T0320962

Handbook of
NATURAL TOXINS

Volume 6
TOXICOLOGY OF PLANT
AND FUNGAL COMPOUNDS

HANDBOOK OF NATURAL TOXINS

Series Editor
Anthony T. Tu
Department of Biochemistry
Colorado State University
Fort Collins, Colorado

Handbook of
NATURAL TOXINS

Volume 6
TOXICOLOGY OF PLANT
AND FUNGAL COMPOUNDS

Edited by

RICHARD F. KEELER
Poisonous Plant Research Laboratory
Agricultural Research Service
U.S. Department of Agriculture
Logan, Utah

ANTHONY T. TU
Department of Biochemistry
Colorado State University
Fort Collins, Colorado

MARCEL DEKKER, INC.   New York • Basel • Hong Kong

Library of Congress Cataloging-in-Publication Data

Toxicology of plant and fungal compounds/edited by Richard F.
Keeler, Anthony T. Tu.
    p.   cm. -- (Handbook of natural toxins; v. 6)
  Includes bibliographical references and index.
  ISBN 0-8247-8375-1
  1. Plant toxins--Toxicology. 2. Mycotoxins--Toxicology.
I. Keeler, Richard F. II. Tu, Anthony T.   III. Series.
RA1250.T69 1991
615.9'52--dc20   90-28581
                                                       CIP

This book is printed on acid-free paper.

MARCEL DEKKER, INC.
270 Madison Avenue, New York, New York 10016

Current printing (last digit):
10 9 8 7 6 5 4 3 2 1

PRINTED IN THE UNITED STATES OF AMERICA

This volume is dedicated to the memory of Ivar Tidestrom, one of several plant taxonomists traversing the western United States in the early 1900s. Without the systematic identification and description of plants and fungi, study of their toxins would be difficult, confirmatory experiments on separate accessions would be impossible, and much valuable research time would be lost. Those who study natural toxins owe a great deal to taxonomists. Ivar Tidestrom made several botanical journeys in the early twentieth century in the western United States from Colorado to California and from southern Arizona to central Idaho. By 1925 he had described and deposited in the U.S. National Herbarium nearly 8000 specimens. His book *Flora of Utah and Nevada*, published in 1925, has been a valuable aid to many researchers since that time. In this photo Ivar Tidestrom is shown on one of his many botanizing trips, but in this instance with a handful of kittens rather than plants (photograph used with permission of the *Journal of Natural Products*).

Preface to the Handbook

Natural toxins are unique toxins which possess some common properties, whether they are obtained from plants, microorganisms, or animals. One common characteristic is that they exert a pronounced effect on the metabolism and biological functions of the intoxicated animals with just a minute quantity. Since ancient times human beings have pondered the physiological effects of various toxins and venoms. How do these natural poisons work? Despite possessing some common nature, each toxin, however, has its unique mode of action and its own characteristic structure.

Drugs are compounds that have specific beneficial effects with a minute quantity. Usually, natural toxins also have very specific effects. Therefore, it is not surprising that many natural toxins are potentially good drugs.

Heretofore, the study of each field of toxins has been taking an independent pathway. Scientists in a specific toxin field are often unaware of the activity in other toxin fields. It is thus desirable to have a primary source of information on all natural toxins so that scientists in a specific discipline of toxin research can easily obtain useful information from other toxin researchers.

This seven-volume handbook of toxins includes the following volumes:

1. *Plant and Fungal Toxins*
2. *Insect Poisons, Allergens, and Other Invertebrate Venoms*
3. *Marine Toxins and Venoms*
4. *Bacterial Toxins*
5. *Reptile Venoms and Toxins*
6. *Toxicology of Plant and Fungal Compounds*
7. *Food Poisoning*

The editor expresses sincere thanks to Maurits Dekker, Chairman of the Board of Marcel Dekker, Inc., for initiating this project.

Anthony T. Tu

Preface to Volume 6

Toxicology has blossomed as a science during the last two decades. That development has been stimulated by a variety of laws passed to protect human populations from careless use and disposal of synthetic chemical compounds such as pesticides, herbicides, and industrial solvents. Naturally occurring toxins also represent hazards of significant magnitude to humans and animals, although they are less frequently the subject of popular press reports.

Natural toxins, including those from plants and fungi, have been responsible for toxicosis of epidemic proportions in humans and animals throughout history. The problems are particularly frequent in domestic livestock. These animals are often fed grains and other feeds that have been improperly dried, cured or stored and on which there is obvious fungal activity with potential toxin production. Furthermore, millions of livestock graze on native plants many of which are poisonous because of contained toxins.

Since the publication, in 1983, of Volume 1 of this series, which was subtitled *Plant and Fungal Toxins*, a great deal of exciting research has been published. We have assembled in this volume 29 chapters describing some of that research. A few chapters update topics previously treated, but most of the chapters describe in depth the toxicologic and chemical aspects of other topics. Accordingly, Volumes 1 and 6 together will provide readers with wide coverage of the general area of plant and fungal toxins.

Chapters in this volume are assembled into three groups: a group on plant toxins, a group on fungal toxins, and a group related to epidemiologic and response considerations. Readers of this volume, as with Volume 1, will see the diversity of chemical classes represented among toxins, the range of effects upon biologic systems, and the variety of expressions of toxicoses. Research on plant and fungal toxins has yielded significant solutions to practical toxicoses problems, provided insight into fundamental chemistry and biology related to the toxicoses, and generated much useful spinoff in the areas of potential drugs, pesticides, and herbicides.

The responsibility for the scientific content of each chapter rests with the individual authors. Any opinions, findings, conclusions, or recommendations expressed in this publication are those of the authors and do not necessarily reflect the view of the U.S. Department of Agriculture, Colorado State University, or any other organization.

Richard F. Keeler
Anthony T. Tu

Contents

PART III. EPIDEMIOLOGY AND RESPONSES

Contributors

Louise C. Abbott Department of Veterinary Biosciences, College of Veterinary Medicine, University of Illinois at Urbana-Champaign, Urbana, Illinois

A. F. Alexander College of Veterinary Medicine, Colorado State University, Fort Collins, Colorado

Dale C. Baker Department of Pathology, Colorado State University, Fort Collins, Colorado

Val Richard Beasley Department of Veterinary Biosciences, College of Veterinary Medicine, University of Illinois at Urbana-Champaign, Urbana, Illinois

John P. Bryant Institute of Arctic Biology, University of Alaska, Fairbanks, Fairbanks, Alaska

William B. Buck Department of Veterinary Biosciences, College of Veterinary Medicine, University of Illinois at Urbana-Champaign, Urbana, Illinois

Thomas D. Bunch Utah State University, Logan, Utah

Greg Bunkers Plant Pathology Department, Montana State University, Bozeman, Montana

Thomas P. Clausen Department of Chemistry, University of Alaska, Fairbanks, Fairbanks, Alaska

Steven M. Colegate Department of Toxicology and Pharmacology, School of Veterinary Studies, Murdoch University, Perth, Murdoch, Western Australia

Louise-Marie Côté Consul-Tox, Inc., Tolono, Illinois

Horace G. Cutler   Department of Plant Physiology, Richard B. Russell Center, Agricultural Research Service, U.S. Department of Agriculture, Athens, Georgia

Andrew M. Dahlem*   College of Veterinary Medicine, University of Illinois at Urbana-Champaign, Urbana, Illinois

Peter R. Dorling   School of Veterinary Studies, Murdoch University, Perth, Murdoch, Western Australia

Stephen O. Duke   Southern Weed Science Laboratory, Agricultural Research Service, U.S. Department of Agriculture, Stoneville, Mississippi

John A. Edgar   Division of Animal Health, CSIRO, Parkville, Victoria, Australia

William L. Epstein   Department of Dermatology, University of California, San Francisco, California

Richard H. Finnell   Department of Veterinary and Comparative Anatomy, Pharmacology, and Physiology, College of Veterinary Medicine, Washington State University, Pullman, Washington

William Gaffield   Western Regional Research Center, Agricultural Research Service, U.S. Department of Agriculture, Albany, California

John E. Garst   Primate Research Institute, New Mexico State University, Holloman Air Force Base, New Mexico

Clive C. Gay   Department of Veterinary Clinical Medicine and Surgery, College of Veterinary Medicine, Washington State University, Pullman, Washington

Wanda M. Haschek   College of Veterinary Medicine, University of Illinois at Urbana-Champaign, Urbana, Illinois

Stephen B. Hooser   College of Veterinary Medicine, University of Illinois at Urbana-Champaign, Urbana, Illinois

Martin J. Humphries   Howard University Cancer Center, Howard University Medical School, Washington, D.C., and University of Manchester, Manchester, England

Clive R. Huxtable   School of Veterinary Studies, Murdoch University, Perth, Murdoch, Western Australia

Lynn F. James   Poisonous Plant Research Laboratory, Agricultural Research Service, U.S. Department of Agriculture, Logan, Utah

Richard F. Keeler   Poisonous Plant Research Laboratory, Agricultural Research Service, U.S. Department of Agriculture, Logan, Utah

---

*   *Current affiliation*: Eli Lilly, Inc., Indianapolis, Indiana

Doug Kenfield* Montana State University, Bozeman, Montana

Wendell W. Kilgore Department of Environmental Toxicology, University of California, Davis, Davis, California

A. Douglas Kinghorn Department of Medicinal Chemistry and Pharmacognosy, College of Pharmacy, University of Illinois at Chicago, Chicago, Illinois

M. W. Lamé Department of Veterinary Pharmacology and Toxicology, University of California, Davis, Davis, California

Kenneth F. Lampe[†] American Medical Association, Chicago, Illinois

Randall A. Lovell[‡] College of Veterinary Medicine, University of Illinois at Urbana-Champaign, Urbana, Illinois

James E. Meeker Toxicology Laboratory, Institute of Forensic Sciences, Oakland, California

Russell J. Molyneux Western Regional Research Center, Agricultural Research Service, U.S. Department of Agriculture, Albany, California

D. Morin Department of Veterinary Pharmacology and Toxicology, University of California, Davis, Davis, California

Sheila A. Newton Howard University Cancer Center, Howard University Medical School, Washington, D.C.

T. N. Oeltmann Departments of Medicine and Biochemistry, Vanderbilt University, Nashville, Tennessee

Kenneth Olden Howard University Cancer Center, Howard University Medical School, Washington, D.C., and National Cancer Institute, Bethesda, Maryland

Kip E. Panter Poisonous Plant Research Laboratory, Agricultural Research Service, U.S. Department of Agriculture, Logan, Utah

Michael A. Pass Department of Physiology and Pharmacology, University of Queensland, St. Lucia, Queensland, Australia

Jack D. Paxton Department of Plant Pathology, University of Illinois at Urbana-Champaign, Urbana, Illinois

Paul B. Reichardt Department of Chemistry, University of Alaska, Fairbanks, Fairbanks, Alaska

---

Current affiliation:
*Kendolynn, Columbia Falls, Montana
[†]Deceased
[‡]Ricerca, Inc., Painesville, Ohio

Loyd D. Rowe Food Animal Protection Research Laboratory, Agricultural Research Service, U.S. Department of Agriculture, College Station, Texas

H. J. Segall Department of Veterinary Pharmacology and Toxicology, University of California, Davis, Davis, California

Gary A. Strobel Plant Pathology Department, Montana State University, Bozeman, Montana

Fumio Sugawara Institute of Physical and Chemical Research, Riken Wakoshi, Saitama, Japan

Anthony T. Tu Department of Biochemistry, Colorado State University, Fort Collins, Colorado

W. M. J. Van Gelder Division of New Crops, Products, and Process Technologies, Agrotechnological Research Institute, Wageningen, The Netherlands

D. Jesse Wagstaff Center for Food Safety and Applied Nutrition, U.S. Food and Drug Administration, Washington, D.C.

Sandra L. White Howard University Cancer Center and Department of Microbiology, Howard University Medical School, Washington, D.C.

Terrie L. Wierenga Poisonous Plant Research Laboratory, Agricultural Research Service, U.S. Department of Agriculture, Logan, Utah

Ronald G. Wiley Neurology Service, Veterans Administration Medical Center, and Vanderbilt University, Nashville, Tennessee

D. W. Wilson Department of Veterinary Pathology, University of California, Davis, Davis, California

William C. Wilson Arthropod-Borne Animal Diseases Research Laboratory, Agricultural Research Service, U.S. Department of Agriculture, Laramie, Wyoming

C. K. Winter University of California, Riverside, Riverside, California

Contents of Previous Volumes

Handbook of
NATURAL TOXINS

Volume 6
TOXICOLOGY OF PLANT
AND FUNGAL COMPOUNDS

I
NATURE AND TOXICITY OF
PLANT TOXINS

A. Alkaloidal Class

1

Metabolism of Pyrrolizidine Alkaloids

H. J. Segall, D. W. Wilson, M. W. Lamé, and D. Morin
University of California, Davis, Davis, California

C. K. Winter
University of California, Riverside, Riverside, California

I. INTRODUCTION

In this chapter we focus principally on the mammalian metabolism of the pyrrolizidine alkaloids (PAs). To ensure that the reader is familiar with the chemistry, distribution, toxicity, and pathology of PAs, a number of earlier review
articles and books are recommended (Bull et al., 1968; McLean, 1970; Peterson
and Culvenor, 1983; Mattocks, 1986).

It has been estimated that as many as 7500 plant species, which is equivalent to 3% of the flowering plants, contain PAs (Smith and Culvenor, 1981).
Historically, the PAs have been associated with the *Senecio* species, as they
have been identified in more than 100 *Senecio* species of the Compositae family.
The PAs are also commonly found in other plant species, especially the Leguminosae (*Crotalaria* species), and the Boraginaceae (*Heliotropium*, *Lindelofia*,
Cynoglossum, and *Amsinckia* species) (Mattocks, 1972b; Culvenor and Jago,
1979). The Compositae and Boraginaceae families producing PAs are distributed worldwide in a variety of climatic conditions, in contrast to the *Crotalaria*
species, which are restricted to subtropical or tropical areas (Peterson and
Culvenor, 1983). Thus one must consider the wide distribution of the PAs
when estimating their deleterious effects on animal and human health. Grains,
bread, milk, honey, and herbal teas contaminated with PAs have either caused
human poisonings or represent potential sources of human poisonings (Hill
et al., 1951; Bras et al., 1954; Mohabbat et al., 1976; Dickinson et al., 1976;
Deinzer et al., 1977; Culvenor et al., 1980; Huxtable, 1980). Many PAs have
been documented to produce toxic effects in laboratory animals, poultry, livestock, and humans (Bull et al., 1968; Huxtable, 1980; Mattocks, 1986). The
toxic syndromes have been shown to vary according to the species: horses,
hepatic and neurological disease; sheep, hemolytic syndrome; cattle, gastrointestinal problems; pigs and dogs, chronic liver disease (Bull et al., 1968).
Pyrrolizidine alkaloid-affected animals are difficult to diagnose and undoubtedly many cases go unreported, as the classic syndromes may not be apparent
until the terminal stages of the disease. At present, no established treatment
is available to reverse the toxicity caused by the PAs.

The present estimate is that 250 PAs have been described which exist as
esters of saturated or monounsaturated heterocyclic pyrrolizidine bases (nec-
ines, Fig. 1) (Mattocks, 1972b; Peterson and Culvenor, 1983; Mattocks, 1986).
Structural requirements to induce significant PA toxicity are (1) unsaturation
at the 1-2 position of the necine base, which allows retronecine esters to exhibit greater toxicity than the saturated necine base platynecine; and (2)
esterification of one of the hydroxyl groups which most frequently occurs
at the C9 position but which may occur at the C7 position with branching of
the ester function (Culvenor et al., 1969, 1976; Mattocks, 1973, 1978, 1981,
1986; Culvenor and Jago, 1979; Peterson and Culvenor, 1983). The toxic
PAs may exist as monoesters or diesters, with cyclic diesters (macrocyclic
diesters) such as senecionine, seneciphylline, and retrorsine usually exhibiting the highest toxicity (Mattocks, 1973, 1986). Esterifying acids of toxic
PAs often have a branched alkyl group (Schoental, 1968; Mattocks, 1981).

It has been demonstrated that PA metabolites originating in the liver rather
than the PAs themselves are the causative agents in PA toxicity (Mattocks,
1972a, 1973, 1986). Evidence for this includes the following: (1) the toxic
effects of the PAs on animals was greatly affected by their prior treatment

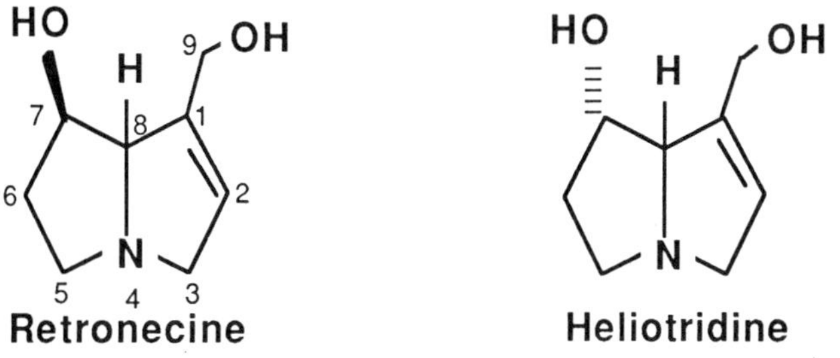

FIGURE 1 Typical PA necine bases.

with a number of drugs that influence the liver-metabolizing enzymes; (2) the major site of damage by the PAs was the liver, which was also the major site of PA metabolism; and (3) no adverse effects were produced when PAs were applied to the skin.

Three established metabolic pathways for the PAs in the liver have been documented in laboratory animals: hydrolysis, N-oxidation, and dehydrogenation to pyrrolic derivatives (Mattocks, 1986). Hydrolysis and N-oxidation are currently thought to represent detoxification mechanisms as opposed to dehydrogenation. The toxicity attributed to the production of toxic pyrroles represents their metabolic activation or dehydrogenation by the liver. An example of the hepatic metabolism of a macrocyclic PA (senecionine) is illustrated in Fig. 2.

II. HYDROLYSIS

Hydrolysis serves as a detoxification mechanism, with the major products of PA esters being the necine base and necic acid moieties (Mattocks, 1972b, 1978, 1986). Neither the necine base nor the necic acid fraction exhibit hepatic or cytotoxic actions. The hepatic enzymes that play a major role in the hydrolysis of PAs are the esterases (Mattocks, 1970, 1982). The hydrolysis rates of PAs have been measured by Mattocks using manometric CO_2 evolution to monitor enzymatic hydrolysis and pH depression to determine alkaline hydrolysis rates of PAs and semisynthetic PA esters (Mattocks, 1982). In an in vitro study using a rat liver homogenate, Mattocks demonstrated that natural and semisynthetic PAs are hydrolyzed by esterases (Mattocks et al., 1986). Mattocks pretreated rats with the esterase inhibitor tri-o-cresylphosphate and admininstered seven synthetic PA cyclic diesters to treated and nontreated animals. Pyrrole levels from PAs most resistant to hydrolysis remained fairly constant, whereas pyrrole levels from compounds susceptible to hydrolysis were increased dramatically in rats pretreated with the esterase inhibitor. Rats not pretreated with the esterase inhibitor exhibited hepatic pyrrole levels inversely related to the in vitro hydrolysis rates of the synthetic PA diesters.

The identification of PA hydrolysis products in vivo and in vitro has only recently attracted much interest. Winter, Segall, and Jones qualitatively determined monocrotalic and senecic acid from methanolic extracts of mouse microsomal incubations of monocrotaline and senecionine, respectively, with their

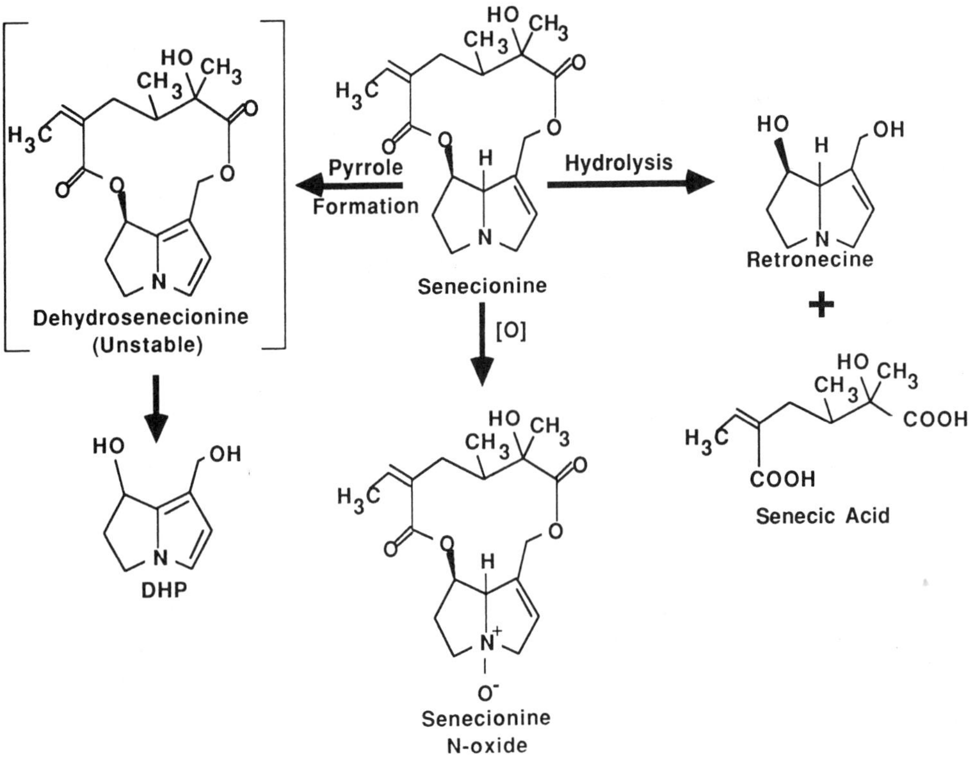

FIGURE 2 Major pathways for the metabolism of the PA senecionine.

trimethylsilyl (TMS) derivatives and gas chromatography/mass spectrometry (GC/MS, Winter et al., 1988). Mattocks developed a thin-layer chromatography (TLC) technique to detect the hydrolysis product (retronecine 7-isovalarate) of retronecine diisovalerate from a rat hepatic esterase preparation (Mattocks, 1982). Thin-layer chromatography was also used to detect the necine base heliotridine from tissue extracts of sheep previously dosed with heliotrine (Jago et al., 1969).

III. N-OXIDATION

A. Formation of *N*-Oxides

Following ingestion, the hepatic microsomal enzymes convert a portion of the PAs to *N*-oxides (Mattocks and White, 1971b; Mattocks, 1981, 1986). Recent evidence indicates that there are two metabolic pathways involving different enzyme systems because pyrroles are also formed in the hepatic microsomes. Chesney and Allen, examining the metabolism of monocrotaline by guinea pig hepatic microsomes, felt that high *N*-oxidase activity and low dehydrogenase activity was present (Chesney and Allen, 1973). Results from a recent study suggest that the resistance of the guinea pig to PA poisoning may be due to resistance of the animal to the toxic effects of pyrroles, rather than from low metabolic pyrrole formation (Winter et al., 1988). White and Mattocks studied the metabolism of retrorsine by initially challenging the rat hepatic mixed-function oxidase system with various concentrations of inducers and inhibitors; they observed significant differences in the amounts of *N*-oxides and pyrrolic metabolites produced (White and Mattocks, 1971). Others felt that a number of cytochrome P450 isozymes may be involved in the two metabolic pathways, with the hepatic flavin monooxygenase playing an important role in the conversion of PAs to *N*-oxides (Buhler and Kedzierski, 1986).

B. Metabolism of *N*-Oxides

Pyrrolizidine *N*-oxides are considered to be relatively unreactive and, due to their polarity, are excreted primarily in the urine (Mattocks, 1971, 1986). The major reaction of PA *N*-oxides involves reduction to the corresponding tert bases, with the intestinal tract the major site of PA *N*-oxide reduction. Retrorsine *N*-oxide was reduced to retrorsine when incubated with rat intestinal contents (Mattocks, 1972a). The levels of pyrrolic metabolites derived from retrorsine *N*-oxides were higher when the *N*-oxide was administered by stomach tube rather than intraperitoneal injection, indicating that the gut plays an important role in the activation of *N*-oxides (Mattocks, 1972a). Mattocks felt that the enzymes of the intestinal flora play an important role in *N*-oxide reduction (Mattocks, 1971). Indicine *N*-oxide was reduced to indicine in the gut of rabbits with lower concentrations of indicine formed following antibiotic treatment, which decreased the bacterial content of the gut (Powis et al., 1979). The reduction of PA *N*-oxides in the liver appears to be a relatively minor reaction. In both rat and rabbit hepatic microsomal incubations, indicine *N*-oxide was reduced to indicine catalyzed by cytochrome P450 and stimulated by an iron(III)-ethylenediaminetetraacetic acid (EDTA) complex. This reaction appeared to be more successful in anaerobic than in aerobic conditions (Powis et al., 1979, 1982; Powis and Wincentsen, 1980). A small percentage of retrorsine *N*-oxide was converted to pyrrolic metabolites when incubated with rat liver slices and the authors thought that the reduction of retrorsine *N*-oxide to retrorsine was the initial step in the production of pyrroles.

C. Analysis of *N*-Oxides

1. Ehrlich Reaction

The analysis of *N*-oxide metabolites has usually been performed using the Ehrlich reaction or modifications of it. The *N*-oxides are converted to pyrroles by the action of iron complexes such as nitroprusside and analyzed using the Ehrlich reaction. Nitrogen oxides were determined initially following the extraction of pyrroles from the appropriate tissue. This assay was complicated by recovery, sensitivity, and reproducibility of the extraction procedure (Mattocks and White, 1970). Mattocks and Bird later eliminated the extraction step and measured the combined pyrroles and *N*-oxides followed by the deduction of pyrrole levels from similar aliquots that had not been treated with the nitroprusside reagent (Mattocks and Bird, 1983b).

2. *Specific* N-*Oxide Detection*

Heliotrine N-oxide was isolated as an in vivo metabolite of heliotrine in sheep from methanolic extracts of the bile, urine, and blood using TLC (Jago et al., 1969). They confirmed their results with a positive Ehrlich reaction and co-chromatography with a heliotrine N-oxide standard. Utilizing senecionine, carbon-14 labeling, and reversed-phase HPLC techniques, Eastman and Segall detected senecionine N-oxide from an in vitro mouse hepatic microsomal fraction (Eastman and Segall, 1982). Reversed-phase HPLC techniques facilitated the detection of N-oxides of jacobine, retrorsine, seneciphylline, and senecionine from hepatic microsomal incubations (Kedzierski and Buhler, 1986a; Ramsdell et al., 1987). A nonchromatographic technique using tandem mass spectrometry facilitated the analysis of senecionine N-oxide from hepatic microsomal incubations using senecionine (Winter et al., 1988a). Using a double-focusing mass spectrometer, collisionally activated decomposition mass-analyzed ion kinetic energy spectrometry (CAD/MIKES) proved to be a successful technique that provided qualitative and semiquantitative results.

IV. DEHYDROGENATION

A. Formation of Pyrrolic Metabolites

The hepatic mixed-function oxidase system is generally regarded as the site of pyrrole formation (Jago et al., 1970; Mattocks and White, 1971b; Mattocks, 1973, 1986). Reduced nicotinamide-adenine dinucleotide phosphate (NADP) plus oxygen are required to induce pyrrole formation with a recent study indicating that cytochrome P450 monooxygenases may play a part in pyrrole production (Buhler and Kedzierski, 1986). The suggested mechanism of pyrrole formation is that enzymatic hydroxylation may occur at one of the carbon atoms (C3 or C8) adjacent to the bridgehead nitrogen (Mattocks and White, 1971b; Mattocks and Bird, 1983b; Mattocks, 1986). Spontaneous decomposition of the elements of water from the recently formed carbinolamine would yield a pyrrole. In an associated reaction, demethylation of PAs containing the otonecine base may yield a C8 hydroxylated carbinolamine which would dehydrate to yield a pyrrole (Culvenor et al., 1971; Mattocks, and White, 1971b; Mattocks, 1972a). The various routes leading to the formation of pyrroles is illustrated in Fig. 3.

Numerous pyrroles have been detected/isolated from in vitro studies using liver microsomes form human embryo liver slices and animals (Jago, 1970; Mattocks and White, 1971b; Chesney and Allen, 1973; White et al., 1973; Culvenor et al., 1976; Mattocks and Bird, 1983b; Segall et al., 1984; Buhler and Kedzierski, 1986). Pyrrole formation has been demonstrated from several in vivo experiments and pyrrolic metabolites have been detected in the liver plus the bile, blood, and urine of rats (Mattocks, 1972a, 1981; White et al., 1973; Hsu et al., 1973a; White, 1977; Lafranconi et al., 1985). A marked decrease in the level of pyrrolic metabolites produced from in vitro incubations of rat lung slices, human embryo lung slices, and rat or rabbit lung slices was noted relative to similar liver tissue preparations (Armstrong and Zuckerman, 1970; Mattocks and White, 1971b; Guengerich, 1977; Hilliker et al., 1983). Mattocks obtained correlations between PA LD_{50} values and liver pyrrole levels in rats given a variety of PAs (Mattocks and White, 1971b).

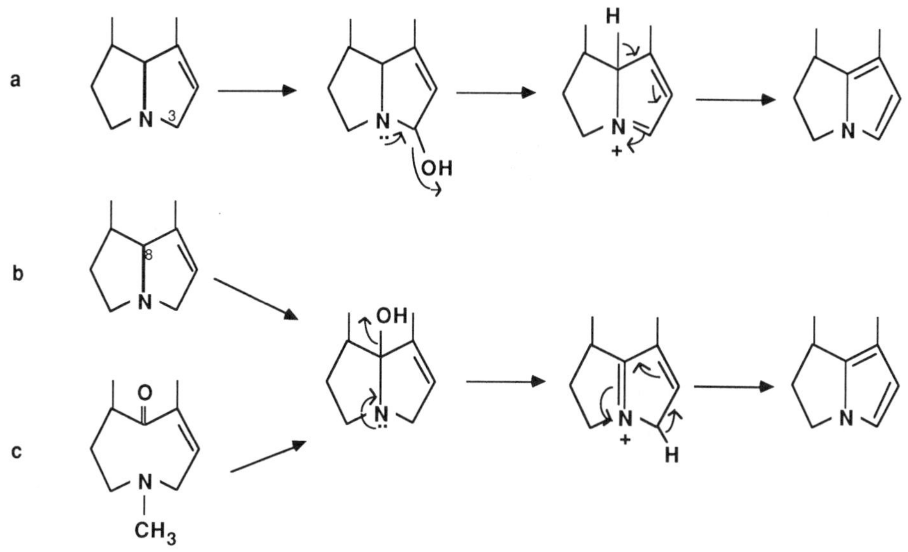

FIGURE 3 Proposed mechanisms of pyrrole formation from (a) C3 hydroxylation, (b) C8 hydroxylation, and (c) demethylation of otonecine base.

Using synthetic PA analogs, similar findings were also obtained (Driver and Mattocks, 1984; Lafranconi et al., 1985).

B. Metabolism of Pyrroles

The toxic effects due to PAs are usually produced by dehydroalkaloid pyrroles originating from PAs that have been metabolized by the hepatic microsomes. Synthetic dehydroalkaloids have produced similar toxic effects, but at lower doses than the parent PAs, provided that they were given intravenously or intraperitoneally (Culvenor et al., 1970; Mattocks, 1969, 1972b, 1986). The dehydroalkaloids have not been isolated directly from in vivo hepatic microsomal preparations as they are highly reactive compounds (Mattocks, 1972b; Peterson and Culvenor, 1983). Secondary metabolic products of the dehydroalkaloids plus cysteine and nonmetabolized PAs have been identified and provide proof of initial dehydroalkaloid formation (Schoental, 1975; Peterson and Culvenor, 1983).

The disappearance of the dehydroalkaloids in biological matrices has been attributed to their ability to act as alkylating agents (Culvenor et al., 1969; Mattocks, 1972b, 1986). Electron rearrangements may displace the ester function of a dehydroalkaloid esterified at the C9 position, forming a species with a positive charge on the nitrogen atom which is in resonance with a C9 carbonium atom (Fig. 4) (Mattocks, 1972b). This reactive intermediate could easily alkylate biological nucleophiles such as sulfhydryls or amines. A similar mechanism could occur with a dehydroalkaloid esterfied at the C7 and C9 positions, which would displace the C7 ester to yield a C7 carbonium ion, thus acting as a bifunctional alkylating agent (Mattocks, 1972b, 1973, 1986). The

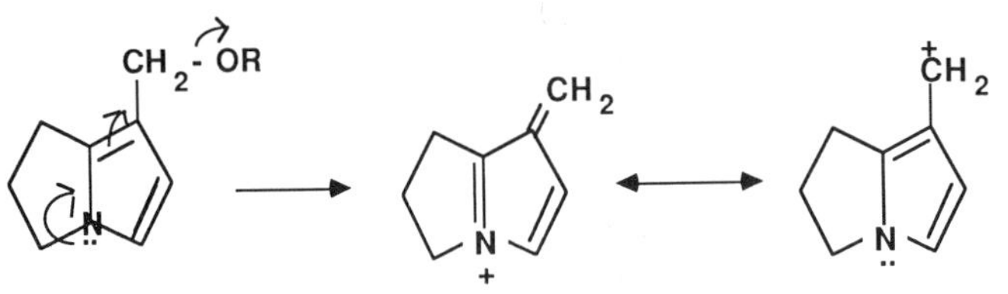

FIGURE 4 Proposed formation of carbonium ion from C9 PA ester.

dehydroalkaloids create toxicity by covalent binding followed by inactivation
of essential biological nucleophiles (Nucleic acids, proteins) which result in
alterations of cell function, damage, or cell death (Bull et al., 1968; McLean,
1970; Mattocks, 1972b, 1973, 1978, 1986).

Dehydroheliotrine has been detected as the primary pyrrolic metabolite
of the heliotrine-based PAs such as heliotrine and lasiocarpine in in vitro incubations of rat hepatic microsomes (Jago, 1970). Its enantiomer, dehydroretronecine [(R)-6,7-dihydro-7B-hydroxyl-1-hydroxymethyl-5H-pyrrolizine, (R)-
DHP] derived from retronecine-based monocrotaline has been identified as a
pyrrolic metabolite from in vivo rat experiments (Hsu et al., 1973a). The
major rat hepatic microsomal metabolite of jacobine (retronecine based) was a
racemic mixture of the R and S enantiomers of DHP, which suggested that
the configuration of the necine pyrrole had not been retained (Kedzierski
and Buhler, 1985). Additional studies confirmed that the metabolic hydrolysis
of the initial dehydroalkaloids occurred with alkyloxygen fission of the C7-
O and C9-O bonds due to an S_N1 mechanism (Kedzierski and Buhler, 1986b).
Necine pyrroles have been shown to be active as alkylating agents, although
to a lesser degree than their parent dehydroalkaloids. Robertson showed
that the nucleoside deoxyguanosine reacted with the [(R)-DHP] in vitro in
an S_N1 reaction, forming an enantiomeric pair of adducts covalently bound
at the C7 position (Robertson, 1982). Binding of [(R)-DHP] with glutathione
and cysteine at the C7 position has been demonstrated in vitro (Robertson
et al., 1977). Additional studies showed the covalent binding of [(R)-DHP]
to DNA as well as nucleotides and nucleosides (Tomer et al., 1986). Synthetic
pyrroles analogous to those formed due to hepatic metabolism covalently bound
to DNA, RNA, and protein when provided to rats in vivo (Guengerich and
Mitchell, 1980). The binding of these analogs to protein in rat hepatic microsomal incubations was inhibited by reduced glutathione, anaerobiosis, carbon
monoxide, and SKF-525A, suggesting that cytochrome P450 may activate the
pyrroles further to more electrophilic species which covalently bind to biological macromolecules (Guengerich and Mitchell, 1980).

C. Other Pyrroles

Segall, Dallas, and Haddon reported the formation of two pyrroles similar to
DHP by incubating senecionine with mouse hepatic microsomes. The two compounds were identified as hydroxydanaidal and methoxydehydroretronecine
(Fig. 5) (Segall et al., 1984). Mattocks and White isolated pyrroles from a
rat microsomal incubation plus the nonhepatotoxic (saturated) PAs rosmarine
and platyphylline (Mattocks and White, 1971a). With these saturated PAs the

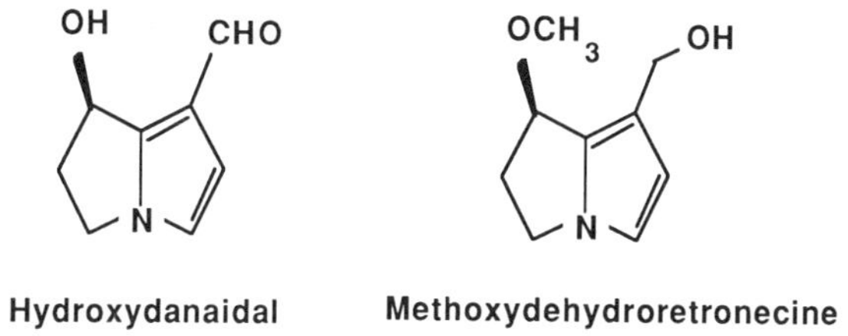
OH
CHO
N
Hydroxydanaidal
OCH3
OH
N
Methoxydehydroretronecine

FIGURE 5 Pyrroles isolated from in vitro mouse hepatic metabolism of senecionine.

observed pyrroline structures were formed in the rings containing the C5 and C7, as opposed to the C1 and C3 ring pyrrole formation from the unsaturated hepatotoxic PAs (Culvenor, 1976).

D. Analysis of Pyrroles (Ehrlich Reaction)

Many of the published PA metabolism studies involving pyrroles have utilized the Ehrlich pyrrole reaction (Mattocks, 1986). Ehrlich's reagent [4-dimethylaminobenzaldehyde (DMBA) in Lewis acid] forms a highly conjugated product by binding to the pyrrole at the nucleophilic C3 carbon adjacent to the pyrroline nitrogen (Fig. 6) (Mattocks, 1968, 1986; Mattocks and White, 1970). The product when measured at 565 nm (λ_{max}) with an inflection point approximately 530 nm yields a mauve to magenta color in boron trifluoride.

Pyrroles have been shown to polymerize rapidly in acid, and since the Ehrlich reaction is performed in acid, polymerization must be monitored carefully for accurate measurements of pyrrole levels to be obtained. To promote the Ehrlich color formation, an ethanolic ascorbic acid solution is added to the samples prior to color formation (Mattocks and White, 1970; Mattocks, 1986). The pyrrole will react with the ascorbic acid, which prevents polymerization while promoting the complex to undergo the Ehrlich reaction (Mattocks and White, 1970). Excess ascorbic acid must be removed following the Ehrlich

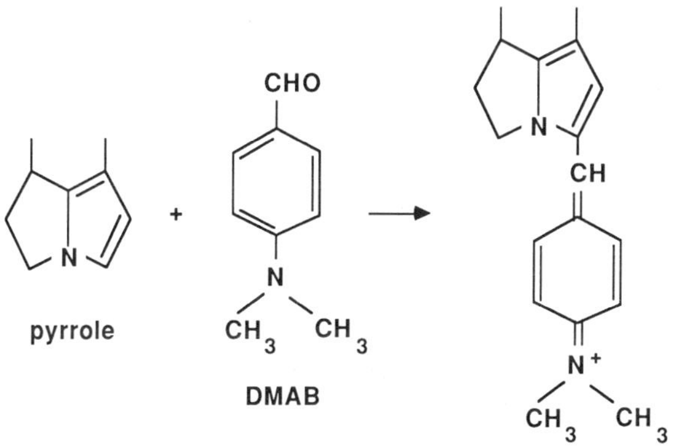
N
pyrrole
+
CHO
N
CH3
CH3
DMAB
N
CH
N+
CH3
CH3

FIGURE 6 Reaction of pyrrole with DMAB (Ehrlich's reagent).

reaction through oxidation with iodine, as excess ascorbic acid causes the Ehrlich color to fade rapidly (Mattocks and Bird, 1983b). In addition, the presence of thiols will increase the λ_{max} of the Ehrlich product and decrease the extinction coefficient (Mattocks and White, 1970; Mattocks and Bird, 1983b). To restore the Ehrlich color, alcoholic mercuric chloride is added to react with thiols and breaks the pyrrole-sulfur bonds (Mattocks and White, 1970; Mattocks and Bird, 1983b).

The versatility of the Ehrlich reaction has allowed the detection of pyrroles from microsomal reactions, blood, urine, and liver tissue (Mattocks, 1967; Mattocks and White, 1970). However, control tissues, especially blood, produced Ehrlich colors with maxima at 504 and 625 nm and absorbtion at 565 nm. Mattocks and White proposed a formula for the corrected pyrrole absorbance to compensate for the 565 and 625-nm absorbances (Mattocks and White, 1970).

The Ehrlich reaction has proven useful in the study of the PAs, yet has been demonstrated to be nonspecific for the detection of PA metabolites. Thus the data obtained using the Ehrlich reaction provides relative rather than quantitative values, as control biological tissues will also have pyrroles that form Ehrlich colors (Mattocks and White, 1970; Mattocks, 1986).

E. Specific Pyrrole Detection

Using thin-layer chromatography (TLC), nuclear magnetic resonance (NMR), and mass spectrometry, Jago et al. (1970) identified the necine pyrrole dehydroheliotrine [(S)-DHP] as the major pyrrole metabolite from in vitro hepatic microsomes incubations. The metabolite of monocrotaline, dehydroretronecine [(R)-DHP], and the enantiomer of dehydroheliotrine was identified as the main pyrrolic metabolite in liver, blood, and urine of rats (Hsu et al., 1973a). A rat dosed with rosemarinine yielded an in vivo pyrrole in the urine, and in vitro rat microsomal and liver slices confirmed this (Mattocks and White, 1971a).

Segall, Dallas, and Haddon using senecionine (radiolabeled and nonradio-labeled) plus mouse hepatic microsomes isolated two pyrroles: hydroxydanaidal and methoxydehydroretronecine using reversed-phase HPLC, with confirmation by NMR and MS (Segall et al., 1984). Another reversed-phase HPLC technique using a styrene-divinylbenzene column aided in the isolation of a racemic mixture of the pyrrole DHP from senecionine, seneciphylline, and retrorsine from in vitro rat and mouse microsomal incubations (Kedzierski and Buhler, 1986a).

A gas chromatography/mass spectrometry (GC/MS) technique identified DHP from mouse hepatic microsomes as a metabolite of senecionine and monocrotaline. Trimethylsilyl (TMS) derivatives of DHP were made with specific ion monitoring of its molecular ion to obtain a detection limit in the range of 15 pg (Winter et al., 1988a).

V. STRUCTURAL FACTORS INFLUENCING PYRROLIZIDINE ALKALOID DEHYDROGENATION, N-OXIDATION, AND HYDROLYSIS

The influence of the PAs on their metabolism by hydrolysis, dehydrogenation, and N-oxidation have been the subject of numerous studies (Mattocks, 1972a,

1986; Mattocks and Bird, 1983b). The degree of lipophilicity and steric factors are important in deciding the relative concentrations of metabolites formed by these pathways. The susceptibility of PAs to hydrolysis is influenced markedly by steric factors. Pyrrolizidine esters sterically hindered were not hydrolyzed as easily as PA esters with short and unbranched acid chains by both base-catalyzed and enzymatic hydrolysis (Mattocks, 1982). Rigidity of the acid chain due to cyclic diester rings or unsaturation or chain branching in proximity to the carbonyl group were major factors in preventing hydrolysis. The stereochemistry of the necine base influenced the susceptibility of PAs to hydrolysis, with esters of retronecine (increased steric hindrance relative to heliotridine esters) undergoing slower hydrolysis than that of heliotridine esters (Mattocks, 1982).

Pyrrole formation from synthetic PA cyclic diesters was shown to increase in rats pretreated with esterase inhibitors (Mattocks et al., 1986). The concentrations of N-oxide and pyrrolic metabolites of PAs appear to be inversely proportional relative to the ease of alkaloid hydrolysis (Mattocks, 1978; Mattocks and Bird, 1983b).

The lipophilicity exhibited by the PAs markedly influences their susceptibility to N-oxidation and dehydrogenation. An increased lipophilicity promotes the formation of pyrrolic and N-oxide metabolites, as the PAs exhibiting high lipophilicity probably are in greater contact with the hepatic microsomal enzymes (Mattocks, 1981; Mattocks and Bird, 1983b; Winter et al., 1988b).

The relative amounts of N-oxide metabolites formed by the hepatic microsomes are also affected by steric factors. The ratio of N-oxide to pyrrolic metabolites was dependent on the type of ester metabolized, with monoesters or cyclic diester PAs forming lower levels of N-oxides than those of acyclic diesters (Mattocks and Bird, 1983b). The steric factors due to the acid moieties appear to offer a possible explanation. The acyclic diesters exhibit free rotation, which provides increased hindrance at the C8 site of the PA nucleus relative to the more rigid cyclic diesters. This would not be conducive to microsomal hydroxylation at this position, which is considered to be the initial step in the dehydrogenation of PAs (Mattocks and White, 1971b; Mattocks and Bird, 1983b; Mattocks, 1986). The increased steric hindrance factor at C8 may also pertain to the acyclic diesters relative to the monoesters.

VI. PYRROLIZIDINE ALKALOIDS AND OTHER METABOLITES

Heliotridine trachelanthate was detected as a biliary and urinary metabolite in sheep and rats provided heliotridine (Fig. 7) (Bull et al., 1968; Jago et al., 1969). Heliotridine trachelanthate was produced by O-demethylation of the heliotrine ester function and exhibited approximately half the toxicity to sheep as heliotrine (parent compound). Rats provided heliotrine excreted the N-oxide of heliotridine trachelanthate in their urine and the metabolite heliotridine-glucuronide was proposed as the major metabolite, as treatment of the urine with β-glucuronidase increased the amount of heliotridine (Bull et al., 1968).

Metabolic hydroxylation has been demonstrated to occur in the acid moieties as well as the PA nucleus. Eastman and Segall isolated 19-hydroxysenec-

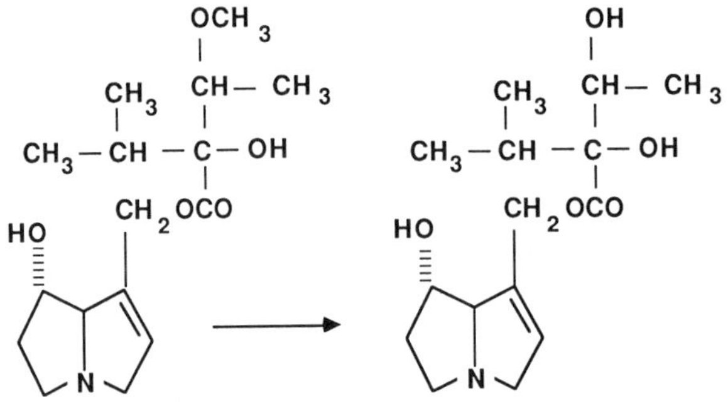

FIGURE 7 O-Demethylation of heliotrine.

ionine from an in vitro incubation of senecionine with mouse hepatic microsomes (Eastman and Segall, 1982).

An additional metabolite appeared to decompose/polymerize rapidly and
to precipitate with the formation of a dark reddish brown/purple color during
the isolation process. Difficulties in isolating this metabolite had been noted
previously (Butler et al., 1970; Mattocks and Bird, 1983a). Recent work
by Segall, Wilson, Dallas, and Haddon identified this metabolite as *trans*-4-
hydroxy-2-hexenal (t-4HH), again using senecionine and mouse hepatic microsomes (Segall et al., 1985). However, as this metabolite may have originated
form either the senecic acid portion or the necine base of senecionine, additional *S. vulgaris* plants were provided 2-[^{14}C]ornithine, as described previously (Green et al., 1981). Previous experiments that provided *Senecio* species 2-[^{14}C]ornithine had yielded specific incorporation at carbons 7, 8, and
9 (Hughes et al., 1964; Bottomley and Geissman, 1964). Separate in vivo
mouse hepatic microsomal experiments using [^{14}C]senecionine derived from
either [^{14}CO$_2$]- or 2-[^{14}C]ornithine were performed. The metabolite t-4HH
was shown to be derived from the retronecine portion of senecionine (Segall
et al., 1985).

The in vivo pathology in rats caused by t-4HH appeared to be similar
to that attributed previously to the reactive pyrroles, and was similar to that
caused by senecionine, which strongly suggested that t-4HH plays an important role in PA toxicity (Segall et al., 1985; Wilson et al., 1986). In rat
hepatocyte cultures and Chinese hamster ovary cells, t-4HH and *trans*-4-
hydroxy-2-nonenal (t-4HN) have caused cytotoxicity and genotoxicity and
have been shown to bind covalently to rat hepatic protein in vivo (Griffin and
Segall, 1986; Grasse et al., 1985). The alkylation of biological nucleophiles
by t-4HH is believed to cause toxicity and is similar to the mechanism of toxicity of the necine pyrroles and dehydroalkaloids. The nucleoside deoxyguanosine was alkylated in vitro by a Michael addition of the free amino group of
deoxyguanosine at the C3 position of t-4HH, followed by cyclization to yield
two pairs of diastereomeric adducts (Fig. 8) (Winter et al., 1986). Winter,
Segall, and Jones also showed that t-4HH reacted similarly with glutathione
in vivo, as a C3 mercapturic acid of t-4HH was identified in the urine of rats

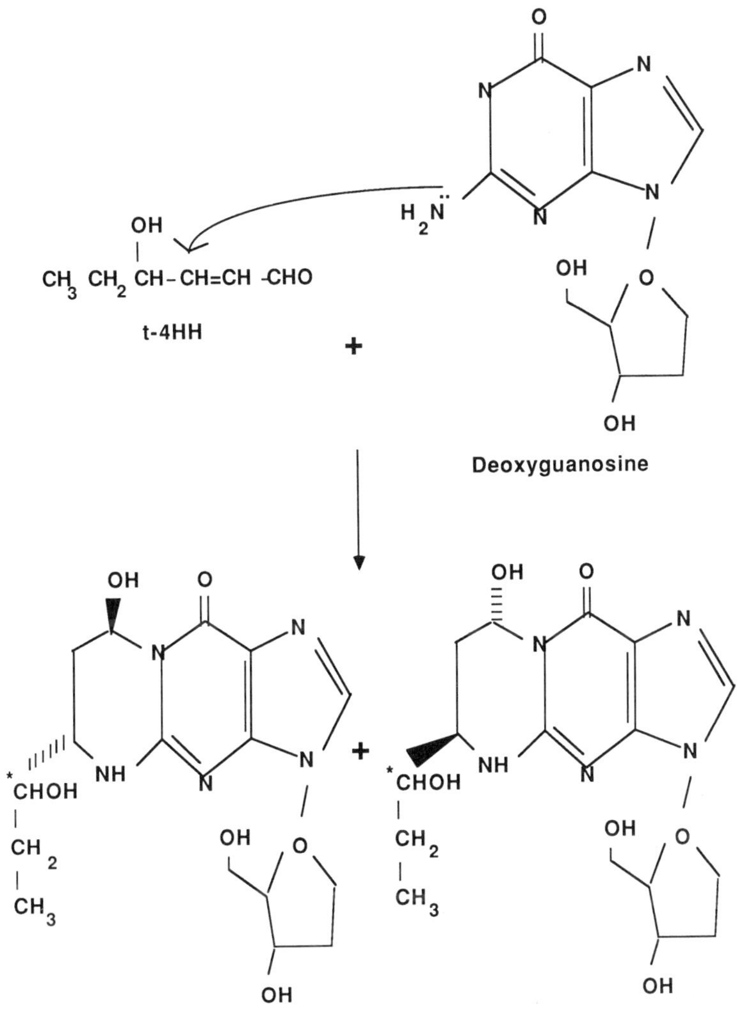

FIGURE 8 Reaction of t-4HH with deoxyguanosine in vitro.

(Winter et al., 1987). The decrease in PA toxicity when glutathione levels were raised may be due to this reaction (White, 1976; Miranda et al., 1981a; Segall et al., 1985). These results suggested similarities in the mechanism of action of the PAs and alkenals and supports the role of t-4HH as an important toxic metabolite of the PAs.

VII. RUMEN METABOLISM

It was demonstrated more than 15 years ago that PAs are susceptible to microbial reduction in the rumen of sheep. It appears that the reductive metabolism in the sheep's rumen is augmented by gram-positive and gram-negative anae-

robes and that vitamin B_{12} may be involved, although this is still debatable
(Russell and Smith, 1968; Lanigan, 1970, 1976). Dick, Dann, Bull, and Culvenor identified the metabolites 7α-hydroxy-1-methylene-8α-pyrrolizidine
and 7α-angeloxy-1-methylene-8α-pyrrolizidine following the incubation of heliotrine and lasiocarpine in sheep rumen liquor and in the sheep's rumen (Fig.
9) (Dick et al., 1963). The parent alkaloids were probably subjected to reductive fission reactions, which led to products possessing a saturated pyrrolizidine nucleus and exomethylene groups adjacent to C1. Following the incubation of heliotrine and lasiocarpine with sheep's rumen contents, 7α-hydroxy-
1α-methyl-8α-pyrrolizidine was reported as the major reductive metabolite,
which represented further reduction of the exomethylene group to a methyl
group (Lanigan and Smith, 1970).

The significance of the reduction of PAs in the rumen has been the subject of a lengthy debate. Sheeps' resistance to PAs may be due to their unique
ability to detoxify PAs in the rumen (Dick et al., 1963; Lanigan and Smith,
1970). Shull, Buckmaster, and Cheeke used sheep rumen fluid incubated
with PAs from *S. jacobaea* and demonstrated that it was more toxic to rats
than were PA preparations from cattle rumen fluid (Shull et al., 1976a). It
appeared to the authors that differences in the hepatic metabolism of the two
species were responsible for the increased PA resistance of sheep. Pyrrolizidine alkaloids from *Echium plantagineum* incubated with sheep hepatic microsomal incubations were five to seven times less toxic than were similar incubations of rat hepatic microsomes (Peterson and Jago, 1984).

VIII. INSECT METABOLISM

Numerous insect species such as grasshoppers, moths, and butterflies accumulate PAs in their tissues by feeding on PA-containing plants (Pliske et al.,
1976; Edgar et al., 1976, 1979; Bernays et al., 1977; Goss, 1979; Schneider
et al., 1982; Boppré et al., 1984). The PAs that the insects sequester make
them less palatable to predators and serves as an important defense mechanism (Edgar et al., 1976, 1979). It has been reported that some moths actually use PAs for nutritional purposes (Goss, 1979).

Both moth and butterfly species are capable of rapidly metabolizing several PAs to dihydropyrrolizine (Edgar et al., 1971, 1973; Culvenor and Edgar,

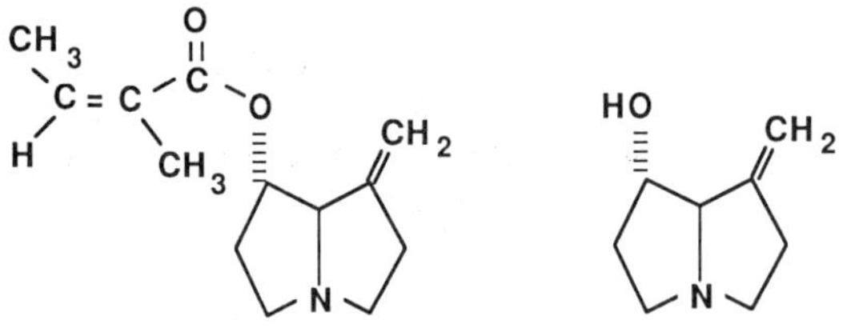

FIGURE 9 Saturated PA metabolites of heliotrine and lasiocarpine formed in
sheep rumen: (a) 7α-angeloxy-1-methylene-8α-pyrrolizidine; (b) 7α-hydroxy-
1-methylene-8α-pyrrolizidine.

1972; Edgar and Culvenor, 1974; Schneider et al., 1982; Komae et al., 1983). Examples of the dihydropyrrolizine metabolites are danaidal and danaidone plus hydroxydanaidal. The latter has also been identified as a metabolite of senecionine in an in vitro mouse hepatic microsomal incubation (Fig. 10) (Segall et al., 1984). These compounds have been found on the coremata, or scent organs, of male moths and hair pencils, or pheromone-disseminating organs, of male butterflies and apparently serve as aphrodisiacs used during courtship (Edgar et al., 1971, 1973; Culvenor and Edgar, 1972; Edgar and Culvenor, 1974; Schneider et al., 1982; Komae et al., 1983).

IX. ENZYME INDUCTION AND INHIBITION

Pretreatment of animals with mixed-function oxidase (MFO) inducers and in-hibitors has had a significant effect on the metabolism of PAs, as the MFO system plays a predominant role in their metabolism (Jago et al., 1970; Mat-tocks and White, 1971b; Buhler and Kedzierski, 1986; Mattocks, 1973, 1986). Pyrrole and N-oxide formation are decreased after pretreatment with the MFO inhibitor SKF-525A, while pretreatment with MFO inducers (pregnenolone-16α-carbonitrile, phenobarbital) increased N-oxide and pyrrole formation (Jago, 1971; Mattocks, 1972a; Chesney and Allen, 1973; White et al., 1973; Tuchweber et al., 1974; Lafranconi and Huxtable, 1984; Buhler and Kedzier-ski, 1986). Male rats predosed with phenobarbitone and administered retror-sine produced increased pyrrole levels for approximately 1 hr, but shortly thereafter pyrrole levels returned to the same levels as in noninduced animals (Mattocks, 1972a).

In a study of the in vitro metabolism of several PAs by hepatic microsomes, the induction of MFO activity in rats predosed with phenobarbital increased formation of the pyrrolic metabolite DHP while N-oxide levels were decreased or unchanged (Buhler and Kedzierski, 1986). The inducer β-naphthoflavone had a negligible effect on DHP formation but markedly decreased N-oxide for-mation. These results suggested that PA dehydrogenation was probably cata-lyzed by a cytochrome P450 isozyme rather than a P448 isozyme with PA de-hydrogenation and N-oxidation catalyzed by different enzyme systems. The addition of n-octylamine to the incubation media in the same study, plus a rise in the pH to enhance flavin monooxygenase activity, did not increase N-oxide formation.

In an in vivo study, rats pretreated with triorthocresylphosphate and dosed with synthetic analogs of PA macrocyclic analogs increased hepatic pyr-role levels (Mattocks et al., 1986). This showed that an important alternative

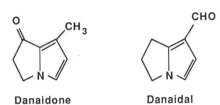

Danaidone   Danaidal

FIGURE 10 Insect PA metabolites.

(competitive pathway) for the metabolism of PAs to pyrrole production (and toxicity) was hydrolysis.

An increase in aldehyde dehydrogenase may provide additional protective measures against PA toxicity. Pregnant mice exhibited a threefold increase in cytosolic aldehyde dehydrogenase levels with increased resistance to PAs (Smolen et al., 1981). The isolation of the alkenal t-4HH may provide a partial explanation for this situation. The in vitro metabolism of t-4HH plus related alkenals by mouse liver aldehyde dehydrogenase was examined (Lamé and Segall, 1986). Kinetic experiments with hepatic cytosol as a source of aldehyde dehydrogenase(s) yielded linear Lineweaver-Burk plots for t-4HH. Diethylaminoethyl (DEAE)-cellulose chromatography of cytosol isolated only a single peak capable of metabolizing t-4HH, which resulted in the majority of activity for the oxidation of t-4HH. Only minor oxidase activity was identified in the mitochondrial fraction.

X. DIETARY/NUTRITIONAL CHANGES

Dietary and nutritional changes can markedly alter hepatic PA metabolism. A low-lipotrope diet fed to rats following monocrotaline ingestion produced lower levels of pyrrole metabolites than were produced in rats fed a normal diet (New berne et al., 1971). Rats starved or fed a low-protein diet exhibited lower in vitro pyrrole production than that of normal rats; this was possibly the result of the decreased MFO activity due to low-protein diets (Mattocks and White, 1971b). Rats fed a pure sucrose diet exhibited reduced pyrrole levels from in vitro microsomal levels and this report suggested that pyrroles may be further metabolized by conjugating with glucuronides (Mattocks, 1972a).

If rats were pretreated with cysteine (which would raise the level of glutathione) and subsequently challenged with retrorsine, a decrease in the level of pyrrolic metabolites occurred (White, 1976). Glutathione thus played a significant role in the metabolism of the pyrroles. Rats pretreated with ethoxyquin and provided with monocrotaline exhibited little change in their pyrrole levels, although ethoxyquin did raise liver glutathione levels (Miranda et al., 1981a). It is possible that pyrrole levels may have increased due to a rise in cytochrome P450 levels or that pyrrole levels were reduced due to glutathione conjugation. Pretreatment of rats for 10 days with 1% dietary cysteine did not affect liver sulfhydryl levels, but reduced the levels of bound pyrroles from PAs of *S. jacobaea* after 2 h. Young female rats provided butylated hydroxyanisole in their diet and monocrotaline exhibited a reduced in vitro hepatic microsomal conversion (Miranda et al., 1981b).

XI. EFFECTS OF PYRROLIZIDINE ALKALOIDS ON METABOLIC SYSTEMS

Male rats fed diets containing 5% *S. jacobaea* for 1 to 4 weeks or 0.5% PA mixture for 3 weeks exhibited reduced hepatic microsomal aryl hydrocarbon hydroxylase activity by both diets with hepatic cytochrome P450 activity lowered after completion of the 0.5% PA mixture (Miranda et al., 1980b). Both diets increased the hepatic microsomal epoxide hydrolase and cytosolic glutathione *S*-transferase activities. Prolonged administration of a diet containing 20% *S. jacobaea* to sheep did not alter the levels of hepatic microsomal aminopyrene *N*-demethylase, epoxide hydrolase, glutathione *S*-transferase or liver glutathione levels (Swick et al., 1983). Rat hepatic microsomal aminopyrene *N*-demethylase and cytochrome P450 activities were reduced following a single dose of a PA mixture of *S. vulgaris* (Shull et al., 1976b). Eastman and Segall showed that alkaloid mixtures from *S. vulgaris* inhibited aminopyrene *N*-demethylase activity but did not affect aniline hydroxylase activity in rat hepatic S-10 fractions (Eastman and Segall, 1980). Additional studies showed that retrorsine was a competitive inhibitor of aminopyrene *N*-demethylase, whereas senecionine and seneciphylline were linear mixed-type inhibitors (Eastman and Segall, 1981). Intraperitoneal injections of monocrotaline in young male rats did not raise epoxide hydrolase activity and decreased aryl hydrocarbon hydroxylase, aminopyrene *N*-demethylase, and glutathione *S*-transferase (Miranda et al., 1980a). Intraperitoneal injections of jacobine increased glutathione *S*-transferase and epoxide hydrolase activities, reduced cytochrome P450 levels, and had no effect upon aryl hydrocarbon hydroxylase activity (Miranda et al., 1980a). Rats injected with dehydromonocrotaline exhibited inhibition of hepatic cell mitosis and DNA synthesis (Hsu et al., 1973b).

Recently, lipid peroxidation was examined as a potential mechanism for cell injury in isolated hepatocytes by t-4HH, the PA senecionine, and related alkenals; but results suggested that lipid peroxidation was not entirely responsible for cellular damage (Griffin and Segall, 1987a). A further study using the same compounds examined the role of calcium homeostasis in isolated rat hepatocytes, but suggested that hepatotoxicity induced by senecionine and t-4HH was not dependent on the influx of extracellular Ca^{2+} (Griffin and Segall, 1987b). Alterations in intracellular Ca^{2+}, possibly associated with depletion of intracellular glutathione, NADPH, and ATP may play a critical role. A follow-up study used the same compounds to determine the sesquestration of Ca^{2+} in mitochondrial and extramitochondrial compartments in isolated hepatocytes (Griffin and Segall, 1989). The results indicated that both senecionine and t-4HH inhibit the sesquestration of Ca^{2+} in mitochondrial and extramitochondrial compartments possibly by inactivating free sulfhydryl groups and oxidizing pyridine nucleotides, respectively.

REFERENCES

Armstrong, S. J., and Zuckerman, A. J. (1970). Production of pyrroles from pyrrolizidine alkaloids by human embryo tissue. *Nature 228*:569-570.

Bernays, E., Edgar, J. A., and Rothschild, M. (1977). Pyrrolizidine alkaloids sequestered and stored by the aposematic grasshopper, *Zonocerus variegatus*. *J. Zool. (Lond.) 182*:85-87.

Boppré, M., Seibt, U., and Wickler, W. (1984). Pharmacophagy in grasshoppers. *Entomol. Exp. Appl. 35*:115.

Bottomley, W., and Geissman, T. A. (1964). Pyrrolizidine alkaloids: the biosynthesis of retronecine. *Phytochemistry 3*:357-360.

Bras, G., Jelliffee, D. B., and Stuart, K. L. (1954). Veno-occlusive disease of liver with non-portal type of cirrhosis occurring in Jamaica. *Arch. Pathol.* 57:285-300.

Buhler, D. R., and Kedzierski, B. (1986). Biological reactive intermediates of pyrrolizidine alkaloids. In *Biological Reactive Intermeidates* III, J. J. Kocsis, D. J. Jollow, C. M. Witmer, J. O. Nelson, and R. Snyder (Eds.). Plenum Press, New York, pp. 611-620.

Bull, L. B., Culvenor, C. C. J., and Dick, A. T. (1968). The pyrrolizidine alkaloids. In *Frontiers of Biology*. North-Holland, Amsterdam.

Butler, W. H., Mattocks, A. R., and Barnes, J. M. (1970). Lesions in the liver and lungs of rats given pyrrole derivatives of pyrrolizidine alkaloids. *J. Pathol.* 100:169-175.

Chesney, C. F., and Allen, J. R. (1973). Resistance of the guinea pig to pyrrolizidine alkaloid intoxication. *Toxicol. Appl. Pharmacol.* 26:385-392.

Culvenor, C. C. J. (1976). Carcinogenic activity of coltsfoot, *Tussilago fareara* L. *Gann* 67:125-129.

Culvenor, C. C. J., and Edgar, J. A. (1972). Dihydropyrrolizine secretions associated with coremata of *Utetheisa* moths (family Arctiidae). *Experientia* 28:627-628.

Culvenor, C. C. J., and Jago, M. V. (1979). Carcinogenic plant products and DNA. In *Chemical Carcinogens and DNA*, P. L. Grover (Ed.). CRC Press, Boca Raton, Fla., pp. 161-186.

Culvenor, C. C. J., Downing, D. T., and Edgar, J. A. (1969). Part 4, Environmental alkylating agents: pyrrolizidine alkaloids as alkylating and antimitotic agents. *Ann. N.Y. Acad. Sci.* 163:837-847.

Culvenor, C. C. J., Edgar, J. A., Smith, L. W., and Tweeddale, H. J. (1970). Dihydropyrrolizines: III. Preparation and reactions of derivatives related to pyrrolizidine alkaloids. *Aust. J. Chem.* 23:1853-1867.

Culvenor, C. C. J., Edgar, J. A., and Smith, L. W. (1971). Active metabolites in the chronic hepatotoxicity of pyrrolizidine alkaloids, including otonecine esters. *Nature (Lond.) New Biol.* 229:255-256.

Culvenor, C. C. J., Edgar, J. A., Jago, M. V., Outteridge, A., and Peterson, J. E. (1976). Hepato- and pneumotoxicity of pyrrolizidine alkaloids and derivatives in relation to molecular structure. *Chem.-Biol. Interact.* 12:299-324.

Culvenor, C. C. J., Clarke, M., Edgar, J. A., Frahn, J. L., Jago, M. V., Peterson, J. E., and Smith, L. W. (1980). Structure and toxicity of the alkaloids of Russian comfrey (*Symphytum × uplandicum* Nyman), a medicinal herb and item of human diet. *Experientia* 36:377-379.

Deinzer, M. L., Thomson, P. A., Burgett, D. M., and Isaacson, D. L. (1977). Pyrrolizidine alkaloids: their occurrence in honey from tansy ragwort (*Senecio jacobaea* L.). *Science* 195:497-499.

Dick, A. T., Dann, A. T., Bull, L. B., and Culvenor, C. C. J. (1963). Vitamin B_{12} and the detoxification of hepatotoxic pyrrolizidine alkaloids in rumen liquor. *Nature* 197:207-208.

Dickinson, J. O., Cooke, M. P., King, R. R., and Mohamed, P. A. (1976). Milk transfer of pyrrolizidine alkaloids in cattle. *J. Am. Vet. Med. Assoc.* 169:1192-1196.

Driver, H. E., and Mattocks, A. R. (1984). The toxic effects in rats of some synthanecine carbamate and phosphate esters analogous to hepatotoxic pyrrolizidine alkaloids. *Chem.-Biol. Interact.* 51:201-218.

Eastman, D. F., and Segall, H. J. (1980). The effect of pyrrolizidine alkaloids (*Senecio vulgaris*) on the liver mixed-function oxidase system. *Toxicol. Lett.* 5:369-374.

Eastman, D. F., and Segall, H. J. (1981). Effects of pyrrolizidine alkaloids senecionine, retrorsine and seneciphylline on aminopyrine *N*-demethylase activity of the rat liver S-10 fraction. *Toxicol. Lett.* 8:217-222.

Eastman, D. F., and Segall, H. J. (1982). A new pyrrolizidine alkaloid metabolite, 19-hydroxysenecionine isolated from mouse hepatic microsomes in vitro. *Drug Metab. Dispos.* 10:696-699.

Edgar, J. A., and Culvenor, C. C. J. (1974). Pyrrolizidine ester alkaloid in danaid butterflies. *Nature* 248:614-165.

Edgar, J. A., Culvenor, C. C. J., and Smith, L. W. (1971). Dihydropyrrolizine derivatives in the hair-pencil secretions of danaid butterflies. *Experientia* 27:761-762.

Edgar, J. A., Culvenor, C. C. J., and Robinson, G. S. (1973). Hairpencil dihydropyrrolizidines of danainae from the New Hebrides. *J. Aust. Entomol. Soc.* 12:144-150.

Edgar, J. A., Cockrum, P. A., and Frahn, J. L. (1976). Pyrrolizidine alkaloids in *Danaus plexippus* and *Danaus chrysippus* L. *Experientia* 32:1535-1537.

Edgar, J. A., Boppré, M., and Schneider, D. (1979). Pyrrolizidine alkaloid storage in African and Australian danaid butterflies. *Experientia* 35:1447-1448.

Goss, G. J. (1979). The interaction between moths and plants containing pyrrolizidine alkaloids. *Environ. Entomol.* 8:487-493.

Grasse, L. D., Lamé, M. W., and Segall, H. J. (1985). In vivo covalent binding of *trans*-4-hydroxy-2-hexenal to rat liver macromolecules. *Toxicol. Lett.* 29:43-49.

Green, C. E., Segall, H. J., and Byard, J. L. (1981). Metabolism, cytotoxicity, and genotoxicity of the pyrrolizidine alkaloid senecionine in primary cultures of rat hepatocytes. *Toxicol. Appl. Pharmacol.* 60:176-185.

Griffin, D. S., and Segall, H. J. (1986). Genotoxicity and cytotoxicity of selected pyrrolizidine alkaloids, a possible metabolite of the alkaloids, and related alkenals. *Toxicol. Appl. Pharmacol.* 86:227-234.

Griffin, D. S., and Segall, H. J. (1987a). Lipid peroxidation and cellular damage caused by the pyrrolizidine alkaloid senecionine, the alkenal *trans*-4-hydroxy-2-hexenal, and related alkenals. *Cell Biol. Toxicol.* 3:379-390.

Griffin, D. S., and Segall, H. J. (1987b). Role of cellular calcium homeostasis in toxic liver injury induced by the pyrrolizidine alkaloid senecionine and the alkenal *trans*-4-OH-2-hexenal. *J. Biochem. Toxicol.* 2:155-167.

Griffin, D. S., and Segall, H. J. (1989). Effects of the pyrrolizidine alkaloid senecionine and the alkenals *trans*-4-OH-hexenal and *trans*-2-hexenal on intracellular calcium compartmentation in isolated hepatocytes. *Biochem. Pharmacol.* 38:391-397.

Guengerich, F. P. (1977). Separation and purification of multiple forms of microsomal cytochrome P-450. *J. Biol. Chem.* 252:3970-3979.

Guengerich, F. P., and Mitchell, M. B. (1980). Metabolic activation of model pyrroles by cytochrome P-450. *Drug Metab. Dispos.* 8:34-38.

Hill, K. R., Rhoades, K., Stafford, J. L., and Aub, R. (1951). Liver disease in Jamaican children (serous hepatosis). *West Indian Med. J.* 1:49-63.

Hilliker, K. S., Garcia, C. M., and Roth, R. A. (1983). Effects of monocrotaline pyrrole on 5-hydroxytryptamine and paraquat uptake by lung slices. *Res. Commun. Chem. Pathol. Pharmacol.* 40:179-197.

Hsu, I. C., Allen, J. R., and Chesney, C. F. (1973a). Identification and toxicological effects of dehydroretronecine, a metabolite of monocrotaline. *Proc. Soc. Exp. Biol. Med.* 144:834-838.

Hsu, I. C., Chesney, C. F., Allen, J. R. (1973b). Chronic effects of monocrotaline pyrrole on hepatic mitosis and DNA synthesis. *Proc. Soc. Exp. Biol. Med.* 142:1133-1136.

Hughes, C. A., Letcher, R., and Warren, F. L. (1964). The senecio alkaloids: Part XVI. The biosynthesis of the necine bases from carbon-14 precursors. *J. Chem. Soc.* 4974-4977.

Huxtable, R. J. (1980). Herbal teas and toxins: novel aspects of pyrrolizidine poisoning in the United States. *Perspect. Biol. Med.* 24:1-14.

Jago, M. V. (1971). Factors affecting the chronic hepatotoxicity of pyrrolizidine alkaloids. *J. Pathol.* 105:1-11.

Jago, M. V., Lanigan, G. W., Bingley, J. B., Piercy, D. W. T., Whittem, J. H., and Titchen, D. A. (1969). Excretion of the pyrrolizidine alkaloid heliotrine in the urine and bile of sheep. *J. Pathol.* 98:115-128.

Jago, M. V., Edgar, J. A., Smith, L. W., and Culvenor, C. C. J. (1970). Metabolic conversion of heliotridine-based pyrrolizidine alkaloids to dehydroheliotridine. *Mol. Pharmacol.* 6:402-406.

Kedzierski, B., and Buhler, D. R. (1985). Configuration of necine pyrroles-toxic metabolites of pyrrolizidine alkaloids. *Toxicol. Lett.* 25:115-119.

Kedzierski, B., and Buhler, D. R. (1986a). Method for determination of pyrrolizidine alkaloids and their metabolites by high-performance liquid chromatography. *Anal. Biochem.* 152:59-65.

Kedzierski, B., and Buhler, D. R. (1986b). The formation of 6-7-dihydro-7-hydroxy-1-hydroxy-methyl-5*H*-pyrrolizidine, a metabolite of pyrrolizidine alkaloids. *Chem.-Biol. Interact.* 57:217-222.

Komae, H., Nishi, A., Hayashi, N., Wesou, C., and Kuwahara, Y. (1983). Components of the sex brand secretions of some danaid butterflies. *Agric. Biol. Chem.* 47:157-158.

Lafranconi, W. M., and Huxtable, R. J. (1984). Hepatic metabolism and pulmonary toxicity of monocrotaline using isolated perfused liver and lung. *Biochem. Pharmacol.* 31:2479-2484.

Lafranconi, W. M., Ohkuma, S., and Huxtable, R. J. (1985). Biliary excretion of novel pneumotoxic metabolites of the pyrrolizidine alkaloid, monocrotaline. *Toxicon* 23:983-992.

Lame, M. W., and Segall, H. J. (1986). Metabolism of the pyrrolizidine alkaloid metabolite *trans*-4-hydroxy-2-hexenal by mouse liver aldehyde dehydrogenase. *Toxicol. Appl. Pharmacol.* 82:94-103.

Lanigan, G. W. (1970). Metabolism of pyrrolizidine alkaloids in the ovine rumen: II. Some factors affecting rate of alkaloid breakdown by rumen fluid in vitro. *Aust. J. Agric. Res.* 21:633-639.

Lanigan, G. W. (1976). *Peptococcus heliotrinreducans*, sp. nov., a cyto-chrome-producing anaerobe which metabolizes pyrrolizidine alkaloids. *J. Gen. Microbiol. 94*:1-10.

Lanigan, G. W., and Smith, L. W. (1970). Metabolism of pyrrolizidine alkaloids in the ovine rumen: I. Formation of 7α-hydroxy-1α-methyl-8α-pyrrolizidine from heliotrine and lasiocarpine. *Aust. J. Agric. Res. 21*:493-500.

Mattocks, A. R. (1967). Spectrophotometric determination of unsaturated pyrrolizine alkaloids. *Anal. Chem. 39*:443-447.

Mattocks, A. R. (1968). Spectrophotometric determination of pyrrolizidine alkaloids—some improvements. *Anal. Chem. 40*:1749-1750.

Mattocks, A. R. (1969). Dihydropyrrolizidine derivatives from unsaturated pyrrolizidine alkaloids. *J. Chem. Soc. C*:1155-1969.

Mattocks, A. R. (1970). Role of the acid moieties in the toxic actions of pyrrolizidine alkaloids on liver and lung. *Nature 228*:174-175.

Mattocks, A. R. (1971). Hepatotoxic effects due to pyrrolizidine alkaloid N-oxides. *Xenobiotica 1*:563-565.

Mattocks, A. R. (1972a). Acute hepatotoxicity and pyrrolic metabolites in rats dosed with pyrrolizidine alkaloids. *Chem.-Biol. Interact. 5*:227-242.

Mattocks, A. R. (1972b). Toxicity and metabolism of *Senecio* alkaloids. In *Phytochemical Ecology: Proceedings of the Phytochemical Society Symposium*, J. B. Harborne (Ed.). Academic Press, New York, pp. 179-200.

Mattocks, A. R. (1973). Mechanisms of pyrrolizidine alkaloid toxicity. In *Pharmacology and the Future of Man*, Vol. 2, G. H. Acheson (Ed.). S. Karger, Basel, pp. 114-123.

Mattocks, A. R. (1978). Recent studies on mechanisms of cytotoxic action of pyrrolizidine alkaloids. In *Effects of Poisonous Plants on Livestock*, R. F. Keeler, K. R. van Kampen, and L. R. James (Eds.). Academic Press, New York, pp. 177-188.

Mattocks, A. R. (1981). Relation of structural features to pyrrolic metabolites in livers of rats given pyrrolizidine alkaloids and derivatives. *Chem.-Biol. Interact. 35*:301-310.

Mattocks, A. R. (1982). Hydrolysis and hepatotoxicity of retronecine diesters. *Toxicol. Lett. 14*:111-116.

Mattocks, A. R. (1986). *Chemistry and Toxicology of Pyrrolizidine Alkaloids.* Academic Press, Orlando, Fla.

Mattocks, A. R., and Bird, I. (1983a). Alkylation by dehydroretronecine, a cytotoxic metabolite of some pyrrolizidine alkaloids: an in vitro test. *Toxicol. Lett. 16*:1-8.

Mattocks, A. R., and Bird, I. (1983b). Pyrrolic and N-oxide metabolites formed from pyrrolizidine alkaloids by hepatic microsomes in vitro: relevance to in vivo hepatotoxicity. *Chem.-Biol. Interact. 43*:209-222.

Mattocks, A. R., and White, I. N. H. (1970). Estimation of metabolites of pyrrolizidine alkaloids in animal tissues. *Anal. Biochem. 38*:529-535.

Mattocks, A. R., and White, I. N. H. (1971a). Pyrrolic metabolites from non-toxic pyrrolizidine alkaloids. *Nature (Lond.) New Biol. 231*:114-115.

Mattocks, A. R., and White, I. N. H. (1971b). The conversion of pyrrolizidine alkaloids to N-oxides and to dihydropyrrolizine derivatives by rat-liver microsomes in vitro. *Chem.-Biol. Interact. 3*:383-396.

Mattocks, A. R., Driver, H. E., Barbour, R. H., and Robins, D. J. (1986).

Metabolism and toxicity of synthetic analogues of macrocyclic diester pyrrolizidine alkaloids. *Chem. -Biol. Interact. 58*: 95-108.

McLean, E. K. (1970). The toxic actions of pyrrolizidine (*Senecio*) alkaloids. *Pharmacol. Rev. 22*: 429-483.

Miranda, C. L., Cheeke, P. R., and Buhler, D. R. (1980a). Comparative effects of the pyrrolizidine alkaloids jocobine and monocrotaline on hepatic drug metabolizing enzymes in the rat. *Res. Commun. Chem. Pathol. Pharmacol. 29*: 573-587.

Miranda, C. L., Cheeke, P. R., and Buhler, D. R. (1980b). Effect of pyrrolizidine alkaloids from tansy ragwort (*Senecio jacobaea*) on hepatic drug-metabolizing enzymes in male rats. *Biochem. Pharmacol. 29*: 2645-2649.

Miranda, C. L., Carpenter, H. M., and Cheeke, P. R. (1981a). Effects of ethoxyquin on the toxicity of the pyrrolizidine alkaloid monocrotaline and on hepatic drug metabolism in mice. *Chem. -Biol. Interact. 37*: 95-107.

Miranda, C. L., Reed, R. L., Cheeke, P. R., and Buhler, D. R. (1981b). Protective effects of butylated hydroxyanisole against the acute toxicity of monocrotaline in mice. *Toxicol. Appl. Pharmacol. 59*: 424-430.

Mohabbat, O., Younos, M. S., Merzad, A. A., Srivastava, R. N., Sediq, G. G., and Aram, G. N. (1976). An outbreak of hepatic veno-occlusive disease in north western Afghanistan. *Lancet 2*(7980): 269-271.

Newberne, P. M., Wilson, R., and Rogers, A. E. (1971). Effects of low-lipotrope diet on the response of young male rats to the pyrrolizidine alkaloid, monocrotaline. *Toxicol. Appl. Pharmacol. 18*: 387-397.

Peterson, J. E., and Culvenor, C. C. J. (1983). Hepatotoxic pyrrolizidine alkaloids. In *Handbook of Natural Toxins*, Vol. 1, R. F. Keeler and A. T. Tu (Eds.). Marcel Dekker, New York, pp. 637-671.

Peterson, J. E., and Jago, M. V. (1984). Toxicity of *Echium plantagineum* (Paterson's curse): II. Pyrrolizidine alkaloid poisoning in rats. *Aust. J. Agric. Res. 35*: 293-304.

Pliske, T. E., Edgar, J. A., and Culvenor, C. C. J. (1976). The chemical basis of attraction of ithomiine butterflies to plants containing pyrrolizidine alkaloids. *J. Chem. Ecol. 2*: 255-262.

Powis, G., and Wincentsen, L. (1980). Pyridine necleotide cofactor requirements of indicine *N*-oxide reduction by hepatic microsomal cytochrome P-450. *Biochem. Pharmacol. 29*: 347-351.

Powis, G., Ames, M. M., and Kovach, J. S. (1979). Metabolic conversion of indicine *N*-oxide to indicine in rabbits and humans. *Cancer Res. 39*: 3564-3570.

Powis, G., Svingen, B. A., and Degraw, C. (1982). Iron-EDTA stimulated reduction of indicine *N*-oxide by the hepatic microsomal fraction, isolated hepatocytes, and the intact rat. *Biochem. Pharmacol. 31*: 293-299.

Ramsdell, H. S., Kedzierski, B., and Buhler, D. R. (1987). Microsomal metabolism of pyrrolizidine alkaloids from *Senecio jacobaea* isolation and quantification of 6,7-dihydro-7-hydroxy-1-hydroxymethyl-5*H*-pyrrolizine and *N*-oxides by high performance liquid chromatography. *Drug Metab. Dispos. 15*: 32-36.

Robertson, K. A. (1982). Akylation of N2 in deoxyguanosine by dehydro-retronecine, a carcinogenic metabolite of the pyrrolizidine alkaloid monocrotaline. *Cancer Res. 42*: 8-14.

Robertson, K. A., Seymour, J. L., Hsai, M.-T., and Allen, J. R. (1977). Covalent interaction of dehydroretronecine, a carcinogenic metabolite of the pyrrolizidine alkaloid monocrotaline, with cysteine and glutathione. *Cancer Res.* 37:3141-3144.

Russell, G. R., and Smith, R. M. (1968). Reduction of heliotrine by a rumen microorganism. *Aust. J. Biol. Sci.* 21:1277-1290.

Schneider, D., Boppré, M., Zweig, J., Horsley, S. B., Bell, T. W., Meinwald, J., Hansen, K., and Diehl, E. W. (1982). Scent organ development in *Creatonotos* moths: regulation by pyrrolizidine alkaloids. *Science* 215:1264-1265.

Schoental, R. (1968). Chemical structures and pathological effects of pyrrolizidine alkaloids. *Isr. J. Med. Sci.* 4:1133-1145.

Schoental, R. (1975). Biochemical basis of liver necrosis caused by pyrrolizidine alkaloids and certain other hepatotoxins. *Biochem. Soc. Trans.* 3:292-294.

Segall, H. J., Dallas, J. L., and Haddon, W. F. (1984). Two dihydropyrrolizine alkaloid metabolites isolated from mouse hepatic microsomes in vitro. *Drug Metab. Dispos.* 12:68-71.

Segall, H. J., Wilson, D. W., Dallas, J. L., and Haddon, W. F. (1985). Trans-4-hydroxy-2-hexenal: a reactive metabolite from the macrocyclic pyrrolizidine alkaloid senecionine. *Science* 229:472-475.

Shull, L. R., Buckmaster, G. W., and Cheeke, P. R. (1976a). Factors influencing pyrrolizidine (*Senecio*) alkaloid metabolism: species, liver sulfhydryls and rumen fermentation. *J. Anim. Sci.* 43:1247-1253.

Shull, L. R., Buckmaster, G. W., and Cheeke, P. R. (1976b). Effects of pyrrolizidine alkaloids on liver microsome mixed-function oxidase activity in rats. *J. Anim. Sci.* 43:1024-1027.

Smith, L. W., and Culvenor, C. C. J. (1981). Plant sources of hepatotoxic pyrrolizidine alkaloids. *J. Nat. Prod.* 44:129-152.

Smolen, A., Peterson, D. R., and Collins, A. C. (1981). Liver cytosolic aldehyde dehydrogenase activity in the pregnant mouse. *Dev. Pharmacol. Ther.* 3:31-49.

Swick, R. A., Miranda, C. L., Cheeke, P. R., and Buhler, D. R. (1983). Effect of phenobarbital on toxicity of pyrrolizidine (*Senecio*) alkaloids in sheep. *J. Anim. Sci.* 56:887-894.

Tomer, K. B., Gross, M. L., and Deinzer, M. L. (1986). Fast atom bombardment and tandem mass spectrometry of covalently modified nucleosides and nucleotides: adducts of pyrrolizidine alkaloid metabolites. *Anal. Chem.* 58:2527-2534.

Tuchweber, B., Kovacs, K., Jago, M. V., and Beaulieu, T. (1974). Effect of steroidal and nonsteroidal microsomal enzyme inducers on the hepatotoxicity of pyrrolizidine alkaloids in rats. *Res. Commun. Chem. Pathol. Pharmacol.* 7:459-480.

White, I. N. H. (1976). The role of liver glutathione in the acute toxicity of retrorsine to rats. *Chem.-Biol. Interact.* 13:333-342.

White, I. N. H. (1977). Excretion of pyrrolic metabolites in the bile of rats given the pyrrolizidine alkaloid retrorsine or the bis-N-ethylcarbamate of synthanecine A. *Chem.-Biol. Interact.* 16:169-180.

White, I. N. H., and Mattocks, A. R. (1971). Some factors affecting the conversion of pyrrolizidine alkaloids to N-oxides and to pyrrolic derivatives in vitro. *Xenobiotica 1*: 503-505.

White, I. N. H., Mattocks, A. R., and Buhler, W. H. (1973). The conversion of the pyrrolizidine alkaloid retrorsine to pyrrolic derivatives in vivo and in vitro and its acute toxicity to various animal species. *Chem.-Biol. Interact. 6*: 207-218.

Wilson, D. W., Segall, H. J., and Lamé, M. W. (1986). Hepatic pathological changes due to hydroxyalkenals. In *Biological Reactive Intermediates III*. D. J. Jollow, C. M. Witmer, J. O. Nelson, and R. Snyder (Eds.). Plenum Press, New York, pp. 853-860.

Winter, C. K., Segall, H. J., and Haddon, W. F. (1986). Formation of cyclic adducts of deoxyguanosine with the aldehydes *trans*-4-hydroxy-2-hexenal and *trans*-4-hydroxy-2-hexenal in vitro. *Cancer Res. 46*: 5682-5686.

Winter, C. K., Segall, H. J., and Jones, A. D. (1987). Distribution of *trans*-4-hydroxy-2-hexenal and tandem mass spectrometric detection of its urinary mercapturic acid in the rat. *Drug Metab. Dispos. 15*: 608-612.

Winter, C. K., Segall, H. J., and Jones, A. D. (1988a). Determination of pyrrolizidine alkaloid metabolites from mouse liver microsomes using tandem mass spectrometry adn gas chromatography/mass spectrometry. *Biomed. Environ. Mass Spectrom. 15*: 265-273.

Winter, C. K., Segall, H. J., and Jones, A. D. (1988b). Species differences in the hepatic microsomal metabolism of the pyrrolizidine alkaloid senecionine. *Comp. Biochem. Physiol. C90*: 429-433.

2

Teratogenicity of Rangeland Lupinus: The Crooked Calf Disease

Richard H. Finnell and Clive C. Gay

College of Veterinary Medicine, Washington State University, Pullman, Washington

Louise C. Abbott *College of Veterinary Medicine, University of Illinois at Urbana-Champaign, Urbana, Illinois*

I. INTRODUCTION

Crooked calf disease is a pattern of congenital anomalies observed in the off-spring of range-grazed beef and dairy cattle in the western United States and Alaska (James, 1977; Keeler, 1973a; Leipold et al., 1969; Shupe et al., 1967a). Usually, no more than 10% of a herd is affected in any one calving season, but up to 40% of calves from a single herd have been reported to be affected (Shupe et al., 1967b; Finnell and Gay, unpublished data). Economic losses for producers are incurred in at least three ways from this condition. First, many of the affected calves die or must be destroyed soon after birth because they cannot stand to suckle or follow the dam. Second, crooked calf disease may be accompanied by dystocia, requiring assistance with calving and potential loss of the dam as well as the calf. Finally, there is the loss of prospective replacement heifers when affected calves are produced (Leipold et al., 1969).

This disease is grossly characterized by the presence of congenital arth-rogryposis of one or both of the forelimbs, typically involving both the elbow and carpal joints. Most often, the elbow joints are immobilized in a flexed position due to malpositioning and malalignment of the ulna and radius with relation to the articular surface of the distal humerus. This is often accompanied by a lateral rotation of the limb distal to the elbow. In crooked calf disease, cutting the flexor tendons of the affected joints does not permit extension of the flexed joint, thereby distinguishing this disease from the condition known as contracted tendons (Leipold et al., 1969, 1977; Shupe et al., 1967a). Whereas many calves born with contracted tendons recover spontaneously or respond favorably to surgical intervention, the anomalies observed with crooked calf disease are permanent (Keeler et al., 1977). Other congenital anomalies in various combinations may also occur in this condition, although arthrogryposis is by far the principal abnormality. Less frequently observed features of crooked calf disease include under- or overextension of the proximal interphalangeal joints, torticollis (cervical scoliosis), scoliosis, and arthrogryposis of the hindlimbs. Muscles from affected limbs are often hypoplastic or atrophied. This loss of muscle mass is usually attributed to disuse of the affected limbs; however, this could also be neurogenic in origin (Shupe et al., 1968). Cleft palate has been reported in several calves affected with crooked calf disease, one of which also displayed subtle facial and neurocranial abnormalities (Shupe et al., 1967a, 1968). Due to problems in ascertainment and reporting of cases, it is uncertain whether orofacial clefts should be included in the less frequently observed features of the crooked calf disease, or if those cases reported represent chance associations. Ankylosis has not been observed in any of the calves that have been necropsied and carefully examined.

A wide spectrum of severity is observed in calves affected with crooked calf disease. The least affected animals usually present with mild contractures of the forelimbs, with or without mild scoliosis and/or torticollis, and are capable of standing up from a recumbent position and walking without any assistance. Although these mildly affected calves survive quite well, the osseous changes are permanent and, with age, usually worsen, since the limbs are subjected to greater load-bearing stresses. The most severely affected animals present with severe contractures of both forelimbs, and the hindlimbs may also be affected. In addition, these animals usually have severe torticollis and/or scoliosis. Even with assistance, severely affected crooked calves are unable to assume a standing position.

Crooked calf disease is considered to be a nonhereditary condition since replacement of breeding stock or the introduction of a different breed of cattle does not prevent its recurring when pregnant cattle continue to graze on rangelands where lupine is present (Shupe et al., 1967a). In addition, when 11 typically crooked-legged heifers were bred to a bull with crooked legs and cleft palate, only normal calves were produced (Shupe et al., 1968). These data all suggest that the transmission of crooked calf disease is nonhereditary.

Given the lack of a familial pattern to outbreaks of the disease, environmental parameters common to the occurrence of crooked calf disease were sought. It was noted that outbreaks occur where cattle graze on rangeland heavily populated with lupine plants, suggesting that maternal ingestion of lupine plants is causally associated with the disorder (Wagnon, 1960; Rimbey, 1969). Field observations (Shupe et al., 1967a; Keeler et al., 1977) as well as feeding trials (Shupe et al., 1967b; Keeler, 1973a,b, 1976) indicate that crooked calf disease is caused by maternal ingestion of anagyrine, a quinolizidine alkaloid found in certain members of the plant genus *Lupinus*. Keeler (1973b) determined that there were four major alkaloid peaks commonly associated with extracts from teratogenic lupines. He subsequently established that the fourth peak, anagyrine, was most probably the teratogenic agent (Keeler, 1973b, 1976). While oral administration of lupine extracts, with or without anagyrine, can routinely cause the classic symptoms of alkaloid toxicity, only administration of those extracts containing the alkaloid anagyrine results in the production of affected offspring in the feeding trial experiments. Teratogenesis occurs with ingestion of 6.5 to 11.9 mg/kg of anagyrine per day for 3 to 4 weeks between days 40 and 75 of gestation (Shupe et al., 1967b; Keeler, 1976). Therefore, the data strongly suggest that it is the anagyrine contained in lupine plants that is the primary teratogenic agent when these plants are ingested by pregnant cows during early gestation (Keeler, 1973a,b, 1976; Shupe, 1970).

Finally, when considering the teratogenicity of lupine plants, it is important to be aware of the significant changes in the production of the toxic alkaloids that occur during the course of their life cycle. The concentration of total and individual alkaloids found in the leaves and stems is higher when the plants are immature and decreases to a much lower level as the plants mature. This is generally true for all portions of the plant, except for intact seeds, which demonstrate an increase in anagyrine concentration as they mature (Keeler et al., 1976). Since there are approximately 100 different species of lupines in the western United States (Kingsbury, 1964), with many species of lupine not containing significant concentrations of anagyrine at any stage of growth, and since the anagyrine content in lupines is variable in those species that do produce the alkaloid (Keeler et al., 1976; Davis, 1982), it is not possible to project a teratogenic dose for the plant material itself.

II. HISTOLOGICAL AND HISTOCHEMICAL STUDIES: PRIMARY MYOPATHY OR FETAL NEUROPATHY?

Several disorders in cattle are characterized by the presence of congenital arthrogryposis. Etiologies include spinal dysraphism (Hulland, 1985) and exposure of the pregnant dam to specific viral agents such as those of Akabane disease (Hartley et al., 1977; Konno et al., 1982; Kurogi et al., 1977; Kirkland et al., 1988) and Bluetongue (Leudke et al., 1977). In our own experience with herds from eastern Washington state afflicted with crooked calf disease, we cannot incriminate a viral etiology for the abnormalities seen in the affected calves. Our test herds in Washington have been examined for evidence of infection with Akabane, BVD, Bluetongue, and IBR viruses, all of which are known to produce either congenital arthrogryposis or cleft palate. Sera from all animals tested were negative for Akabane virus, and colostrum-deprived calves were negative for BVD, Bluetongue, and IBR viruses as well as negative for virus isolation from tissue samples (Abbott et al., 1986).

Both gross and histological examinations of tissues were performed on affected neonatal Angus × Hereford calves (four female and four male), approximately 2 days old, originally submitted from a ranch in eastern Washington. Calves were submitted to the Washington Animal Disease Diagnostic Laboratory (WADDL) at Washington State University and subsequently eutha-

TABLE 1 Macroscopic Findings from Necropsy

Calf no.	Gender	Arthrogryposis Forelimb	Hindlimb	Shortened humerus	Torticollis	Costochondral junction	Brain weight (g)
2255	Male	Yes[a]	No	Left only	Yes	Indented[b]	232.4
2252	Male	Yes[a,c]	No	Both[d]	Yes	Normal	213.4
2254	Female	Yes	No	Both[d]	None	Indented[b]	201.3
2259	Male	Yes[c]	No	None	Yes	Indented[b,e]	215.5
2253	Female	Yes[a,f]	No	None	Yes	Normal	224.0
2257	Female	Yes[a,f,g]	No	None	Yes	Normal	200.6
2258	Male	Yes[f,g]	No	None	Yes	Normal	219.2
2256	Female	Yes[f,g]	No	None	None	Normal	213.2

[a]Left limb deviated laterally at the elbow.
[b]Costochondral junctions on left side are medially indented.
[c]Right limb deviated at the elbow.
[d]Abnormal shape as well as shortened.
[e]Costochondral junctions on right side are medially indented.
[f]Right limb deviated medially at the carpus.
[g]Left limb deviated laterally at the carpus.

nized by barbiturate overdose. Each of the calves presented with varying
degrees of the crooked calf disease, the details of which are presented in
Table 1. Radiographs of the limbs, skull, and vertebral column from two of
the eight animals were also obtained. Samples were taken from the following
sites for light-microscopic investigation: brain (brainstem, cerebellum, cerebral cortex), heart, liver, lung, pancreas, adrenal gland, kidney, spleen,
and radial and femoral nerves. In addition, the external intercostalis,
brachialis, triceps brachii, biceps brachii, longissimus dorsi, biceps femoris,
vastus lateralis, and semitendinosus skeletal muscles were all sampled. All
tissues processed for light microscopy were fixed in 10% neutral buffered
formalin. After routine paraffin embedding, sections were cut at 4 µm, stained
with hematoxylin and eosin (HE), and examined.

Samples of the following skeletal muscles from four affected Angus × Hereford calves were additionally processed for special histochemical examination:
brachialis, triceps brachii, longissimus dorsi, vastus lateralis, and semitendinosus muscles. Muscle samples used as controls for the histochemistry were
taken from the same skeletal muscles of an unaffected, male Holstein calf.
A square block of tissue 2 to 3 cm thick was dissected from the superficial
surface of each muscle at the midpoint of the muscle belly. Blocks of tissue
from the longissimus muscles were taken from the superficial surface located
at the midpoint between the last rib and the tuber coxae. From the center
of these larger pieces of tissue, a block of muscle approximately 10 × 5 × 5
mm was trimmed off the superficial surface, placed on a small piece of cork,

and frozen in isopentane cooled to -160°C by liquid nitrogen. The frozen tissue was maintained on dry ice or in a -70°C freezer or until transverse serial sections of 10 μm thickness were cut on a cryostat at -20°C. Adenosine triphosphatase (ATPase) at pH 10.3 and NADH-tetrazolium reductase (NADH-tr) reactions were used to analyze different enzyme activities in the muscle fibers. Areas of each muscle sample containing 200 to 500 fibers were photographed. Counts of type I and type II fibers were made from the photographs of the sections reacted with ATPase. In addition to the counts, the muscle samples were examined for the presence of any abnormal fibers that can be visualized with ATPase or NADH-tr reactions, but not with HE.

Extensive histopathological examination of neonatal calves exhibiting crooked calf disease, based on hematoxylin and eosin (HE)-stained muscle samples, does not reveal any consistent primary lesion of skeletal muscle or nervous tissue (Abbott et al., 1986). Rather, varied responses have been observed, including myositis, myodegeneration, muscle atrophy and necrosis, cellulitis, and perineuritis in various muscles or nerves (Table 2). It is likely that these various findings are, at least in part, a result of pressure or trauma due to the calves' inability to stand, although some of the lesions could have been initiated prior to birth.

Repeated gross and histologic examination of all major soft-tissue organ systems failed to reveal any evidence of abnormality (Abbott et al., 1986). All reports of examinations of brains and spinal cords from affected calves indicate that no gross or histologic abnormalities have been uncovered. Further, the average brain weight observed from affected calves is not significantly different from normal standards developed for neonatal dairy calves, according to Washington Animal Disease Diagnostic Laboratory records.

It is noteworthy that radiographs of the affected calves do not usually reveal osseous abnormalities that are as severe as might be predicted on the basis of the visible, gross abnormalities (Abbott et al., 1986; Shupe et al., 1967b). The most common radiographic abnormalities observed are subluxation and lateral or medial deviation of joints in the affected limbs—in particular, the malpositioning of the ulna and radius with respect to the distal humerus (Shupe et al., 1967a,b). Occasional abnormally shaped articular surfaces of long bones are also described (Abbott et al., 1986). In spite of severe torticollis, there may be no radiographic efidence of vertebral abnormalities. However, the most often observed abnormalities of the vertebral column are rotation of the vertebral column and wedging of the vertebral bodies (Keeler et al., 1977). Taken together, these data suggest that animals affected with the crooked calf disease suffer from a soft-tissue defect that interferes with the normal strength and location of the collateral support structures, rather than from a primarily hard-tissue defect.

One of the most likely soft-tissue defects that must be considered in crooked calf disease is a primary myopathy. To ascertain if a primary myopathy exists in calves affected by crooked calf disease, muscle histochemistry has been examined (Abbott et al., 1986). Adenosine triphosphatase at pH 10.3 and NADH-tr reactions are used to analyze different enzyme activities in skeletal muscle fibers (Dubowitz and Brooke, 1973). Use of these histochemical stains not only allows differentiation of type I and type II muscle fibers, they also allow visualization of abnormal fibers that are not visualized with HE. Type I fibers have high oxidative and low glycolytic activity, yield-

TABLE 2 Histologic Findings from Tissue Samples from Affected Angus Calves

Calf no.	Abnormality observed in muscle or nerve tissue							Additional findings in tissue other than muscle or nerve
	Myositis	Myodegeneration	Muscle atrophy	Muscle necrosis	Cellulitis	Perineuritis	Neuritis	
2255	Biceps Brachii m.[b]	None	Brachialis m.[a]	Biceps Brachii m.[c] Semitendinosus m.[c]	None	Radial n.[b]	None	Hemorrhagic adrenal cortex
2252	External Intercostalis m.[c,e]	External Intercostalis m.[c] Semitendinosus m.[c]	None	None	None	None	Radial n.[d] Femoral n.[d]	
2254	None	None	None	None	None	None	None	
2259	None	Muscle[c,f]	None	None	None	None	None	Mild multifocal hepatitis
2253	Brachialis m.[c,e] Triceps Brachii m.[c,e]	Brachialis m.[c] Triceps Brachii m.[c]	None	Brachialis m.[c] Triceps Brachii m.[c]	None	None	None	Multifocal, suppurative meningoencephalitis
2257	None	None	None	None	Semitendinosus m.[b]	None	None	Mild, diffuse hypoplasia of adrenal cortex with edema
2258	None	External Intercostalis m.[c]	None	None	Brachialis m.[b]	Radial n.[b]	None	
2256	None	None	None	None	None	Femoral n.[c]	None	Locally extensive suppurative alveolitis

[a] Denervation.
[b] Histiocytic, neutrophilic.
[c] Multifocal.
[d] Neutrophilic.
[e] Nonsuppurative.
[f] Muscle not identified.

ing low ATPase activity. Type II fibers have low oxidative and high glycolytic activity, giving them high ATPase activity (Dubowitz and Brooke, 1973).
While normal ratios for type I to type II fibers in cattle have yet to be determined, the data do not suggest that any abnormalities in percentages of fiber
types exist in the muscles sampled (Abbott et al., 1986). Neither was any
abnormal type grouping of fibers, such as that associated with reinnervation
of muscle, which involves whole fascicles (Dubowitz and Brooke, 1973), observed in any calves affected with crooked calf disease.

Many changes in the architecture of individual muscle fibers are not recognizable with HE staining but can be revealed with ATPase or NADH-tr staining. Pathologic changes that can be revealed include target fibers, central
cores, tubular aggregates, and whorling of the interfibrillar network (Dubowitz and Brooke, 1973). No such pathological changes were seen in the
affected calves. Besides a primary myopathy, other possible causes for congenital arthrogryposis include fetal neuropathy—either peripheral, central, or
both—and excessive compression of the fetus. Many nonhereditary examples
of congenital arthrogryposis are associated with denervation muscle atrophy
and exhibit gross or microscopic lesions of the spinal cord (Herzog and Adam,
1968; Hulland, 1985; Keeler, 1976). Other reported examples of congenital
arthrogryposis in cattle are hereditary with an autosomal recessive mode of
transmission (Hadlow, 1973). One such hereditary form of arthrogryposis
is the hereditary syndrome of arthrogryposis and palatoschisis found in
Charolais cattle (Leipold et al., 1969; Nawrot et al., 1980; Russell et al.,
1985). The pattern of limb and axial anomalies in affected Charolais calves
is similar to that seen in crooked calf disease. Although this syndrome in
Charolais cattle was originally attributed to spinal dysraphism (Leipold et al.,
1969), recent evidence suggests a neurogenic abnormality of differentiation
in the central nervous system of the affected fetuses and may involve integration of neural pathways that influence functioning of lower motor neurons
(Russell et al., 1985).

The possibility that a central nervous system lesion exists, resulting in
reduced or complete absence of movement of the affected body parts in the
developing fetus, especially during the period of rapid growth, has not yet
been ruled out as a factor in crooked calf disease. However, at necropsy,
the brainstems of the eight affected calves we examined did not reveal any
gross lesions. Preliminary histological examination of spinal cords from calves
affected with crooked calf disease shows no differences from spinal cords from
control animals (L. Abbott, personal observation). Further histological examination needs to be undertaken to eliminate definitively the possibility of a
central nervous system lesion causing clinical signs associated with crooked
calf disease.

III. PATHOGENESIS OF CROOKED CALF DISEASE:
MALFORMATION OR DEFORMATION COMPLEX?

The pathogenesis of crooked calf disease remains, at best, poorly understood.
Most often the abnormalities described in affected calves have been referred
to by investigators as structural malformations. However, our examination of

many affected calves, along with the negative findings of a primary myopathy or neuropathy as described in Section II, makes us question whether the clinical findings in crooked calf disease are indeed malformations or whether they are actually deformations. Although this may seem to be a trivial distinction, it is highly significant when it comes to understanding the pathogenesis of this disorder.

To better understand the pathogenesis of crooked calf disease, two groups of affected neonatal Angus × Hereford crooked calves were obtained from a ranch in eastern Washington. The first group consisted of four 2-day-old calves. After a complete physical examination, radiographs of the limbs, skull, and vertebral columns were obtained for these calves. The second group consisted of two male and four female calves that were slightly older, although less than 7 days of age. These animals were examined similarly.

Within the initial group, there was a broad spectrum of severity observed in the affected calves. The least-affected animal presented with mild contractures of the left forelimb and was ambulatory. The next animal presented with contractures of the left forelimb and torticollis. This animal was able to stand and walk limited distances. The third calf presented with bilateral contractures of the forelimbs and torticollis. It could stand with assistance but was unable to walk. The most severely affected animal presented with severe contractures of the right hindlimb. In addition, it had extreme torticollis and scoliosis. Even with help, this animal was unable to assume a standing position. Examination of the second group of calves indicated contractures of at least one forelimb in all the calves, while the hindlimbs were involved in only two animals. Torticollis was a consistent feature in three calves, while only one animal had obvious scoliosis. Small umbilical hernias were noted in three animals. None of the affected calves presented with orofacial anomalies such as cleft or high-arched palates. There was no evidence of abnormality in any of the major organ systems.

Radiographs obtained from the three most severely affected group I (2-day-old) calves showed all osseous structures to be within normal limits and free of any overt malformations. In the most severely affected calf, the metatarsal and metacarpal-phalangeal articulations appeared to be subluxated in the affected limbs. Despite the severe torticollis, there was no evidence of vertebral abnormalities on the radiographs. Muscle samples taken from the group II calves revealed no significant or consistent degenerative, inflammatory, fibrotic, or necrotizing change in any section, affecting muscle, fascia, peripheral nerve, or blood vessel. Similarly, there were no subtle muscle changes such as centralization of nuclei, vacuolation, loss of striations, fiber kinking, or hyalinization of cytoplasm.

The 10 affected calves that we examined extensively presented with the classic features of crooked calf disease. These included asymmetrical limb contractures, torticollis, and scoliosis; subluxation and medial deviation of affected limbs; and the absence of abnormal skeletal muscle histology. These findings are consistent with the results of a previous study on affected crooked calves from the same herd (Abbott et al., 1986).

In past reports of crooked calf disease, the abnormalities observed in affected calves have been considered as structural malformations. The term *structural malformation* is specific to a primary structural defect that results from a localized error in morphogenesis (Christiansen, 1975). The insult

leading to the morphogenetic error takes place prior to, or during organogenesis, thereby causing the structure to be improperly or poorly formed.
The absence of any skeletal malformation, such as hemivertebra or bone a-
genesis, suggests that the anomalies seen in crooked calf disease do not meet
the criteria for structural malformations but better fit the description of structural deformations. A structural deformation is an alteration in the shape
and/or structure of a body part that has previously undergone normal differentiation (Jones, 1983a). Since the structure initially is normally developed,
the event leading to the deformation must take place after the onset of organogenesis. Further, as in crooked calf disease, all parts of the structure must
be present. In cattle, organogenesis of the forelimb occurs between days 24
and 45 of gestation (Evans and Ack, 1973). The critical period for lupine-
induced teratogenesis has most often been cited as between days 40 and 75 of
gestation; however, affected calves have been produced in feeding trials when
exposure was between 70 and 100 days (Shupe et al., 1967b). This places
the critical period for lupine-induced limb anomalies after the period of limb
organogenesis, thus supporting a deformational origin of the defects.

Structural deformations may result from restricted fetal movement caused
by intrauterine constraint. The origin of the constraint can be either intrinsic or extrinsic to the fetus itself (Jones, 1983b). Intrinsically derived deformations usually result from a genetically based neuropathy or myopathy
that affects the ability of the fetus to avoid normal forces imposed by the
uterine wall. Since the primary defect involves an alteration in a programmed
developmental sequence within the fetus, the structural defects tend to be
symmetrically distributed and not amenable to reversal. An example that fits
this description is the autosomal recessive syndrome of arthrogryposis and
palatoschisis in Charolais cattle, where a primary neuropathy leads to bi-
laterally symmetrical deformations of the limbs (Russell et al., 1985). In contrast, the lack of a primary myopathy or neuropathy in crooked calf disease,
along with the asymmetrical pattern of the limb defects, rules out an intrinsic
origin for the deformation seen in the disease.

In extrinsically derived deformations, the fetus is capable of normal movement, but the space available for movement is restricted. The constraint applied by such a restriction can be very localized, resulting in asymmetry of
limb involvement which is often reversible with time. Although there have
been no reports in reversal of the limb defects in crooked calf disease, surgical treatment has been successful in correcting congenital arthrogryposis of
the carpal joints in calves with similar if not identical defects (Verschooten
et al., 1969). This finding, along with the asymmetry of the defects, classi-
fies the anomalies seen in crooked calf disease as extrinsically derived deformations.

The mechanism by which lupine imposes constraint on fetal movement is a
matter of interesting speculation. In cattle, simple fetal movements occur at
a fairly consistent level from the end of the first trimester until term (Fraser,
1976). At this time, the pregnant uterus in a primiparous heifer is located
in the restricted area of the pelvic cavity. It remains there until the second
trimester, at which time it drops down into the large abdominal cavity for
the remainder of the pregnancy. In contrast, the uterus of multiparous cows
most often lies on the floor of the abdominal cavity from the beginning of pregnancy (Roberts, 1986). Consequently, the uterus of the heifer occupies a

more restricted area compared to the uterus of a cow during the time when lupine induces teratogenesis. It follows that the space available for fetal movement would be less in the uterus of a heifer compared to that of a cow. If additional constraint were imposed on the uterus by the anagyrine in lupine, this would cause a further restriction in the area available for fetal movement which would affect the heifer's fetus to a greater degree than the cow's. This could help explain why the majority of crooked calves are born to heifers.

There is indirect evidence that the alkaloid anagyrine may cause uterine constraint by inducing contractions. When administered to pregnant cattle between days 50 and 75 of gestation, coniine, the teratogenic alkaloid in *Conium maculatum* (poison hemlock), causes arthrogryposis similar to that observed in crooked calf disease (Keeler, 1974). In strips of uterine muscle from guinea pigs, maintained under physiologic conditions in an organ bath, coniine significantly increases the duration of spontaneous uterine contractions (Steven Taylor, personal communication). Thus the possibility exists that like coniine, anagyrine affects uterine smooth muscle, resulting in contractions of a long duration. Based on the discussion above, it is possible to devise a theoretical mechanism for lupine-induced structural deformations as shown in Fig. 1. The maternal ingestion of anagyrine-containing lupine late in the first trimester of pregnancy causes uterine contractions which restrict the area available for fetal movement. If these contractions take place in the uterus of a heifer, the constraint imposed by the uterine location within the pelvic canal restricts fetal movement to a greater degree than the same contractions taking place in the flaccid uterus within the abdominal cavity of a cow. Alternatively, prolonged contractions in the heifer could delay dropping of the uterus into the abdominal cavity, thereby limiting fetal movement to the area within the pelvic canal. In either case, the constraint imposed by the uterine wall restricts fetal movement and results in the structural deformations seen in crooked calf syndrome.

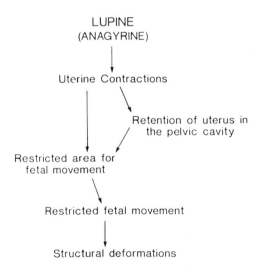

FIGURE 1 Theoretical mechanism for lupine-induced structural deformations.

IV. CONCLUSIONS

It is clear that certain species of the genus *Lupinus* contain toxic alkaloids that pose a serious reproductive hazard to cattle that graze on infested pastures. When sufficient concentrations of anagyrine, found in the plants, are consumed during early gestation the risk for producing abnormal offspring can be as low as 10% or as high as 40%. This causes a considerable economic loss to the producer, since the affected animal must be destroyed; by so doing, the number of future breeding stock is diminished. Only through understanding the mechanism of anagyrine-induced teratogenesis can one begin to propose remedies to avoid the loss.

In the work described in the preceding sections, detailed examinations of calves with the classic features of the crooked calf disease are essentially free of any soft-tissue organ defects, myopathy, or fetal neuropathy. The presence of limb contractures, scoliosis, and torticollis in the absence of abnormal radiographic findings strongly suggests that these abnormal findings are not structural malformations, but rather must be considered deformations. We believe that the uterine environment of a heifer grazing on lupine containing high concentrations of anagyrine is such that it restricts fetal movement and results in structural deformations. The validity of this mechanism remains to be tested. What is clear is that teratogens can cause not only malformations, but as in the case with lupine, can also cause extrinsically derived deformations.

REFERENCES

Abbott, L. C., Finnell, R. H., Chernoff, G. F., Parish, S. M., and Gay, C. C. (1986). Crooked calf disease: a histological and histochemical examination of eight affected calves. *Vet. Pathol.* 23:734-740.

Christiansen, R. L. (1975). Classification and nomenclature of morphological defects. *Lancet 1*:513.

Davis, A. M. (1982). The occurrence of anagyrine in a collection of western American lupines. *J. Range Manage.* 35:81-84.

Dubowitz, V., and Brooke, M. H. (1973). *Muscle Biopsy: A Modern Approach.* Philadelphia, W. B. Saudners, p. 5.

Evans, H. E., and Sack, W. O. (1973). Prenatal development of domestic and laboratory mammals: growth curves, external features and selected references. *Anat. Histol. Embryol.* 8:11-45.

Fraser, A. F. (1976). Some features of an ultrasonic study of bovine fetal kinesis. *Appl. Animal Ethol.* 2:379-383.

Hadlow, W. J. (1973). Myopathies of animals. In *The Striated Muscle*, C. M. Pearson and F. K. Mostofi (Eds.). Williams & Wilkins, Baltimore, p. 364.

Hartley, W. J., De Saram, W. G., Della-Porta, A. J., Snowdown, W. A., and Shepherd, N. C. (1977). Pathology of congenital bovine epizootic arthrogryposis and hydranencephaly and its relationship to Akabane virus. *Aust. Vet. J.* 53:319.

Herzog, A., and Adam, R. (1968). Zur Neuromyodysplasia congenita (kongenitale Arthrogrypose) der Hintergliedmassen beim Kalb: I. Pathologische

Anatomie und Histologie der Muskulatur arthrogrypotischer Gliedmassen. *Dtsch. Tieraerztl. Wochenschr. 75*:237.

Hulland, T. J. (1985). Muscles and tendons. In *Pathology of Domestic Animals*, 3rd ed., Vol. 1, K. V. F. Jubb, P. C. Kennedy, and N. Palmer (Eds.). Academic Press, Orlando, Fla., p. 151.

James, L. F. (1977). Plant-induced congenital malformations in animals. *World Rev. Nurt. Diet. 26*:208.

Jones, K. L. (1983a). Introduction. *Semin. Perinatol. 7*:237-238.

Jones, M. C. (1983b). Intrinsic versus extrinsically derived deformational defects: a clinical approach. *Semin. Perinatol. 7*:247-249.

Keeler, R. F. (1973a). Lupin alakloids from teratogenic and nonteratogenic lupins: I. Correlation of crooked calf disease incidence with alkaloid distribution determined by gas chromatography. *Teratology 7*:23-30.

Keeler, R. F. (1973b). Lupin alkaloids from teratogenic and nonteratogenic lupins: II. Identification of the major alkaloids by tandem gas chromatography-mass spectrometry in plants producing crooked calf disease. *Teratology 7*:31.

Keeler, R. F. (1974). Coniine, a teratogenic principle from *Conium maculatum* producing congenital malformations in calves. *Clin. Toxicol. 7*:195-206.

Keeler, R. F. (1976). Lupin alkaloids from teratogenic and nonteratogenic lupins: III. Identification of anagyrine as the probable teratogen by feeding trails. *J. Toxicol. Environ. Health 1*:887-898.

Keeler, R. F., Cronin, E. H., and Shupe, J. L. (1976). Lupin alkaloids from teratogenic and nonteratogenic lupins: IV. Concentration of total alkaloids, individual major alkaloids, and the teratogen anagyrine as a function of plant part and stage of growth and their relationship to crooked calf disease. *J. Toxicol. Environ. Health 1*:899-908.

Keeler, R. F., James, L. F., Shupe, J. L., and Van Kempen, K. R. (1977). Lupine induced crooked calf disease and a management method to reduce incidence. *J. Range Manage. 30*:97-102.

Kingsbury, N. M. (1964). *Poisonous Plants of the United States and Canada.* Prentice-Hall, Englewood Cliffs, N.J.

Kirkland, P. D., Barry, R. D., Harper, P. A. W., and Zelski, R. Z. (1988). The development of Akabane virus-induced congenital abnormalities in cattle. *Vet. Rec. 122*:582-586.

Konno, S. Moriwaki, M., and Nakagawa, M. (1982). Akabane disease in cattle: congenital abnormalities caused by viral infection spontaneous disease. *Vet. Pathol. 19*: 246.

Kurogi, H., Inaba, Y., Takahashi, E., Sato, K., Satoda, K., Goto, Y., Omori, T., and Matumoto, M. (1977). Congenital abnormalities in newborn calves after inoculation of pregnant cows with Akabane virus. *Infect. Immun. 17*:338.

Leipold, W. H., Cates, W. F., Radostits, O. M., and Howell, W. E. (1969). Spinal dysraphism, arthrogryposis and cleft palate in newborn Charolais calves. *Can. Vet. J. 10*:268.

Leipold, H. W., Husby, F., Brundage, A. L., and Shupe, J. L. (1977). Congenital defects of calves on Kodiak island. *J. Am. Vet. Med. Assoc. 170*:1408.

Leudke, A. J., Jochim, M. M., and Jones, R. H. (1977). Bluetongue in cattle: effects of *Culicoides variipennis*-transmitted Bluetongue virus on pregnant heifers and their calves. *Am. J. Vet. Res. 38*:1687.

Nawrot, P. S., Howell, W. E., and Leipold, H. W. (1980). Arthrogryposis: an inherited defect in newborn calves. *Aust. Vet. J. 56*:359.

Rimbey, C. W. (1969). Crooked calf disease. *Calif. Agric. 23*(May):7-8.

Roberts, S. J. (1986). *Veterinary Obstetrics and Genital Diseases (Theriogenology)*. Stephen J. Roberts, Burlington, Vt., p. 20.

Russell, R. G., Doige, C. E., Oteruelo, F. T., Hare, D., and Singh, E. (1985). Variability in limb malformation and possible significance in the pathogenesis of an inherited congenital neuromuscular disease of Charolais cattle (syndrome of arthrogryposis and palatoschisis). *Vet. Pathol. 22*: 2-12.

Shupe, J. L. (1970). Crooked calf syndrome. In *Bovine Medicine and Surgery and Herd Health Management*, W. J. Gibbons, E. J. Catcott, and J. F. Smithcors (Eds.). American Veterinary Publications, Wheaton, Il., p. 306.

Shupe, J. L., James, L. F., and Binns, W. (1967a). Observations on crooked calf disease. *J. Am. Vet. Med. Assoc. 151*:191-197.

Shupe, J. L., Binns, W., James, L. F., and Keeler, R. F. (1967b). Lupine, a cause of crooked calf disease. *J. Am. Vet. Med. Assoc. 151*:198-203.

Shupe, J. L., Binns, W., James, L. F., and Keeler, R. F. (1968). A congenital deformity in calves induced by the maternal consumption of lupine. *Aust. J. Agric. Res. 19*:335.

Verschooten, F., De Moor, A., Desmet, P., Watte, R., and Gunst, O. (1969). Surgical treatment of congenital arthrogryposis of the carpal joint, associated with contraction of the flexor tendons in calves. *Vet. Rec. 85*: 140-171.

Wagnon, K. A. (1960). Lupine poisoning as a possible factor in congenital deformities in cattle. *J. Range Manage. 13*:89-91.

3

Investigations of the Teratogenic Potential of the Lupine Alkaloid Anagyrine

James E. Meeker

Toxicology Laboratory, Institute of Forensic Sciences, Oakland, California

Wendell W. Kilgore

University of California, Davis, Davis, California

I. INTRODUCTION

On the basis of circumstantial evidence, the quinolizidine alkaloid anagyrine from *Lupinus latifolius* was implicated by Kilgore et al. (1981) as being responsible for a human deformity. Ingestion of various species of lupine has resulted in outbreaks of acute poisoning of sheep and cattle. Couch (1926) determined that the poisonous properties of lupines were due primarily to alkaloids. Wagnon (1960) reported that congenital crooked calf disease was suspected by California ranchers to be due to maternal ingestion of *Lupinus laxiflorus*. Keeler (1973a,b, 1976) and Keeler et al. (1976) implicated anagyrine as the probable compound responsible for crooked calf disease.

The genus *Lupinus* is a member of the family Leguminosae (Fabacease, pea family) (Abrams, 1960; Kinghorn and Balandrin, 1983; Munz, 1973). Lupines are present in North and South America, Europe, and Australia (Cooper and Johnson, 1984; Everist, 1974). There are perhaps 200 species of lupines, mostly in North and South America (Abrams, 1960; Herman, 1966). In the United States, lupines are most common in the western states (Kingsbury, 1964; James et al., 1985). California alone has more than 80 native species (Abrams, 1960; Kingsbury, 1964; Munz, 1973). Lupines are annual or perennial herbs which usually grow about 1 m high (Munz, 1973). The perennials generally start growth early in the spring, flower in June, and form seeds in July or August (James et al., 1985). The flowers range in color from blue or purple to yellow or white (Herman, 1966).

   L. latifolius (broadleaved lupine), the species of lupine implicated by Kilgore et al. (1981) as being responsible for a human deformity, is found primarily in the western United States and adjacent Baja Mexico (Vaughn and Dunn, 1977). It grows in open woods and thickets (below 7000 ft), canyons, or hillsides along the coastal ranges of California from San Diego County to Humboldt County and in the Sierra Nevada (Abrams, 1960; Munz, 1973).

   Several species of *Lupinus* are cultivated for use as fodder and green manure (Everist, 1974). Herman (1966) states that in general the plants are palatable and are sometimes a good source of forage before the pods have set. The seeds of *L. albus*, *L. luteus*, and *L. angustifolia* were at one time used in Europe as a substitute for coffee (Pammel, 1911). Hatzold et al. (1983) suggest that lupine species should be employed on a greater scale for animal and human nutrition. *L. mutabilis* has long been used as a food crop in the Andean highland. The species of lupine used as fodder generally consists of "sweet" lupines which have a low alkaloid concentration. With an increase in alkaloid content the plants become less palatable and are referred to as "bitter" lupines. Kingsbury (1964) states that alkaloids are universally bitter in taste.

   Keeler et al. (1976) have shown that the concentration of quinolizidine alkaloids in lupines varies with the plant parts and stages of maturity. The alkaloids are high in concentration in aboveground parts early in plant growth, and as the lupines approach the flower stage, the alkaloid content decreases significantly. In the mature seed stage, the leaves and stems are low, but the seeds are extremely high in total alkaloid concentration.

   Ingestion of various species of lupine has resulted in massive outbreaks of poisonings of sheep and to a lesser extent cattle. Pammel (1911) reported that in Montana during the year 1900, 3000 sheep were poisoned by lupines and resulted in 1900 mortalities. Also, four horses were poisoned with three mortalities due to lupine ingestion. The toxic signs usually appear in livestock within 1 to 2 h after ingestion of toxic lupines (Pammel, 1911; Kingsbury, 1964) and include nervousness, difficult breathing, loss of muscular control, excess salivation, convulsions, coma, and death (Keeler, 1968). Several authors have noted that the poisoning of livestock usually resulted from ingestion of mature lupines with the toxic principle mainly in the seeds (Pammel, 1911; Marsh and Clawson, 1916; Marsh, 1929; James, 1980). Marsh and Clawson (1916) were among the first to report that the poisoning of range sheep was due to the alkaloids found in lupines. Couch (1926) proved that the poisonous properties of lupines were due to the alkaloids and the toxicity of lupines varies among species because of variations in the quantities and types of alkaloids present. Couch (1926) observed that there was little difference in dosage between the toxic and lethal levels of lupines.

Congenital deformities in cattle have been shown to result from the maternal ingestion of certain lupine plants. Wagnon (1960) reported that congenital crooked calf disease (CCD) was suspected by California ranchers to be due to the maternal ingestion of *L. laxiflorus*. Shupe et al. (1967) proved that ingestion of certain species of lupine by pregnant cows resulted in CCD. The deformity is characterized by twisted or bowed limbs (arthrogryposis), twisted or bowed spine (scoliosis), twisted neck (torticollis), and cleft palate (Keeler et al., 1977). Detailed studies were performed by Keeler (1973a,b, 1976) and Keeler et al. (1976) to identify the compound responsible for the teratogenic effects of lupines. Keeler's investigations concentrated on the quinolizidine alkaloids because Landauer (1960) had previously shown that the quinolizidine alkaloid cytisine was teratogenic in chick embryos. Keeler's efforts implicated the quinolizidine alkaloid anagyrine as the probable teratogen.

Kilgore et al. (1981) reported that a baby boy from the mountainous backcountry of northwestern California (Trinity County) was born with severe bilateral deformities of the distal thoracic limbs. The deformities included bilateral radial hypoplasia, curvature of the ulna, absent thumbs, and webbed fingers on one hand (Fig. 1). Subsequently, Lazerson and Ortega (1984) determined that the child also suffered from red cell aplasia thought to be an anagyrine-induced stem cell defect. The hypothesis in this case was that the child's deformities resulted from in utero exposure to anagyrine from maternal ingestion of milk from goats that had foraged on teratogenic lupines. The evidence for Kilgore et al.'s hypothesis consisted of statements by the mother that lupines grew abundantly where the mother permitted the does to forage and that she had often seen the does feed on the lupines. Also, other animals that she owned had reproductive problems the year her child was born. She stated that her goats also gave birth to kids stillborn or with deformed legs and that puppies born to a neighbor's dog that had been given the goat's milk during pregnancy were born with "flippers" instead of paws. Further, the mother stated she regularly drank goat's milk during her pregnancy. Finally, the child's deformities showed similarities to those seen in calves of pregnant cows exposed to teratogenic lupines (Shupe et al., 1967) in that the deformities involved primarily skeletal deformities of the limbs. The lupines collected from Trinity County were identified as *L. latifolius* and were subsequently shown by Meeker and Kilgore (1987) to contain a high percentage of anagyrine. Kilgore et al. (1981) also noted that *Nicotiana*, *Conium*, and *Veratrum* plants were found in the area near the child's home. Keeler (1978a) and Crowe (1978) have reported these plants to be teratogenic to cattle and sheep.

II. ALKALOIDS OF *LUPINUS LATIFOLIUS*

L. latifolius in the early preflower state (Fig. 2) was collected during May 1983 in Trinity County, California. The capillary gas chromatography (GC) profile of the alkaloid extract is presented in Fig. 3 and the chemical structures corresponding to the numbered peaks are presented in Fig. 4. The six peaks, identified by mass spectrometry, correspond to (I) 5,6-dehydrolupanine, (II) lupanine, (III) aphylline, (IV) aphyllidine, (V) 4-hydroxylupanine, and (VI) anagyrine. Peak V consistently had an adjacent GC peak, but a fragmentation pattern was not obtained upon mass spectral analysis, and the substance remains unidentified.

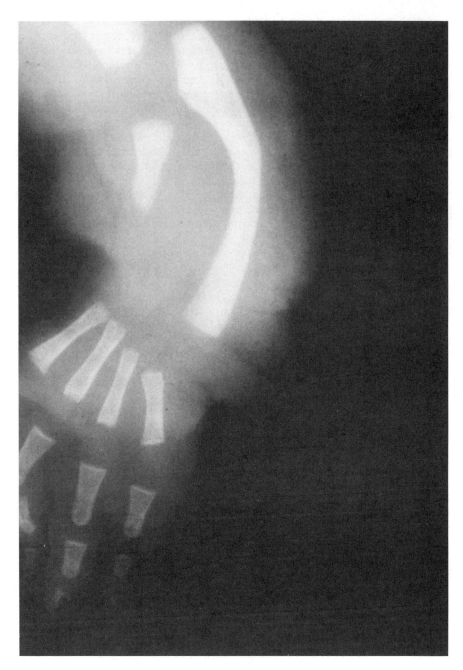

FIGURE 1 Radiograph of distal thoracic limb with radial hypoplasia, curvature of the ulna, and absent thumb.

FIGURE 2 Lupine plants collected from Trinity County, California, May 1983.

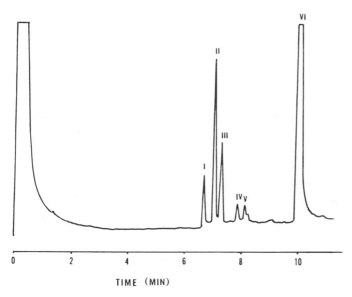

TIME (MIN)

FIGURE 3 Capillary gas chromatogram of the alkaloids extracted from *L. lati-folius*. See Fig. 4 for identification of peaks I to VI.

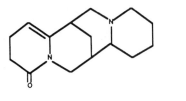

I. 5,6-DEHYDROLUPANINE

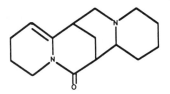

IV. APHYLLIDINE

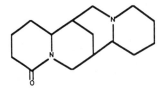

II. LUPANINE

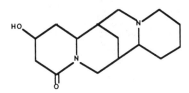

V. 4-HYDROXYLUPANINE

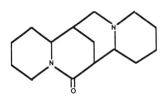

III. APHYLLINE

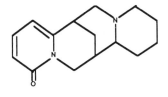

VI. ANAGYRINE

FIGURE 4 Structures of the alkaloids identified in *L. latifolius*.

The alkaloid content of *L. latifolius* is presented in Table 1. The total alkaloid content was calculated at 1.334% of the plant dry weight. Anagyrine represents the major alkaloid present, accounting for 86% of the total alkaloids and 1.14% of the plant dry weight. Lupanine, aphylline, and 5,6-dehydrolupanine represent 6.4, 3.9, and 1.9% of the total alkaloids, respectively. On a dry-weight basis there were 0.086% of lupanine, 0.052% of aphylline, and 0.026% of 5,6-dehydrolupanine. Aphyllidine and 4-hydroxylupanine were also identified in small quantities. The mass spectral data are presented in Table 2. The references cited are those that aided in the identification of individual alkaloids.

Wink and Hartmann (1980) and Cho and Martin (1971) have alluded to the biogenetic origin of quinolizidine in lupine plants. Both have suggested that the biosynthesis of the α-pyridone alkaloids such as anagyrine are assumed to derive from lupanine via 5,6-dehydrolupanine as a key intermediate. The alkaloids identified in *L. latifolius* are consistent with their hypothesis. Another alkaloid present in this investigation was 4-hydroxylupanine, which

TABLE 1 Alkaloid Content of *L. Latifolius*

Peak	Alkaloid	Percent total alkaloid (SE)[a]	Percent plant dry weight (SE)[a]
I	5,6-Dehydrolupanine	1.92 (0.10)	0.026 (0.002)
II	Lupanine	6.49 (0.11)	0.086 (0.001)
III	Aphylline	3.87 (0.02)	0.052 (0.002)
IV	Aphyllidine	0.78 (0.02)	0.0103 (0.0003)
V	4-Hydroxylupanine	1.27 (0.04)	0.017 (0.001)
VI	Anagyrine	85.66 (0.02)	1.143 (0.036)
	Total alkaloid content		1.334 (0.042)

[a]Average and SE are based on $n = 3$.
Source: Adapted from Meeker and Kilgore (1987).

could be an intermediate in the conversion of lupanine to 5,6-dehydrolupanine via an initial hydroxylation of lupanine to yield 4-hydroxylupanine, which could then be further oxidized to 5,6-dehydrolupanine.

Keeler (1973a) reported that lupines with an anagyrine concentration of over 1.44 g/kg were generally teratogenic when fed to pregnant cows. Davis and Stout (1986) reported that there are 14 known species of lupine with anagyrine at teratogenic concentrations. Table 3 summarizes their results, showing the teratogenic species and their respective anagyrine concentration and percentage of total alkaloids. Davis and Stout (1986) reported that *L. latifolius* Agardh. contained anagyrine at 6.04 g/kg dry plant weight and 26% of the total alkaloids. The *L. latifolius* from Trinity County contained anagyrine at 11.43 g/kg dry plant weight and 86% of the total alkaloids. Both values are remarkably high relative to other reported values for lupines in general. Keeler (1973a) reported finding anagyrine levels up to 7.31 g/kg dry plant weight and 50% of the total alkaloids in *Lupinus caudatus* and 6.76 g/kg and 37% in *Lupinus sericeus*. He also reported finding anagyrine at 10.41 g/kg dry plant weight and 52% of the total alkaloids in an unidentified species from central Idaho. Davis (1982) reported finding anagyrine values ranging from 1.35 to 9.83 g/kg of dry plant weight for *L. caudatus* harvested in May 1978, while *L. sericeus* showed ranges of 3.54 to 5.76 g/kg for the same period. Davis and Stout (1986) also reported finding anagyrine at 10.27 g/kg dry plant weight and 53% of the total alkaloids in *Lupinus montigenus*.

TABLE 2 Mass Spectral Data of the Alkaloids of *L. latifolius*

Peak	Alkaloid	M[+]	Characteristic ions (relative abundance)	References
I	5,6-Dehydro-lupanine	246	246(100), 98(54), 245(44), 247(16), 97(15)	Cho and Martin (1971a)
II	Lupanine	248	136(100), 248(79), 247(72), 149(65), 150(55)	Cho and Martin (1971a); Schuman et al. (1968)
III	Aphylline	248	136(100), 247(54), 220(54), 137(44), 138(29)	Schumann et al. (1968)
IV	Ahyllidine	246	246(100), 136(59), 245(52), 134(29), 217(18)	Schumann et al. (1968)
V	4-Hydroxy-lupanine	264	264(100), 263(52), 136(35), 247(28), 134(23)	Cho and Martin (1971b); Hatzold et al. (1983)
VI	Anagyrine	244	244(100), 98(93), 146(46), 160(29), 243(26)	Keeler (1973b); Neuner-Jehle et al. (1964)

Source: Adapted from Meeker and Kilgore (1987).

It is reasonable that a goat foraging on *L. latifolius* from Trinity County could be exposed to a relatively high level of anagyrine before the acute toxic effects resulting from the total alkaloid consumption became apparent. This would allow for a higher concentration of anagyrine in goat's milk relative to alkaloid proviles from lupines containing a lesser percentage of anagyrine.

III. BLOOD KINETICS AND MILK TRANSFER OF ALKALOIDS IN LACTATING GOATS

A search of the available literature showed that few authors have studied the transfer of teratogenic alkaloids into the milk of livestock. One of the earliest reported instances of toxins being excreted into milk was the "milk sickness" incident in the early nineteenth century, later shown to be caused by consumption of milk from cattle poisoned by ingestion of *Eupatorium rugosum* (white snakeroot) (Kingsbury, 1964). Couch (1930) reported that the poison tremetol, found in *E. rugosum* and *Aplopappus heterophyllus* (rayless goldenrod), may be transmitted through the milk or meat of the animals and thus endanger the humans. James and Hartley (1977) determined that the toxin of certain plants of the *Astragalus* and *Oxytropis* (locoweed) could pass through the milk of cows and sheep in sufficient quantity to poison animals consuming the

TABLE 3 Lupine Species with Anagyrine at Teratogenic Concentrations

Lupinus species	Anagyrine concentration (g/kg)	Percent of total alkaloids	Total alkaloids (g/kg)
L. albicaulis Doug. (pine lupine)	2.08	18.2	11.43
L. alpestris A. Nels (mountain silvery lupine)	3.36	23.4	14.35
L. andersonii S. Wats. (Anderson's lupine)	3.15	30.9	10.20
L. argenteus Pursh. (silvery lupine)	3.34	18.3	18.22
L. burkei S. wats (Burke's lupine)	1.59	8.8	18.10
L. caudatus Kell. (tailcup lupine)	2.94	33.6	8.75
L. erectus Hend. (tall silvery lupine)	1.59	18.2	8.72
L. evermanii Rydb. (Everman's lupine)	4.62	21.5	21.52
L. latifolius Agardh. (broadleaf lupine)	6.04	25.9	23.33
L. leucophyllus Dougl. (velvet lupine)	2.90	34.6	8.38
L. littoralis Doug. (seashore lupine)	3.31	38.1	8.68
L. montigenus Heller (Mt. Rose lupine)	10.27	52.6	19.54
L. polyphyllus Lindl. (Washington lupine)	6.10	28.0	21.76
L. sericeus Pursh. (silky lupine)	6.84	36.6	18.71

Source: Adapted from Davis and Stout (1986).

milk. Of special interest, James et al. (1967) reported that some sheep and cattle poisoned by locoweed may give birth to offspring with skeletal malformations.

The pyrrolizidine alkaloids (PA) have been shown to be transferred into the milk of livestock. Dickinson et al. (1976) reported that in lactating cows given 10 g/kg per day of *Senecio jacobaea* (tansy ragwort) orally, the pyrrolizidine alkaloid content of the milk ranged from 0.094 to 0.167 µg/mL. Dickin-

son claims that the milk extraction procedure yielded a 20% recovery of the
PA; therefore, the values should be multiplied by a factor of 5 to approximate
the actual PA concentration. King (1980) reported that after the administration of tansy ragwort via rumen cannula at a rate of 1% of body weight, the
mean PA concentrations from cows and goats milk was 0.684 and 0.381 μg/mL,
respectively. Goeger et al. (1982) found that PA are transferred in goats'
milk and may produce hepatotoxic effects to rats fed milk containing 7.5 ng
of PA per gram of milk (dry weight). Deinzer et al. (1982) found PA concentrations ranged from 0.33 to 0.81 μg/mL in the milk of goats fed tansy ragwort. All the previous authors indicate that the occurrence of PA in livestock
milk are unlikely to represent a significant human health hazard.

The quinolizidine alkaloid cytisine was reported by Long (1917) to be excreted into the milk of goats that had foraged on *Cytisus weldeni*. Although
the goats were uninjured, the milk was stated to be poisonous to humans.
Muenscher (1951) lists lupine as a plant that produces undesirable flavors
in milk and milk products. Craigmill et al. (1982) found anagyrine in goats'
milk that was sampled 10 to 24 h after oral exposure to 2 to 3 g of toxic lupine.

The blood kinetics and transfer of anagyrine into the milk of goats was
studied, with emphasis being placed on obtaining information on the maximum
milk concentration. The quinolizidine alkaloids were extracted from the blood
and milk by acid-base partition using the organic solvent 1-chlorobutane.
This extraction procedure is essentially a modification of that described by
Foerster et al. (1978) and Baselt (1980). A simplified flowchart diagram of
the blood extraction procedure is presented in Fig. 5. This procedure is a
sensitive, relatively easy, and rapid method for analyzing the quinolizidine
alkaloids in biological fluids and should prove effective for studying the biological fate of other classes of alkaloids.

Lactating does were orally exposed to the alkaloids extracted from *L. latifolius* at approximately 80 mg/kg with anagyrine and lupanine representing
86% and 7% of the total alkaloids, respectively. A representative gas chromatography profile of the alkaloids extracted from the blood of a goat 1 h after
exposure to the alkaloids is presented in Fig. 6. Peaks II and VI were identified by mass spectral analysis as lupanine and anagyrine. The corresponding
24-h blood kinetic curve for anagyrine and lupanine is presented in Fig. 7.

The blood kinetics data showed that the alkaloids were detected in the
blood within 15 min, and peak goat blood concentrations of the quinolizidine
alkaloids occurred at approximately 1 h after oral exposure to the alkaloid
extract. Peak anagyrine concentrations ranged from 1.22 to 2.41 μg/mL while
lupanine ranged from 0.48 to 1.37 μg/mL. The alkaloids were essentially eliminated from the blood after 24 h. The average elimination half-life for anagyrine and lupanine was 2.24 and 2.87 h, respectively. The findings are in
agreement with Pammel (1911) and Kingsbury (1964), who state that toxic
signs may appear in livestock within 1 to 2 h after ingestion of toxic lupines.
Also, the short average elimination half-life indicates that the quinolizidine
alkaloids are rapidly excreted. Kingsbury (1964) and Marsh and Clawson
(1916) alluded to the possibility that the poisonous principle of lupines was
rapidly excreted and was not a cumulative poison.

A representative gas chromatogram of the alkaloids extracted from milk
samples collected 2.5 h after the final dose to goats orally exposed to four
separate 70-mg/kg doses of the alkaloids extracted from *L. latifolius* at 2.5-h

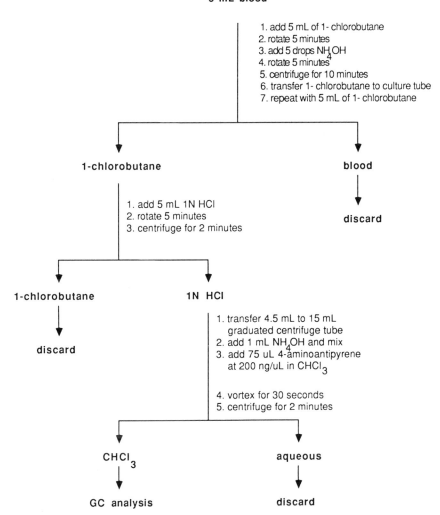

FIGURE 5 Alkaloid extraction procedure from whole blood.

intervals is presented in Fig. 8. Toxic signs were noted in goats 1 h after the final dose with corresponding total blood alkaloid concentrations ranging from 5.3 to 8.0 μg/mL. The signs included decreased motor activity, loss of appetite, and hanging of the head while butting against a fence. These signs are similar to those seen in sheep poisoned by toxic lupines (Marsh, 1929). The signs persisted for several hours but were absent by the following morning.

The maximum total quinolizidine alkaloid milk concentration was 39 μg/mL, with anagyrine and lupanine accounting for approximately 19 and 14 μg/mL, respectively. The total alkaloid concentration decreased to 5.25 μg/mL at 24

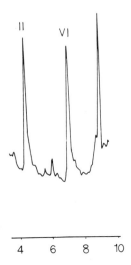

FIGURE 6 Capillary gas chromatogram of the alkaloids extracted from the blood of a goat 1 h after oral exposure to a single dose (77 mg/kg) of the alkaloids extracted from *L. latifolius*. Peak identifications: II, lupanine; VI, anagyrine.

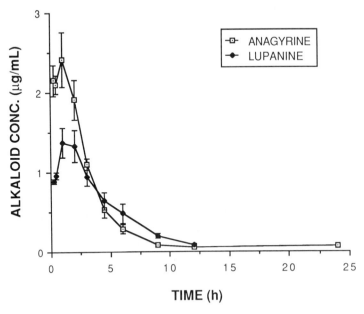

FIGURE 7 Goat blood concentrations following a single oral exposure to 77 mg/kg of the alkaloids extracted from *L. latifolius*.

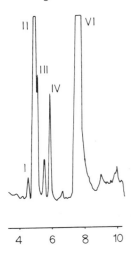

FIGURE 8 Capillary gas chromatogram of the alkaloids extracted from milk collected 2.5 h after the final dose from a goat exposed orally to four separate 70-mg/kg doses of the alkaloids of *L. latifolius* separated by 2.5-h intervals. Peak identification: I, 5,6-dehydrolupanine; II, lupanine; III, aphylline; IV, aphyllidine; VI, anagyrine.

h and 6.30 µg/mL at 48 h. The average milk production was 270 mL for the 2.5 h milk sampling, 330 mL at 24 h, and increased to 915 mL at 48 h. The decrease in milk production was most likely a result of fasting the goats for about 30 h and presumably had no significant effect on the concentration of alkaloids in the milk. Rasmussen (1971) states that the concentration of a drug in milk is independent of the volume of milk in the mammary gland, which indicates that mammary excretion is a diffusion process. Yovo et al. (1984) report the oral LD_{50} of lupanine in the mouse as 410 mg/kg, and cytisine has a reported oral LD_{50} in the mouse of 101 mg/kg (Merck, 1983), although it should be noted that the acute toxicity of quinolizidine mixtures had not been studied previously. It is felt that the potential for acute intoxication is low in humans consuming milk that contains quinolizidine alkaloids.

On the basis of the relative percentage of anagyrine and lupanine in the plant extract versus the percentages determined in different biological fluids (Fig. 9), it appears that to some extent anagyrine may be reduced to lupanine. The relative percentage of anagyrine to lupanine in the original plant extract was 93% to 7%, while the relative percentages in the biological fluids averaged 63% to 37% for anagyrine and lupanine, respectively. The changes in the relative percentage of the original plant extract possibly are a result of metabolic reduction of anagyrine to lupanine in the goat rumen. Baldwin and Emery (1960) characterized the rumen as having strong reduction capabilities, while De Corte-Baeten and Debackere (1978) note that rumen microfauna are capable of rapid reductive biotransformations. Prins (1978) showed a reductive degradation of the pyrrolizidine alkaloids in the rumen, which ultimately led to the reduction of a double bond within the pyrrolizidine nucleus. Another fact, which may contribute to the changes in the relative percentages of anagyrine

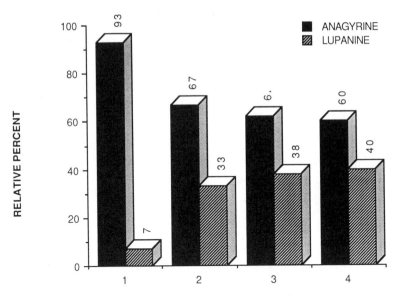

FIGURE 9 Relative percentages of anagyrine and lupanine in different biological fluids. 1, Original plant extract; 2, blood sampled 1 h after exposure
to a single oral dose of 77 mg/kg of the alkaloid extract; 3, blood sampled 2.5
h after oral exposure to four doses, separated by 2.5 h, of 70 mg/kg of the
alkaloid extract; 4, milk sampled 2.5 h after oral exposure to four doses, separated by 2.5 h, of 70 mg/kg of the alkaloid extract.

and lupanine, is the difference in the elimination half-life. The average $t_{1/2}$
values for anagyrine and lupanine were 2.24 and 2.87 h, respectively. Thus,
based on the $t_{1/2}$ values, the ratio of anagyrine to lupanine would tend to
decrease from the initial ratio as the time after exposure increases. Selective
metabolism of anagyrine over lupanine could also account for the changes in
the relative percentages. The unsaturated ring in anagyrine might be more
susceptible to oxidation by liver microsomes, resulting in a more rapid elimination. Another mechanism that might contribute to the changes in relative
percentages is differential absorption. This mechanism would appear to contribute the least to these changes, because of the structural similarities between anagyrine and lupanine and the fact that peak blood concentrations
of both alkaloids occurred about 1 h after oral exposure to the alkaloid extract.

IV. TERATOGENIC INVESTIGATIONS OF ANAGYRINE

Wagnon (1960), Shupe et al. (1967), and Keeler (1976) have performed experimental feeding trials of lupine plants or alkaloid extracts with pregnant cows
in order to produce crooked calf disease. In reviewing their experimental
procedures and results, the following conclusions can be made. Pregnant
cows are most susceptible to the teratogenic effects of lupines during days
40 to 70 of gestation. If the feeding of lupines does not include a large proportion of this gestational period, the occurrence of deformities is reduced.

The maternal daily dose of anagyrine required to produce moderate deformities consistently in calves was estimated at 6.5 to 11.9 mg/kg during the suscepti- ble gestation period. The severity of malformations was directly related to the amount of anagyrine exposure. In the majority of cases in which calves were born with deformities, the dams experienced moderate to severe signs of toxic- ity during the alkaloid treatment. The signs of maternal toxicity included de- pression, incoordination, stilted gait, muscular twitching, and recumbency.

The average gestation period of the cow is 280 days (Jainudeen and Hafez, 1980). The critical period for the bovine limb development is during weeks 3.5 through 6.5 (Noden and De Lahunta, 1985), with the forelimb bud visible on day 25 (Jainudeen and Hafez, 1980). The importance of this is that, as mentioned earlier, pregnant cows are most susceptible to the teratogenic ef- fects of lupines during days 40 to 70 of gestation. Thus, in designing the teratology study with laboratory rats, it seemed logical to perform two types of studies. The first to involve the administration of the alkaloids during the critical period of organogenesis (days 6 to 15) and the second to include the late organogenesis and early histogenesis periods (days 12 to 19).

The overall experimental design of a study in which Sprague-Dawley rats were exposed to anagyrine levels ranging from 0.86 to 86 mg/kg per day is presented in Table 4. As mentioned previously, in the majority of cases in which calves were born with deformities, the dams experienced moderate to severe signs of toxicity during the alkaloid treatment. It was noted that ex- posure to 50 mg/kg of the alkaloids to pregnant rats once daily resulted in a decrease in the maternal weight gain during the exposure period relative to the control rats, but no other signs of toxicity were observed. Preliminary investigations showed that exposure of female rats to 100 mg/kg of the lupine alkaloids once daily would produce lethal effects after the third dose. Based on the short half-life of the alkaloids, the dose was decreased by one-half and administered twice daily. Thus the dose of the alkaloids extracted from *L. latifolius* was adjusted to 37.5 to 50 mg/kg twice daily to maintain moderate to severe signs of maternal toxicity without producing maternal lethality.

TABLE 4 Anagyrine Rat Teratology Experimental Design

Group	Number of rats	Dose[a] (g/kg)	Dosing days
I	6	Vehicle control	6-15
II	3	1.0	6-15
III	3	10.0	6-15
IV	3	50.0	6-15
V	3	75-100[b]	6-15
VI	3	75-100[b]	12-19

[a]The dose is based on the total alkaloid administered; anagyrine represents 86% of the total alkaloids.
[b]The rats were dosed twice daily with 37.5 to 50 mg/kg of the alkaloids extracted from *L. latifolius*.

Maternal weight gain in the experimental rats was less than that of the controls at or above 50 mg/kg of total lupine alkaloids, and signs of toxicity were noted at 75 to 100 mg/kg which included decreased motor activity, scruffiness, rigid posture with difficulty moving, severe head tremors, and moderate to severe whole-body tremors. Early fetal resorptions were observed in three of six litters exposed to 75 to 100 mg/kg of the lupine alkaloids. Reduced fetal length was observed in fetuses exposed to 50 mg/kg, while decreases in both fetal weights and lengths were noted at the 75 to 100 mg/kg levels of exposure to the lupine alkaloids. The reductions in fetal weights and lengths are most likely secondary to the maternal toxic effects. No visceral or skeletal effects were observed in any of the treatment groups.

Although early fetal resorptions were observed in some rat litters exposed to 75 to 100 mg/kg of the lupine alkaloids, these probably resulted secondarily to the severe maternal toxicity. Palmer (1978) states that in a majority of cases the embryotoxicity probably occurs secondarily to a primary effect on the maternal organism. Decreases in fetal lengths were observed in the male and female fetuses at the 50-mg/kg dose level (group IV), while decreases in both fetal weights and lengths were noted in male and female fetuses at the 75- to 100-mg/kg levels of exposure to the lupine alkaloids (groups V and VI). There was also a reduction in the maternal weight gain in groups IV, V, and VI. Palmer (1978) notes that retardation of mean fetal weight correlates closely with reduced maternal weight gain. Even though fetal size was reduced, there was no retardation of skeletal ossification. Thus the reductions in fetal weights and lengths were most likely secondary to the maternal weight reductions.

Thus it appears that anagyrine is not teratogenic in Sprague-Dawley rats. This is in agreement with Keeler's (1976) observation that the testing for teratogenic effects of anagyrine in laboratory animals had not been encouraging. Of interest, the known human teratogen, thalidomide, was not teratogenic in rats (Pliess, 1962; Somers, 1962; Fratta et al., 1965) but produced skeletal deformities in rabbits (Somers, 1962; Fratta et al., 1965) and dogs (Weidman et al., 1963; Delatour et al., 1965). As mentioned previously, Kilgore et al. (1981) reported possible skeletal deviations in dogs resulting from exposure to anagyrine. Thus studies aimed at testing the teratogenic potential of anagyrine should involve other species, such as the rabbit, dog, goat, or subhuman primate.

V. CONCLUSIONS

An important finding is the occurrence of the suspected teratogen anagyrine in goats milk at approximately 19 µg/mL, which may well have a health impact on pregnant women consuming the milk. The average daily milk consumption of an adult human, as reported by van der Kreek (1983), is 8 mL per kilogram of body weight. At this rate, a 70-kg person could be exposed to about 10 mg of anagyrine per day (0.14 mg/kg per day). The teratogen thalidomide has caused skeletal deformities in humans at daily dose levels ranging from 0.5 to 2.0 mg/kg (Council on Environmental Quality, 1981; Schardein, 1985). Thus only a $3\frac{1}{2}$-fold difference exists between the lowest thalidomide dose that produces teratogenic effects and the calculated level of exposure to anagyrine.

Goeger et al. (1982) note that goats are commonly raised on small farms in marginal agricultural areas. Often, the milk from a dairy goat raised under such conditions is consumed by a single family, which could allow for a significant exposure to anagyrine. However, the risk of exposure to plant toxins in milk for the general population is minimal, because the practice of pooling milk from many herds in a wide geographical area, as is done in the dairy cattle industry, ensures that a toxin will usually be diluted far below levels toxic to humans.

Goats appear to be less susceptible to the acute toxic effects of the quinolizidine alkaloids than are cows and sheep. Thus goats may consume large quantities of teratogenic lupines, which allows for high levels of anagyrine in the milk before any acute toxic signs are observed. Without the observation of toxic signs an individual has little indication of the potential exposure to anagyrine via ingestion of contaminated milk.

With the large number of teratogenic plants in the environment, further investigations should be conducted to study the milk transfer and teratogenic risk of plant extractives to humans. Keeler (1978b) and Keeler et al. (1977) discuss grazing management methods to reduce the incidence of congenital deformities in livestock. These methods should be observed by people that consume dairy products from marginal agricultural areas, where teratogenic plants are often found in abundance.

REFERENCES

Abrams, L. (1960). *Illustrated Flora of the Pacific States Washington, Oregon, and California*, Vol. II. Stanford University Press, Stanford, Calif.

Baldwin, R. L., and Emery, R. S. (1960). The oxidation-reduction potential of rumen contents. *J. Dairy Sci.* 43:506-511.

Baselt, R. C. (1980). *Analytical Procedures for Therapeutic Drug Monitoring and Emergency Toxicology*. Biomedical Publications, Davis, Calif.

Cho, Y. D., and Martin, R. O. (1971). Resolution and unambiguous identification of microgram amounts of 22 lupin alkaloids by sequential use of thin-layer and gas-liquid chromatography and mass spectrometry. *Anal. Biochem.* 44:49-57.

Cooper, R., and Johnson, A. M. (1984). *Poisonous Plants in Britain and Their Effects on Animals and Man*. H.M. Stationery Office, London.

Couch, J. F. (1926). Relative toxicity of the lupine alkaloids. *J. Agric. Res.* 32:51-56.

Couch, J. F. (1930). The toxic constituent of rayless goldenrod (*Aplopappus heterophyllus*). *J. Agric. Res.* 40:649-658.

Council on Environmental Quality. (1981). *Hazards to Human Reproduction*. U.S. Government Printing Office, Washington, D.C.

Craigmill, A. L., Crosby, D. G., Kilgore, W. W., Poppen, N. K., and Hedrick, K. (1982). Passage of toxic alkaloids into goats milk. *Proc. 3rd Int. Conf. Goat Prod. Dis.*, Tucson, Ariz., Jan. 10-15.

Crowe, M. W. (1978). Tobacco—a cause of congenital arthrogryposis. In *Effects of Poisonous Plants on Livestock*, R. F. Keeler, K. R. Van Kampen, and L. F. James (Eds.). Academic Press, New York, pp. 419-427.

Davis, A. M. (1982). The occurrence of anagyrine in a collection of western American lupines. *J. Range Manage. 35*:81-84.

Davis, A. M., and Stout, D. M. (1986). Anagyrine in western American lupines. *J. Range Manage. 39*(1):29-30.

De Corte-Baeten, K., and Debackere, M. (1978). The non-absorption of chloramphenicol after oral administration in adult ruminants: a tentative explanation from in-vitro studies. *J. Vet. Pharmacol. Ther. 1*:192-134.

Deinzer, M. L., Arbogast, B. L., Buhler, D. R., and Cheeke, P. R. (1982). Gas chromatographic determination of pyrrolizidine alkaloids in goat's milk. *Anal. Chem. 54*:1811-1814.

Delatour, P., Dams, R., and Favre-Tissot, M. (1965). Embryopathies chez le chein. *Therapie 20*:573-589.

Dickinson, J. O., Cooke, M. P., King, R. R., and Mohamed, P. A. (1976). Milk transfer of pyrrolizidine alkaloids in cattle. *J. Am. Vet. Med. Assoc. 169*:1192-1196.

Everist, S. E. (1974). *Poisonous Plants of Australia*. Angus & Robertson, North Ryde, Australia.

Foerster, E. H., Hatchett, D., and Garriott, J. C. (1978). A rapid, comprehensive screening procedure for basic drugs in blood or tissues by gas chromatography. *J. Anal. Toxicol. 2*:50-55.

Fratta, I. D., Sigg, E. B., and Maiorana, K. (1965). Teratogenic effects of thalidomide in rabbits, rats, hamsters, and mice. *Toxicol. Appl. Pharmacol. 7*:268-286.

Goeger, D. E., Cheeke, P. R., Schmitz, J. A., and Buhler, D. R. (1982). Effect of feeding milk from goats fed tansy ragwort (*Senecio jacobaea*) to rats and calves. *Am. J. Vet. Res. 43*:1631-1633.

Hatzold, T., Elmadfa, I., Gross, R., Wink, M., Hartmann, T., and Witte, L. (1983). Quinolizidine alkaloids in seeds of *Lupinus mutabilis*. *J. Agric. Food Chem. 31*:934-938.

Herman, F. J. (1966). *Notes of Western Range Forbes*, Agricultural Handbook 293, U.S. Department of Agriculture, Forest Service, U.S. Government Printing Office, Washington, D.C.

Jainudeen, M. R., and Hafez, E. S. S. (1980). Gestation, prenatal physiology and parturition. In *Reproduction in Farm Animals*, E. S. E. Hafez (Ed.). Lea & Febiger, Philadelphia, pp. 247-268.

James, L. F. (1980). Plant poisoning in livestock. *Mod. Vet. Pract. 61*(12).

James, L. F., and Hartley, W. J. (1977). Effects of milk from animals fed locoweed on kittens, calves, and lambs. *Am. J. Vet. Res. 38*:1263-1265.

James, L. F., Shupe, J. L., and Binns, W. (1967). Abortive and teratogenic effects of locoweed on sheep and cattle. *Am. J. Vet. Res. 28*:1379-1388.

James, L. F., Keeler, R. F., Johnson, A. E., Williams, M. C., Cronin, E. H., and Olsen, J. D. (1985). *Plants poisonous to livestock in the western states*, Bull. No. 415. U.S. Department of Agriculture, U.S. Government Printing Office, Washington, D.C.

Keeler, R. F. (1968). Toxic and teratogenic alkaloids of western range plants. *J. Agric. Food Chem. 17*:473-482.

Keeler, R. F. (1973a). Lupin alkaloids from teratogenic and nonteratogenic lupins: I. Correlation of crooked calf disease incidence with alkaloid distribution determined by gas chromatography. *Teratology 7*:23-30.

Keeler, R. F. (1973b). Lupin alkaloids from teratogenic and nonteratogenic lupins: II. Identification of the major alkaloids by tandem gas chromatography-mass spectrometry in plants producing crooked calf disease. *Teratology 7*:31-35.

Keeler, R. F. (1976). Lupin alkaloids from teratogenic and nonteratogenic lupins: III. Identification of anagyrine as the probable teratogen by feeding trials. *J. Toxicol. Environ. Health 1*:887-898.

Keeler, R. F. (1978a). Alkaloid teratogens from *Lupinus, Conium, Veratrum,* and related genera. In *Effects of Poisonous Plants on Livestock,* R. F. Keeler, K. R. Van Kempen, and L. F. James (Eds.). Academic Press, New York, pp. 397-408.

Keeler, R. F. (1978b). Reducing incidence of plant-caused congenital deformities in livestock by grazing management. *J. Range Manage. 31*:355-360.

Keeler, R. F., Cronin, E. H., and Shupe, J. L. (1976). Lupin alkaloids from teratogenic and nonteratogenic lupins: IV. Concentration of total alkaloids, individual major alkaloids and the teratogen anagyrine as a function of plant part and stage of growth and their relationship to crooked calf disease. *J. Toxicol. Environ. Health 1*:899-908.

Keeler, R. F., James, L. F., Shupe, J. L., and Van Kampen, K. R. (1977). Lupine-induced crooked calf disease and a management method to reduce incidence. *J. Range Manage. 30*(2):97-102.

Kilgore, W. W., Crosby, D. G., Craigmill, A. L., and Poppen, N. K. (1981). Toxic plants as possible human teratogens. *Calif. Agric. 35*:6.

King, R. R. (1980). Transfer of pyrrolizidine alkaloids from *Senecio jacobaea* into the milk of cattle and goats and the effects on calves and kids consuming the milk. *Diss. Abstr. Int. B40*:94.

Kinghorn, A. D., and Balandrin, M. F. (1983). Quinolizidine alkaloids of the Leguminosae: structural types, analysis, chemotaxonomy, and biological activities. In *Alkaloids: Chemical and Biological Perspectives,* Vol. II, S. W. Pelletier (Ed.). Wiley, New York, pp. 105-148.

Kingsbury, J. M. (1964). *Poisonous Plants of the United States and Canada.* Prentice-Hall, Englewood Cliffs, N.J.

Landauer, W. (1960). Nicotine-induced malformations in chicken embryos and their bearing on the phenocopy problem. *J. Exp. Zool. 143*:107-122.

Lazerson, J., and Ortega, J. A. (1984). Anagyrine induced red cell aplasia and skeletal dysplasia. *Blood 64*:106a.

Long, H. C. (1917). *Plants Poisonous to Live Stock.* Cambridge University Press, Cambridge.

Marsh, C. D. (1929). *Stock-poisoning plants of the range,* Bull. No. 1245. U.S. Department of Agriculture, Washington, D.C.

Marsh, C. D., and Clawson, A. B. (1916). *Lupines as poisonous plants,* Bull. No. 405, U.S. Department of Agriculture, Washington, D.C.

Meeker, J. E., and Kilgore, W. W. (1987). Identification and quantitation of the alkaloids of *Lupinus latifolius. J. Agric. Food Chem. 35*:431-433.

Merck and Company. (1983). *The Merck Index: An Encyclopedia of Chemicals, Drugs and Biologicals,* 10th ed. Merck and Company, Rahway, N.J.

Muenscher, W. C. (1951). *Poisonous Plants of the United States.* Macmillan, New York.

Munz, P. A. (1973). *A California Flora and Supplement.* University of California Press, Berkeley.

Noden, D. M., and De Lahunta, A. (1985). *The Embryology of Domestic Animals*: *Developmental Mechanisms and Malformations*. Williams & Wilkins, Baltimore.

Palmer, A. K. (1978). The design of subprimate animal studies. In *Handbook of Teratology*, Vol. 4, J. G. Wilson and F. C. Fraser (Eds.). Plenum Press, New York, pp. 215-253.

Pammel, L. H. (1911). *A Manuel of Poisonous Plants*: *Chiefly of Eastern North America with Brief Notes on Economic and Medicinal Plants and Numerous Illustrations*. Torch Press, Cedar Rapids, Iowa.

Pliess, G. (1962). Thalidomide and congenital abnormalities. *Lancet 1*:1128-1129.

Prins, R. A. (1978). Nutritional impact of intestinal drug-microbe interactions. In *Nutrition and Drug Interrelations*, Academic Press, New York, pp. 189-251.

Rasmussen, F. (1971). Excretion of drugs by milk. In *Handbook of Experimental Pharmacology*, Vol. 28, B. B. Brodie and J. R. Gilette (Eds.). Springer-Verlag, New York, pp. 390-402.

Schardein, J. L. (1985). *Chemically Induced Birth Defects*. Marcel Dekker, New York.

Shupe, J. L., Binns, W., James, L. F., and Keeler, R. F. (1967). Lupine: a cause of crooked calf disease. *J. Am. Vet. Med. Assoc. 151*:198-203.

Somers, G. F. (1962). Thalidomide and congenital abnormalities. *Lancet 1*: 912-913.

Van der Kreek, F. W. (1983). Animal drugs and the evaluation of residues in milk and meat. In *Veterinary Pharmacology and Toxicology*, Y. Ruckebusch, P. Toutain, and G. D. Koritz (Eds.). AVI, Westport, Conn.

Vaughn, P., and Dunn. D. B. (1977). The *Lupinus latifolius* Agardh. complex. *Trans. Mo. Acad. Sci. 10*:89-101.

Wagnon, K. A. (1960). Lupine poisoning as a possible factor in congenital deformities in cattle. *J. Range Manage. 13*:89-91.

Weidman, W. H., Young, H. H., and Zollman, P. E. (1963). The effect of thalidomide on the unborn puppy. *Proc. Staff Meet. Mayo Clin. 38*:518-522.

Wink, M., and Hartmann, T. (1980). Production of quinolizidine alkaloids by photomixotrophic cell suspension cultures: biochemical and biogenetic aspects. *Planta Med. 40*:149-155.

Yovo, K., Huguet, F., Pothier, J., Durand, M., Breteau, M., and Narcisse, G. (1984). Comparative pharmacological study of sparteine and its ketonic derivative lupanine from seeds of *Lupinus albus*. *Planta Med. 50*: 420-424.

4

Myopathy in Cattle Caused by *Thermopsis montana*

Dale C. Baker

Colorado State University, Fort Collins, Colorado

Richard F. Keeler

Poisonous Plant Research Laboratory, Agricultural Research Service, USDA, Logan, Utah

I. INTRODUCTION

Very few plants have been experimentally proven to cause primarily myocardial and/or skeletal muscle injury in animals, and for those plants that do so, the chemical constituent(s) responsible are not known in all cases. Several plant species or molds on plants are capable of causing muscular degeneration, but the degeneration is secondary, incidental, or only part of a constellation of abnormalities (Allen, 1978; Sullivan, 1985).

There are several plants that cause a myopathy that is the predominant expression of injury in the animal. Cottonseed meal (when used as a feed supplement for monogastrics and young ruminants) and *Eupatorium rugosum* (white snakeroot) cause myocardial injury, or myocardial and skeletal muscle injury, respectively (Holmberg et al., 1988; Rogers et al., 1975; Smith, 1957; White et al., 1985). The toxic compounds in these plants are the alcohols gossypol and trematol, respectively, and are capable of causing injury to horses, cattle, and swine as well as other species (Couch, 1927; Rogers et al., 1975;

Smith, 1957). White snakeroot is a problem in cattle and causes trembling (Couch, 1933). Description of a myopathy, however, has only been documented in horses fed frozen plant material experimentally (White et al., 1985). Long-term ingestion of the plant causes myocardial degeneration and resulting fibroplasia with mild skeletal muscular degeneration (White et al., 1985). In the acute intoxications, horses experience weakness and have dark urine, skeletal and myocardial muscular degeneration, and elevated serum creatine kinase activity. *Aplopappus heterophyllus* (rayless goldenrod) in the southwestern United States contains trematol and has been associated with a similar syndrome of trembles in cattle; however, a myopathy has not been substantiated with this plant (Couch, 1930; Zalkow et al., 1962). Rayless goldenrod may be an unrecognized problem in the southwest. Gossypol intoxication was a problem primarily in swine fed cottonseed meal mixed into feed as a protein source. Gossypol causes acute hepatocellular necrosis and myocardial necrosis, with the centrilobular hepatic necrosis attributed to direct action by gossypol and anoxia from acute heart failure resulting from myocardial injury (Holmberg et al., 1988). Adult ruminants are resistant to cottonseed meal, and gossypol is apparently modified in the rumen to nonreactive protein complexes (Reiser and Fu, 1962). Young ruminant animals are susceptibel to gossypol because their rumen is not fully functional and is more like that of a monogastric animal than that of an adult ruminant (Holmberg et al., 1988). *Cassia* plant species cause injury to skeletal muscle and myocardium mainly in cattle, but also have been reported to be a problem in sheep and goats (O'Hara et al., 1969; Rowe et al., 1987; see also Chapter 16). *Cassia occidentalis* and *Cassia obtusifolia* cause widespread myodegeneration in cattle grazing pastures containing these plants (O'Hara et al., 1969). The syndrome is characterized by dark brown or red urine, incoordination, and recumbency near the time of death with gross and microscopic myodegeneration of cardiac and skeletal muscle. *Cassia roemeriana* has been demonstrated to cause injury to cattle and goats fed this plant experimentally (Rowe et al., 1987). Although several compounds have been isolated from *Cassia* species, the toxic compound responsible for muscle injury is unknown (Kim et al., 1971; Lal and Gupta, 1973). There is ultrastructural evidence that mitochondrial swelling is the first morphologic change of injured myofibers in the *Cassia*-induced myopathy and is likely a reflection of interruption of oxidative metabolism and depletion of adenosine triphosphate (ATP) (Read et al., 1968). Plants in England and Australia have been associated with peroxidative injury to muscle associated with unsaturated fatty acids in the plants and low serum α-tocopherol concentrations in the animals (Walker, 1985; McMurray and Rice, 1982).

Other plants have been associated with a myopathy, but usually only secondarily to other organ system injury in the animal or as only a minor component of the overall injury to the animal. *Karwinskia humboldtiana* (coyotillo) has been demonstrated to cause a skeletal and myocardial myopathy in goats due to an unidentified chemical constituent of the plant (Dewan et al., 1965). Since the identification of a myopathy, coyotillo has been shown to cause demyelination of peripheral nerves and peripheral and central nervous system axonal degeneration (Charlton and Pierce, 1970; Charlton et al., 1970). The relationship of these two observations in animals intoxicated by *K. humboldtiana* is not determined; however, the myopathy may be secondary to the neuropathy. Gardiner (1956) in Australia reported a myopathy induced by *Lupinus* as a part of the syndrome lupinosis. Lupinosis has been unequivocally ascribed to contamination on *Lupinus* by the fungus *Phomopsis leptostromiformis* (Gardiner and Petterson, 1972; Van Warmelo et al., 1970). The myopathy, and more significantly a severe hepatopathy, have since been induced by the purified *Phomopsis* peptide toxin phomopsin (Allen, 1978). Thus the myopathy is only a minor feature of the syndrome, in which hepatic disease is the most severe and life-threatening facet. *Vinca villosa* is associated with disseminated granulomatous and often eosinophilic inflammation involving many tissues, but also involves the myocardium with associated necrosis and regeneration of the myocardium (Panciera et al., 1966). Myocardial injury in this disease is not considered the cause of death and is only a component of the syndrome.

II. IDENTIFICATION OF MYOPATHY IN CATTLE CAUSED
   BY *THERMOPSIS MONTANA*

Early reports of *Thermopsis montana* toxicosis in cattle described a condition in cattle grazing pastures containing this plant (Chase and Keeler, 1983; Keeler et al., 1986). The plant has widespread distribution in the western United States and is found in Utah, Colorado, Idaho, Montana, Oregon, Washington, and Nevada (Rydberg, 1917). Prolonged recumbency or sudden death are severe sequelae of ingestion of *T. montana* (Keeler et al., 1986). Recumbency may last several days, during which time grazing animals are not able to rise to reach water or feed, and it is this expression of toxicity that is believed to account for many death losses in range animals through dehydration (Keeler et al., 1986). Initial investigation of this problem demonstrated that cattle developed elevated serum aspartate transaminase and creatine kinase activities near the time of recumbency, but it could not be determined if the injury was neurological or muscular in nature (Keeler et al., 1986). Subsequent investigation determined that the recumbency was associated with muscular degeneration (myopathy) and clinical recovery correlated with healing and repair of injured myofibers (Baker and Keeler, 1989). Those cattle that died suddenly after being dosed with dried, ground *Thermopsis* plant material had acute hyaline degeneration of skeletal muscle, and the cause of death was assumed to be respiratory arrest (Fig. 1). Those cattle that did not die following initial administration of plant material also had hyaline degeneration of myofibers and loss of cross-striations, and satellite nuclear proliferation and repair of myofibers following the initial insult (Fig. 2) (Baker and Keeler, 1989). Clinical recovery corresponded with repair of myofibers. The myopathy in all cases involved only skeletal muscles, with myocardium remaining unaffected (Baker and Keeler, 1989). None of the cattle had an elevated body temperature during the episode of muscle degeneration. Myoglobin was not detected in the urine of any of these calves. As in previous experiments, the serum creative kinase (CK) and aspartate transaminase (AST) activities were significantly elevated in days 1 and 7, respectively (Baker and Keeler, 1989).

III. COMPOUNDS OF *THERMOPSIS MONTANA*
    RESPONSIBLE FOR THE MYOPATHY

Because *T. montana* had alkaloids similar to *Lupinus* species (Couch, 1926) and the toxic properties of the plant did not deteriorate over time as is the

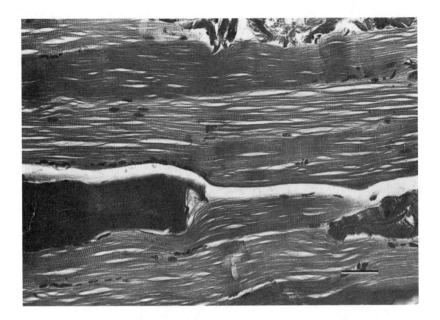

FIGURE 1 Acute hyaline degeneration and myofiber fragmentation in skeletal muscle myofiber in calf that was administered dried, ground *T. montana* twice and died less than 36 h after the first administration. Bar = 152 μm.

case with trematol, the clinical toxicosis was speculated to be induced by one or more of the rather stable quinolizidine alkaloids of the plant (Keeler et al., 1986). That early work (Keeler et al., 1986) determined that there were five main alkaloids present. By tandem gas chromatographic/mass spectrometric (GC/MS) and optical rotation analysis (Keeler et al., 1986), four of those alkaloids proved to be (-)-anagyrine, (-)-thermopsine, cytisine, and N-methylcytisine and the fifth was later identified as 5,6-dehydrolupanine (Keeler and Baker, unpublished observations) (Fig. 3). Even though levels of individual alkaloids were measured and varied between plant collections, a correlation was not apparent between any individual alkaloid level and clinical recumbency (Keeler et al., 1986).

In an effort to determine the compound in *T. montana* that was responsible for the observed myopathy, alkaloid extracts of *T. montana*, *Laburnum anagyroides*, and a *Lupinus* sp. were prepared and administered by gavage to calves (Keeler and Baker, unpublished observations). The alkaloid extract from *T. montana* was expected to establish whether the alkaloid class of compounds could reproduce the clinical syndrome and myopathy observed when the dried, ground plant was fed to the calves. The *Lupinus* and *L. anagyroides* alkaloid extracts were prepared and selected because each plant contains one or more but not all of the five alkaloids present in *Thermopsis*, and consequently certain alkaloids could be excluded or incriminated as the specific toxic compound.

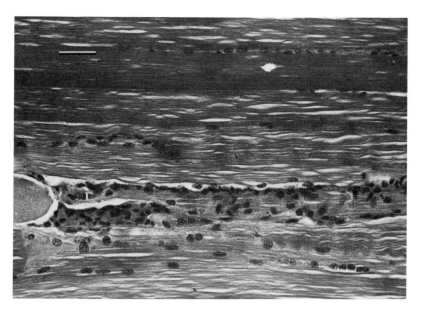

FIGURE 2 There is variation of myofiber diameter and satellite nuclear proliferation, indicating repair of previously injured myofibers in this specimen.
This calf was administered *T. montana* plant material four times (once every 24
h) and examined several days later after recumbency developed. Bar = 170 μm.

Three alkaloid peaks were evident by GC analysis of the *Lupinus* purified
alkaloid preparation utilized for gavage. Retention times by gas chromatography (against cytisine, lupanine, and anagyrine standards) and mass spectrometric fragmentation patterns permitted unequivocal identification of peaks
1 and 3 as lupanine and anagyrine. Peak 2 was unidentified but was not present in the *Thermopsis* preparation. One major alkaloid peak (cytisine) was
present in the *L. anagyroides* alkaloid extract preparation.

Animals administered the *Thermopsis* purified alkaloid preparation had
signs of generalized tremors, fasciculation of individual muscle groups, irregular gait, and involuntary, prolonged recumbency lasting several days or
until euthanasia. Animals gavaged with the *Laburnum* alkaloid extract had
oral frothing, anorexia, and an irregular gait. Animals gavaged with the
Lupinus purified alkaloid preparation had generalized tremors, protrusion of
the nictitating ocular membranes, irregular gait, difficulty in remaining standing, fasciculation of individual muscle groups, and temporary involuntary
recumbency.

Microscopic examination of muscle groups from calves administered the
alkaloid extract of *T. montana* demonstrated a mild to severe acute hyaline
degeneration of myofibers similar to those calves administered ground *T. montana* plant material. There was also satellite nuclear proliferation and infiltration of degenerate myofibers by macrophages. Occasional mineralization of
myofibers was also evident. Calves in experimental groups administered an
alkaloid extract from *Lupinus* sp. and *L. anagyroides* by gavage did not have

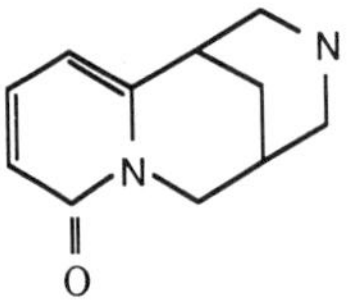

cytisine

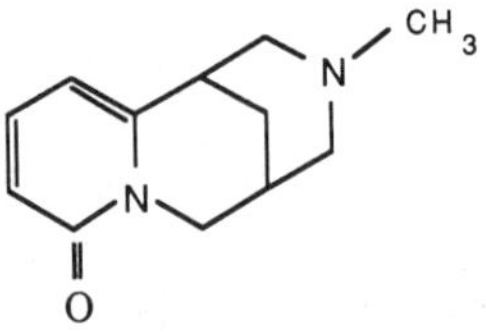

N-methylcytisine

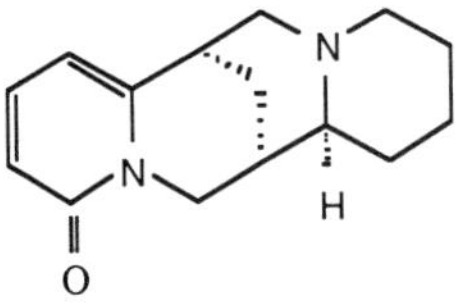

(-)-thermopsine

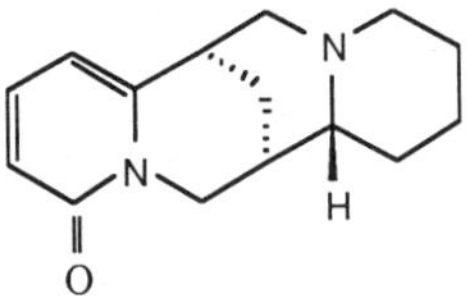

(-)-anagyrine

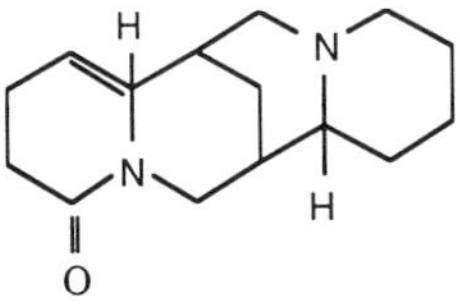

5,6 dehydrolupanine

FIGURE 3 The five quinolizidine alkaloids identified in the *T. montana* purified alkaloid extract. Optical activity (configuration) of anagyrine and
thermopsine were determined by optical rotation analysis, while that of cytisine, *N*-methylcytisine, and 5,6 dehydrolupanine are presumed from the literature [see Keeler (1989)].

any gross abnormalities of any muscle group. Microscopically, in both these
experimental groups there was diffuse myofiber nuclear proliferation with
multifocal hyaline or granular degeneration of myofibers throughout most muscles examined. There was satellite nuclear proliferation with focal areas of
myofiber degeneration and increased number of macrophages.

IV. CONCLUSIONS

Prolonged recumbency and microscopic evidence of severe myopathy similar
in grade to that induced by *T. montana* plant material were induced by only
one of the three purified alkaloid preparations, the *Thermopsis* purified alkaloid preparation. It induced clinical recumbency and microscopic evidence of
myopathy even more severe than did plant material with dose levels (as total
alkaloid) a little over twice as high as total alkaloid in the plant doses (Keeler
and Baker, unpublished observations). We believe the compound(s) responsible for the clinical myopathy and resulting clinical recumbency resides in the
alkaloid fraction because of fraction purity and dosage consideration.

The *Lupinus* purified alkaloid preparation (at an anagyrine dose approximately equivalent to that in the *Thermopsis* plant material) did cause microscopic skeletal muscle injury, but only transient involuntary recumbency in one of three animals dosed. No transient or prolonged recumbency was induced in any of the three animals dosed with the *Laburnum* alkaloid extract even though the level of the alkaloid cytisine was over five times as high as the cytisine level in the *Thermopsis* plant material. Even so, in these three animals there was mild to moderate evidence of myopathy. These data suggest that of the five alkaloids present in the *Thermopsis* plant material, neither anagyrine nor cytisine alone can account for the severe recumbency-inducing potential of the *Thermopsis* plant material or alkaloid preparation therefrom, but they were capable of causing skeletal muscle necrosis and degeneration. The mild to moderate microscopic evidence of myopathy at those dose levels with the *Lupinus* and *Laburnum* preparations and the severe effects with the *Thermopsis* preparation suggest a common etiologic feature among the three preparations.

The alkaloids present in *T. montana* and the subsequent purified alkaloid preparations are quinolizidine alkaloids. Alkaloids of that class have not been incriminated in causing myopathy in any animal species despite widespread ingestion in food and feeds (Keeler, 1989; Kinghorn and Balandrin, 1984; Mears and Mabry, 1971). Couch (1926) described depression in animals administered quinolizidine alkaloids and muscle spasms and tremors when sparteine was administered, but the occurrence of a myopathy was not examined adequately. In addition to the common feature of compound class, these alkaloids all have an α-pyridone A-ring. Only very few of the known quainolizidine alkaloids possess α-pyridone A-rings (Keeler, 1989; Kinghorn and Balandrin, 1984; Mears and Mabry, 1971). Perhaps the α-pyridone A-ring quinolizidine alkaloids as a group are responsible for the myopathy and resulting recumbency (Keeler and Baker, unpublished observations). Although the various α-pyridone-containing alkaloids might vary in potency, their effects could be additive, and this could readily account for the greater potency of the *Thermopsis* alkaloid preparation compared to the other preparations.

Neither structure nor configuraiton of quinolizidine alkaloids with α-pyridone A-rings is helpful in speculating on the mechanism of injury to skeletal muscle, and it is therefore premature to speculate about the mechanism of effect until the toxin(s) is unequivocally identified.

REFERENCES

Allen, J. G. (1978). The emergence of a lupinosis-associated myopathy in sheep in Western Australia. *Aust. Vet. J.* 54:548-549.

Baker, D. C., and Keeler, R. F. (1989). Myopathy in cattle caused by *Thermopsis montana*. *J. Am. Vet. Med. Assoc.* 194:1269-1272.

Charlton, K. M. and Pierce, K. R. (1970). A neuropathy in goats caused by experimental coyotillo (*Karwinskia humboldtiana*) poisoning: II. Lesions in the peripheral nervous system—teased fiber and acid phosphatase studies. *Pathol. Vet.* 7:385-407.

Charlton, K. M., Pierce, K. R., Storts, R. W., and Bridges, C. H. (1970). A neuropathy in goats caused by experimental coyotillo (*Karwinskia hum-*

boldtiana) poisoning: V. Lesions in the central nervous system. *Pathol. Vet.* 7:435-447.

Chase, R. L., and Keeler, R. F. (1983). Mountain thermopsis toxicity in cattle. *Utah Sci.* 44:28-31.

Couch, J. F. (1926). Relative toxicity of lupine alkaloids. *J. Agric. Res.* 32:51-67.

Couch, J. F. (1927). The toxic constituent of richweed or white snakeroot (*Eupatorium urticaefolium*). *J. Agric. Res.* 35:547-576.

Couch, J. F. (1930). The toxic constituent of rayless goldenrod. *J. Agric. Res.* 40:649-658.

Couch, J. F. (1933). Trembles (or milk sickness). *U.S. Dep. Agric. Circ.* 306:1-11.

Dewan, M. L., Hensen, J. B., Dollahite, J. W., and Bridges, C. H. (1965). Toxic myodegeneration in goats produced by feeding mature fruits of the coyotillo plant (*Karwinski humboldtiana*). *Am. J. Pathol.* 46:215-226.

Gardiner, M. R. (1956). The pathology of lupinosis in sheep. *Pathol. Vet.* 2:417-445.

Gardiner, M. R., and Petterson, D. S. (1972). Pathogenesis of mouse lupinosis induced by a fungus (*Cytospora* spp.) growing on dead lupines. *J. Comp. Pathol.* 82:5-13.

Holmberg, C. A., Weaver, L. D., Guterbock, W. M., Genes, J., and Montgomery, P. (1988). Pathological and toxicological studies of calves fed a high concentration cotton seed meal diet. *Vet. Pathol.* 25:147-153.

Keeler, R. F. (1989). Quinolizidine alkaloid in range and grain lupins. In *Toxicants of Plant Origin: Alkaloids*, Vol. 1, P. R. Cheeke (Ed.). CRC Press, Boca Raton, Fla., pp. 133-167.

Keeler, R. F., Johnson, A. E., and Chase, R. C. (1986). Toxicity of *Thermopsis montana* in cattle. *Cornell Vet.* 76:115-127.

Kim, H. L., Camp, B. J., and Grigsby, R. D. (1971). Isolation of n-methyl-morpholine from seeds of *Cassia occidentalis* L. (coffee senna). *J. Agric. Res.* 19:198-199.

Kinghorn, A. D., and Balandrin, M. F. (1984). Quinolizidine alkaloids of the Leguminosae: structural types, analysis, chemotaxonomy, and biological activity. In *Alkaloids: Chemical and Biological Perspectives*, Vol. 2, S. W. Pelletier (Ed.). Wiley, New York, pp. 105-148.

Lal, J., and Gupta, P. C. (1973). Anthraquinone glycoside from the seeds of *Cassia occidentalis* Linn. *Experientia* 29:141-142.

McMurray, C. H., and Rice. D. A. (1982). Vitamin E and selenium deficiency diseases. *Ir. Vet. J.* 36:57-67.

Mears, J. A., and Mabry, T. J. (1971). Alkaloids in the Leguminosae. In *Chemotaxonomy of the Leguminosae*, J. B. Harborne, D. Boulter, and B. L. Turner (Eds.). Academic Press, New York, pp. 73-178.

O'Hara, P. J., Pierce, K. R., and Read, W. K. (1969). Degenerative myopathy associated with ingestion of *Cassia occidentalis* L.: clinical and pathologic features of the experimentally induced disease. *Am. J. Vet. Res.* 30:2173-2180.

Panciera, R. J., Johnson, L., and Osburn, B. I. (1966). A disease of cattle grazing hairy vetch pasture. *J. Am. Vet. Med. Assoc.* 148:804-808.

Read, W. K., Pierce, K. R., and O'Hara, P. J. (1968). Ultrastructural lesions of an acute toxic cardiomyopathy of cattle. *Lab. Invest.* 18:227-231.

Reiser, R., and Fu, H. C. (1962). The mechanisms of gossypol detoxification by ruminant animals. *J. Nutr. 76:*215-218.

Rogers, P. A. M., Henaghan, T. P., and Wheeler, B. (1975). Gossypol poisoning in young calves. *Ir. Vet. J. 29:*9-13.

Rowe, L. D., Corrier, D. E., Reagor, J. C., and Jones, L. P. (1987). Experimentally induced *Cassia roemeriana* poisoning in cattle and goats. *Am. J. Vet. Res. 48:*992-998.

Rydberg, P. A. (1917). *Flora of the Rocky Mountains and adjacent plains.* Steinman and Felt Press, Lancaster, Pa., p. 456.

Smith, H. A. (1957). The pathology of gossypol poisoning. *Am. J. Pathol. 33:*353-365.

Sullivan, N. D. (1985). The nervous system. In *Pathology of Domestic Animals*, K. V. F. Jubb, P. C. Kennedy, and N. Palmer (Eds.). Academic Press, New York, p. 263.

Van Warmelo, K. T., Marasas, W. F. O., Adelaar, T. F., Kellerman, T. S., van Rensberg, I. B. J., and Minne, J. A. (1970). Experimental evidence that lupinosis of sheep is a mycotoxicosis caused by the fungus *Phomopsis leptostromiformis* (Kuhn, Bubak). *J. S. Afr. Vet. Med. Assoc. 41:*235-247.

Walker, K. H. (1985). Toxicity in sheep due to *Ixiolaena brevicompta.* In *Plant Toxicology*, A. A. Seawright, M. P. Hegarty, L. F. James, and R. F. Keeler (Eds.). Queensland Poisonous Plant Committee, Yeerongpilly, Australia, pp. 401-047.

White, J. L., Shivaprasad, H. L., Thompson, L. J., and Buck, W. B. (1985). White snakeroot (*Eupatorium rugosum*) poisoning: clinical effects associated with cardiac and skeletal muscle lesions in experimental equine toxicosis. In *Plant Toxicology*, A. A. Seawright, M. P. Hegarty, L. F. James, and R. F. Keeler (Eds.). Queensland Poisonous Plant Committee, Yeerongpilly, Australia, pp. 411-422.

Zalkow, L. H., Burke, N., Cabat, G., and Grula, E. A. (1962). Toxic constituents of rayless goldenrod. *J. Med. Pharm. Chem. 5:*1342-1351.

5

Toxicosis from Steroidal Alkaloids of *Solanum* Species

Dale C. Baker

Colorado State University, Fort Collins, Colorado

Richard F. Keeler

Poisonous Plant Research Laboratory, Agricultural Research Service, USDA, Logan, Utah

William Gaffield

Western Regional Research Center, Agricultural Research Service, USDA, Albany, California

I. INTRODUCTION

A few members of the *Solanum* genus are commonly cultivated for human consumption. These plants are known to contain several types of steroidal alkaloids that are toxic. Some of these steroidal alkaloids of cultivated *Solanums* are also teratogenic in animal model systems. Many wild, noncultivated *Solanum* species also contain steroidal alkaloids that have proven to be teratogenic to hamsters. During investigation of potato (*Solanum tuberosum*) and noncultivated *Solanum*-induced teratogenesis, it was noted that feeding pregnant dams sufficient plant material to cause cranial and facial defects in developing fetuses also caused a small percentage of the dams to die. Maternal toxicosis is known to complicate examination of fetal teratogenesis (Khera, 1984), and we were therefore prompted to investigate the mechanism of injury and death by these *Solanum* materials in hamsters.

II. *SOLANUM TUBEROSUM* TOXICOSIS (SOLANIDANE ALKALOIDS)

Reports of human intoxication by sprouted or spoiled potatoes have been recorded for many years, especially during periods of famine or food shortage (Harris and Cockburn, 1918; McMillan and Thompson, 1979; Willimott, 1933). Fatalities are rare but have occurred (Hansen, 1925). Intoxication of domesticated animals has also been reported with occasional fatalities (Adam, 1978; Craig and Kehoe, 1925; Konig, 1953). Early reports of intoxication and death in humans recorded clinical symptoms of headache, vomiting, diarrhea, and debility (Harris and Cockburn, 1918) either with few lesions, with gastric and intestinal inflammation (Willimott, 1933), or with oral and esophageal ulceration (Ruhlue, 1961).

These early reports (Harris and Cockburn, 1918) associated the clinical symptoms and death with increased concentration of the glycoalkaloid solanine in potatoes that were allowed to sprout. Sprouts, flowers, and leaf parts as well as greened skins of tubers and spoiled tubers have high concentrations of glycoalkaloids. Since these early reports, solanine was found to be a mixture of α-solanine and α-chaconine (Kuhn et al., 1955a,b), and occasionally with compounds having a shorter carbohydrate chain of both solanine and chaconine (the β and γ forms). These glycoalkaloids have the same parent aglycone solanidine (Fig. 1). Other less abundant steroidal glycoalkaloid types (α-solamarine, β-solamarine) and the aglycones (tomatidenol, demissidine, 5β-solanidan-3α-ol) are sometimes found in cultivated potatoes, but are not present in sufficient concentrations to be considered important (Jadhave et al., 1981). Little is known about the biological activity of these minor alkaloids.

Since those early investigations, the major glycoalkaloids of potatoes have been investigated and their toxicity determined. The LD_{50} for α-chaconine and α-solanine for vairous species is tabulated (Tables 1 and 2). Most of the evaluations of glycoalkaloids activity have been by intraperitoneal administration (Norred et al., 1976; Nishie et al., 1971). Oral administration of [³H]-α-chaconine in hamsters suggested that α-chaconine was absorbed well, but this is at odds with studies in other species (Alozie et al., 1979). α-Solanine and α-chaconine in rats and mice, at least, are poorly absorbed from the intestine with a considerably higher LD_{50} dose for oral administration versus intraperitoneal (IP) administration (Tables 1 and 2) (Jadhav et al., 1981). None of the studies, even those in which glycoalkaloids were administered by gavage or orally, could determine the cause of death (Gull et al., 1970; Konig, 1953). Solanine was determined to inhibit acetylcholinesterase activity (Orgell et al., 1958), and that inhibition is considered by some to be the mechanism of death (Morgan and Coxon, 1987). Since that observation, purified major glycoalkaloids and their aglycones and some major and minor wild potato alkaloids and aglycones have been evaluated and found to inhibit cholinesterase activity (Bushway et al., 1987) (Table 3). An outbreak of potato poisoning in schoolboys suggested that the level of glycoalkaloids was not sufficient to

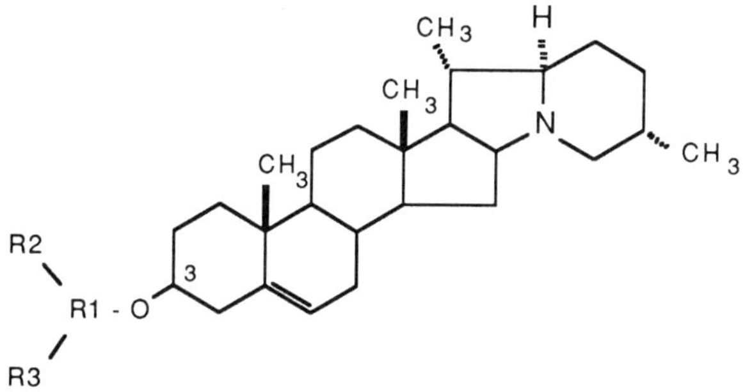

FIGURE 1 Solanidane alkaloid skeleton: solanidine (OH at C3); α-solanine (R1 = galactose, R2 = glucose, R3 = rhamnose: α-solanine); β-solanine (R1 and R2 only); γ-solanine (R1 only); α-chaconine (R1 = glucose, R2 and R3 = rhamnose); β-chaconine (R1 and R2 only); γ-chaconine (R1 only).

cause intoxication unless there were additional compounds (spirostane sapogenins or their glycosolated derivatives as saponins) in the potatoes to enhance absorption of the solanidine glycoalkaloids (McMillan and Thompson, 1979). The hypothesis suggests that the spirostane saponins may be an irritant to the alimentary tract, causing diarrhea and vomiting and thereby promoting absorption of α-solanine and α-chaconine. The presence of solanidane alkaloids and spirostane saponins together in potatoes was not examined then or since.

Recently, severe gastric and intestinal mucosal necrosis was associated with potato sprout material and crude alkaloid preparations from potato sprouts administered by gavage to hamsters (Baker et al., 1987, 1988) (Figs. 2 and 3; normal intestinal mucosa Fig. 4). Even though sufficient sprout material and alkaloid extract were administered to cause death of hamsters, brain cholinesterase activity was only minimally depressed (84 to 90% of normal). In previous studies by others, administration of α-chaconine to rats IP at a sufficient dose to cause death to two-thirds of the rats depressed the cholinesterase activity to 18% of normal, with rats intoxicated at a sublethal dose having

TABLE 1 Dosage of α-Chaconine and Lethality for Various Animal Species

Animal	Route of adminsitration	Amount (mg/kg)	Effects	Reference
Mouse	IP	19.2	50% death	Nishie et al. (1975)
Rabbit	IP	30, 40	0/2 death in <12 h	Nishie et al. (1975)
	IP	50	1/3 death in <12 h	Nishie et al. (1975)
	IP	60	1/1 death in <12 h	Nishie et al. (1975)
Rat	IP	10, 30, 60, 90	0/3, 1/3, 2/3, 3/3 dead in 4 h	Alozie et al. (1978)
	IP	84	50% death	Chaube and Swinyard (1976)

TABLE 2 Dosage of α-Solanine and Lethality for Various Animal Species

Animal	Route of administration	Amount (mg/kg)	Effects	Reference
Man	Oral	225	Toxic	Ruhlue (1961)
Sheep	Oral	500	Lethal	Konig (1953)
	IV	50	Lethal	Konig (1953)
	Oral	17	Toxic	Konig (1953)
Rat	Gavage	590	50% death	Gull et al. (1970)
	IP	75	50% death	Gull et al (1970)
	IP	67	50% death	Chaube and Swinyard (1976)
Mouse	IP	32.3	50% death	Patil et al (1972)
	IP	30	50% death	Sharma et al. (1978)
Rabbit	IP	20	Overnight death	Nishie et al. (1971) (1971)
	IP	30	Death in 6 h	Nishie et al. (1971)
	IP	30, 40, 50	0/1, 1/1, 1/1 dead within 24 h	Nishie et al. (1975)

TABLE 3 Anticholinesterase Activity of Glycoalkaloids and Their Aglycones Present in Wild and Cultivated Potatoes[a]

Compound	Average cholinesterase inhibition (%)
Glycoalkaloids	
α-Chaconine	26.8
β$_2$-Chaconine	23.3
α-Solanine	26.3
Dehydrocommersonine	18.5
Commersonine	20.2
Demissine	21.6
Tomatine	4.2
Aglycones	
Solanidine	15.4
Demissidine	11.3
Tomatidine	4.2

[a]Determinations at similar concentrations of compound with reactant.
Source: Data from Busway et al. (1987).

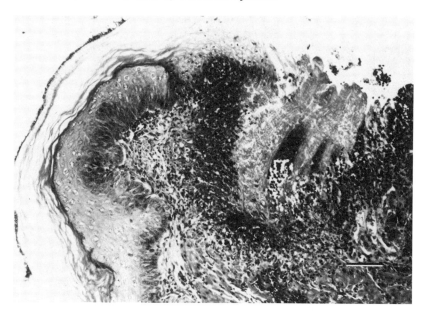

FIGURE 2 Gastric glandular mucosa at the junction of the squamous fore-stomach epithelium and the glandular mucosal epithelium from a hamster administered by gavage 50 mg of α-solanine purified from potato sprout material. There is severe necrosis of the glandular mucosal epithelium and hyperemia of adjacent mucosa. Bar = 294 μm.

79% cholinesterase activity (Alozie et al., 1978). The crude alkaloid preparation previously administered to hamsters (Baker et al., 1987) contained primarily chaconine and solanine alkaloids; however, other steroidal compounds (sapogenins and saponins as suggested previously) could have been in the preparation as well (Baker et al., 1987). Even so, it was thought that the alkaloids α-solanine and α-chaconine were responsible for the mucosal epithelial necrosis that caused secondary fluid-filled intestinal lumens, septicemia, and probable shock (Baker et al., 1988). Portions of the crude mixture of chaconine and solanine previously administered to those hamsters (Baker et al., 1987) was then further purified to yield α-solanine and α-chaconine, and also hydrolyzed to yield solanidine. Each of these preparations was administered by gavage to hamsters in equimolar concentrations (50 mg per hamster for glycoalkaloids, 23 mg per hamster for aglycone) and each glycoalkaloid caused severe clinical depression and gastric and proximal small intestinal mucosal necrosis with fluid-filled intestinal lumens. The aglycone did not cause any lesions (Baker et al., 1989b). The glycoalkaloid-induced lesions were the same as those present in hamsters administered potato sprout material. Acetylcholinesterase inhibition by the steroidal alkaloids of potatoes did not appear to be the most important mechanism of injury (Baker et al., 1988). Also, the glycoalkaloids were capable of causing gastric and intestinal mucosal injury without contaminating saponins or sapogenins as had been thought necessary by McMillan and Thompson (1979).

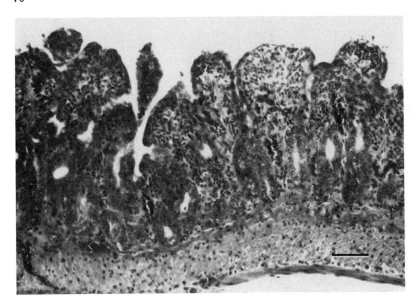

FIGURE 3 Small intestine from a hamster administered by gavage 50 mg of α-solanine purified from sprout material. There is marked necrosis and blunting of intestinal villi with loss of covering epithelium. Bar = 294 μm.

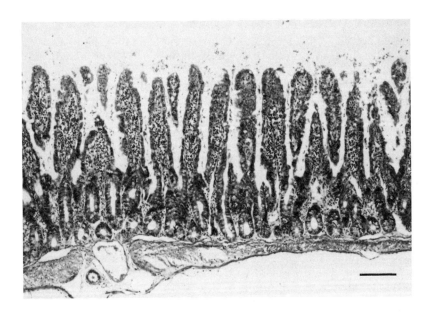

FIGURE 4 Small intestine from a control hamster administered water by gavage. Bar = 714 μm.

III. *SOLANUM* TOXICOSIS (SPIROSOLANE ALKALOIDS)

Other *Solanum* plant species have been administered to pregnant hamsters to evaluate the teratogenicity of the steroidal alkaloids that they contain (Keeler et al., 1989). These plant species evaluated contained spirosolane glycoalkaloids (Fig. 5) rather than the solanidane type in *S. tuberosum*. Two of the plant species tested caused death of pregnant hamsters (Baker et al., 1989a). *Solanum eleagnifolium* contained solasodine glycoalkaloid(s) and caused the death of six of eight hamsters fed 0.6 to 1.0g of ground plant material (Baker et al., 1989a). These hamsters had lesions similar to those in hamsters administered *S. tuberosum* with gastric and small intestinal mucosal necrosis and fluid-filled intestinal lumens (Figs. 6 and 7). *Solanum dulcamara* also caused death in 8 of 10 hamsters administered 1.4 to 2.0 g of dried, ground plant material (Baker et al., 1989a). *S. dulcamara* contained one-third the total alkaloid concentration of *S. eleagnifolium*, but had an equal mixture of solasodine glycoalkaloid(s) and probably soladulcidine glycoalkaloids. The lesions in the hamsters administered *S. dulcamara* plant material could not be differentiated from lesions in hamsters administered either *S. eleagnifolium* or *S. tuberosum* (gastric and small intestinal mucosal epithelial necrosis). Two additional *Solanum* plant species were fed (*Solanum melongena* and *Solanum sarrachoides*). They contained only solasodine glycoalkaloid(s), and neither cause death or lesions, but the alkaloid concentration was considerably less than in *S. eleagnifolium* (Baker et al., 1989a).

The glycoalkaloid fraction from *S. eleagnifolium* was isolated and purified and 45 mg per hamster administered by gavage. The glycoalkaloid fraction material caused gastric and intestinal mucosal necrosis and fluid-filled intestinal lumens within 24 h of similar severity, as did the ground whole plant and the mixed solanidine glycoalkaloids from *S. tuberosum* (Baker et al., 1989a).

Spirosolane alkaloids and glycoalkaloids also occur in cultivated tomato (*Lycopersicon esculentum* Mill.) plants. Tomatine is a glycoalkaloid of a spirosolane aglycone (tomatidine, Fig. 8). Tomatine was administered by gavage to hamsters (Baker et al., 1989b) and caused gross changes in the gastric glandular mucosa and intestinal mucosa similar to changes induced by equimolar doses of solanine and chaconine (Baker et al., 1989b). Tomatine causes only slight inhibition of acetylcholinesterase activity in vitro compared with solanine and chaconine (Bushway et al., 1987).

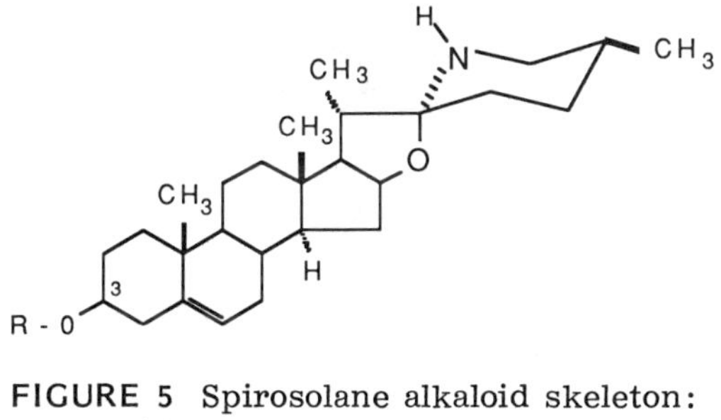

FIGURE 5 Spirosolane alkaloid skeleton: solasodine (R = H); solasodine glycoalkaloids contain various carbohydrates at C3.

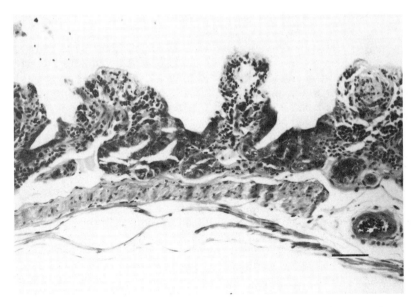

FIGURE 6 Small intestine from a hamster administered dried, ground seed material from *S. eleagnifolium* by gavage. There is blunting of villi with low cuboidal to squamous epithelium covering the villi. Bar = 300 µm.

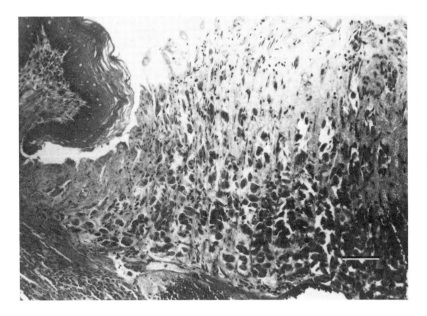

FIGURE 7 Gastric glandular mucosa at the junction of the squamous fore-stomach epithelium and the glandular mucosal epithelium from a hamster administered dried, ground seed material from *S. eleagnifolium* by gavage. There is severe necrosis of the glandular mucosal epithelium. Bar = 286 µm.

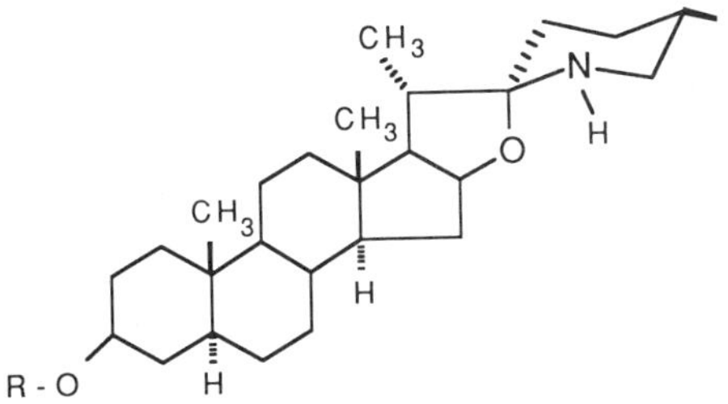

FIGURE 8 Tomatidine alkaloid (spirosolane type) with carbohydrate substitu-

tions at R to make glycoalkaloids (tomatine; R = $-$gal$-$glc $<^{\text{xyl}}_{\text{glc}}$).

IV. MECHANISM OF INJURY BY STEROIDAL ALKALOIDS

It has been generally considered that the mechanism of injury and death of
humans and animals exposed to solanidine glycoalkaloids from *S. tuberosum*
(α-solanine and α-chaconine) is acetylcholinesterase inhibition, which eventually leads to respiratory failure (Morgan and Coxon, 1987; Brimblecombe,
1977). Recent investigations in hamsters suggest that animals administered
α-solanine or α-chaconine have intestinal and gastric mucosal necrosis with
secondary fluid loss, septicemia, and bacteremia and only slight acetylcholinesterase inhibition (Baker et al., 1987, 1988). Lethal central nervous system
acetylcholinesterase inhibition in rats administered α-chaconine IP or organo-
phosphate compounds IP was 18 and 41% of the reference activity, respectively
(Alozie et al., 1978; Baker et al., 1988). Acetylcholinesterase activity associated with lethally intoxicated hamsters orally administered α-solanine and
α-chaconine by gavage were 84 to 90% of control activity (Baker et al., 1987).
Solasodine glycoalkaloids in *S. eleagnifolium* and *S. dulcamara* have not been
evaluated in vitro for cholinesterase inhibitory activity. Oral administration
of lethal concentrations of α-solanine and α-chaconine to hamsters does not
cause sufficient acetylcholinesterase inhibition to account for death.
　　Steroidal alkaloids have some of the same physical properties that are
ascribed to saponins (hemolysis of erythrocytes, forming foam in an aqueous
solution), even though steroidal alkaloids are not considered saponins by definition (George, 1965; Price et al., 1987; Wall and Davis, 1970). Solanine has
been demonstrated to cause hemolysis of erythrocytes in vitro (Konig, 1953).
Saponins have been reported to cause intestinal irritation and corrosion when
consumed in the diet (Sollmann, 1957). There is also evidence that saponins
increase intestinal permeability and enterocyte turnover and induce ultrasturc-
tural alterations of villous enterocytes (Alvarez and Torres-Pinedo, 1982;
Johnson et al., 1986; Cassidy et al., 1981). Some saponins are structurally
related to steroidal alkaloids, of course. Diosgenin and glycosolated forms
of diosgenin (Saponin, ICN Biochemicals, Cleveland, Ohio) are structurally
similar to solasodine and glycoalkaloids of solasodine. Neither diosgenin nor
Saponin cause gross lesions in the intestinal mucosa when administered by
gavage to hamsters (Baker et al., 1989b), even though equimolar amounts of
solasodine glycoalkaloids (extracted from *S. eleagnifolium*) did cause intestinal

and gastric mucosal hemorrhage (Baker et al., 1989b). The glycoalkaloids of tomatidine, solasodine, and solanidine all caused severe intestinal epithelial necrosis and appeared more toxic than diosgenin at equimolar concentrations (Baker et al., 1989b). The gastrointestinal lesions may result from the saponin-like effect of these glycoalkaloids, an ability to disrupt cell membranes more easily than saponins, or it may be a result of other undetermined mechanisms. The cause of death in hamsters orally administered the steroidal glycoalkaloids appears to be secondary to septicemia and bacteremia associated with the intestinal lesions rather than cholinesterase inhibition, and the mechanism of the gastrointestinal epithelial injury has not been determined.

REFERENCES

Adam, S. E. I. (1978). Toxicity of indigenous plants and agricultural chemicals in farm animals. *J. Toxicol. Clin. Toxicol. 13*:269-280.

Alozie, S. O., Sharma, R. P., and Salunkhe, D. K. (1978). Inhibition of rat cholinesterase isoenzymes in vitro and in vivo by the potato alkaloid α-chaconine. *J. Food Biochem. 2*:259-276.

Alozie, S. O., Sharma, R. P., and Salunkhe, D. K. (1979). Excretion of α-chaconine-^{3}H, a steroidal glycoalkaloid from *Solanum tuberosum* L. and its metabolites in hamsters. *Pharmacol. Res. Commun. 11*:483-490.

Alvarez, J. R., and Torres-Pinedo, R. (1982). Interaction of soybean lectin, soyasaponins and glycinin with rabbit jejunal mucosa in vitro. *Pediatr. Res. 16*:728-731.

Baker, D. C., Keeler, R., and Gaffield, W. (1987). Lesions of potato sprout and extracted potato sprout alkaloid toxicity in Syrian hamsters. *J. Toxicol. Clin. Toxicol. 25*:199-208.

Baker, D. C., Keeler, R., and Gaffield, W. (1988). Mechanism of death in hamsters gavaged potato sprout material. *Toxicol. Pathol. 16*:333-339.

Baker, D. C., Keeler, R., and Gaffield, W. (1989). Pathology of hamsters gavaged *Solanum* plant species containing steroidal alkaloids. *Toxicon 27*:1331-1337.

Baker, D. C., Keeler, R., and Gaffield, W. (1989b). Steroidal alkaloid toxicity in hamsters. *Am. J. Pathol.* (in preparation).

Brimblecombe, R. W. (1977). Drugs acting on central cholinergic mechanisms and affecting respiration. *Pharmacol. Ther. B3*:65-74.

Bushway, R. J., Savage, S. A., and Ferguson, B. S. (1987). Inhibition of acetylcholinesterase by solanaceous glycoalkaloids and alkaloids. *Am. Potato J. 64*:409-413.

Cassidy, M. M., Lightfoot, F. G., Grau, L. E., Story, J. A., Kritchevsky, D., and Vahouny, G. V. (1981). Effect of chronic intake of dietary fibers on the ultrastructural topography of rat jejunum and colon: a scanning electron microscopy study. *Am. J. Clin. Nutr. 34*:218-228.

Chaube, S., and Swinyard, C. A. (1976). Teratological and toxicological studies of alkaloids and phenolic compounds from *Solanum tuberosum*. *J. Toxicol. Appl. Pharmacol. 36*:227-237.

Craig, J. F., and Kehoe, D. (1925). Plant poisoning. *Vet. Rec. 38*:795-825.

George, A. J. (1965). Legal status of toxicity of saponins. *Food Costmet. Toxicol.* 3:85-91.

Gull, S. D., Isenberg, F. M., and Bryan, H. H. (1970). Alkaloid toxicology of *Solanum tuberosum. Hortic. Sci.* 5:316.

Hansen, A. A. (1925). Two fatal cases of potato poisoning. *Science 61*:340-341.

Harris, R. W., and Cockburn, T. (1918). Alleged poisoning by potatoes. *Analyst 43*:133-137.

Jadhav, S. J., Sharma, R. P., and Salunkhe, D. K. (1981). Naturally occurring toxic alkaloids in foods. *Crit. Rev. Toxicol.* 9:21-104.

Johnson, I. T., Gee, J. M., Price, K. R., Curl, C. L., and Fenwock, G. R. (1986). Influence of saponins on gut permeability and active nutrient transport in vitro. *J. Nutr. 116*:2270-2277.

Keeler, R. F., Baker, D. C., and Gaffield, W. (1990). Teratogenicity of spirosolane-containing *Solanum* species. *Toxicon 28*:(in press).

Khera, K. S. (1984). Maternal toxicity—a possible factor in fetal malformations in mice. *Teratology 29*:411-416.

Konig, H. (1953). Untersuchungen über Solanin Wirkung bein Rind und Schaft im Zusammenhang mit Kartoffelkraut-Futterung. *Schweiz. Arch. Tierheilkd.* 95:97-118.

Kuhn, R., Low, I., and Trischmann, H. (1955a). Die Konstitution des Solanins. *Chem. Ber.* 88:1492-1506.

Kuhn, R., Low, I., and Trischmann, H. (1955b). Die Konstitution des Chaconins. *Chem. Ber.* 88:1690-1696.

McMillan, M., and Thompson, J. C. (1979). An outbreak of suspected solanine poisoning in schoolboys: examination of criteria of solanine poisoning. *Q. J. Med.* 48:227-243.

Morgan, M. R. A., and Coxon, D. T. (1987). Tolerances: glycoalkaloids in potates. In *Natural Toxicants in Food: Progress and Prospects*, D. H. Watson (Ed.). VCH Publishers, New York, pp. 221-230.

Nishie, K., Gumbmann, M. R., and Keyl, A. C. (1971). Pharmacology of solanine. *Toxicol. Appl. Pharmacol.* 19:81-82.

Nishie, K., Norred, W. P., and Swain, A. P. (1975). Pharmacology and toxicology of chaconine and tomatine. *Res. Commun. Chem. Pathol. Pharmacol.* 12:657-668.

Norred, W. P., Nishie, K., and Osman, S. F. (1976). Excretion, distribution and metabolic fate of ^{3}H-α-chaconine. *Res. Commun. Chem. Pathol. Pharmacol.* 13:161-171.

Orgell, W. H., Vaidya, K. A., and Dahm, P. A. (1958). Inhibition of human plasma cholinesterase in vitro and by extracts of solanaceous plants. *Science 128*:1136-1137.

Patil, B. C., Sharma, R. P., Salunkhe, D. K., and Salunkhe, K. (1972). Evaluation of solanine toxicity. *Food Cosmet. Toxicol.* 10:395-398.

Prince, K. R., Johnson, I. T., and Fenwock, G. R. (1987). The chemistry and biological significance of saponins in food and feedingstuffs. *Crit. Rev. Food Sci. Nutr.* 26:27-135.

Ruhlue, R. (1961). Beitrag zur Pathologie und Toxikologie des Solanins. *Arch. Pharm. (Weinheim) 284*:67-74.

Sharma, R. P., Willhite, C. C., Shupe, J. L., and Salunkhe, D. K. (1978). Acute toxicity and histopathological effects of certain glycoalkaloids and extracts of *Alternaria solani* or *Phytophthora infestans* in mice. *Toxicol. Lett. 3:* 349-355.

Sollmann, T. (1957). *A Manual of Pharmacology*. W. B. Saunders, Philadelphia, pp. 667-670.

Wall, M. E., and Davis, K. H. (1970). The chemistry, pharmacology and toxicology of steroidal glycosides. In *Toxins of Animal and Plant Origin*, Vol. 2, *Proceedings of the 2nd International Symposium of Animal and Plant Toxins*, A. DeVries and E. Kochua (Eds.). Gordon and Breach Science Publisher, New York, pp. 597-624.

Willimott, S. G. (1933). An investigation of solanine poisoning. *Analyst 58:* 431-439.

6

Teratogenic *Solanum* Species and the Responsible Teratogens

Richard F. Keeler

Poisonous Plant Research Laboratory, Agricultural Research Service, USDA, Logan, Utah

Dale C. Baker

Colorado State University, Fort Collins, Colorado

William Gaffield

Western Regional Research Center, Agricultural Research Service, USDA, Albany, California

I. INTRODUCTION

Studies on the possible teratogenicity of various *Solanum* species are of fairly recent origin. Several steroidal alkaloids from *Veratrum californicum* were identified in 1966 as the teratogens responsible for natural outbreaks of carnio-facial defects in sheep from maternal ingestion of that plant (Keeler and Binns, 1966). These alkaloidal teratogens have a number of structural similarities to some of the solanum alkaloids, so the latter were suspected as possible terato-gens (Keeler, 1970a).

Historically, epidemics of cyclopia and related congenital deformities in sheep were common in certain high-intensity lambing operations in Idaho. Hundreds of lambs per year were affected (Binns et al., 1963), and the na-ture of the effects was highly variable. They included single or double globe cyclopia, hypoplastic maxilla and premaxilla, pronounced mandibular curva-ture, and occasionally a skin-covered proboscis above a cyclopic single eye. Cebocephaly or brain tissue deficits were also common (Binns et al., 1963). *V. californicum* ingested or gavaged on day 14 of gestation induced the condi-tion in experimental ewes (Binns et al., 1965). Results from administering plant extracts and fractions suggested that the teratogen was an alkaloid (Keeler and Binns, 1964). Subsequent testing of individual alkaloids dis-closed that only three induced the condition in experimental lambs: jervine, cyclopamine, and its glycoside cycloposine (Keeler and Binns, 1968). The three teratogens are structurally related C-nor-D-homo steroidal alkaloids of the jerveratrum series with fused furanopiperidine moieties attached spiro at carbon 17 of the modified steroid (Fig. 1). Closely related compounds devoid of the furan ring did not induce craniofacial defects (Keeler, 1970a). A wide variety of experimental ruminants (Binns et al., 1972) as well as nonruminant laboratory animals were susceptible (Keeler, 1970b, 1971, 1975; Bryden et al., 1973; Bryden and Keeler, 1973), and it appeared that the insult was di-rectly on the embryo by the alkaloid teratogen rather than by metabolites, because both treated chick embryos as well as sheep embryos from ewes ad-ministered jervine or cyclopamine by intrauterine injection were susceptible (Bryden et al., 1973; Bryden and Keeler, 1973).

Thus *Solanum* species teratogenicity was investigated because of the struc-tural similarity between the *Veratrum* alkaloid teratogens and certain *Solanum*

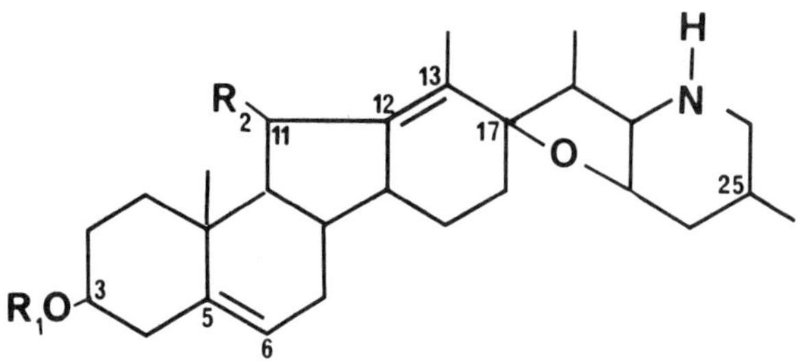

FIGURE 1 Three teratogenic C-nor-D-homo-jerveratrum steroidal alkaloids of *V. californicum*: cyclopamine (R_1 = H, R_2 = H_2), jervine (R_1 = H, R_2 = O), and cycloposine (R_1 = glucose, R_2 = H_2).

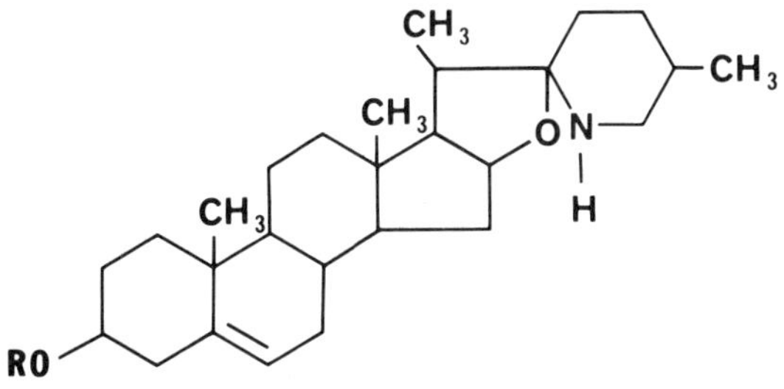

FIGURE 2 Spirosolane-type steroidal alkaloids present in *Solanums* as aglycone (R = H) or glycoside (R = various sugars).

alkaloids, and the possibility that both plant genera as well as constituent
alkaloids might give rise to similar defects in the human and animal population.
Candidate *Solanum* alkaloids which showed structural similarity to the *Veratrum*
teratogens included those from among the spirosolane and solanidane groups
(Figs. 2 and 3).

Another reason to investigate possible teratogenicity of *Solanum* species
arose because of an hypothesis advanced by Renwick (1972) which claimed
that avoidance of blighted potatoes by pregnant women would reduce the incidence of anencephaly and spina bifida (ASB) in newborn babies by 95%. As
support for his hypothesis, Renwick reported evidence that suggested to him
that there was a direct correlation between incidence of potato blight induced
by *Phytophthora infestans* and the incidence of spina bifida and anencephaly
in newborn babies. He further speculated that the potato alkaloids might be
considered among several compound classes as possible responsible terato-
gen(s) and that the active agent was probably synthesized by the potato as
a consequence of the blight.

In Volume 1 of the *Handbook of Natural Toxins* is found a chapter "Naturally Occurring Teratogens from Plants" (Keeler, 1983) in which literature
to 1981 on the subject at hand was briefly reviewed. In the present chapter
the early work is covered in much greater detail along with extensive coverage
of research since 1981 on the teratogenicity of *Solanum* species and their teratogens. This chapter, along with Chapters 5, 7, and 8, explore not only the

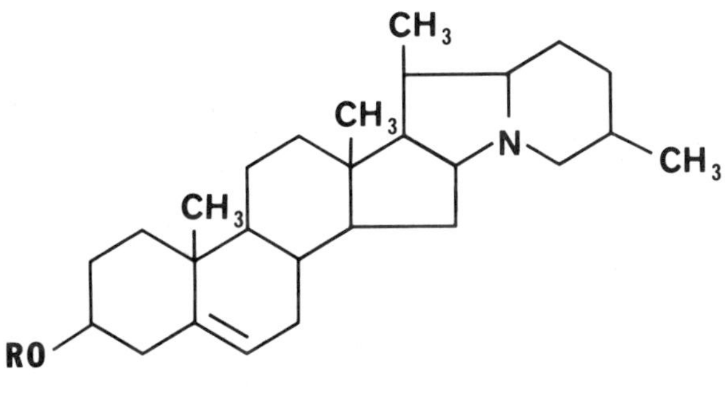

FIGURE 3 Solanidane-type steroidal alkaloids present in *Solanums* as aglycone (R = H) or glycoside (R = various sugars).

teratogenicity, but also the toxicity, analysis, and chemistry of *Solanum* species and their alkaloids.

II. POTENTIAL TERATOGENICITY OF *SOLANUM* SPECIES
BASED ON SIMILARITY OF CONSTITUENT ALKALOIDS
TO KNOWN TERATOGENS

Steroidal alkaloids are present in several genera, including the *Veratrum* and
Solanum (Kupchan and By, 1968; Schreiber, 1968). Early work which identified the *Veratrum* C-nor-D-homo-jerveratrum series steroidal alkaloids as potent teratogens led to consideration of experimental approaches that would
determine the structural and configurational features essential for teratogenic properties of steroidal alkaloids (Keeler, 1970a). Testing of isolated
Veratrum alkaloids suggested the apparent necessity of an intact furan ring
(Keeler, 1970a) which may confer some rigidity to the molecule. But the essential structural and configurational features could only be identified by
empirical testing of model compounds, including representatives from each of
the jerveratrum, spirosolane, and solanidane groups. If essential features
could be identified clearly, it would be possible to assess the potential teratogenicity of members of the *Solanum* species.

Utilizing naturally occurring compounds, an early approach tested *Solanum*
alkaloids bearing close structural and configurational similarity to cyclopamine.
The rigid conformation of cyclopamine, conferred by the spiro fused furanopiperidine moiety, is nearly duplicated by the spirosolanes, tomatidine, and
solasodine, which provide a pair of C22 isomers placing the piperidine nitrogen atom on opposite sides of the steroidal plane. Furthermore, the sapogenin,
diosgenin, provides a nonnitrogenous analog of solasodine. Experiments comparing the teratogenicity of these three compounds in hamsters to that of the
Veratrum alkaloids jervine and cyclopamine, were informative. Jervine, cyclopamine, and solasodine were teratogenic, but tomatidine and diosgenin were not
(Keeler et al., 1976). Clearly, the nitrogen atom in the piperidine ring was
essential for teratogenicity and its configurational position was critical (Keeler
et al., 1976). The spiro connection between rings D and E in the jerveratrum
compounds and between E and F in the spirosolanes positioned the nitrogen of
the piperidine ring either α or β (below or above, respectively) with regard
to the steroid plane. Alkaloids with the nitrogen α (Fig. 4) were teratogenic.
The early supposition that the furan conferred rigidity essential to the molecule's activity (Keeler, 1970a) was probably less important than the nitrogen
configuration resulting from the spiro connection. Variations in teratogenic
potency were thought to arise either from the degree of nitrogen projection
in the α direction or else the relative basicity of the alkaloids (Keeler et al.,
1976).

In further efforts to identify the structural and configurational features
required of a steroidal alkaloid teratogen, Brown (Brown and Keeler, 1978a,b)
prepared a series of jervine and cyclopamine analogs for assay in hamsters.
Results showed that neither the 5,6 or 12,13 double bonds nor C3 substituents
played an essential role in teratogenicity. Alterations at the nitrogen atom,
however, induced marked variation in teratogenicity. *N*-Methyljervine was
active, suggesting that the nitrogen could be tertiary as well as secondary,

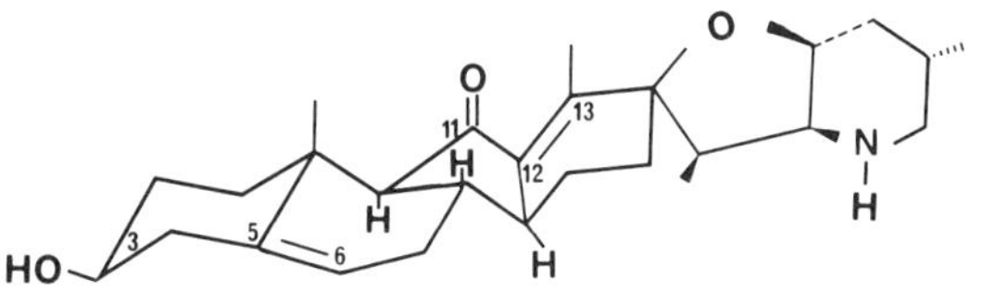

(a)

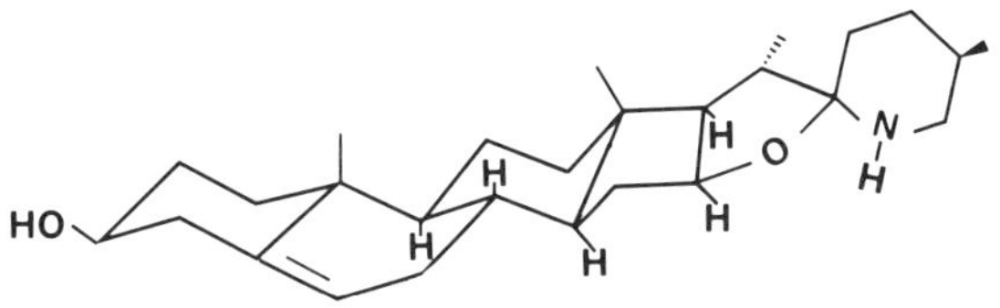

(b)

FIGURE 4 Examples of α-oriented nitrogen atoms in the (a) jerveratrum and (b) spirosolane alkaloid series (cyclopamine and solasodine, respectively).

but the N-methylmethiodide derivative, with no available electrons on the nitrogen, was inactive. Bonding to the active biological site probably occurred through the nitrogen atom. Other substitutions on the nitrogen atom altered activity, perhaps because of bulk, basicity changes, or other reasons.

Because the tertiary amine, N-methyljervine, was teratogenic, Brown believed that tertiary nitrogen solanidanes, common to certain *Solanum* species, having nitrogen-bonding capabilities α to the plane of the steroid should be teratogenic (Brown and Keeler, 1978c). Epimers of solanidine and demissidine (5,6-dihydrosolanidine) of different configuration at carbons 22 and 25 had been synthesized in 1961 by Sato and Ikekawa (1961). These configurational epimers vary with respect to the projection of the free-electron pair on the nitrogen (Fig. 5). For testing in hamsters, Brown prepared two 22S,25R epimers with the electron pair projecting α, and one 22R,25S epimer with the electron pair projecting β (Brown and Keeler, 1978c). Both of the 22S,25R isomers were teratogenic, while the single 22R,25S epimer (the naturally occurring *Solanum* alkaloid demissidine) was not teratogenic. The other naturally occurring 22R,25S epimer, solanidine, was not tested (Brown and Keeler, 1978c).

Based on these experimental results, a steroidal alkaloid might be expected to be teratogenic if it possessed a basic nitrogen atom in the terminal non-steroidal F ring shared or unshared with ring E, provided that there were nitrogen-bonding capabilities α to the plane of the steroid. Thus *Solanum* species that contained alkaloids which met those configurational requirements might be considered as potential teratogenic plants.

III. TERATOGENICITY OF *SOLANUM TUBEROSUM* AND OTHER *SOLANUM* SPECIES CONTAINING SOLANIDANE ALKALOIDS

Renwick's hypothesis (Renwick, 1972) stimulated a great deal of research activity in ensuing years because ASB in humans was of significant incidence

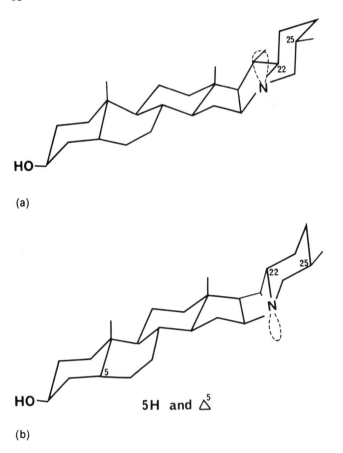

(a)

(b)

FIGURE 5 Solanidane epimers with the nitrogen-atom free-electron pair projecting β (a) or α (b) to the steroid plane.

in many parts of the world [approaching 0.35% of live births in some areas
(Leck et al., 1968)], and also due to the agricultural importance of potatoes
as a primary foodstuff. The startling claim of the hypothesis that ASB could
be reduced by 95% through potato avoidance led to follow-up research and to
controversy. The hypothesis was based on an apparent epidemiologic correlation between incidence of blight and incidence of ASB, so some research centered on epidemiologic aspects. Several workers who believed that other epidemiologic interpretations were more appropriate (Elwood and MacKenzie,
1973; Emanuel and Sever, 1973; Field and Kerr, 1973; Kinlen and Hewitt,
1973; McMahon et al., 1973; Spiers et al., 1974) cast doubt on the validity
of the epidemiologic relationship upon which the hypothesis was based. Particularly compelling evidence against the hypothesis that potato avoidance
would reduce ASB by 95% was the birth of ASB children to mothers on potato
avoidance trials (Nevin and Merrett, 1975).

    In the first laboratory animal study concerning the question of potential
teratogenicity of potatoes, Poswillo et al. (1972) found cranial osseous defects

in marmosets born to dams dosed with certain potato preparations. Later experiments failed to confirm the observation (Poswillo et al., 1973). Swinyard and Chaube (1973) determined that injection of extracted potato alkaloids or of pure solanine to pregnant rats and rabbits produced no neural tube defects in their offsping. Ruddick et al. (1974) claimed that freeze-dried *Phytophthora*-blighted "Kennebec" potatoes were not teratogenic in rats. Nishie et al. (1975) reported that tomatine, α-chaconine, and α-solanine failed to produce teratogenic effects in chicks. According to Bell et al. (1976), the intraperitoneal injection of solanine in pregnant mice did not produce terata. Chaube and Swinyard (1976) reported no neural tube defects in offspring from rats given acute or chronic intraperitoneal injection of a α-chaconine or α-solanine, although some fetuses were dead. But Pierro and co-workers (1977) found α-chaconine but not α-solanine was teratogenic in inbred NAW/Pr mice when dams were dosed on day 8 or 9 of gestation. Mun and associates (1975) showed that both pure solanine and glycoalkaloids extracted from *Phytophthora*-blighted potatoes produced "rumplessness or trunklessness" in chick embryos when eggs were treated early in their development. Jelinek et al. (1976) found that chick deformities were induced by an ethanol extract of boiled potatoes infected with *P. infestans*, an equivalent amount of extract of healthy potatoes, or by solanine in amounts corresponding to the solanine concentration in either extract. Sharma et al. (1978) found no teratogenic or embryolethal effects in hamsters from 50% blighted potatoes in the diet. In limited testing in miniature swine and rabbits, Sharma et al. (1978) observed rare instances of anencephaly and spina bifida occulta, but incidence was not statistically significant because of limited numbers of animals.

Neither blight-infested tuber material nor aged, high-alkaloid tuber material was teratogenic in rats, mice, hamsters, or rabbits when gavaged at the primitive streak/neural plate stage of embryonic development (Keeler et al., 1974, 1975). However, sprouts containing 200 to 400 times as much alkaloid as tubers were teratogenic in Simonsen hamsters. Exencephaly and encephalocele were usually induced (Keeler et al., 1978). Sprouts from six different cultivars produced terata, but neither tubers nor peels from these same cultivars were teratogenic at doses up to four times as high as sprout dosages. Approximately 2500 to 3500 mg/kg of dried sprout material was required to induce the malformations. Presumably, this teratogenic effect of potato sprouts in Simonsen hamsters was due to alkaloids since the 3% acetic acid-extracted total glycoalkaloid fraction (TGA) from the sprouts also produced the effects. Pregnant Simonsen hamsters were dosed with 370 mg/kg of a total glycoalkaloid preparation from Kennebec sprouts, and of 21 litters carried to term, 8 had a total of 23 deformed offspring (Keeler, 1984).

Renwick and colleagues attempted to identify the teratogen of potato sprouts and measure the in vivo retention of it in tissues of humans and hamsters. Renwick claimed (1982) that the two major potato alkaloid glycosides, α-solanine and α-chaconine, induced a high incidence of exencephaly and encephalocele in offspring from pregnant hamsters gavaged the compounds on day 8 of gestation. Twenty of 34 live litters had malformed individuals and about 24% of all offspring of these litters in α-solanine-gavaged animals were deformed. These two solanidane glycosides are the principal alkaloidal glycosides in U.S. potato cultivars and the only alkaloidal glycosides present in British cultivars (Renwick, 1982). Renwick and colleagues (1984) demonstrated that the British potato cultivar Arran Pilot is teratogenic in Simonsen hamsters, and showed through extraction and isolation experiments coupled with teratogenicity trials that both α-solanine and α-chaconine isolated from the Arran Pilot cultivar were teratogenic. Both glycoalkaloids induced birth defects in offspring in over half the litters, which led to Renwick's conclusion that potato sprout teratogenicity could be accounted for essentially by these two compounds.

Naturally occurring solanidanes, α-chaconine and α-solanine, are considered to possess the 22R,25S configuration [β projection of nitrogen free-electron pair above the steroidal plane (Schreiber, 1968)]. Earlier data (Brown and Keeler, 1978c) on the teratogenicity of solanidane epimers would not have led to the prediction that these compounds are teratogenic unless enzyme-catalyzed inversion of the electron pair takes place through configurational alteration in vivo or unless some of the 22S,25R epimer was present in potatoes and in glycoside preparations.

Renwick and co-workers (Claringbold et al., 1982) also studied the kinetics of retention of tritiated solanidine in human subjects to extend the data of Nevin and Merrett (1975), who had shown that potato avoidance by mothers during pregnancy did not prevent the birth of ASB offspring among mothers who had delivered ASB children previously. If potato alkaloids (solanidine or its glycosides) were responsible for induction of ASB, significant tissue storage would have to occur, followed by release during pregnancy into maternal circulation and thence to the embryo. In these experiments (Claringbold et al., 1982), solanidine [identity confirmed by mass spectroscopy (MS)] was oxidized with mercuric acetate and subsequently reduced with tritiated sodium borohydride, resulting in a mixture of tritiated solanidines which was then administered to human subjects by intravenous injection. Urinary and fecal excretion rates of radiolabel were sufficiently slow so that 90% or more of the label was retained somewhere in the body and excreted with a half-life of from 34 to 68 days. Unfortunately, it was not determined whether the sequestered label was still in the form of solanidine rather than a metabolite. However, solanidine was isolated and identified in human postmortem liver samples from subjects that had died from cardiovascular disease. If the retained label was still in the form of unchanged solanidine, an approximation of 50 mg was calculated as the retained body burden of solanidine from daily intake and absorption of 1 mg/day. If solanidine stored in innocuous loci was mobilized during the stress of pregnancy, mobilization might lead to sufficient embryonic insult to induce ASB (Claringbold et al., 1982). Alozie et al. (1979) had earlier shown binding and slow excretion of orally administered tritiated α-chaconine in hamsters.

IV. TERATOGENICITY OF *SOLANUM* SPECIES CONTAINING SPIROSOLANE ALKALOIDS

Spirosolane alkaloids such as the teratogen solasodine (Fig. 4) are common in several plant genera used as food by humans or foraged by livestock. These plants include many members of the *Solanum* genus, particularly those encountered by grazing livestock, although *S. melongena* (eggplant), *S. quitoense* (naranjilla), and some cultivars of *S. tuberosum* are ingested by humans.

To test the potential teratogenicity of spirosolane-containing *Solanum* species, the induction of birth defects has been assayed in hamsters administered four spirosolane alkaloid-containing *Solanum* species—*S. eleagnifolium, S. dulcamara, S. sarrachoides,* and *S. melongena* (eggplant) (Keeler et al., unpublished observations). Compared to the induction of birth defects by *S. tuberosum,* which contains mainly solanidane glycosides, and to the incidence of defects in controls, *S. eleagnifolium* and *S. dulcamara* fruit both induced a high-percentage incidence of deformed litters (20.4 and 16.3, respectively) that was statistically significant ($P < 0.001$). While percentage incidence of deformed litters induced by both *S. sarrachoides* and *S. melongena* fruit (9.5 and 7.6, respectively) was higher than controls (3.4), in neither case was the incidence found to be statistically significant ($P > 0.05$). By comparison, deformed litter incidence induced by sprouts of *S. tuberosum* was 24.0% ($P < 0.001$). Terata induced by all *Solanum* species were mainly exencephaly and encephalocele (Fig. 6).

A comparison by gas chromatographic (GC) analysis of purified alkaloid extracts of the test *Solanum* species before and after hydrolysis revealed no measurable free solasodine, other spirosolanes, or any nonspirosolane steroidal alkaloid aglycones in unhydrolyzed total alkaloid fractions of fruit of *S. eleagnifolium, S. sarrachoides, S. dulcamara,* or *S. melongena* (Keeler et al., unpublished observations). All alkaloid material was apparently present in the glycoside form. In contrast, sprouts of *S. tuberosum* contained 33% solanidine (the only aglycone found) in the free form and 67% as glycoside, which was freed only upon hydrolysis. GC/MS analysis of hydrolysates of the purified extracts revealed that solasodine was a principal or sole aglycone of the alkaloid glycosides in all of the *Solanum* test species except *S. tuberosum* (Keeler et al., unpublished observations). In the latter, solanidine was the sole aglycone. Among the test species, exclusive of *S. tuberosum,* only *S. dulcamara* contained glycosides other than solasodine glycosides. In addition to solasodine glycosides, another glycoside, possibly based on soladulcidine or a close relative, was present in *S. dulcamara.*

Considerable variation in both toxicity and teratogenicity was observed among the different *Solanum* species (Keeler et al., unpublished observations). Gross and histopathologic toxic effects included gastric and small intestinal mucosal necrosis in dams dying or showing overt toxicity signs from *Solanum* gavage (Baker et al., 1989). *S. tuberosum,* which contains solanidane-type alkaloids, and *S. eleagnifolium,* which contains spirosolane-type alkaloid(s), were equally toxic to the dam and teratogenic to concepti at approximately equal alkaloid dose elvels. If alkaloids alone were responsible for the toxicity and teratogenicity, it appeared that solanidane and solasodine glycosides were about equally toxic and teratogenic and that potency was determined by alkaloid dose level since *S. sarrachoides* and *S. melongena* were devoid of teratogenicity and almost nontoxic at alkaloid levels 1/4 to 1/20 that of *S. eleagnifolium.* But because *S. dulcamara* at about 1/10 the alkaloid dose level was approximately equally toxic and teratogenic compared to *S. eleagnifolium,* there must be other important factors that determine teratogenic potency. Aglycone structural identity undoubtedly plays a considerable role in determining teratogenic potency, as do configurational aspects (Keeler et al., 1976; Brown and Keeler, 1978c). The alkaloid glycosides of *S. dulcamara* administered comprised approximately equal amounts of a solasodine glycoside and what was speculated to be a soladulcidine glycoside. Perhaps spirosopane

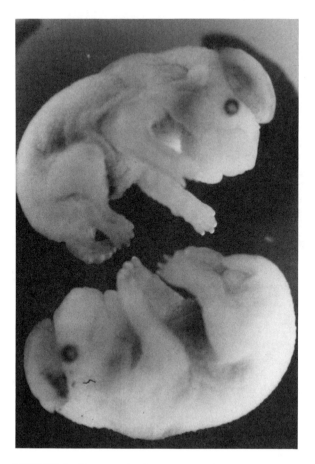

FIGURE 6 Exencephalic hamster fetuses induced by maternal gavage of *S. dulcamara*.

glycosides are not of equal potency. Alternatively, the emulsifying activity of saponins present in impure preparations may promote gastrointestinal absorption of alkaloids as suggested by Morgan and Coxon (1987). But clearly spirosolane alkaloid-containing *Solanum* species must be considered as potentially teratogenic.

V. DOSAGE AND MECHANISM CONSIDERATIONS

Although the data clearly show that several *Solanum* species are teratogenic in the Simonsen hamster, an examination of both the incidence of deformities and the required dose levels leaves several questions unanswered. Table 1 contains data that compare both toxicity and teratogenicity of two *Solanum* plants and several extracts and alkaloids of both the solanidane and the spirosolane types (Keeler et al., unpublished observations). *S. tuberosum* sprouts

TABLE 1 Toxicity and Teratogenicity of Two *Solanum* Plants, Extracts, and Alkaloids Gavaged to Simonsen Hamsters on Day 8 of Gestation[a]

Preparation	Dose[b] (g/kg BW)	Number pregnant surviving dams	Percentage dam deaths among treated animals	Percentage deformed litters from surviving dams
A. *Solanum tuberosum* (sprouts)	2.2 ± 0.3 (= 0.046 alkaloid)	96	14	24
B. Crude alkaloidal glycosides (from A)	0.245 ± 0.03	38	34	18
C. α-Chaconine	0.173 ± 0.007	29	26	66
D. α-Solanine	0.200	35	8	57
E. (22S, 25R)-Aglycones	0.13 ± 0.05	14	7	57
F. (22R, 25S-Aglycone	0.23 ± 0.08	10	9	10
G. *Solanum eleagnifolium* (fruits)	2.5 (= 0.04 alkaloid)	49	23	20
H. Solasodine glycoside (from G)	0.47 1 0.13	16	38	0
I. Solasodine				
a	0.200	10	0	10
b	1.4 ± 0.2	51	4	37
J. Tomatine	0.53 ± 0.12	34	36	6
K. Tomatidine	1.95 ± 0.75	38	0	—

[a]Data adapted from the following sources: items A, G, H, Ia, and J from Keeler et al. (unpublished observations); item B from Gaffield, Keeler, and Baker (unpublished observations); items C and D from Renwick et al. (1984); items E and F from Brown and Keeler (1978c); and items Ib and K from Keeler et al. (1976).

[b]In some cases treatment levels were goruped for convenience of reporting. Dose levels consequently show the range of doses included in each category.

from the Kennebec cultivar (A) and crude glycoside derived therefrom (B) were both teratogenic to concepti and toxic to the dam at levels tested. According to Renwick et al. (1984), the alkaloids α-chaconine (C) and α-solanine (D), derived from the Arran Pilot cultivar, were even more teratogenic and α-solanine was far less toxic to the dam than were roughly equal molar levels of B. In earlier work (Brown and Keeler, 1978c), (22S,25R)-solanidane epimers (E) were quite teratogenic, while a (22R,25S)-solanidane epimer (F) was essentially devoid of teratogenicity at molar levels close to B, C, and D. None of the solanidane epimers showed appreciable toxicity in the dam. The spirosolane-containing fruit of *S. eleagnifolium* (G), when gavaged at levels quite toxic to the dam, induced terata readily, but the solasodine glycoside derived therefrom (H) did not induce terata at levels that were even more toxic to the dam. Solasodine aglycone was not toxic to the dam nor teratogenic to concepti at approximately equivalent molar levels (Ia), but at levels about eight times as high (Ib) was decidedly teratogenic but still not toxic to the dam. Neither the glycoside tomatine (J) nor its aglycone tomatidine (K) were teratogenic at molar levels even higher than those of the solasodine (I) and solasodine glycoside (H) pair. Tomatine, but not tomatidine, was decidedly toxic to the dam.

Several questions related to dosage are still unclear after a critical examination of the data in Table 1. Based on known teratogenicity of alkaloidal aglycones, the teratogenicity of *Solanum* species should be due to their alkaloidal content, particularly the content of glycosidic alkaloids. Both the much lower activity of the crude alkaloidal glycoside (B) compared to *S. tuberosum* sprouts (A) from which B was derived and the lack of teratogenicity of the spirosolane glycoside (H) compared to *S. eleagnifolium* (G) from which H was derived (even though H was dosed at over 10 times the dose of G) are difficult to reconcile. Furthermore, if α-chaconine (C) and α-solanine (D) from the Arran Pilot cultivar are comprised of solanidine whose nitrogen free-electron pair projects β to the steroidal plane rather than α, the greater teratogenicity of C and D on a molar equivalent basis compared to the α-aglycone epimer (E) and vastly more teratogenic than the β-aglycone epimer (F) is difficult to reconcile.

Solanum species teratogenicity is apparently more complex than may be readily explained by dose levels of suspected alkaloidal teratogens. Perhaps C and D contained some of the α-aglycone (the 22S,25R) epimer. Pakrashi and co-workers (1977, 1978) reported the presence of a 22S,25R epimer, solanogantine, in a *Solanum* species, *S. giganteum*, along with two solanidanes of β-nitrogen configuration. So there is precedence in the *Solanum* genus for 22S,25R epimers. Alternatively, the presence of saponins in the preparations may promote gastrointestinal absorption of the alkaloids (Morgan and Coxon, 1987). Chapter 8 suggests another intriguing teratogenic possibility concerning the presence of either N- or C-oxidized analogs as either metabolites or minor plant constituents.

The toxicity induced by several *Solanum* species and their alkaloids, discussed at length in Chapter 5, is of interest here due to its impact on mode of action of the *Solanum* teratogens. Concern has been expressed that toxicity effects in dams and resultant effects in concepti, rather than direct effects on concepti, may often be the cause of observed terata (Khera, 1984; Black and Marks, 1986). Although there is a high incidence and severity of dam toxicosis upon administration of *Solanum* spp. and their alkaloids, dam toxicity does not appear to be responsible for the teratogenic effects. For example, among spirosolanes, the aglycone solasodine (Table 1, Ia) when dosed at 1.4 ± 0.2 g/kg body weight induced a high incidence of terata in concepti but was essentially without toxicity, while the solasodine glycoside from *S. eleagnifolium* (Table 1, H) at a molar dose of about one-eighth that level induced no terata but caused nearly 50% dam deaths from gastric and proximal small intestinal mucosal necrosis. Furthermore, the aglycone tomatidine (Table 1, K) was nontoxic and nonteratogenic, yet its glycoside tomatine (Table 1, J) at doses about one-eighth the molar equivalent induced no terata at a statistically significant level but was very toxic to dams. Among solanidanes, the sprouts (A) from *S. tuberosum* were much more teratogenic and much less toxic on an alkaloid dose basis than was the crude glycoside (B) extracted therefrom. In each incidence, the nature of the toxicity was always a gastric and proximal small intestinal mucosal necrosis (Baker et al., 1989) (see also Chapter 5). Were dam toxicity responsible for teratogenicity, one would expect a close parallel in incidence between the two effects. Thus although the mechanism of action in *Solanum* species teratogenesis is unknown, it does not result from dam toxicity.

VI. *SOLANUM* TERATOGENIC HAZARDS OF THE REAL WORLD

Based on present knowledge, the question of real-world teratogenic hazard from ingestion of *Solanum* species centers on whether humans, domestic livestock, or wild animal species are affected by the teratogenic solanidane or spirosolane alkaloids present in these plants. Clearly, a limited number of classes and strains of laboratory animals are susceptible to induction of terata by *Solanum* plant parts or their alkaloidal constituents. But whether that represents a real-world problem remains to be determined.

The question of possible teratogenicity of potatoes in humans cannot be answered with certainty because while one hamster strain, chick embryos, and one mouse strain are susceptible to plant parts or their alkaloids, most lab animals have not been adversely affected. If these data are extrapolated to humans, the teratogenicity of potato sprouts in the Simonsen hamster (Keeler et al., 1978) does not appear to represent a real-world hazard because an equivalent dose in an average pregnant woman (50 to 70 kg in weight) would be over 1000 g wet weight of sprouts. Sprouts are not ordinarily consumed by humans in any quantity because of the bitter taste conferred by their high alkaloid level. But, of course, animal species and strains do differ in susceptibility, and whether there is a real-world teratogenic hazard to humans from consuming potatoes remains to be clarified. If further research establishes unequivocally that there is undue tissue storage of a potato teratogen, which is not metabolized to an inactive form but which is released during pregnancy as Renwick suggests (Renwick et al., 1984), the birth of ASB children to mothers on potato avoidance trials as reported by Nevin and Merrett (1975) could be explained. On the other hand, it seems appropriate to acknowledge that genetic errors may account for most ASB births. Perhaps potatoes or their alkaloids play a role in human birth defects in some multifactorial way.

Genetic susceptibility differences among individuals in the very diverse human population could then play a very striking role if potatoes or associated compounds were even slightly teratogenic in humans.

Potato waste from processing plants, which is fed to livestock, often contains a high content of sprouts. If species susceptibility to potato-induced birth defects is broad enough, livestock may develop terata. Whether there are real-world teratogenic hazards from solanidane alkaloids centers largely on potatoes. Tubers are consumed by humans, and the halum or other wastes by livestock.

Spirosolane alkaloids, on the other hand, such as the teratogen solasodine and its glycosides, are found in several *Solanum* species used as food by humans in addition to plants foraged by livestock. A tabular listing (Schreiber, 1968) of plant sources of solasodine either as aglycone or glycoside suggested that it had been isolated by 1968 from about 100 different plants, including various *Solanum* species. Some of these plants are grazed by livestock and a few of them are common foods. For example, *S. melongena* (eggplant), *S. quitoense* (the Andean naranjilla), and *S. intrusum* (wonderberry) are among those used as food. Several dozen *Solanum* species are listed by Everist (1974) and Kingsbury (1964) as plants reported to induce toxicity in livestock. Thus frequent livestock contact with these plants must occur.

Spirosolanes, other than solasodine, that might be suspect as teratogenic if ingested by humans or animals include soladulcidine (5,6-dihydrosolasodine) isolated from *S. dulcamara, S. megacarpa,* and other species (Schreiber, 1968, 1979) and solanaviol, the C12α-ol analog of solasodine, from *S. aviculare* (Kaneko et al., 1980).

VII. CONCLUSIONS

Several *Solanum* species have proven to be teratogenic in various laboratory animal assays. The active agents appear to be solanidane and spirosolane steroidal alkaloids, probably as their glycosides. Teratogenicity of these alkaloids is not unexpected since they bear certain structural and configurational similarities to the known steroidal alkaloid teratogens from *Veratrum*. The teratogenic *Solanum* species also induce severe toxicity in the ingesting dam, but the teratogenic effects in their offspring are apparently unrelated to maternal toxicity. Whether there are real-world teratogenic hazards for humans and animals upon ingestion of these *Solanum* species is a question that cannot yet be answered with complete assurance.

REFERENCES

Alozie, S. O., Sharma, R. P., and Salunkhe, D. K. (1979). Excretion of α-chaconine-^{3}H, a steroidal glycoalkaloid from *Solanum tuberosum* L. and its metabolites in hamsters. *Pharmacol. Res. Commun. 11*:483-490.

Baker, D. C., Keeler, R. F., and Gaffield, W. (1989). Pathology in hamsters gavaged *Solanum* plant species containing steroidal alkaloids. *Toxicon 27*:1331-1337.

Bell, D. P., Gibson, J. G., McCarroll, A. M., McClean, G. A., and Geraldine, A. (1976). Embyrotoxicity of solanine and aspirin in mice. *J. Reprod. Fertil.* 46:257-259.

Binns, W., James, L. F., Shupe, J. L., and Everett, G. (1963). A congenital cyclopian-type malformation in lambs induced by maternal ingestion of a range plant, *Veratrum californicum. Am. J. Vet. Res.* 24:1164-1175.

Binns, W., Shupe, J. L., Keeler, R. F., and James, L. F. (1965). Chronologic evaluation of teratogenicity in sheep fed *Veratrum californicum. J. Am. Vet. Med. Assoc.* 147:839-842.

Binns, W., Keeler, R. F., and Balls, L. D. (1972). Congenital deformities in lambs, calves, and goats resulting from maternal ingestion of *Veratrum californicum*: hare lip, cleft palate, ataxia, and hypoplasia of metacarpal bones. *Clin. Toxicol.* 5:245-261.

Black, D. L., and Marks, T. A. (1986). Inconsistent use of terminology in animal development toxicology studies: a discussion. *Teratology 33*: 333-338.

Brown, D., and Keeler, R. F. (1978a). Structure-activity relation of steroid teratogens: 1. Jervine ring system. *J. Agric. Food Chem.* 26:561-563.

Brown, D., and Keeler, R. F. (1978b). Structure-activity relation of steroid teratogens: 2. N-substituted jervines. *J. Agric. Food Chem.* 26:564-566.

Brown, D., and Keeler, R. F. (1978c). Structure-activity relation of steroid teratogens: 3. Solanidan epimers. *J. Agric. Food Chem.* 26:566-569.

Bryden, M. M., and Keeler, R. F. (1973). Effects of alkaloids of *Veratrum californicum* on developing embryos. *J. Anat.* 116:464.

Bryden, M. M., Perry, C., and Keeler, R. F. (1973). Effects of alkaloids of *Veratrum californicum* on the developing chick embryo. *Teratology* 8:19-27.

Chaube, S., and Swinyard, C. A. (1976). Teratological and toxicological studies of alkaloids and phenolic compounds from *Solanum tuberosum. J. Toxicol. Appl. Pharmacol.* 36:227-237.

Claringbold, W. D. B., Few, J. D., and Renwick, J. H. (1982). Kinetics and retention of solanidine in man. *Xenobiotica 12*:293-302.

Elwood, J. H., and MacKenzie, G. (1973). Associations between the incidence of neurological malformations and potato blight outbreaks over 50 years in Ireland. *Nature 243*:476-477.

Emanuel, I. S., and Sever, L. E. (1973). Questions concerning the possible association of potatoes and neural tube defects, and an alternative hypothesis relating to maternal growth and development. *Teratology 8*:325-331.

Everist, S. L. (1974). *Poisonous Plants of Australia.* Angus & Robertson, London, pp. 652-680.

Field, B., and Kerr, C. (1973). Potato blight and neural tube defects. *Lancet 2*:507-508.

Jelinek, R., Kyzlink, V., and Blattny, C., Jr. (1976). An evaluation of the embryo-toxic effects of blighted potatoes on chicken embryos. *Teratology 14*:335-342.

Kaneko, K., Niitsu, K., Yoshida, N., and Mitsuhashi, H. (1980). Structure of solanaviol, a new steroidal alkaloid from *Solanum aviculare. Phytochemistry 19*:299-302.

Keeler, R. F. (1970a). Teratogenic compounds of *Veratrum californicum* (Durand): IX. Structure-activity relationships. *Teratology 3*:169-174.

Keeler, R. F. (1970b). Teratogenic compounds of *Veratrum californicum* (Durand): X. Cyclopia in rabbits produced by cyclopamine. *Teratology* 3:175-180.

Keeler, R. F. (1971). Teratogenic compounds of *Veratrum californicum* (Durand): XI. Gestational chronology and compound specificity in rabbits. *Proc. Soc. Exp. Biol. Med. 136*:1174-1189.

Keeler, R. F. (1975). Teratogenic effects of cyclopamine and jervine in rats, mice, and hamsters. *Proc. Soc. Exp. Biol. Med. 149*:302-306.

Keeler, R. F. (1983). Naturally occurring teratogens from plants. In *Handbook of Natural Toxins*, Vol. 1, *Plant and Fungal Toxins*, R. F. Keeler and A. T. Tu (Eds.). Marcel Dekker, New York, pp. 161-199.

Keeler, R. F. (1984). Mammalian teratogenicity of steroidal alkaloids. In *Isopentenoids in Plants: Biochemistry and Function*, W. D. Nes, G. Fuller, and L.-S. Tsai (Eds.). Marcel Dekker, New York, pp. 531-562.

Keeler, R. F., and Binns, W. (1964). Chemical compounds of *Veratrum californicum* related to congenital ovine cyclopian malformation: extraction of active material. *Proc. Soc. Exp. Biol. Med. 116*:123-127.

Keeler, R. F., and Binns, W. (1966). Teratogenic compounds of *Veratrum californicum* (Durand): II. Production of ovine fetal cyclopia by fractions and alkaloid preparations. *Can. J. Biochem. 44*:829-838.

Keeler, R. F., and Binns, W. (1968). Teratogenic compounds of *Veratrum californicum* (Durand): V. Comparison of cyclopian effects of steroidal alkaloids from the plant and structurally related compounds from other sources. *Teratology 1*:5-10.

Keeler, R. F., Douglas, D. R., and Stallknecht, G. F. (1974). Failure of blighted Russet Burbank potatoes to produce congenital deformities in rats. *Proc. Soc. Exp. Biol. Med. 146*:284-286.

Keeler, R. F., Douglas, D. R., and Stallknecht, G. F. (1975). The testing of blighted, aged, and control Russet Burbank potato tuber preparations for ability to produce spina bifida and anencephaly in rats, rabbits, hamsters, and mice. *Am. Potato J. 52*:125-132.

Keeler, R. F., Young, S., and Brown, D. (1976). Spina bifida, exencephaly, and cranial bleb produced by the solanum alkaloid solasodine. *Res. Commun. Chem. Pathol. Pharmacol. 13*:723-730.

Keeler, R. F., Young, S., Brown, D., Stallknecht, G. F., and Douglas, D. (1978). Congenital deformities produced in hamsters by potato sprouts. *Teratology 17*:327-334.

Khera, K. S. (1984). Maternal toxicity—a possible factor in fetal malformations in mice. *Teratology 29*:411-416.

Kingsbury, J. M. (1964). *Poisonous Plants of the United States and Canada*. Prentice-Hall, Englewood Cliffs, N.J.

Kinlen, L., and Hewitt, A. (1973). Potato blight and anencephaly in Scotland. *Br. J. Prev. Soc. Med. 27*:208-213.

Kupchan, S. M., and By, A. W. (1968). Steroid alkaloids: the *Veratrum* group. In *The Alkaloids*, Vol. 10, R. H. F. Manske (Ed.). Academic Press, New York, pp. 193-285.

Leck, I., Record, R. G., McKeown, T., and Edwards, J. H. (1968). The incidence of malformations in Birmingham, England, 1950-1959. *Teratology 1*:263-280.

McMahon, B. S., Yen, S., and Rotham, K. J. (1973). Potato blight and neural tube defects. *Lancet 1*:598-599.

Morgan, M. R. A., and Coxon, D. T. (1987). Tolerances: glycoalkaloids in potatoes. In *Natural Toxicants in Food: Progress and Prospects*, D. H. Watson (Ed.). Ellis Horwood, Chichester, West Sussex, England.

Mun, A. M., Barden, E. S., Wilson, J. M., and Hogan, J. M. (1975). Teratogenic effects in early chick embryos of solanine and glycoalkaloids from potatoes infected with late-blight *Phytophthora infestans*. *Teratology* 11:73-78.

Nevin, N. C., and Merrett, J. D. (1975). Potato avoidance during pregnancy in women with a previous infant with either anencephaly and/or spina bifida. *Br. J. Prev. Soc. Med.* 12:657-668.

Pakrashi, S. C., Chakravarty, A. K., and Ali, E. (1977). Solanogantine, a novel 3-amino-22βH-solanidane from *Solanum giganteum*. *Tetrahedron Lett.* 7:645-648.

Pakrashi, S. C., Chakravarty, A. K., Ali, E, Dhar, T. K., and Dan, S. (1978). Studies on Indian medicinal plants: Part XLVII. Novel 3-amino-solanidanes from *Solanum giganteum*. *J. Indian Chem. Soc.* 55:1109-1113.

Pierro, L. J., Haines, J. S., and Osman, S. F. (1977). Teratogenicity and toxicity of purified α-chaconine and α-solanine. *Teratology* 15:31A.

Poswillo, D. E., Sopher, D., and Mitchell, S. J. (1972). Experimental induction of foetal malformation with "blighted" potato: a preliminary report. *Nature* 239:462-464.

Poswillo, D. E., Sopher, D., Mitchell, S. J., Coxon, D. T., Curtis, R. F., and Price, K. R. (1973). Investigations into the teratogenic potential of imperfect potatoes. *Teratology* 8:339-348.

Renwick, J. H. (1972). Hypothesis: anencephaly and spina bifida are usually preventable by avoidance of a specific but unidentified substance present in certain potato tubers. *Br. J. Prev. Soc. Med.* 26:67-88.

Renwick, J. H. (1982). Food and malformation. *Practitioner* 226:1947-1953.

Renwick, J. H., Claringbold, W. D. B., Earthy, M. E., Few, J. D., and McLean, C. S. (1984). Neural-tube defects produced in Syrian hamsters by potato glycoalkaloids. *Teratology* 30:371-381.

Ruddick, J. A., Harwig, J., and Scott, P. M. (1974). Nonteratogenicity in rats of blighted potatoes and compounds contained in them. *Teratology* 9:165-168.

Sato, Y., and Ikekawa, N. (1961). Chemsitry of the spiroaminoketal side chain of solasodine and tomatidine: V. The synthesis of the isomeric solani-danones. *J. Org. Chem.* 26:1945-1947.

Schreiber, K. (1968). Steroid alkaloids: the *Solanum* group. In *The Alkaloids*, Vol. 10, R. H. F. Manske (Ed.). Academic Press, New York, pp. 1-192.

Schreiber, K. (1979). The steroid alkaloids of *Solanum*. In *The Biology and Taxonomy of the Solanaceae*, J. G. Hawkes, R. N. Lester, and A. D. Skelding (Eds.). Academic Press, New York, pp. 193-202.

Sharma, R. P., Willhite, C. C., Wu, M. T., and Salunkhe, D. K. (1978). Teratogenic potential of blighted potato concentrate in rabbits, hamsters and miniature swine. *Teratology* 18:55-62.

Spiers, P. S., Pietrzyk, J. J., Piper, J. M., and Glebatis, D. M. (1974). Human potato consumption and neural-tube malformation. *Teratology* 10:125-128.

Swinyard, C. A., and Chaube, S. (1973). Are potatoes teratogenic for experimental animals? *Teratology* 10:349-358.

7

Steroidal Glycoalkaloids in *Solanum*: Consequences for Potato Breeding and for Food Safety

W. M. J. Van Gelder

Agrotechnological Research Institute, Wageningen, The Netherlands

I. INTRODUCTION

Steroidal glycoalkaloids (SGAs) are a class of natural toxins occurring in the food crops potato (*Solanum tuberosum*), tomato (*Lycopersicon esculentum*), and eggplant or aubergine (*Solanum melongena*), and in many other species of the family Solanaceae. The SGAs consist of a C27-steroidal alkaloid (SA) (Fig. 1) and a sugar moiety often a di-, tri-, or tetrasaccharide.

The edible parts of potato, tomato, and eggplant usually contain only small quantities of SGAs, but many environmental factors can induce *de novo* synthesis and accumulation of SGAs in potatoes, sometimes resulting in toxic and in rare instances in fatal concentrations. Cases of poisoning, especially in the first half of this century, have generated much research activity on the potato SGAs. The withdrawal from commerce in the United States in 1970, of the variety Lenape, which caused incidences of illness due to its excessive tuber SGA levels (Zitnak and Johnston, 1970), and a published hypothesis, suggesting a toxin present in certain potato tubers to be involved in human birth defects (Renwock, 1972), led to an increase of research on the toxicity and teratogenicity of the potato SGAs and on the factors affecting their accumulation in potato tubers. The evidence that Lenape inherited the ability to synthesize high levels of SGAs from its wild ancestor *Solanum chacoense* (Sinden et al., 1984) forces potato breeders to realize that introgression of genes from wild species into the cultivated potato can go together with transmission of hazardous levels of SGAs.

In this chapter we deal with the consequences, from the viewpoints of food safety and of breeding efficiency, of the utilization of wild *Solanum* species in potato breeding programs. The literature describing the ability of the potato tuber to accumulate, under particular environmental conditions, unexpectedly high concentrations of SGAs is also discussed comprehensively, because this accumulation can take place just as readily when wild-type SGAs have been transmitted to potatoes. The complex methodology for SGA analysis is reviewed and emphasis is given to procedural difficulties which lead easily to experimental errors. A recently developed instrumental method, enabling the efficient determination of the SGA composition of wild *Solanum* species in a single analysis (Van Gelder et al., 1988a,b), is described in more detail. Other aspects of SGAs are briefly discussed, and for detailed information on these aspects, reviews are cited.

It is recommended that the SGA contents of the current potato varieties be controlled by cultivation techniques and adequate postharvest treatment. Breeding efforts can prevent the introduction into future varieties of undesired levels or types of SGAs.

II. OCCURRENCE AND CHEMISTRY OF STEROIDAL GLYCOALKALOIDS

In 1820, Desfosses reported the discovery of a new organic base, isolated from berries of black nightshade (*Solanum nigrum*). One hundred milligrams of this compounds, which he named solanée, administered orally to a dog, caused considerable vomiting and unconsciousness. A compound similar to solanée was found in potato and was named solanine (Baup, 1826). The discovery of the natural toxin solanine in one of the world's main food crops has generated much research activity, which has been ongoing for over 160 years. It took 130 years before the composition of solanine was finally revealed as a mixture of two glycosidic classes of glycoalkaloids, the α, β, and γ forms of solanine and of chaconine (Table 1), which have the same alkaloidal aglycone solanidine but different sugar moieties (Kuhn and Löw, 1954; Kuhn et al., 1955a,b). About 90 to 95% of the solanidine in potato was found glycosidic-bound in α-solanine and α-chaconine (Kuhn and Löw, 1954; Kuhn et al., 1955b; Pasesnishenko and Guseva, 1956).

The chemistry and occurrence of the SAs and SGAs of *Solanum* have been reviewed up to 1981 (Prelog and Jeger, 1953, 1960; Schreiber, 1968; Ripperger and Schreiber, 1981). More than 80 aglycones possessing the C27 carbon skeleton of cholestane were described. They are divided into five groups, representing different types of structures: the solanidanes (e.g., solanidine), the spirosolanes (e.g., tomatidine), the epiminocholestanes (e.g., solafloridine), the 3-aminospirostanes (e.g., paniculidine), and the group with a solanocapsine skeleton (Fig. 1). Other structures, such as the jervanes, occur in the *Veratrum*-type SAs of the Liliaceae (Ripperger and Schreiber, 1981).

In the genus *Solanum*, the SAs are glycosidic-bound via the hydroxyl group at carbon atom 3. They occur often in combination with different glycosidic groups, examples of which are solatriose, chacotriose, and lycotetraose. As a result, numerous naturally occurring SGAs have been reported for *Solanum*, but until now, only a limited number of them have been detected in the tuber-bearing species (Table 1). In this review SGA content means the sum of the concentrations of the SGAs quantified simultaneously; SGA (or SA) composition means that the different types of SGAs (or aglycones) are separated and quantified individually.

III. TOXICITY OF STEROIDAL GLYCOALKALOIDS

Reviews on the toxicology, pharmacology, and teratology of SAs and SGAs are given by McMillan and Thompson (1979), Jadhav et al. (1981), Morris and Lee (1984), and Keeler (1986). Additional information on these subjects is presented in other chapters of this volume. Therefore, the toxicity of the SGAs will be discussed in general in relation to their safety limits in potatoes.

According to Morris and Lee (1984) up to 30 deaths and over 2000 documented cases of SGA poisoning of humans, involving potato, have been recorded. Numerous and massive outbreaks were described in the nineteenth century and in the first six decades of the twentieth century (Zitnak, 1977; Verbist and Monnet, 1979; McMillan and Thompson, 1979). Only a few cases of poisoning seem to have occurred in the past two decades (McMillan and Thompson, 1979; Norberg, 1987). However, it has recently been stated in several reports that the extent of minor SGA poisonings is unknown since the symptoms are common to many ailments and can easily be mistaken for severe digestive discomfort (gastroenteritis), with nausea, diarrhea, vomiting, stomach cramps, headache, and dizziness (Wood and Young, 1974; *British Medical Journal*, 1979; Verbist and Monnet, 1979; Sinden, 1987).

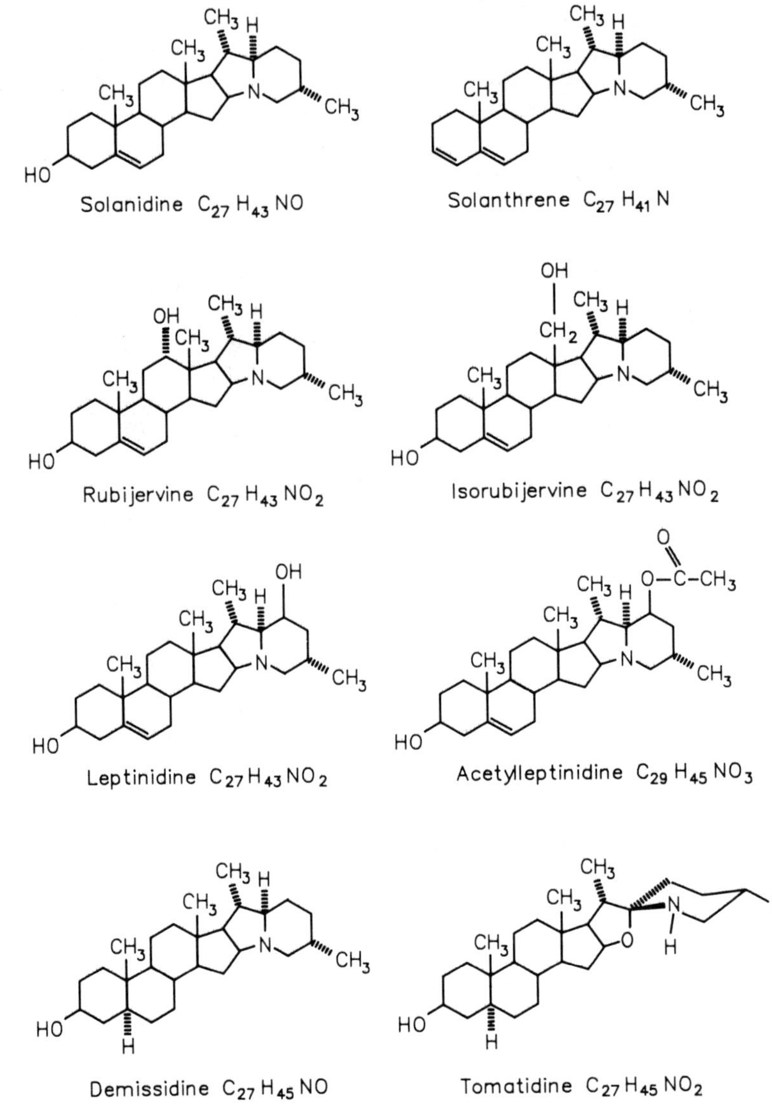

Solanidine $C_{27}H_{43}NO$

Solanthrene $C_{27}H_{41}N$

Rubijervine $C_{27}H_{43}NO_2$

Isorubijervine $C_{27}H_{43}NO_2$

Leptinidine $C_{27}H_{43}NO_2$

Acetylleptinidine $C_{29}H_{45}NO_3$

Demissidine $C_{27}H_{45}NO$

Tomatidine $C_{27}H_{45}NO_2$

FIGURE 1 Structural formulas of steroidal alkaloids of the *Solanum* groups solanidanes, spirosolanes, solanocapsines, epiminocholestanes, and 3-aminospirostanes.

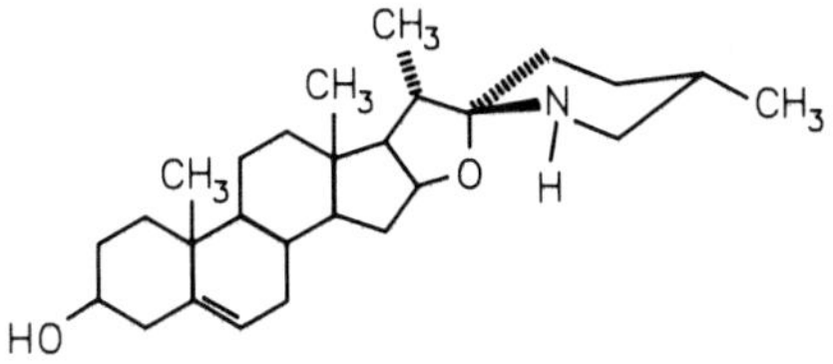

Tomatidenol $C_{27}H_{43}NO_2$

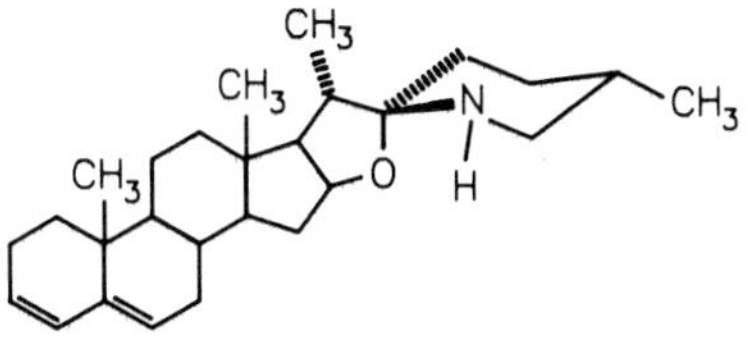

Tomatidadiene $C_{27}H_{41}NO$

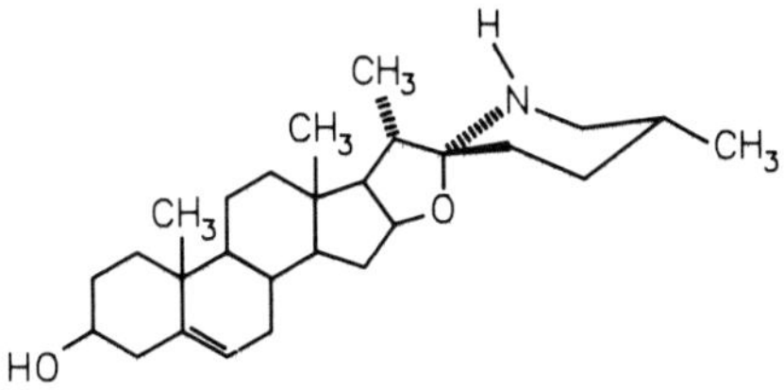

Solasodine $C_{27}H_{43}NO_2$

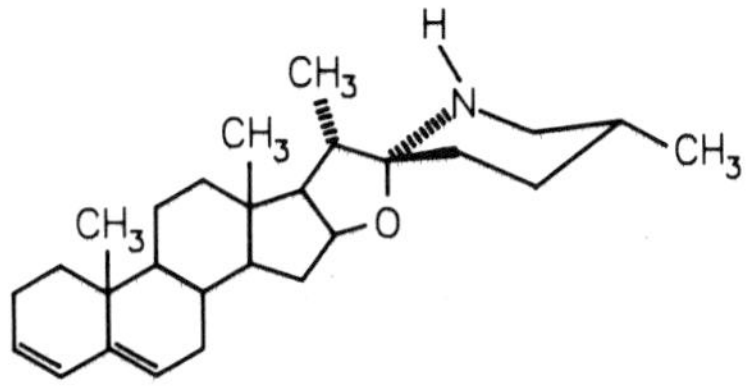

Solasodiene $C_{27}H_{41}NO$

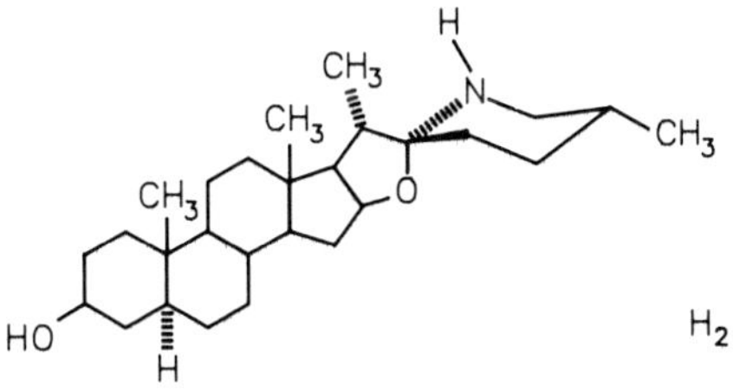

Soladulcidine $C_{27}H_{45}NO_2$

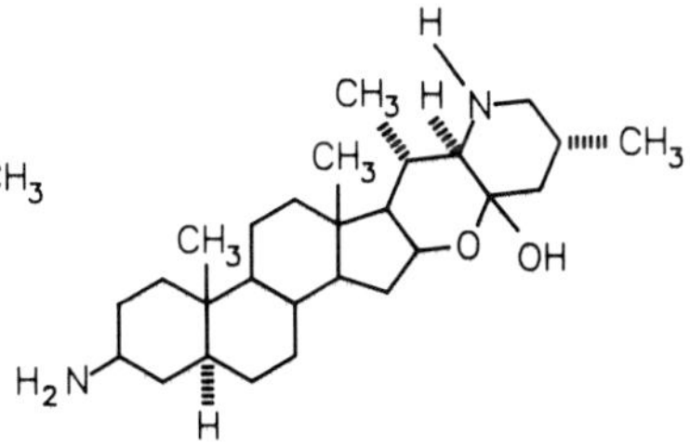

Solanocapsine $C_{27}H_{46}N_2O_2$

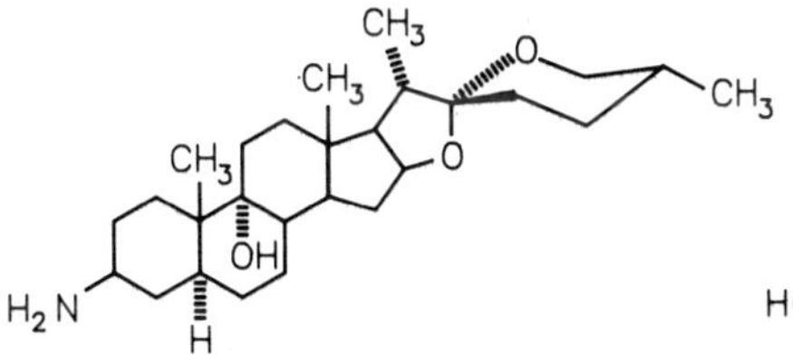

Paniculidine $C_{27}H_{45}NO_3$

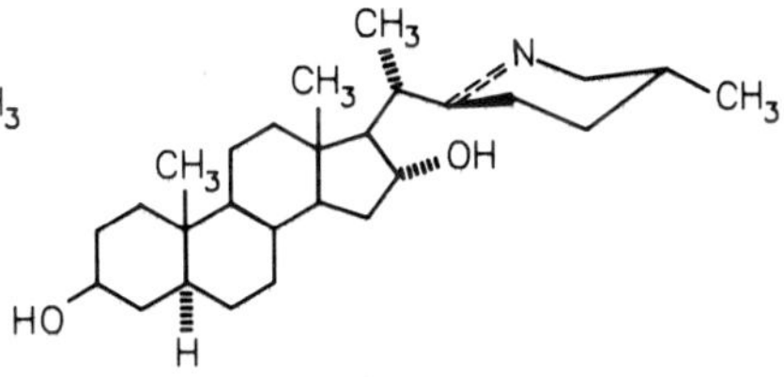

Solafloridine $C_{27}H_{45}NO_2$

FIGURE 1 (continued)

TABLE 1 Steroidal Glycoalkaloids of Tuber-Bearing *Solanum* Species

Steroidal glycoalkaloid	Glycoside group	Glycoside structure[a]
Solanidine[b] glycosides		
α-Solanine	Solatriose	1. R-Gal$<^{\text{Rham}}_{\text{Glu}}$
β-Solanine[c]	Solabiose	2. R-Gla-Glu
γ-Solanine[c]	Galactose	3. R-Gal
α-Chaconine	Chacotriose	4. R-Glu$<^{\text{Rham-1}}_{\text{Rham-2}}$
β$_1$-Chaconine[c]	Chacobiose	5. R-Glu-Rham-1
β$_2$-Chaconine[c]	Chacobiose	6. R-Glu-Rham-2
γ-Chaconine[c]	Glucose	7. R-Glu
Dehydrocommersonine	Commertetraose	8. R-Gal-Glu$<^{\text{Glu}}_{\text{Glu}}$
Demissidine[b] glycosides		
Demissine	Lycotetraose	9. R-Gal-Glu$<^{\text{Glu}}_{\text{Xyl}}$
Commersonine	Commertetraose	8
Leptinidine[b] glycosides		
Leptinine I	Chacotriose	4
Leptinine II	Solatriose	1
Acetylleptinidine[b] glycosides		
Leptine I	Chacotriose	4
Leptine II	Solatriose	1
Tomatidenol[b] glycosides		
α-Solamarine	Solatriose	1
β-Solamarine	Chacotriose	4
Solasodine[b] glycosides		
Solasonine	Solatriose	1
Solamargine	Chacotriose	4
Tomatidine[b] glycosides		
Tomatine	Lycotetraose	9
Sisunine (neotomatine)	Commertetraose	8

[a]R, corresponding aglycone; Gal, galactose; Rham, rhamnose; Glu, glucose; Xyl, xylose.
[b]Aglycone, structures given in Fig. 1.
[c]Minor steroidal glycoalkaloids may be hydrolysis artefacts or metabolites.

As early as 1924, Bömer and Mattis concluded that potatoes with contents of solanidine glycosides exceeding 200 mg/kg are potentially hazardous to humans, because they had found that potatoes involved in poisoning showed contents of solanidine glycosides exceeding 250 mg/kg fresh weight. Since then, many authors have interpreted this statement as "potatoes containing amounts of solanidine glycosides below 200 mg/kg are safe for consumption." However, surprisingly little information on the subacute and possible chronic toxicity of the solanidine glycosides is available to support this statement. Lepper (1949) regarded a level of solanidine glycosides in potatoes of 150 mg/kg as too high for consumption, and Ross et al. (1978) suggested that from the viewpoint of selecting cultivars for human consumption, the limit should be 60 to 70 mg/kg.

Solanidine and solasodine showed long (several weeks) half-times of excretion in humans and in hamsters (Claringbold et al., 1982; Harvey et al., 1985). This, in combination with continuous intake, as occurs when potatoes are a normal constituent in the diet, has been suggested by Claringbold et al. (1982) and Renwick et al. (1984) to lead potentially to a considerable body burden, especially in relation to pregnancy. Consequently, the acceptable level for solanidine glycosides in potatoes (in the literature on SGAs often called the "safety limit") is still open to debate. Additional toxicological studies by experts on the possible chronic effects of the potato SGAs seem necessary for establishing adequate acceptable levels.

Potatoes containing elevated levels of solanidine glycosides cause a bitter taste or burning sensation in the throat when consumed (Sinden et al., 1976; Ross et al., 1978). This has been suggested as indicative of levels of SGAs in potatoes too high for safe consumption. However, certain methods of food preparation can mask the bitter taste (Sizer et al., 1980) and the bitterness varies for different SGAs. For instance, chaconine is much more bitter than solanine (Zitnak, 1977) and certain SGAs from wild species, such as those containing leptinidine and the saturated aglycones, do not produce bitterness (Kuhn and Löw, 1961; Ross, 1986). Moreover, individuals seem to vary in their perception of SGA bitterness (Zitnak, 1977). These factors and the many cases of SGA poisoning show that the taste of potatoes is not a reliable indicator for SGA levels too high for consumption.

Apart from the information on the potato SGAs and the limited information on the acute toxicity of α-tomatine (Jadhav et al., 1981), there is hardly any information on the toxicity of the SGAs of wild *Solanum* species. However, a relationship between biological activity and chemical structure of SGAs has been demonstrated. The teratogenic effect on experimental animals (Keeler, 1986), the antifeedant activity against the Colorado potato beetle (Kuhn and Löw, 1961), the cardiotonic activity on the frog heart (Nishie et al., 1975, 1976), and the antifungal activity of the SGAs (Kusano et al., 1987) all varied depending on chemical structure. Therefore, alien SGAs, which potentially could be introduced into the food chain by breeding, should not be allowed in food crops until adequate acceptable levels have been derived.

IV. BIOSYNTHESIS OF STEROIDAL GLYCOALKALOIDS

The biosynthetic pathway of the SAs is closely related to that of the steroidal sapogenins, which occur together with the SAs in *Solanum*. They follow the

general path of steroidal biosynthesis, starting from acetylcoenzyme A via
the usual intermediates, mevalonic acid, squalene, cycloartenol, and cholesterol. The steps in the pathway from cholesterol to the aglycones have been
elucidated only partially. Figure 2 shows the (partially hypothetical) pathway
for the biosynthesis of the SGAs. Dormantiol and dormantinone have been
isolated from solanidine-synthesizing *Veratrum* species (Kaneko et al., 1977),
but have not yet been proven by tracer experiments to be intermediates. The
amino acid arginine was suggested as the nitrogen source for solanidine in
this biosynthesis route (Kaneko et al., 1976).

It is thought that at least in the case of the solanidine and solasodine
glycosides, the glycosylation of the aglycone occurs stepwise to the γ, β, and
finally the α forms of the SGAs (Liljegren, 1971; Jadhav and Salunkhe, 1973;
Lavintman et al., 1977). Further details on the biosynthesis of the SGAs
can be found in reviews by Jadhav et al. (1981), Ripperger and Schreiber
(1981), and Heftmann (1983).

V. DISTRIBUTION OF STEROIDAL GLYCOALKALOIDS IN POTATO

SGAs are usually found in all organs of the plant, with the highest concentrations in regions of high metabolic activity, such as flowers, unripe berries,
young leaves, and sprouts. Potato (*S. tuberosum*) contains only solanidine
glycosides. The most extensive study up to now on the distribution of the
solanidine glycosides in different organs and tuber tissues of potato was carried out by Lampitt et al. (1943). They investigated different cultivars, the
results of which are summarized in Table 2. In addition, data from other
reports are compiled.

Field-grown normal tubers of most of the current potato varieties show
average levels of solanidine glycosides up to 100 mg/kg fresh weight; only
very few *S. tuberosum* varieties produce tubers showing average levels exceeding 150 mg/kg (Sinden and Webb, 1974; Wood and Young, 1974; Patchett
et al., 1977; Ross et al., 1978; Bintcliffe et al., 1982; Bhuva and Parnell,
1983; Parnell et al., 1984; Van Gelder, 1985a; Lammerink, 1985; Morris and
Petermann, 1985; Uppal, 1987). Small tubers usually show high levels of solanidine glycosides (Verbist and Monnet, 1979; Van Gelder et al., 1988a) and
have been suggested to be responsible for cases of gastroenteritis (Verbist
and Monnet, 1979).

The solanidine glycosides are often concentrated in about a 1.5-mm layer
under the skin of the potato tuber—according to Fischer and Thiele (1929),
in the first 10 cell layers of the storage tissue. Peeling removes 60 to 96%
of these toxins (Wood and Young, 1974; Bushway et al., 1983; Uppal, 1987).
If potatoes contain high concentrations of SGAs, they can be present throughout the flesh. Then, peeling may remove only 30 to 35% of the total amount
present (Zitnak, 1961; Wood and Young, 1974; Verbist and Monnet, 1979).

Morris and Petermann (1985) found that the amount of α-solanine varied
from 28 to 57% of the total amount of solanidine glycosides in potato tubers.
Free solanidine, up to 33% of the total amount (free and glycosidic-bound solanidine) present, has been reported to occur in bitter potato tubers (Zitnak,

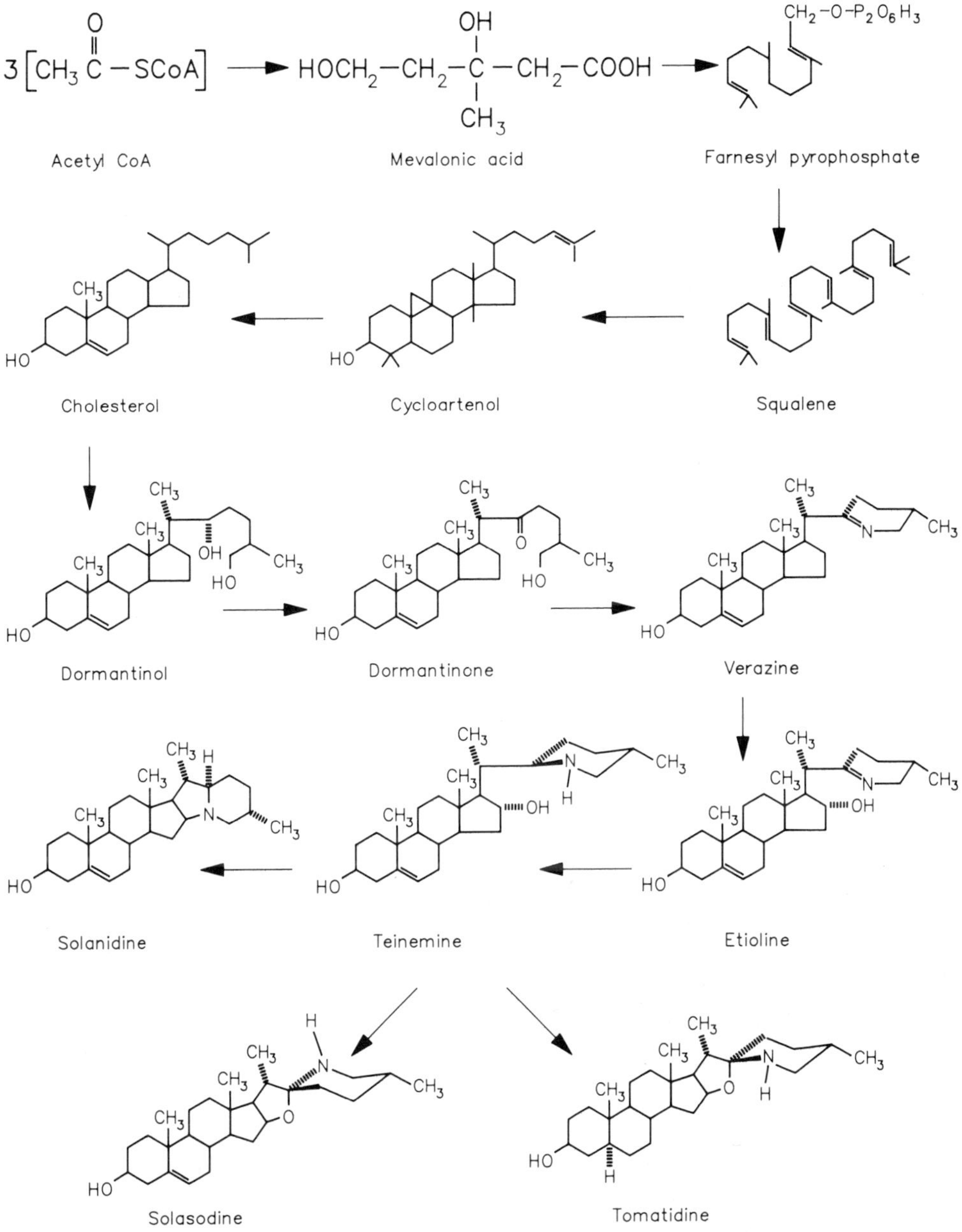

FIGURE 2 Partially hypothetical biosynthetic pathway of steroidal alkaloids in *Solanum* species.

TABLE 2 Concentrations of Solanidine Glycosides in Various Parts of the Potato Plant (*Solanum tuberosum*)

Plant tissue	Solanidine glycosides (mg/kg fresh weight)		References
	Lampitt et al. (1943)	Other studies	
Normal tubers			
Whole tuber	25-100	11-150	Many; see text
Skin, 2-3% of tuber	300-640		
Peel, 10-12% of tuber	150-155	150-1068	Wood and Young (1974), Zitnak (1981), Bushway et al. (1983)
Flesh	12-60	1-100	Zitnak (1981), Bushway et al. (1983)
Small tubers			
10-40 g		96-448	Verbist and Monnet (1979)
0.3-17 g		92-522	Van Gelder et al. (1988a)
Bitter tubers		250-800	Zitnak (1961)
Sprouts	1950-17,700[a]	2000-4360	Bömer and Mattis (1924), Wood and Young (1974), Fitzpatrick et al. (1977)
Stolons	150-540		
Roots	180-400		
Stems	23-33		
Lateral stems		30-71	Kozukue et al. (1987)
Leaves	550-610	230-1000	Wood and Young (1974), Kozukue et al. (1987)
Growing tops	300-860		
Flowers	2150-4160	3000-5000	Wood and Young (1974), Kozukue et al. (1987)
Petals		3060-4970	Kozukue et al. (1987)
Calyxes		4770-5710	Kozukue et al. (1987)
Fruits	420	560-1080	Bömer and Mattis (1924)

[a]Extreme high levels were due to illumination of sprouts.

1961), but Lampitt et al. (1943) could not detect free solanidine in tubers of nine varieties, not even after light exposure for 18 weeks.

VI. FACTORS AFFECTING STEROIDAL GLYCOALKALOID LEVELS IN POTATO TUBERS

A. Genetic Variation

It is generally accepted that the level of solanidine glycosides is a genetically controlled characteristic (Jadhav et al., 1981; Sinden et al., 1984). The many reports on the levels of solanidine glycosides in tubers of numerous varieties show that considerable genetic variation exists within *S. tuberosum*. However, environmental effects on the SGA levels are often also reflected in the values. Interactions between genotype and environment have been demonstrated, but in general the ranking order of genotypes remains quite constant under different environmental conditions (Patchett et al., 1977; Sinden et al., 1984; Lammerink, 1985). Under unusual environmental or improper handling conditions, cultivars with genetically determined high levels of solanidine glycosides more easily accumulate excessive amounts in their tubers than do cultivars with low levels (Jadhav et al., 1981; Van Gelder, 1988a).

B. Growing Conditions and Maturity of the Potato Tuber

Levels of solanidine glycosides in the tuber may vary widely among crops of a single variety grown on different locations or in different years. This is ascribed to the varying environmental conditions (Sinden and Webb, 1972, 1974; Parnell et al., 1984; Van Gelder and Dellaert, 1988). Most of the environmental variation seems to result from climatic influences (Maga, 1980; Jadhav et al., 1981). An unusually cool growing season accompanied by an abnormally high number of overcast days, probably resulting in an immature potato crop, has been associated especially with incidences of illness caused by toxic levels of solanidine glycosides (Börner and Mattis, 1924; Norberg, 1987). Immaturity has been associated with higher than normal or even excessive levels of solanidine glycosides (Börner and Mattis, 1924; Wolf and Duggar, 1946; Ahmed and Müller, 1979). Tuber size and maturity, within a variety, are inversely related to the level of solanidine glycosides. This is because these SGAs are formed early during tuber development and are "diluted" during the process of enlarging and maturation, and also because the SGAs are concentrated in the peel, which is proportionally a greater part of smaller tubers.

When tubers are exposed to bright sunlight in the field, they can accumulate extremely high SGA levels (Baerug, 1962; Zitnak, 1961, 1977). Therefore, the tubers must be well covered with soil during their growth. Molybdenum application to the soil (Munshi and Mondy, 1988) and foliar application of the plant hormone indoleacetic acid (Ponnampalam and Mondy, 1986) resulted in a decreased solanidine glycoside synthesis in the tubers. The method of irrigation of the potato crop can lead to an increase in SGA synthesis in the tubers (Gosselin et al., 1988).

Other environmental factors that have been investigated in relation to SGA accumulation during growth of potato tubers have been reviewed by Jadhav et al. (1981). In general, planting date, fertilization with major elements, and soil type have only little effect and are not associated with potentially hazardous levels of solanidine glycosides. This conclusion is supported by a fertilization experiment which showed that nitrogen and potassium had little effect on the accumulation of solanidine glycosides (Ahmed and Müller, 1979), and further supported by a year × location study (Van Gelder and Dellaert, 1988) which showed that on a sandy soil the level of solanidine glycosides was only slightly (although statistically significant, $P < 0.001$) higher ($\bar{x}$ = 215 mg/kg) than on a clay soil ($\bar{x}$ = 183 mg/kg).

To control the accumulation of solanidine glycosides in potato tubers during growth, it is important that potato breeders develop varieties with low average levels, that tubers are well covered with soil during growth, and that they are harvested at maturity. When the crop has been exposed to physiological stress, especially in the case of unusual climatic conditions, it is wise to check its SGA content.

C. Light Exposure and Irradiation

When potatoes are exposed to light, their levels of solanidine glycosides may increase considerably. The increase is positively related to the light intensity and the duration of the exposure (Jadhav and Salunkhe, 1975; Maga, 1980; Zitnak, 1981; Jadhav et al., 1981; Sinden et al., 1984; Uppal, 1987) and is strongly dependent on the cultivar (Zitnak, 1977). Upon exposure to bright sunlight (35,000 to 50,000 lx) for 6 h, the solanidine glycoside level of freshly harvested tubers increased from 50 to above 200 mg/kg (Baerug, 1962). Levels as high as 450 mg/kg have been reported for tubers left in the field at low temperatures for 72 h (Zitnak, 1961, 1977). The solanidine glycoside levels of immature and small tubers increased more during light exposure (up to 480 mg/kg) than those of mature and large tubers (up to 200 mg/kg) (Bömer and Mattis, 1924; Wolf and Dugar, 1946; Lepper, 1949; Sinden and Webb, 1974; Patchett et al., 1977). Artificial light during storage or marketing also induces *de novo* synthesis of solanidine glycosides. The increases are usually not as dramatic as those resulting from sunlight, and varieties with levels normally below 100 mg/kg, usually do not exceed 150 mg/kg upon artificial light exposure (Ahmed and Müller, 1981; Sinden et al., 1984; Lammerink, 1985; De Maine et al., 1988).

D. Storage Conditions

Storage of potato tubers can increase their levels of solanidine glycosides (Cronk et al., 1974; Ahmed and Müller, 1981), but the literature is conflicting with respect to the influence of the temperature and the duration of the storage period. Storage in the dark at various temperatures between 0 and 28°C for 12 weeks (Nair et al., 1981; Linnemann et al., 1985) or between 10 and 15°C for up to 7 months (Zitnak, 1953, quoted in Jadhav et al., 1981; Lammerink, 1985) hardly affected the accumulation of solanidine glycosides. Storage under humid conditions at 4°C resulted in high levels of solanidine glycosides after 6 weeks (Zitnak, 1953 quoted in Jadhav et al., 1981). Storage at 4°C resulted in a slight increase after 3 months in a study by Wu and

Salunkhe (1976), but in nonelevated levels after 3 to 8 months in other studies (Wolf and Duggar, 1946; Fitzpatrick et al., 1977; Bostock et al., 1983).

It is concluded that potato tubers can be stored for a considerable period
of time, probably up to 8 months or even longer, without a significant increase
in the levels of solanidine glycosides, provided that the storage conditions are
optimal. Indications can be found in the literature that storage in the dark at
about 9 to 15°C and at a low air humidity is to be preferred, but further research is needed on the effects of storage conditions on the accumulation of
SGAs. This is even more important now in view of the currently increasing
interest for cold storage (2 to 4°C) of potatoes as an alternative to the use
of chemical sprouting inhibitors.

E. Tuber Injury

Damage to tubers resulting from dropping, puncturing, cutting, hammering,
or brushing, or resulting from diseases or animals, stimulated SGA synthesis
(Sinden and Webb, 1974; Wu and Salunkhe, 1976; Ahmed and Müller, 1978;
Olsson, 1986; Mondy et al., 1987). This effect is thought to be a physiological defense mechanism. In slightly injured tubers the levels of solanidine
glycosides can increase by 200 to 300%; when the damage was visible, the contents were unusually high (Sinden and Webb, 1974). In the case of severe
damage, tubers showed toxic levels of solanidine glycosides (Olsson, 1986).
Increased levels were found in both the peel and the flesh, and they accumulated mainly in the first few weeks after induction (Wu and Salunkhe, 1976).
The extent of the SGA accumulation depends strongly on the type of injury,
on the cultivar, and on the storage conditions after induction of the injury.
Damaged tubers stored at 4 or 5°C in the dark accumulated less solanidine
glycosides than tubers stored at 20 or 21°C or than tubers stored in the light
(Wu and Salunkhe, 1976; Ahmed and Müller, 1978; Mondy et al., 1987). Probably, the tuber defense mechanism is more active at higher temperatures.
Olsson (1986) observed a high correlation between the initial solanidine glycoside levels of varieties and breeding clones and the levels after damage, and
concluded that potato breeders should select for low SGA levels. Fitzpatrick
et al. (1978b) carried out analyses for SGA levels of damaged potatoes purchased on the retail market. They found elevated but nontoxic levels, but
they did not rule out damage causing abnormally elevated SGA levels of potatoes available on the retail market.

Although growers and those involved in marketing usually prevent injury
that deteriorates the outward appearance of potatoes, the reports above also
concur in showing that injury to potatoes should be avoided from the viewpoint of food safety.

F. Potato Processing

Peeling of potatoes removes a considerable part of the solanidine glycosides.
This part may vary for different cultivars and depends on the levels of solanidine glycosides in the tubers (see Section V). SGAs are fairly heat-stable
compounds; their melting points, at which some SGAs may start decomposing,
vary in general from 230 to 280°C (Prelog and Jeger, 1960; Schreiber, 1968;
Ripperger and Schreiber, 1981). At these temperatures their aglycones show

no decomposition, and even during gas chromatography at 280 to 320°C they show little or no decomposition (Van Gelder, 1985b). It is therefore not surprising that steam cooking (Baker et al., 1955), boiling, baking, and microwaving of potatoes did not affect their levels of solanidine glycosides, although during frying of potato peels 16 to 22% of these SGAs were lost (Bushway and Ponnampalam, 1981).

When during the manufacturing of potato chips (crisps), french fries, and so on, half products such as slices and strips are left for some time before frying or cooking, considerable accumulation of SGAs (up to 290 mg/kg) can occur (Maga, 1981; Ahmed and Müller, 1978). Fitzpatrick et al. (1977) reported concentrations of SGAs up to 1630 mg/kg for aged potato slices. In aged slices of the variety Kennebec, the tomatidenol glycosides α-solamarine and β-solamarine, not originating from *S. tuberosum*, were detected in addition to α-solanine and α-chaconine (Shih and Kuć, 1974; Fitzpatrick et al., 1977). The foregoing results are especially important in the light of the results of Sizer et al. (1980), who showed that during the frying process water was lost, which resulted in a three- to fourfold concentration of SGAs. They also showed that commercially purchased chips (crisps) containing most of the potato skin varied in SGA contents from 95 to 720 mg/kg. The excessively high SGA level caused no noticeable bitterness, but perhaps the bitterness was masked by salt or the high oil content. Nowadays bitterness could also be masked by other flavor additives. Because infants and adolescents may consume relatively large amounts of chips (crisps), it is important that potatoes be peeled well and that delays in processing of slices or otherwise nonintact potatoes be avoided.

VII. CONTROL OF STEROIDAL GLYCOALKALOID ACCUMULATION IN POTATO TUBERS

The basis for the production of a potato crop safe for consumption is to breed varieties that accumulate genetically determined low levels of SGAs under the various expected growth and postharvest conditions. In addition, several measures for further controlling SGA accumulation by cultivation and storage techniques have been recommended in the preceding paragraphs and in literature reviews (Jadhav et al., 1981; Sinden et al., 1984; Woolfe, 1987). Beyond this, a large number of physical and chemical treatments have been developed to control postharvest accumulation of SGAs. Among these are vacuum packaging and packaging in colored polyethylene bags, ionizing radiation, submerging in water to which often chemicals were added, heating of tubers, and treating them with waxes, chemicals, or oils. Some treatments simultaneously inhibited SGA accumulation in, and greening and/or sprouting of, the tubers. The efficacy and limitations of these treatments have been reviewed extensively (Salunkhe and Wu, 1979; Maga, 1980; Jadhav et al., 1981).

VIII. STEROIDAL GLYCOALKALOID ANALYSIS

The methodology for SGA analysis is very complex, which is apparent from the structures of this class of compounds (Fig. 1 and Table 1). This is illus-

trated by the hundreds of publications describing the development or modifications of methods, of which over 60 have appeared during the past decade
only. In this review, emphasis will be given (1) to those particular aspects
of SGA methodology which present analytical problems leading to errors in
detection or quantification, and (2) to recent developments in instrumental
analytical techniques which now enable efficient multicomponent SGA analysis.

A. Sampling

Original reports as well as reviews on SGA analysis generally neglect the sampling of potato tubers when describing or evaluating the basic steps of a procedure. However, the levels of SGAs of individual tubers can vary considerably, showing coefficients of variation of up to 60% (Ross et al., 1978; Van
Gelder et al., 1988a). An analysis of individual tubers of two varieties revealed that for obtaining representative values, samples should preferably
consist of at least 15 tubers (Van Gelder, 1987). In many studies referred
to in this chapter, samples consisted of only four to six tubers. There is
no doubt that these small sample sizes are responsible for at least some of
the conflicting literature reports on SGAs.

B. Extraction

This procedural step has received much attention in methods development,
as it is generally recognized that it has a large effect on the accuracy of SGA
analysis. In earlier reports, time-consuming Soxhlet extractions (Wolf and
Duggar, 1946; Dabbs and Hilton, 1953; Baker et al., 1955) or exhaustive re-
flux boiling (Sachse and Bachmann, 1969) have been evaluated. Smittle (1971)
and Bretzloff (1971) introduced the rapid and effective extraction by blending tuber samples for some minutes in methanol-water-trichloroacetic acid mixtures. However, solvents containing acid can lead to losses due to hydrolysis
of SGAs (Caddle et al., 1978). A bisolvent extraction system using chloroform and methanol introduced by Wang et al. (1972) has been criticized by
some authors (Mackenzie and Gregory, 1979; Speroni and Pell, 1980) but
proved most satisfactory when applied by others provided that the solvent
layers were allowed to separate for a sufficiently long period of time (Clement
and Verbist, 1980; Van Gelder, 1984; Morgan et al., 1985). A very simple
and rapid procedure for sample preparation, consisting of homogenization of
tuber samples and dilution, can be applied in combination with immunoassays,
because in these assays antibodies highly specific to SGAs are used (Morgan
et al., 1983).

C. Purification

Certain steps for the purification of SGA extracts, reported in the literature,
may cause considerable losses of SGAs. Precipitation of proteins to prevent
their interference with quantification of SGAs (Rooke et al., 1943; Schwarze,
1962, 1963; Ross et al., 1978; Blincow et al., 1982; Deahl and Sinden, 1987)
should be avoided, because it results in losses due to coprecipitation of SGAs.
Baker et al. (1955) reported such losses of solanidine glycosides up to 20%,
and Olsson (1986) of about 10%, of the total SGA content of potatoes. Slijm

and Weinans (1973) found 25 to 80% of the solanidine glycosides in the heat-precipitated tuber proteins from six potato cultivars that varied considerably in their levels of proteins and of SGAs. During an earlier evaluation of literature methods for determining the contents of solanidine glycosides in potato tubers, losses of 15 to 35% were found to be due to coprecipitation of SGAs and proteins (Van Gelder, results not published).

A considerable experimental error will occur when SGAs with different aglycones are present in a sample and the purification and concentration of the SGAs is performed by alkaline precipitation at pH 9.4 to 10 and 70°C. Under these conditions the alkali-soluble leptines as well as a variable amount of other SGAs (e.g., demissine) will be lost (Kuhn and Löw, 1961; Gregory et al., 1981; Sinden et al., 1986), while the solanidine glycosides are quantitatively precipitated (Sachse and Bachmann, 1969).

When high concentrations of SGAs are present, such as in wild Solanaceae species, losses may occur due to interactions between SGAs and other compounds present (Osman, 1983); especially complex formation between SGAs and sterols (Heftmann, 1967; Roddick, 1974, 1979, 1980). The solubility of such complexes, for instance those of a tomatine-sterol and a solanine-sterol complex, varied considerably. However, aglycones do not form complexes with sterols (Arneson and Durbin, 1968; Roddick, 1979, 1980).

D. Quantification

Until about 1930, SGA levels were usually measured using gravimetric methods. The obvious disadvantages of these methods were that other plant constituents were extracted and weighed together with the SGAs, or that exhaustive purification led to considerable losses. After Alberti (1932) reported the color reaction between the solanidine glycosides and the Marquis reagent, concentrated sulfuric acid and formaldehyde, many colorimetric methods for determining the levels of solanidine glycosides based on this or similar reactions were developed. These methods have been widely used and are reviewed by Jadhav et al. (1981) and Coxon (1984).

Several other techniques have been applied for determining SGA levels. Heftmann and Schwimmer (1973) described a radioligand assay based on the precipitation of tomatine with 4-[^{14}C]cholesterol and subsequent measurement of the radioactivity remaining in solution. This method was modified by Roddick (1979), who used stigmasterol instead of radioactive cholesterol and who used gas chromatography (GC) for quantification. This method was also made applicable to the potato SGAs (Roddick, 1980). A method for the comprehensive determination of the total content of potato SGAs, based on titration of the basic nitrogen of the aglycone obtained by hydrolysis, was described by Fitzpatrick and Osman (1974). As different types of aglycones could be quantified simultaneously, this method would be useful in breeding programs for determining the total SGA contents of clones containing wild germplasm. After this method had been used in many studies, it was realized that variable losses of SGAs could occur during several steps of the procedure. Although several modifications were proposed (Fitzpatrick et al., 1978a; Mackenzie and Gregory, 1979; Speroni and Pell, 1980; Bushway et al., 1980a), chromatographic methods, discussed hereafter, have superseded this titrimetric assay. Marzouk and Boukef (1983) determined solasodine by using cholesterol oxidase and found their method to be sensitive, reproducible, and simple, but they realized that interference from other compounds containing the Δ^5-3β-ol sterol skeleton can occur. An automated method for determining the level of solanidine glycosides, based on their cholinesterase inhibitor activity, has been proposed by Schwerdtfeger (1984). This method needs further evaluation and its protein precipitation step must be avoided.

Almost any of the foregoing methods has one or more of the following limitations: laboriousness and length of the procedure, the use of corrosive or toxic chemicals, interference from other plant constituents, and lack of sensitivity and losses due to necessary purification or hydrolysis. A technique not suffering from these disadvantages is quantitative enzyme immunoassay. The first immunoassays for SGAs were radioimmunoassays developed for solanidine and its glycosides by Vallejo and Ercegovich (1979) and for solasodine and its glycosides by Weiler et al. (1980). These methods have met with little enthusiasm, probably because of the need to apply radioactive labels. A more tractable method, the enzyme-linked immunosorbent assay (ELISA) for "total glycoalkaloids" in potato tubers, was described by Morgan et al. (1983). The anti-SGA-antiserum raised showed specificity toward solanidine, demissidine, and their glycosides. Spirosolanes such as tomatidine did not cross-react and are thus not quantified. Comparative studies (Morgan et al., 1985; Hellenäs, 1986) showed that the results of the ELISA for potato SGAs agreed well with those of different colorimetric reference methods and with those of a high-pressure liquid chromatography (HPLC) method. This ELISA method can be used for the screening of breeding clones for low levels of solanidine (and demissidine) glycosides.

E. Chromatographic Analysis of the Steroidal Glycoalkaloid Composition

Thin-layer chromatography (TLC) methods are especially valuable for qualitative analysis of SAs and SGAs. Solvent systems for the separation on silica gel G of many of these compounds have been developed (Boll, 1962; Schreiber et al., 1963; Schwarze, 1963; Hunter et al., 1976). Baerheim Svendsen and Verpoorte (1983) reviewed and listed the chromatographic variables presented in the literature. Specific and sensitive reagents for visualization of SAs and SGAs are available (Jellema et al., 1980; Baerheim Svendsen and Verpoorte, 1983) and quantification by densitometry, although generally quite difficult, is feasible (Ahmed and Müller, 1978; Caddle et al., 1978; Jellema et al., 1981, 1982).

In the past decade, TLC analysis of SAs and SGAs has been superseded by HPLC and GC, which are complementary techniques. For chromatographing thermolabile, strongly polar, high-boiling, or nonvolatile compounds, HPLC is often preferable. Advantages of GC are the availability of highly sensitive detector systems which can be generally applicable: for instance, the flame ionization detector (FID) or very selective detectors such as the thermoionic (nitrogen-specific) detector (NPD) (Van Gelder et al., 1988b). A recent and important variant of GC useful for the analysis of SAs is capillary GC, also called high-resolution GC (HRGC), which enables very efficient separations of complex mixtures in relatively short periods of time. Capillary GC with narrow-bore columns of 0.1 mm inner diameter and a column length of 50 m or even more offers the ultimate separation efficiency, and thus resolution, at this moment. However, these improvements are attended by a proportionate increase in the complexity of the technique and of the number of problems that can be encountered. Therefore, capillary GC demands a much more careful approach than "packed" GC.

HPLC and GC can be applied successfully for the separation and individual quantification of SGAs and their aglycones. This is true when only a single SGA is present in plant material, but also when a certain aglycone occurs glycosidically bound to different sugar moieties.

Bushway et al. (1979, 1980b) reported an HPLC method for the separation and quantification of α-solanine and α-chaconine using a "carbohydrate analysis column" and tetrahydrofuran-water-acetonitrile (53:17:30) as mobile phase. Morris and Lee (1981) developed a method for the separation of α-solanine and α-chaconine within 3 min, using a radially compressed reversed-phase C18 column and acetonitrile-water-ethanolamine (45:55:0.1) as mobile phase. Solanidine and all of its known glycosides could be separated in several analyses using different column packings and mobile phases. Modifications of these methods have been reported (Bushway, 1982a,b), the more recent ones describing the use of solid-phase extraction columns (Sep-Pak columns) for efficient sample cleanup (Morris and Petermann, 1985; Carman et al., 1986; Bushway et al., 1986). Hellenäs (1986) reported average losses of potato SGAs of 14%, which were mainly due to the Sep-Pak purification step, so this step should be applied with care and recovery experiments are essential.

Separation and quantification using HPLC has been described for solasodine (Nes et al., 1980), for solasonine and solamargine (Cham and Wilson, 1987), for solasodine and several of its mono-, di-, and triglycosides (Crabbe and Fryer, 1980), and for some solanidine (α-solanine and α-chaconine) and solasodine glycosides (α-solasonine, α-solamargine, and β-solamargine) (Eldridge and Hockridge, 1983). Bushway and Storch (1982) separated by semipreparative HPLC α-solanine and α-chaconine, extracted from flowers of the potato cultivar Katahdin, and demissine and commersonine, extracted from *S. demissum* flowers.

In many *Solanum* species, several SAs may occur simultaneously, and each of them may be bound to various sugar moieties (Schreiber, 1968; Ripperger and Schreiber, 1981). When in such cases many SGAs occur in a single species, the separation efficiency of HPLC will be insufficient. A GC method for the separation of SGAs and their aglycones on a 3% OV-1 column programmed up to 350°C has been described (Herb et al., 1975). This method could potentially be applied to a complex mixture of SGAs such as that occurring in wild *Solanum* species (Osman et al., 1979). However, this method suffered from several disadvantages. The samples had to be derivatized by permethylation, which is difficult and laborious, and the chromatographic separation lasted for almost 2 h. Only relative quantification was possible; thus a separate analysis for the total SGA content was required. Moreover, due to the high GC operating temperature, column deterioration occurred after only 100 analyses (Herb et al., 1975; Osman et al., 1978; Gregory et al., 1981).

An alternative approach consists of extraction and hydrolysis of the SGAs, separation and individual quantification of the aglycones, and expression of their contents as glycosidic-bound SAs. Acid hydrolysis of SGAs usually leads to considerable losses (Coxon et al., 1979; MacKenzie and Gregory,

1979), which can vary largely for different samples and for different SGAs (Davies and Blincow, 1984; Van Gelder, 1984). Hydrolysis in a two-phase system, consisting of an aqueous acid phase and an immiscible organic liquid phase, allowed simultaneous and quantitative recovery of aglycones from different types of SGAs (Van Gelder, 1984, 1985b). For the hydrolysis of a variety of plant samples, a two-phase system consisting of hydrochloric acid and chloroform was suitable (Van Gelder and De Ponti, 1987; Van Gelder et al., 1988a).

For the separation and individual quantification of aglycones, HPLC, GC using packed columns and capillary GC are potentially useful. However, HPLC is not to be preferred as two analyses, one for the more polar and one for the less polar SAs were required, and both analyses were time consuming (Hunter et al., 1980). Although quantitative data were not given, the chromatograms revealed that the detector responses varied greatly for the different SAs, which would have limited the quantification by this technique. In general, ultraviolet and refractive index detectors used in HPLC are not sensitive to saturated SAs, such as demissidine, tomatidine, and soladulcidine, whereas GC detectors such as FID and NPD are very sensitive to all types of SAs (Van Gelder et al., 1988b).

GC using packed columns has been applied to derivatized SAs and directly injected SAs (Osman and Sinden, 1977; Coxon et al., 1979; King, 1980; Juvik et al., 1982), but it did not enable the separation of Δ^5- and 5α-aglycone pairs such as solanidine and demissidine (Osman and Sinden, 1977; King, 1980; Van Gelder, 1985b). Qualitative analysis of mixtures of glycosidic-bound solanidine and demissidine has been achieved by applying hydrolysis conditions that yielded solanthrene from the former and demissidine from the latter, which aglycones were then separated by GC (Osman and Sinden, 1977).

A capillary GC method for the analysis of SAs from *Solanum* species (Van Gelder, 1985b) enabled the rapid separation and quantification in a single analysis of a number of underivatized SAs, including solanidine and demissidine. Chromatograms obtained for wild species of *Solanum* (Van Gelder and Jonker, 1986) and of *Lycopersicon* (Van Gelder and De Ponti, 1987) showed that in addition to a number of identified SAs, several unidentified compounds were present in extracts prepared using a procedure rather selective for SAs. Therefore, the capillary GC method was extended by applying a dual detector system (FID and NPD) for unambiguous differentiation between SAs and non-nitrogen-containing compounds (Fig. 3) (Van Gelder et al., 1988b). Figure 4 shows the separation by capillary GC, using postanalysis reprocessing of the simultaneously obtained NPD and FID data of a large number of SAs added to a potato tuber extract. They included the Δ^5- and 5α-aglycone pairs solanidine-demissidine, solasodine-soladulcidine, and tomatidenol-tomatidine. This capillary GC method was developed so that nitrogen-containing and nonnitrogen-containing compounds present in Solanaceae plant material cannot interfere with the SAs. First, the procedure for sample preparation is rather selective. The bisolvent extraction does not extract potentially interfering proteins and exploits the differences in polarity between the glycosidic-bound SAs and the nonpolar plant constituents, such as the sterols; the two-phase hydrolysis step eliminates most of the polar (non-SA) compounds because the glycosidic-bound SAs are converted to their apolar aglycones, which are collected in the organic phase. Second, the SAs require high temperatures for their elu-

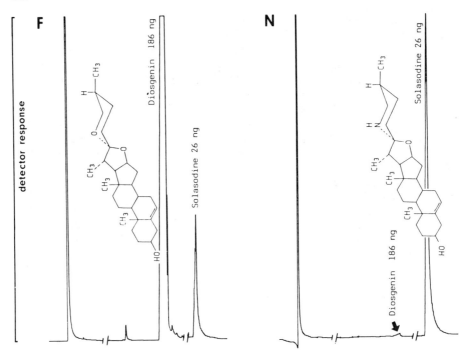

FIGURE 3 Responses of flame ionization detection (F) and specific-nitrogen detection (N) of the steroidal alkaloid solasodine and its oxygen analog, the steroidal sapogenin diosgenin. (After Van Gelder et al., 1988b.)

tion during capillary GC, so compounds that are present together with the SAs preelute. Third, simultaneous NPD and FID unambiguously differentiates between SAs and steroidal sapogenins, which might have been (partly) iso-lated together with the SAs and which may have similar retention times. Only when unknown SAs, which are easily detected by this method, are present in Solanaceae species do they need to be characterized and/or identified by spec-trometric techniques.

IX. STEROIDAL GLYCOALKALOIDS IN *SOLANUM* SPECIES USED IN POTATO BREEDING

Wild and primitive *Solanum* species are being used in potato breeding to intro-duce into the cultivated potato a variety of desirable characteristics, such as disease and insect resistance; tolerance to frost, heat, and other physio-logical stresses; and improved yield, starch content, and processing quality. The utilization of wild germplasm should be approached with caution because together with the valuable traits, hazardous levels of solanidine glycosides or alien types of SGAs can be introduced into cultivars.

In 1970, the commercial variety Lenape had to be removed from commerce in the United States because its SGA concentration regularly reached hazard-

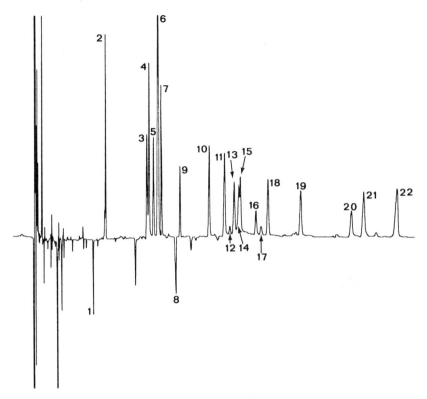

FIGURE 4 Separation of steroidal alkaloids spiked to a potato tuber extract using capillary GC and postanalysis reprocessing of FID and NPD data. Peak identification: 1, 5α-cholestane (internal standard); 2, solanthrene; 3, solanidine; 4, demissidine; 5, solasodiene; 6, demissidan-3-one; 7, tomatidadiene; 8, diosgenin (internal standard); 9, solanid-4-en-3-one; 10, rubijervine; 11, solasodine; 12, soladulcidine; 13, tomatidenol; 14, tomatidine; 15, isorubijervine; 16, tomatidan-3-one; 17, solanocapsine; 18, cyclopamine; 19, veratramine; 20, deacetylmuldamine (teinimine); 21, jervine; 22, N-acetyltomatidine. For chromatographic conditions, see Van Gelder et al. (1988b). Thanks are due to Dr. W. Gaffield, Berkeley; Dr. R. F. Keeler, Logan; Professor D. N. Kirk, London; Dr. S. F. Osman, Philadelphia; and Dr. S. L. Sinden, Beltsville, for providing steroidal alkaloids.

ous levels up to 350 mg/kg in Canada and 650 mg/kg in the United States (Zitnak and Johnston, 1970; Sinden and Webb, 1972, 1974). It was concluded from indirect evidence that the *S. chacoense* ancestor of Lenape was the source of these high SGA levels (Zitnak and Johnston, 1970; Sinden et al., 1984).

Only limited information on the inheritance of SGAs, covering only relatively few *Solanum* species and few SGAs has been presented [Schwarze, 1962, 1963; Sanford and Sinden, 1972; McCollum and Sinden, 1979; Sinden et al., 1986 (see also the review by Sinden et al., 1984)]. Conclusions relevant from the viewpoints of food safety and breeding efficiency that can be drawn from the inheritance studies are as follows:

1. The use of wild species in potato breeding programs can lead to extremely high levels of SGAs in hybrid breeding clones. Once such high levels are introduced into hybrid parental clones, excessive levels will persist at least among some of the offspring.
2. It may be possible to select cultivars showing low SGA levels after limited backcrossing of hybrids showing high levels. On the other hand, it may also be likely that wild-type SGAs or excessive levels of solanidine glycosides may persist through many backcrosses to species not showing these characteristics [see also Sinden and Sanford (1981) and Grassert and Lellbach (1987)].
3. Recombination of genes regulating the glycoside composition and genes controlling the aglycone type can occur during hybridization. This may lead to synthesis of SGAs not formed in either of the parents and to complex SGA compositions [see also Schmiediche et al. (1980) and Osman et al. (1986)]. Analogously, hybridization may lead to recombination of genes regulating the synthesis of different types of aglycones (Shih and Kuć, 1974). This may result in aglycones not present in either of the parents or even in the formation of novel SAs.

Limited surveys on the quantitative SA or SGA compositions of tubers of *Solanum* species have been presented by Osman et al. (1978), Van Gelder and Jonker (1986), and Johns and Osman (1986), and a more extended survey has been presented recently (Van Gelder et al., 1988a). Table 3 shows the SA compositions, expressed as glycoalkaloids, of tubers of *Solanum* species used in potato breeding. These compositions vary considerably between species, both qualitatively and quantitatively. Variation also exists within species, which reflects intraspecific heterogeneity and also variation in environmental conditions. Genetic variation can be utilized by potato breeders because it enables selection of crossing parents, which combine the desired trait with the least unfavorable SGA composition.

Most of the *Solanum* species produce very small tubers under conditions necessary for successful propagation. As discussed before, this may have contributed to their high SGA levels. Van Gelder et al. (1988a) showed that tubers of cultivars, grown under the same conditions and corresponding in small size to tubers of wild species, had SGA levels two to three times higher than those of field-grown normal tubers. If the relation between SGA level and the size and maturity of tubers is similar for cultivars and species, the high levels of the species' tubers are partly explained by this factor. However, some *Solanum* species have extremely high SGA levels even when this factor is taken into consideration. Such species and their hybrid progeny must be monitored for SGAs during breeding programs.

Van Gelder et al. (1989a) analyzed the minor and trace SAs of some *Solanum* species using several methods, including capillary GC/mass spectrometry and high-resolution mass spectrometry. Several SAs not reported before were characterized as solanidanes. Some of them may have been intermediates in SGA metabolism or stress metabolites.

S. vernei is being used widely in potato breeding (Ross, 1986) and was thought to contain only α-solanine and α-chaconine (Holden, 1981; Sinden et al., 1984) on the basis of an analysis of a foliage sample reported by Schrei-

TABLE 3 Steroidal Glycoalkaloid Composition of Tubers of *Solanum* Species Used in Potato Breeding[a]

Solanum species	Solanidine glycosides	Demissidine glycosides	Solasodine glycosides	Tomatidenol glycosides	Tomatidine glycosides	Other SGAs
S. acaule	8	231	—	—	127	—
S. berthaultii	160	—	—	—	—	140
S. brevicaule	1566	—	—	—	—	75
S. bukasovii	820	—	—	—	—	—
S. canasence	344	—	—	—	—	Traces
S. commersonii	1485	400	—	—	—	165
S. demissum	—	630	—	—	780	—
S. gourlayi	1382	—	—	—	—	—
S. leptophyes	1016	—	—	—	—	Traces
S. multidissectum	360	—	—	—	—	55
S. oplosence	500	—	—	—	—	—
S. sucrense	1167	—	—	—	—	Traces
S. phureja	24	—	—	—	—	—
S. venturii	1499	—	—	—	—	—
S. vernei	4909	—	1606	290	—	400

[a] Average values of different accessions/genotypes and years of growth. Concentrations in mg/kg fresh tubers; traces ≤ 2.5 mg/kg.
Sources: Van Gelder and Jonker (1986) and Van Gelder et al. (1988a).

ber (1963). However, recently, solasodine was found as the sole aglycone
in the leaves of *S. vernei*, while in the tubers, solanidine, solasodine, and
several unidentified SAs were detected (Van Gelder et al., 1988a). These
and many other discrepancies between the reports by different authors may
have been the result of intraspecific heterogeneity, of differences in the growing conditions applied, and of the physiological age and conditions of the plant
samples analyzed; but imperfection of the analytical techniques, as discussed
in the methodological section of this chapter, will also have played an important role.

The reports above show that for the analyses of wild *Solanum* species,
high-resolution, sensitive techniques must be used. Additional studies on
the identity and on the inheritance of the wild-type SGAs must be carried
out to investigate the potential transmission of these toxins to the food crop.

X. CONCLUDING REMARKS

Although studies on the chronic toxicity of the solanidine glycosides have
not been carried out, it is generally believed that most of the current potato
varieties are safe for consumption, provided that the crop is grown, harvested, and treated further as recommended in the paragraphs on the accumulation and control of SGAs.

The SGA levels in potatoes which are considered normal and those which
are believed to be potentially toxic to humans differ by a factor of 2 to 3.
This margin is extremely narrow compared to margins that are usually established in food science, especially in view of the many factors that lead to a
considerable accumulation of SGAs. It is recommended that the ingestion by
the public of the overall amount of SGAs from the various Solanaceae food
crops should not be allowed to rise. In this respect, the National Institute
of Agricultural Botany (NIAB) at Cambridge, United Kingdom, has recently
presented a mean level for solanidine glycosides of 60 mg/kg fresh unpeeled
potato as a guideline for breeders to bear in mind when submitting new varieties for national list testing (Parnell et al., 1984).

Of many *Solanum* species available to the breeder, one or more accessions
have now been analyzed for their SGAs. However, the varying and sometimes
conflicting data in the literature show that these cannot generally be used as
a guide in potato breeding.

There is hardly any doubt that the many environmental and physiological
factors that affect the biosynthesis of the solanidine glycosides in the current
potato varieties will also affect the biosynthesis of the various SGAs in *Solanum*
species. It must therefore be pointed out that in future varieties containing
wild species germplasm, genes for the synthesis of wild-type SGAs can be
suppressed under normal growth conditions or postharvest handling conditions
of potatoes. This can result in levels of these SGAs that are not detected.
However, under particular environmental or physiological (stress) conditions
such genes may be enhanced in expression (cf. Shih and Kuć, 1974; Fitzpatrick et al., 1977), which may lead to accumulation of high levels of the corresponding SGAs.

The advent of new techniques in cell biology, such as somatic hybridization, enables the recombination of genes from tuberiferous and genetically

very different nontuberiferous *Solanum* species or even more distant species
from other genera of Solanacae. Studies on the SA and SGA compositions
of somatic hybrids appear necessary to evaluate their potential for synthesizing novel or hybrid SAs or SGAs.

SGAs that do not occur in potato varieties considered safe for consumption must be excluded from new varieties until proper safety limits have been
established. However, it might be easier and wiser for breeders to exclude
alien SGAs from the food chain rather than to await long-term toxicological
evaluation studies and to rely on monitoring of the accumulation of alien SGAs
in the food product that would be necessary under a variety of environmental
conditions.

REFERENCES

Ahmed, S. S., and Müller, K. (1978). Effect of wound-damages on the glyco-
    alkaloid content in potato tubers and chips. *Lebensm.-Wiss. Technol.*
    11:144-146.

Ahmed, S. S., and Müller, K. (1979). Seasonal changes and the effect of
    nitrogen- and potash-fertilization on the solanine and α-chaconine content
    in various parts of the potato plant. *Z. Pflanzenernaehr. Bodenkd. 142:*
    275-279.

Ahmed, S. S., and Müller, K. (1981). Einfluss von Lagerzeit, Licht und
    Temperatur auf den Solanin- und α-Chaconingehalt mit und ohne Keim-
    hemmungsmittel behandelter Kartoffeln. *Potato Res. 24*:93-99.

Alberti, B. (1932). Zum Nachweis von Solanin. *Z. Unters. Lebensm. 64:*
    260-262.

Arneson, P. A., and Durbin, R. D. (1968). Studies on the mode of action
    of tomatine as a fungitoxic agent. *Plant Physiol. 43*:683-686.

Baerheim Svendsen, A., and Verpoorte, R. (1983). *Chromatography of
    Alkaloids.* Part A: *Thin-Layer Chromatography.* Elsevier, Amsterdam.

Baerug, R. (1962). Influence of different rates and intensities of light on
    solanine content and cooking quality of potato tubers. *Eur. Potato J.*
    5:242-251.

Baker, L. C., Lampitt, L. H., and Meredith, O. B. (1955). Solanine, glyco-
    side of the potato: III. An improved method of extraction and determina-
    tion. *J. Sci. Food Agric. 6*:197-202.

Baup, M. (1826). Extrait d'une lettre de M. Baup aux redacteurs sur plu-
    siers nouvelles substances. *Ann. Chim. Phys. 31*:108-109.

Bhuva, V. S., and Parnell, A. (1983). The effect of site and genotype on
    the glycoalkaloid content of first and second early potato varieties. *J.
    Natl. Inst. Agric. Bot. 16*:229-230.

Bintcliffe, E. J. B., Clydesdale, A., and Draper, S. R. (1982). Effects of
    genotype, site and season on the glycoalkaloid content of potato tubers.
    J. Natl. Inst. Agric. Bot. 16:86-91.

Blincow, P. J., Davies, A. M. C., Blintcliffe, E. J. B., Clydesdale, A.,
    Draper, S. R., and Allison, M. J. (1982). A screening method for the
    determination of glycoalkaloids in tubers of potato varieties. *J. Natl.
    Inst. Agric. Bot. 16*:92-97.

Boll, P. M. (1962). Alkaloidal glycosides from *Solanum dulcamara*: II. Three new alkaloidal glycosides and a reassessment of soladulcamaridine. *Acta Chem. Scand.* *16*:1819-1830.

Börner, A., and Mattis, H. (1924). Der Solaningehalt der Kartoffeln. *Z. Unters. Nahr-Genussm.* *47*:97-127.

Bostock, R. M., Nuckles, E., Henfling, J. W. D. M., and Kuć, J. A. (1983). Effects of potato tuber age and storage on sesquiterpenoid stress metabolite accumulation, steroid glycoalkaloid accumulation, and response to abscisic and arachidonic acids. *Phytopathology* *73*:435-438.

Bretzloff, C. W. (1971). A method for the rapid estimation of glycoalkaloids in potato tubers. *Am. Potato J.* *48*:158-162.

British Medical Journal. (1979). Solanine poisoning. Dec. 8:1458-1459.

Bushway, R. J. (1982a). High-performance liquid chromatographic separation of potato glycoalkaloids using a radially compressed amino column. *J. Chromatogr.* *247*:180-183.

Bushway, R. J. (1982b). High-performance liquid chromatographic determination of the metabolites of the potato glycoalkaloids, α-chaconine and α-solanine, in potato tubers and potato products. *J. Liq. Chromatogr.* *5*:1313-1322.

Bushway, R. J., and Ponnampalam, R. (1981). α-Chaconine and α-solanine content of potato products and their stability during several modes of cooking. *J. Agric. Food Chem.* *29*:814-817.

Bushway, R. J., and Storch, R. H. (1982). Semi-preparative high-performance liquid chromatographic separation of potato glycoalkaloids. *J. Liq. Chromatogr.* *5*:731-742.

Bushway, R. J., Barden, E. S., Bushway, A. W., and Bushway, A. A. (1979). High-performance liquid chromatographic separation of potato glycoalkaloids. *J. Chromatogr.* *178*:533-541.

Bushway, R. J., Wilson, A. M., and Bushway, A. A. (1980a). Determination of total glycoalkaloids in potato tubers using a modified titration method. *Am. Potato J.* *57*:561-565.

Bushway, R. J., Barden, E. S., Wilson, A. M., and Bushway, A. A. (1980b). Analysis of potato glycoalkaloids by high-performance liquid chromatography. *J. Food Sci.* *45*:1088-1089.

Bushway, R. J., Bureau, J. L., and McGann, D. F. (1983). Alpha-chaconine and alpha-solanine content of potato peels and potato peel products. *J. Food Sci.* *48*:84-86.

Bushway, R. J., Bureau, J. L., and King, J. (1986). Modification of the rapid high-performance liquid chromatographic method for the determination of potato glycoalkaloids. *J. Agric. Food Chem.* *34*:277-279.

Caddle, L. S., Stelzig, D. A., Harper, K. L., and Young, R. J. (1978). Thin-layer chromatographic system for identification and quantification of potato tuber glycoalkaloids. *J. Agric. Food Chem.* *26*:1453-1454.

Carman, A. S., Jr., Kuan, S. S., Ware, G. M., Francis, O. J., Jr., and Kirshenheuter, G. P. (1986). Rapid high-performance liquid chromatographic determination of the potato glycoalkaloids α-solanine and α-chaconine. *J. Agric. Food Chem.* *34*:279-282.

Cham, B. E., and Wilson, L. (1987). HPLC of glycoalkaloids from *Solanum sodomaeum*. *Planta Med.* 59-62.

Claringbold, W. D. B., Few. J. D., and Renwick, J. H. (1982). Kinetics and retention of solanidine in man. *Xenobiotica 12*:293-302.

Clement, E., and Verbist, J. F. (1980). The quantitation of solanine in tubers of *Solanum tuberosum* L: a comparative study of nine colourimetric methods. *Lebensm.-Wiss. Technol. 13*:202-206 (in French).

Coxon, D. T. (1984). Methodology for glycoalkaloid analysis. *Am. Potato J. 61*:169-183.

Coxon, D. T., Price, K. R., and Jones, P. G. (1979). A simplified method for the determination of total glycoalkaloids in potato tubers. *J. Sci. Food Agric. 30*:1043-1049.

Crabbe, P. G., and Fryer, C. (1980). Rapid quantitative analysis of solasodine, solasodine glycosides and solasodine by high-pressure liquid chromatography. *J. Chromatogr. 187*:87-100.

Cronk, T. C., Kuhn, G. D., and McArdle, F. J. (1974). The influence of stage of maturity, level of nitrogen fertilization and storage on the concentration of solanine in tubers of three potato cultivars. *Bull. Environ. Contam. Toxicol. 11*:163-168.

Dabbs, D. H., and Hilton, R. J. (1953). Methods of analysis for solanine in tubers of *Solanum tuberosum*. *Can. J. Technol. 31*:213-220.

Davies, A. M. C., and Blincow, P. J. (1984). Glycoalkaloid content of potatoes and potato products sold in the UK. *J. Sci. Food Agric. 35*:553-557.

Deahl, K. L., and Sinden, S. L. (1987). A technique for rapid detection of leptine glycoalkaloids in potato foliage. *Am. Potato J. 64*:285-290.

De Maine, M. J., Bain, H., and Joyce, J. A. L. (1988). Changes in the tuber glycoalkaloid content of potato cultivars on exposure to light. *J. Agric. Sci. Camb. 11*:57-58.

Desfosses, M. (1820). Extrait d'une lettre de M. Desfosses, pharmacien, à Besançon, à M. Roubiquet. *J. Pharm. 6*:374-376.

Eldridge, A. C., and Hockridge, M. E. (1983). High-performance liquid chromatographic separation of eastern black nightshade (*Solanum ptycantum*) glycoalkaloids. *J. Agric. Food Chem. 31*:1218-1220.

Fischer, R., and Thiele, J. (1929). Uber den Solaninnachweis in der Kartoffel mit Blutgelatine. *Oesterr. Bot. Z. 78*:325-334.

Fitzpatrick, T. J., and Osman, S. F. (1974). A comprehensive method for the determination of total potato glycoalkaloids. *Am. Potato J. 51*:318-323.

Fitzpatrick, T. J., Herb, S. F., Osman, S. F., and McDermott, J. A. (1977). Potato glycoalkaloids: increases and variations of ratios in aged slices over prolonged storage. *Am. Potato J. 54*:539-544.

Fitzpatrick, T. J., MacKenzie, J. D., and Gregory, P. (1978a). Modifications of the comprehensive method for total glycoalkaloid determination. *Am. Potato J. 55*:247-248.

Fitzpatrick, T. J., McDermott, J. A., and Osman, S. F. (1978b). Evaluation of injured commercial potato samples for total glycoalkaloid content. *J. Food Sci. 43*:1617-1618.

Gosselin, B., Mondy, N. I., and Evans, W. D. (1988). Effect of method of irrigation on the total glycoalkaloid and nitrate-nitrogen content of Rosa potatoes. *Am. Potato J. 65*:99-103.

Grassert, V., and Lellbach, H. (1987). Untersuchungen des Glykoalkaloid-gehalts von Kartoffelhybriden mit Resistenz gegen die Kartoffelnematoden *Globodera rostochiensis* und *Globodera pallida*. *Biochem. Physiol. Pflanz.* *182*:473-479.

Gregory, P., Sinden, S. L., Osman, S. F., Tingey, W. M., and Chessin, D. A. (1981). Glycoalkaloids of wild tuber-bearing *Solanum* species. *J. Agric. Food Chem.* *29*:1212-1215.

Harvey, M. H., McMillan, M., Morgan, M. R., and Chan, H. W.-S. (1985). Solanidine is present in sera of healthy individuals and in amounts dependent on their dietary potato consumption. *Hum. Toxicol.* *4*:187-194.

Heftmann, E. (1967). Biochemistry of steroidal sapogenins and glycoalkaloids. *Lloydia 30*:209-231.

Heftmann, E. (1983). Biogenesis of steroids in Solanaceae. *Phytochemistry* *22*:1843-1860.

Heftmann, E., and Schwimmer, S. (1973). A radioligand assay of tomatine. *Phytochemistry 12*:2661-2663.

Hellenäs, K.-E. (1986). A simplified procedure for quantification of potato glycoalkaloids in tuber extracts by HPLC: comparison with ELISA and a colorimetric method. *J. Sci. Food Agric.* *37*:776-782.

Herb, S. F., Fitzpatrick, T. J., and Osman, S. F. (1975). Separation of potato glycoalkaloids by gas chromatography. *J. Agric. Food Chem.* *23*: 520-523.

Holden, J. H. W. (1981). The contribution of breeding to the improvement of potato quality. *Survey Pap. 8th Trienn. Conf. Eur. Assoc. Potato Res.*, Munich, pp. 37-53.

Hunter, I. R., Walden, M. K., Wagner, J. R., and Heftmann, E. (1976). Thin-layer chromatography of steroidal alkaloids. *J. Chromatogr. 118*: 259-262.

Hunter, I. R., Walden, M. K., and Heftmann, E. (1980). High-performance liquid chromatography of *Solanum* and *Veratrum* alkaloids. *J. Chromatogr. 198*:363-366.

Jadhav, S. J., and Salunkhe, D. K. (1973). Enzymatic glucosylation of solanidine. *J. Food Sci. 301*:1099-1100.

Jadhav, S. J., and Salunkhe, D. K. (1975). Formation and control of chlorophyll and glycoalkaloids in tubers of *Solanum tuberosum* L. and evaluation of glycoalkaloid toxicity. *Adv. Food Res. 21*:307-354.

Jadhav, S. J., Sharma, R. P., and Salunkhe, D. K. (1981). Naturally occurring toxic alkaloids in foods. *Crit. Rev. Toxicol. 9*:21-104.

Jellema, R., Elema, E. T., and Malingré, Th. M. (1980). Optical brighteners as thin-layer chromatographic detection reagents for glycoalkaloids and steroid alkaloids in *Solanum* species. *J. Chromatogr. 189*:406-409.

Jellema, R., Elema, E. T., and Malingré, Th. M. (1981). Fluorodensitometric determination of potato glycoalkaloids on thin-layer chromatograms. *J. Chromatogr. 210*:121-129.

Jellema, R., Elema, E. T., and Malingré, Th. M. (1982). A rapid quantitative determination of the individual glycoalkaloids in tubers and leaves of *Solanum tuberosum* L. *Potato Res. 25*:247-255.

Johns, T., and Osman, S. F. (1986). Glycoalkaloids of *Solanum* series *Megistacrolobum* and related potato cultigens. *Biochem. Syst. Ecol. 14*: 651-655.

Juvik, J. A., Stevens, M. A., and Rick, C. M. (1982). Survey of the genus *Lycopersicon* for variability in α-tomatine content. *Hortic. Sci.* 17:764-766.

Kaneko, K., Tanaka, M. W., and Mitsuhashi, H. (1976). Origin of nitrogen in the biosynthesis of solanidine by *Veratrum grandiflorum*. *Phytochemistry* 15:1391-1393.

Kaneko, K., Tanaka, M. W., and Mitsuhashi, H. (1977). Dormantinol, a possible precursor in solanidine biosynthesis from budding *Veratrum grandiflorum*. *Phytochemistry* 16:1247-1250.

Keeler, R. F. (1986). Teratology of steroidal alkaloids. In *Alkaloids: Chemical and Biological Perspectives*, Vol. 4, S. W. Pelletier (Ed.). Wiley, New York, pp. 389-425.

King, R. R. (1980). Analysis of potato glycoalkaloids by gas-liquid chromatography of alkaloid components. *J. Assoc. Off. Anal. Chem.* 63:1226-1230.

Kozukue, N., Kozukue, E., and Mizuno, S. (1987). Glycoalkaloids in potato plants and tubers. *Hortic. Sci.* 22:294-296.

Kuhn, R., and Löw, I. (1954). Die Konstitution des Solanins. *Angew. Chem.* 66:639-640.

Kuhn, R., and Löw, I. (1961). Zur Konstitution der Leptine. *Chem. Ber.* 94:1088-1095.

Kuhn, R., Löw, I., and Trischmann, H. (1955a). Die Konstitution des Solanins. *Chem. Ber.* 88:1492-1507.

Kuhn, R., Löw, I., and Trischmann, H. (1955b). Die Konstitution des α-Chaconins. *Chem. Ber.* 88:1690-1693.

Kusano, G., Takahashi, A., Sugiyama, K., and Nozoe, S. (1987). Antifungal properties of *Solanum* alkaloids. *Chem. Pharm. Bull.* 35:4862-4867.

Lammerink, P. (1985). Total glycoalkaloid content of new potato cultivars. *N.Z. J. Exp. Agric.* 13:413-414.

Lampitt, L. H., Bushill, J. H., Rooke, H. S., and Jackson, E. M. (1943). Solanine: glycoside of the potato: II. Its distribution in the potato plant. *J. Soc. Chem. Ind. Lond.* 62:48-51.

Lavintman, N., Tandecarz, J., and Cardini, C. E. (1977). Enzymatic glycosylation of steroid alkaloids in potato tuber. *Plant Sci. Lett.* 8:65-70.

Lepper, W. (1949). Solaningehalte von 58 Kartoffelsorten. *Z. Lebensm.-Unters. Forsch.* 88:264-273.

Liljegren, D. R. (1971). Glucosylation of solasodine by extracts from *Solanum laciniatum*. *Phytochemistry* 10:3061-3064.

Linnemann, A. R., Es, A. van, and Hartmans, K. J. (1985). Changes in the content of L-ascorbic acid, glucose, fructose, sucrose and total glycoalkaloids in potato (cv. Bintje) stored at 7, 16 and 28°C. *Potato Res.* 28:271-278.

MacKenzie, J. D., and Gregory, P. (1979). Evaluation of a comprehensive method for total glycoalkaloid determination. *Am. Potato J.* 56:27-33.

Maga, J. A. (1980). Potato glycoalkaloids. *Crit. Rev. Food Sci. Nutr.* 12:371-405.

Maga, J. A. (1981). Total and individual glycoalkaloid composition of stored potato slices. *J. Food Process. Preserv.* 5:23-28.

Marzouk, Z., and Boukef, K. (1983). Etude comparative de deux techniques de dosage de la solasodine. *Plant. Med. Phytother.* 17:139-146.

McCollum, G. D., and Sinden, S. L. (1979). Inheritance study of tuber glycoalkaloids in a wild potato, *Solanum chacoense* Bitter. *Am. Potato J. 56*:95-113.

McMillan, M., and Thompson, J. C. (1979). An outbreak of suspected solanine poisoning in schoolboys: examination of criteria of solanine poisoning. *Q. J. Med. 48*:227-243.

Monday, N. I., Leja, M., and Gosselin, B. (1987). Changes in total phenolic, total glycoalkaloid, and ascorbic acid content of potatoes as a result of bruising. *J. Food Sci. 52*:631-633.

Morgan, M. R. A., McNerney, R., Matthew, J. A., Coxon, D. T., and Chan, H. W.-S. (1983). An enzyme-linked immunosorbent assay for total glycoalkaloids in potato tubers. *J. Sci. Food Agric. 34*:593-598.

Morgan, M. R. A., Coxon, D. T., Bramham, S., Chan, H. W.-S., Van Gelder, W. M. J., and Allison, M. J. (1985). Determination of the glycoalkaloid content of potato tubers by three methods including enzyme-linked immunosorbent assay. *J. Sci. Food Agric. 36*:282-288.

Morris, S. C., and Lee, T. H. (1981). Analysis of potato glycoalkaloids with radially compressed high-performance liquid chromatographic cartridges and ethanolamine in the mobile phase. *J. Chromatogr. 219*:403-410.

Morris, S. C., and Lee, T. H. (1984). The toxicity and teratogenicity of Solanaceae glycoalkaloids, particularly those of the potato (*Solanum tuberosum*): a review. *Food Technol. Aust. 36*:118-124.

Morris, S. C., and Petermann, J. B. (1985). Genetic and environmental effects on levels of glycoalkaloids in cultivars of potato (*Solanum tuberosum* L.). *Food Chem. 18*:271-282.

Munshi, C. B., and Mondy, N. I. (1988). Effect of soil applications of molybdenum on the biochemical composition of Katahdin potatoes: nitrate nitrogen and total glycoalkaloids. *J. Agric. Food Chem. 36*:688-960.

Nair, P. M., Behere, A. G., and Ramaswamy, N. K. (1981). Glycoalkaloids of *Solanum tuberosum* Linn. *J. Sci. Ind. Res. 40*:529-535.

Nes, W. D., Heftmann, E., Hunter, I. R., and Walden, M. K. (1980). Determination of solasodine in fruits of *Solanum khasianum* by a combination of chromatofuge and high-pressure liquid chromatography. *J. Liq. Chromatogr. 3*:1687-1696.

Nishie, K., Norred, W. P., and Swain, A. P. (1975). Pharmacology and toxicology of chaconine and tomatine. *Res. Commun. Chem. Pathol. Pharmacol. 12*:657-668.

Nishie, K., Fitzpatrick, T. J., Swain, A. P., and Keyl, A. C. (1976). Positive inotropic action of Solanaceae glycoalkaloids. *Res. Commun. Chem. Pathol. Pharmacol. 15*:601-607.

Norberg, H. (1987). Magnum bonum—en död potatis? *Lantbrukstidskr. Stockholms län 1987*(1):17-18.

Olsson, K. (1986). The influence of genotype on the effects of impact damage on the accumulation of glycoalkaloids in potato tubers. *Potato Res. 29*:1-12.

Osman, S. F. (1983). Glycoalkaloids in potato. *Food Chem. 11*:235-247.

Osman, S. F., and Sinden, S. L. (1977). Analysis of mixtures of solanidine and demissidine glycoalkaloids containing identical carbohydrate units. *J. Agric. Food Chem. 25*:955-957.

Osman, S. F., Herb, S. F., Fitzpatrick, T. J., and Schmiediche, P. (1978). Glycoalkaloid composition of wild and cultivated tuber-bearing *Solanum* species of potential value in potato breeding programs. *J. Agric. Food Chem. 26*:1246-1248.

Osman, S. F., Zacharius, R. M., Kalan, E. B., Fitzpatrick, T. J., and Krulick, S. (1979). Stress metabolites of the potato and other Solanaceous plants. *J. Food Prot. 42*:502-507.

Osman, S. F., Johns, T. A., and Price, K. R. (1986). Sisunine, a glycoalkaloid found in hybrids between *Solanum acaule* and *Solanum × ajanhuiri*. *Phytochemistry 25*:967-968.

Parnell, A., Bhuva, V. S., and Bintcliffe, E. J. B. (1984). The glycoalkaloid content of potato varieties. *J. Natl. Inst. Agric. Bot. 16*:535-541.

Pasesnishenko, V. A., and Guseva, A. R. (1956). Quantitative determination of potato glycoalkaloids and their preparative separation. *Biochemistry (USSR) 21*:606-611.

Patchett, B. J., Cunningham, P. S., and Lill, R. E. (1977). Glycoalkaloid levels in New Zealand potatoes. *N.Z. J. Exp. Agric. 5*:55-57.

Ponnampalam, R., and Mondy, N. I. (1986). Effect of foliar application of indole-acetic acid on the total glycoalkaloids and nitrate nitrogen content of potatoes. *J. Agric. Food Chem. 34*:686-688.

Prelog, V., and Jeger, O. (1953). The chemistry of *Solanum* and *Veratrum* alkaloids. In *The Alkaloids*, Vol. III, R. H. F. Manske and H. L. Holmes (Eds.). Academic Press, New York, pp. 247-312.

Prelog, V., and Jeger, O. (1960). Steroid alkaloids: the *Solanum* group. In *The Alkaloids*, Vol. VII, R. H. F. Manske (Ed.). Academic Press, New York, pp. 343-361.

Renwick, J. H. (1972). Anencephaly and spina bifida are usually preventable by avoidance of a specific but unidentified substance present in certain potato tubers. *Br. J. Prev. Soc. Med. 26*:67-88.

Renwick, J. H., Claringbold, W. D. B., Earthy, M. E., Few, J. D., and McLean, A. C. (1984). Neural-tube defects produced by Syrian hamsters by potato glycoalkaloids. *Teratology 30*:371-381.

Ripperger, H., and Schreiber, K. (1981). *Solanum* steroid alkaloids. In *The Alkaloids*, Vol. XIX, R. G. A. Rodrigo (Ed.). Academic Press, New York, pp. 81-192.

Roddick, J. G. (1974). The steroidal glycoalkaloid α-tomatine. *Phytochemistry 13*:9-25.

Roddick, J. G. (1979). Complex formation between solanaceous steroidal glycoalkaloids and free sterols in vitro. *Phytochemistry 18*:1467-1470.

Roddick, J. G. (1980). A sterol-binding assay for potato glycoalkaloids. *Phytochemistry 19*:2455-2457.

Rooke, H. S., Bushill, J. H., Lampitt, L. H., and Jackson, E. M. (1943). Solanine, glycoside of the potato: I. Its isolation and determination. *J. Soc. Chem. Ind. Lond. 62*:20-24.

Ross, H. (1986). Potato breeding—problems and perspectives: advances in plant breeding. *J. Plant Breed. Suppl. 13*:1-130.

Ross, H., Pasemann, P., and Nitsche, W. (1978). Der Glykoalkaloidgehalt von Kartoffelsorten in seiner Abhängigkeit von Anbauort und-jahr und seiner Beziehung zum Geschmack. *Z. Pflanzenzuecht. 80*:64-79.

Sachse, J., and Bachmann, F. (1969). Uber die Alkaloidbestimmung in *Solanum tuberosum* L. *Z. Lebensm.-Unters. Forsch.* 141:262-274.

Salunkhe, D. K., and Wu, M. T. (1979). Control of postharvest glycoalkaloid formation in potato tubers. *J. Food Prot.* 42:519-525.

Sanford, L. L., and Sinden, S. L. (1972). Inheritance of potato glycoalkaloids. *Am. Potato J.* 49:209-217.

Schmiediche, P. E., Hawkes, J. G., and Ochoa, C. M. (1980). Breeding of the cultivated potato species *Solanum × Juzepczukii* Buk. and *Solanum × Curtilobum* Juz. et Buk: I. A study of the natural variations of *S. × Juzepczukii, S. × Curtilobum* and their wild progenitor, *S. acaule* Bitt. *Euphytica* 29:685-704.

Schreiber, K. (1963). Uber die Alkaloidglykoside knollen-tragender *Solanum-Arten. Kulturpflauhe* 11:422-450.

Schreiber, K. (1968). Steroid alkaloids: the *Solanum* group. In *The Alkaloids*, Vol. X, R. H. F. Manske (Ed.). Academic Press, New York, pp. 1-192.

Schreiber, K., Aurich, O., and Osske, G. (1963). *Solanum*-Alkaloide: XVIII. Dünnschichtchromatographie von *Solanum*-Steroidalkaloiden und Steroidsapogeninen. *J. Chromatogr.* 12:63-69.

Schwarze, P. (1962). Methoden zum Solaninnachweiss und zur Solaninbestimmung in Kartoffelzuchtmaterial. *Zuechter* 32:155-160.

Schwarze, P. (1963). Uber den Glykoalkaloidgehalt und die Zusammensetzung des Glykoalkaloidkomplexes in Nachkommen der Artkreuzung *Solanum tuberosum × Solanum chacoense. Zuechter* 33:275-281.

Schwerdtfeger, E. (1984). The automated kinetic assay of solanine. *Acta Hortic.* 163:79-82.

Shih, M.-J., and Kuć, J. (1974). α- and β-Solamarine in Kennebec *Solanum tuberosum* leaves and aged tuber slices. *Phytochemistry* 13:997-1000.

Sinden, S. L. (1987). Potato glycoalkaloids. *Acta Hortic.* 207:41-47.

Sinden, S. L., and Sanford, L. L. (1981). Origin and inheritance of solamarine glycoalkoids in commercial potato cultivars. *Am. Potato J.* 58:305-325.

Sinden, S. L., and Webb, R. E. (1972). Effect of variety and location on the glycolalkaloid content of potatoes. *Am. Potato J.* 49:334-338.

Sinden, S. L., and Webb, R. E. (1974). Effect of environment on glycoalkaloid content of six potato varieties at 39 locations. *U.S. Dep. Agric. Tech. Bull.* 1472.

Sinden, S. L., Deahl, K. L., and Aulenbach, B. B. (1976). Effect of glycoalkaloids and phenolics on potato flavor. *J. Food Sci.* 41:520-523.

Sinden, S. L., Sanford, L. L., and Webb, R. E. (1984). Genetic and environmental control of potato glycoalkaloids. *Am. Potato J.* 61:141-156.

Sinden, S. L., Sanford, L. L., and Deahl, K. L. (1986). Segregation of leptine glycoalkaloids in *Solanum chacoense* Bitter. *J. Agric. Food Chem.* 34:372-377.

Sizer, C. E., Maga, J. A., and Craven, C. J. (1980). Total glycoalkaloids in potatoes and potato chips. *J. Agric. Food Chem.* 28:578-579.

Slijm, P., and Weinans, R. (1973). *Contents of solanine and protein in potato varieties*, Report 21103, Dec. 5, 1973. Avebé, Veendam, The Netherlands (in Dutch).

Smittle, D. A. (1971). A comparison and modification of methods of total glycoalkaloid analysis. *Am. Potato J.* 48:410-413.

Speroni, J. J., and Pell, E. J. (1980). Modified method for tuber glycoalkaloid and leaf glycoalkaloid analysis. *Am. Potato J.* 57:537-542.

Uppal, D. S. (1987). Varietal and environmental effect on the glycoalkaloid content of potato (*Solanum tuberosum* L.). *Plant Foods Hum. Nutr.* 37: 333-340.

Vallejo, R. P., and Ercegovich, C. D. (1979). Analysis of potato for glycoalkaloid content by radioimmunoassay (RIA). *Natl. Bur. Stand. (U.S.) Spec. Publ.* 519:333-340.

Van Gelder, W. M. J. (1984). A new hydrolysis technique for steroid glycoalkaloids with unstable aglycones from *Solanum* spp. *J. Sci. Food Agric.* 35:487-494.

Van Gelder, W. M. J. (1985a). Plant breeding as a tool for improving product quality. *Bedrijfsontwikkeling 16:*474-478 (in Dutch).

Van Gelder, W. M. J. (1985b). Determination of the total C27-steroidal alkaloid composition of *Solanum* species by high-resolution gas chromatography. *J. Chromatogr.* 331:285-293.

Van Gelder, W. M. J. (1987). Research on the C27-steroidal alkaloid composition of potato: development of an efficient and quantitative method for determining the total C27-steroidal alkaloid composition of wild species, inter-specific hybrids and cultivars of *Solanum*, Research report EC, Contract No. 4910. Directorate-General for Agriculture, European Communities, Brussels.

Van Gelder, W. M. J., and Dellaert, L. M. W. (1988). Alkaloids in potatoes. *Prophyta 42S:*236-238 (in Dutch).

Van Gelder, W. M. J., and De Ponti, O. M. B. (1987). α-Tomatine and other steroidal glycoalkaloids in fruits of tomato lines resistant to the glasshouse whitefly (*Trialeurodes vaporariorum* Westw.). *Euphytica* 36:555-561.

Van Gelder, W. M. J., and Jonker, H. H. (1986). Steroidal alkaloid composition of tubers of exotic *Solanum* species of value in potato breeding determined by high-resolution gas chromatography. In *Potato Research of Tomorrow*, A. G. B. Beekman (Ed.). Pudoc, Wageningen, The Netherlands, pp. 166-169.

Van Gelder, W. M. J., Vinke, J. H., and Scheffer, J. J. C. (1988a). Steroidal glycoalkaloids in tubers and leaves of *Solanum* species used in potato breeding. *Euphytica 37S:*147-158.

Van Gelder, W. M. J., Jonker, H. H., Huizing, H. J., and Scheffer, J. J. C. (1988b). Capillary gas chromatography of steroidal alkaloids in Solanaceae: retention indices and simultaneous flame-ionisation/nitrogen-specific detection. *J. Chromatogr.* 442:133-145.

Van Gelder, W. M. J., Tuinstra, L. G. M. Th., Van der Greef, J., and Scheffer, J. J. C. (1989a). Mass spectrometric characterization of novel steroidal alkaloids in *Solanum*: implications for potato breeding. *J. Chromatogr.* 482:13-22.

Verbist, J. F., and Monnet, R. (1979). A propos de la teneur en solanine des petits tubercules nouveaux de pomme de terre (*Solanum tuberosum* L.). *Potato Res.* 22:239-244.

Wang, S. L., Bedford, C. L., and Thompson, N. R. (1972). Determination of glycoalkaloids in potatoes (*S. tuberosum*) with a bisolvent extraction method. *Am. Potato J.* *49*: 302-308.

Weiler, E. W., Krüger, H., and Zenk, M. H. (1980). Radioimmunoassay for the determination of the steroidal alkaloid solasodine and related compounds in living plants and herbarium specimens. *Planta Med.* *39*: 112-124.

Wolf, M. J., and Duggar, B. M. (1946). Estimation and physiological role of solanine in the potato. *J. Agric. Res.* *73*: 1-32.

Wood, F. A., and Young, D. A. (1974). TGA in potatoes. *Can. Dep. Agric. Publ. 1533.*

Woolfe, J. A. (1987). *The Potato in the Human Diet.* Cambridge University Press, Cambridge.

Wu, M. T., and Salunkhe, D. K. (1976). Changes in glycoalkaloid content following mechanical injuries to potato tubers. *J. Am. Soc. Hortic. Sci.* *101*: 329-331.

Zitnak, A. (1961). The occurrence and distribution of free alkaloid solanidine in Netted Gem potatoes. *Can. J. Biochem. Physiol.* *39*: 1257-1265.

Zitnak, A. (1977). Steroids and capsaicinoids of Solanaceous food plants. In *Nightshades and Health*, N. F. Childers and G. M. Russo (Eds.). Somerset Press, Somerville, N.J., pp. 41-91.

Zitnak, A. (1981). Photoinduction of glycoalkaloids in cured potatoes. *Am. Potato J.* *58*: 415-421.

Zitnak, A., and Johnston, G. R. (1970). Glycoalkaloid content of B5141-6 potatoes. *Am. Potato J.* *47*: 256-260.

8

Solanum Glycoalkaloids: Plant Toxins Possessing Disparate Physiologically Active Structural Entities

William Gaffield

Western Regional Research Center, Agricultural Research Service, USDA, Albany, California

Richard F. Keeler

Poisonous Plant Research Laboratory, Agricultural Research Service, USDA, Logan, Utah

Dale C. Baker

Colorado State University, Fort Collins, Colorado

I. INTRODUCTION

Numerous species of the plant families Solanaceae, Liliaceae, and Veratreae, especially those of genera *Solanum*, *Lycopersicon*, and *Veratrum*, produce steroidal alkaloids. Included among the steroidal alkamines isolated from these species are a wide variety of compounds containing the C27 cholestane skeleton

(Ripperger and Schreiber, 1981). The steroidal alkaloids have been considered by some not as true alkaloids in the biogenetic sense but instead as "pseudoalkaloids" or "alcaloida imperfecta" which are simple derivatives of naturally occurring nitrogen-free substances (Hegnauer, 1963). They become alkaloidlike because at a late stage of their biosynthesis, nitrogen is introduced into the molecule. True alkaloids have been defined as structurally complex, basic, nitrogen-heterocyclic compounds of plant origin which manifest significant pharmacological activity. More recently, Pelletier has questioned the classification of natural nitrogenous compounds based on biogenesis and has recommended that structure alone should determine whether or not a compound is defined as an alkaloid (Pelletier, 1983).

Whereas steroidal sapogenins are based on a spirostane skeleton [1], many *Solanum* glycoalkaloids are derived from either the solanidane framework [2], which contains an indolizidine system (e.g., solanines, chaconines), or spirosolanes [3], which incorporate an oxazaspirodecane moiety (e.g., solasonine, tomatine). The Solanaceae or nightshade family encompasses many agricultural crop plants important to humans, such as potato, tomato, eggplant, capsicum, and naranjilla (Jadhav et al., 1981; Morris and Lee, 1984). While the purpose of natural toxicants has been claimed to be as chemical defense agents against pests and disease (Roddick, 1987), the presence of a basic nitrogen group renders alkaloids quite toxic to warm-blooded organisms. It is well known that substitution of nitrogen for carbon in tetracyclic steroids produces compounds with a variety of biological effects; for example, several nitrogen-containing steroids (derivatives of 3-oxo-4-aza-5α-androstane-17β-carboxamide) are competitive inhibitors of testosterone 5α-reductase, whereas the carbon analogs are not (Rasmusson et al., 1986). Because *Solanum* glycoalkaloids are present in edible parts of the aforementioned food plants and have been implicated in numerous human and livestock poisonings and fatalities due to their powerful physiological and pharmacological activity (Morris and Lee, 1984), intensive chemical studies have focused for over half a century on the two major steroidal glycoalkaloids, α-solanine [4] and α-chaconine [5]. These alkaloids share a common aglycone (solanidine) and differ only in their carbohydrate moiety.

The biologically active glycoalkaloids may be viewed as comprised of three diverse structural entities: a polar, water-soluble oligosaccharide portion of up to five monosaccharide units attached at C3; a nonpolar, lipophilic steroidal framework; and a nitrogen heterocylic moiety which is known to produce various toxic effects (e.g., tomatine [6]). Slight alterations in structure or configuration can exert profound effects on their biological properties. Conversely, nonnitrogenous steroidal saponins are present in nonedible parts of other food plants (e.g., oats, peanuts, and sugarbeets) and have not been incriminated as causing serious incidences of poisoning (Price et al., 1987). The greater lytic effect of chaconine than solanine on a variety of plant membranes, coupled with the total lack of activity of solanine on several systems, demonstrates the key role played by the triose in this interaction, which has been speculated to result either from different responses of the alkaloids to degradative enzymes or in their ability to reach binding sites in membranes (Roddick et al., 1988). Furthermore, β_2-chaconine, which differs from α-chaconine only by lacking a rhamnose group, does not display membrane lytic activity. In this chapter, which complements others in this volume on terato-

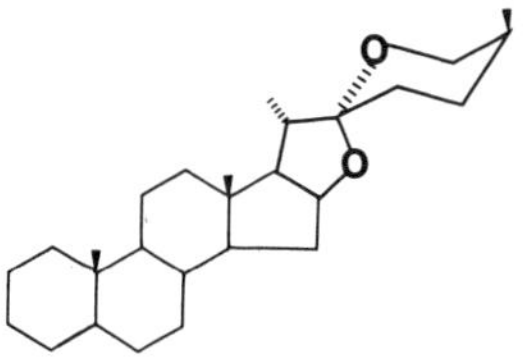

[1]

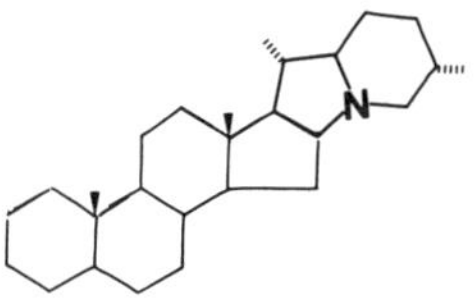

[2]

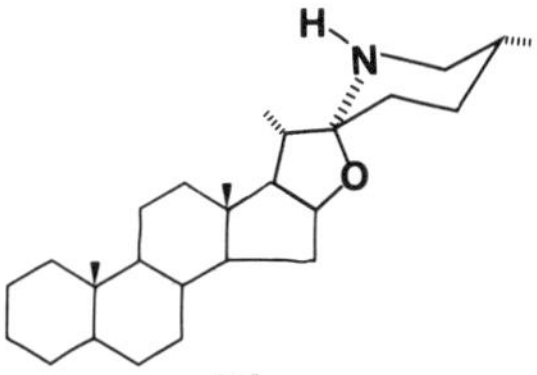

[3]

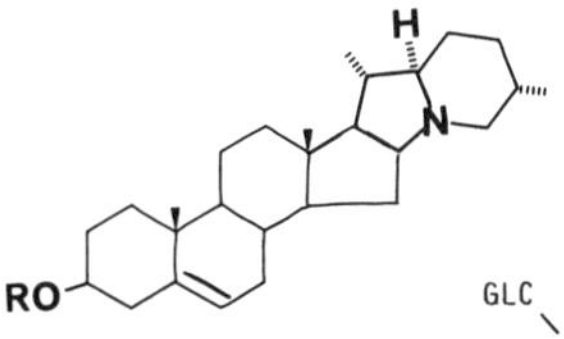

RO—

[4] α-SOLANINE, R =

GLC
\
GAL ⁻
/
RHA

[5] α-CHACONINE, R =

RHA
\
GLC —
/
RHA

[7] SOLANIDINE, R = H

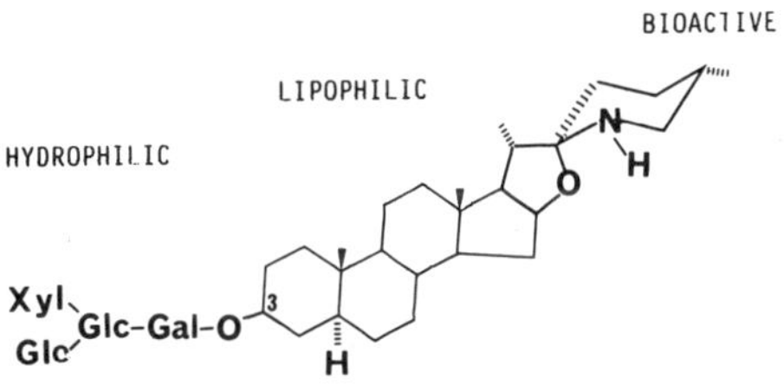

BIOACTIVE

LIPOPHILIC

HYDROPHILIC

Xyl
\
Glc-Gal-O
/
Glc

[6]

genicity, toxicity, and analysis of *Solanum* species and their alkaloids, we explore why diverse biological effects may be due not only to the amount of alkaloids present in plant material but also to their molecular structures.

II. CHEMICAL INTERRELATIONSHIPS AMONG *SOLANUM* ALKALOIDS

Due in part to the wide diversity of sugar residues of *Solanum* glycoalkaloids, the isolation and structural elucidation of numerous new steroidal alkamines and their glycosides have been recorded during the past 20 years. Historical-ly, steroidal alkaloids presented chemists with difficult and challenging struc-tural problems. A brief summary of several highlights in the classical chemical determination of structure of key steroidal alkaloids is provided to illustrate the chemical interrelationship of the spirostanes, spirosolanes, and solanidanes.

Solanine was first isolated from *S. nigrum* (morel) in 1821 (Desfosses, 1821), followed by its isolation a few years later from potatoes (Baup, 1826). In 1861, solanine from potatoes was shown (Zwenger and Kind, 1861) to be a glycoside and its alkaloidal aglycone named solanidine [7]. In 1905, "solanine" from *S. sodomeum* berries was shown (Oddo and Colombano, 1905) to be different from that from *S. tuberosum* and was subsequently named solasonine, from which solasodine [8] was obtained upon acidic hydrolysis. The typical steroid dehydrogenation product γ-methylcyclopentenophenanthrene [9] was isolated upon selenium dehydrogenation of both solanidine and solasodine, and along with the formation of sparingly soluble digitonides from the two alkaloids established the location of glycoside attachment to the steroid at the secondary hydroxyl group on C3 (Prelog and Jeger, 1953). Of the four different structures postulated for solanidine in the 1940s (Reichstein and Reich, 1946), the indolizidine nucleus [7] present in two of them (Rochelmeyer, 1942; Prelog and Szpilfogel, 1942; Craig and Jacobs, 1943) furnished the simplest explanation for the formation of 2-ethyl-5-methylpyridine [10] upon selenium dehydrogenation and was subsequently confirmed by partial synthesis of 5β-solanidan-3β-ol from sarsasapogenin [11] (Prelog and Szpilfogel, 1944; Uhle and Jacobs, 1945). The structure of solasodine was established when its second oxygen atom was found to be present as a cyclic ether (Briggs et al., 1950), followed by partial synthesis (Uhle, 1953) of the spirosolane from a steroid sapogenin.

Reactions converting tomatidine [12] into solanidan-3β-ol (5α-H [7]) permitted elucidation of the configuration of most of the solanidane ring system (Sato and Latham, 1956). The generation of $R(+)$- and $S(-)$-5-methyl-2-piperidone, [13] and [14], upon oxidation of soladulcidine (5α-H [8]) and tomatidine, respectively, along with 3β-acetoxy-5α-pregn-16-ene-20-one [15], established the C25 stereochemistry of the two alkaloids (Schreiber, 1965). Because chemical degradations destroyed the C22 stereocenter of the spirosolanes, chiroptical techniques were used (Schreiber, 1968) to demonstrate that solasodine and tomatidine possessed opposite configurations at this center and X-ray crystallography was employed (Hohne et al., 1966) to establish the configurations of the solanidanes. Nearly all natural solanidanes possess 20S, 22R, 25S, and NS configuration (see below). In 1954, Kuhn revealed (Kuhn and Löw, 1954) that the identity of the glycoalkaloid "solanine" was primarily a mixture of two classes of glycosides, α-solanine [4] and α-chaconine [5], whose trioses differ with respect to one sugar. With the advent of modern spectral techniques such as mass spectrometry, X-ray crystallography, circular dichroism, and nuclear magnetic resonance (NMR) spectroscopy, by which over 200 steroidal alkaloids and their derivatives have been characterized, relatively straightforward application of these powerful methods often will enable the molecular structure of a newly isolated steroidal alkaloid to be determined (Highet and Wheeler, 1985).

III. BIOLOGICAL ACTIVITY OF STRUCTURALLY DIVERSE INDOLIZIDINE ALKALOIDS

The indolizidine alkaloids, which bear a fused 6/5 ring system, occupy a structurally intermediate position between the pyrrolizidine and quinolizidine

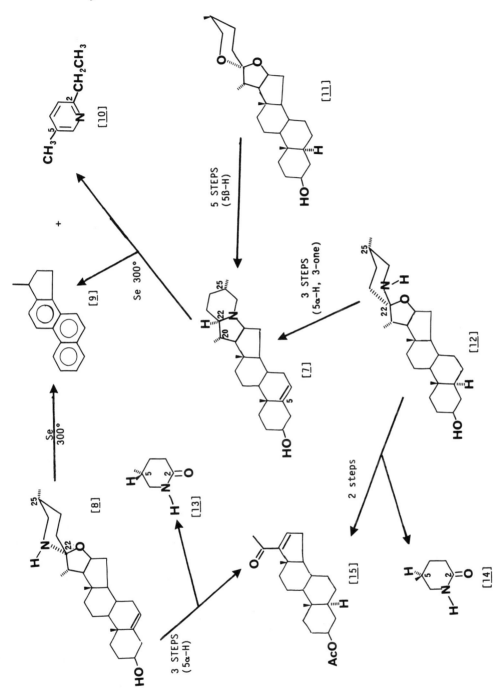

classes, but in contrast to the latter groups have usually not been clearly
identified as a specific class of alkaloids (Elbein and Molyneux, 1987). Several plant families include simple indolizidines that are highly functionalized
with polar substituents such as hydroxy and amino groups. Important members of this group are slaframine, swainsonine, and castanospermine (Elbein
and Molyneux, 1987; Broquist, 1985). Other simple indolizidines, such as
the gephyrotoxins, occur as constituents of neotropical poison-dart frogs
(Daly and Spande, 1986). If the azabicyclic indolizidine nucleus is embedded
within a fused polycyclic ring system, as in the steroidal alkaloids occurring
in the Solanaceae, the resultant alkaloid is no longer considered to be simple.
Several biological properties of structurally diverse indolizidines will be considered, with emphasis on their common azabicyclic functionality.

The pharmacological activities of the dendrobatid alkaloids are due to the
evolutionary development of these skin toxins as part of a chemical defense
system used to protect the brightly colored dendrobatid frogs from predators
(Daly, 1982). Dart envenomation with poison frog secretions presumably dates
from pre-Colombian times by the Noanamá and Emberá Indians of South America
and persists today despite the advance of civilization (Märki and Witkop, 1963).
Synthetic compounds related closely to 223AB [16] represent a class of noncompetitive blockers of neuromuscular transmission (Daly and Spande, 1986).
An alkyl-substituted indolizidine, 239CD [17], causes long-lasting locomotor
difficulties and prostration after subcutaneous administration to mice (Daly
et al., 1978). The tricyclic gephyrotoxins (see Fig. 1) antagonize neuromuscular transmission and are relatively weak muscarinic antagonists (Daly and
Spande, 1986). A simple member of the pumiliotoxin A series, pumiliotoxin 251D [18], provided the key to structural elucidation of more complex pumiliotoxins, A [19] and B [20], although 251D's activity in potentiating frog muscle contraction was much less than that of its two congeners (Daly and Spande,
1986). Pumiliotoxin B and its relatives appear to exert selective effects on
nerve and muscle which are linked to apparent facilitation of evoked calcium
translocation across both plasma and internal membranes of calcium storage
organelles. This apparent facilitation of calcium translocation may be due to
pumiliotoxin B's ability to cause repetitive firing after stimulation of nerve
or muscle (Daly and Spande, 1986).

Disparate observations of excessive salivation ("slobbering") by midwestern U.S. farm animals following consumption of moldy forage, of *Swainsona* pea toxicity in Australian livestock, and of locoweed poisoning on western
U.S. rangelands has resulted in the isolation of several highly substituted
octahydroindolizidine alkaloids, which are the causative agents of these diseases. The alkaloid slaframine [21] was isolated and characterized from cultures of the fungus *Rhizoctonia leguminicola*, a contaminant of "slobber forage"
(Gardiner et al., 1968). A potent parasympathomimetic secretogogue, slaframine was found to be responsible for slobbering, lacrimation, diarrhea,
feed refusal, anorexia, and even death, associated with consumption of red
clover and other legume forages infected with *R. leguminicola* (Aust and Broquist, 1965; Rainey et al., 1965). Slaframine was shown to be a powerful
cholinergic stimulator of the exocrine glands, especially the salivary glands.

The solution of the *Swainsona* toxicity problem provides a classic example
of the application of several scientific disciplines to natural products research
(Chapter 9, this volume). *Swainsona* toxicity was recognized to be patho-

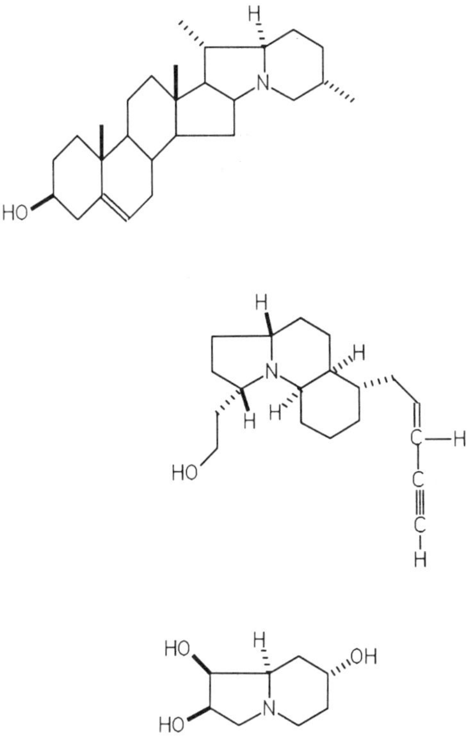

FIGURE 1 Some structurally diverse indolizidine alkaloids: (top to bottom) solanidine, gephyrotoxin [X-ray structure, see Daly et al. (1977)], and swainsonine.

logically and biochemically similar to mannosidosis, a lysosomal storage disease resulting from a genetic deficiency of the enzyme α-mannosidase (Dorling et al., 1978). Using this enzyme as a probe, the novel trihydroxyindolizidine alkaloid swainsonine [22] was isolated, identified, and shown to be a powerful inhibitor of lysosomal α-mannosidase (Colegate et al., 1979). This finding provided the impetus for the examination and subsequent isolation of swainsonine from spotted locoweed (*Astragalus lentiginosus*) which produce the "loco" syndrome in livestock (Molyneux and James, 1982). The locoweed toxin had remained unknown for over 70 years (Marsh, 1909) due, in part, to the polyhydroxyindolizidine's extreme water solubility, lack of a suitable chromophore for ultraviolet monitoring, and failure to react with standard alkaloid spray reagents (Molyneux et al., 1989). Swainsonine inhibits both major types of mammalian-α-D-mannosidases (acidic and intermediate) and some plant mannosidases (Elbein and Molyneux, 1987). It is quite specific in its inhibition of α-mannosidases and has been found to be without effect on β-mannosidase and various other glycosidases (Dorling et al., 1980; Kang and Elbein, 1983). A deficiency of lysosomal α-D-mannosidase manifests an accumulation of mannose-rich oligosaccharides in the lysosomal cellular system. The undigested sugars form foamy vacuolar inclusions which eventually disrupt cellular func-

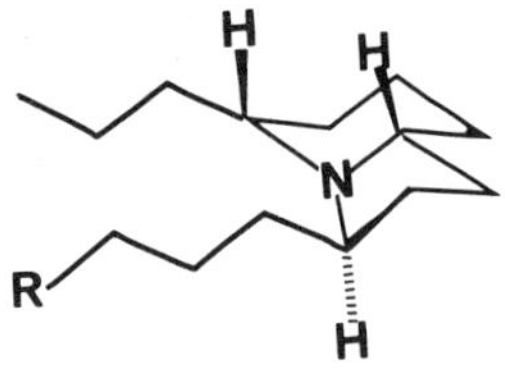

[16], 223 AB, R = -CH₃

[17], 239 CD, R = -CH₂OH

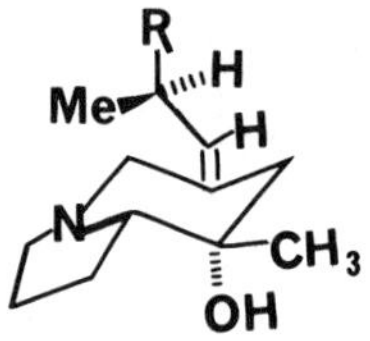

[18], 251 D, R = -CH₂CH₂CH₂CH₃

[19], A, R = -CH₂-CH = C-C-C₂H₅ (CH₃; HO H)

[20], B, R = -CH₂-CH = C-C-C-CH₃ (CH₃ OH; HO H)

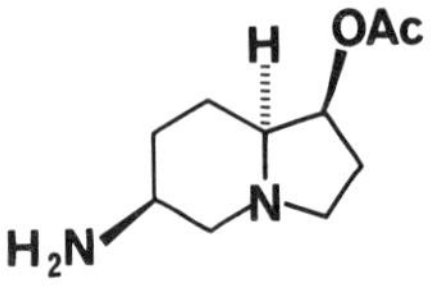

[21]

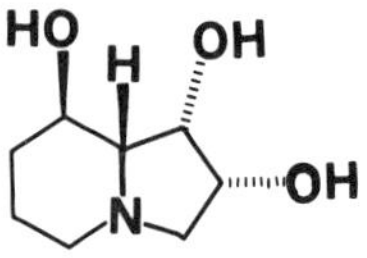

[22]

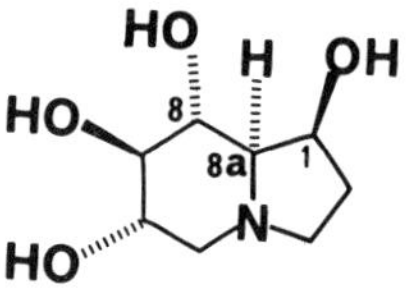

[23]

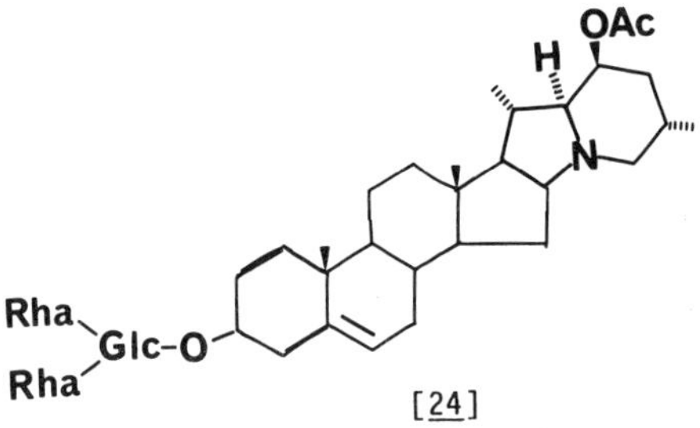

[24]

tion. Thus a phenocopy of the genetic lysosomal storage disease, α-mannosidosis, can result from the action of a single alkaloid, swainsonine, on a specific enzymatic locus.

Chestnut-like seeds produced by the Australian tree *Castanospermum australe* (Moreton Bay chestnut), which have been reported to be toxic to animals and to have caused gastrointestinal symptoms in early European settlers, yielded a toxic tetrahydroxyindolizidine alkaloid, castanospermine (Hohenschutz et al., 1981). Castanospermine [23], which is a less specific enzyme inhibitor than swainsonine, has the ability to inhibit both α- and β-lysosomal glucosidases and glucosidases I and II (Pan et al., 1983; Saul et al., 1983). The inhibition of glucosidase I, the initial processing glycosidase that removes the outermost glucose residue from the glycoprotein, disrupts N-linked glycoprotein biosynthesis and distribution, as does swainsonine, although by a different mechanism.

The toxic effects of several steroidal glycoalkaloids (and their aglycones) are relatively similar in the six species of animals studied, with α-chaconine [5] being most lethal and solasodine [8] least toxic (Morris and Lee, 1984). Glycoalkaloids appear to exhibit two toxic actions, one on cholinesterase affecting the nervous system (Orgell et al., 1958) and another affecting the gastrointestinal tract and general body metabolism (Harris and Cockburn, 1918). Solanine [4], leptine I [24], and chaconine [5] are strong inhibitors of human-plasma or eel cholinesterase, while tomatine [6] is only a weak inhibitor (Orgell, 1963; Bushway et al., 1987). This effect of glycoalkaloids on the nervous system could account for several of the neurological symptoms (drowsiness, apathy, confusion, weakness, depression, and unconsciousness) observed upon ingestion of glycoalkaloids. Another toxic effect exhibited by glycoalkaloids is related to their saponinlike properties. This results in disruption of membranes in the gastrointestinal tract and elsewhere that are characterized by hemolytic and hemorrhagic damage in addition to accumulation of excess fluid in body cavities (Harris and Cockburn, 1918; König and Staffe, 1953). Death of experimental animals from ingestion of either potato sprouts or major potato alkaloids (α-solanine, α-chaconine) has usually been attributed to central nervous system depression resulting from acetylcholinesterase inhibition (Morgan and Coxon, 1987). Recently, hamsters administered potato sprout material have been shown to develop severe gastric and proximal small intestinal mucosal necrosis accompanied by only slight acetylcholinesterase inhibition (Baker et al., 1988). Thus shock from fluid shifting, tissue necrosis, septicemia, and bacteremia are probably more important than acetylcholinesterase inhibition in producing death in hamsters administered potato sprouts (Chapter 5).

A considerable variation and selectivity exists between toxicity and teratogenicity among *Solanum* alkaloids (Table 1). Studies of spirosolanes in rats and hamsters have shown that solasodine [8] was teratogenic, in contrast to tomatidine [12] and diosgenin [25], a nonnitrogenous sapogenin analog of solasodine (Keeler et al., 1976). The absence of terata induction by diosgenin and tomatidine demonstrated that both the presence of the nitrogen in the F-ring and its configurational position with respect to the steroidal plane were critical for teratogenicity. Although terata were not observed upon dosing laboratory mammals with naturally occurring (22*R*,25*S*)-demissidine (5α-H [7]), malformations were induced in hamsters upon administration of a synthetic

TABLE 1 Toxicity and Teratogenicity of Steroidal Alkaloid
Glycosides and Their Aglycones

	Toxicity	Teratogenicity
Solasodine [8]	-	+
Solasodine glycoside ex *Solanum eleagnifolium*[a]	+	-
Tomatidine [12]	-	-
Tomatine [6]	+	-
(22R,25S)-Demissidine [5α-H [7]]	-	-
(22S,25R)-Solanidine [26]	-	+
α-Chaconine [5]	+	+
α-Solanine [4]	+	+

[a]See Chapter 6.
Sources: Keeler (1984, 1986) and Morris and Lee (1984).

epimer, (22S,25R)-solanidine [26] (Brown and Keeler, 1978). This teratogen
appears, on the basis of conformational analysis, to project the nitrogen lone
pair of electrons below the steroidal plant (i.e., alpha) in concordance with
other teratogenic *Veratrum* and spirosolane alkaloids (Keeler, 1984, 1986).
Conversely, the naturally occurring (22R,25S)-solanidanes project the lone
pair of electrons above the steroidal plane (i.e., beta; see [27]) (Brown and
Keeler, 1978; Brown, 1978). Thus the conclusion (Renwick et al., 1984) that
potato sprout teratogenicity can be solely accounted for by the presence of
α-solanine and α-chaconine (presumably of 22R,25S configuration) is at vari-
ance with simple expectations based on the teratogenicity of epimeric solanidanes. A complete description of *Solanum* teratogenicity is provided in Chapter 6 of this volume.

IV. MODE OF ACTION OF TOXIC INDOLIZIDINE ALKALOIDS

Although extensive research has been conducted on the toxic and pharmacologic properties of organic compounds, the elucidation of the mechanism of
action of these varied agents, particularly at the molecular level, is extremely
difficult due to the chemical, physical, and metabolic complexities of living
systems. Many of the toxic and pharmacologic effects of organic compounds
appear to result from noncovalent, and thus reversible, interactions with cellular components or molecules. However, in the past 30 years the toxic manifestations of many genotoxic agents, some allergens, and certain drugs have
often arisen from covalent interactions of the compounds or their metabolites
with cellular macromolecules. Identification of the products of these reactions
has revealed that the reactive forms of these structurally diverse agents are
electrophilic. An example of alkaloids that by themselves are not toxic but

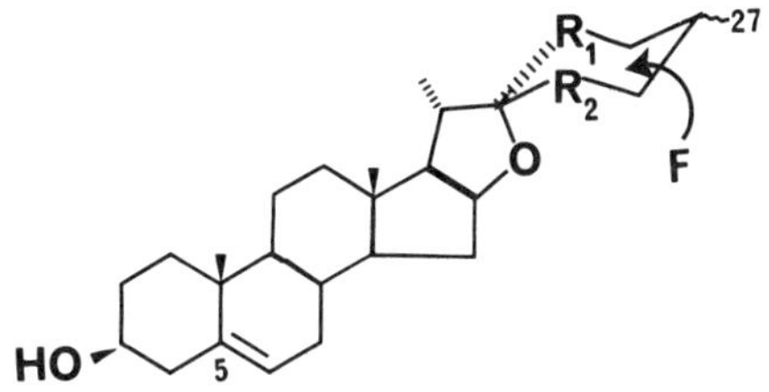

	R_1	R_2		C-27
SOLASODINE [8]	NH	CH_2		α
TOMATIDINE [12]	CH_2	NH	(5α-H)	α
DIOSGENIN [25]	CH_2	O		β

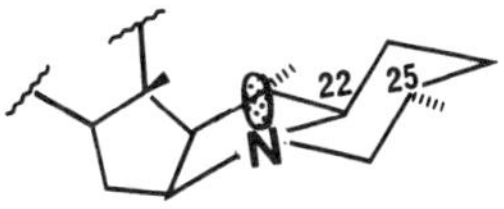

NITROGEN β
22R, 25S-SOLANIDANES
[27]

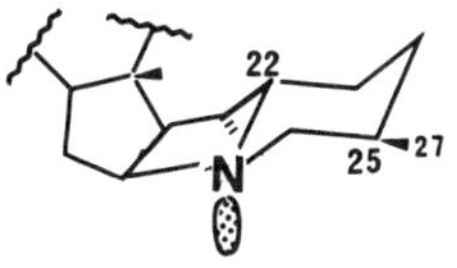

NITROGEN α
22S,25R-SOLANIDANES
[26]

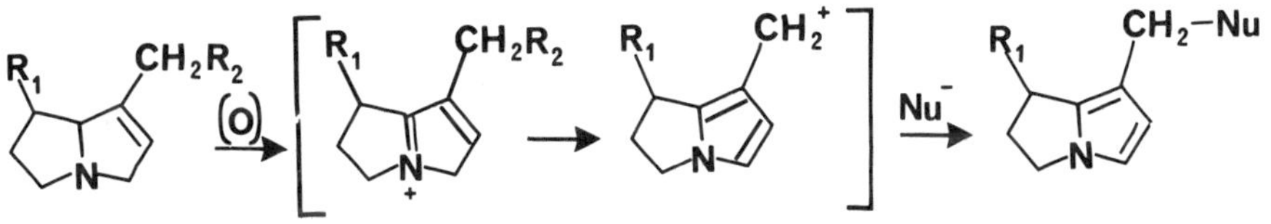

[28]

which upon bioactivation generate a toxic metabolite are the pyrrolizidine alkaloids. These bicyclic compounds, with a fused 5/5 ring system, undergo oxidation by liver multifunction oxidases to the corresponding pyrrole, which
upon hydrolysis produces a highly alkylating (electrophilic) exocyclic methylene group [28] that can react with cellular nucleophiles (Nu = nucleophile)
(Mattocks and White, 1971; White and Mattocks, 1971). Multifunction oxidases
are normally responsible for detoxification processes of the liver, and the
generation of toxic pyrrole from a nontoxic pyrrolizidine appears to be an
unfortunate metabolic consequence.

A significant induction period, which is required before salivary and pancreatic excretion occurs following slaframine administration, led to evidence
that bioactivation of slaframine was necessary for expression of activity (Aust,
1969). A rat liver microsomal system requiring NADPH and flavoprotein oxidase acts on slaframine to yield a 6-ketoimine [29], thought to be the active
compound (Guengerich and Aust, 1977). Iminium ion [29] bears a close structural relationship to the acetylcholine ion [30] because an alkylated quaternary nitrogen atom and an acetyl ester are separated by two adjacent carbon
atoms, C1 and C8a. Activated slaframine apparently binds to muscarinic
acetylcholine receptors.

[29]   [30]

[31]   [32]

JERVINE [33], R = O
CYCLOPAMINE [34], R = H₂

[7]   [35]   [36]

H⁻ or CN⁻

A pharmacophore, or common electronic message, incorporates a specific arrangement of essential chemical groups common to bioactive molecules that is recognized by a single receptor. The concept of a pharmacophore is useful in developing and testing hypotheses about which chemical groups are important for a specific biological activity and what the three-dimensional arrangement of these groups is in the receptor bound or "active" conformation of each molecule. The determination of the pharmacophore requires the initial examination of each three-dimensional pattern of candidate functional groups

which results from an energetically accessible conformation. Each active analog must be capable of presenting a pattern that appears in the set of possible
patterns determined for each compound. One plausible explanation for biological inactivity arises when an inactive compound, capable of presenting
the pharmacophore, requires a novel volume. Part of this novel volume may
be occupied by the receptor and may preclude binding of the compound in
question. Such an explanation can rationalize the different activities of enantiomers.

Swainsonine, which has been referred to as a "sugar impersonator" (Fellows, 1985), does not require metabolic activation in order to express its bioactivity. The inhibitory activity of swainsonine has been speculated to result
from the structural similarity of its protonated form [31] to the mannosyl cation [32] (Dorling et al., 1980). The absolute configuration of swainsonine
supports this contention because C2, C1, and C8a of [31] are equivalent to
C2, C3, and C5, respectively, of [32]. The close relationship of the two
structures would appear to satisfy geometric requirements for recognition by
the active site of the enzyme, resulting in enzyme-substrate reaction. Castanospermine, [23], whose substitution pattern resembles swainsonine about
C1, C8, and C8a, is a glucose analog and a specific glucosidase inhibitor.

Because some of the diverse species (insects, fungi, nematodes, animals,
humans) susceptible to glycoalkaloid toxicity do not possess mechanisms to
activate xenobiotics, *Solanum* glycoalkaloids probably exert their toxic effects
directly on the organisms (Jadhav et al., 1981; Morris and Lee, 1984). In
fact, certain pathogenic fungi are insensitive to glycoalkaloids, due to their
ability to metabolize them into innocuous compounds (Holland and Taylor, 1979;
Arneson and Durbin, 1967). Although many reports indicate that solanine
and chaconine may protect plants from their predators through unpalatable
taste and anticholinesterase activity, the fungistatic/fungicidal effects of the
two alkaloids in vitro result from complexation with membrane sterols leading
to destabilization and the formation of pores in strategic membranes (Roddick,
1987). Tomatine presumably attacks membranes as a weak surfactant by virtue of its amphipathic properties before complexing with 3β-hydroxysterols.
The sterol-binding hypothesis gained acceptance when 1:1 molecular complexes
were formed in vitro between tomatine, or other glycoalkaloids and saponins,
and 3β-hydroxysterols abundant in animal cells (cholesterol), fungal cells
(ergosterol), and plant cells (sitosterol) (Schulz and Sander, 1957). Because
the ratios of solanine and chaconine found in potato tissue (about 65% chaconine in tubers and about 75% chaconine in shoots) are those most effective
against animal and fungal membranes, the resultant synergism between the
two glycoalkaloids in disrupting membranes may explain the apparent dilemma
of considerable material and energy resources of the plant being channeled
into the synthesis of solanine although it is biologically less active than chaconine (Roddick et al., 1988).

Prominent gross and histopathologic effects observed upon administration
to hamsters of several solanaceous plants included gastric glandular necrosis
and small intestinal mucosal necrosis (Baker et al., 1989). Lesions produced
in hamsters by solasodine glycoside containing plants *S. dulcamara* and *S.
eleagnifolium* were identical to lesions resulting from *S. tuberosum* sprout
material, suggesting that the steroidal alkaloid toxins acted directly on the
glandular mucosa of the stomach and small intestine without undergoing meta-

bolic activation (Baker et al., 1989). Thus induction of both death, and gastric and intestinal necrosis, are not confined to ingestion of solanidane glycosides (Baker et al., 1988) but may also result from spirosolane glycosides.

After extensive research, epidemics of cyclopia and related congenital deformities (hypoplastic maxilla and premaxilla, pronounced mandibular curvature, cebocephaly, and brain tissue deposits) in sheep were established to result from ingestion of the toxic range plant *Veratrum californicum* (false hellebore) on the fourteenth day of gestation (Binns et al., 1965). A direct teratogenic insult on the embryo by parent alkaloid, rather than a metabolite, was shown by the susceptibility of both jervine [33] and cyclopamine [34]-treated chick embryos as well as sheep embryos from ewes administered jervine or cyclopamine by intrauterine injection (Bryden et al., 1973; Bryden and Keeler, 1973).

Environmentally produced terata inductions share certain common features: stage sensitivity, dose-response relationships, threshold effects, and genetic variability. Mechanisms of teratogenesis may include interference with normal cell migration, programmed cell death, and differentiation, in addition to destruction or delay of progenitor lines. Among the problems involved in understanding a particular teratogenesis are the qualitative identification of species-specific metabolites, the quantitative estimation of the teratogenic potential of each parent compound and its individual metabolites, and the quantitative estimation of the species-specific pharmacokinetic parameters. Even after over 25 years of intensive investigation of thalidomide-induced phocomelia, the mechanism of embryopathy of this widely studied teratogen is still controversial, and 16 proposed hypotheses (Table 2) remain untested by either rigorous experimental or observational methods (Stephens, 1988).

Two postulated mechanisms of action have been proposed for jervine- and cyclopamine-induced teratogenesis. Because of cyclopamine's potent inhibition of catecholamine release mediated by the nicotine cholinergic receptor, interaction between cyclopamine and the acetylcholine receptor has been proposed as a mechanism for *Veratrum* teratogenicity (Sim et al., 1985). In more extensive research on inhibition of proteoglycan synthesis, the production of limb defects by jervine, the specific nature of which is dependent on the developmental stage of embryonic exposure, has been studied. Jervine compromises rapidly developing chondrogenic precursors, showing these adverse effects before and during chondrogenesis but not afterward. Jervine's teratogenic effects do not directly alter the synthesis of cartilage-specific products but instead prevent formation of cartilage rudiments by extensively damaging the rapidly multiplying precursor cells for these structures (Campbell et al., 1985, 1987).

Terata expression differences between known *Veratrum* teratogens (cyclopamine and jervine) and proposed *Solanum* teratogens (spirosolanes and solanidanes) suggest that the two groups of alkaloids may be binding to different receptor sites. Whereas *Veratrum* teratogens induce a high incidence of cebocephalics (Keeler et al., 1978), deformities in offspring from hamsters administered various *Solanum* species were expressed generally as exencephaly or encephalocele or occasionally as cebocephaly and hare lip (Keeler et al., 1990). Variation in either absorption or clearance rates could produce a shift in insult timing to cause terata expression or pattern variation, and structurally similar teratogens can produce dissimilar deformities by altering differ-

TABLE 2 Proposed Thalidomide Mechanisms of Action[a]

Biochemical mechanisms
   B-vitamin antagonism
   Interference with glutamic acid metabolism
   Chelation of bivalent cations or accumulation of polar
     metabolites
   Pteroylglutamic acid antagonism
   Acylation
   Nucleic acid synthesis
   Intercalation into DNA
   Uncoupler of oxidative phosphorylation
   Cycloheximide-like inhibition of protein synthesis

Cellular mechanisms
   Cell death
   Cell-cell interactions

Tissue- and organ-level mechanisms
   Axial limb artery degeneration
   A "more primitive paw pattern"
   Faulty chondrification and calcification
   Decreased mesonephric induction of chondrogenesis
   Direct effect on the limb bud

[a]See Stephens (1988).

ent sequential reactions present in the lengthy reaction sequences involved in the formation of morphologic features.

Because of the high dam toxicity and lack of terata induced upon administration of tomatine as well as the solasodine glycoside from *S. eleagnifolium* to hamsters compared to high teratogenicity and lack of toxicity observed with solasodine, dam toxicity is clearly not responsible for *Solanum* teratogenicity (see Chapter 6). Whether the craniofacial defects produced by solanidanes and spirosolanes [including spirosolane-containing *Solanum* species (Keeler et al., 1990)] are mechanistically related must await both confirmation of *S. tuberosum* (potato) teratogenicity due to α-solanine and α-chaconine, where C22, C25 stereoisomeric integrity is established, and definitive structural determination of the highly toxic and teratogenic spirosolanes from wild *Solanum* species. Alternative suggestions regarding possible minor plant constituents or indolizidine metabolites are presented in the following section.

V. POTENTIAL TERATOGENIC METABOLITES OR MINOR CONSTITUENTS OF *SOLANUM* SPECIES

Subtle stereoselectivity of mammalian teratogenicity compared to toxicity is dramatically emphasized by the malformations induced in hamsters upon ingestion of solasodine and (22S,25R)-solanidine, in contrast to their stereoisomeric analogs tomatidine and (22R,25S)-solanidine (i.e., demissidine), respectively

(Table 1). On the other hand, both of the spirosolanes and both solanidines are nontoxic at the dosages tested. Although metabolic activation does not appear to be required for *Solanum* alkaloid teratogens to express their biological effects, several oxidative transformations could conceivably occur either in vivo or in the plant which might result in the formation of minor teratogenic components. Potential products of indolizidine oxidation include iminium ions, C-hydroxylated indolizidines, and indolizidine N-oxides.

Iminium ions have been chemically generated from solanidanes (e.g., solanidine [7]) upon reaction with either mercuric acetate or N-bromosuccinimide, yielding primarily the $\Delta^{22,N}$ ion [36] (Screiber and Horstmann, 1966). Conversion of the naturally occurring 22R-solanidine into an iminium ion upon biological oxidation offers the potential, upon reduction, of producing the 22S epimer. However, a reducing agent approaching from the β-side of the steroid encounters significant congestion, particularly from the C18 methyl group, clearly favoring regeneration of the 22R-solanidine. Nucleophilic addition of either hydride (Adam et al., 1967) or cyanide (Schreiber and Horstmann, 1966) to the $\Delta^{22,N}$ iminium ion of solanidine gave 22α substitution in each instance. Even if biological oxidation-reduction produced (22S,25S)-solanidine with an α-projecting nitrogen atom (i.e., [26] with αC27), the fact remains that the incidence of birth anomalies observed in hamsters treated with this alkaloid was insignificant (Brown and Keeler, 1978). Low activity was suggested to result from shielding of the nonbonding electron pair by 1,3-diaxial interactions with both the C27 and C21 methyl groups, resulting in a nitrogen less accessible to binding sites. Epimeric solanidanes of unspecified stereochemistry have been reported to occur in European potato cultivars (Van Gelder et al., 1987). Additional C-22, C-25 isomers of steroidal indolizidines, such as solanogantine [37] (3β-NH_2,5α-H) (Pakrashi et al., 1977), solanogantamine [38] (3β-NH_2,5α-H) and isosolanogantamine [38] (3α-NH_2, 5α-H) (Chakravarty et al., 1984) have been isolated from the Indian medicinal plant *S. giganteum*.

Two iminium ions, neither of which has been isolated but whose existence has been inferred from deuterium labeling studies, have been considered plausible intermediates in the final stages of swainsonine biosynthesis (Harris et al., 1988). One of these, [39], may provide the substrate onto which the 8-hydroxy group is introduced. Thus, a dehydroindolizidine iminium ion of a steroidal glycoalkaloid could be positioned to undergo β-oxidation similar to that postulated to occur in simple polyhydroxylated indolizidines.

A glycoside of 23β-hydroxysolanidine, [40], has been obtained upon oxidation of solanidine with microsomal fractions from *Solanum* leaves after addition of NADPH (Osman et al., 1987). Certain accessions of *S. chacoense* contain, in addition to solanine and chaconine, leptines (cf. [24]) and leptinidines (Schreiber, 1968). The 23-acetoxy-substituted forms (leptines) of the more common *Solanum* glycoalkaloids, which have not been detected in tubers but occur primarily in plant foliage, are potent feeding deterrents for insect pests such as the Colorado potato beetle (Sinden et al., 1986).

In view of the possible presence of 23β-hydroxylated steroidal glycoalkaloids, either as in vivo metabolites or minor plant constituents, consideration of the β-hydroxyamines as potential teratogens is warranted because of the following observations: (1) the occurrence of birth defects in range animals upon consumption of swainsonine containing *Astragalus* species (Molyneux

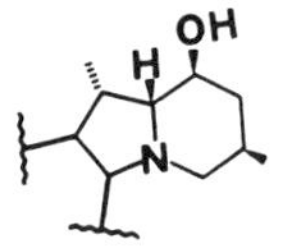

[37]

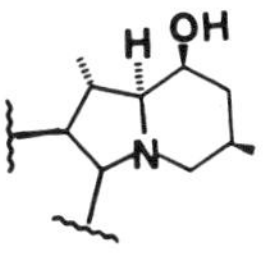

[38]

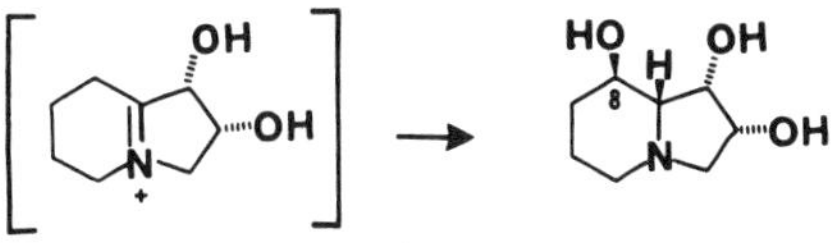

[39]

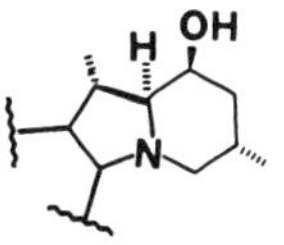

[40] 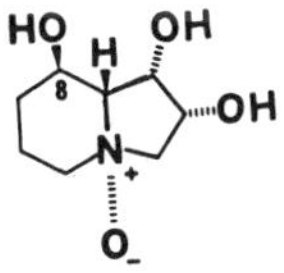   [41] 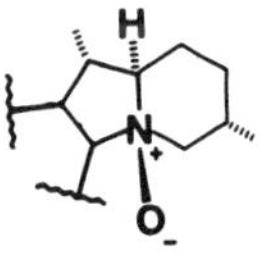   [42]

et al., 1985); (2) the conclusion that α-substituted piperidines bearing a three-carbon fragment are potential teratogens (Keeler and Crowe, 1985); and (3) the greater hydrophilicity of 23-hydroxy and 23-acetoxy steroidal glycoalkaloids, which could result in greater fetal absorption and distribution [e.g., α-solanine and α-chaconine are reported to be teratogenic (Renwick et al., 1984), in contrast to the aglycone demissidine (Brown and Keeler, 1978)].

Amine N-oxides are often hygroscopic, unstable compounds that rapidly yield intractable products, making their isolation and characterization difficult. Frequently, they are hard to detect either due to their lack of reaction with chromatographic spray reagents or to the weak molecular ions produced in their mass spectra because of thermal deoxygenation at normal probe temperatures (Molyneux, 1988; Bremer and Van Thuc, 1980). Although amine N-oxides are considerably less lipophilic and more water soluble than are their corresponding free bases and are usually regarded as detoxification products, the natural occurrence of N-oxides in plants and the role of N-oxidation in animal metabolism has posed intriguing questions concerning their biochemistry and function. Thus in *Senecio* spp. the highly polar N-oxides, which are often present in greater quantities than the free amine, appear to be the molecular form by which the pyrrolizidine alkaloids are synthesized, translocated, and accumulated (Toppel et al., 1988). Furthermore, the N-oxide form of the pyrrolizidine alkaloid riddelliine is capable of producing typical *Senecio* toxicosis in cattle and the total alkaloid content of the plant, representing both free base and N-oxide rather than free base alone, is the determining factor in the toxicity of *S. riddelli* (Molyneux et al., 1990).

Indolizidines with fused 6/5 rings, such as swainsonine and solanidanes, could theoretically invert during N-oxide formation, although such a transformation should be energetically unfavorable, so that the N-oxide of swainsonine [41] probably exists in a trans relationship to the bridgehead hydrogen, as does the nitrogen lone pair (Molyneux and James, 1982; Molyneux et al., 1985). Preliminary studies have suggested that swainsonine N-oxide may inhibit α-mannosidase (Molyneux and James, 1982). Because swainsonine acts as an inhibitor in its protonated form, which bears close structural similarities to the mannosyl cation, swainsonine N-oxide can be regarded as an ionized species. The cation would be structurally identical in the protonated base and the N-oxide (Molyneux et al., 1985). Although *Solanum* alkaloid N-oxides have not been isolated, the saltlike derivatives have been synthesized from solanidan-3β-ol [42] and Δ^2-solanidine (Briggs et al., 1950; Szpilfogel, 1951). Biological evaluation of solanidane N-oxides could provide insight into whether or not replacement of the β-projecting electron pair with a polar oxygen atom on the S-tertiary nitrogen atom affects teratogenic properties of steroidal glycoalkaloids.

VI. EPILOGUE

The biological properties and mode of action of several toxic indolizidine alkaloids, some of whose effects are better understood than those of toxic and teratogenic *Solanum* alkaloids, have been presented. If a pathologic condition or morphologic event could be correlated with a biochemical probe, the resulting bioassay should facilitate isolation and structural determination of key bioactive *Solanum* alkaloids. Detailed study and comparison of the action and effects of toxic and teratogenic agents of established structure increase the potential for utilizing such compounds in experiments designed to recognize specific morphologic events at very early developmental stages.

REFERENCES

Adam, G., Horstmann, C., and Schrieber, K. (1967). Photochemische Reaktionen: IX. Notiz zur stereospezifischen Photoreduktion von Steroid-Imoniumverbindungen. *Chem. Ber. 100*:1753-1655.

Arneson, P. A., and Durbin, R. D. (1967). Hydrolysis of tomatine by *Septoria lycopersici*: a detoxification mechanism. *Phytopathology 57*:1358-1360.

Aust, S. D. (1969). Evidence for the bioactivation of slaframine. *Biochem. Pharmacol. 18*:929-932.

Aust, S. D., and Broquist, H. P. (1965). Isolation of a parasympathomimetic alkaloid of fungal origin. *Nature 205*:204.

Baker, D. C., Keeler, R. F., and Gaffield, W. (1988). Mechanism of death in Syrian hamsters gavaged potato sprout material. *Toxicol. Pathol. 16*:333-339.

Baker, D. C., Keeler, R. F., and Gaffield, W. (1989). Pathology in hamsters administered *Solanum* plant species that contain steroidal alkaloids. *Toxicon. 27*:1331-1337.

Baup, M. (1826). Extrait d'une lettre sur plusieurs nouvelles substances. *Ann. Chim. Phys. 31*:108-109.

Binns, W., Shupe, J. L., Keeler, R. F., and James, L. F. (1965). Chronologic evaluation of teratogenicity in sheep fed *Veratrum californicum*. *J. Am. Vet. Med. Assoc. 147*:839-842.

Bremer, J. B., and Van Thuc, L. (1980). The characterization and thermolysis of *cis*- and *trans*-(±)laudanosine *N*-oxide. *Aust. J. Chem. 33*:379-394.

Briggs, L. H., Harvey, W. E., Locker, R. H., McGillivray, W. A., and Seelye, R. N. (1950). Solanum alkaloids: V. Solasodine. *J. Chem. Soc.* 3013-3020.

Broquist, H. P. (1985). The indolizidine alkaloids, slaframine and swainsonine: contaminants in animal forages. *Annu. Rev. Nutr. 5*:391-409.

Brown, D. (1978). Structure-activity relation of steroidal amine teratogens. In *Effects of Poisonous Plants on Livestock*, R. F. Keeler, K. R. Van Kampen, and L. F. James (Eds.). Academic Press, New York, pp. 409-418.

Brown, D., and Keeler, R. F. (1978). Structure-activity relation of steroid teratogens: 3. Solanidan epimers. *J. Agric. Food Chem. 26*:566-569.

Bryden, M. M., and Keeler, R. F. (1973). Effects of alkaloids of *Veratrum californicum* on developing embryos. *J. Anat. 116*:464.

Bryden, M. M., Perry, C., and Keeler, R. F. (1973). Effects of alkaloids of *Veratrum californicum* on chick embryos. *Teratology 8*:19-27.

Bushway, R. J., Savage, S. A., and Ferguson, B. S. (1987). Inhibition of acetyl cholinesterase by solanaceous glycoalkaloids and alkaloids. *Am. Potato J. 64*:409-413.

Campbell, M. A., Brown, K. S., Hassell, J. R., Horigan, E. A., and Keeler, R. F. (1985). Inhibition of limb chondrogenesis by a *Veratrum* alkaloid: temporal specificity in vivo and in vitro. *Dev. Biol. 111*:464-470.

Campbell, M. A., Horton, W., and Keeler, R. (1987). Comparative effects of retinoic acid and jervine on chondrocyte differentiation. *Teratology 36*:235-243.

Chakravarty, A. K., Das, B., Ali, E., and Pakrashi, S. C. (1984). Studies on Indian medicinal plants: Part 77. Structure and stereochemistry of some new steroidal alkaloids from *Solanum pseudocapsicum* and *Solanum giganteum* by nuclear magnetic resonance spectroscopy. *J. Chem. Soc. Perkin Trans. 1*:467-474.

Colegate, S. M., Dorling, P. R., and Huxtable, C. R. (1979). A spectroscopic investigation of swainsonine: an α-mannosidase inhibitor isolated from *Swainsona canescens*. *Aust. J. Chem. 32*:2257-2264.

Craig, L. C., and Jacobs, W. A. (1943). The veratrine alkaloids: XX. Further correlations in the veratrine group: the relationship between the veratrine bases and solanidine. *J. Biol. Chem. 149*:451-464.

Daly, J. W. (1982). Alkaloids of neotropical poison frogs (*Dendrobatidae*). In *Progress in the Chemistry of Organic Natural Products*, Vol. 41, W. Herz, H. Grisebach, and G. W. Kirby (Eds.). Springer-Verlag, Berlin, pp. 205-340.

Daly, J. W., and Spande, T. F. (1986). Amphibian alkaloids: chemistry, pharmacology, and biology. In *Alkaloids: Chemical and Biological Perspectives*, Vol. 4, S. W. Pelletier (Ed.). Wiley, New York, pp. 1-274.

Daly, J. W., Witkop, B., Tokuyama, T., Nishikawa, T., and Karle, I. L. (1977). Gephyrotoxins, histrionicotoxins and pumiliotoxins from the neotropical frog *Dendrobates histrionicus*. *Helv. Chim. Acta 60*:1128-1140.

Daly, J. W., Brown, G. B., Mensah-Dwumah, M., and Myers, C. W. (1978). Classification of skin alkaloids from neotropical poison-dart frogs (*Dendrobatidae*). *Toxicon. 16*:163-188.

Desfosses, M. (1821). Examen du principe narcotique de la Morelle (*Solanum nigrum*), etc. *J. Pharm. 7*:414-417.

Dorling, P. R., Huxtable, C. R., and Vogel, P. (1978). Lysosomal storage in *Swainsona* spp. toxicosis: an induced mannosidosis. *Neuropathol. Appl. Neurobiol. 4*:285-295.

Dorling, P. R., Huxtable, C. R., and Colegate, S. M. (1980). Inhibition of lysosomal α-mannosidase by swainsonine, an indolizidine alkaloid isolated from *Swainsona canescens*. *Biochem. J. 191*:649-651.

Elbein, A. D., and Molyneux, R. J. (1987). The chemistry and biochemistry of simple indolizidine and related polyhydroxy alkaloids. In *Alkaloids: Chemical and Biological Perspectives*, Vol. 5, S. W. Pelletier (Ed.). Wiley, New York, pp. 1-54.

Fellows, L. (1985). The sugar-shaped weapons of plants. *New Sci.* (1469): 40-41.

Gardiner, R. A., Rinehart, K. L., Jr., Snyder, J. J., and Broquist, H. P. (1968). Slaframine: absolute stereochemistry and a revised structure. *J. Am. Chem. Soc. 90*:5639-5640.

Guengerich, F. P., and Aust, S. D. (1977). Activation of the parasympathomimetic alkaloid slaframine by microsomal and photochemical oxidation. *Mol. Pharmacol. 13*:185-195.

Harris, F. W. and Cockburn, T. (1918). Alleged poisoning by potatoes. *Analyst 43*:133-137.

Harris, C. M., Schneider, M. J., Ungemach, F. S., Hill, J. E., and Harris, T. M. (1988). Biosynthesis of the toxic indolizidine alkaloids slaframine and swainsonine in *Rhizoctonia leguminicola*: metabolism of 1-hydroxy-indolizidines. *J. Am. Chem. Soc. 110*:940-949.

Hegnauer, R. (1963). The taxonomic significance of alkaloids. In *Chemical Plant Taxonomy*, T. Swain (Ed.). Academic Press, New York, pp. 389-427.

Highet, R. J., and Wheeler, J. W. (1985). The study of alkaloid structures by spectral methods. In *The Alkaloids*, Vol. 24, A. Brossi (Ed.). Academic Press, New York, pp. 287-348.

Hohenschutz, L. D., Bell, E. A., Jewess, P. J., Leworthy, D. P., Pryce, R. J., Arnold, E., and Clardy, J. (1981). Castanospermine, a 1,6,7,8-tetrahydroxyoctahydroindolizidine alkaloid, from seeds of *Castanospermum australe*. *Phytochemistry 20*:811-814.

Hohne, E., Schreiber, K., Ripperger, H., and Worch, H.-H. (1966). *Solanum* Alkaloide: LX. Röntgenstruckturanalyse von Demissidin-hydrojodid zur absoluten Konfiguration der Solanidane und 22,26-Iminocholestane an C-22. *Tetrahedron 22*:673-678.

Holland, H. L., and Taylor, G. J. (1979). Transformations of steroids and the steroidal alkaloid, solanine, by *Phytophthora infestans*. *Phytochemistry 18*:437-440.

Jadhav, S. J., Sharma, R. P., and Salunkhe, D. K. (1981). Naturally occurring toxic alkaloids in foods. *Crit. Rev. Toxicol. 9*:21-104.

Kang, M. S., and Elbein, A. D. (1983). Mechanism of inhibition of jack bean α-mannosidase by swainsonine. *Plant Physiol. 71*:551-554.

Keeler, R. F. (1984). Mammalian teratogenicity of steroidal alkaloids. In *Isopentenoids in Plants: Biochemistry and Function*, W. D. Nes, G. Fuller, and L.-S. Tsai (Eds.). Marcel Dekker, New York, pp. 531-562.

Keeler, R. F. (1986). Teratology of steroidal alkaloids. In *Alkaloids: Chemical and Biological Perspectives*, Vol. 4, S. W. Pelletier (Ed.). Wiley, New York, pp. 389-425.

Keeler, R. F., and Crowe, M. W. (1985). Anabasine, a teratogen form the *Nicotiana* genus. In *Plant Toxicology*, A. A. Seawright, M. P. Hegarty, L. F. James, and R. F. Keeler (Eds.). Queensland Poisonous Plant Committee, Yeerongpilly, Australia, pp. 324-333.

Keeler, R. F., Young, S., and Brown, D. (1976). Spina bifida, exencephaly, and cranial bleb produced in hamsters by the *Solanum* alkaloid solasodine. *Res. Commun. Chem. Pathol. Pharmacol. 13:*723-730.

Keeler, R. F., Young, S., Brown, D., Stallknecht, G. F., and Douglas, D. (1978). Congenital deformities produced in hamsters by potato sprouts. *Teratology 17:*327-334.

Keeler, R. F., Baker, D. C., and Gaffield, W. (1990). Spirosolane-containing *Solanum* species and induction of congenital craniofacial malformations. *Toxicon* (in press).

König, H., and Staffe, A. (1953). Action of solanine upon blood pressure and blood catalase of sheep. *Dtsch. Tieraerztl. Wochenschr. 60:*150-153.

Kuhn, R., and Löw, I. (1954). Die Konstitution des Solanins. *Angew. Chem. 66:*639-640.

Märki, F., and Witkop, B. (1963). The venom of the Colombian arrow poison frog *Phyllobates bicolor. Experientia 19:*329-338.

Marsh, C. D. (1909). *The locoweed disease of the plains*, Bull. No. 112. U.S. Department of Agriculture, Bureau of Animal Industry, Washington, D.C., pp. 1-130.

Mattocks, A. R., and White, I. N. H. (1971). Conversion of pyrrolizidine alkaloids to *N*-oxides and to dihydropyrrolizidine derivatives by rat-liver microsomes in vitro. *Chem.-Biol. Interact. 3:*383-396.

Molyneux, R. J. (1988). The chemistry of pyrrolizidine and indolizidine alkaloids and their role as constituents of toxic range plants. *Rev. Latinoam. Quim. 19:*135-141.

Molyneux, R. J., and James, L. F. (1982). Loco intoxication: indolizidine alkaloids of spotted locoweed (*Astragalus lentiginosus*). *Science 216:*190-191.

Molyneux, R. J., James, L. F., and Panter, K. E. (1985). Chemistry of toxic constituents of locoweed (*Astragalus* and *Oxytropis*) species. In *Plant Toxicology*, A. A. Seawright, M. P. Hegarty, L. F. James, and R. F. Keeler (Eds.). Queensland Poisonous Plant Committee, Yeerongpilly, Australia, pp. 266-278.

Molyneux, R. J., James, L. F., Panter, K. E., and Ralphs, M. (1989). The occurrence and detection of swainsonine in locoweeds. In *Swainsonine and Related Glycosidase Inhibitors*, L. F. James, A. D. Elbein, R. J. Molyneux, and C. D. Warren (Eds.). Iowa State University Press, Ames, IA, pp. 100-117.

Molyneux, R. J., Johnson, A. E., Olsen, J. D., and Baker, D. C. (1990). Toxicity of pyrrolizidine alkaloids from Riddell's groundsel (*Senecio riddellii*) to cattle. *Amer. J. Vet. Res.* (in press).

Morgan, M. R. A., and Coxon, D. T. (1987). Tolerances: glycoalkaloids in potatoes. In *Natural Toxicants in Food: Progress and Prospects*, D. H. Watson (Ed.). Ellis Horwood, New York, pp. 221-230.

Morris, S. C., and Lee, T. H. (1984). The toxicity and teratogenicity of solanaceae glycoalkaloids, particularly those of the potato (*Solanum tuberosum*): a review. *Food Technol. Aust.* 36:118-124.

Oddo, G., and Colombano, A. (1905). Ueber die Producte, die man aus *Solanum sodomaeum* Linn. extrahirt. *Chem. Ber.* 38:2755-2758.

Orgell, W. H. (1963). Inhibition of human plasma cholinesterase in vitro by alkaloids, glycosides and other natural substances. *Lloydia* 26:36-43.

Orgell, W. H., Vaidya, K. A., and Dahm, P. A. (1958). Inhibition of human plasma cholinesterase in vitro by extracts of solanaceous plants. *Science* 128:1136-1137.

Osman, S., Sinden, S. L., Deahl, K., and Moreau, R. (1987). The metabolism of solanidine by microsomal fractions from *Solanum chacoense*. *Phytochemistry* 26:3163-3165.

Pakrashi, S. C., Chakravarty, A. K., and Ali, E. (1977). Solanogantine, a novel 3-amino-22βH-solanidane from *Solanum giganteum*. *Tetrahedron Lett.* 7:645-648.

Pan, Y. T., Hori, H., Saul, R., Sanford, B. A., Molyneux, R. J., and Elbein, A. D. (1983). Castanospermine inhibits the processing of the oligosaccharide portion of the influenza viral hemagglutinin. *Biochemistry* 22:3975-3984.

Pelletier, S. W. (1983). The nature and definition of an alkaloid. In *Alkaloids: Chemical and Biological Perspectives*, Vol. 1, S. W. Pelletier (Ed.). Wiley, New York, pp. 1-31.

Prelog, V., and Jeger, O. (1953). The chemistry of *Solanum* and *Veratrum* alkaloids. In *The Alkaloids*, Vol. 3, R. H. F. Manske and H. L. Holmes (Eds.). Academic Press, New York, pp. 247-312.

Prelog, V., and Szpilfogel, S. (1942). Uber Steroide und Sexualhormone: 79. Uber das 2-Athyl-5-methyl-pyridin, ein Dehydrierungsprodukt des Solanidins. *Helv. Chim. Acta* 25:1306-1313.

Prelog, V., and Szpilfogel, S. (1944). Steroide und Sexualhormone: 92. Uber die Stereoisomeren Dihydrosolanidine. *Helv. Chim. Acta* 27:390-400.

Price, K. R., Johnson, I. T., and Fenwick, G. R. (1987). The chemistry and biological significance of saponins in foods and feedingstuffs. *Crit. Rev. Food Sci. Nutr.* 26:27-135.

Rainey, D. P., Smalley, E. B., Crump, M. H., and Strong, F. M. (1965). Isolation of salivation factor from *Rhizoctonia leguminicola* on red clover hay. *Nature* 205:203-204.

Rasmusson, G. H., Reynolds, G. F., Steinberg, N. G., Walton, E., Patel, G. F., Liang, T., Cascieri, M. A., Cheung, A. H., Brooks, J. R., and Berman, C. (1986). Azasteroids: Structure-activity relationships for inhibition of 5α-reductase and of androgen receptor binding. *J. Med. Chem.* 29:2298-2315.

Reichstein, T., and Reich, H. (1946). The chemistry of the steroids. *Annu. Rev. Biochem.* 15:155-192.

Renwick, J. H., Claringbold, W. D. B., Earthy, M. E., Few, J. D., and McLean, C. S. (1984). Neural-tube defects produced in Syrian hamsters by potato glycoalkaloids. *Teratology* 30:371-381.

Ripperger, H., and Schreiber, K. (1981). *Solanum* steroid alkaloids. In *The Alkaloids*, Vol. 19, R. G. A. Rodrigo (Ed.). Academic Press, New York, pp. 81-192.

Rochelmeyer, V. H. (1942). Solatubine. *Arch. Pharm. (Weinheim)* 280:453-455.

Roddick, J. G. (1987). Antifungal activity of plant steroids. *Am. Chem. Soc. Symp. Ser.* 325:286-303.

Roddick, J. G., Rijnenberg, A. L., and Osman, S. F. (1988). Synergistic interaction between potato glycoalkaloids α-solanine and α-chaconine in relation to destabilization of cell membranes: ecological implications. *J. Chem. Ecol.* 14:889-902.

Sato, Y., and Latham, H. G., Jr. (1956). Chemistry of dihydrotomatidines. *J. Am. Chem. Soc.* 78:3146-3150.

Saul, R., Chambers, J. P., Molyneux, R. J., and Elbein, A. D. (1983). Castanospermine, a tetrahydroxylated alkaloid that inhibits β-glucocerebrosidase. *Arch. Biochem. Biophys.* 221:593-597.

Schreiber, K. (1965). *Solanum* alkaloide: XLVIII. Abbau von Solactulcidin und Tomatidin zu den Enantiomeren 5-Methyl-piperidonen-(2). *Liebigs Ann. Chem.* 682:219-227.

Schreiber, K. (1968). Steroid alkaloids: the *Solanum* group. In *The Alkaloids*, Vol. 10, R. H. F. Manske (Ed.). Academic Press, New York, pp. 1-192.

Schreiber, K., and Horstmann, C. (1966). Dehydrierung von Demissidin mit Quecksilber(II)-Acetate bzw. N-Brom-succinimid. *Chem. Ber.* 99: 3183-3193.

Schulz, G., and Sander, H. (1957). Cholesterol-tomatide: a new compound for the analysis and preparation of steroids. *Hoppe-Seyler's Z. Physiol. Chem.* 308:122-126.

Sim, F. R. P., Livett, B. G., Browne, C. A., and Keeler, R. F. (1985). Studies on the mechanism of *Veratrum* teratogenicity. In *Plant Toxicology*, A. A. Seawright, M. P. Hegarty, L. F. James, and R. F. Keeler (Eds.). Queensland Poisonous Plant Committee, Yeerongpilly, Australia, pp. 344-348.

Sinden, S. L., Sanford, L. L., and Deahl, K. L. (1986). Segregation of leptine glycoalkaloids in *Solanum chacoense* Bitter. *J. Agric. Food Chem.* 34:372-377.

Stephens, T. D. (1988). Proposed mechanisms of action in thalidomide embryopathy. *Teratology* 38:229-239.

Szpilfogel, S. (1951). Uber Steroide und Sexaualhormone: 175. Uber einige N-oxyde in der Solanidin-Reihe. *Helv. Chim. Acta* 34:843-846.

Toppel, G., Witte, L., and Hartmann, T. (1988). N-Oxidation and degradation of pyrrolizidine alkaloids during germination of *Crotalaria scassellatii*. *Phytochemistry* 27:3757-3760.

Uhle, F. C. (1953). The transformation of kryptogenin to solasodine. *J. Am. Chem. Soc.* 75:2280-2281.

Uhle, F. C., and Jacobs, W. A. (1945). The veratrine alkaloids: 24. The octahydropyrrocoline ring system of the tertiary bases: conversion of sarsasapogenin to a solanidine derivative. *J. Biol. Chem.* 160:243-248.

Van Gelder, W. M. J., Hopmans, C. W. J., Jonker, H. H., and van Eeuwijk,
    F. A. (1987). Biosynthesis and metabolism of C-27 steroidal alkaloids
    in leaves of potato. *Abstr. Conf. Pap. Posters, 10th Trienn. Conf. Eur.
    Assoc. Potato Res.*, pp. 276-277.
White, I. N. H., and Mattocks, A. R. (1971). Factors affecting the conver-
    sion of pyrrolizidine alkaloids to *N*-oxides and to pyrrolic derivatives in
    vitro. *Xenobiotica 1*: 503-505.
Zwenger, C., and Kind, A. (1861). Ueber das Solanin und dessen Spaltungs-
    producte, *Ann. Chem. Pharm. 118*:129-151.

9

Swainsonine: A Toxic Indolizidine Alkaloid from the Australian *Swainsona* Species

Steven M. Colegate, Peter R. Dorling, and Clive R. Huxtable

School of Veterinary Studies, Murdoch University, Perth, Murdoch, Western Australia

I. INTRODUCTION

Intoxication of farm stock following ingestion of plants belonging to the *Swainsona* genus has never been of major national economic significance in Australia, but has placed a financial burden on individual farm owners where localized outbreaks have occurred (Huxtable and Dorling, 1982a). It was recognized at an early stage that the clinical signs and pathological findings in *Swainsona* toxicosis were very similar to those observed with locoweed (*Astragalus* and *Oxytropis* species) intoxication of animals in the United States (Hartley, 1978). In the early 1970s, pathological and biochemical investigations of *Swainsona* toxicosis indicated that the disease process might involve the storage of material within lysosomes (Huxtable, 1970, 1972). A lysosomal storage process was subsequently demonstrated and shown to involve the induced storage of endogenous, mannose-rich oligosaccharides following ingestion of the plants (Dorling et al., 1978). Determination of the biological mechanism of the toxicosis led to development of an in vitro enzymatic assay for all plant extracts and subsequent purification procedures. This allowed ready access to the purified toxin, which was subsequently shown by spectroscopic analysis to be an indolizidine-triol (Colegate et al., 1979). The proposed structure of the toxin, given the trivial name swainsonine, was confirmed by x-ray diffraction analysis of its diacetate (Skelton and White, 1980).

The presence of swainsonine in the American locoweeds was subsequently established (Molyneux and James, 1982) and is the subject of a detailed review in this volume (Chapter 10). Swainsonine was also shown to be a metabolite of the mold *Rhizoctonia leguminicola* in association with slaframine, the causative factor of a slobbering disease of cattle that are fed spoiled red clover hay (Schneider et al., 1983). As interest in the compound increased it was also found to be a metabolite of the mold *Metarhizium anisopliae*, and this was used as the basis for large-scale production of swainsonine (Hino et al., 1985). Swainsonine quickly found a use as an in vivo inhibitor of acid α-D-mannosidase in investigations of lysosomal storage phenomena. It was shown to inhibit the posttranslational, glycoprotein processing enzyme Golgi mannosidase II (Elbein et al., 1981) and the effects of the resultant changes in glycoprotein structures have been investigated in a variety of systems. Swainsonine has been shown to exert immunomodulatory effects by stimulating natural killer cell activity, thereby reducing the extent of metastasis of some tumors.

The specific action of swainsonine was postulated to be a result of structural similarities between the swainsonine and mannosyl cations (Dorling et al., 1980). This initiated a search for other naturally occurring carbohydrate analogs which also act as enzyme inhibitors. The activities of a wide range of naturally occurring piperidine and pyrrolidine sugar analogs has been reviewed by Fellows (1986). The activity of swainsonine and similar glycosidase inhibitors stimulated research into the synthesis of swainsonine and its stereoisomers. It also stimulated research into the stereospecific synthesis of other hydroxylated piperidines and pyrrolidines with stereochemistries predicted to affect particular glycosidases.

II. CLINICAL ASPECTS OF *SWAINSONA* INTOXICATION

Certain species of the plant genus *Swainsona* have long been recognized to present a hazard to grazing animals. Livestock will not normally eat these plants unless there is a shortage of alternative feed. Therefore, outbreaks of poisoning tend to follow rains at the end of periods of drought or feed shortage. Animals can ingest these plants for 2 to 6 weeks before clinical signs of intoxication become obvious,. It seems that affected animals can develop a morbid preference for the plant, thus compounding the problem. In general, the clinical signs of intoxication are similar in cattle, sheep, and horses and have been described in some detail by Huxtable and Dorling (1982a). The first sign of poisoning is a progressive loss of condition followed, over a period of weeks to months, by signs of nervous dysfunction, such as high or low carriage of the head; head tremor; excess lachrymation; hyperesthesia; an excitable, apprehensive, and sometimes aggressive demeanor; and a dysmetric, ataxic gait. Increasing incoordination and weakness may lead to death from misadventure.

There is evidence to suggest that there is significant impairment of fertility in cows that ingest *Swainsona* spp. However, field observations imply no such impairment in sheep, and there is no information with respect to horses. In cattle, at least, it has been suggested that animals initially exposed to *Swainsona* as an adult will survive longer as chronic cases. Affected cattle exposed to *Swainsona* from birth may not display nervous signs for up to 8 to 12 months of age but may die within a few weeks after the onset of such signs. It has been reported that sheep may show progressive weight loss and emaciation with no overt neurological signs, while there was an early onset of edema of the lower limbs and prepuce in horses involved in experimental feeding trials (Huxtable and Dorling, 1982a). It has been suggested that for clinical signs to be manifested, the intake of *Swainsona* should be at a sufficiently high rate and that the higher this rate is, the more severe is the expression of the toxicosis (Huxtable and Dorling, 1982a). Animals will not be affected by low intake rates.

III. ISOLATION AND STRUCTURAL ELUCIDATION OF SWAINSONINE

A. Isolation

The isolation of the toxin responsible for the toxicosis ultimately depended upon the prior determination of the mechanism by which the effects of *Swainsona* ingestion were manifested.

1. Mechanism of the Toxicosis

Biochemical and ultrastructural evidence indicated that the widespread, cellular vacuolation observed in intoxicated animals was a lysosomal storage phenomenon (Huxtable, 1970, 1972). The options were either that some exogenous material derived from the plant was unable to be degraded by the lysosomal hydrolases or that some component of the plant was affecting the normal functioning of the lysosomal enzymes, resulting in storage of incompletely degraded endogenous material. To test this hypothesis, aqueous extracts of the plant, of the lymph nodes of an unaffected sheep, and of the lymph nodes of an intoxicated sheep were compared by gel filtration. The results clearly indicated a marked increase in the amount of some endogenous material in the affected animal compared to the control. This material was not present in the plant extract (Dorling et al., 1978).

This material gave a positive response to tests for the presence of a reducing sugar entity and had an apparent molecular weight of less than 300
daltons as determined by gel filtration. Acid hydrolysis of the material and
subsequent gas-liquid chromatography of the hydrolysate demonstrated the
significant presence of the anomers of mannose and glucosamine. The overall
and relative abundances of these sugars were very similar to those observed
in cases of hereditary mannosidosis (Ockerman, 1969, 1973; Jolly, 1975), in
which a deficiency of lysosomal α-mannosidase results in storage of mannose-
and *N*-acetylglucosamine-rich oligosaccharides. This suggested that *Swainsona* intoxication was perhaps a manifestation of the inhibition of lysosomal
α-mannosidase by a factor in the plant. Indeed, aqueous extracts of the plant
potently and specifically inhibited the ability of acid α-D-mannosidase to release the fluorescent aglycone from the synthetic substrate, 4-methylumbelli-
feryl mannopyranoside. This enzymatic activity thus formed the basis of a
facile, in vitro assay for monitoring all plant extracts and subsequent purification steps for the presence of the toxin (Dorling et al., 1978).

2. Extraction and Purification of the Toxin

With the availability of the in vitro enzymatic assay procedure, the extraction and purification of the inhibitor proceeded rapidly (Colegate et al., 1979).
The dried plant was milled to a fine powder and extracted exhaustively with
ethyl acetate. After evaporation of the solvent, the ethyl acetate extractives
were reextracted with water and filtered. The filtrate, acidified if necessary,
was applied to a strong cation-exchange resin column. After copious washing of the column with water, the α-mannosidase inhibitory activity was eluted
from the resin with dilute ammonia solution. The active solution, after the
acidity and conductivity were appropriately adjusted, was applied to a cellulose based, weak cation-exchange column which was then eluted with a sodium
chloride gradient. The active fractions were pooled and lyophilized to afford
a mixture which was then treated with ammoniated chloroform to extract the
inhibitor. Subsequent crystallization and recrystallization of the resultant gel
provided the inhibitor, swainsonine, as sheaves of fine white needles (Colegate et al., 1979).

B. Structural Elucidation

The spectroscopic data for the toxin implied the indolizidine-triol structure
[1] for swainsonine (Colegate et al., 1979) and this was confirmed by the
x-ray diffraction analysis of the diacetate of swainsonine [2] (Skelton and
White, 1980).

[1] R = H
[2] R = COCH₃

1. Assignment of Structure

The chromatographic properties of swainsonine indicated the probable presence of a readily protonated nitrogen atom. This was confirmed by a combustion elemental analysis which indicated an empirical formula of $C_8H_{15}NO_3$. That this was also the molecular formula was shown by the high-resolution electron impact mass spectrum (EIMS). The molecular ion peak observed at a mass-to-charge (m/e) ratio of 173.1054 correlated well with that expected for $C_8H_{15}NO_3$ (173.1051).

The eight carbon centers were made evident by the broadband decoupled ^{13}C-nuclear magnetic resonance (NMR) spectrum. As the eight signals all occurred upfield of 75 ppm, the possibility of unsaturation was eliminated, which therefore required the compound to be bicyclic. On reintroduction of partial coupling in an off-resonance decoupled experiment, the four lower field signals appeared as doublets, implying methine (C-H) carbons, whilst the four higher field carbons appeared as triplets, implying methylene (C-H$_2$) carbons. The chemical shifts of the methine carbons (δ 72.5, 69.4, 68.7, 66.1 ppm) and two of the methylene carbons (δ 60.4, 51.3 ppm) were consistent with direct bonding to either an oxygen or a nitrogen atom.

Acetylation of swainsonine with acetic anhydride at room temperature led to a diacetate or to a triacetate if it was refluxed with acetic anhydride and pyridine. The EIMS of the diacetate and triacetate showed the appropriate molecular ion peaks and also showed fragmentations corresponding to losses of two or three acetoxy groups, respectively. The ^{13}C- and ^{1}H-NMR spectra of the acetates showed the additional carbonyl and methyl carbons and the acetoxy methyl protons expected.

The 90-MHz ^{1}H-NMR spectrum of swainsonine, a complex series of multiplets occurring upfield of 5 ppm, and the 90MHz ^{1}H-NMR spectrum of the diacetate were carefully analyzed using double-resonance decoupling techniques and induced double-resonance techniques. These NMR procedures gave information on the interaction of the protons with each other and allowed the development of the partial structure [3] for swainsonine. Assignment of partial

[3]

structure [3] necessitated a tertiary nitrogen atom since the ^{13}C-NMR spectrum indicated that six of the carbons were directly bonded to an oxygen or a nitrogen atom. This tertiary nature of the nitrogen atom was confirmed by recording the ^{1}H-NMR spectrum of swainsonine in the presence of trifluoroacetic acid (TFA). The addition of TFA has the effect of quaternizing the nitrogen atom, which causes a downfield shift for protons on carbons directly bonded to the nitrogen (Hamlow et al., 1964). Thus five protons were substantially shifted downfield on the addition of TFA, allowing expansion of the partial structure [3] to [4]. This left only the obvious insertion of the remaining methylene group to complete the indolizidine-triol structure [5], which was completely supported by the observed fragmentation pattern in the high-resolution EIMS.

[4]   [5]

2. Stereochemistry of Swainsonine

Relative stereochemistry

Spectroscopic analysis: In addition to the 16 possible stereoisomers, dictated by the four asymmetric centers in the molecule, the ring fusion could either be trans (with the bridgehead proton 8a on the opposite side of the plane of the molecule to the lone pair of electrons on nitrogen), cis (same side), or inverting between the two conformations. Previous work with azabicyclic alkaloids (Luning and Lundin, 1967; Rader et al., 1965) has demonstrated that characteristic absorption bands in the region 2700 to 2900 cm^{-1}, are observed in the infrared (IR) spectra of these fused-ring heterocycles under certain conditions. These Bohlmann absorption bands (Bohlmann, 1957) are observed when two or more protons, on carbons α to the nitrogen atom, are in a trans-diaxial relationship to the lone pair of electrons on the nitrogen atom. The IR spectra of swainsonine and its acetate derivatives clearly showed these strong Bohlmann absorption bands and thus implied this particular relationship for the α protons and the nitrogen lone-pair electrons. By examination of molecular models of swainsonine it was apparent that this Bohlmann criterion is realized only when the rings are trans-fused. This results in H5$_{axial}$ and H8a being trans-diaxial to the lone pair of electrons on the nitrogen atom. To begin describing the relative stereochemistry of swainsonine, the lone pair of electrons on nitrogen was arbitrarily oriented such that it was below the plane of the rings. Therefore, H8a must be above the plane of the rings and was thus labeled β.

The relative, spatial relationship of vicinal protons can be estimated by consideration of the Karplus equation, which relates the dihedral angle of interaction of the protons with their coupling constant (Williams and Fleming, 1966). Thus, by due consideration of the experimentally derived coupling constants in the ^{1}H-NMR spectra of swainsonine and its acetate derivatives, by rationalization of the magnitude of these coupling constants using molecular models and by comparison with similar fused-ring heterocycles, the protons H1, H2, and H8a were judged to be cis to each other and trans to H8.

Therefore, the relative stereochemistry of swainsonine and of the acetates was predicted to be 1α,2α,8β,8aβ, as shown in structure [1].

X-ray diffraction analysis: Due to the inherent uncertainty in predicting the proton-proton spatial relationships based on the observed coupling constants, it was considered prudent to examine the structure by x-ray diffraction techniques (Skelton and White, 1980). Crystals of 1,2-diacetoxyswainsonine [2], which was predicted to have the same relative stereochemistry and the same conformational ring-fusion preference as swainsonine, were of sufficient size and quality for this procedure. In addition to confirming the spectroscopically deduced structure for swainsonine, the x-ray diffraction data indicated that the molecular dimensions of swainsonine diacetate were generally as expected. The six-membered ring was shown to adopt a normal "chair" conformation, with the hydroxyl substituent and the five-membered ring junctions being equatorially oriented. The five-membered ring has a pseudoenvelope conformation and there is some suggestion of a long hydrogen bond between the C8 hydroxyl substituent and the C1 oxygen. There does not seem to be any steric reason for nonacetylation of the C8 hydroxyl substituent, and it may be that under the very mild acetylation conditions used (Colegate et al., 1979), hydrogen bonding between the C1 and C2 hydroxyls may account for the preferential acetylation of the C1 and C2 hydroxyls of swainsonine. Thus this preferential acetylation may result from the ease of acetylation of the C1 and C2 hydroxyls rather than from any hindrance to the acetylation of the C8 hydroxyl.

Absolute stereochemistry. The absolute stereochemistry of the molecule was determined by Schneider et al (1983) by reacting the 1,2-acetonide derivative of swainsonine with a racemic mixture of 2-phenylbutanoic anhydride [asymmetric induction method of Horeau (1961)]. The resulting enantiomeric excess indicated that the 8-hydroxyl substituent was dextrorotatory and therefore was labeled R. Thus the structure of swainsonine could be absolutely described as (1S,2R,8R,8aR)-1,2,8-trihydroxyoctahydroindolizine [1].

IV. OCCURRENCE OF SWAINSONINE AND ITS N-OXIDE IN THE *SWAINSONA* SPECIES

Molyneux isolated the N-oxide of swainsonine from *Astragalus lentiginosus* (Molyneux and James, 1982) and has suggested that the relative configuration and the conformation of the N-oxide should be the same as for swainsonine (Molyneux et al., 1985). The ^{1}H- and ^{13}C-NMR data for the N-oxide, prepared by oxidizing swainsonine in ethanolic hydrogen peroxide, fully supported that suggestion (Colegate et al., 1989). For example, the coupling constants between the protons on carbons 8a and 8, carbons 1 and 8a, carbons 1 and 2, and carbons 3 and 2 were similar in magnitude to those observed for swainsonine and therefore implied a similar relative stereochemistry. As expected, there was a marked downfield shift of the resonance positions for the protons bonded to carbons 3, 5, and 8a (α to the nitrogen atom) in the N-oxide compared to the analogous resonances in swainsonine. This downfield shift was similar to the shift observed for these protons when the ^{1}H-NMR spectrum of swainsonine was recorded using D_2O/trifluoroacetic acid (TFA) as the solvent and is to be expected of protons on carbons bonded directly to a quaternized nitrogen atom. Additionally, the ^{13}C-NMR spectrum of the N-oxide showed a large downfield shift (8 to 15 ppm) for the resonances of C3, C5, and C8a compared to swainsonine, which was again a manifestation of the electron-withdrawing effect that the ionized nitrogen atom exerts on carbons directly bonded to it. However, the trans-fused nature of the indolizidine structure is still in doubt since all attempts at trying to observe the Bohlmann bands in the IR spectrum have been unsuccessful. Molyneux et al. (1985) have conducted an extensive survey of the *Astragalus* and *Oxytropis* species for the occurrence of swainsonine and its N-oxide.

A. Distribution of the *Swainsona* Species

Except for one doubtful species reported to exist in New Zealand, the *Swainsona* genus is restricted to Australia. There are 55 species of *Swainsona* in Australia, with representatives of the genus occurring in all states. However, only seven of the species have any reported toxicity, and these are confined to the mainland states, with a concentration in the inland, more arid regions. Members of the family Leguminosae, the *Swainsonas* are herbs or low shrubs which have compound leaves consisting of odd numbers of leaflets and a bare tip. The pea-shaped flowers (papilionaceous) are usually large and showy and colored in hues of blue, purple, red, and in a few species, yellow and white (Everist, 1981). A botanical classification by Hutchinson (Heywood, 1971) allocated the *Swainsona* genus to the tribe Coluteae of the Leguminosae subfamily Lotoideae. The allocation of the *Astragalus* and *Oxytropis* genera to the adjacent tribe Astragaleae demonstrates the close relationship between the Australian *Swainsonas* and the North American locoweeds.

1. S. canescens

Swainsona canescens (Benth.) A. Lee is a low, spreading bush, up to 1 m in diameter, which grows on heavy soils in arid areas, especially those subject to seasonal inundation, such as dam catchment areas, road verges, and dry creek beds. The leaves and stems are covered with fine hairs, which give the plant a gray appearance and its colloquial, West Australian name of "grey Swainson pea." The flowers are on elongated racemes and vary in color from purple on the lower part of the raceme to yellow nearer the tip. It is a plant of the open pastoral range country, and an almost hairless variety, *S. canescens* var. *horniana*, grows in the more easterly parts of the distribution range.

2. S. galegifolia

Swainsona galegifolia (Andr.) R. Br. regrows annually from a perrennial root stock and has small, hairless leaflets and fairly large, bright red to purple flowers on long, erect racemes. Known as the smooth Darling pea (syn. *S. coronillifolia*), this species is the most common cause of *Swainsona* toxicosis, with documented cases of poisoning dating back to the early days of European settlement in Australia. It grows prolifically during spring, following sufficient winter rain, and it is at this time that most cases of poisoning occur. Growing in a range of soils, from heavy clays to light loams, the species is often a contaminant of semi-improved pasture.

3. *S. greyana*

Swainsona greyana Lindl., or Darling pea, usually has large, bright pink flowers except in the variation *cadellii*, which has white flowers. A perennial herb, regrowing from a deep, persistent rootstock, this species has a more southerly range than *S. galegifolia* and is reputed to be the most toxic of the *Swainsona* species.

4. *S. procumbens*

Swainsona procumbens F. Muell. is a prostrate herb with blue-purple flowers, the lower petal (keel petal) of which has a characteristic spiraled tip. Commonly known as Broughton pea, it has also been collected from Mt. Barker in Western Australia, which is well outside the normal range, but human involvement in this occurrence cannot be ruled out.

5. *S. luteola*

Swainsona luteola F. Muell., or dwarf Darling pea, grows in late winter and in spring, and poisoning usually occurs when other feed is scarce. It is a small procumbent herb which grows on clays and clay-loams in open grassland. The small flowers are usually blue and are crowded onto short racemes.

6. *S. swainsonioides*

Swainsona swainsonioides (Benth.) A. Lee is very similar to *S. procumbens* in appearance and occupies much the same range. Field evidence has been highly incriminating of this species, but no feeding tests have yet been recorded.

7. *S. brachycarpa*

Similarly, *S. brachycarpa* is listed as a toxic species, but the evidence is less than convincing since the known toxic species, *S. galegifolia* and *S. luteola*, were also growing in the pasture that caused an outbreak of poisoning in horses (O'Sullivan and Goodwin, 1977).

B. Analysis Method and Results

Samples of the leaves, stems, or seeds of the different species were air-dried and milled to a fine powder. Extraction of the samples, spiked with a known quantity of tetrahydroxyindolizidine castanospermine [6] as an internal standard, for 48 h with ethanol was followed by a chromatographic cleanup of the extract. The appropriate chromatographic fraction was lyophilized and derivatized by trimethylsilylation to afford a sample suitable for gas-liquid chromatographic (GLC) analysis. Castanospermine was used as an internal standard only after it was established that each sample did not contain any native castanospermine. Using this analytical method, the leaves, stems, and seeds of *S. galegifolia*, whole plant and seeds of *S. canescens*, leaves and seeds of *S. maccullochliana*, and seeds of *S. greyana* and an undetermined *Swainsona* species were analyzed for the presence of swainsonine and its *N*-oxide. In contrast to the results of the *Astragalus* and *Oxytropis* survey (Molyneux et al., 1985), none of the *Swainsona* species tested contained any of the *N*-oxide

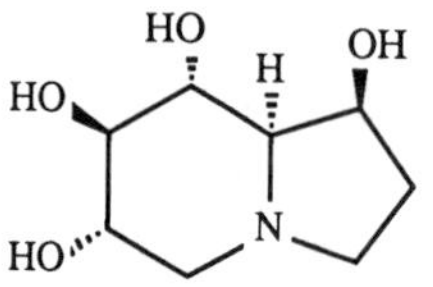

[6] 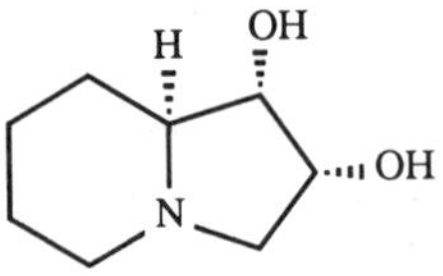   [7]

of swainsonine. It was evident from this preliminary survey that not all the
Swainsonas contain swainsonine and that the highest content of swainsonine
was detected in *Swainsona greyana* (3900 ppm), which is reputed to be the
most toxic of the species. *Swainsona canescens*, from which swainsonine was
originally isolated, contained a relatively small amount of the toxic alkaloid
(182 ppm in leaves and 33 ppm in seeds) (Dorling et al., 1989a).

V. SYNTHESIS OF SWAINSONINE

A. Chemical Synthesis

The synthetic challenge afforded by the swainsonine molecule, in conjunction
with the biochemical uses of swainsonine, has led several research groups to
pursue the synthesis of this compound. A nonenantioselective, heterocyclic
approach was adopted for the synthesis of 8a-*epi*-8-dehydroxyswainsonine [7]
(Colegate et al., 1984). Extension and modification of this procedure to pre-
pare swainsonine were forestalled by several successful, enantiospecific syntheses. Adams et al. (1985) employed the "asymmetric epoxide" methodology,
developed for the synthesis of polyhydroxylated natural products (Katsuki
et al., 1982), to synthesize swainsonine in 21 steps and 6.6% overall yield
from *trans*-1,4-dichloro-2-butene and N-benzyl-p-toluenesulfonamide (which
provided a suitably protected nitrogen resistant to oxidation and which would
not act as an intramolecular nucleophile for the epoxide functions). Stereochemical control of the synthesis was provided by the asymmetric epoxidation
of intermediate alkenes, which allows access to each of the 16 stereoisomers
of swainsonine. Indeed, this group also reported the synthesis of the "D-
gluco" [8] and "D-galacto" [9] isomers of swainsonine.

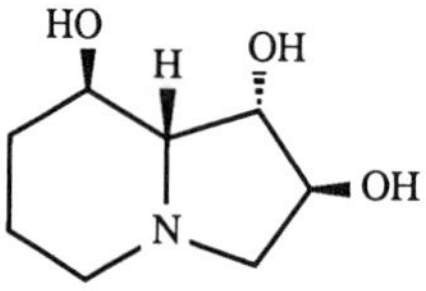

[8] 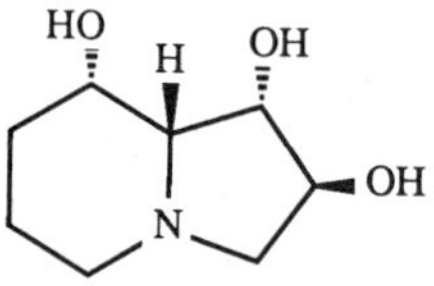   [9]

The stereochemical similarity between swainsonine and D-mannose prompted
several syntheses of swainsonine in which the stereochemistry of the hydroxyl
substituents was controlled by using carbohydrate precursors. Thus D-mannose and D-glucose were used as chiral synthons in the enantioselective synthesis of swainsonine. These syntheses involve preparation of the appropriately substituted and protected aminodeoxy carbohydrates, which then require
chain extension and ring closures to afford the indolizidine system and hence

(-)-swainsonine (Ali et al., 1984, 1985; Fleet et al., 1984a; Setoi et al., 1985; Suami et al., 1984, 1985; Yasuda et al., 1984). A short, enantioselective synthesis of (-)-swainsonine, in seven steps from 2,3-O-isopropylidene-D-erythrose via an intramolecular 1,3 dipolar cycloaddition of an unactivated olefinic azide, has been reported (Bennett et al., 1989). Modification of these syntheses has made it possible to synthesize various stereoisomers of swainsonine (Adams et al., 1985; Yasuda et al., 1985; Iimura et al., 1986; Tadano et al., 1986a,b) which have subsequently been investigated for their enzyme inhibition activities.

B. Biosynthesis

The indolizidine alkaloids swainsonine and slaframine [10] are both metabolites of the fungus *Rhizoctonia leguminicola*. Infection of red clover hay by this mold causes a "slobbers" syndrome in animals that ingest the infected feed (Rainey et al., 1965; Aust and Broquist, 1965). Both swainsonine and slaframine (the causative factor in the slobbers syndrome) are obtained from mycelial mats of the mold grown in liquid culture containing red clover hay infusion (Schneider et al., 1983). The biosynthesis of these alkaloids (Fig. 1) is interesting in that they have opposing configurations at C1 and C8a. Using ^{14}C- and ^{3}H-labeled precursors, it was shown that both alkaloids totally incorporate L-pipecolic acid derived from L-lysine (Guengerich et al., 1973a). Incorporation of L-pipecolic acid provides the piperidine ring and C1 of the alkaloids.

The role of acetate in the formation of L-pipecolic acid was indicated by the incorporation of one deuterium atom, from acetate-d_3, into swainsonine. Condensation of malonic acid with pipecolic acid (with concomitant decarboxylation) was indicated as the source of C2 and C3 of the alkaloids. The resultant pipecolyl acetate could then undergo cyclization and reduction to form the (8aS)-1-oxoindolizidine [11], at which stage the biosynthetic pathways to swainsonine and slaframine may diverge. Reduction of the carbonyl from the β face of this oxoindolizidine affords (1S,8aS)-1-hydroxyindolizidine [12], which is then functionalized at C6 and acetylated to yield slaframine [10]. The isotopic label from a mixture of *cis*- and *trans*-DL-[1-^{3}H]-1-hydroxyindolizidine is incorporated into both swainsonine and slaframine (Guengerich et al., 1973b). It has been demonstrated that two deuterium atoms are lost in the biotransformation of pipecolic-d_9 acid to swainsonine. One of these losses occurs at C3 of pipecolic acid when the C8-hydroxyl of swainsonine is introduced. The site of the other loss of deuterium was shown, by ^{2}H-NMR, to be C2 of pipecolic acid, which corresponds to C8a of swainsonine (Schneider et al., 1982). The latter loss indicated an epimerization step about C8a of the indolizidine system.

It has been shown that the (1S,2R,8aS) enantiomer of 1,2-dihydroxyindolizidine [7] is a minor metabolite of *R. leguminicola*. The biosynthetic relationship of this diol to swainsonine was demonstrated by refeeding the tritiated diol to the fungus. There was subsequently observed a high level of tritium incorporation (45%) into swainsonine. This conversion of the diol to swainsonine provided the rationale for assigning the absolute stereochemistry of the diol. It also provides strong evidence that the diol is included in a biosynthetic pathway to swainsonine. This pathway, however, may only be a minor one which occurs when synthesis of the diol is enhanced by swamping the "usual"

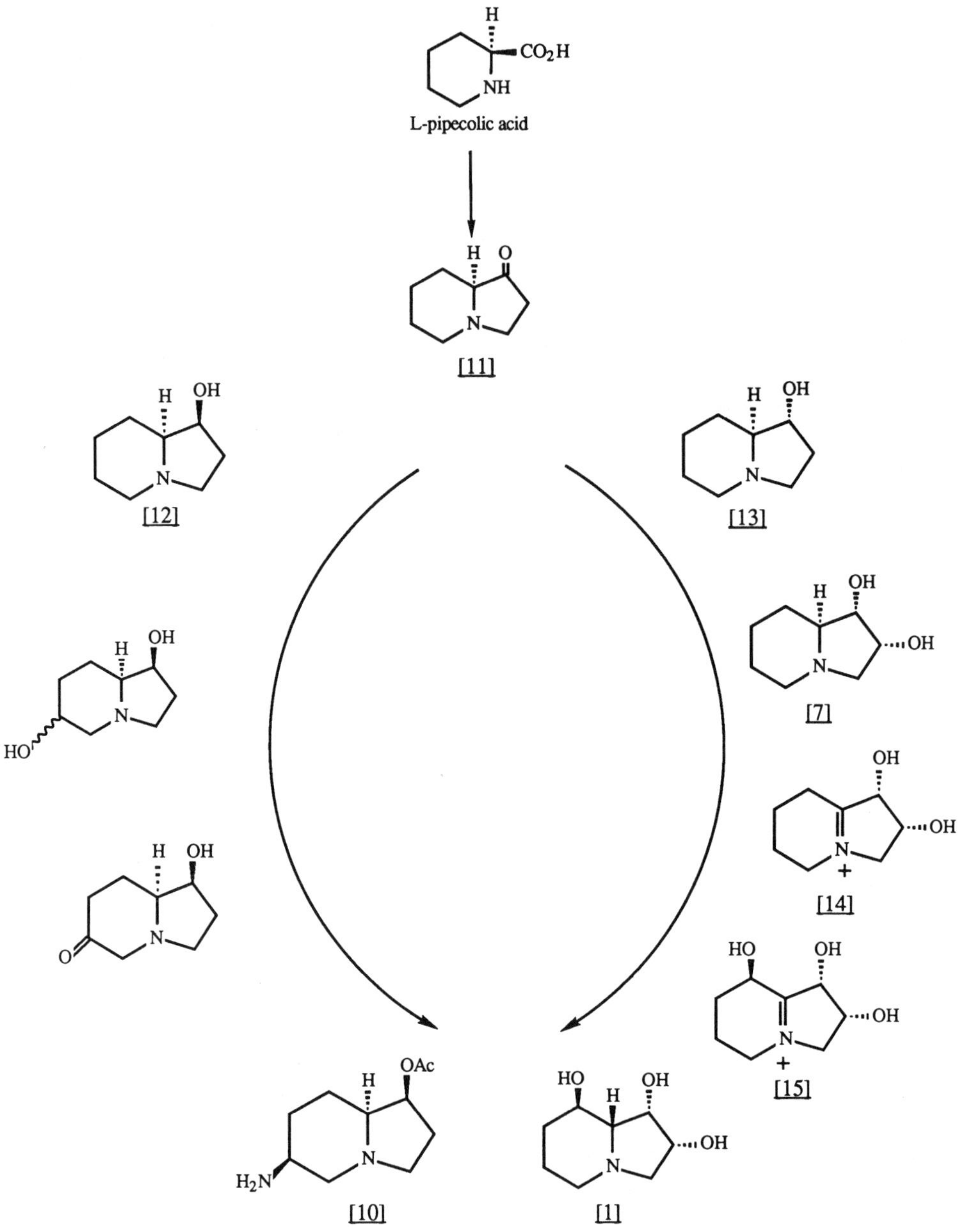

FIGURE 1 Proposed biosynthetic pathway to swainsonine in *R. leguminicola*.

swainsonine pathway with excess, exogenous 1-hydroxyindolizidine (Harris et al., 1987).

To more fully elucidate the later sequences involved in the biosynthesis of swainsonine, Harris et al. (1988a) have utilized the specifically labeled enantiomers of the 1-hydroxyindolizidines [12] and [13]. Their work supports the proposal that the biosynthetic pathways to slaframine and swainsonine diverge at the oxo-indolizidine [11] stage. The route to swainsonine continues via (1R,8aS)-1-hydroxyindolizidine [13], which is subsequently hydroxylated to the cis-diol [7]. This diol is oxidized to the iminium ion [14], which may then undergo further hydroxylation to [15]. Reduction of this iminium ion [15], resulting in overall epimerization about C8a, results in the formation of swainsonine (Fig. 1). It has been proposed that the biosynthesis of swainsonine in the diablo locoweed follows a similar route to that in the fungus *R. leguminicola* (Harris et al., 1988b).

VI. BIOLOGICAL PROPERTIES AND EFFECTS OF SWAINSONINE

Swainsonine is a potent inhibitor of acid α-D-mannosidase, causing the lysosomal storage of endogenous, mannose-rich oligosaccharides. This storage induces a phenocopy of the lysosomal storage disease mannosidosis, which results from genetic deficiency of lysosomal α-D-mannosidase (Dorling et al., 1978; Huxtable and Dorling, 1982b; Jolly et al., 1981). Swainsonine will also inhibit the glycoprotein processing Golgi mannosidase II to produce modified glycoproteins.

A. Enzymology

Swainsonine has been shown to inhibit lysosomal α-D-mannosidase, cytosolic α-D-mannosidase, and Golgi α-D-mannosidase II. Lysosomal α-mannosidase is an exo-glycosidase with a pH optimum of about 4.5. It is able to hydrolyze α-(1-2), α-(1-3), and α-(1-6) mannosidic linkages and is involved primarily in the catabolism of glycoproteins. Biochemical evidence suggested that swainsonine was a specific, reversible, substrate-site-directed inhibitor of α-D-mannosidase and that it would be concentrated within the acid environment of the lysosomes (Dorling et al., 1980). This reversibility of inhibition of jack bean α-mannosidase is in contrast to the findings of Tulsiani et al. (1985), who demonstrated partial reversibility with lysosomal α-mannosidase and Golgi mannosidase II but reported the irreversible inhibition of jack bean α-mannosidase. Kang and Elbein (1983) also demonstrated the very specific competitive nature of swainsonine as an inhibitor of α-D-mannosidase. They showed that swainsonine may be tightly bound to the enzyme and is only slowly removed. McGee and Murray (1986) showed that swainsonine inhibition of α-mannosidases from different sources can vary and that the inhibition of cowpea α-mannosidase appears to be noncompetitive.

The Golgi α-mannosidases Ia, Ib, and II are involved in the modification of asparagine-linked oligosaccharides of glycoproteins. The Golgi α-mannosidase II has a pH optimum of about 5.75 and is able to hydrolyze the α-(1-3) and α-(1-6) mannosidic linkages of its special substrate, whereas the α-mannosidases Ia and Ib have α-(1-2) specificity. Based on structures of stored oligosaccharides, it was initially thought that swainsonine inhibited Golgi α-mannosidases Ia and Ib (Elbein et al., 1981). However, while swainsonine was found to be a potent inhibitor of α-mannosidase II, it was reported to have no effect on α-mannosidase I in vitro (Tulsiani et al., 1982). Despite this report, later studies on the effects of swainsonine and some of its epimers suggested that Golgi α-mannosidase I may be inhibited, thereby partially accounting for the structures of the induced storage products (Cenci di Bello et al., 1983, 1989). Golgi α-mannosidase II has been shown to be inhibited by swainsonine in vitro, by assay with suitable substrates, and in vivo by structural analysis and comparison of the stored oligosaccharides (Elbein et al., 1981; Tulsiani et al., 1982; Cenci di Bello et al., 1989).

The cytosolic α-mannosidase has an α-(1-2) mannosidic specificity and a pH optimum of 6.5. A similar activity has been found in the endoplasmic reticulum of rat liver (Bischoff and Kornfeld, 1983), and it has been suggested that the cytosolic α-mannosidase activity may arise from the endoplasmic reticulum by proteolysis or by disruption during extraction (Winchester, 1984). Swainsonine inhibits that portion of soluble mouse liver α-mannosidase activity which is not retained on concanavalin A and which is therefore presumed to be cytosolic. Chotai et al. (1983) have also reported inhibition of a neutral α-mannosidase by swainsonine. Thus neutral α-mannosidase isolated from normal human and human mannosidosis fibroblasts is inhibited by swainsonine. Neutral, cytosolic α-D-mannosidase isolated form human liver was also shown to be inhibited by swainsonine (89% inhibition by a 1 mM solution of swainsonine compared to 100% inhibition of the lysosomal α-mannosidase at the same swainsonine concentration) (Cenci di Bello et al., 1989). However, Tulsiani et al. (1982, 1984) have reported that swainsonine, at similar concentrations, did not inhibit cytosolic α-mannosidase isolated from rat liver. A possible explanation for this inconsistency and for the variability of reported inhibition constants (K_i) for 50% inhibition of acidic α-D-mannosidase has been proffered by Dorling et al. (1989b) and concerns the choice and concentrations of substrates used.

B. Effect on Glycoprotein Synthesis

Glycoproteins are abundant and widely dispersed in nature, being found in fungi, green plants, bacteria, viruses, and animal cells. The biological functions and importance of intracellular, cell-surface, and secreted glycoproteins include intercellular adhesion, pinocytosis, cellular recognition, receptor activity, protection of the associated protein against proteolytic degradation, and transfer of metabolites across cellular membranes. These and other biological functions have been described extensively in the literature.

Biosynthesis of N-linked glycoproteins involves transfer of the oligosaccharide from its isoprenoid carrier, dolichol phosphate, to the nascent peptide in the endoplasmic reticulum. Modification of the "core" oligosaccharide then ensues in the endoplasmic reticulum [loss of three terminal glucose units and possibly 1 α-(1-2)-linked mannose unit] and in the Golgi apparatus. Modification within the Golgi involves the participation of various mannosidases and transferases and results in the production of complex, hybrid, and high-mannose glycans (Winchester, 1984).

The role of the carbohydrate entity in affecting the biological function of glycoproteins remains a matter for conjecture and debate. Olden et al. (1982) have reviewed the experimental data for various hypotheses and proposed that the carbohydrate entity is responsible for directing the glycoprotein to specific cellular organelles via interaction with intracellular membrane receptors. This localization function of the carbohydrate entity may not, according to their model, be restricted solely to the lysosomal enzymes. They suggest further that the carbohydrate entity is required for the conformational and proteolytic stability of the associated protein. However, the carbohydrate entity may not be strictly required for the secretion of extracellular products or for the expression of the specific activity of the associated protein.

Inhibition of one or more of the steps in the biosynthesis of the glycoproteins is a valuable method for investigating how alterations in glycosylation can affect the biological role of the glycoproteins. For example, inhibition of the synthesis of the oligosaccharide carrier, dolichol phosphate, or inhibition of the initial transfer of sugars to dolichol phosphate, by antibiotics such as tunicamycin, will prevent glycosylation of the protein by the "core" oligosaccharide. A variety of compounds are known to inhibit different stages in the posttranslational processing of glycoproteins. Elbein (1987) has comprehensively reviewed inhibitors of the synthesis of lipid-linked saccharides, of glycoprotein processing, of dolichol phosphate synthesis, and of transport of glycoproteins in addition to compounds that modify protein synthesis and structure.

Swainsonine modifies the processing of asparagine-linked glycoproteins by inhibiting the Golgi mannosidase II. This enzyme is crucial in the posttranslational processing of the oligosaccharide chains of a glycoprotein. In normal situations, depending on the glycoprotein, there may be a mixture of complex, hybrid, high-mannose, or other types of oligosaccharide chains attached to the one peptide. In swainsonine intoxication, due to the inhibition of α-mannosidase II, the production of complex oligosaccharides is blocked, with a consequent increase in the hybrid structure (Dorling et al., 1989b).

This predomination of the hybrid glycan, however, does not appear to have very much effect on the viability of the resultant glycoproteins (Dorling et al., 1989b; Elbein, 1987). However, treatment with swainsonine does appear to accelerate intracellular transport (Yeo et al., 1985), block the receptor-mediated uptake of mannose-terminated glycoproteins by macrophages (Chung et al., 1984), block the glucocorticoid stimulation of resorptive cells (Bar-Shavit et al., 1984), affect the in vivo "homing" of lymphoma cells (Hooghe et al., 1984), and restore the immunological response in immunodeficient mice (Kino et al., 1985).

C. Lysosomal Storage

Intense cytoplasmic vacuolation of cells in many tissues is the most characteristic lesion associated with exposure to swainsonine and is well developed within 10 days in samples examined by routine light microscopy. Vacuolation regresses rapidly on withdrawal of the toxin, generally vanishing within 2 weeks, although some neurones are reported to retain vacuoles for up to 1 month (Huxtable and Dorling, 1982b). It was predicted, on ultrastructural and biochemical grounds, that these vacuoles were secondary lysosomes (Huxtable,

1970,1972), and this was confirmed subsequently by histochemical and immuno-logical techniques (Novikoff et al., 1985). The vacuolation is believed to represent the proliferation and enlargement of lysosomes which are storing accumulated, mannose-rich oligosaccharides consequent to the inhibition of acid α-mannosidase (Huxtable and Dorling, 1982b).

The onset of storage may be monitored by the appearance of vacuolated lymphocytes in peripheral blood smears (Huxtable and Gibson, 1970). Guinea pigs developed obvious neurovisceral mannoside storage, including neurones in the central nervous system and peripheral ganglia, within 4 weeks of initiating a dose of 100 μg/mL of swainsonine in their drinking water. In rats receiving a similar dose of swainsonine, multisystem storage occurred but did not significantly affect nerve cell bodies in the central nervous system (Huxtable and Dorling, 1982b). As little as 5 μg/mL of swainsonine in the drinking water of rats induced visceral vacuolation (Novikoff et al., 1985), but levels of over 400 μg/mL are required before vacuolation will occur in the central nervous system (Dorling et al., 1989b). This seems to indicate a very efficient blood-brain barrier in the rat.

In swainsonine intoxication, this storage material is derived predominantly from hybrid glycans resulting from the concurrent inhibition of Golgi mannosidase II. This is in contrast to genetic mannosidosis, a lysosomal storage disease resulting from a deficiency of acid α-D-mannosidase, in which the stored material is derived from complex glycans reflecting the viability of the post-translational processing enzymes. Minor, between-species differences in stored mannosides can be explained by the presence (in rats, guinea pigs, cats, and humans, for example) or by the absence (in pigs, sheep, cattle, and goats, for example) of endoenzymes that catalyze the hydrolysis of linkages between the core chitobioside and the protein chain of glycoproteins. This hydrolysis may involve an endohexosaminidase or an asparagine-hexosamine hydrolytic activity (Dorling et al., 1989b).

Hepatic, lysosomal glycoprotein degradation in the rat has been shown to require the initial hydrolysis of the carbohydrate entity from the protein chain (Winkler and Segal, 1984a,b). The failure to demonstrate storage of oligosaccharides in the liver of swainsonine-treated rats, despite intense vacuolation (Novikoff et al., 1985), inplies that rat liver lacks the necessary endoenzymes to initiate the degradation process and that storage of intact glycoproteins may be occurring. The rat kidney, however, does apparently have this glycoprotein degrading capability since treatment with swainsonine does induce oligosaccharide storage (Dorling et al., 1989b).

Increased levels of acid α-mannosidase activity in the plasma and tissues of animals treated with swainsonine and a restoration of α-mannosidase activity following disruption of the cells have been interpreted to question the validity of the original proposal (Dorling et al., 1978) that lysosomal storage is a direct effect of the inhibition of the lysosomal α-mannosidase (Tulsiani and Touster, 1983). However, it is maintained that mannoside storage is a consequence of the inhibition of the lysosomal enzyme rather than a manifestation of the inability of lysosomal hydrolases to degrade the modified oligosaccharides resulting from inhibition of the posttranslational processing enzyme, mannosidase II. The observations on α-mannosidase activity levels can be explained and, indeed, might be expected on the basis of lysosomal turnover and intracellular localization of swainsonine (Dorling et al., 1989b).

The rapid resolution of storage following cessation of swainsonine administration indicates further that the lysosomal complement of hydrolases is capable of "handling" the accumulated oligosaccharides, which, after all, are not abnormal but simply present in abnormal relative amounts.

The clinical effects of swainsonine intoxication relate temporally to the development and intensification of lysosomal storage (Huxtable and Dorling, 1982a). Indeed, the clinical signs and morphologic changes associated with swainsonine intoxication are essentially the same as for the genetic lysosomal storage disorder α-mannosidosis (Dorling et al., 1978, 1985; Huxtable and Dorling, 1982b). The mannosides that are stored in either case differ in structure since in mannosidosis there is no inhibition of the processing enzyme α-mannosidase II as there is with swainsonine intoxication. The close similarity between genetic mannosidosis and the effects of swainsonine intoxication suggests that the induction of mannoside storage in lysosomes is the critical factor in swainsonine intoxication. The lysosomal storage induced by swainsonine may be implicated in the detrimental effects on the fetus since the involvement of lysosomal disorders in teratogenesis is well documented (Lloyd and Beck, 1969). The combined effects of fetal and maternal mannosidosis in swainsonine intoxication may contribute to birth defects and abortion.

D. Neuropathologic Effects

As clinical neurologic deficits are a feature of severe swainsonine intoxication, the neuropathology has been of particular interest. The intensity and distribution of mannoside storage by neurones is influenced by the dose rate of swainsonine, and it appears that in the rat the blood-brain barrier to swainsonine is higher than in most other species. Lysosomal mannoside storage in neurones is confined to the perikaryon and is similar in all respects to the process occurring in other tissues. In addition, however, the storage process is accompanied by the formation of axonal spheroids (also termed "axonal dystrophy") at numerous sites in the central and peripheral nervous systems (Huxtable and Dorling, 1982b). These spheroids, located mainly toward the distal extremities of long axons, are localized swellings crowded with mitochondria, granulomembranous dense bodies, and vesicular, tubular, and membranous arrays (Huxtable and Dorling, 1985). The spheroids are identical, in morphology, to those seen in a number of neuropathological conditions, including other lysosomal storage diseases (Jellinger, 1973). There is some evidence that spheroid formation in an axon is a direct consequence of lysosomal storage in the parent cell body, but the mechanism of their formation remains undefined. It has been proposed that axonal spheroid formation represents a distal degenerative process which may be related to abortive attempts to regenerate specialized endings during normal turnover of these structures. However, in swainsonine-treated rats in which selected dystrophic axons were subjected to focal crush injury and allowed to regenerate, successful regeneration was completed before new spheroids were formed. It was suggested subsequently that spheroid formation may reflect a blockade of retrograde axonal transport of obsolete organelles, destined for return to the perikaryon for degradation, and their distal accumulation. These studies also implied that neither mannoside storage nor spheroid formation caused significant functional impairment of the neurones (Pritchard et al., 1989a).

Other studies have revealed yet another type of neuronal lesion associated with the storage process. Distorting enlargements of the axon hillock and axon initial segment develop in some higher areas of the brain. These meganeurites may be accompanied by dendritic outgrowths (secondary neurites) and by the formation of aberrant synapses. In cats, such changes have been observer in both genetic mannosidosis and in swainsonine intoxication (Walkley et al., 1986). In the latter it has been shown that the initiation of aberrant neurite growth on cortical pyramidal neurones was influenced both by the intensity of lysosomal storage and by the age of the animal. It was also suggested that the immature brain is most susceptible to neuritogenic influences (Walkley and Siegel, 1985). This process appears irreversible in such animals. Despite neuronal vacuolation and the formation of meganeurites in thalamic nuclei in mature, swainsonine-intoxicated sheep, dendritic outgrowths and aberrant synapses were not observed. On cessation of swainsonine exposure there was a significant regression of the meganeurites (Huxtable et al., 1982).

The formation of meganeurites with secondary neuritic processes has been observed in a wide range of lysosomal storage diseases and it seems likely that such lesions are responsible for the clinical neurologic deficits that occur. Irreversible lesions of this nature could account for the persistence of neurologic disease long after the resolution of lysosomal storage in animals suffering severe swainsonine intoxication (Huxtable and Dorling, 1982a; Dorling et al., 1989b).

E. Appetite Suppression

Among the initial signs of swainsonine intoxication are included loss of condition and retardation of growth of young animals. Indeed, chronic weight loss is observed in sheep grazing *Swainsona* even though the intake of plant (and hence swainsonine intake) was not sufficient to induce neurologic disease (Hartley, 1978). The effect of swainsonine on growth rate was investigated experimentally using weanling rats (Pritchard et al., 1989b). The rats received approximately 8 or 46 mg/kg per day of swainsonine via a subcutaneously implanted miniosmotic pump. At the lower dose rate, intense mannoside storage was induced except at neuronal sites protected by the blood-brain barrier. At the higher dose rate, extensive storage was also induced in the neurones of the central nervous system. Both dose rates caused a significant retardation of body-weight gain, which was shown to be due to a profound suppression of appetite in affected animals. At the higher dose rate there was also a reduction in water intake and urine output. There is no current explanation for these effects observed in naturally and experimentally intoxicated animals, apart from stating that the effects appear to be related to the lysosomal storage syndrome. The birth of underweight lambs is perhaps not surprising in view of these effects of swainsonine on appetite, water intake, and the growth rate of postnates.

F. Immunomodulatory and Anticancer Effects

The swainsonine-induced inhibition of the posttranslational processing enzyme α-mannosidase II appears to contribute little to the expression of clinical signs of the toxicosis, despite affecting the structures of the stored oligo-saccharides. However, it does seem to have a pronounced effect on the pro-liferation of activated lymphocytes and the metastasis of some tumor cells. The importance of the role of the carbohydrate entity of cell-surface glyco-proteins in various stages of the metastatic cascade (Dennis and Laforte, 1987) and in the proliferation of activated lymphocytes has been suggested by many studies (Pulverer et al., 1988). For example, the proliferation of activated T lymphocytes is promoted by interleukin 2 (IL-2), a glycoprotein produced by T helper cells (Morgan et al., 1976).

The effect of swainsonine and other inhibitors of glycoprotein processing on immunoenhancement, resulting from an increased proliferation of activated lymphocytes, and on the inhibition of metastasis of tumor cells is considered in detail by Olden in Chapter 26 of this volume. Let it suffice to state at this stage that treatment with swainsonine enhances the immune response in immunocompromised hosts (Kino et al., 1985) and effectively inhibits the colo-nization of the lung by B16-F10 melanoma cells in mice (Humphries et al., 1988). It also enhances mitogen-induced IL-2 production and receptor ex-pression in human lymphocytes, in contrast to castanospermine [6], bromo-conduritol [16], 1-deoxynojirimycin [17], and 1-deoxymannojirimycin [18], in-hibitors of glucosidase I, glucosidase II, glucosidases I and II, and mannosi-dase I, respectively, which do not enhance the immune response (Pulverer et al., 1988). The antimetastatic effects apparently result from the ability of swainsonine to enhance natural killer cell activity by stimulating T helper cells to produce IL-2, which, in turn, promotes the proliferation of activated T lymphocytes.

[16]   [17]   [18]

VII. STRUCTURE–ACTIVITY RELATIONSHIPS

A. Swainsonine

A study of the effect of nucleophiles and pH on the activity of α-D-mannosi-dase indicated a concerted mechanism for mannoside hydrolysis involving two ionizable groups (De Prijcker and De Bruyne, 1975). The glycosidic oxygen is protonated, by a proton donor such as the histidine imidazolium ion (pK $\sim$ 6), the aglycone cleaved off, and the resultant mannosyl cation simultaneously stabilized by a carboxylate ion (pK $\sim$ 3). Thus one of the more obvious hy-potheses for the activity of swainsonine is that it can block the mannosyl sub-strate site of the enzyme. This becomes more acceptable when the absolute configuration of swainsonine is compared to that of mannose or, more specif-ically, when the swainsonine cation is compared to the mannosyl cation (Fig. 2) (Schneider et al., 1983). Additional support for such a hypothesis was the

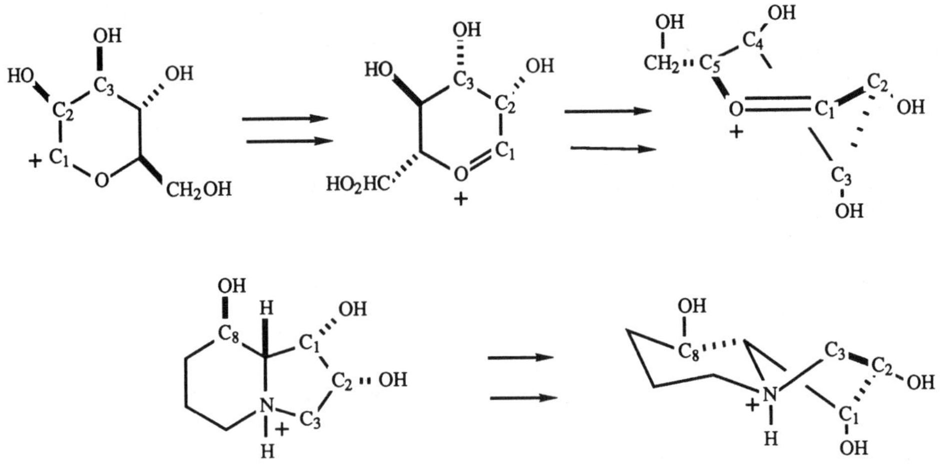

FIGURE 2 Comparison of swainsonine cation with mannosyl cation.

biochemical evidence which suggested that swainsonine was a specific, reversible, substrate-site-directed inhibitor of α-D-mannosidase, and that it would be concentrated within the acid environment of the lysosomes (Dorling et al., 1980). Further, it was shown that the presence of all three unsubstituted hydroxyl substituents was required for the specificity and potency of swainsonine. Thus the 1,2-diacetate of swainsonine was inactive (Colegate et al., 1989), while absence of the 8-hydroxyl substituent, as in the synthetic 8-deoxy-8a-epi-swainsonine [7], resulted in a significant decrease in potency and specificity of its enzyme inhibition activity (Colegate et al., 1984). Periodate oxidation of swainsonine destroyed its enzyme inhibition activity, which was not restored on subsequent reduction of the resultant carbonyls with sodium borohydride (Kang and Elbein, 1983).

It was suggested (Colegate et al., 1979) that synthesis of stereoisomers of swainsonine may yield specific, potent inhibitors of other enzymes and thus provide useful tools for biochemical investigations. Subsequently, a vast array of naturally occurring and synthetic polyhydroxylated indolizidine, pyrrolidine, and piperidine alkaloids have also been related to carbohydrate structures and investigated for enzyme inhibition activity. The resultant availability of synthetic stereoisomers of swainsonine and of the pyrrolidine analogs has allowed more detailed studies of the structural requirements for swainsonine activity. Thus the 2-epi-swainsonine (a glucose analog) [8] did not inhibit jack bean α-mannosidase but did inhibit fungal α-glucosidase, as might be expected, and the 2,8-di-epi-swainsonine (a galactose analog) [9] did not inhibit α-mannosidase but was a mild inhibitor of β-glucosidase (Elbein et al., 1987). The 8a-epi (Tadano et al., 1986a), the 8-epi (Iimura et al., 1986; Tadano et al., 1986b), and the 1,8-di-epi (Iimura et al., 1986; Tadano et al., 1986b) isomers of swainsonine, [19]-[21], each showed reduced activity against α-D-mannosidase with 93%, 15%, and 20%, respectively, of the activity of swainsonine.

[19] [20] [21]

A recent report describes the in vitro activities of swainsonine [1], five stereoisomers of swainsonine ([19]-[23]), and the pyrrolidine analogues of swainsonine and its 8a-epi and 8,8a-di-epi isomers ([24]-[26]) as inhibitors of lysosomal, Golgi, and cytosolic α-D-mannosidases (Cenci di Bello et al., 1989). The results suggested that the chirality of each of the hydroxyl substituents in swainsonine was important in determining the inhibitory potential. Thus, inverting the chirality of any of the hydroxyl substituents, as in compounds [8], [9], [20], and [21], effectively curtailed the ability to inhibit the α-mannosidases tested. It is of interest to note that compared to swainsonine, inversion of the bridgehead proton H8a, as in compound [19], did not dramatically affect the IC_{50}. However, when the bridgehead proton was inverted in conjunction with the C8 hydroxyl as in compound [22], there was observed a restoration of the loss of inhibitory activity resulting from inversion of the C8 hydroxyl alone [20]. In this study it was found, using purified human lysosomal α- mannosidase, that swainsonine was a more potent inhibitor than the synthetic pyrrolidine analog of swainsonine, 1,4-dideoxy-1,4-imino-D-mannitol [24]. This is in contrast to the findings of Fleet et al. (1984b), who found the opposite when the two compounds were compared using jack bean α-mannosidase. The synthetic pyrrolidine analogs of the two active swainsonine isomers (8a-epi [19] and 8,8a-di-epi [22]), 1,4-dideoxy-1,4-imino-D-talitol [25] and 1,4-dideoxy-1,4-imino-L-allitol [26], were also shown to be active as α-mannosidase inhibitors, albeit each with a lower IC_{50} (1.2×10^{-4} M) than swainsonine (7×10^{-8} M) and their analogous swainsonine isomers (7.5×10^{-5} M and 2×10^{-6} M, respectively).

As might be expected from the in vitro enzyme inhibition studies, it was shown that the active swainsonine isomers [19] and [22] also induced storage of mannose-rich oligosaccharides in cultured human fibroblasts. The structures of these oligosaccharides were consistent with the inhibition of the processing α-mannosidases. The same study indicated that the pyrrolidine analogs of swainsonine and of the active isomers of swainsonine ([24]-[26]) inhibited the glycoprotein processing enzymes to a lesser extent and were consequently less effective at inducing accumulation of oligosaccharides and in affecting glycoprotein processing (Cenci di Bello et al., 1989).

[22] [23]

HO
H   OH
HO–CH$_2$
.... OH
N
H

[**24**]

HO
H   OH
HO–CH$_2$
.... OH
N
H

[**25**]

HO
H   OH
HO–CH$_2$
.... OH
N
H

[**26**]

B. Other Glycosidase Inhibitors

From the available enzyme inhibition studies on swainsonine and its stereoisomers, it is apparent that the presence and stereochemistry of the three hydroxyl substituents are important for the potent and specific activity of swainsonine. However, it has become clear from glycosidase inhibition studies of
the various stereoisomers of swainsonine and of other hydroxy indolizidine,
piperidine, and pyrrolidine alkaloids that predictions of glycosidase inhibition
activity based on carbohydrate structure analogies should be treated cautiously.

The 2-*epi*-swainsonine isomer [8] (analogous to D-glucose) does indeed
inhibit fungal α-glucosidase but, unexpectedly, still inhibits Golgi mannosidase II rather than glucosidase I or II. The 2,8-di-*epi*-swainsonine [9]
(analogous to D-galactose) does not inhibit galactosidases but is a mild inhibitor of β-glucosidase and does not affect any glycoprotein-processing enzymes
(Elbein et al., 1987).

Castanospermine, a 1,6,7,8-tetrahydroxyindolizidine [6] isolated from
the seeds of the Australian leguminous tree *Castanospermum australe* (Moreton
Bay chestnut) (Hohenschutz et al., 1981), has been shown to inhibit α- and
β-glucosidases and β-glucocerebrosidase (Saul et al., 1983). Castanospermine
was also shown to be an inhibitor of glucosidase I and II and thereby to affect
glycoprotein processing (Szumilo et al., 1986). This activity might be expected on the basis that the relative stereochemistry of the hydroxyl substituents on C6, C7, and C8 of castanospermine compare favorably with D-glucose.
It may also be noted that the relative stereochemistry of the C1, C8, and C7
hydroxyl substituents can also be compared to D-glucose. However, because
the piperidine alkaloid deoxynojirimycin [17] is also a potent inhibitor of α-
glucosidases (Fellows, 1986), it is tempting to associate the relative stereochemistry of the C6, C7, and C8 hydroxyls with the C2, C3, and C4 hydroxyls
of D-glucose. This association presents a dilemma when 6-*epi*-castanospermine
[27] (Molyneux et al., 1987) is considered because the relative stereochemistry
of the C6, C7, and C8 hydroxyls now is analogous to D-mannose and deoxymannojirimycin [18], an effective mannosidase inhibitor (Fellows, 1986). However, 6-*epi*-castanospermine was shown to be inactive against α-mannosidase
and β-glucosidase but to be a potent inhibitor of α-glucosidase (Molyneux
et al., 1987). Perhaps this indicates that comparison of the relative stereochemistry of the hydroxyl substituents in castanospermine or its stereoisomers
with the stereochemistry of monosaccharides should begin with the C1 hydroxyl
substituent. This suggestion would thus predict that the 6-*epi*-castano-
spermine might be an inhibitor of α-glucosidases and further that the 1-*epi*-
castanospermine [28] might then be a good inhibitor of α-mannosidases. Despite the similarity of both castanospermine and its 6-epimer in inhibiting α-

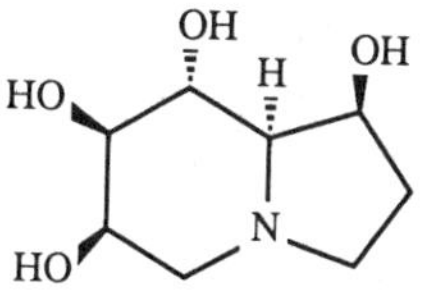

[27] 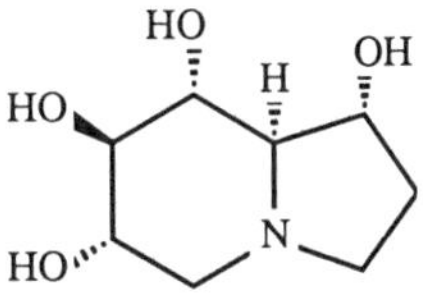   [28] 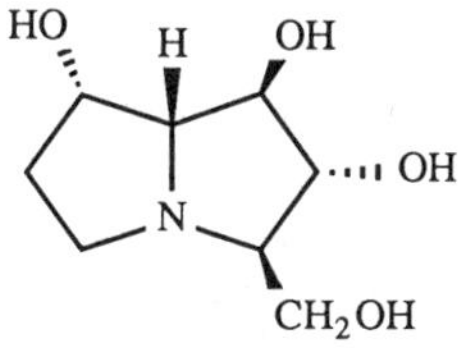   [29]

glucosidase, there are important differences in their inhibitory spectra (Elbein, 1987) which indicate caution when attempting to predict activity based
on sugar structure analogies alone.

The recent isolation of australine [29] from the Moreton Bay chestnut
(*C. australe*) has added a unique glycosidase inhibitor to the fold. This alkaloid is not only reported to be the first example of a pyrrolizidine-based glycosidase inhibitor but also to be the first tetrahydroxypyrrolizidine alkaloid
isolated and the first with the hydroxymethyl substituent at the C3 position
rather than the normal C1 (Molyneux et al., 1988). Australine, with its relative stereochemistry being analogous to that of D-glucose, is a potent, specific inhibitor of amyloglucosidase (an *exo*-1,4-α-glucosidase). It does not,
however, have any effect on β-glucosidase, α- and β-mannosidase, or α- and
β-galactosidase.

Although the preceding examples and those included in a review of the
biological activity of polyhydroxylated indolizidine, piperidine, and pyrrolidine alkaloids (Fellows, 1986) indicate that accurate predictions of enzyme
inhibition activity will involve more than a simplistic comparison with monosaccharides, there are at least two notable examples of the specific design and
synthesis of potent enzyme inhibitors. Thus 1,4-dideoxy-1,4-imino-D-manni-
tol (a mannose analog) [24] (Fleet et al., 1984b) and 1,5-dideoxy-1,5-imino-
L-fucitol (a fucose analog) [30] (Fleet et al., 1985) are potent inhibitors of
α-D-mannosidase and α-L-fucosidase, respectively. It has been suggested

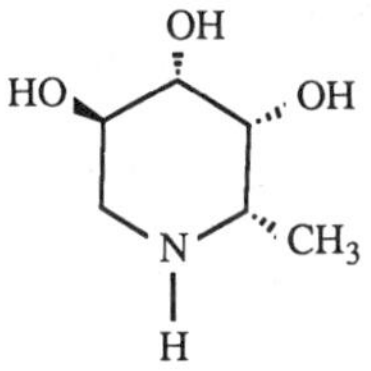

[30]

that a prerequisite for these polyhydroxylated alkaloids to possess glycosidase
inhibition activity is that they include at least three hydroxyl substituents at
positions β to the nitrogen atom (Elbein and Molyneux, 1987). This condition,
in conjunction with monosaccharide structural analogies, may serve as a rational
basis for synthetic aspirations or for screening compounds for inhibition activity.

VIII. CONCLUSIONS

The clinical signs of *Swainsona* or swainsonine intoxication are believed to be
manifestations of the resulting lysosomal storage syndrome. The similarity of

clinical signs and morphology of the intoxication to those of genetic α-mannosidosis support the conclusion that swainsonine intoxication provides an excellent experimental model for genetic α-mannosidosis (Huxtable and Dorling,
1982b). It is difficult to assign any clinical deficits to the effect of swainsonine on glycoprotein processing. However, this very effect may be the basis
for the immunomodulation and antimetastatic effects of swainsonine.

When making analogies between the structures of the polyhydroxylated
alkaloids and the monosaccharides, there exists an intrinsically arbitrary factor which perhaps renders the use of terms such as "D-gluco" swainsonine
for the 2-epi isomer, for example, potentially confusing. The original comparisons between the structures of swainsonine and D-mannose correlated the
C2-OH, C1-OH, and C8a of swainsonine with the C2-OH, C3-OH, and C5 of
mannose (Schneider et al., 1983). Even though the comparative stereochemistry around these particular carbon centers in swainsonine may indeed render the molecule "mannosyl-like" enough for activity, using these carbon centers as descriptors for sugar analogies is clearly deficient. For example,
this method of comparison affords no analogous structure for the 8-epimer,
and since the C4 of the sugar is ignored, swainsonine can equally be compared
to D-talose. Others (Adams et al., 1985) have compared the C2-OH, C1-OH,
and C8-OH of swainsonine with the C2-OH, C3-OH, and C4-OH of mannose
when drawing analogies between swainsonine and its 2-epi [8] and 2,8-di-epi
[9] isomers with mannose, glucose, and galactose, respectively. This view
would also therefore predict the 8-epimer of swainsonine [20] to be analogous
to D-talose and 1,8-di-epimer [21] to be analogous to D-idose. However, a
different interpretation seems to compare the C2-OH, C1-OH, C8a-H, and
C8-OH of swainsonine to the C2-OH, C3-OH, C4-OH, and C5-OH of D-mannose
or, indeed, with the C2-OH, C3-OH, C4-H, and C4-CHOH of the furanose
isomer of D-mannose (Cenci di Bello et al., 1989; Elbein et al., 1987; Fleet
et al., 1984b). This alternative view would predict the 2,8-di-epimer, the
2-epimer, the 8-epimer, and the 1,8-di-epimer of swainsonine to be uniquely
analogous to L-idose, D-glucose, L-gulose, and L-galactose, respectively. Although the latter method presents a unique "sugar" name for the epimers (in
contrast to the previous two methods), it may be that the chiral centers used
for comparison may not have any relevance to the requirements for activity.
Thus it is probably prudent to refer to the stereochemical isomers of these
alkaloids as particular epimers of the parent compound rather than as "sugar"
analogs.

Despite the unreliable predictability of enzyme inhibition activity of naturally occurring and synthetic polyhydroxylated indolizidine, piperidine, and
pyrrolidine alkaloids, the fact remains that these classes of compounds can
provide specific enzyme inhibitors which then can be used in studies of glycoprotein processing, the effects of altered glycoprotein processing (reflecting
the biological role of the carbohydrate entity), and in studies of pathological,
physiological, and biochemical conditions such as lysosomal storage, immunodeficient, and cancerous disease states.

ACKNOWLEDGMENTS

The authors wish to thank Dr. Russell Molyneux, Dr. Isabelle Cenci di Bello,
and Dr. Thomas Harris for making the prepublication proofs of their work

(Molyneux et al., 1988; Cenci di Bello et al., 1989; Harris et al., 1988a) available. Marie-Louise Colegate is thanked for her efforts in the typing and rearrangement of this review.

REFERENCES

Adams, C. E., Walker, F. J., and Sharpless, K. B. (1985). Enantioselective synthesis of swainsonine, a trihydroxylated indolizidine alkaloid. *J. Org. Chem. 50*: 420-422.

Ali, M. H., Hough, L., and Richardson, A. C. (1984). A chiral synthesis of swainsonine from D-glucose. *J. Chem. Soc. Chem. Commun.* 447-448.

Ali, M. H., Hough, L., and Richardson, A. C. (1985). Synthesis of the indolizidine alkaloid swainsonine from D-glucose. *Carbohydr. Res. 136*: 225-240.

Aust, S. D., and Broquist, H. P. (1965). Isolation of a parasympathomimetic alkaloid of fungal origin. *Nature* (Lond.) *205*: 204.

Bar-Shavit, Z., Kahn, A. J., Pegg, L. E., Stone, R. R., and Teitelbaum, S. L. (1984). Glucocorticoids modulate macrophage surface oligosaccharides and their bone binding activity. *J. Clin. Invest. 73*: 1277-1283.

Bennett, R. B., Choi, J.-R., Montgomery, W. D., and Cha, J. K. (1989). A short, enantioselective synthesis of (-)-swainsonine. *J. Am. Chem. Soc., 111*: 2580-2582.

Bischoff, J., and Kornfeld, R. (1983). Evidence for an α-mannosidase in endoplasmic reticulum of rat liver. *J. Biol. Chem. 258*: 7907-7910.

Bohlmann, F. (1957). Configuration determination of quinolizidine derivatives. *Angew. Chem. 69*: 641-642.

Cenci di Bello, I., Dorling, P. R., and Winchester, B. (1983). The storage products in genetic and swainsonine-induced human mannosidosis. *Biochem. J. 215*: 693-696.

Cenci di Bello, I., Fleet, G., Namgoong, S. K., Tadano, K.-I., and Winchester, B. (1989). Structure-activity relationship of swainsonine. *Biochem. J. 259*: 855-861.

Chotai, K., Jennings, C., Winchester, B., and Dorling, P. R. (1983). The uptake of swainsonine, a specific inhibitor of α-D-mannosidase, into normal human fibroblasts in culture. *J. Cell. Biochem. 21*: 107-117.

Chung, K. M., Shephard, V. L., and Stahl, P. (1984). Swainsonine and castanospermine blockade of mannose glycoprotein uptake by macrophages. *J. Biol. Chem. 259*: 14637-14641.

Colegate, S. M., Dorling, P. R., and Huxtable, C. R. (1979). A spectroscopic investigation of swainsonine: an α-mannosidase inhibitor isolated from *Swainsona canescens*. *Aust. J. Chem. 32*: 2257-2264.

Colegate, S. M., Dorling, P. R., and Huxtable, C. R. (1984). The synthesis and biological activity of (±)-(1α,2α,8aα)-indolizidine-1,2-diol. *Aust. J. Chem. 37*: 1503-1509.

Colegate, S. M., Dorling, P. R., and Huxtable, C. R. (1989). Structural elucidation of swainsonine: relationship of structure to activity. In *Swainsonine and Related Glycosidase Inhibitors*, L. F. James, A. D. Elbein, J. Molyneux, and C. D. Warren (Eds.). Iowa State University Press, Ames, Iowa, pp. 91-99.

De Prijcker, J., and De Bruyne, C. K. (1975). Effect of added nucleophiles and pH on α-D-mannosidase-catalyzed reactions. *Carbohydr. Res. 43:* 173-182.

Dennis, J. W., and Laforte, S. (1987). Tumour cell surface carbohydrate and the metastatic phenotype. *Cancer Metastasis Rev.* 5:185-203.

Dorling, P. R., Huxtable, C. P., and Vogel, P. (1978). Lysosomal storage in *Swainsona* spp. toxicosis: an induced mannosidosis. *Neuropath. Appl. Neurobiol.* 4:285-295.

Dorling, P. R., Huxtable, C. P., and Colegate, S. M. (1980). Inhibition of lysosomal α-mannosidase by swainsonine, an indolizidine alkaloid isolated from *Swainsona canescens. Biochem. J. 191:*649-651.

Dorling, P. R., Huxtable, C. R., Colegate, S. M., and Winchester, B. G. (1985). The pathogenesis of chronic *Swainsona* sp. toxicity. In *Plant Toxicology*, A. A. Seawright, M. P. Hegarty, L. F. James, and R. F. Keeler (Eds.). Queensland Poisonous Plants Committee, Yeerongpilly, Australia, pp. 255-265.

Dorling, P. R., Colegate, S. M., and Huxtable, C. R. (1989a). Toxic species of the plant genus *Swainsona*. In *Swainsonine and Related Glycosidase Inhibitors*, L. F. James, A. D. Elbein, J. Molyneux, and C. D. Warren (Eds.). Iowa State University Press, Ames, Iowa, pp. 14-22.

Dorling, P. R., Colegate, S. M., and Huxtable, C. R. (1989b). Swainsonine, a toxic indolizidine alkaloid. In *Toxicants of Plant Origin*, Vol. 1, *Alkaloids*, P. R. Cheeke (Ed.). CRC Press, Boca Raton, Fla., references therein, L. F. James, A. D. Elbein, J. Molyneux, and C. D. Warren (Eds.). Iowa State University Press, Ames, Iowa, pp. 237-250.

Elbein, A. D. (1987). Inhibitors of the biosynthesis and processing of N-linked oligosaccharide chains. *Annu. Rev. Biochem.* 56:497-534.

Elbein, A. D., and Molyneux, R. J. (1987). The chemistry and biochemistry of simple indolizidine and related polyhydroxylated alkaloids. In *Alkaloids: Chemical and Biological Perspectives*, Vol. 5, S. W. Pelletier (Ed.). Wiley, New York, pp. 1-54.

Elbein, A. D., Solf, R., Dorling, P. R., and Vosbeck, K. (1981). Swainsonine: an inhibitor of glycoprotein processing. *Proc. Natl. Acad. Sci. USA 78:*7393-7397.

Elbein, A. D., Szumilo, T., Sanford, B. A., Sharpless, K. B., and Adams, C. (1987). Effect of isomers of swainsonine on glycosidase activity and glycoprotein processing. *Biochemistry 26:*2502-2510.

Everist, S. L. (1981). *Poisonous Plants of Australia*, 2nd ed. Angus & Robertson, Sydney, Australia, pp. 481-489.

Fellows, L. E. (1986). The biological activity of polyhydroxyalkaloids from plants. *Pestic. Sci.* 17:602-606.

Fleet, G. W. J., Gough, M. J., and Smith, P. W. (1984a). Enantiospecific synthesis of swainsonine (1*S*,2*R*,8*R*,8a*R*)-1,2,8-trihydroxyoctahydroindolizine, from D-mannose. *Tetrahedron Lett. 25:*1853-1956.

Fleet, G. W. J., Smith, P. W., Evans, S. V., and Fellows, L. E. (1984b). Design synthesis and preliminary evaluation of a potent α-mannosidase inhibitor: 1,4-dideoxy-1,4-imino-D-mannitol. *J. Chem. Soc. Chem. Commun.* 1240-1241.

Fleet, G. W. J., Shaw, A. N., Evans, S. V., and Fellows, L. E. (1985). Synthesis from D-glucose of 1,5-dideoxy-1,5-imino-L-fucitol, a potent α-L-fucosidase inhibitor. *J. Chem. Soc. Chem. Commun.* 841-842.

Guengerich, F. P., Di Mari, S. J., and Broquist, H. P. (1973a). Isolation and characterization of a 1-pyrindene fungal alkaloid. *J. Am. Chem. Soc.*, *95*: 2055-2056.

Guengerich, F. P., Snyder, J. J., and Broquist, H. P. (1973b). Biosynthesis of slaframine, (1*S*,6*S*,8a*S*)-1-acetoxy-6-aminooctahydroindolizine, a parasympathomimetic alkaloid of fungal origin: 1. Pipecolic acid the slaframine biogenesis. *Biochemistry 12*: 4264-4269.

Hamlow, H. P., Okuda, S., and Nakagawa, N. (1964). Nuclear magnetic resonance effects of cyclic tertiary amines. *Tetrahedron Lett.* 2553-2559.

Harris, C. M., Schneider, M. J., Ungemach, F. S., Hill, J. E., and Harris, T. M. (1988a). Biosynthesis of the toxic indolizidine alkaloids slaframine and swainsonine in *Rhizoctonia leguminicola*: metabolism of 1-hydroxy-indolizidines. *J. Am. Chem. Soc.*, *110*: 940-949.

Harris, C. M., Campbell, B. C., Molyneux, R. J., and Harris, T. M. (1988b). Biosynthesis of swainsonine in the diablo locoweed (*Astragalus oxyphysus*). *Tetrahedron Lett.* *29*: 4815-4818.

Harris, T. M., Harris, C. M., Hill, J. E., and Ungemach, F. S. (1987). (1*S*,2*R*,8a*S*)-1,2-Dihydroxyindolizidine formation by *Rhizoctonia leguminicola*, the fugus that produces slaframine and swainsonine. *J. Org. Chem.* *52*: 3094-3098.

Hartley, W. J. (1978). A comparative study of Darling Pea (*Swainsona* spp.) poisoning in Australia with locoweed (*Astragalus* and *Oxytropis* spp.) poisoning in North America. In *Effects of Poisonous Plants on Livestock*, R. F. Keeler, K. R. Van Kampen, and L. F. James (Eds.). Academic Press, New York, p. 363.

Heywood, V. H. (1971). In *Chemotaxonomy of the Leguminosae*, J. B. Harbourne, D. Bouter, and B. L. Turner (Eds.). Academic Press, New York, pp. 1-29.

Hino, M., Nakayama, O., Tsurumi, Y., Adachi, K., Shibata, T., Terano, H., Kohsaka, M., Aoki, H., and Imanaka, H. (1985). Studies of an immunomodulator, swainsonine: I. Enhancement of immune response by swainsonine in vivo. *J. Antibiot.* *38*: 926-935.

Hohenschutz, L. D., Bell, E. A., Jewess, P. J., Leworthy, D. P., Pryce, R. J., Arnold, E., and Clardy, J. (1981). Castanospermine, a 1,6,7,8-tetrahydroxyoctahydroindolizine alkaloid, from seeds of *Castanospermum australe*. *Phytochemistry 20*: 811-814.

Hooghe, R. J., Scaaf-Lafontaine, N., Hooghe-Peters, E. L., Plaetse, F. V., De Saint-Georges, L., Dorling, P. R., and Janowski, M. (1984). Integrity of glycoprotein complex sugars is required for homing but not for several other membrane-mediated functions. *Cell Biochem. Funct. 2*: 102-106.

Horeau, A. (1961). Principe et applications d'une nouvelle méthode de détermination des configurations dite "par dédoublement partial." *Tetrahedron Lett.* 506-512.

Humphries, M. J., Matsumoto, K., White, S. L., Molyneux, R. J., and Olden, K. (1988). Augmentation of murine natural killer cell activity by swainsonine, a new antimetastatic immunomodulator. *Cancer Res. 48*: 1410-1415.

Huxtable, C. R. (1970). Ultrastructural changes caused by *Swainsona galegifolia* poisoning in the guinea pig. *Aust. J. Exp. Biol. Med. Sci. 48*: 71-80.

Huxtable, C. R. (1972). The effect of ingesiton of *Swainsona galegifolia* on the liver lysosomes of the guinea pig. *Aust. J. Exp. Biol. Med. Sci.* *50*:109-118.

Huxtable, C. R., and Dorling, P. R. (1982a). Poisoning of livestock by *Swainsona* spp.: current status. *Aust. Vet. J.* *59*:50-53.

Huxtable, C. R., and Dorling, P. R. (1982b). Mannosidosis: swainsonine-induced mannosidosis. *Am. J. Pathol.* *107*:124-126.

Huxtable, C. R., and Dorling, P. R. (1985). Mannoside storage and axonal dystrophy in sensory neurones of swainsonine-treated rats: morphogenesis of lesions. *Acta Neuropathol.* *68*:65-73.

Huxtable, C. R., and Gibson, A. (1970). Vacuolation of circulating lymphocytes in guinea pigs and cattle ingesting *Swainsona galegifolia*. *Aust. Vet. J.* *46*:446-448.

Huxtable, C. R., Dorling, P. R., and Walkley, S. U. (1982). Onset and regression of neuroaxonal lesions in sheep with mannosidosis induced experimentally with swainsonine. *Acta Neuropathol.* *58*:27-33.

Iimura, Y., Hotta, Y., Fukabori, C., Tadano, K.-I., and Suami, T. (1986). Synthesis of (-)-8-*epi*-swainsonine and (-)-1,8-di-*epi*-swainsonine, stereoisomers of indolizidine alkaloid, swainsonine. *J. Carbohydr. Chem.* *5*: 147-152.

Jellinger, K. (1973). Neuroaxonal dystrophy: its natural history and related disorders. *Prog. Neuropathol.* *2*:129.

Jolly, R. D. (1975). Mannosidosis of Angus cattle: a prototype control programme for some genetic diseases. *Adv. Vet. Sci. Comp. Med.* *19*:1-20.

Jolly, R. D., Winchester, B. G., Gehler, J., Dorling, P. R., and Dawson, G. (1981). Mannosidosis: a comparative review of biochemical and related clinicopathological aspects of three forms of the disease. *J. Appl. Biochem.* *3*:273-291.

Kang, M. S., and Elbein, A. D. (1983). Mechanisms of inhibition of jack bean α-mannosidase by swainsonine. *Plant Physiol.* *71*:551-554.

Katsuki, T., Lee, A. W. M., Ma, P., Martin, V. S., Masamune, S., Sharpless, K. B., Tuddenham, D., and Walker, F. J. (1982). Synthesis of saccharides and related polyhydroxylated natural products: I. Simple alditols. *J. Org. Chem.* *47*:1373-1378.

Kino, T., Inamura, N., Nakahara, K., Kiyoto, S., Goto, T., Terano, H., Kohsaka, M., Aoki, H., and Imanaka, H. (1985). Studies of an immunomodulator, swainsonine: II. Effect of swainsonine on mouse immunodeficient systems and experimental murine tumor. *J. Antibiot.* *38*:936-940.

Lloyd, J. B., and Beck, F. (1969). Lysosomes and congenital malformation. *Biochem. J.* *115*:32-34.

Luning, B., and Lundin, C. (1967). Orchidaceae alkaloids: VI. Synthesis and relative configuration of 5,7-dimethyloctahydroindolizines. *Acta Chem. Scan.* *21*:2136-2142.

McGee, C. M., and Murray, D. R. (1986). Comparative studies of acid glycosidases from three legumes. *Ann. Bot.* (*Lond.*) *57*:179-190.

Molyneux, R. J., and James, L. F. (1982). Loco intoxication: indolizidine alkaloids of spotted locoweed (*Astragalus lentigenosus*). *Science* *216*:190-191.

Molyneux, R. J., James, L. J., and Panter, K. E. (1985). Chemistry of toxic constituents of locoweed (*Astragalus* and *Oxytropis*) species. In *Plant Toxicology*, A. A. Seawright, M. P. Hegarty, L. F. James, and

R. F. Keeler (Eds.). Queensland Poisonous Plants Committee, Yeeron-gpilly, Australia, pp. 266-278.

Molyneux, R. J., Roitman, J. N., Dunnheim, G., Szumilo, T., and Elbein, A. D. (1987). 6-Epicastanospermine, a novel indolizidine alkaloid that inhibits α-glucosidase. *Arch. Biochem. Biophys. 251*:450-457.

Molyneux, R. J., Benson, B., Wong, R. Y., Tropea, J. E., and Elbein, A. D. (1988). Australine, a novel pyrrolizidine alkaloid glucosidase inhibitor from *Castanospermum australe. J. Nat. Prod. 51*(6):1198-1206.

Morgan, O., Ruscetti, F., and Gallo, R. (1976). Selective in vitro growth of T lymphocytes from normal human bone marrow. *Science 193*:1007-1009.

Novikoff, P. M., Touster, O., Novikoff, A. B., and Tulsiani, D. P. (1985). Effects of swainsonine on rat liver and kidney: biochemical and morphological studies. *J. Cell Biol. 101*:339-349.

Ockerman, P. A. (1969). Mannosidosis: isolation of oligosaccharide storage material from brain. *J. Pediatr. 75*:360-365.

Ockerman, P. A. (1973). In *Lysosomes and Storage Diseases*, H. G. Hers and F. van Hoof (Eds.). New York, pp. 292-304.

Olden, K., Parent, J. B., and White, S. L. (1982). Carbohydrate moieties of glycoproteins: a re-evaluation of their function. *Biochim. Biophys. Acta 650*:209-232.

O'Sullivan, B. M., and Goodwin, J. A. (1977). An outbreak of *Swainsona* poisoning in horses. *Aust. Vet. J. 53*:446-446.

Pritchard, D. H., Huxtable, C. R., Dorling, P. R., and Colegate, S. M. (1989a). Some characteristics of axonal dystrophy in swainsonine toxicosis. In *Swainsonine and Related Glycosidase Inhibitors*, L. F. James, A. D. Elbein, J. Molyneux, and C. D. Warren (Eds.). Iowa State University Press, Ames, Iowa, pp. 76-82.

Pritchard, D. H., Huxtable, C. R., Dorling, P. R., and Colegate, S. M. (1989b). The effect of swainsonine on the growth rate of young rats. In *Swainsonine and Related Glycosidase Inhibitors*, L. F. James, A. D. Elbein, J. Molyneux, and C. D. Warren (Eds.). Iowa State University Press, Ames, Iowa, pp. 360-366.

Pulverer, G., Beuth, J., Ko, H. L., Yassin, A., Ohshima, Y., Roszkowski, K., and Uhlenbruch, G. (1988). Glycoprotein modifications of sarcoma L-1 tumor cells by tunicamycin, swainsonine, bromoconduritol or 1-desoxy-nojirimycin treatment inhibits their metastatic lung colonization in Balb/c-mice. *J. Cancer Res. Clin. Oncol. 114*:217-220.

Rader, C. P., Young, R. L., and Aaron, H. S. (1965). Azabicyclic alcohols: III. Stereochemistry of the 7- and 8-hydroxyindolizidines. *J. Org. Chem. 30*:1563-1539.

Rainey, D. P., Smalley, E. B., Crump, M. H., and Strong, F. M. (1965). Isolation of salivation factor from *Rhizoctonia leguminicola* on red clover hay. *Nature* (Lond.) *205*:203-204.

Saul, R., Chambers, J. P., Molyneux, R. J., and Elbein, A. D. (1983). Castanospermine, a tetrahydroxylated alkaloid that inhibits α-glucosidase and α-glucocerebrosidase. *Arch. Biochem. Biophys. 221*:265-275.

Schneider, M. J., Ungemach, F. S., Broquist, H. P., and Harris, T. M. (1982). Biosynthesis of swainsonine in *Rhizoctonia leguminicola*: epimerization at the ring fusion. *J. Am. Chem. Soc., 104*:6863-6864.

Schneider, M. J., Ungemach, F. S., Broquist, H. P., and Harris, T. M. (1983). (1*S*,2*R*,8*R*,8a*R*)-1,2,8-Trihydroxyindolizidine (swainsonine), an α-mannosidase inhibitor from *Rhizoctonia leguminicola*. *Tetrahedron* *39*:29-32.

Setoi, H., Takeno, H., and Hashimoto, M. (1985). Enantiospecific total synthesis of (-)-swainsonine: new applications of sodium borohydride reduction. *J. Org. Chem. 50*:3948-3950.

Skelton, B. W., and White, A. H. (1980). Crystal structure of swainsonine diacetate. *Aust. J. Chem. 33*:435-439.

Suami, T., Tadano, K.-I., and Iimura, Y. (1984). Total synthesis of (-)-swainsonine, and an α-mannosidase inhibitor isolated from *Swainsona canescens*. *Chem. Lett. 3*:513-516.

Suami, T., Tadano, K.-I., and Iimura, Y. (1985). Total synthesis of (-)-swainsonine, and an α-mannosidase inhibitor isolated from *Swainsona canescens*. *Carbohydr. Res. 136*: 67-75.

Szumilo, T., Kaushal, G. P., and Elbein, A. D. (1986). Purification and properties of glucosidase I from mung bean seedlings. *Arch. Biochem. Biophys. 247*:261-271.

Tadano, K.-I., Hotta, Y., Morita, M., Suami, T., Winchester, B., and Cenci di Bello, I. (1986a). Synthesis of (-)-8a-*epi*-swainsonine, (1S,2R,8R, 8aS)-octahydro-1,2,8-indolizinetriol. *Chem. Lett. 5*:2105-2108.

Tadano, K.-I., Iimura, Y., Hotta, Y., Fukabori, C., and Suami, T. (1986b). Synthesis of (-)-8-*epi*-swainsonine and (-)-1,8-di-*epi*-swainsonine, stereoisomers of physiologically interesting indolizidine alkaloid, swainsonine. *Bull. Chem. Soc. Jpn. 59*:3885-3892.

Tulsinani, D. R. P., and Touster, O. (1983). Swainsonine, a potent mannosidase inhibitor, elevates rat liver and brain lysosomal α-D-mannosidase, decreased Golgi α-D-mannosidase II, and increased the plasma levels of several acid hydrolases. *Arch. Biochem. Biophys. 224*:594-600.

Tulsiani, D. R. P., Harris, T. M., and Touster, O. (1982). Swainsonine inhibits the biosynthesis of complex glycoproteins by inhibition of Golgi mannosidase II. *J. Biol. Chem. 257*:7936-7939.

Tulsiani, D. R. P., Broquist, H. P., James, L. F., and Touster, O. (1984). The similar effects of swainsonine and locoweed on tissue glycosidases and oligosaccharides of the pig indicate that the alkaloid is the principal toxin responsible for the induction of locoism. *Arch. Biochem. Biophys. 232*:76-85.

Tulsiani, D. R. P., Broquist, H. P., and Touster, O. (1985). Marked differences in the swainsonine inhibition of rat liver lysosomal α-D-mannosidase, rat liver Golgi mannosidase II, and jack bean α-D-mannosidase. *Arch. Biochem. Biophys. 236*:427-434.

Walkley, S. U., and Siegel, D. A. (1985). Ectopic dendritogenesis occurs on cortical pyramidal neurons in swainsonine-induced feline α-mannosidosis. *Dev. Brain Res. 20*:143-148.

Walkley, S. U., Wurzelmann, S., and Siegel, D. A. (1986). Ultrastructural changes in cerebral cortical neurons in swainsonine-induced and inherited feline α-mannosidosis appear identical. *J. Cell Biol. 103*:A76.

Williams, D. H., and Fleming, I. (1966). *Spectroscopic Methods in Organic Chemistry*. McGraw-Hill, New York, p. 104.

Winchester, B. (1984). Role of α-mannosidases in the biosynthesis and catabolism of glycoproteins. *Biochem. Soc. Trans. 12*:522-524.

Winkler, J. R., and Segal, H. L. (1984a). Inhibition by swainsonine of the degradation of endocytosed glycoproteins in isolated rat liver parenchymal cells. *J. Biol. Chem. 259*:1958-1962.

Winkler, J. R., and Segal, H. L. (1984b). Swainsonine inhibits glycoprotein degradation by isolated rat liver lysosomes. *J. Biol. Chem. 259*:15369-15372.

Yasuda, N., Tsutsumi, H., and Takaya, T. (1984). Total synthesis of swainsonine. *Chem. Lett. 3*:1201-1204.

Yasuda, N., Tsutsumi, H., and Takaya, T. (1985). Synthesis of two stereoisomers of swainsonine. *Chem. Lett. 4*:31-34.

Yeo, T. K., Yeo, K. T., Parent, J. B., and Olden, K. (1985). Swainsonine treatment accelerates intracellular transport and secretion of glycoproteins in human hepatoma cells. *J. Biol. Chem. 260*:2565-2569.

10

Swainsonine, the Locoweed Toxin: Analysis and Distribution

Russell J. Molyneux

Western Regional Research Center, Agricultural Research Service, USDA, Albany, California

Lynn F. James

Poisonous Plant Research Laboratory, Agricultural Research Service, USDA, Logan, Utah

I. INTRODUCTION

The closely related genera *Astragalus* and *Oxytropis* of the plant family Leguminosae are circumglobal in distribution. The North American species have been subjected to extensive taxonomic analysis and *Astragalus* has been classified into 368 species and 184 varieties (Barneby, 1964), whereas *Oxytropis* has been grouped into 35 species (Barneby, 1952). In the western United States certain individual species of these genera have been classified as "locoweeds" because of their propensity to cause a neurological disease known as locoism in livestock that consume them (Marsh, 1909). The signs of such poisoning are depression, dull staring eyes, staggering gait, muscular incoordination, rough coat, and nervousness when stressed. Affected animals may also become solitary and exhibit difficulty in eating and drinking, emaciation, and sexual dysfunction (James et al., 1981). In addition, the locoweeds have been shown to cause birth defects and abortion (James et al., 1967), and to be associated with congestive right-heart failure when consumed at high altitudes (about 3000 m) (Panter et al., 1988). It has been suggested that livestock may become habituated to locoweed but it has not been possible to confirm this observation experimentally (Ralphs and Molyneux, 1989). Locoweed toxicity has been observed in many animal species, including wild and domesticated livestock as well as experimental animals. A comprehensive discussion of the various syndromes is presented in Volume 1 of this Handbook (James, 1983).

It should be noted that many species of *Astragalus* are acutely toxic due to the presence of glucose derivatives of 3-nitropropanol or 3-nitropropionic acid (Williams and James, 1978), or are chronically toxic due to the presence of accumulated selenium, possibly as organoselenium derivatives (Hartley et al., 1985). However, only those *Astragalus* and *Oxytropis* species capable of producing the neurological defect of locoism can properly be regarded as locoweeds. The extension of the term "locoweed" to other toxic species of the genera is inaccurate and misleading terminology. There is some evidence that *Astragalus* and *Oxytropis* species found in other parts of the world, such as China (G. R. Cao, personal communication) and Peru (K. E. Panter, personal communication), may produce a disease in livestock that is identical to locoism, but the colloquial nature of the term and the difficulty of accurately defining the syndromes may have prevented a direct correlation with the situation in the western United States. Nevertheless, C. D. Marsh (1909) astutely noted the similarity of locoism to the "pea-struck" syndrome produced by consumption of certain *Swainsona* species in Australia.

The comprehensive work of Marsh over a number of years during the early part of this century established the etiology of the locoweed disease as a consequence of consuming particular species of the genera *Astragalus* and *Oxytropis*. Moreover, the majority of the syndromes produced by these plants were delineated during this period, providing the fundamental definition of the disease as it is known at present. Undoubtedly, the locoweeds are the major single cause of livestock losses due to poisonous plants in western rangelands even today, and losses due to death are far outweighed economically by malnourishment, lack of weight gain, and reduced reproductive performance. The problem is frequently unpredictable and sporadic in nature, resulting in poisoning episodes which may be catastrophic to individual producers or localities under ecological conditions which are such that locoweed populations may explode. Such episodes are most commonly associated with species such as *Astragalus lentiginosus*, *A. mollissimus*, *A. wootonii*, *Oxytropis sericea*, and *O. lambertii* which have historically been incriminated as locoweeds. A tabulation of these species from three primary sources is provided in Table 1. Despite such useful observations it should be recognized

TABLE 1 *Astragalus* and *Oxytropis* Species Incriminated as Locoweeds from Field Observations

Species[a]	Marsh (1909, 1924)	Sampson and Malmsten (1935)	Barneby (1952, 1964)
A. agricidus			×
A. allochrous	×		
A. asymmetricus		×	×
A. bisulcatus	×		
A. canadensis		×	
A. diphysus	×		
A. douglasii			×
A. drummondi	×		
A. hornii		×	
A. lentiginosus[b]	×	×	×
A. malacus			×
A. miguelensis			×
A. miser			×
A. mollissimus[b]	×		×
A. nothoxys	×		×
A. nuttallii		×	
A. oocarpus		×	
A. oxyphysus		×	×
A. pubentissimus[b]			×
A. purshii		×	
A. rattani			×
A. tetrapterus			×
A. thurberi	×		×
A. wootoni[b]	×		×
O. besseyi	×		×
O. lambertii	×		×
O. lagopus	×		×
O. sericea[b]	×		×

[a]Nomenclature according to Barneby.
[b]Principal ("classic") locoweed species.

that the potential exists for a previously unincriminated *Astragalus* and *Oxytropis* species to respond to ecological change with massive population growth or with greatly increased levels of the locoweed toxin.

It is apparent that none of the problems described above, caused by the locoweeds, can be confronted without the isolation and identification of the toxin and subsequent development of analytical methods to detect it. The former task has now been achieved with the identification of swainsonine as the toxin of both locoweeds and *Swainsona* species. It is the purpose of this chapter to discuss briefly the isolation and structural properties of swainsonine and to present in some detail analytical methods that have been developed for the alkaloid. Finally, recent results on the occurrence and distribution of swainsonine in nature are dealt with. It is anticipated that the application of analytical methodology will provide a predictive tool that will enable scientists and producers to displace the locoweeds from their preeminent position as livestock poisons, which they have occupied since the earliest settlement of the western United States.

II. SWAINSONINE: THE LOCOWEED TOXIN

A. Isolation and Identification

Swainsonine [1] was first isolated and the structure elucidated, in an exemplary demonstration of the advantages of interdisciplinary cooperation, from the Australian legume *Swainsona canescens* (Colegate et al., 1979) (see also Chapter 9 in this volume). The latter species and other members of the genus are closely related botanically to the American locoweeds and produce, upon consumption by animals, a toxicosis analogous to locoism. This communality, remarked upon some 75 years earlier by Marsh, led to the isolation of swainsonine, together with swainsonine *N*-oxide [2], from the spotted locoweed, *Astragalus lentiginosus* (Molyneux and James, 1982). Swainsonine has subsequently been detected in a number of different *Swainsona*, *Astragalus*, and *Oxytropis* species, although there is a distinction between the Australian and North American genera in that only the latter elaborate the *N*-oxide (Molyneux et al., 1985, 1989; Dorling et al., 1989). In addition to its occurrence in these legumes, swainsonine is produced together with the indolizidine alkaloid slaframine [3] by *Rhizoctonia leguminicola*, which is, as its name implies, a fungus infesting leguminous forages, especially red clover (Schneider et al., 1983). It has also been isolated from a second microorganism, *Metarhizium anisopliae* (Hino et al., 1985). It is interesting to speculate vis-à-vis the compounding effect on swainsonine content if *R. leguminicola*, or some other as yet undiscovered swainsonine-producing fungus, were to infest a locoweed species.

At the time of its initial isolation, swainsonine (1,2,8-trihydroxyindolizidine) was unique as a polyhydroxyindolizidine alkaloid. Shortly thereafter, castanospermine [4], a tetrahydroxyindolizidine alkaloid (Hohenschutz et al., 1981), was isolated from seeds of the Moreton Bay chestnut (*Castanospermum australe*), a large Australian rain forest tree of the family Leguminosae, quite different in appearance in all but the seed pods from *Swainsona* and the locoweeds, which are herbaceous species. Nevertheless, the seeds are toxic to horses and cattle (McKenzie et al., 1988). Castanospermine has also been

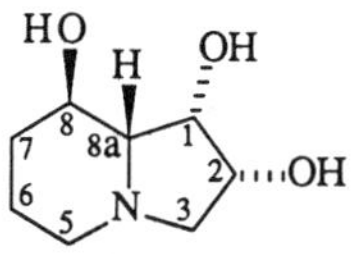

[1]

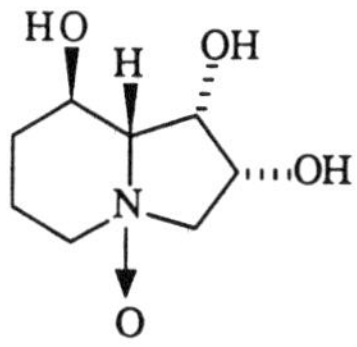

[2]

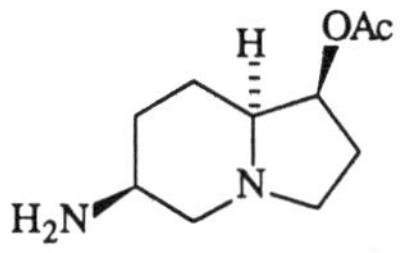

[3]

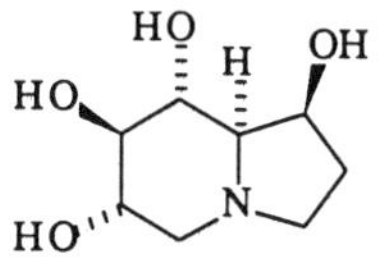

[4]

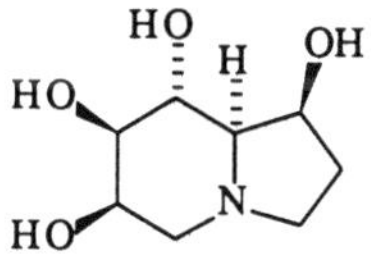

[5]

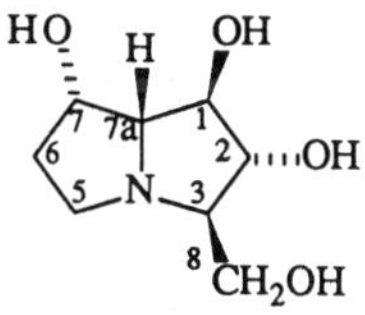

[6]

isolated or identified in a number of species of *Alexa*, leguminous trees native to Central and South America (Nash et al., 1988a). *C. australe* has recently yielded 6-epicastanospermine [5] (Molyneux et al., 1986), australine [6] (Molyneux et al., 1988), and 3,8-diepialexine (3-epiaustraline) (Nash et al., 1988b). Although the australines must by convention be regarded as pyrrolizidine alkaloids, it is apparent from close examination of their structures that they can be viewed as indolizidine alkaloids in which the six-membered ring has undergone a formal ring contraction with extrusion of a $-CH_2OH$ group. It is therefore obvious that swainsonine can no longer be regarded as unique, but rather must be seen as the vanguard of a general class of polyhydroxyindolizidine alkaloids, occurring primarily in legumes and having novel and specific biochemical properties as glycosidase inhibitors (Elbein and Molyneux, 1987). Undoubtedly, many more structurally related alkaloids remain to be discovered.

B. Structure and Properties

The physical properties of swainsonine are atypical of most classes of alkaloids. It is extremely soluble in water and hydroxylic solvents, only moderately soluble in polar, nonhydroxylic solvents, and quite insoluble in nonpolar solvents. Swainsonine *N*-oxide possesses these same properties to an even more pronounced degree, and the two alkaloids can be separated by capitalizing upon the fact that whereas swainsonine has limited solubility in chloroform, the *N*-oxide is completely insoluble in the same solvent. Conventional techniques for isolation and purification of alkaloids, which generally involve partitioning into acidic solution, basification, and back extraction with water-immiscible organic solvents, cannot be used to isolate swainsonine. The crude plant extract is most conveniently purified by passage of the aqueous acid-soluble portion through a column of Dowex 50W-X8 ion-exchange resin in its ammonium ion form and elution with dilute ammonium hydroxide. After such purification steps the alkaloid can be crystallized from chloroform saturated with ammonia, although the process has proved to be difficult and erratic even in the hands of experienced workers.

The structure of swainsonine was determined by spectroscopic methods, in particular, mass spectrometry, and ^{1}H- and ^{13}C-nuclear magnetic resonance spectroscopy (Colegate et al., 1979). The hydroxyl groups at C1 and C2 bear a cis relationship to one another, and examination of molecular models indicates that the conformation of the molecule is such that hydrogen bonding of either group to the nitrogen-atom lone pair can occur (Fig. 1). It is interesting to note that swainsonine [1] is unique among the known simple polyhydroxy indolizidine alkaloids in possessing a β-configuration at the bridgehead carbon atoms. This may be a consequence of its novel biosynthesis from precursors with an α-configuration at this position, via an iminium ion (Harris et al., 1988a,b).

In its structural features swainsonine has much in common with the simple sugars, and it is presumably this similarity that confers glycosidase inhibitory properties upon it and related polyhydroxy alkaloids (see below). At the same time, swainsonine possesses the general alkaloidal property of basic character and therefore exists as a salt at low pH, whereas the *N*-oxide is essentially a neutral, yet polar species.

C. Biochemistry and Mode of Action

Swainsonine is a potent, specific inhibitor of a number of α-mannosidases. It was inferred that the toxin of *S. canescens* possessed such a property even before its isolation and structural identification as a trihydroxyindolizidine alkaloid, since consumption of the plant produced a phenocopy of the genetically controlled lysosomal storage disease, mannosidosis (Dorling et al., 1978). This disease is characterized by an insufficiency of the enzyme α-mannosidase. The recognition of this similarity led to the use of the enzyme as a biochemical probe for a plant constituent with inhibitory properties, ultimately shown to be swainsonine. The pure alkaloid was subsequently demonstrated to be a competitive inhibitor of lysosomal α-mannosidase (Dorling et al., 1980).

In mammalian tissues there are three structurally differentiated forms of α-mannosidase, each possessing different pH optima and different subcellular locations: acidic α-mannosidase, localized in the lysosomes; intermediate α-mannosidase, concentrated in the Golgi; and neutral α-mannosidase, localized in the cytosol. The Golgi α-mannosidase has been further classified into mannosidase IA/IB and mannosidase II. Each of the enzymes exhibits a specificity for particular mannosyl linkages and functions in the degradation of the oligosaccharide moiety of various glycoproteins. The inhibition of these essential processing steps leads to lysosomal storage of improperly processed

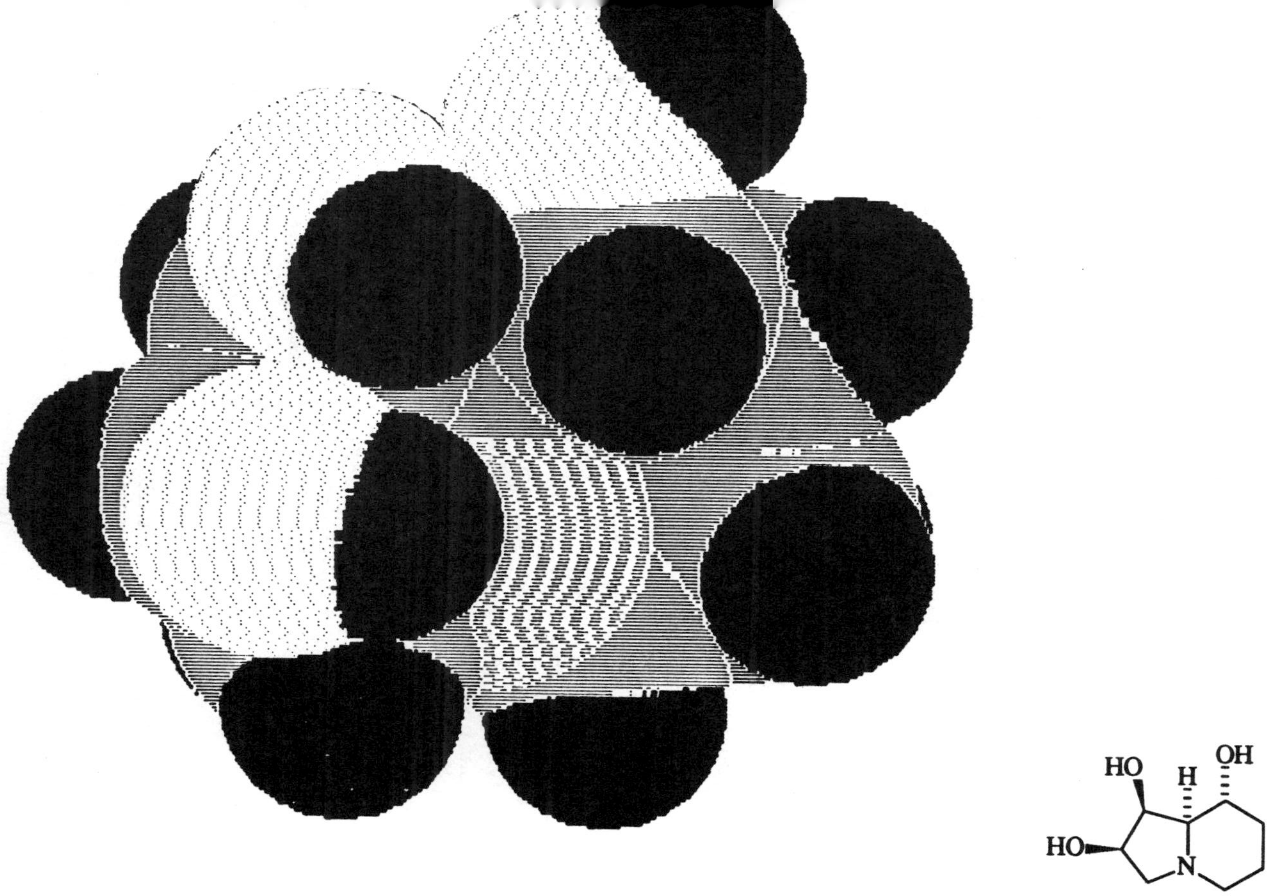

SWAINSONINE

FIGURE 1 Energy-minimized molecular model of swainsonine, illustrating proximity of cis-1,2-diol groups to nitrogen lone pair.

glycoprotein, which is consequently unable to undergo subsequent trimming steps and cellular excretion of the protein end product. The consequent ac- cumulation of such intermediates within the cell leads to vacuolation and even- tual clinical expression of the storage disease.

It has been shown that swainsonine completely inhibits acidic α-mannosi- dases isolated from various tissues, which have a pH optimum of 4.0, at a concentration of 20 mM (Dorling et al., 1980). In addition, swainsonine has been found to be a potent inhibitor of Golgi mannosidase II but not of mannosi- dases IA and IB (Tulsiani et al., 1982). Further studies showed that the alkaloid was extremely specific, failing to inhibit β-mannosidase, α- of β-glu- cosidase, α- or β-galactosidase, β-hexosaminidase, or α-fucosidase, even at much higher concentrations than that at which it is effective against α- mannosidase (Kang and Elbein, 1983). Experiments using cell cultures from viral, animal, and human sources have demonstrated that swainsonine can be absorbed into cells and inhibit the biosynthesis of the N-linked glycopro- teins, but no evidence of cell-growth inhibition of cytotoxicity has been ob- served even at very high concentrations (Elbein et al., 1983).

In contrast to swainsonine, other polyhydroxyindolizidine and polyhy- droxypyrrolizidine alkaloids do not inhibit α-mannosidase. Thus castano- spermine [4] inhibits α- and β-glucosidase (Saul et al., 1983, 1984) and 6- epicastanospermine inhibits α-glucosidase (Molyneux et al., 1986), which is also inhibited by australine (Tropea et al., 1989).

D. Toxicology

Treatment of rats, guinea pigs, or sheep with swainsonine causes excretion of abnormal "high-mannose" oligosaccharides in the urine. The use of high- performance liquid chromatography to analyze the profiles of these metabo- lites indicated the presence of specific oligosaccharides characteristic of in- hibition of both lysosomal α-mannosidase and Golgi mannosidase II. The de- fect in glycoprotein processing appeared to produce no clinical effects on the animals, but the associated accumulation of lysosomal storage products pro- duced the same symptoms as locoweed consumption (Abraham et al., 1983). Comparative experiments, using pigs treated with swainsonine and with loco- weed, resulted in similar decreases in liver Golgi mannosidase II levels and increases in tissue oligosaccharide levels. The profiles and structures of the accumulated oligosaccharides, together with the altered enzyme activities and similar clinical signs, provide compelling evidence for swainsonine as the locoism-producing toxin in *Astragalus* and *Oxytropis* species (Tulsiani et al., 1984).

The question of whether or not swainsonine is responsible for other syn- dromes attributed to locoweed consumption is far more problematic. There is no doubt that the alkaloid interferes with a fundamental biochemical pro- cess of all cells (i.e., glycoprotein processing) and could theoretically be responsible for many apparently unrelated syndromes. The relationship of swainsonine to abortion, birth defects, sexual dysfunction, and habituation (if it occurs) remains to be proven. It is noteworthy, however, that the alka- loid does possess the structural features proposed as essential for terato- genicity [i.e., a saturated piperidine ring with a three-carbon atom or longer side chain attached α to the nitrogen atom (e.g., coniine)] (Keeler, 1983).

In the case of swainsonine this propyl side chain is modified by fusion to the nitrogen atom itself. The opportunity to produce terata may be greatly reduced by the extreme water solubility of swainsonine. Feeding experiments with swainsonine in rats (Pritchard et al., 1989) and in dairy cattle (Daniel et al., 1989) demonstrate that it is not metabolized to any appreciable extent and is rapidly excreted. It is probable, therefore, that if swainsonine is in fact capable of inducing terata, the amount reaching the fetus would only be sufficient to produce insult when the consumption of locoweed is exceptionally high or sustained for a long period. It has been shown that locoweed fed to mice from days 6 to 15 at a swainsonine dose rate of 4 mg/kg body weight per day failed to result in either maternal or fetal toxicity (Berry et al., 1989).

On the other hand, swainsonine is undoubtedly transferred in the milk to their offspring by animals feeding on locoweed. Thus both cattle consuming white locoweed (*Oxytropis sericea*) at high altitudes, and their unweaned calves, showed symptoms of congestive right-heart failure attributable to swainsonine ingestion (James et al., 1983). Moreover, milk from cattle fed locoweed has produced symptoms of locoism in kittens, calves, and lambs (James and Hartley, 1977). Such results naturally raise the specter of swainsonine entering the human food chain. In general, this is unlikely to be a problem, due to the modern practice of blending milk from many different sources (James et al., 1989b). Nevertheless, in situations where persons, especially young children, may depend on milk from a family cow, the risk of swainsonine ingestion via this route should be assessed, given suitable analytical methods.

III. SWAINSONINE ANALYSIS

A. Analytical Requirements

The identification of swainsonine as the causative agent of locoism, and probably of many of the other toxic syndromes attributable to locoweeds, does not per se resolve the problem of economic loss caused by these plants. It is, however, the crucial step required to develop the essential techniques to prevent or control such losses. Suitable analytical techniques, once available, can be used to devise management procedures that may be applied in a predictive manner to the following problems:

1. To establish those *Astragalus* and *Oxytropis* species, additional plant genera, and microorganisms that contain significant levels of swainsonine and may thus possess the potential to induce locoism
2. To determine the particular plant parts in which swainsonine may accumulate and at what growth stage the plant may be most (or least) toxic
3. To establish the maximum tolerated dose, without deleterious effects, for livestock species of concern
4. To determine the rate and extent of excretion of swainsonine and its potential for accumulation in meat or milk
5. To measure the transfer of swainsonine in pregnant animals to the fetal unit and its potential to produce abortion or terata
6. To investigate the effect of swainsonine ingestion levels on reproduc-

tive performance

7. To establish whether or not a relationship exists between the swain-sonine content of the plant and a potential for habituation in animals consuming it

In order to deal with such questions, the analytical techniques must be, above all, specific for swainsonine. In addition, it is desirable that they also be sensitive, accurate, rapid, and convenient. Unfortunately, these require-ments conflict with the physical properties of swainsonine. Although it may be quite naturally classified as an indolizidine alkaloid, with fundamental structural features in common with the other bicyclic alkaloid classes, the pyrrolizidines and quinolizidines, certain structural details set it apart. Thus the high degree of hydroxylation confers an exceptional solubility in water and other hydroxylic solvents and a corresponding lack of solubility in most organic solvents. In many respects swainsonine is somewhat of a "pseudo-alkaloid," with significant similarities to both simple sugars and amino sugars. The simpler monocyclic polyhydroxylated piperidine (e.g., deoxynojirimycin) and pyrrolidine alkaloids also have chemical and biochemical properties in com-mon with swainsonine and castanospermine (Elbein and Molyneux, 1987) and may conveniently be regarded as hypothetical fragments of the indolizidine ring system (Fig. 2). Such structural analogies are suggestive of the most appropriate analytical techniques and provide valuable leads as to methods that may be modified to provide specific analyses for swainsonine.

B. Qualitative Thin-Layer Chromatographic Analysis

Thin-layer chromatography (TLC) possesses many of the features requisite to providing answers to the problems arising from locoweed toxicity. It is rapid, convenient, and has the potential, as demonstrated in the case of the pyrrolizidine alkaloids (Mattocks and Jukes, 1987), to be adapted to a field situation. As an analytical tool its specificity and sensitivity depend most heavily on an appropriate detection method; with sufficient effort solvent sys-tems capable of resolving structurally similar compounds can usually be de-veloped.

In contrast to most alkaloids, including the pyrrolizidine and quinolizi-dine groups, swainsonine fails to react with general alkaloid detection re-agents such as iodoplatinate and Dragendorff's, except at unacceptably high concentrations. Also at high concentrations it reacts with ninhydrin to give, not a typical purple amino acid coloration but rather, a nondescript yellow-brown spot. Although the latter spray reagent may conveniently be used to locate the alkaloid on preparative TLC plates, it is neither specific nor sensitive enough for analytical purposes. The acetate derivatives of swain-sonine and castanospermine do respond readily to Dragendorff's reagent, in-dicating that the lack of reactivity with the alkaloid itself involves some type of interaction of the hydroxyl groups with the heterocyclic nitrogen atom. Nevertheless, the advantages of TLC, primarily speed and convenience, are lost if such derivatives must be prepared prior to analysis.

The structural analogies of swainsonine and related indolizidine alkaloids to the pyrrolizidine necine bases have provided an entrée to an analytical method for the former which is specific, sensitive, and convenient for the

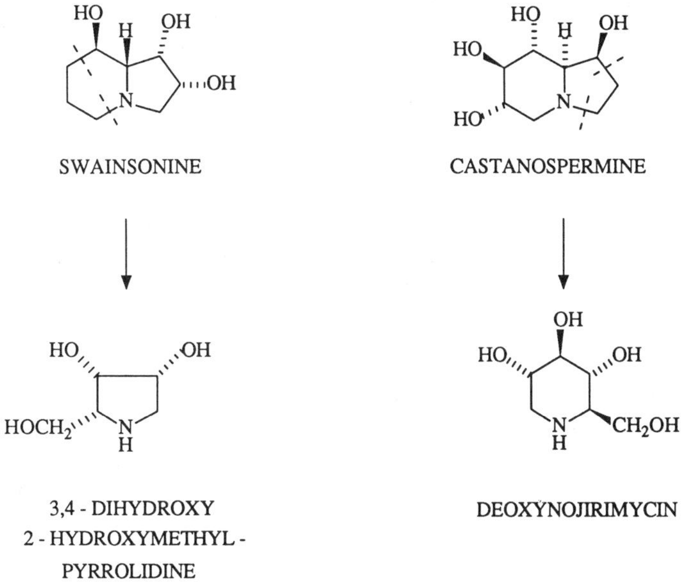

FIGURE 2 Hypothetical fragmentation of polyhydroxyindolizidine alkaloids to pyrrolidine and piperidine structural equivalents.

screening of plant extracts. It has been shown that pyrrolizidine alkaloids (e.g., retronecine) possessing a degree of unsaturation, when sprayed with a solution of *o*-chloranil, undergo oxidation to pyrrolic derivatives which are capable of condensing with Ehrlich's reagent to give an intense purple-colored spot (Molyneux and Roitman, 1980). The latter condensation requires the presence of a free position alpha to the nitrogen atom of the pyrrole ring system. This dual, sequential spray reagent has been used routinely to analyze plant extracts for pyrrolizidine alkaloids, both the simple necine bases and the more commonly found mono- and di-ester derivatives.

Since swainsonine possesses a pyrrolidine ring moiety, an analogous condensation with Ehrlich's reagent will occur if the pyrrolic ring system can be generated. In contrast to the pyrrolizidine alkaloids, however, swainsonine is lacking in unsaturation and an oxidation process is inappropriate for generation of the essential pyrrole. Nevertheless, the presence of several hydroxyl groups in the molecule suggests that a double dehydration process would lead to the pyrrolic ring system. This can, in fact, be achieved by an initial spray reagent containing acetic anhydride. Subsequent treatment with the Ehrlich's reagent spray yields a purple-colored spot, as with the pyrrolizidine alkaloids, except that the reaction is less rapid and heating of the TLC plate is required for full development of color. An additional advantage of the method is that swainsonine *N*-oxide undergoes a Polonovski rearrangement with acetic anhydride, so that a single dehydration step is all that is required and the purple color develops with greater facility. The free-base and *N*-oxide forms of the alkaloid can thus be readily distinguished, both by the speed of color formation and by the much lower mobility of the latter in suitable solvent systems (e.g., $CHCl_3:MeOH:NH_4OH:H_2O$, 70:26:2:2 or 4:4:1:1). The minimum detection level for swainsonine on the TLC plate is on the order of 0.5 μg, and for the N-oxide, about 0.05 μg. The contrasting routes to pyrrolic intermediates, capable of reacting positively with Ehrlich's reagent, are illustrated for retronecine and swainsonine in Fig. 3.

Related polyhydroxyindolizidine alkaloids such as castanospermine (4), 6-epicastanospermine [5], and their corresponding N-oxides are detectable at similar levels, although a rearrangement of the double bonds from the six- to the five-membered ring, following the initial dehydration step, is necessary for generation of the pyrrolic system. In contrast, the novel polyhydroxy-pyrrolizidine alkaloid australine [6], which co-occurs with castanospermine in *C. australe* (Molyneux et al., 1988), can generate a pyrrole directly but fails to react with Ehrlich's reagent since the position alpha to the hetero-cyclic nitrogen atom is blocked by the hydroxymethyl group.

This TLC method for swainsonine has been used to screen extracts from a number of *Astragalus* and *Oxytropis* species and various plant parts. In addition, it has been used to show that swainsonine occurs in the milk of cows fed on locoweed (Molyneux et al., 1985).

C. Quantitative Gas Chromatographic Analysis

Gas chromatography (GC) fulfills those analytical criteria which are absent from the TLC method, namely sensitive and accurate quantitation. It is, however, far less rapid and convenient, requiring the use of specialized equipment. Although swainsonine has significant volatility, subliming at about 100°C under vacuum, attempts to analyze it and related alkaloids directly by GC have been unsuccessful (Molyneux, unpublished results). Although a single peak was obtained, the detector response was not consistent, most probably due to dehydration of the molecule at the temperature of the injector or column. Given this situation, the structural analogy of the alkaloids to the simple sugars, for which a number of derivatization methods have been developed to facilitate GC analysis, proved most useful. The trimethylsilyl (TMS) derivatives were chosen since selection can be made from among a considerable variety of commercially available reagents.

Initial experiments with swainsonine, treated with bis(trimethylsilyl)tri-fluoroacetamide (BSTFA), gave a single peak on a 30-m DB-1 fused silica column. The peak was shown by GC/mass spectrometry to be due to the tri-TMS derivative. It is interesting to note that fragmentation of this derivative proved to be analogous to that of the underivatized alkaloid, namely cleavage of the bonds beta to the nitrogen atom in the five-membered ring, leaving the six-membered ring moiety and its substituent hydroxyl group (either de-rivatized or underivatized) intact. The same fragmentation pattern has been found in all other polyhydroxy-indolizidine alkaloids examined, thus providing valuable information as to the distribution of hydroxyl groups between the two rings of the bicyclic system. Unfortunately, castanospermine failed to react completely with BSTFA, giving three major peaks on GC. However, de-rivatization with hexamethyldisilazane-trimethylchlorosilane (HMDS-TMCS) gave a single peak, shown by GC/MS to be the tetra-TMS derivative. It has been found that N-methyl-N-trimethylsilyltrifluoroacetamide (MSTFA) is the best general silylating reagent, yielding single derivatives with all polyhydroxy-

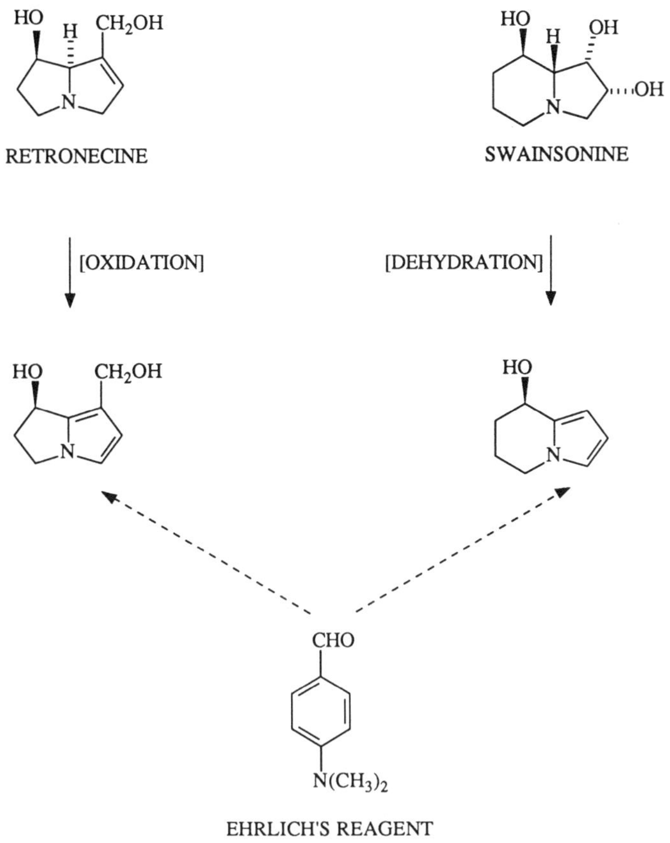

FIGURE 3 Hypothetical pyrrole derivatives, generated from retronecine and swainsonine, capable of condensation with Ehrlich's reagent.

indolizidine, polyhydroxy-pyrrolizidine, polyhydroxy-pyrrolidine, and poly-hydroxy-piperidine derivatives so far examined. In general, as might be expected, it appears that an increasing number of hydroxyl substituents (and consequently, TMS moieties) leads to longer retention times on GC. Retention times for a number of such alkaloids are listed in Table 2.

Standardization of the GC with pure swainsonine showed that the detector response was linear, with a minimum detection level of 150 pg. Sensitivity of this order indicates that quantitative analysis can be carried out on quite small samples of plant material. In fact, it has been found that a single seed of *Astragalus lentiginosus*, weighing 2.2 mg, contains sufficient swainsonine for an aliquot of 0.5% of the extract to give a detector response corresponding to 39 ng. Analysis of vegetative plant material, including flowers, leaves, and stems, can readily be performed on 0.5-g samples. Many additional peaks are observed in the GC of these extracts, possibly due to other polyhydroxy alkaloids, but the swainsonine peak is well resolved and easily quantitated. Specificity for such alkaloids could be increased even more by the use of a nitrogen-specific detector. The GC method is therefore both sensitive and

TABLE 2 Retention Times for Polyhydroxy Alkaloid TMS
Derivatives on Gas Chromatography

Alkaloid	Retention time (min)
Pyrrolidine class	
Fagomine	11.44
Deoxynojirimycin	16.78
Deoxymannojirimycin	14.29
Pyrrolizidine class	
Australine	16.93
3-Epiaustraline	17.53
Indolizidine class	
Swainsonine	13.97
6-Epicastanospermine	17.71
Castanospermine	18.80
Castanospermine *N*-oxide	19.67

accurate, and suitable for a comprehensive survey of swainsonine occurrence
not only within individual species and varieties but also between plant parts
and at different growth stages.

D. Potential Analytical Methods

The significance of swainsonine and related alkaloids as toxins, their importance as tools in the study of glycoprotein processing, and their potential applications in medicine or for production of animal models of genetic lysosomal
storage disease indicate that increasingly sensitive analytical methods, or
procedures adapted to analysis of specific tissues or fluids, will be required.
The advantages and disadvantages of those most likely to be adapted in the
future are therefore briefly discussed in this section.

High-performance liquid chromatography (HPLC) is a convenient technique generally available in a majority of laboratories, especially those performing routine clinical analyses. The physical properties of swainsonine,
namely its extreme water solubility and lack of a chromophore suitable for
spectrophotometric detection, detract from the suitability of HPLC as an analytical technique. Nevertheless, the selection of appropriate reagents should
yield derivatives suitable for HPLC analysis. As with GC analysis, the hydroxyl groups would appear to be the most amenable to derivatization. Appropriate derivatives would be those with chromophores absorbing strongly in
the ultraviolet or visible region of the spectrum, or strongly fluorescent compounds that would provide extremely high sensitivity. The use of 7-[(chloro-
carbonyl)methoxy]-4-methylcoumarin would appear to be a particularly suitable reagent for the formation of fluorescent ester derivatives of the hydroxyl groups (Karlsson et al., 1985). The presence of the cis-1,2-diol group
in swainsonine suggests that the formation of cyclic boronate derivatives having chromophoric or fluorescent properties should be investigated. Deriva-

tization of swainsonine with ferroceneboronic acid has recently been shown
to yield a cyclic ester with an abundant molecular ion for GC/MS detection
(Brooks et al., 1989). Unfortunately, the ester must be further treated with
BSTFA to derivatize the remaining hydroxyl group, in order to obtain adequate volatility. Cyclic boronate esters would be specific for the cis-diol
moiety and would not be applicable to other polyhydroxyindolizidine alkaloids
such as castanospermine, which lack such functionality. In the future it may
be possible to apply HPLC to analysis of swainsonine without derivatization
using mass spectrometric detection (HPLC-MS), providing a suitable column-
solvent system combination can be found.

Tandem mass spectrometry (MS/MS) is a rapidly evolving technique that
utilizes two coupled mass analyzers to provide separation of ions of selected
mass, which then undergo fragmentation and analysis. The technique bears
a direct analogy to GC/MS but without the requirement for chemical cleanup
and derivatization. The speed of analysis is markedly increased since the
time required for separation is essentially instantaneous in the mass spectrometer. The technique can be applied to crude plant extracts or even plant
material since only ions of a particular mass (M^+ 173 for swainsonine) are selected from the complex matrix for analysis in the second mass analyzer.
MS/MS has been applied to pyrrolizidine alkaloids as a class (Haddon and
Molyneux, 1983) and also to individual alkaloids.

Immunoassay techniques [enzyme-linked immunosorbent assay (ELISA)
and radioimmunoassay (RIA)] are commonly used in clinical chemistry and
for trace amounts of environmental toxins. The methodology for detection
of individual compounds requires the development of appropriate haptens of
remarkable specificity, and monoclonal or polyclonal antibody production which
may involve considerable time and effort. Nevertheless, if swainsonine or
other polyhydroxyindolizidine alkaloids fulfill their potential as clinical drugs
(Humphries et al., 1988; Walker et al., 1987), or if routine analysis of meat
and milk samples is required to prevent entry of the alkaloids into the food
chain, such effort may be justified. Immunoassay methods are extremely sensitive, specific, and easy to use once they are developed.

IV. DISTRIBUTION OF SWAINSONINE

A. General Occurrence

The discovery of swainsonine and its unique biological properties is relatively
recent. Despite this, the alkaloid has been isolated from three quite different general sources: (1) poison pea or Darling pea (*Swainsona*) species in
Australia, (2) locoweed (*Astragalus* and *Oxytropis*) species in North America,
and (3) microorganisms (*Rhizoctonia leguminicola* and *Metarhizium anisopliae*).
In view of the diverse nature, both geographically and as species, of these
sources it is most probable that swainsonine will be found to occur in additional plants or fungi. It may, in fact, prove to be an alkaloid of fairly wide
distribution, having remained undiscovered previously because of the cryptic nature of its chemical and physical properties.

Whereas *Swainsona* is restricted to Australia, *Astragalus* and *Oxytropis*
species occur worldwide and it appears likely that livestock losses occurring
in other regions of the world, especially South America (K. E. Panter, per-

sonal communication), the interior regions of China (G. R. Cao, personal communication) and the USSR, and possibly also South Africa, may in fact be previously unrecognized manifestations of the well-established locoweed disease of North America. The occurrence of swainsonine in two unrelated microorganisms increases the probability that it will be found in others. In this context it is interesting to note that the biosynthetic pathway to swainsonine from pipecolic acid (Fig. 4) is identical in *R. leguminicola* (Harris et al., 1988a) and in the Diablo locoweed, *A. oxyphysus* (Harris et al., 1988b), suggesting that swainsonine production is a desirable trait. Since legumes such as red clover are a natural substrate for the fungus, it seems probable that at some time in the evolutionary past the genes for swainsonine biosynthesis were transferred from microorganism to plant, or vice versa.

The general occurrence of polyhydroxyindolizidine alkaloids in plants of the Leguminosae indicate that this family would be the most rewarding in which to search for additional swainsonine-producing genera. This chemotaxonomic approach has already proved productive in the case of castanospermine, which has recently been found to occur in a number of *Alexa* species native to South America (Nash et al., 1988a) in addition to its original source, the monotypic species *C. australe* from Australia (Hohenschutz et al., 1981).

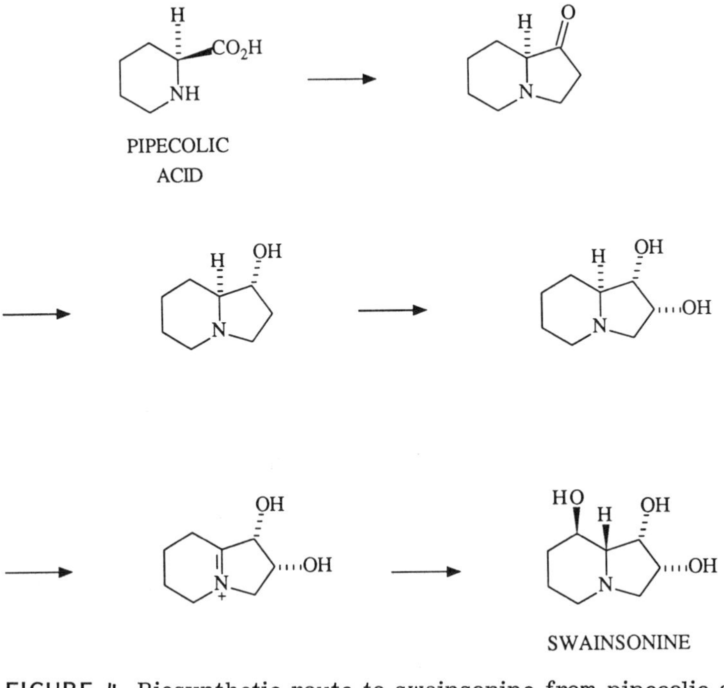

FIGURE 4 Biosynthetic route to swainsonine from pipecolic acid in *R. leguminicola* and *A. oxyphysus* (Harris et al., 1988a,b).

B. Occurrence of Swainsonine by Species or Variety

The analytical methods for swainsonine discussed earlier have been developed so recently that there has been no concerted effort to date to establish its distribution within the genera *Astragalus* and *Oxytropis*. Such an approach has proved useful in the case of the nitrotoxins. Over 250 species have been analyzed, and particular taxonomic sections have been found to be the most likely to produce nitropropanol glycosides (Williams and Barneby, 1977). However, there is no guarantee that a similar approach will prove applicable to the situation with swainsonine.

Species of *Astragalus* and *Oxytropis* analyzed to date have been collected in an opportunistic or serendipitous manner and efforts have quite naturally been concentrated on species which are incriminated as locoweeds on the basis of field observations. All species classified as true locoweeds that have been examined do, in fact, contain swainsonine. These are listed in Table 3. Additional species not previously identified as locoweeds have now been shown to contain greater or lesser amounts of swainsonine. The more significant of these are also included in Table 3. It should be realized that a considerable number of species which do contain swainsonine may not present a problem of locoism because of their very limited distribution or inaccessibility to livestock. Nevertheless, it is useful to identify swainsonine-containing species because of the unpredictability of ecological change, which may on occasion result in juxtaposition of livestock, or even wildlife such as deer or elk, with burgeoning populations of such species and consequently threaten the wellbeing of the animals.

Despite the relatively small number of plant species that have been analyzed, a number of interesting observations have been made which indicate the need for systematic examination. For example, certain *Astragalus* species are known accumulators of selenium and are established as toxic (Alkali Disease) due to the presence of this element. Two of these, *A. bisulcatus* and *A. praelongus*, have been shown qualitatively by TLC to contain moderate

TABLE 3 Occurrence of Swainsonine in *Astragalus* and *Oxytropis* Species

Locoweeds	Other species
A. asymmetricus	*A. bicristatus*
A. bisulcatus	*A. didymocarpus*
A. lentiginosus	*A. pycnostachyus*
A. mollissimus	*A. succumbens*
A. oocarpus	*A. trichopodus*
A. oxyphysus	*O. kansunsis*
A. wootoni	*O. ochrocephala*
O. lambertii	
O. sericea	

amounts of swainsonine and their toxicity, sometimes alluded to as "Blind Staggers," may be a combination of syndromes produced by both selenium and swainsonine (Molyneux et al., 1985), although recent research has raised some question as to the association of Blind Staggers with selenium-accumulating plants (James et al., 1989a). On the other hand, *A. conjunctus, A. falcatus, A. hoodianus, A. leucolobus, A. purshii, A. reventiformis,* and *A. whitneyi,* which contain moderate levels of nitrotoxins (Williams and Barneby, 1977), have been found to be devoid of swainsonine. Whether or not the two classes of toxin are mutually exclusive awaits the analysis of a larger cross section of samples.

Interesting preliminary results have been obtained from the analysis of species that are not native to North America. Thus, whereas the native species *Oxytropis lambertii* and *O. sericea* contain significant amounts of swainsonine, *O. riparia,* a native of the USSR that has become established in southwestern Montana, contains none of the alkaloid (Williams and Molyneux, 1988). In fact, its high nutritional value indicates that it may have some utility as a forage plant. In contrast, leaf and stem samples of *O. ochrocephala* and *O. kansunsis,* collected from the Ninxia and Gansu regions of China, were found to contain 0.012% and 0.021% swainsonine, respectively (Molyneux and Cao, unpublished results). Such levels are quite typical of those found in locoweed samples, and the syndromes of toxicity observed in horses in these areas may be the first manifestation of locoism due to *Oxytropis* established other than in North America.

Determinations of swainsonine content at the varietal level within a given species have been extremely limited. Five of the 37 varieties of *A. lentiginosus* have been examined (var. *diphysus, lentiginosis, micans, nigricalysis,* and *wahweapensis*) and all contain swainsonine, albeit in varying amounts. Cattle grazing Wahweap milkvetch (*A. lentiginosus* var. *wahweapensis*) developed clinical signs of locoweed poisoning (Ralphs et al., 1988), corroborating the evidence for swainsonine as the locoweed toxin. In contrast, two varieties of *A. flavus* showed considerable differences. *A. flavus* var. *argillosus* contained 0.035% swainsonine, whereas var. *flavus* contained only 0.001%, a barely detectable amount. This indicates that until much more data is available, it would be unwise to extrapolate the swainsonine content of a particular variety within a species to the species in general.

C. Occurrence of Swainsonine by Plant Part and Growth Stage

For the purpose of controlling livestock losses caused by locoweed consumption, it is essential that the swainsonine content of individual plant parts, at various growth stages, be determined. The availability of such information would enable producers to restrict the access of their animals to the plants when they are most toxic.

Initial results have shown that there are considerable differences in swainsonine content between various plant parts, with the highest levels concentrated in the seed. GC analysis of swainsonine can readily be performed on a single seed weighing only a few milligrams. For example, the swainsonine content of *A. lentiginosus* seed was shown to be 0.35%. Moreover, this seed sample was 17 years old at the time of analysis, indicating that swainsonine is retained in plant material for considerable periods. This was confirmed with vegetative material from *A. lentiginosus* var. *diphysus*, in which green plant material contained 0.037% swainsonine, and dry, senescent, overwintered stem material contained 0.023% (Ralphs and Molyneux, 1989). It appears probable that, provided the situation warrants sacrifice of the material, a single seed from an herbarium specimen could be used to determine the swainsonine content.

The most comprehensive study of swainsonine variation with plant part has been for *Oxytropis sericea* during the seasons 1984-1986. The swainsonine level ranged from 0.007 to 0.079% in leaf, 0.08 to 0.103% in flowers, and 0.022 to 0.154% in seed and pod samples (Molyneux et al., 1989). It is noteworthy that the swainsonine content tends to be highest in the reproductive parts of the plant. For this reason, analyses of plant samples should, whenever possible, be performed on pod/seed samples in order to maximize the potential for detection of swainsonine. Analysis of additional plant parts can then be carried out on those species warranting the greatest concern. Obviously, if the swainsonine content of the seed is very low, there is little likelihood that the vegetative parts will be hazardous to livestock.

Data on the variation of swainsonine with growth stage and season is extremely limited and restricted to the *O. sericea* series discussed above. The swainsonine content was twice as high in 1985 as in 1984, with 1986 being intermediate in level. Swainsonine content in the flower/seedhead and in the leaf reached a maximum at the immature pod stage. At the mature pod stage, the level in the seedhead declined to approximately 60 to 70% of the maximum, but the decline in leaf samples was far more marked, the swainsonine content amounting to about 25 to 30% of the maximum. These observations may be explained by an interesting experiment that provides some insight as to the biosynthesis of swainsonine and its transport within the plant. A spotted locoweed plant (*A. lentiginosus*), grown in the laboratory, was opportunistically colonized by the green pea aphid (*Acyrthosiphon pisum*). Analysis by TLC of the honeydew (excreta) of these insects showed that it contained high levels of swainsonine (Dreyer et al., 1985). Since the pea aphid is known to feed solely on the phloem, the swainsonine must be biosynthesized in the leaves and transported in the phloem to other parts of the plant, where it becomes preferentially concentrated. The high concentration of alkaloid within the seeds may serve a protective function in order to ensure reproduction of the plant.

The latter experiment serves to illustrate an additional point with regard to analysis of plant samples for swainsonine. The utility of any analytical technique is limited primarily by the problems of sampling. Thus at the suborgan level it is physically difficult to collect plant parts or obtain sufficient material for analysis. We have found, however, that certain insects can be used to advantage to gather selectively quite specific microscopic parts of the plant and that the residue of such predation, the insects themselves, or their excreta, can then be analyzed for swainsonine, to ascertain its localization and transport within the plant. For example, seed beetles of the genus *Acanthoscelides* frequently infest locoweeds, the larvae feeding on the endosperm but leaving the seed coat unattacked (Johnson, 1970). The latter can then be analyzed to determine the localization of the alkaloid within the seed itself. Such observations should be capitalized on to better understand the role of swainsonine within the plant.

V. CONCLUSIONS

Both qualitative and quantitative methods of analysis for swainsonine are now established. These methods will undoubtedly evolve further in the direction of greater sensitivity, selectivity, and convenience. However, such techniques are merely tools, not an end in themselves. They provide the means with which to study the far more interesting problems of swainsonine occurrence and distribution in plants, fungi and animals. More significantly, they may at last provide the essential information necessary to prevent livestock losses due to locoweeds, a problem that has affected producers for over a century.

REFERENCES

Abraham, D., Blakemore, W. F., Jolly, R. D., Sidebotham, R., and Winchester, B. (1983). The catabolism of mammalian glycoproteins. *Biochem. J. 215*: 573-579.

Barneby, R. C. (1952). A revision of the North American species of *Oxytropis* DC. *Proc. Calif. Acad. Sci. 4th Ser. 27*: 177-312.

Barneby, R. C. (1964). Atlas of North American Astragalus: Parts I and II. *Mem. N.Y. Bot. Gard. 13*.

Berry, D. L., Molyneux, R. J., James, L. F., and Willhite, C. C. (1989). Developmental toxicology of the indolizidine alkaloids castanospermine and swainsonine in rodents. In *Swainsonine and Related Glycosidase Inhibitors*, L. F. James, A. D. Elbein, R. J. Molyneux, and C. D. Warren (Eds.). Iowa State University Press, Ames, pp. 417-424.

Brooks, C. W. J., Cole, W. J., and Robins, D. J. (1989). Gas chromatography-mass spectrometry of cyclic boronate derivatives of some alkaloid and terpenoid diols. *Heterocycles 28*: 151-156.

Colegate, S. M., Dorling, P. R., and Huxtable, C. R. (1979). A spectroscopic investigation of swainsonine: an α-mannosidase inhibitor isolated from *Swainsona canescens*. *Aust. J. Chem. 32*: 2257-2264.

Daniel, P. F., Warren, C. D., James, L. F., and Jolly, R. D. (1989). A comparison of swainsonine-induced and genetic α-mannosidosis in Aberdeen Angus cattle. In *Swainsonine and Related Glycosidase Inhibitors*, L. F. James, A. D. Elbein, R. J. Molyneux, and C. D. Warren (Eds.). Iowa State University Press, Ames, pp. 331-343.

Dorling, P. R., Huxtable, C. R., and Vogel, P. (1978). Lysosomal storage in *Swainsona* spp. toxicosis: an induced mannosidosis. *Neuropathol. Appl. Neurobiol. 4*: 285-295.

Dorling, P. R., Huxtable, C. R., and Colegate, S. M. (1980). Inhibition of lysosomal α-mannosidase by swainsonine, an indolizidine alkaloid isolated from *Swainsona canescens*. *Biochem. J. 191*: 649-651.

Dorling, P. R., Colegate, S. M., and Huxtable, C. R. (1989). Toxic species of the plant genus *Swainsona*. In *Swainsonine and Related Glyco-*

sidase Inhibitors, L. F. James, A. D. Elbein, R. J. Molyneux, and C.
D. Warren (Eds.). Iowa State University Press, Ames, pp. 14-22.

Dreyer, D. L., Jones, K. C., and Molyneux, R. J. (1985). Feeding deterrency of some pyrrolizidine, indolizidine, and quinolizidine alkaloids towards pea aphid (*Acyrthosiphon pisum*) and evidence for phloem transport of indolizidine alkaloid swainsonine. *J. Chem. Ecol.* 11:1045-1051.

Elbein, A. D., and Molyneux, R. J. (1987). The chemistry and biochemistry of simple indolizidine and related polyhydroxy alkaloids. In *Alkaloids: Chemical and Biological Perspectives*, Vol. 5, S. W. Pelletier (Ed.). Wiley, New York, pp. 1-54.

Elbein, A. D., Pan, Y. T., Solf, R., and Vosbeck, K. (1983). Effect of swainsonine, an inhibitor of glycoprotein processing, on cultured mammalian cells. *J. Cell Physiol.* 115:265-275.

Haddon, W. F., and Molyneux, R. J. (1983). Tandem mass spectrometry for agricultural problems. In *Tandem Mass Spectrometry*, F. W. McLafferty (Ed.). Wiley-Interscience, New York, pp. 451-464.

Harris, C. M., Schneider, M. J., Ungemach, F. S., Hill, J. E., and Harris, T. M. (1988a). Biosynthesis of the toxic indolizidine alkaloids slaframine and swainsonine in *Rhizoctonia leguminicola*: metabolism of 1-hydroxy-indolizidines. *J. Am. Chem. Soc.* 110:940-949.

Harris, C. M., Campbell, B. C., Molyneux, R. J., and Harris, T. M. (1988b). Biosynthesis of swainsonine in the Diablo locoweed (*Astragalus oxyphysus*). *Tetrahedron Lett.* 29:4815-4818.

Hartley, W. J., James, L. F., Broquist, H., and Panter, K. E. (1985). Pathology of experimental locoweed and selenium poisoning in pigs. In *Plant Toxicology*, A. A. Seawright, M. P. Hegarty, L. F. James, and R. F. Keeler (Eds.). Queensland Poisonous Plants Committee, Yeerongpilly, Australia, pp. 141-149.

Hino, M., Nakayama, O., Tsurumi, Y., Adachi, K., Shibata, T., Terano, H., Kohsaka, M. Aoki, H., and Imanaka, H. (1985). Studies of an immunomodulator, swainsonine: I. Enhancement of immune response by swainsonine in vitro. *J. Antibiot.* 38:926-935.

Hohenschutz, L. L., Bell, E. A., Jewess, P. J., Leworthy, D. P., Pryce, R. J., Arnold, E., and Clardy, J. (1981). Castanospermine, a 1,6,7,8-tetrahydroxyindolizidine alkaloid, from seeds of *Castanospermum asutrale*. *Phytochemistry* 20:811-814.

Humphries, M. J., Matsumoto, K., White, S. L., Molyneux, R. J., and Olden, K. (1988). Augmentation of natural killer cell activity by swainsonine, a new antimetastatic immunomodulator. *Cancer Res.* 48:1410-1415.

James, L. F. (1983). Neurotoxins and other toxins from *Astragalus* and related genera. In *Handbook of Natural Toxins*, Vol. 1, *Plant and Fungal Toxins*, R. F. Keeler and A. T. Tu (Eds.). Marcel Dekker, New York, pp. 445-462.

James, L. F., and Hartley, W. J. (1977). Effects of milk from animals fed locoweed on kittens, calves and lambs. *Am. J. Vet. Res.* 38:1263-1265.

James, L. F., Shupe, J. L., Binns, W., and Keeler, R. F. (1967). Abortive and teratogenic effects of locoweed on sheep and cattle. *Am. J. Vet. Res.* 28:1379-1388.

James, L. F., Hartley, W. J., and Van Kampen, K. R. (1981). Syndromes of *Astragalus* poisoning. *J. Am. Vet. Med. Assoc.* 178:146-150.

James, L. F., Hartley, W. J., Van Kampen, K. R., and Nielsen, D. B.
     (1983). Relationship between the ingestion of the locoweed *Oxytropis
     sericea* and congestive right-sided heart failure in cattle. *Am. J. Vet.
     Res. 44*:254-259.

James, L. F., Mayland, H. F., Miller, M. R., Panter, K. E., and Baker,
     D. C. (1989a). Selenium poisoning in livestock. In *Selenium in Agri-
     culture and the Environment*, L. W. Jacobs (Ed.), Soil Science Society
     of America Special Publication No. 23. American Society of Agronomy,
     Madison, Wis., pp. 123-132.

James, L. F., Molyneux, R. J., and Panter, K. E. (1989b). The potential
     for toxic principals of *Astragalus* and related plants to appear in milk
     and meat. *Vet. Hum. Toxicol.* (in press).

Johnson, C. D. (1970). Biosystematics of the Arizona, California, and Ore-
     gon species of the seed beetle Acanthoscelides Schilsky (Coleoptera:
     Bruchidae). *Univ. Calif. Publ. Entomol. 59*:1-116.

Kang, M. S., and Elbein, A. D. (1983). Mechanism of inhibition of jack bean
     α-mannosidase by swainsonine. *Plant Physiol. 71*:551-554.

Karlsson, K.-E., Wiesler, D., Alasandro, M., and Novotny, M. (1985). 7-
     [(Chlorocarbonyl)methoxy]-4-methylcoumarin: a novel fluorescent re-
     agent for the precolumn derivatization of hydroxy compounds in liquid
     chromatography. *Anal. Chem. 57*:229-234.

Keeler, R. F. (1983). Naturally occurring teratogens from plants. In *Hand-
     book of Natural Toxins*, Vol. 1, *Plant and Fungal Toxins*, R. F. Keeler
     and A. T. Tu (Eds.). Marcel Dekker, New York, pp. 161-199.

Marsh, C. D. (1909). *The locoweed disease of the plains*, Bull. No. 112.
     U.S. Department of Agriculture, Bureau of Animal Industry, Washington,
     D.C., pp. 1-130.

Marsh, C. D. (1924). *Stock-poisoning plants of the range*, Bull. No. 1245.
     U.S. Department of Agriculture, Bureau of Animal Industry, Washington,
     D.C., pp. 1-36.

Mattocks, A. R., and Jukes, R. (1987). Improved field tests for toxic pyr-
     rolizidine alkaloids. *J. Nat. Prod. 50*:161-166.

McKenzie, R. A., Reichmann, K. G., Dimmock, C. K., Dunster, P. J., and
     Twist, J. O. (1988). The toxicity of *Castanospermum australe* seeds
     for cattle. *Aust. Vet. J. 65*:165-167.

Molyneux, R. J., and James, L. F. (1982). Loco intoxication: indolizidine
     alkaloids of spotted locoweed (*Astragalus lentiginosus*). *Science 216*:190-
     191.

Molyneux, R. J., and Roitman, J. N. (1980). Specific detection of pyrroli-
     zidine alkaloids on thin-layer chromatograms. *J. Chromatogr. 195*:412-
     415.

Molyneux, R. J., James, L. F., and Panter, K. E. (1985). Chemistry of
     toxic constituents of locoweed (*Astragalus* and *Oxytropis*) species. In
     Plant Toxicology, A. A. Seawright, M. P. Hegarty, L. F. James, and
     R. F. Keeler (Eds.). Queensland Poisonous Plants Committee, Yeerong-
     pilly, Australia, pp. 266-278.

Molyneux, R. J., Roitman, J. N., Dunnheim, G., Szumilo, T., and Elbein,
     A. D. (1986). 6-Epicastanospermine, a novel indolizidine alkaloid that
     inhibits α-glucosidase. *Arch. Biochem. Biophys. 251*:450-457.

Molyneux, R. J., Benson, M., Wong, R. Y., Tropea, J. E., and Elbein, A.

D. (1988). Australine, a novel pyrrolizidine alkaloid glucosidase inhibitor from *Castanospermum australe*. *J. Nat. Prod.* 51:1198-1206.

Molyneux, R. J., James, L. F., Panter, K. E., and Ralphs, M. H. (1989). The occurrence and detection of swainsonine in locoweeds. In *Swainsonine and Related Glycosidase Inhibitors*, L. F. James, A. D. Elbein, R. J. Molyneux, and C. D. Warren (Eds.). Iowa State University Press, Ames, pp. 100-117.

Nash, R. J., Fellows, L. E., Dring, J. V., Stirton, C. H., Carter, D., Hegarty, M. P., and Bell, E. A. (1988a). Castanospermine in *Alexa* species. *Phytochemistry* 27:1403-1404.

Nash, R. J., Fellows, L. E., Plant, A. C., Fleet, G. W. J., Derome, A. E., Baird, P. D., Hegarty, M. P., and Scofield, A. M. (1988b). Isolation from *Castanospermum australe* and x-ray crystal structure of 3,8-diepialexine, (1R,2R,3S,7S,8R)-3-hydroxymethyl-1,2,7-trihydroxypyrrolizidine[2S,3R,4R,5S,6R)-2-hydroxymethyl-1-aza-bicyclo[3.3.0]octan-3,4,6-triol]. *Tetrahedron* 44:5959-5964.

Panter, K. E., James, L. F., Neilson, D., Molyneux, R. J., Ralphs, M. H., and Olsen, J. D. (1988). The relationship of *Oxytropis sericea* (green and dry) and *Astragalus lentiginosus* with high mountain disease in cattle. *Vet. Hum. Toxicol.* 30:318-323.

Pritchard, D. H., Huxtable, C. R., Dorling, P. R., and Colegate, S. M. (1989). The effect of swainsonine on the growth rate of young rats. In *Swainsonine and Related Glycosidase Inhibitors*, L. F. James, A. D. Elbein, R. J. Molyneux, and C. D. Warren (Eds.). Iowa State University Press, Ames, pp. 360-366.

Ralphs, M. H., and Molyneux, R. J. (1989). Livestock grazing locoweed and the influence of swainsonine on locoweed palability and habituation. In *Swainsonine and Related Glycosidase Inhibitors*, L. F. James, A. D. Elbein, R. J. Molyneux, and C. D. Warren (Eds.). Iowa State University Press, Ames, pp. 39-49.

Ralphs, M. H., James, L. F., Nielsen, D. B., Baker, D. C., and Molyneux, R. J. (1988). Cattle grazing Wahweap milkvetch in southeastern Utah. *J. Anim. Sci.* 66:3124-3130.

Sampson, A. W., and Malmsten, H. E. (1935). *Stock-poisoning plants of California*, Bull. No. 593. University of California College of Agriculture, Berkeley, pp. 1-90.

Saul, R., Chambers, J. P., Molyneux, R. J., and Elbein, A. D. (1983). Castanospermine, a tetrahydroxylated alkaloid that inhibits β-glucocerebrosidase. *Arch. Biochem. Biophys.* 221:593-597.

Saul, R., Molyneux, R. J., and Elbein, A. D. (1984). Studies on the mechanism of castanospermine inhibition of α- and β-glucosidases. *Arch. Biochem. Biophys.* 230:668-675.

Schneider, M. J., Ungemach, F. S., Broquist, H. P., and Harris, T. M. (1983). (1S,2R,8R,8aR)-1,2,8-Trihydroxyoctahydroindolizine (swainsonine), an α-mannosidase inhibitor from *Rhizoctonia leguminicola*. *Tetrahedron* 39:29-32.

Tropea, J. E., Molyneux, R. J., Kaushal, G. P., Pan, Y. T., Mitchell, M., and Elbein, A. D. (1989). Australine, a pyrrolizidine alkaloid that inhibits amyloglucosidase and glycoprotein processing. *Biochemistry* 28:2027-2034.

Tulsiani, D. R. P., Harris, T. M., and Touster, O. (1982). Swainsonine inhibits the biosynthesis of complex glycoproteins by inhibition of Golgi mannosidase II. *J. Biol. Chem. 257:* 7936-7939.

Tulsiani, D. R. P., Broquist, H. P., James, L. F., and Touster, O. (1984). The similar effects of swainsonine and locoweed on tissue glycosidases and oligosaccharides of the pig indicate that the alkaloid is the principal toxin responsible for the induction of locoism. *Arch. Biochem. Biophys. 232:* 76-85.

Walker, B. D., Kowalski, M., Goh, W. C., Kozarsky, K. Krieger, M., Rosen, C., Rohrschneider, L., Haseltine, W. A., and Sodroski, J. (1987). Inhibition of human immunodeficiency virus syncytium formation and virus replication by castanospermine. *Proc. Natl. Acad. Sci. USA 84:* 8120-8124.

Williams, M. C., and Barneby, R. C. (1977). The occurrence of nitro-toxins in North American *Astragalus* (Fabaceae). *Brittonia 29:* 310-326.

Williams, M. C., and James, L. F. (1978). Livestock poisoning from nitro-bearing *Astragalus*. In *Effects of Poisonous Plants on Livestock*, R. F. Keeler, K. R. Van Kampen, and L. F. James (Eds.). Academic Press, New York, pp. 379-389.

Williams, M. C., and Molyneux, R. J. (1988). Toxicological investigations on Ruby Valley pointvetch. *J. Range Manage. 41:* 399-400.

I
NATURE AND TOXICITY OF PLANT TOXINS

B. Other Classes

11

New Techniques for the Isolation and Identification of Phorbol Esters and Structurally Related Diterpenes

A. Douglas Kinghorn

University of Illinois at Chicago, Chicago, Illinois

I. INTRODUCTION

The purification and structural determination of the toxic constituents of cro-ton oil, the seed oil of *Croton tiglium* L. (Euphorbiaceae), presented a major challenge to natural products chemists that took until the 1960s to resolve, when it was established that these substances are a complex mixture of esters of the tetracyclic diterpene phorbol (Hecker and Schmidt, 1974). Phorbol esters were found to be responsible not only for the purgative and skin-irritant effects of croton oil, but also for its tumor-promoting (cocarcinogenic) properties, wherein carcinomas were produced on mouse skin after repeated doses of croton oil subsequent to a single subeffective dose of a carcinogen (Berenblum, 1941; Hecker and Schmidt, 1974). The phorbol esters are still among the most potent tumor promoters known for mouse skin (Itai et al., 1988). In addition to tumor promotion, the phorbol esters exhibit a wide range of other biochemical and cellular effects, and, for example, alter cell morphology, serve as lymphocyte mitogens, induce platelet aggregation, elevate cyclic guanosine 5'-monophosphate (GMP) levels, stimulate ornithine decarboxylase, and exhibit antileukemic activity (Blumberg, 1980, 1981). Mechanistically, the phorbol esters appear to bind to a receptor site that is represented by a portion of protein kinase C, an enzyme that has an important role in signal transduction for several hormones and other biologically active substances. It is thought that tumor-promoting agents such as phorbol esters activate protein kinase C by substituting for endogenous diacylglycerol, which is normally produced in the turnover of inositol phospholipids (Nishizuka, 1984; Blumberg, 1988).

In the more than 20 years since the isolation and structure elucidation of the phorbol esters of croton oil, biologically active esters of a large number of polyfunctional diterpene alcohols structurally related to phorbol have been isolated from many toxic plants in the families Euphorbiaceae and Thymelaeaceae. The diterpene moieties of the skin-irritant and tumor-promoting esters of this type are based on the tigliane, daphnane, and ingenane carbon skeletons, and such compounds have been subjected to frequent literature reviews (Hecker, 1968, 1981; Hecker and Schmidt, 1974; Evans and Taylor, 1983; Kinghorn, 1983, 1985; Tyler and Howden, 1985a; Evans, 1986). New examples of these compounds continue to be discovered, primarily as a result of the bioactivity-guided fractionation of plant extracts that exhibit antileukemic, cytotoxic, piscicidal, or skin-irritant activities (Badawi et al., 1983; Handa et al., 1983; Jolad et al., 1983; Pettit et al., 1983; Powell et al., 1985; Tyler and Howden, 1985b; Adolf et al., 1988; Gonzáles Urones et al., 1988).

In this chapter, mention will first be made of the distribution of genera in the plant families Euphorbiaceae and Thymelaeaceae that biosynthesize phorbol and related diterpene esters. A short section will ensue on the toxic potential that ingestion of or contact with plants containing these diterpenes may present to livestock and humans. Reference will then be made to the structural variation exhibited by these toxins. Finally, a consideration of modern methods for the isolation, screening, and structure elucidation of the phorbol esters and related compounds will be presented, hopefully to facilitate the more rapid detection and identification of this group of toxins by those encountering these compounds as plant constituents in the future.

II. DITERPENE ESTER DISTRIBTUION, TOXIC EFFECTS, AND STRUCTURAL TYPES

A. Occurrence of Diterpene Esters of the Phorbol Type in the Plant Kingdom

Tigliane, daphnane, and ingenane diterpene ester toxins have proven to be of somewhat restricted distribution in their plant families of origin. These compounds have been isolated and characterized from only 14 of the approximately 300 genera in the Euphorbiaceae (*Aleurites, Baliospermum, Croton, Elaeophorbia, Euphorbia, Excoecaria, Hippomane, Hura, Jatropha, Micranda, Ostodes, Sapium, Stillingia, Synadenium*) and 12 of the 50 or so genera of the Thymelaeaceae (*Aquilaria, Daphne, Daphnopsis, Diarthron, Dirca, Gnidia, Lasiosyphon, Pimelea, Stellera, Synaptolepis, Thymelaea,* and *Wikstroemia*) (Willis, 1973; Kinghorn, 1983, 1985; Rizk et al., 1984; Borris et al., 1988). In the Euphorbiaceae, the toxic diterpene ester-bearing genera seem to be limited in distribution to the subfamilies Crotonoideae and Euphorbiodeae (Webster, 1975; Kinghorn, 1979). Toxic diterpene ester constituents have so far been found only in the subfamilies Aquilarioideae and Thylemaeoideae of the Thymelaeaceae (Gilg, 1984; Borris et al., 1988).

B. Toxic Potential for Livestock and Humans

Ingestion of plants in the families Euphorbiaceae and Thymelaeaceae that biosynthesize diterpene esters of the phorbol type causes severe symptoms of toxicity in livestock. For example, the feeding of cattle with the foliage or untreated meal of the tung oil tree (*Aleurites fordii* Hemsl.) leads to anorexia, emaciation, hemorrhagic diarrhea, and necrotic erosions of the gastrointestinal tract, with death usually occurring after 1 to 3 weeks (Kingsbury, 1964). The ingestion of repeated small doses of *Pimelea* species leads to St. George disease of cattle, which is characterized by chronic weight loss, and edema leading to submandibular swelling, with death resulting from congestive heart failure (Freeman et al., 1979). Contact by livestock with the latices of euphorbiaceous plants that contain toxic diterpene esters leads to severe skin inflammation, loss of hair, and swelling around the eyes and mouth (Kinghorn, 1985).

Although perhaps less commonly experienced than with livestock, the symptoms of intoxication by these diterpene ester-containing plants are equally severe in humans. Croton oil has been documented as causing bloody diarrhea, gastroenteritis, cyanosis, delirium, and respiratory disturbances, and the ingestion of as few as four *C. tiglium* seeds has led to fatal consequences (Hecker and Schmidt, 1974). Contact with the eyes of skin by the latices of euphorbiaceous species produces very severe toxic symptoms in humans. For example, the symptoms caused by the accidental entry to the eye of a drop of the latex of *Euphorbia lactea* Haw. were conjunctival hyperemia, edema, pain, corneal striae, and chemosis of the eyelids and cornea. Contact with the sap of the garden plant, *Euphorbia myrsinites* L., led to severe erythematous papulovesiculation on the trunks and faces of several children who were playing near a stand of these plants (Kinghorn, 1985).

There has been some discussion of the extent to which repeated exposure to plants containing phorbol and related diterpene esters might contribute to the genesis of human cancer. Professional gardeners involved in the cultivation of ornamental euphorbiaceous and thymelaeaceous species might be at a considerable occupational risk, since such plants could be contacted on a regular basis (Hecker, 1981). Also, considerable concern has been accorded to the plant *Croton flavens* L., the leaves of which are used to make an herbal tea in the Caribbean island of Curaçao. It has been hypothesized that the levels of phorbol esters present in teas made from this plant part are sufficiently high not only to cause chronic irritation of the esophagus, but also to serve as a cocarcinogenic element that may be involved in producing the much higher than average rates of esophageal cancer encountered among certain members of the population in Curaçao (Weber and Hecker, 1978). In addition, the phorbol esters have recently been demonstrated to be inducers of the Epstein-Barr virus, for which there is a strong etiological association with some human tumors, such as nasopharyngeal carcinoma. Those areas with the highest incidence of nasopharyngeal carcinoma in China have been correlated with a correspondingly high utilization of the phorbol ester-containing plants that are the sources of tung oil (*Aleurites fordii*) and croton oil (*Croton tiglium*), which are employed as herbal medicines for the treatment of gastrointestinal disturbances (Hirayama and Ito, 1981; Ito et al., 1983b). Furthermore, it has also been demonstrated that soil samples taken from areas under which euphorbiaceous and thymelaeaceous plants known to contain phorbol esters are growing can also possess Epstein-Barr virus-inducing activity, and it has been suggested that these diterpenes can be adsorbed to the soil and enter the human nasal cavity at intervals as soil dust (Ito et al., 1983a).

C. Structural Diversity of Toxic Diterpene Esters in the Plant Families Euphorbiaceae and Thymelaeaceae

The structures of the hydrocarbons tigliane, daphnane, and ingenane are shown in Fig. 1 ([1]-[3], respectively). All of the tumor-promoting and skin-irritant diterpene esters found to date in the species of the families Euphorbiaceae and Thymelaeaceae are based on these three skeleta. While toxins of all three types have been isolated from euphorbiaceous species, only tigliane and daphnane diterpene esters have as yet been reported from species in the Thymelaeaceae. There are also a number of macrocyclic diterpenoids obtained from species in the Euphorbiaceae that have been found to exhibit biological activity, especially as antileukemic and/or cytotoxic agents. Such compounds are biogenetically related to the tigliane, daphnane, and ingenane diterpenoids, and the structures of the hydrocarbons represented by two classes of bioactive macrocyclic diterpenoids that will be mentioned in this review are also shown in Fig. 1 (i.e., lathyrane, [4]; casbane, [5]).

The structural variation exhibited by compounds based on each of the skeleta, tigliane, daphnane, and ingenane, will be considered in turn. For example, there are now a total of 25 esters of the tigliane diterpene alcohols phorbol (Fig. 2, [6]) and 4-deoxy-4α-phorbol (Fig. 2, [7]) which have been isolated from the seed oil of *C. tiglium* (croton oil). The Hecker group isolated 11 native phorbol 12,13-diesters that were all shown to be tumor-promoting agents on mouse skin (Fig. 2, [8]-[18], respectively). These can be divided into A-factors (Fig. 2, [8]-[11]) and B-factors (Fig. 2, [12]-[18]), which, in turn, have a long-chain acyl substituent at C12 and C13. The most abundant as well as potent biologically active compound from croton oil has proven to be 12-O-tetradecanoylphorbol-13-acetate (TPA, Fig. 2, [8]) (Hecker, 1968; Hecker and Schmidt, 1974). In addition to the active phorbol 12,13-diesters, Hecker and colleagues have described the presence of "cryptic cocarcinogens" in croton oil, which are phorbol 12,13,20-triesters. Although these are not biologically active per se, they are capable of being hydrolyzed and thus rendered biologically active. Three non-naturally occur-

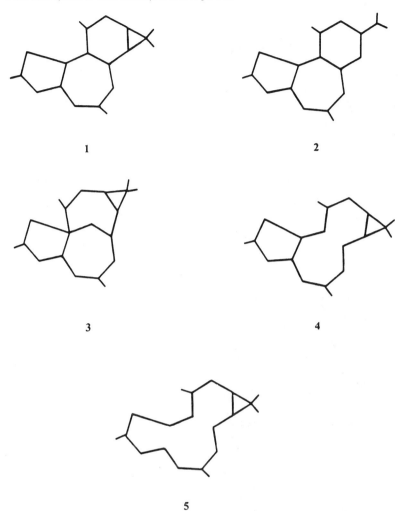

FIGURE 1 Structures of the hydrocarbon skeletons of five biogenetically related diterpenes ([1]-[5]).

ring phorbol diester hydrolytic products (Fig. 2, [19]-[21]) have been obtained by partial hydrolysis of phorbol triesters (Hecker and Schmidt, 1974). Recent work in this laboratory has enabled 11 additionally diterpene ester constituents of croton oil to be isolated and fully characterized. Compounds [22]-[28] (Fig. 2) are short-chain esters of phorbol, while compounds [29]-[32] (Fig. 2) are short-chain esters of 4-deoxy-4α-phorbol. Compounds [27], [28], and [32] (Fig. 2) are monoesters of their respective diterpene alcohols (Marshall and Kinghorn, 1984).

The foregoing description of the phorbol ester constituents found to date in croton oil exemplifies the complex structural variations that can occur in just one euphorbiaceous species. Naturally occurring toxic esters of various

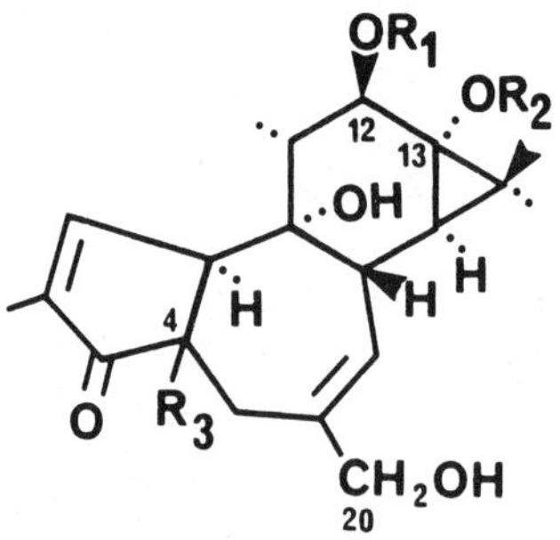

Compound	R_1	R_2	R_3
6	H	H	β-OH
7	H	H	α-H
8	Tetradecanoate	Acetate	β-OH
9	Decanoate	Acetate	β-OH
10	Dodecanoate	Acetate	β-OH
11	Hexadecanoate	Acetate	β-OH
12	2-Methylbutyrate	Dodecanoate	β-OH
13	2-Methylbutyrate	Decanoate	β-OH
14	Tiglate	Decanoate	β-OH
15	Acetate	Dodecanoate	β-OH
16	2-Methylbutyrate	Octanoate	β-OH
17	Tiglate	Octanoate	β-OH
18	Acetate	Decanoate	β-OH
19	Tiglate	Butyrate	β-OH
20	Tiglate	Dodecanoate	β-OH
21	Butyrate	Dodecanoate	β-OH
22	Tiglate	Isobutyrate	β-OH
23	Tiglate	Acetate	β-OH
24	2-Methylbutyrate	Isobutyrate	β-OH
25	2-Methylbutyrate	Acetate	β-OH
26	Acetate	Acetate	β-OH
27	Tiglate	H	β-OH
28	H	Acetate	β-OH
29	Tiglate	Isobutyrate	α-H
30	Tiglate	Acetate	α-H
31	2-Methylbutyrate	Acetate	α-H
32	H	Acetate	α-H

FIGURE 2 Structures of phorbol ([6]), 4-deoxy-4α-phorbol ([7]), and esters of these diterpene alcohols ([8]-[32]) that have been obtained from hydrophilic and hydrophobic extracts of croton oil.

deoxygenated and hydroxylated phorbol esters are also known, including those
of 4-deoxyphorbol, 12-deoxyphorbol, 12-deoxy-5-hydroxyphorbol, 12-deoxy-
16-hydroxyphorbol, and 16-hydroxyphorbol. These compounds have been
described in some detail by Evans and Taylor (1983).

     Compounds in the daphnane ester series also typically occur in plants
in complex mixtures. For example, in a recent study, 17 skin irritants and

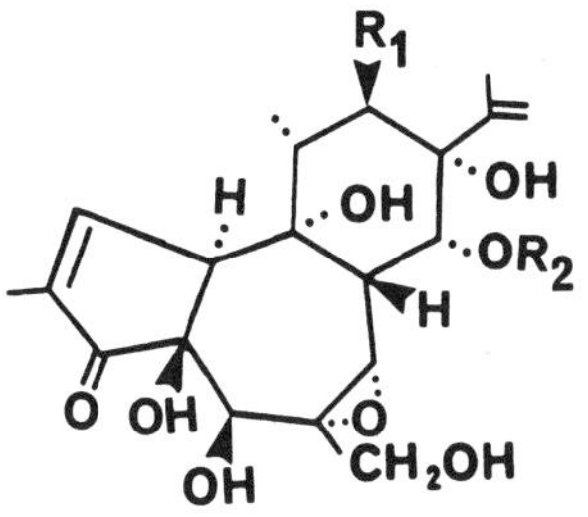

Compound	R$_1$	R$_2$
33	H	H
34	OH	H
35	H	E COCH=CH(CH$_2$)$_{12}$CH$_3$

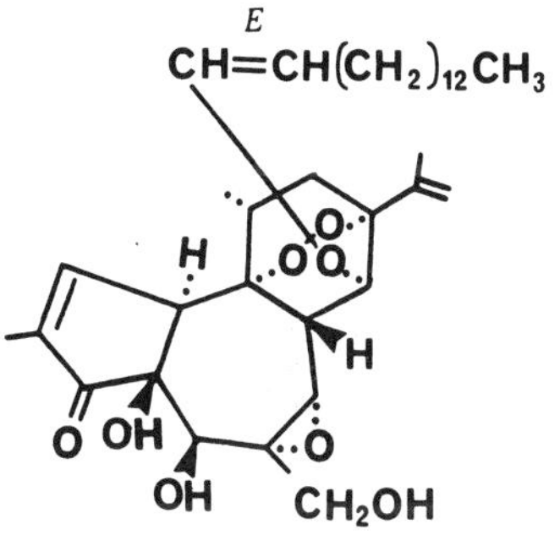

36 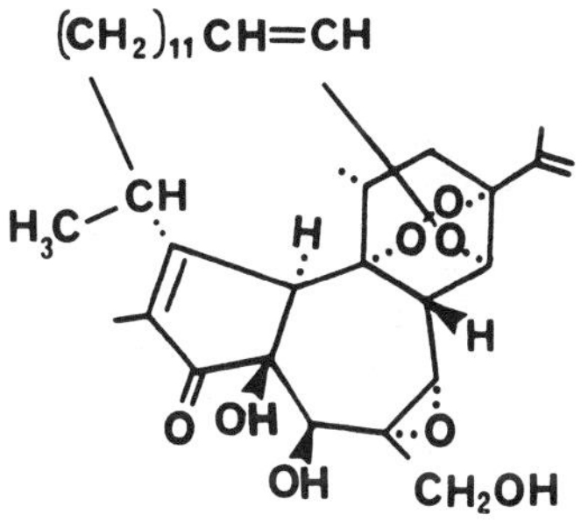   37

FIGURE 3 Structures of 5β-hydroxyresiniferonol-6α,7α-oxide ([33]), 5β,12β-dihydroxyresiniferonol-6α,7α-oxide ([34]), and three daphnane esters ([35]-[37]) isolated from two *Synaptolepis* species.

tumor promoters of this type were isolated and characterized from the roots of the two African species, *Synaptolepis kirkii* Oliv. and *S. retusa* H. H. W. Pearson (Thymelaeaceae) (Adolf et al., 1988). The majority of these compounds were daphnane esters based on the parent alcohols, 5β-hydroxy-resiniferonol-6α,7α-oxide (Fig. 3, [33]) and 5β,12β-dihydroxyresiniferonol-6α,7α-oxide (Fig. 3, [34]). Within this group, a few were conventional esters, such as compound [35] (Fig. 3), while most were 9,13,14-orthoesters, as exemplified by compound [36] (Fig. 3). 1α-Alkyldaphnane esters were also found as toxic constituents of these two plants. Compounds in this class are intramolecular 9,13,14-*ortho*-(2-hexadecenoic acid) esters, in which the subterminal carbon atom of their orthoester chain is linked covalently with α-stereochemistry to C1 of the parent hydroxyresiniferonol alcohol. The structure of the most abundant 1α-alkyldaphnane derivative, [37], isolated from both of the *Synaptolepis* species investigated, is shown in Fig. 3 (Adolf et al., 1988).

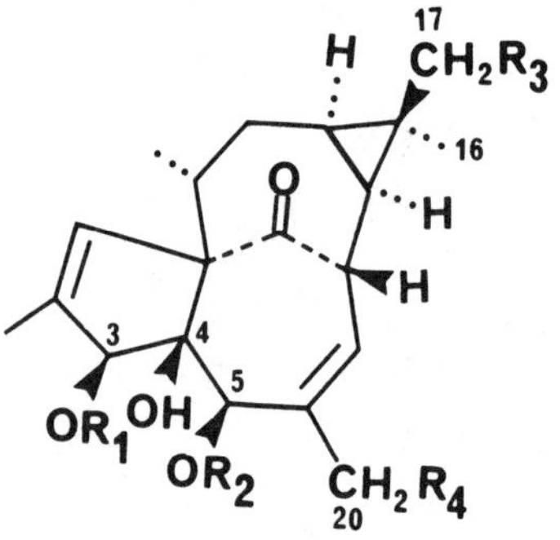

Compound	R_1	R_2	R_3	R_4
38	H	H	OH	OH
39	H	H	H	OH
40	H	H	OH	H
41	Deca-2,4,6-trienoate	H	O-Angelate	OH
42	Angelate	Acetate	O-Acetate	O-Acetate
43	Angelate	H	O-Acetate	O-Acetate
44	Angelate	H	H	O-Acetate
45	Angelate	H	O-Acetate	H

FIGURE 4 Structures of 17-hydroxyingenol ([38]), ingenol ([39]), 20-deoxy-17-hydroxyingenol ([40]), and five ingenane derivatives ([41]-[45]) isolated from the latex of *Euphorbia hermentiana*.

Diterpene toxins of the ingenane series are again found as mixtures of closely related compounds. For example, we have worked on the highly irritant latex of *Euphorbia hermentiana* Lem. (syn. *E. trigona* Haw.) (Euphorbiaceae), a cactiform species sold in the United States as a household plant. This was found to contain five ingenane polyol compounds, based on the parent diterpene alcohols, 17-hydroxyingenol (Fig. 4, [38]), ingenol (Fig. 4, [39]), and 20-deoxy-17-hydroxyingenol (Fig. 4, [40]). Three of the ingenane diterpenes isolated were esters of 17-hydroxyingenol (Fig. 4, [41]-[43]), with one each of ingenol (Fig. 4, [44]) and 20-deoxy-17-hydroxyingenol (Fig. 4, [45]). The most potent skin irritant of the compounds isolated was 3-O-n-(deca-2,4,6-trienoyl)-17-O-[Z-2-methyl-2-butenoyl]-17-hydroxyingenol (Fig. 4, [41]) (Lin et al., 1983; Kinghorn, 1987). It was necessary to resolve these compounds from several macrocyclic diterpenes of the lathyrane type that also occurred in the latex samples examined (Lin and Kinghorn, 1983).

It has not been possible in the limited space available for this chapter to describe any more than a few examples of the major structural variations exhibited by the toxic diterpenoids occurring in plants of the Euphorbiaceae and Thymelaeaceae. More extensive descriptions of the structures of both the toxic and nontoxic diterpenoids biosynthesized by plants in these families have been published (Evans and Taylor, 1983; Evans, 1986).

III. PHORBOL ESTER ISOLATION AND SCREENING PROCEDURES

A. Purification Methods

There are a number of factors that have to be taken into account during the purification of bioactive diterpene esters based on the tigliane, daphnane, and ingenane skeleta from plant sources. First, as mentioned previously, these compounds tend to occur in the plant in very complex mixtures. Normally, they are also found in low yields. Furthermore, these substances are labile to varying degrees, as may be shown by comparing the stability of 12-O-tetradecanoylphorbol-13-acetate (TPA) (Fig. 2, [8]) from croton oil, with that of another phorbol 12,13-diester, 12-O-undecadienoylphorbol-13-acetate (Fig. 5, [46]), which was isolated as a cytotoxic constituent from the stems and fruits of *Ostodes paniculata* Blume (Handa et al., 1983). TPA is known to autoxidize on storage to a β-epoxide (Fig. 5, [47]), an aldehyde (Fig. 5, [48]), and a $\Delta^{5,6}$-7β-hydroperoxide (Fig. 5, [49]), depending on whether it is kept in solution or in the solid form (Hecker and Schmidt, 1975). Whereas TPA was converted to its hydroperoxide analog relatively slowly in the solid form, compound [46] (Fig. 5) was found to decompose significantly to its hydroperoxide derivative, ostodin (Fig. 5, [50]), within a week of storage under nitrogen at 4°C (Handa et al., 1983). Ingenol esters are even unstable to silica gel, and naturally occurring ingenol 3-acylates can transesterify to the corresponding 5-acylates during chromatography (Sorg and Hecker, 1982). A further factor complicating the isolation of phorbol and structurally related esters is their inherent toxicity, and adequate provisions must be taken in the laboratory to prevent personnel from contacting their skin or eyes with

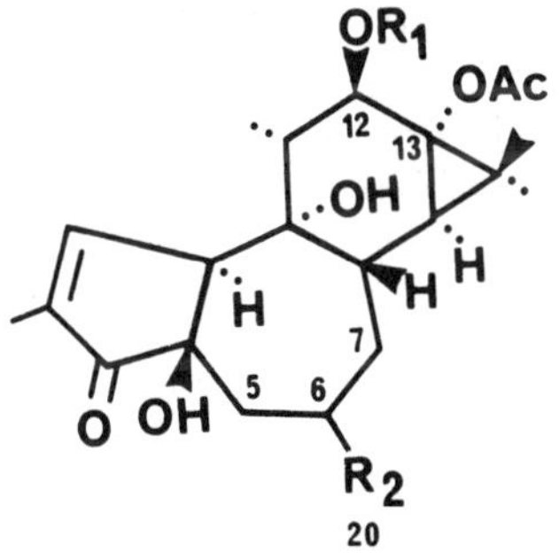

Compound	R_1	R_2	Other
46	CO(CH=CH)C$_8$H$_{15}$	CH$_2$OH	$\Delta^{7,8}$
47	CO(CH$_2$)$_{12}$CH$_3$	α-CH$_2$OH	6,7-β-epoxide
48	CO(CH$_2$)$_{12}$CH$_3$	CHO	$\Delta^{7,8}$
49	CO(CH$_2$)$_{12}$CH$_3$	CH$_2$OH	$\Delta^{5,6}$; 7β-OOH
50	CO(CH=CH)C$_8$H$_{15}$	CH$_2$OH	$\Delta^{5,6}$; 7β-OOH

FIGURE 5 Structures of a cytotoxic phorbol diester constituent of *Ostodes paniculata* ([46]) and several phorbol 12,13-diester decomposition products ([47]-[50]).

these irritant substances. It is recommended that purification procedures
for toxic diterpene esters be carried out in hoods as far as possible, and that
protective goggles, masks, and gloves be worn when handling these compounds or plant extracts or fractions containing them.

The first successful isolation procedures for the phorbol esters of *Croton
tiglium* seed oil were somewhat protracted and consisted of bioactivity-guided
multiple liquid-liquid distributions and column chromatography on the methanol-
soluble portion of croton oil (Hecker and Schmidt, 1974). Many other isolation
schemes for these compounds have been published, and almost all are based on
combinations of chromatographic methods. For several years we have used
droplet countercurrent chromatography (DCCC) in combination with low-pressure liquid chromatography over phase-bonded silica gel phases for the resolution of diterpene homologs in the tigliane, ingenane, and lathyrane classes
(Lin and Kinghorn, 1983; Lin et al., 1983; Marshall and Kinghorn, 1984; Marshall et al., 1985a). The use of DCCC in this manner permits the complete
purification of phorbol esters in only a few days rather than the much longer
periods needed to be expended during more traditional phorbol ester isolation
methods using the Craig countercurrent distribution apparatus (Hecker and
Schmidt, 1974). The DCCC technique is particularly suitable for labile compounds much as the phorbol and structurally related diterpene esters, since
solutes are protected from exposure to the atmosphere during this procedure.
In addition, chromatography over Florisil (Rizk et al., 1984), centrifugal-
liquid chromatography (Taylor et al., 1981), rotation locular countercurrent
chromatography (Pieters and Vlietinck, 1986), and vacuum-liquid chromatography (Pieters and Vlietinck, 1989) have all been used successfully for the
partial purification of phorbol, daphnane, and ingenol esters. For the final
purification of these diterpene ester toxins, preparative thin-layer chromatography over silica gel G (Badawi et al., 1983; Handa et al., 1983; Lin and
Kinghorn, 1983; Lin et al., 1983; Marshall and Kinghorn, 1984) has been used
routinely in our laboratory, although other groups have used partition thin-
layer chromatography employing buffered kieselguhr G plates containing 20%
diethylene glycol as stationary phase (Brooks et al., 1987), or low- or high-
pressure reversed-phase column chromatography (Jolad et al., 1983; Pettit
et al., 1983; Powell et al., 1985; Tyler and Howden, 1985b; Adolf et al., 1988).

The use of overpressured layer chromatography (OPLC) has been applied
to the resolution of the phorbol diesters of *C. tiglium* seed oil. The croton
oil A-factors and B-factors (compounds with a long-chain acyl substituent
affixed to C12 and C13, respectively) were initially separated from a hydrophilic residue by low-pressure column chromatography over silica gel H. Good
resolution was then obtained for the individual A- and B-factors when they
were subjected to reversed-phase OPLC using a high-performance TLC reversed-phase sorbent layer. Certain compounds, including the most biologically active croton oil constituent, 12-O-tetradecanoylphorbol-13-acetate (Fig.
2, [8]), were shown to be homogeneous by extraction of the chromatographic
zones after solvent development and analysis by chemical ionization mass
spectrometry (Erdelmeier et al., 1988).

B. Screening Techniques

There are occasions when, to save time, it is desirable to demonstrate the
presence of absence of phorbol esters in plant parts of species in the Euphor-

biaceae and Thymelaeaceae, or products made from these species. Therefore, there have been several attempts to devise methods to detect phorbol esters rapidly in plant extracts and fractions. These may be divided into chemical and biological methods and are discussed in turn.

1. Chemical Methods

The initial phytochemical methods developed for the microanalysis of phorbol esters did not detect individual native ester homologues based on common parent diterpene alcohols, but only the diterpene portions of each toxin, in the form of their acetates. It has been found that it is difficult to resolve diterpene ester homologs by adsorption chromatography, and that the acetates of diterpene alcohols are more stable than the native diterpene esters. Thus, in an extensive chemotaxonomic study of this type, small latex samples (5 to 10 mL) or portions of fresh herbs (100 g) of approximately 60 *Euphorbia* and *Elaeophorbia* species were subjected to solvent extraction, hydrolysis, and acetylation. The resultant diterpene acetates were then identified by a combination of thin-layer chromatography, gas-liquid chromatography, and mass spectrometry (Evans and Kinghorn, 1977). More recently, it has been demonstrated that diterpene acetates are amenable to analysis by gas chromatography/mass spectrometry (Kinghorn et al., 1986).

Several chromatographic methods have been devised for the qualitative screening of naturally occurring diterpene esters. For example, the 12-deoxyphorbol esters present in a number of *Euphorbia* species were identified after solvent extraction using a combination of adsorption and partition thin-lyer chromatographic (TLC) methods, and electron impact mass spectrometry (Evans et al., 1975). Bauer et al. (1983) found that high-performance liquid chromatography (HPLC) over a C18 phase-bonded silica phase was suitable for the resolution of many of the phorbol esters in croton oil and the ingenol esters in the latex of *Euphorbia canariensis*. This promising methodology could well be extended to the analysis of phorbol and related diterpene esters in other species in the families Euphorbiaceae and Thymelaeaceae. In our laboratory we have developed a two-dimensional TLC (2D-TLC) technique for the rapid analysis of phorbol esters, which has been applied to the resolution of the phorbol 12,13-diester constituents of croton oil. Advantage was taken of the commercial availability of TLC plates with coupled normal and reversed zones. Initial development of a hydrophilic extract of croton oil in the first dimension using silica gel (NP) permitted the separation of a triester zone as well as the A- and B-factor diester zones. Subsequent development on a reversed-phase (RP) octadecylsilyl silica gel layer resulted in the detection of about 15 phorbol diesters. As with the reversed-phase OPLC separation referred to earlier, TPA was detected as a discrete zone as shown in Fig. 6 and was found to be uncontaminated by any other phorbol ester constituents of croton oil by mass spectrometry. Application of this new 2D-TLC procedure demonstrated the presence of many phorbol ester constituents of croton oil that still remain to be characterized, especially triester representatives (Erdelmeier et al., 1988).

There have been only a few chemical methods proposed for the quantitation of phorbol esters. In one such procedure, diterpene alcohols were produced from naturally occurring esters in the latices of *Euphorbia* species by hydrolysis, and acetylated and quantitated using gas-liquid chromatography,

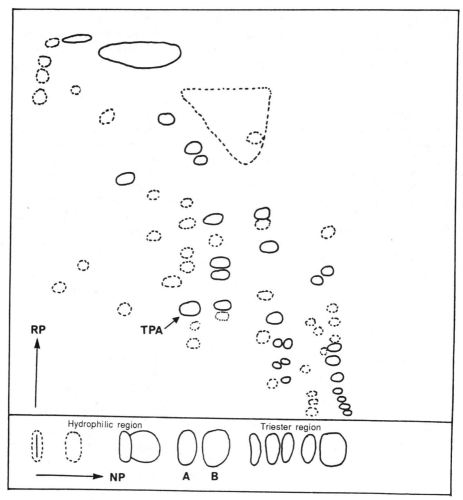

FIGURE 6 Resolution of the major croton oil toxin, TPA, by two-dimensional thin-layer chromatography. A and B represent croton oil phorbol diesters of Hecker's types A and B, respectively, with NP (normal-phase separation) and RP (reversed-phase separation) being expressive of the two development modes used. TLC zones giving a similar color reaction to TPA when visualized with ethanolic sulfuric acid (60% v/v) are marked with solid lines, while the zones with dotted lines indicate presumed nonphorbol ester constituents of croton oil.

employing codeine as an internal standard (Kinghorn and Evans, 1974). The daphnane orthoesters from *Daphne genkwa* Sieb. et Zucc. roots, which are used in China as human abortifacient substances, were determined quantitatively in a parenteral formulation using a spectrophotometric procedure (Wang et al., 1986). The relative proportions of phorbol 12,13-diesters and phorbol 12,13,20-triesters in croton oil have been quantitatively determined using ^{1}H-nuclear magnetic resonance (NMR) spectroscopy (Pieters and Vlietinck, 1986). A similar procedure was employed to quantitate the respective proportions of the biologically active ingenol 3-monoesters and biologically inactive diterpenes present in the latex of *Euphorbia ingens* E. Mey (Pieters and Vlietinck, 1989). Recently, Hecker and co-workers have proposed potentially useful methods for the HPLC analysis of ingenol esters in *Euphorbia lathyris* L. latex (Gminski et al., 1988) and of phorbol esters in *Croton tiglium* seed oil (Gläser et al., 1988).

While chemical methods do permit the specific detection of diterpenoids in specific structural classes (tigliane, daphnane, and ingenane esters, etc.), they suffer from the disadvantage of producing a lack of differentiation between the biologically active and nonbiologically active representatives in a given diterpene ester class.

2. Biological Methods

In an important early paper, acetone extracts of the latices of 10 *Euphorbia* species were screened in Berenblum experiments for their tumor promotion activity in mice, with the carcinogen 9,10-dimethyl-1,2-benzanthracene being used as an initiating agent, and doses of each latex extract applied repeatedly to the backs of mice. All the species tested were found to be active as tumor-promoting agents, as evidenced by the production of papillomas at the time of sacrifice 26 weeks after beginning the experiments, and a correlation was made between observed epidermal hyperplasia and tumor-promoting effects (Roe and Peirce, 1961). The isolation of the cocarcinogenic principles of croton oil was also achieved with the use of Berenblum experiments (Hecker, 1968; Hecker and Schmidt, 1974). However, because the determination of tumor-promoting activity of plant extracts and fractions is very time consuming, more rapid alternative biological methods have been devised to screen for phorbol esters. For example, all the tumor-promoting agent diterpene esters of species in the Euphorbiaceae and Thymelaceaceae are also skin-irritant substances, so phorbol and related diterpene esters may be predicted as being present in those species in these families that produce inflammation in mouse ears (Hecker and Schmidt, 1974; Kinghorn and Evans, 1975; Upadhyay et al., 1980; Fellhauer and Hecker, 1986). Other methods that have been used to predict the presence of these compounds in plant extracts are piscicidal activity assessment (Kupchan et al., 1976; Niwa et al., 1982; Tyler and Howden, 1985a,b), determination of in vivo activity against P388 lymphocytic leukemia (Fellhauer and Hecker, 1986; Tyler and Howden, 1985a), Epstein-Barr virus-inducing activity (Ito et al., 1983a,b; Ohigashi et al., 1985), and a selective [^{3}H]phorbol dibutyrate binding assay (Beutler et al., 1988). As noted previously, the phorbol esters and related toxins exhibit a wide range of other biological effects, and of these, the development of selective screens for these compounds in plant extracts based on ornithine decarboxylase induction in mouse skin (Ohigashi et al., 1982) and protein kinase C activation (Brooks et al., 1987; Ellis et al., 1987) might prove possible in the future.

IV. METHODS FOR THE STRUCTURE DETERMINATION
OF TOXIC DITERPENE ESTERS

A. X-ray Crystallographic Studies

Historically, it was necessary to use x-ray studies to determine the structure
of the diterpene moiety of each prototype tigliane, daphnane, and ingenane
ester toxin. Thus the correct structure of phorbol was finalized after the
performance of x-ray crystallography on crystals of neophorbol 13,20-diace-
tate 3-*p*-bromobenzoate (Hoppe et al., 1967) and phorbol 5-bromofuroate (Pettersen et al., 1967). The structure of daphnetoxin, the first daphnane ester
toxin to be structurally established, was determined in a similar manner on
crystals of its bis-bromoacetate derivative (Stout et al., 1970). Single-crystal
x-ray analysis was conducted on the 20-*p*-iodobenzoate of gnidimacrin, the
first 1α-alkyldaphnane ester toxin to be structurally characterized (Kupchan
et al., 1976). In 1970, the structure of ingenol was confirmed after the x-
ray structure analysis of ingenol 3,5,20-triacetate (Zechmeister et al., 1970).
Other representatives of this toxin class, as well as derivatives of biogenetically related diterpenes from the families Euphorbiaceae and Thymelaeaceae,
have also been subjected to x-ray crystallography (Evans and Taylor, 1983).

B. Spectroscopic Methods

Reviews are available that summarize the considerable body of literature on
the ultraviolet (UV), infrared (IR), [1]H-nuclear magnetic resonance (^{1}H-NMR),
^{13}C-NMR-nuclear magnetic resonance spectroscopic (^{13}C-NMR), electron-
impact mass spectrometric (MS), and circular dichroism (CD) parameters of
toxic diterpene esters in the tigliane, daphnane, and ingenane classes (Hecker
and Schmidt, 1974; Evans and Taylor, 1983; Evans, 1986). In recent years,
there have been significant advances in NMR spectroscopy, which now permit the more facile structure determination of diterpene ester toxins of unknown structure than was the case formerly. Particularly significant is the
routine availability of high-field NMR instrumentation in many laboratories,
which not only substantially reduces the degree of signal overlapping in complex NMR natural product spectra, but also enables complete [1]H- and [13]C-
NMR spectral determinations to be produced on only milligram quantities of
compound. Furthermore, increasing use can now be made of newly developed
one-dimensional (1D) and two-dimensional (2D) NMR pulse sequences (Benn
and Günther, 1983) to help unravel the structures of the tigliane, daphnane,
and ingenane ester toxins. Space does not permit a comprehensive review
of the past use of modern NMR and other spectroscopic techniques in the
structure elucidation of diterpene ester toxins of the Euphorbiaceae and Thymelaeaceae, but a few examples are mentioned in the following paragraphs
on the application of these methods on phorbol and biogenetically related compounds that have been conducted in our laboratory.

12-*O*-Tiglylphorbol-13-isobutyrate (Fig. 2, [22]) is one of the several
novel short-chain phorbol and 4-deoxy-4α-phorbol esters obtained from croton oil using DCCC as a primary isolation techniques, as mentioned earlier
in this review. The stages in the structural determination of this phorbol
12,13-diester using spectroscopic methods are briefly outlined. As an initial
step, the elemental formula of this isolate was established as $C_{29}H_{40}O_8$ by

high-resolution mass spectrometry. The compound exhibited a UV λ_{max} at 225 nm and prominent absorption maxima in its IR spectrum at 3418, 1706, and 1078 cm^{-1}. The well-resolved ^{1}H-NMR spectrum of compound [22], which was run at 360 MHz, enabled this compound to be assigned as a 12,13-diester of the diterpene alcohol, phorbol, by comparison with data published previously. Furthermore, it was possible to infer from the ^{1}H-NMR spectrum that the two ester substituents of the compounds were tiglic acid and isobutyric acid, although their relative positions of substitution could not be determined by this method alone (Marshall and Kinghorn, 1984). Electron-impact MS has proven to be very useful for establishing the number and relative positions of the ester substituents of phorbol 12,13-diesters, since it has been found that the C12 acyl substituents are lost from the molecular ion as an acyloxy radical, while the C13 acyl substituents are eliminated as whole acids (Hecker and Schmidt, 1974; Evans and Taylor, 1983). Thus the observation of a fragment ion at m/z 417 in the mass spectrum of the toxin, representing a loss of 99 amu from the molecular ion, indicated that the longer-chain tiglyl ester unit was affixed to C12, and that the shorter-chain isobutyrate ester was therefore attached to C13. This was confirmed by the generation of the monoester phorbol 12-tiglate (Fig. 2, [27]) on hydrolysis with weak methanolic KOH (Marshall and Kinghorn, 1984). It has previously been noted that the C13 ester substituents of phorbol 12,13-diesters are more susceptible to hydrolysis than are C12 units (Hecker and Schmidt, 1974). On complete hydrolysis and acetylation of 12-O-tiglylphorbol-13-isobutyrate (Fig. 2, [22]), the known compound phorbol 12,13,20-triacetate (Fig. 7, [51]) was produced, thereby confirming the identity of the diterpene alcohol moiety of the toxin (Marshall and Kinghorn, 1984).

A 2D ^{1}H-^{13}C-heteronuclear shift correlation (HETCOR) NMR experiment was used to resolve the previously ambiguous C16 and C17 methyl proton chemical shifts in the ^{1}H-NMR spectrum of phorbol 12,13,20-triacetate (Fig. 7, [51]) (Marshall, 1985). Confirmation of these new assignments (H$_3$-16, δ1.232; H$_3$-17, δ1.250) was made using an NOE (nuclear Overhauser enhancement) difference experiment in which irradiation of the C17 methyl protons resulted in a significant enhancement of the similarly oriented C8 and C11 proton signals. No such enhancement of these resonances was observed when the C16 methyl-proton ^{1}H-NMR signal of compound [51] was selectively irradiated (Marshall et al., 1985b).

NMR NOE difference experiments have also been used to revise the structures of three toxic ingenane derivatives (Fig. 4, [41]-[43]), that were isolated from the latex of *Euphorbia hermentiana*, as mentioned in Section II.C. The most potent skin irritant compound in this series, [41] (Fig. 4), was identified initially by spectral data comparison as an ester of 16-hydroxyingenol with the same structure as the known compound, *Euphorbia* factor I$_5$ (the 16-angelate-3-decatrienoate of 16-hydroxyingenol, a constituent of *Euphorbia ingens* E. Mey latex) (Lin et al., 1983; Opferkuch and Hecker, 1982). However, some doubt was cast on this assignment by the later isolation and characterization of a 17-hydroxyingenol ester (as opposed to a 16-hydroxyingenol ester) from *Euphorbia kamerunica* latex by Connolly et al. (1984a). Complete hydrolysis and acetylation of compound [41] (Fig. 4), yielded a product that was proven to be 17-hydroxyingenol 3,5,17,20-tetraacetate (Fig. 8, [52]), after the performance of an NOE NMR difference experiment, which

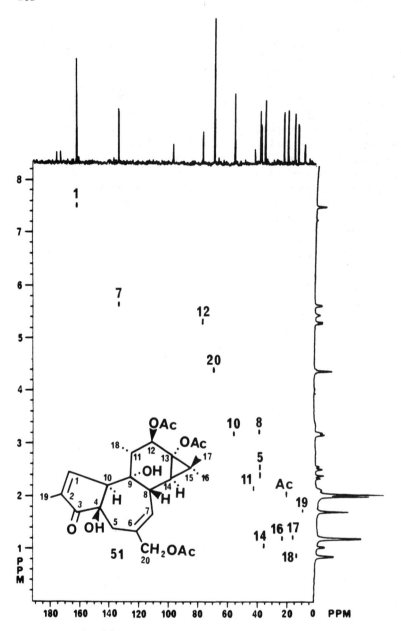

FIGURE 7 ^{1}H-^{13}C HETCOR NMR spectrum of phorbol 12,13,20-triacetate ([51]). The normal ^{13}C- and ^{1}H-NMR spectra of this compound are shown at the top and along the right-hand side of the figure, respectively.

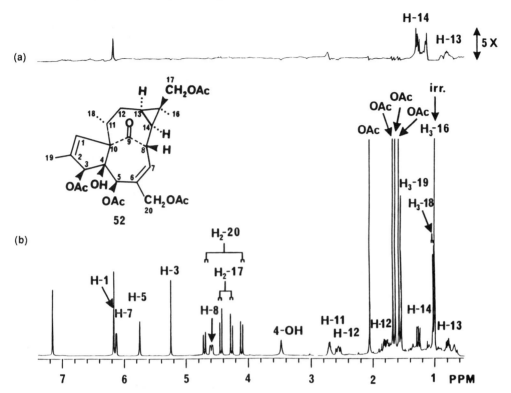

FIGURE 8 17-Hydroxyingenol 3,5,17,20-tetraacetate ([52]): (a) NOE difference spectrum; (b) normal ^{1}H-NMR spectrum.

is shown in Fig. 8. Figure 8a shows the NOE difference NMR spectrum of compound [52], while its normal ^{1}H-NMR spectrum run in deuterobenzene is shown in Fig. 8b. Irradiation of C16 methyl signal at $\delta 1.00$ ppm resulted in enhancements of the C13 and C14 proton signals (Fig. 8a, magnified five times), indicating that the C16 methyl group exhibits the same configuration as H13 and H14 (i.e., α), and that, therefore, the acyloxymethyl group affixed to C15 is β-oriented. Compound [41] (Fig. 4) was therefore reassigned as 3-O-n-(deca-2,4,6-trienoyl)-17-hydroxyingenol-17-angelate. Compounds [42] and [43] (Fig. 4) also afforded 17-hydroxyingenol 3,5,17,20-tetraacetate on hydrolysis and acetylation, and therefore were also reassigned as 17-hydroxyingenol esters. An additional NOE difference NMR experiment on the hydrolyzed, acetylated product of compound [45] (Fig. 4) demonstrated that this compound was an ester of 20-deoxy-17-hydroxyingenol (Kinghorn, 1987). As a result of the necessity for structural reassignment of these ingenane compounds from *E. hermentiana* latex, it may be suggested that not only should the identity of *Euphorbia* factor I_5 be reexamined, but that on biogenetic grounds, esters of all phorbol and ingenol diterpene alcohols originally assigned with a 16-hydroxymethyl unit might in actuality be 17-hydroxylated compounds.

It was pointed out earlier in this chapter that a series of ingol esters were obtained from the skin-irritant fraction of *E. hermentiana* latex. These compounds, which are based on the lathyrane diterpene skeleton, were obtained in approximately the same overall yield as the ingenane derivatives, and several proved to be significantly cytotoxic when tested against P388 lymphocytic leukemia cells (Lin et al., 1983; Lin, 1986). The relative stereochemistry of ingol 3,7,8,12-tetraacetate was determined by single-crystal x-ray crystallography by Lotter and colleagues (1979). Connolly and co-workers (1984b) reexamined the published ORTEP diagram obtained for ingol tetraacetate, and determined that the relative configurations at C8 and C13 were opposite to those reported previously. Confirmation of this reassignment was obtained in this laboratory by the performance of a 2D NOE (NOESY) NMR experiment on ingol tetraacetate, obtained from *E. hermentiana* latex (Fig. 9). Given that the C12 and C19 protons are β-oriented, the observations of NOEs between H7 and H8, H8 and H12, H8 and H19, and H12 and H19 indicate that the C7 and C8 protons are cis and β. The observation of an NOE between the C12 and C13 protons clearly indicates that these are cis, and that therefore the C20 methyl group is alpha and trans to the C12 proton (Lin, 1986). The revised structure of ingol 3,7,8,12-tetraacetate proposed by Connolly et al. (1984b) and confirmed in our NMR experiments in shown in Fig. 9 ([53]). All naturally occurring ingol esters, therefore, also bear this same relative stereochemistry.

For a final example of a modern NMR technique that has been applied to the structure determination of bioactive diterpene esters, reference will be made to the use of the selective INEPT method on an oxygenated casbanoid diterpene isolated from *Agrostistachys hookeri* Benth. & Hook. f. (Euphorbiaceae). Four such compounds were found to be cytotoxic against P388 lymphocytic leukemia cells (Choi et al., 1986, 1988). As stated earlier in this chapter, casbane is biogenetically related to the tigliane, daphnane, and ingenane diterpenes. The most abundant compound in this series, agrostistachin (Fig. 10, [54]), was structurally determined using a combination of 1D and 2D NMR techniques, and confirmed by single-crystal x-ray crystallography (Choi et al., 1986). Unequivocal assignments of the ^{13}C-NMR chemical shifts of the quaternary carbons, C2, C6, and C12, were obtained after application of the selective INEPT technique, a method recently developed to assist in the assignment of ^{13}C-NMR spectra (Bax, 1984). A portion of the downfield region of the ^{13}C-NMR spectrum of agrostistachin is shown in Fig. 10a. Irradiation at the H7 position resulted in a selective enhancement of C6 (Fig. 10b), along with other carbon atoms two or three bonds distant from the irradiation site (C5, C8, and C9), which are not shown on this portion of the spectrum. Analogous irradiations of H10 and H4 resulted in the selective enhancements of C12 (Fig. 10c) and C2 (Fig. 10d). In this manner, the chemical shifts of C2, C6, and C12 of agrostistachin were assigned at δ137.92, δ133.21, and δ137.32, respectively (Choi, 1988).

Thus far there appear to have been no publications that demonstrate the application of the newer 1D and 2D NMR techniques on compounds in the daphnane ester series, presumably because of the difficulties involved in getting large enough quantities of these ocmpounds in pure form. However, useful compilations of high-field ^{1}H-NMR (Badawi et al., 1983; Jolad et al., 1983; Pettit et al., 1983; Powell et al., 1985; Tyler and Howden, 1985b) and [13]C-

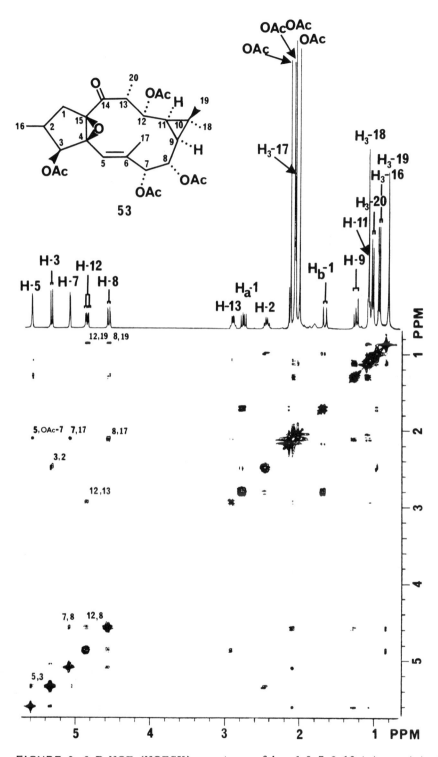

FIGURE 9 2-D NOE (NOESY) spectrum of ingol 3,7,8,12-tetraacetate ([53]).

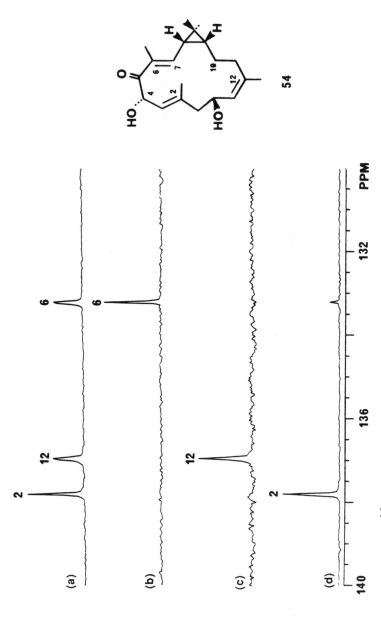

FIGURE 10 ^{13}C-NMR spectra of agrostistachin ([54]): (a) portion of the proton-noise decoupled spectrum; (b-d) selective INEPT spectra obtained by irradiation of H7, H10, and H4, respectively.

NMR spectral data (Jolad et al., 1983; Pettit et al., 1983; Powell et al., 1985) of various daphnane derivatives have appeared in the literature.

V. SUMMARY AND CONCLUSIONS

The phorbol and structurally related diterpene esters that are biosynthesized by plants in certain genera of the families Euphorbiaceae and Thymelaeaceae are highly potent substances biologically. When plants containing these diterpene ester toxins are ingested or contacted, they may present a severe health hazard to livestock and humans alike. The isolation and identification of the phorbol esters is complicated by the tendency of these labile compounds to occur in their plants of origin in complex mixtures in low concentration levels. New methods of analysis, isolation, and structure determination, however, have facilitated the detection and identification of these compounds in recent years, and should become much more widely employed for this purpose in the future.

The full consequences of the threat that phorbol esters may play in the environment are as yet incompletely realized. Until more information is known, caution should be exercised in the use of animal feeds, ornamental and garden plants, herbal remedies, and products obtained from euphorbiaceous and thymelaeaceous plants that may contain these toxins.

ACKNOWLEDGMENTS

The author is grateful to Drs. Y.-H. Choi, C. A. J. Erdelmeier, L.-J. Lin, and G. T. Marshall for performing some of the laboratory studies mentioned in this chapter. This chapter is dedicated to Professor Norman R. Farnsworth on the occasion of his sixtieth birthday.

REFERENCES

Adolf, W., Seip, E. H., Hecker, E., and Dossaji, S. F. (1988). Irritant principles of the mezereon family (Thymelaeaceae): V. New skin irritants and tumor promoters of the daphnane and 1α-alkyldaphnane type from *Synaptolepis kirkii* and *Synaptolepis retusa*. *J. Nat. Prod.* 51:662-674.

Badawi, M. M., Handa, S. S., Kinghorn, A. D., Cordell, G. A., and Farnsworth, N. R. (1983). Plant anticancer agents: XXVII. Antileukemic and cytotoxic constituents of *Dirca occidentalis* (Thymelaeaceae). *J. Pharm. Sci.* 72:1285-1287.

Bauer, R., Tittel, G., and Wagner, H. (1983). Isolation and detection of phorbol esters in croton oil with HPLC: a new method for diterpene ester screening in the Euphorbiaceae. *Planta Med.* 48:10-16.

Bax, A. (1984). Structure determination and spectral assignment by pulsed polarization transfer via long-range ^{1}H-^{13}C couplings. *J. Magn. Reson.* 57:314-318.

Benn, R., and Günther, H. (1983). Modern pulse methods in high-resolution NMR spectroscopy. *Angew. Chem. Int. Ed. Engl.* 22:350-380.

Berenblum, I. (1941). The cocarcinogenic action of croton resin. *Cancer Res.* *1*:44-48.

Beutler, J. A., Alvarado, A. B., and McCloud, T. G. (1988). Screening of Euphorbiaceae for bioactive phorbol esters using a ^{3}H-PDBu binding assay. *Int. Cong. Nat. Prod. Res.*, Park City, Utah, July 17-21 (abstract P-5).

Blumberg, P. M. (1980). In vitro studies on the mode of action of the phorbol esters, potent tumor promoters: Part I. *Crit. Rev. Toxicol.* *8*:153-197.

Blumberg, P. M. (1981). In vitro studies on the mode of action of the phorbol esters, potent tumor promoters: Part II. *Crit. Rev. Toxicol.* *8*:199-234.

Blumberg, P. M. (1988). Protein kinase C as the receptor for the phorbol ester tumor promoters: Sixth Rhoads Memorial Award Lecture. *Cancer Res.* *48*:1-8.

Borris, R. P., Blaskó, G., and Cordell, G. A. (1988). Ethnopharmacologic and phytochemical studies of the Thymelaeaceae. *J. Ethnopharmacol.* *24*:41-91.

Brooks, G., Morrice, N. A., Ellis, C., Aitken, A., Evans, A. T., and Evans, F. J. (1987). Toxic phorbol esters from Chinese tallow tree stimulate protein kinase C. *Toxicon* *25*:1229-1233.

Choi, Y.-H. (1988). Biologically active constituents of *Agrostistachys hookeri* and *Abrus precatorius*. Ph.D. dissertation, University of Illinois at Chicago.

Choi, Y.-H., Kim, J., Pezzuto, J. M., Kinghorn, A. D., Farnsworth, N. R., Lotter, H., and Wagner, H. (1986). Agrostistachin, a novel cytotoxic macrocyclic diterpene from *Agrostistachys hookeri*. *Tetrahedon Lett.* *27*:5795-5798.

Choi, Y.-H., Pezzuto, J. M., Kinghorn, A. D., and Farnsworth, N. R. (1988). Plant anticancer agents: XLVI. Cytotoxic casbane-type constituents of *Agrostistachys hookeri*. *J. Nat. Prod.* *51*:110-116.

Connolly, J. D., Fakunle, C. O., and Rycroft, D. S. (1984a). Five ingol esters and a 17-hydroxyingenol ester from the latex of *Euphorbia kamerunica*: assignment of esters using [13]C N.M.R. methods. *Tetrahedon Lett.* *25*:3773-3776.

Connolly, J. D., Fakunle, C. O., and Rycroft, D. S. (1984b). A reassessment of the relative stereochemistry of ingol tetra-acetate. *J. Chem. Res. (Synop.)* 366-367.

Ellis, C. A., Brooks, S. F., Brooks, G., Evans, A. T., Morrice, N., Evans, F. J., and Aitken, A. (1987). The effects of phorbol esters with different biological effects on protein kinase C. *Phytother. Res.* *1*:187-190.

Erdelmeier, C. A. J., Van Leeuwen, P. A. S., and Kinghorn, A. D. (1988). Phorbol ester constituents of croton oil: separation by two-dimensional TLC and rapid purification utilizing reversed-phase overpressure layer chromatography (RP-OPLC). *Planta Med.* *54*:71-75.

Evans, F. J. (Ed.). (1986). *Naturally Occurring Phorbol Esters*. CRC Press, Boca Raton, Fla.

Evans, F. J., and Kinghorn, A. D. (1977). A comparative phytochemical study of the diterpenes of some species of the genera *Euphorbia* and *Elaeophorbia* (Euphorbiacaeae). *Bot. J. Linn. Soc. 74*:23-35.

Evans, F. J., and Taylor, S. E. (1983). Pro-inflammatory, tumor-promoting and antitumor diterpenes of the plant families Euphorbiaceae and Thymelaeaceae. *Fortsch. Chem. Org. Naturst. 44*:1-99.

Evans, F. J., Schmidt, R. J., and Kinghorn, A. D. (1975). A microtechnique for the identification of diterpene ester inflammatory toxins. *Biomed. Mass Spectrom. 2*:126-130.

Fellhauer, M., and Hecker, E. (1986). Screening of Thymelaeaceae species for irritant, cocarcinogenic and antineoplastic activity. *Planta Med. 52*: 553-554.

Freeman, P. W., Ritchie, E., and Taylor, W. C. (1979). The constituents of Australian *Pimelea* spp.: I. The isolation and structure of the toxin of *Pimelea simplex* and *P. trichostachya* form B responsible for St. George disease of cattle. *Aust. J. Chem. 32*:2495-2506.

Gilg, E. (1984). Thymelaeaceae. In *Die Natürlichen Pflanzenfamilien*, Part III, Section 6a, A. Engler and K. Prantl (Eds.). Verlag von Welhelm Engelmann, Leipzig, East Germany, pp. 216-245.

Gläser, S., Sorg, B., and Hecker, E. (1988). A method for the quantitative determination of polyfunctional diterpene esters of the tigliane type in *Croton tiglium*. *Planta Med. 54*:580.

Gminski, R., Sorg, B., and Hecker, E. (1988). Quantitative determination of polyfunctional diterpene esters of the ingenane type in *Euphorbia lathyris* by HPLC. *Planta Med. 54*:580.

Gonzáles Urones, J., Basabe Barcala, P., Sexmero Cuadrado, M. J., and Sànchez Marcos, I. (1988). Diterpenes from the latex of *Euphorbia broteri*. *Phytochemistry 27*:207-212.

Handa, S. S., Kinghorn, A. D., Cordell, G. A., and Farnsworth, N. R. (1983). Plant anticancer agents: XXIII. Isolation of a phorbol diester and its $\Delta^{5,6}$-7β-hydroperoxide derivative from *Ostodes paniculata*. *J. Nat. Prod. 46*:123-126.

Hecker, E. (1968). Cocarcinogenic principles from the seed oil of *Croton tiglium* L. and from other Euphorbiaceae. *Cancer Res. 28*:2338-2349.

Hecker, E. (1981). Cocarcinogenesis and tumor promoters of the diterpene ester type as possible carcinogenic risk factors. *J. Cancer Res. Clin. Oncol. 99*:103-124.

Hecker, E., and Schmidt, R. (1974). Phorbol esters—the irritants and cocarcinogens of *Croton tiglium* L. *Fortsch. Chem. Org. Naturst. 31*:377-467.

Hecker, E., and Schmidt, R. (1975). Autoxidation of phorbol esters under normal storage conditions. *Cancer Res. 35*:1375-1377.

Hirayama, T., and Ito, Y. (1981). A new view of the etiology of nasopharyngeal carcinoma. *Prev. Med. 10*:614-622.

Hoppe, W., Brandl, F., Strell, I., Rörhl, M., Gassmann, I., Hecker, E., Bartsch, H., Kriebich, G., and v. Szczepanski, Ch. (1967). X-ray structure analysis of neophorbol. *Angew. Chem. Int. Ed. Engl. 6*:809-810.

Itai, A., Kato, Y., Tomioka, N., Iitaka, Y., Endo, Y., Hasegawa, M., Shudo, K., Fujiki, H., and Sakai, S.-I. (1988). A receptor model for tumor promoters: rational superposition of teleocidins and phorbol esters. *Proc. Natl. Acad. Sci. USA 85*: 3688-3692.

Ito, Y., Ohigashi, H., Koshimizu, K., and Yi, Z. (1983a). Epstein-Barr virus-activating principle in the ether extracts of soils collected from under plants which contain active diterpene esters. *Cancer Lett. 19*: 113-117.

Ito, Y., Yanase, S., Tokuda, H., Kishishita, M., Ohigashi, H., Hirota, M., and Koshimizu, K. (1983b). Epstein-Barr virus-activation by tung oil, extracts of *Aleurites fordii* and its diterpene ester 12-O-hexadecanoyl-16-hydroxyphorbol-13-acetate. *Cancer Lett. 18*: 87-95.

Jolad, S. D., Hoffmann, J. J., Timmermann, B. N., Schram, K. H., Cole, J. R., Bates, R. B., Klenk, R. E., and Tempesta, M. S. (1983). Daphnane diterpenes from *Wikstroemia monticola*: wikstrotoxins A-D, huratoxin, and excoecariatoxin. *J. Nat. Prod. 46*: 675-680.

Kinghorn, A. D. (1979). Cocarcinogenic irritant Euphorbiaceae. In *Toxic Plants*, A. D. Kinghorn (Ed.). Columbia University Press, New York, pp. 137-159.

Kinghorn, A. D. (1983). Carcinogenic and cocarcinogenic toxins. In *Handbook of Natural Toxins*, Vol. 1, *Plant and Fungal Toxins*, R. F. Keeler and A. T. Tu (Eds.), Marcel Dekker, New York, pp. 239-298.

Kinghorn, A. D. (1985). Skin-irritant and tumor-promoting compounds of species of the Euphorbiaceae. In *Plant Toxicology*, A. A. Seawright, M. Hegarty, L. F. James, and R. F. Keeler (Eds.). Queensland Poisonous Plants Committee, Yeerongpilly, Australia, pp. 357-366.

Kinghorn, A. D. (1987). Biologically active compounds from plants with reputed medicinal and sweetening properties. *J. Nat. Prod. 50*: 1009-1024.

Kinghorn, A. D., and Evans, F. J. (1974). A quantitative gas-liquid chromatographic method for phorbol and related diterpenes as their acetates. *J. Pharm. Pharmacol. 26*: 408-412.

Kinghorn, A. D., and Evans, F. J. (1975). A biological screen of selected species of the genus *Euphorbia* for skin irritant effects. *Planta Med. 28*: 325-335.

Kinghorn, A. D., Lin, L.-J., Marshall, G. T., and Hussain, R. A. (1986). Application of high-field NMR techniques and GC/MS to phorbol ester structure determination and analysis. *J. Toxicol. Toxin Rev. 5*: 254.

Kingsbury, J. M. (1964). *Poisonous Plants of the United States and Canada*. Prentice-Hall, Englewood Cliffs, N.J.

Kupchan, S. M., Shizuri, Y., Murae, T., Sweeny, J. G., Haynes, H. R., Shen, M.-S., Barrick, J. C., Bryan, R. F., van der Helm, D., and Wu, K. K. (1976). Gnidimacrin and gnidimacrin 20-palmitate, novel macrocyclic antileukemic diterpenoid esters from *Gnidia subcordata*. *J. Am. Chem. Soc. 98*: 5719-5720.

Lin, L.-J. (1986). Studies in natural product structure elucidation and synthesis. Ph.D. dissertation, University of Illinois at Chicago.

Lin, L.-J., and Kinghorn, A. D. (1983). 8-Methoxyingol esters from the latex of *Euphorbia hermentiana*. *Phytochemistry 22*: 2795-2799.

Lin, L.-J., Marshall, G. T., and Kinghorn, A. D. (1983). The dermatitis-producing constituents of *Euphorbia hermentiana* Lem. latex. *J. Nat. Prod. 46*: 723-731.

Lotter, H., Opferkuch, H. J., and Hecker, E. (1979). Crystal structure and stereochemistry of ingol-3,7,8,12-tetraacetate. *Tetrahedone Lett.* 20: 77-78.

Marshall, G. T. (1985). New phorbol ester constituents from croton oil. Ph.D. dissertation, University of Illinois at Chicago.

Marshall, G. T., and Kinghorn, A. D. (1984). Short-chain phorbol ester constituents of croton oil. *J. Am. Oil Chem. Soc.* 61: 1220-1225.

Marshall, G. T., Klocke, J. A., Lin, L.-J., and Kinghorn, A. D. (1985a). Effects of diterpene esters of tigliane, daphnane, ingenane, and lathyrane types on the pink bollworm, *Pectinophora gossypiella* Saunders (Lepidoptera: Gelechiidae). *J. Chem. Ecol.* 11: 191-206.

Marshall, G. T., Lin, L.-J., and Kinghorn, A. D. (1985b). Unambiguous ^{1}H-NMR assignment of phorbol triacetate using a two-dimensional NMR technique. *J. Nat. Prod.* 48: 823-825.

Nishizuka, Y. (1984). The role of protein kinase C in cell surface signal transduction and tumor promotion. *Nature 308*: 693-698.

Niwa, M., Takamizawa, H., Takematsu, H., and Hirata, Y. (1982). Piscicidal constituents of *Stellara chamaejasme* L. *Chem. Pharm. Bull. 30*: 4518-4520.

Ohigashi, H., Hirota, M., Ohtsuka, T., Koshimizu, K., Fujiki, H., Suganuma, M., Yamaizumi, Z., and Sugimura, T. (1982). Resiniferonol-related diterpene esters from *Daphne odora* Thunb. and their ornithine-decarboxylase-inducing activity in mouse skin. *Agric. Biol. Chem. 46*: 2605-2608.

Ohigashi, H., Koshimizu, K., Jato, J., Tokuda, H., Hiramatsu, S, and Ito, Y. (1985). Epstein-Barr virus inducing activity of Euphorbiaceae plants growing in Cameroon. *Sci. Technol. Rev. (Health Sci.)* 2: 65-71.

Opferkuch, H. J., and Hecker, E. (1982). On the active principles of the spurge family (Euphorbiaceae): IV. Skin irritant and tumor promoting diterpene esters from *Euphorbia ingens* E. Mey. *J. Cancer Res. Clin. Oncol. 103*: 255-268.

Pettersen, R. C., Ferguson, G., Crombie, L., Games, M. L., and Pointer, D. J. (1967). The structure and stereochemistry of phorbol, diterpene parent of co-carcinogens of croton oil. *Chem. Commun.* 716-717.

Pettit, G. R., Zou, J.-C., Goswami, A., Cragg, G. M., and Schmidt, J. M. (1983). Antineoplastic agents: 88. *Pimelea prostrata*. *J. Nat. Prod.* 46: 563-568.

Pieters, L. A., and Vlietinck, A. J. (1986). Rotation locular counter-current chromatography and quantitative [1]H-nuclear magnetic resonance spectroscopy of the phorbol ester constituents of croton oil. *Planta Med.* 52: 465-468.

Pieters, L. A. C., and Vlietinck, A. J. 1989). Vacuum liquid chromatography and quantitative ^{1}H NMR spectroscopy of tumor-promoting diterpene esters. *J. Nat. Prod.* 52: 186-190.

Powell, R. G., Weisleder, D., and Smith, C. E., Jr. (1985). Daphnane diterpenes from *Diarthron vesiculosum*: vesiculosin and isovesiculosin. *J. Nat. Prod.* 48: 102-107.

Rizk, A. M., Hammouda, F. M., Ismail, S. E., El-Missiry, M. M., and Evans, F. J. (1984). Irritant resiniferonol derivatives from Egyptian *Thymelaea hirsuta* L. *Experientia 40*: 808-809.

Roe, F. J. C., and Peirce, W. E. H. (1961). Tumor promotion by *Euphorbia* latices. *Cancer Res. 21*:338-344.

Sorg, B., and Hecker, E. (1982). On the chemistry of ingenol: II(1). Esters of ingenol and $\Delta^{7,8}$-isoingenol. *Z. Naturforsch. B37*:748-756.

Stout, G. H., Balkenol, W. G., Poling, M., and Hickernell, G. L. (1970). The isolation and structure of daphnetoxin, the poisonous principle of *Daphne* species. *J. Am. Chem. Soc. 92*:1070-1071.

Taylor, S. E., Gafur, M. A., Choudhury, A. K., and Evans, F. J. (1981). Nitrogen-containing phorbol derivatives of *Sapium indicum*. *Phytochemistry 20*:2749-2751.

Tyler, M. I., and Howden, M. E. H. (1985a). Antitumor and irritant diterpenoid esters of Thymelaceaceae species. In *Plant Toxicology*, A. A. Seawright, M. Hegarty, L. F. James, and R. F. Keeler (Eds.). Queensland Poisonous Plants Committee, Yeerongpilly, Australia, pp. 367-374.

Tyler, M. I., and Howden, M. E. H. (1985b). Antineoplastic and piscicidal 1-alkyldaphnane orthoesters from *Pimelea* species. *J. Nat. Prod. 48*:440-445.

Upadhyay, R. R., Bakhtavar, F., Mohseni, H., Sater, A. M., Saleh, N., Tafazuli, A., Dizaji, F. N., and Mohaddes, G. (1980). Screening of *Euphorbia* from Azabaijan for skin irritant activity and for diterpenes. *Planta Med. 38*:151-154.

Wang, M.-Z., Liu, J.-S., Song, L.-L., Xiang, B.-R., and An, D.-K. (1986). Application of orthogonal function spectrophotometry to the determination of total diterpene esters in yuanhua (*Daphne genkwa* Sieb. et Zucc.) root injection. *Acta Pharm. Sin. 21*:119-123.

Weber, J., and Hecker, E. (1978). Cocarcinogens of the diester type from *Croton flavens* L. and esophageal cancer in Curaçao. *Experientia 34*: 679-682.

Webster, G. T. (1975). Conspectus of a new classification of the Euphorbiaceae. *Taxon 24*:593-601.

Willis, J. C. (1973). *A Dictionary of the Flowering Plants and Ferns* (revised by H. K. Airy-Shaw). Cambridge University Press, Cambridge.

Zechmeister, K., Brandl, F., Hoppe, W., Hecker, E., Opferkuch, H. J., and Adolf, W. (1970). Structure determination of the new tetracyclic diterpene ingenol-triacetate with triple product methods. *Tetrahedon Lett.* 4075-4078.

12

Ricin and Related Plant Toxins: Mechanism of Action and Neurobiological Applications

Ronald G. Wiley

Veterans Administration Medical Center, and Vanderbilt University, Nashville, Tennessee

T. N. Oeltmann

Vanderbilt University, Nashville, Tennessee

I. MECHANISM OF ACTION

There have been several recent reviews of the plant toxin ricin and its mechanism of action (Olsnes and Pihl, 1982; Olsnes and Sandvig, 1983, 1985, 1988). The purpose of this review is to outline our current knowledge of ricin and related toxins, mechanisms of entry, the mechanism for the translocation of the toxic subunit into the cytoplasm, and the mechanism by which ribosomes are inactivated by the toxic subunit. Ricin, abrin, and modeccin are similar in structure and mechanism of toxicity. Ricin, abrin, and modeccin are all composed of two nonidentical subunits which have unique functions, as illustrated in Fig. 1. In all three instances, the B subunits are lectins that bind the toxins to cell surface receptors containing terminal galactose residues. This binding to the cell surface by the B-chains is an obligatory first step in the intoxication of intact cells. The toxic action of these plant proteins is associated exclusively with the A-chains. The A-chains are enzymes that

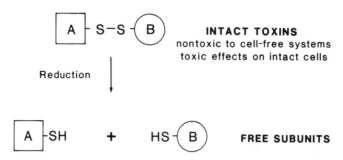

FIGURE 1 Schematic representation of the subunit structure of cytotoxic ribosome-inactivating lectins. A number of these proteins isolated from plants have the same basic structure of a binding subunit (B-chain) and an effector subunit (A-chain) which is an endoglycosidase that inactivates ribosomes, thus inhibiting protein synthesis. The subunits can be separated and individually purified by reduction of a disulfide bond.

inactivate the eukaryotic ribosome and thus inhibit protein synthesis. The extreme toxicity of these proteins is due to the fact that the free A-chains are enzymes, and the presence of a single A-chain molecule within the cytosol is sufficient to kill a cell. Some of the physical properties of these toxins have been summarized by Olsnes and Pihl (1982) and are listed in Table 1.

Ricin is synthesized as a single polypeptide during the maturation of castor beans. It accumulates in the storage granules of the seeds (Youle and Huang, 1976). After synthesis, the toxin is cleaved into two polypeptides, termed the A- and the B-chain, linked by a disulfide bond (Olsnes and Pihl, 1982; Lord, 1985; Harley and Lord, 1985). The molecular weight of the A-chain is 30,625 kilodaltons (kD), and the molecular weight of the B-chain is 31,431 kD. The B-chain has been shown to contain two galactose binding sites (Houston and Dooley, 1982). These two binding sites have slightly different affinities for lactose as determined by equilibrium studies (Zentz et al., 1978). Binding of the toxin to galactose moieties on the cell surface, which is required for the toxic effect on intact cells, takes place at these sites.

Both the A and B polypeptide chains of ricin are glycoproteins (Olsnes and Pihl, 1982), with the majority of the carbohydrate located in the B-chain. These carbohydrate groups play a role in binding of the toxin to certain cells containing mannose receptors such as macrophages (Simmons et al., 1986).

The primary structure of ricin has been determined by Funatsu et al. (1978, 1979). In addition, ricin has been crystallized and its structure has been solved at 2.8 A (Montfort et al., 1987). There are four internal disulfide bridges present in the B-chain and none in the A-chain. The intact toxins contain no reactive sulfhydryl groups in either the absence or presence of urea (Olsnes et al., 1975; Wei et al., 1975). However, one buried sulfhydryl group was observed in position 171 of ricin A-chain when treated with sodium dodecyl sulfate (Cawley and Houston, 1979). The free A- and B-chains contain one additional sulfhydryl group each.

TABLE 1 Physical Properties of Ricin, Abrin, and Modeccin (1)

Protein	Molecular weight[a]	pI	Carbohydrate (residues)/molecule of protein	
			Mannose	Glucosamine
Abrin				
Intact	65,000	6.1	10	1.6
A-chain	30,000	4.6	0	0
B-chain	35,000	7.2	9.7	1.9
Ricin				
Intact	62,057	7.1	15.6	2.4
A-chain	30,625	7.5	4.3	0.4
B-chain	31,432	4.8	10.7	1.33
Modeccin				
Intact	63,000	6.2-7.1		
A-chain	28,000	5.8-6.1		
B-chain	38,000	7.3-8.2		

[a]The molecular weights were estimated by polyacrylamide gel electrophoresis in the presence of sodium dodecyl sulfate. Only for ricin, which has been sequenced (10,11), are the values exact.

While weak hydrophobic interactions are sufficient to maintain the association of the two chains, the intact disulfide bond between the A- and B-chains appear to play an important role in the toxic effect on cells (Lappi et al., 1978). However, biological activity requires that the covalent link between the two chains be reduced since covalent interchain cross-linking of ricin and abrin results in nontoxic molecules, whereas similar treatment of the individual A- and B-chains has no effect on their functions.

There are differences in both the amounts and types of carbohydrates present in abrin and ricin (Olsnes et al., 1975). The majority of the carbohydrates in the toxins are located in the B-chains (Table 1). Ricin contains three oligosaccharide moieties, one consisting of $(GlcNAc)_2(Man)_4$ in the A-chain and two in the B-chain consisting of $(GlcNAc)_2(Man)_6$ and $(GlcNAc)_2(Man)_7$ (Foxwell et al., 1985). In all cases, the oligosaccharide chains were found to be of the N-linked type. No O-linked carbohydrates have been detected. In addition, abrin, ricin, and modeccin all bind to concanavalin A, suggesting that mannose residues are terminal.

A. Binding of Ricin to Cells

Ricin and abrin bind to sites at the cell surface which contain terminal galactose residues. Depending on the cell type, between 10^6 and 10^8 toxin molecules can be bound per cell (Sandvig et al., 1976). While the majority of the binding sites are carried by glycoproteins with terminal galactose residues, there is at least one report of binding to cells by glycolipids (Hughes and Gardas, 1976).

As mentioned above, the toxin has two binding sites for galactose, and these two sites have somewhat different affinities for the sugar. These two sites most probably exhibit different affinities for galactose contained in glyco-proteins of the cell surface as well. Whether both sites, or only the high-affinity site, are involved in cell binding is not clear at this time.

Ricin may also be bound to certain cells by an entirely different mechanism. Ricin is a glycoprotein and contains mannose-rich N-linked oligosaccharides in both of its constituent subunits. On the surface of cells of the reticulo-endothelial system, mannose receptors are present that have been shown to bind these carbohydrates (Simmons et al., 1986; Wileman et al., 1985; Skilleter and Foxwell, 1986). Further, it has been demonstrated that binding by these mannose receptors results in subsequent cell death (Simmons et al., 1986). Deglycosylation of the toxin abolished both binding and intoxication by the mannose receptor pathway (Foxwell et al., 1987).

Ricin binding and uptake has been investigated at the ultrastructural level, utilizing ligand conjugates or immunocytochemical detection methods. Both monovalent and polyvalent conjugates of ricin and peroxidase bind even-ly to the cell surface at 4°C, including microvilli and various coated and un-coated cell-surface pits. By using a ricin-gold conjugate, an even surface labeling has also been obtained at 4°C (van Deurs et al., 1985).

Altogether, ultrastructural studies using various approaches indicate that ricin binding sites are more or less evenly distributed over the entire cell surface. In addition, while cell surface-bound toxin is internalized at 37°C, the cell surface never becomes depleted of binding sites (van Deurs et al., 1985). One possible explanation for this is that the internalization of ricin binding sites is a relatively slow process, and, in fact, some binding sites may not be internalized at all. In fact, it has been demonstrated that some of the toxin is rapidly recycled to the cell surface (Sandvig and Olsnes, 1979).

B. Internalization of Ricin

Endocytosis as a mechanism for the penetration of a toxin was first demon-strated with diphtheria toxin (Draper and Simon, 1980). Diphtheria toxin has been shown to require transport to an acidic compartment prior to trans-location into the cytosol (Sandvig and Olsnes, 1980). Since the pH required for translocation is found only in intracellular vesicles, such as endosomes and lysosomes (Mellman et al., 1986), it was suggested that transport of diph-theria toxin to one of these compartments must precede translocation to the cytoplasm. In a series of elegant experiments, Sandvig and Olsnes demon-strated that the translocation indeed takes place from the endosomes (Sand-vig and Olsnes, 1981). However, in the case of ricin and abrin, low pH is not required for entry. Sandvig et al. (Sandvig and Olsnes, 1982a; Sandvig et al., 1979) demonstrated that these toxins are most active when the acidifi-cation of intracellular vesicles is inhibited. On the other hand, compounds which increase the pH of intracellular vesicles protect cells from the toxic effects of modeccin (Sandvig et al., 1979).

Several morphological studies have suggested that a fraction of the ricin bound to the cell surface is endocytosed (van Deurs et al., 1985, 1986, 1987; Sandvig et al., 1987). However, the exact mechanism of ricin uptake or internalization is still unknown. The fact that ricin has been observed in coated pits on the cell surface of various cell types (van Deurs et al., 1985; Sandvig et al., 1987) suggests that at least a fraction of the bound ricin is taken up via these structures. However, it does not exclude the possibility that some ricin is also being taken up by other pathways.

One such alternative pathway could be smooth pits and vesicles as described for albumin-gold (Ghitescu et al., 1986). Smooth pits appear at the cell surface 5 to 10 times more frequently than coated pits. Smooth pits at the cell surface may represent recycling vesicles carrying membrane from intracellular endocytic compartments back to the cell surface (Mellman, 1984). Other smooth pits at the cell surface may represent secretory vesicles coming from the Golgi complex or the trans-Golgi network. A second possible alternative to the coated pits at the cell surface as candidates for the alternative endocytic pathway would be larger, uncoated invaginations (Sandvig et al., 1987). It is clear that at least some ricin molecules bound to the cell surface are taken up via coated pits and vesicles, while other experimental evidence suggests that ricin is internalized via a nonclathrin-coated pathway as well.

Internalization of ricin has been studied by means of morphological techniques. Ricin has been detected intracellularly in endosomes using immunoperoxidase cytochemistry (van Deurs et al., 1986) and immunogold cytochemistry (van Deurs et al., 1988). Ricin conjugates such as ricin-HRP have been traced to endosomes a few minutes after exposure to the cells (van Deurs et al., 1986, 1987). Thus, as for other internalized ligands, endosomes are the first intracellular location for endocytosed ricin, be it taken up by coated pits or smooth pits, or both.

Endosomes are acidified compartments (Mellman et al., 1986) where the low pH is responsible for the dissociation of many ligands from their receptors. This dissociation is a prerequisite for further sorting and trafficking of the ligand to lysosomes and the receptor back to the cell surface (Wileman et al., 1985; Mellman et al., 1986; Goldstein et al., 1985). Internalized ricin also remains attached to its binding sites at the low pH in endosomes. Van Deurs et al. (1988) has shown that only 22% of the ricin initially bound at pH 7 was found to be released at pH 5.0. This is consistent with earlier biochemical studies which demonstrated that internalized ricin molecules are recycled to the cell surface, probably attached to their binding sites (Sandvig and Olsnes, 1979).

Sandvig and Olsnes (1979) have shown that a small fraction of internalized ricin molecules are transferred to lysosomes and are slowly degraded. These may be the ricin molecules which are released from their receptor in the endosome. Whether this slow degradation of ricin is due to slow delivery to lysosomes or to the fact that ricin is very resistant to proteolytic enzymes is still open to question. While there are a number of compounds that inhibit the degradation of internalized ricin (colchicine, cytochalasin B, NaN_3, weak bases), none of these compounds inhibited the endocytosis of ricin or the recycling of the endocytosed toxin back to the cell surface (Sandvig and Olsnes, 1979). Altogether, the current data suggest that the sorting of internalized ricin with respect to further routing, to the Golgi or lysosomes, takes place in the endosomal system. The transfer of the A-chains of ricin, abrin, and modeccin to the cytosol requires Ca^{2+} (Sandvig and Olsnes, 1982b). Replacement of Ca^{2+} by Co^{2+} or removal of Ca^{2+} with EGTA prevents the toxic effect, although the endocytic uptake of the toxin remains unchanged.

The exact mechanism by which internalized ricin is translocated to the cytosol, where the A-chain inactivates the ribosomal 60S subunit is not clear. Ricin A-chains, like the A-fragment of diphtheria toxin and other bacterial and plant toxins, are probably translocated across the membrane of one or more intact intracellular compartment(s). The compartment where translocation takes place is different for different toxins. The A-fragment of diphtheria toxin, for example, is translocated rapidly after uptake of the toxin into endosomes, where the low pH favors this process (Draper and Simon, 1980; Sandvig and Olsnes, 1980). In contrast, it takes about 60 to 90 min after initial uptake of ricin before its cytotoxic effect can be measured biochemically. In addition, the low pH found in endosomes and lysosomes is not required for ricin A-chain translocation (van Deurs et al., 1988). Thus, while it cannot be ruled out completely that ricin A-chains are translocated to the cytoplasm from lysosomes and/or endosomes, it does not appear to be the case since when the pH in lysosomes is increased by treatment of cells with 10 mM NH_4Cl, the cells remain sensitized to ricin (Sandvig et al., 1979). Normal lysosomal function does not appear to be required for ricin entry into the cytosol.

Thus one can speculate that optimal ricin A-chain translocation requires a pH that is not very acidic. Although the trans-Golgi network (TGN) is thought to have a lower pH than the cytosol (Anderson and Pathak, 1985), the TGN is probably only mildly acidic. Youle and Colombatti (1987) demonstrated that a hybridoma cell secreting antibodies against ricin was also resistant to the toxic effects of ricin. They suggested that the internalized ricin was inactivated by the anti-ricin antibodies during their transport through the Golgi complex. In addition, they were able to demonstrate that only 1% of the total internalized ricin was translocated to the cytosol. Although other possibilities cannot be ruled out completely, evidence has accumulated which is consistent with the concept that ricin must reach the TGN in order to exert its cytotoxic effect.

C. Mechanism of Ricin Toxicity

Once the ricin subunit A reaches the cytoplasm, it exerts its toxic effect by its ability to enzymatically inactivate the 28S ribosomal RNA. Recently, Endo et al. (Endo et al., 1987; Endo and Tsurugi, 1987) have demonstrated that this unique activity of the ricin A-chain occurs by specific modification of the A_{4324} residue of 28S rRNA of eukaryotic ribosomes. Further, they have established that the ricin A-chain is a highly specific N-glycosidase and that its activity is not nucleotide sequence-specific, as the target sequence that is modified (AGUACGAGAGGAAC) is modified only when the sequence is contained within an eukaryotic ribosome. Thus the overall structure/conformation of the ribosome must also play a role in the process of inactivation by ricin A-chain. The thus modified ribosome is no longer capable of supporting protein synthesis and cell death results. The same mechanism of ribosome inactivation has also been described for abrin and modeccin (Endo et al., 1987) and has recently been reviewed (Endo, 1988).

D. Summary

A schematic presentation of our current knowledge and speculations about endocytosis and intracellular pathways of ricin leading to cell death is dia-

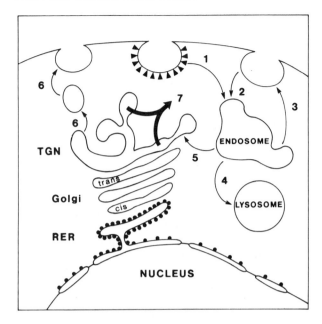

FIGURE 2 Schematic representation of current understanding of the intracellular sorting and routing of the toxic lectin, ricin. The sequence of events
begins with binding to cell surface oligosaccharides followed by endocytosis
via coated (1) and uncoated (2) pits and vesicles. Ricin is then routed to
endosomes, the surface membrane (3), lysosomes (4), the trans-Golgi network
(TGN: 5), and the cytosol (7). Ricin may also return to the surface membrane from the Golgi (6). RER indicates rough endoplasmic reticulum.

grammed in Fig. 2. Binding sites or receptors (membrane glycoproteins and
glycolipids) for ricin are numerous and uniform over the cell surface. Some
receptor-bound ricin is rapidly internalized, while some may not be endocytosed at all. This may account for the apparent slow uptake of cell-bound
ricin. Both coated (route 1) and smooth pits and vesicles (route 2) may participate in the uptake of ricin. Ricin then reaches the endosomal system,
where most ricin molecules remain attached to their membrane binding sites
regardless of the low pH of the endosome. Some ricin molecules, presumably
still attached to the binding sites, are recycled to the cell surface by vesicular and tubular structures budding off from the membrane of the endosomal
system (route 3). Still other ricin molecules, perhaps those which detach
from the binding sites at the low pH, are transported to lysosomes, where
they are slowly degraded (route 4). More important, some ricin molecules
follow their membrane binding sites to the Golgi complex, in particular to the
TGN (route 5), from where they may be either routed back to the cell surface along the secretory pathway (route 6) or the A-chains of some ricin molecules that reach the TGN may be translocated across the membrane to reach
the cytosol, where they inactivate the ribosome and subsequently inhibit protein synthesis (route 7). Regardless of the exact sequence of events that
delivers the A subunit into the cytoplasm, the specific enzymatic modification

of the 28S rRNA leads to inactivation of the ribosome, irreversible inhibition of protein synthesis, and subsequent death of the cell.

II. NEUROBIOLOGICAL APPLICATIONS

A. Study of Nervous System Glycoconjugates

Ricin toxin (RCA-II, RCA_{60}) and ricinus agglutinin (RCA-I, RCA_{120}) have been used to study the glycosylation of nervous system macromolecules based on the specificity of these lectins for N-acetyl galactosamine (GalNAc) and galactose (Gal), respectively. Several workers have examined ricin binding to central nervous system (CNS) membranes using radioiodinated or peroxidase conjugated ricin. In general, ricin binds weakly to adult brain membrane preparations (Gurd, 1977). Several reports have shown periods during early development where ricin binds abundantly to specific neuronal structures (Hatten and Sidman, 1977; Hatten et al., 1979; Huch and Hatten, 1981; Mc-Laughlin et al., 1980), but ricin binding decreases with maturation of the CNS. Growth cone (growing axon tip) preparations from fetal brain contain many glycoproteins that bind ricin, at least one of which is not present in adult axon terminals (Greenberger and Pfenninger, 1986). In the adult, ricin binds primarily to cerebral capillaries (Kelly et al., 1976), macrophages (Pfenninger and Maylie-Pfenninger, 1981), and perhaps, extracellular synaptic cleft material (Bittiger and Schnebli, 1974). Limited ricin binding in adult brain may be due to addition of sialic acid to CNS glycoconjugates considering that ricin will bind avidly to adult CNS membranes after pretreatment with neuraminidase (Gurd, 1977; McLaughlin et al., 1980; DeSilva et al., 1979; Hart and Wood, 1985). Alternatively, the molecules that ricin binds to in developing brain are not present in the adult CNS. In any case, with few exceptions (Salvaterra et al., 1977; Shirakawa et al., 1983), the functional identities of ricin-binding molecules are unknown. Consequently, the biological significance of ricin binding to nervous tissue is unclear.

In vitro studies have shown binding, uptake, and internalization of ricin by neurons of peripheral autonomic (Gonatas et al., 1975) and sensory ganglia (Gonatas et al., 1977; Streit et al., 1985) and by microglia (Groeger et al., 1983). Uptake and axonal transport of ricin have been used to characterize nerve terminal macromolecules in vivo. From the anterior chamber of the eye, injection of radioiodinated ricin results in accumulation of label in the ipsilateral superior cervical ganglion within 14 h (Dumar et al., 1979). Compared to ricin, wheat germ agglutinin was much more abundantly taken up and axonally transported. Several other studies have confirmed that ricin and ricin-horseradish peroxidase (HRP) conjugates are taken up and axonally transported to perikarya by sensory and motor neurons of the peripheral nervous system (Harper et al., 1980; Wiley et al., 1982; Yamamoto et al., 1984). However, in keeping with the paucity of ricin binding to adult CNS neurons, ricin is not taken up and axonally transported by CNS neurons (66).

These studies suggest that a modest abundance of ricin-binding moieties are present on neurons of the peripheral nervous system and that these neurons can take up ricin by endocytosis and accumulate ricin in their perikarya. Neurons in the developing CNS, and particularly axonal growth cones, also contain some ricin-binding moieties, but adult CNS neurons either do not express these substances or add sialic acid to them. The significance of ricin uptake by peripheral neurons with respect to the fatal toxicity of systemically administered ricin remains to be elucidated. However, the lethal dose of all the toxic lectins is one to two orders of magnitude lower after intraventricular injection into the cerebrospinal fluid than when given systemically (Strocchi et al., 1979; Wiley and Oeltmann, unpublished).

B. Lesioning Neurons with Ricin and Related Toxins

Anatomically selective neural lesions of peripheral sensory, motor, and autonomic neurons are possible using ricin and the other toxic lectins, abrin, modeccin, volkensin, and viscumin. Harper et al. (1980) originally reported that injection of ricin into submandibular salivary glands of rats resulted in cytotoxic changes in neurons of the ipsilateral superior cervical ganglion. Wiley et al. (1982) subsequently demonstrated that subepineurial injection of ricin, abrin, or modeccin into peripheral nerve could be used to selectively destroy sensory and motor neurons projecting axons through the injected nerve (see Fig. 3). This observation has been confirmed by several others (Yamamoto et al., 1983, 1984, 1985; Johnson et al., 1985; Leong and Tan, 1987; Henry et al., 1987; Ling and Leong, 1987; Paul and Devor, 1987; Pubols and Foglesong, 1988). In addition, axonal transport and accumulation of ricin in perikarya of sensory and motor neurons has been reported using ricin-HRP conjugates (Wiley et al., 1982) or antiricin immunohistochemistry (Yamamoto et al., 1984, 1985). Autoradiography using [^{3}H]leucine incorporation shows

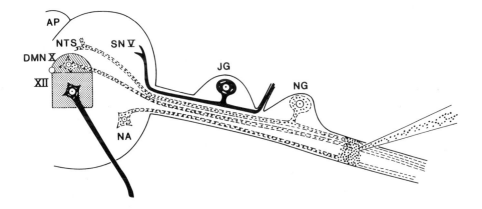

FIGURE 3 Schematic of the suicide transport strategy as demonstrated by subepineurial vagus nerve injections. Small dots indicate toxin. NG, nodose ganglion of vagus (sensory neurons); JG, jugular ganglion; DMNX, dorsal motor nucleus of the vagus (motor neurons); NA, nucleus ambiguous (motor neurons); NTS, nucleus tractus solitarius (sensory terminal field). Adjacent nonvagal structures: XII, hypoglossal nucleus; AP, area postrema; and SN V, spinal nucleus of the trigeminal nerve. Dashed neurons are those destroyed by vagal injection of ricin. The black neurons are not affected by the injection.

profound inhibition of protein synthesis in vagal motor and sensory neurons
within 18 h after ricin injection into the cervical vagus nerve (Wiley, 1985).

The use of ricin to make anatomically specific lesions of peripheral sensory
and motor neurons has been described in detail (Wiley and Oeltmann, 1986).
The most reliable technique has involved careful pressure microinjection subepineurially so that all the toxin remains contained within the nerve sheath.
However, even with great care to prevent leakage, animals may develop systemic ricin poisoning because the dose necessary to ablate a large peripheral
nerve completely may be too great (Paul and Devor, 1987). This problem
can be overcome by the use of concurrent systemic administration of antiricin
antisera, which protects animals against systemic ricin poisoning without affecting the suicide transport effect (Wiley and Oeltmann, 1989).

The cytopathology of ricin effect on neurons has been described in several settings, including vagal injections (Wiley et al., 1982; Ling and Leong,
1987), sciatic nerve injections (Yamamoto et al., 1984, 1985; Paul and Devor,
1987; Pubols and Foglesong, 1988), submandibular salivary gland injections
(Harper et al., 1980), and tooth pulp application (Henry et al., 1987). Figures 4 to 7 show the neuropathological effects of viscumin, the toxic lectin
from mistletoe, which are identical to those seen with ricin. The earliest
change detectable at the light microscopic level is chromatolysis followed by
perikaryal swelling, nuclear and nucleolar degeneration, and eventual dis-
integration of the neurons. At the ultrastructural level, the earliest change
is disaggregation of polyribosomes followed by disorganization of the rough
endoplasmic reticulum, resulting in many small clear vesicles within the perikaryal cytoplams.

A number of toxic lectins and related axonally transported cytotoxins
have been studied for suicide transport activity in the rat peripheral and
central nervous systems. Table 2 summarizes those data. In general, all
the ribosome-inactivating cytotoxins tested destroy vagal sensory neurons,
but the cytotoxin from *Shigella dysenteriae* does not efficiently destroy vagal
motor neurons (Wiley et al., 1985). Also, ricin is not active as a suicide transport agent within the rat CNS (Wiley et al., 1983).

Specific applications of the suicide transport technique have included:

1. Anatomical mapping studies (Yamamoto et al., 1983; Johnson et al.,
1985; Leong and Tan, 1987; Aldskogius et al., 1988), which usually combine
ricin with silver degeneration techniques or electron microscopy. These studies have demonstrated the usefulness of ricin for this purpose.

2. Modeling of motor neuron degenerations (Yamamoto et al., 1985; Palladini et al., 1986). The relationship of ricin effect on motor neurons to the
naturally occurring disease remains unclear.

3. Studies of neuropathic pain and plasticity of somatosensory pathways
after peripheral nerve damage (Yamamoto et al., 1984; Nennesmo and Kristensson, 1986; Wiesenfeld-Hallin et al., 1987; Wall et al., 1988; Pubols and Bowen,
1988). Compared to peripheral nerve transection, ricin produces much greater loss of sensory neurons with degeneration of their central terminals.
Peripheral nerve transection usually results in delayed partial loss of sensory
neurons. Interestingly, current data do not reveal any behavioral difference between animals with peripheral neurectomy by ricin as compared to
transection; however ricin-ablated nerves do not form neuromas (Nennesmo

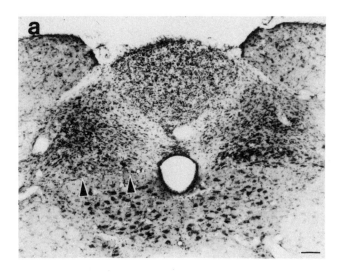

FIGURE 4a Suicide transport effects of 0.4 μg of viscumin injected into the cervical vagus nerve of a rat as shown in Fig. 3. The animal was sacrificed 4 days after toxin injection. Sections are stained with cresyl violet.(a) Transverse section of medulla showing loss of motor neurons from the dorsal motor nucleus (arrowheads) ipsilateral to the toxin injection.

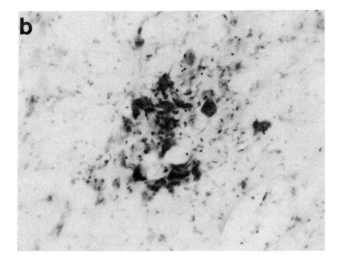

FIGURE 4b Left nucleus ambiguous ipsilateral to toxin injection showing partial loss of neurons and increased mononuclear cells.

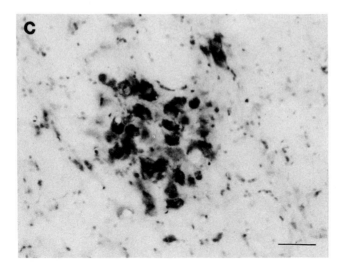

FIGURE 4c Right nucleus ambiguous showing normal architecture.

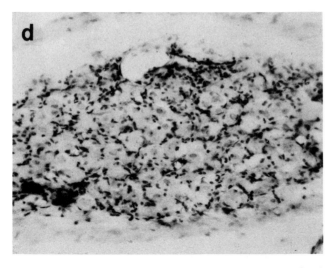

FIGURE 4d Left nodose ganglion ipsilateral to the toxin injection showing massive chromatolysis of virtually all sensory neurons.

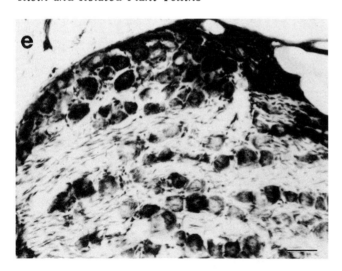

FIGURE 4e Right nodose ganglion showing normal cytologic appearance of vagal sensory neurons. All magnification bars indicate 100 μm. Bar in (c) also applies to (b); bar in (e) also applies to (d).

and Kristensson, 1986). The therapeutic implications of these observations remain to be elucidated.

    4. Mapping cellular localization of neurotransmitter receptors (Helke et al., 1985, 1986). In the case of substance P receptors, ricin lesions have proven very effective in establishing that the receptors are on motor neurons. This use of ricin will probably be exploited much more in the future. A number of similar studies using agents active within the CNS are currently underway.

    5. Disease-related applications include eradication of latent herpes simplex virus in trigeminal sensory neurons (Hino et al., 1988), production and analysis of glial fibrillary bundles (Yamamoto et al., 1986), and treatment of equine neuromas (Cummings et al., 1988).

Future directions in this field involve use of modeccin and volkensin in peripheral nerves (Wiley and Stirpe, 1987) and in the CNS (Wiley and Stirpe, 1988). Indeed, modeccin and volkensin are very active suicide transport agents on at least some CNS pathways in the rat. Also, conjugates of the A-chain effector moieties to various carriers (Oeltmann and Wiley, 1986; Ovadia et al., 1988) are being explored for their usefulness in making selective neural lesions. Future suicide transport agents based on antineuronal antibodies may prove extraordinarily valuable in making highly selective neural lesions for experimental and possibly therapeutic purposes.

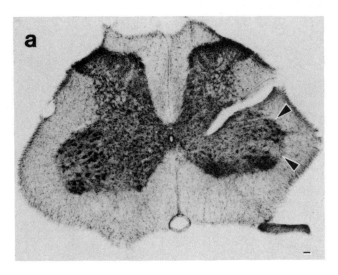

(a)

FIGURE 5 Effects of 2.8 µg of viscumin injected subepineurially into the sciatic nerve of a rat. The animal was sacrificed after 5 days. Sections are stained with cresyl violet. (a) Transverse section of the spinal cord showing loss of sciatic motor neurons from the right ventrolateral region (arrowheads) ipsilateral to the toxin injection; (b) left L_5 dorsal root ganglion showing normal appearance of sciatic sensory neurons; (c) right L_5 dorsal root ganglion showing many chromatolytic sensory neurons. Magnification bars indicate 100 µm. Bar in (c) also applies to (b).

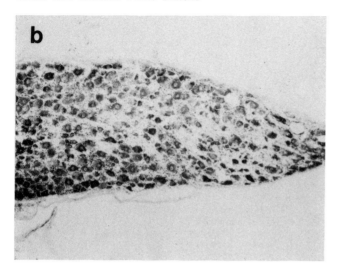

(b)

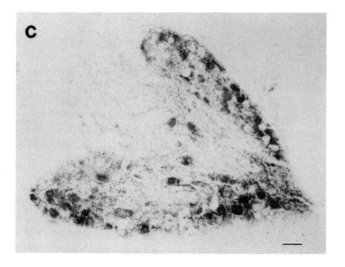

(c)

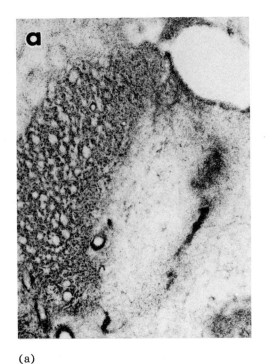

(a)

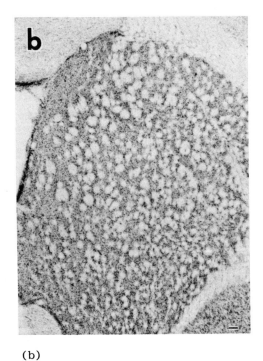

(b)

FIGURE 6 Effects of 0.4 µg of viscumin injected into the left caudate nucleus of a rat. The animal was sacrificed after 15 days. Sections are stained with cresyl violet. (a) Left caudate nucleus showing injection site (right lower half of section); (b) right caudate nucleus showing normal cytoarchitecture;

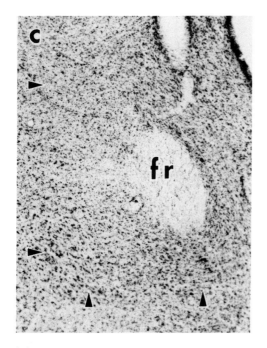

(c)

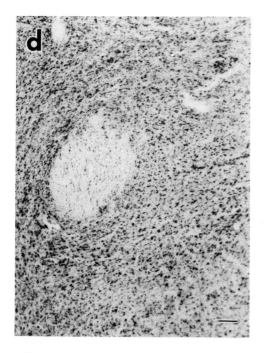

(d)

FIGURE 6 (continued) (c) left parafascicular nucleus of the thalamus (outlined by arrowheads) showing partial loss of neurons that project to the ipsilateral caudate nucleus; (d) right parafascicular nucleus showing normal
appearance. fr indicates fasciculus retroflexus. Magnification bars indicate
100 μm. Bar in (b) also applies to (a); bar in (d) also applies to (c).

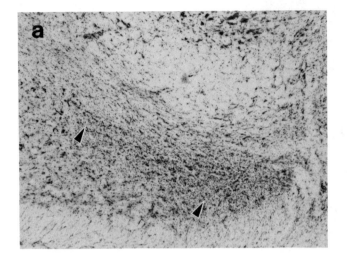

(a)

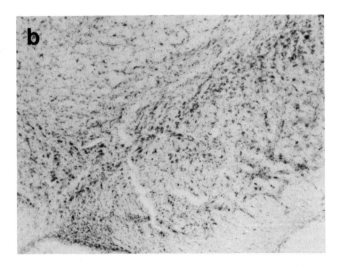

(b)

FIGURE 7 Substantia nigra sections from same rat as in Fig. 6. (a) and (b) are stained with cresyl violet; (c) and (d) are stained with immunoperoxidase technique for tyrosine hydroxylase to identify dopaminergic neurons of the substantia nigra pars compacta that project to the ipsilateral caudate nucleus. (a) Left substantia nigra showing loss of pars compacta neurons (arrowheads); (b) right substantia nigra showing normal appearance;

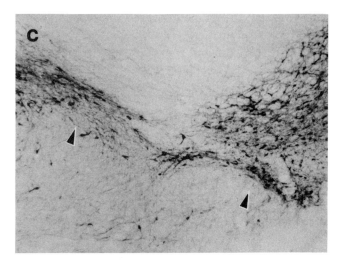

(c)

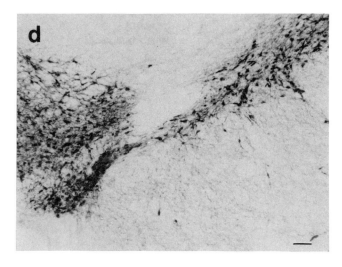

(d)

FIGURE 7 (continued) (c) left substantia nigra stained for tyrosine hydroxylase showing partial loss of neurons (arrowheads) that project to the ipsilateral caudate nucleus; (d) right substantia nigra stained for tyrosine hydroxylase showing normal abundance of dopaminergic neurons. Sections
shown in (c) and (d) are adjacent to (a) and (b), respectively. Magnification bar in (d) indicates 100 μm and applies to all panels.

TABLE 2 Suicide Transport Properties of Toxic Lectins

Toxin	Source	Suicide transport activity[a]	
		PNS	CNS
Ricin	*Ricinus communis*	++	0
Abrin	*Abrus precatoris*	++	0
Viscumin	*Viscum album*	++	+/-
Modeccin	*Adenia digitata*	++	++
Volkensin	*Adenia volkensii*	++	++
Shiga toxin	*Shigella dysenteriae*	+	0

[a]Suicide transport activity in the peripheral nervous system was assessed after subepineurial vagal injection; CNS activity was assessed after caudate nucleus injection. In the PNS, + indicates destruction of sensory neurons only, ++ indicates destruction of both sensory and motor neurons. In the CNS, +/- means partial destruction of the ipsilateral substantia nigra and parafascicular nucleus of the thalamus at near lethal doses, ++ indicates profound destruction of those structures at sublethal doses. 0 indicates no activity at any dose tested.

REFERENCES

Aldskogius, H., Wiesenfeld-Halin, Z., and Kristensson, K. (1988). Selective neuronal destruction by *Ricinus communis* agglustinin I and its use for the quantitative determination of sciatic nerve dorsal root ganglion cell numbers. *Brain Res. 461*: 215-220.

Anderson, R. G. W., and Pathak, R. K. (1985). Vesicles and cisternae in the trans Golgi apparatus of human fibroblasts are acidic compartments. *Cell 40*: 635-643.

Bittiger, H., and Schnebli, H. P. (1974). Binding of concanavalin A and ricin to synaptic junctions of rat brain. *Nature 249*: 370-371.

Cawley, D. B., and Houston, L. L. (1979). Effect of sulfhydryl reagents and protease inhibitors on sodium dodecyl sulfate-heat-induced dissociation of *Ricinus communis* agglutinin. *Biochem. Biophys. Acta 581*: 51-62.

Cummings, J. F., Fubini, S. L., and Todhunter, R. J. (1988). Attempts to prevent equine post neurectomy neuroma formation through retrograde transport of two neurotoxins, doxorubicin and ricin, *Equine Vet. J. 20*: 451-456.

DeSilva, N. S., Gurd, J. W., and Schwartz, C. (1979). Developmental alteration of rat brain synaptic membranes: reaction of glycoproteins with plant lectins. *Brain Res. 165*: 283-293.

Draper, R., and Simon, M. (1980). The entry of diphtheria toxin into the mammalian cell cytoplasm: evidence for lysosomal involvement. *J. Cell Biol. 87*: 849-854.

Dumas, M., Schwab, M. E., and Thoenen, H. (1979). Retrograde axonal transport of specific macromolecules as a tool for characterizing nerve terminal membranes, *J. Neurobiol. 10*:179-197.

Endo, Y. (1988). Mechanism of action of ricin and related toxins on the inactivation of eukaryotic ribosomes. In *Immunotoxins*, A. E. Frankel (ed.). Kluwer Academic Publishers, Norwell, Mass., pp. 75-89.

Endo, Y., and Tsurugi, K. (1987). RNA *N*-glycosidase activity of ricin A-chain: mechanism of action of the toxic lectin ricin on eukaryotic ribosomes. *J. Biol. Chem. 262*:8128-8130.

Endo, Y., Mitsui, M., Motizuki, M., and Tsurugi, K. (1987). The mechanism of action of ricin and related toxic lectins on eukaryotic ribosomes: the site and the characteristics of the modification in 28 S ribosomal RNA caused by the toxins. *J. Biol. Chem. 262*:5908-5912.

Foxwell, B. M., Donovan, T. A., Thorpe, P. E., and Wilson, G. (1985). The removal of carbohydrates from ricin with endoglycosidases H, F, and D and -mannosidase. *Biochem. Biophys. Acta 840*:193-203.

Foxwell, B. M. J., Blakey, D. C., Brown, A. N. F., Donovan, T. A., and Thorpe, P. E. (1987). The preparation of deglycosylated ricin by recombination of glycosidase-treated A- and B-chains: effects of deglycosylation on toxicity and in vivo distribution. *Biochem. Biophys. Acta 923*: 59-65.

Funatsu, G., Yoshitaka, S., and Funatsu, M. (1978). Primary structure of isoleucine chain of ricin D. *Agric. Biol. Chem. 42*:501-503.

Funatsu, G., Kimura, M., and Funatsu, M. (1979). Primary structure of alanine chain of ricin D. *Agric. Biol. Chem. 43*:2221-2224.

Ghitescu, L., Fixman, A., Simionescu, M., and Simionescu, N. (1986). Specific binding sites for albumin restricted to plasmalemmal vesicles of continuous capillary endothelium: receptor-mediated transcytosis. *J. Cell Biol. 102*:1304-1311.

Golstein, J. L., Brown, M. S., Anderson, R. G. W., Russell, D. W., and Schneider, W. J. (1985). Receptor-mediated endocytosis: concepts emerging from the LDL receptor system. *Annu. Rev. Cell Biol. 1*:1-40.

Gonatas, N. K., Steiber, A., Kim, S. U., Graham, D. I., and Avrameas, S. (1975). Internalization of neuronal plasma membrane ricin receptors into the Golgi apparauts. *Exp. Cell Res. 94*:426-431.

Gonatas, N. K., Kim, S. U., Steiber, A., and Avrameas, S. (1977). Internalization of lectins in neuronal GERL. *J. Cell Biol. 73*:1-13.

Greenberger, L. M., and Pfenninger, K. H. (1986). Membrane glycoproteins of the nerve growth cone: diversity and growth regulation of oligosaccharides. *J. Cell Biol. 103*:1369-1382.

Groeger, B. K., Williams, L. G., Pigott, J., Ziska, P., O'Dell, D. S., Williams, D. J., Franz, H., and Debbage, P. L. (1983). Affinities of ricin 120 and mistletoe lectin 1 for membrane components of liver and nervous tissue. In *Lectins*, Vol. III, T. C. Bog-Hanson and G. A. Spengler (Eds.). Walter de Gruyter, West Berlin, pp. 179-187.

Gurd, J. W. (1977). Synaptic membrane glycoproteins: molecular identification of lectin receptors. *Biochemistry 16*:369-374.

Harley, S. M., and Lord, J. M. (1985). In vitro endoproteolytic cleavage of castor bean lectin precursors. *Plant Sci. 41*:(*Lucknow*) 111-116.

Harper, C. G., Gonatas, J. O., Mizutani, T., and Gonatas, N. K. (1980). Retrograde transport and effects of toxic ricin in the autonomic nervous system. *Lab. Invest.* *42*:396-404.

Hart, C. E., and Wood, J. G. (1985). A comparative study of the intracellular lectin binding sites of neurons in culture with neurons in situ. *J. Comp. Neurol.* *239*:155-162.

Hatten, M. E., and Sidman, R. L. (1977). Plant lectins detect age and region pecific differences in cell surface carbohydrates and cell reassociation behavior of embryonic mouse cerebellar cells. *J. Supramol. Struct.* *7*:267-275.

Hatten, M. E., Schachner, M., and Sidman, R. L. (1979). Histochemical characterization of lectin binding in mouse cerebellum. *Neuroscience 4*: 921-935.

Helke, C. J., Charlton, C. G., and Wiley, R. G. (1985). Suicide transport of ricin demonstrates the presence of substance P receptors on medullary somatic and autonomic motor neurons. *Brain Res.* *328*:190-195.

Helke, C. J., Charlton, C. G., and Wiley, R. G. (1986). Studies on the cellular localization of spinal cord substance P receptors. *Neuroscience 19*:523-533.

Henry, M. A., Westrum, L. E., Johnson, L. R., and Canfield, R. C. (1987). Ultrastructure of degenerative changes following ricin application to feline dental pulps. *J. Neurocytol.* *16*:601-611.

Hino, M., Sekizawa, T., and Openshaw, H. (1988). Ricin injection eliminates latent *Herpes simplex* virus in the mouse. *J. Infect. Dis.* *157*: 1270-1271.

Houston, L. L., and Dooley, T. P. (1982). Binding of two molecules of 4-methylumbelliferyl galactose or 4-methylumbelliferyl N-acetylgalactosamine to the B-chain of ricin and *Ricinus communis* agglutinin and to purified ricin B-chain. *J. Biol. Chem.* *257*:4147-4151.

Huck, M. E., and Hatten, M. E. (1981). Developmental stage-specific changes in lectin binding to mouse cerebellar cells in vitro. *J. Neurosci.* *1*:1075-1084.

Hughes, R. C., and Gardas, A. (1976). Phenotypic reversion of ricin-resistant hamster fibroblasts to a sensitive state after coating with glycolipid receptors. *Nature 264*:63-66.

Johnson, L. R., Westrum, L. E., Henry, M. A., and Canfield, R. C. (1985). Toxic ricin demonstrates a dual dental projection. *Brain Res.* *345*:379-383.

Kelly, P., Cotman, C. W., Gentry, C., and Nicolson, G. L. (1976). Distribution and mobility of lectin receptors on synaptic membranes of identified neurons in the central nervous system. *J. Cell Biol.* *71*:487-496.

Lappi, D. A., Kapmeyer, W., Beglau, J. M., and Kaplan, N. O. (1978). The disulfide bond connecting the chains of ricin. *Proc. Natl. Acad. Sci. USA 75*:1096-1102.

Leong, S. K., and Tan, C. K. (1987). Central projections of rat sciatic nerve fibers as revealed by *Ricinus communis* agglutinin and horseradish perxidase tracers. *J. Anat.* *154*:15-26.

Ling, E. A., and Leong, S. K. (1987). Effects of intraneural injection of *Ricinus communis* agglutinin-60 into the rat vagus nerve. *J. Neurocytol.* *16*:373-387.

Lord, J. M. (1985). Synthesis and intracellular transport of lectin and storage protein precursors in endosperm from castor bean. *Eur. J. Biochem. 146*: 403-409.

McLaughlin, B. J., Wood, J. G., and Gurd, J. W. (1980). The localization of lectin binding sites during photoreceptor synaptogenesis in the chick retina. *Brain Res. 191*: 345-357.

Mellman, I. (1984). Membrane recycling during endocytosis. In *Lysosomes in Biology and Pathology*, J. T. Dingle, R. T. Dean, and W. Sly (Eds.). Elsevier, Amsterdam, pp. 201-229.

Mellman, I., Ruchs, R., and Helenius, A. (1986). Acidification of the endocytic and exocytic pathways. *Annu. Rev. Biochem. 55*: 663-700.

Montfort, W., Villafranca, J. E., Monzingo, A. F., Ernst, S., Katzin, B., Rutenber, E., Xuong, N. H., Hamlin, R., and Robertus, J. D. (1987). The 3-dimensional structure of ricin at 2.8A. *J. Biol. Chem. 262*: 5398-5403.

Nennesmo, I., and Kristensson, K. (1986). Effects of retrograde axonal transport of *Ricinus communis* agglutinin I on neuroma formation. *Acta Neuropathol. 70*: 279-283.

Oeltmann, T. N., and Wiley, R. G. (1986). Wheat germ agglutinin-ricin A-chain conjugate is neuronotoxic after vagal injection. *Brain Res. 377*: 221-228.

Olsnes, S., and Pihl, A. (1982). Toxic lectins and related proteins. In *Molecular Action of Toxins and Viruses*, P. Cohen and S. van Heyningen (Eds.). Elsevier/North Holland, Amsterdam, pp. 51-105.

Olsnes, S., and Sandvig, K. (1983). Entry of toxic proteins into cells. In *Receptor-Mediated Endocytosis: Receptors and Recognition*, Series B, Vol. 15, P. Cuatrecasas and T. F. Roth (Eds.). Chapman & Hall, London, pp. 188-236.

Olsnes, S., and Sandvig, K. (1985). Entry of polypeptide toxins into animal cells. In *Endocytosis*, I. Pastan and M. C. Willingham (Eds.). Plenum Press, New York, pp. 195-234.

Olsnes, S., and Sandvig, K. (1988). How protein toxins enter and kill cells. In *Immunotoxins*, A. E. Frankel (ed.). Kluwer Academic Publishers, Norwell, Mass., pp. 39-73.

Olsnes, S., Refsnes, K., Christensen, T. B., and Pihl, A. (1975). Studies on the structure and properties of the lectins from *Abrus precatorius* and *Ricinus communis*. *Biochem. Biophys. Acta 405*: 1-10.

Ovadia, M., Wiley, R. G., Hager, C., LaRocca, C., and Oeltmann, T. N. (1988). Synthesis and in vitro and in vivo activity of a hybrid composed of ricin B chain-barley ribosome-inactivating protein. *Arch. Biochem. Biophys. 264*: 168-175.

Palladini, G., Medolago-Albani, L., Guerrisi, R., Millefiorini, M., Antonini, G., Filippini, C., Conforti, A., and Palatinsky, E. (1986). The response of ventral horn neurons to ricin: an experimental abiotrophy model. *Pathol. Biol. 34*: 1047-1053.

Paul, I., and Devor, M. (1987). Completeness and selectivity of ricin "suicide transport" lesions in rat dorsal root ganglia. *J. Neurosci. Methods 22*: 103-111.

Pfenninger, K. H., and Maylie-Pfenninger, M.-F. (1981). Lectin labelling of sprouting neurons: I. Regional distribution of surface glycoconjugates. *J. Cell Biol. 89*: 536-546.

Pubols, L. M., and Bowen, D. C. (1988). Lack of central sprouting of pri-
    mary afferent fibers after ricin deafferentation. *J. Comp. Neurol.* 275:
    282-287.

Pubols, L. M., and Foglesong, M. E. (1988). Acute and chronic effects of
    the neurolytic agent ricin on dorsal root ganglia, spinal cord and nerves.
    J. Comp. Neurol. 275: 271-281.

Salvaterra, P. M., Gurd, J. M., and Mahler, H. R. (1977). Interactions
    of the nicotinic acetylcholine receptor from rat brain with lectins. *J.
    Neurochem.* 29: 345-353.

Sandvig, K., and Olsnes, S. (1979). Effect of temperature on the uptake,
    excretion and degradation of abrin and ricin by HeLa cells. *Exp. Cell
    Res.* 121: 15-25.

Sandvig, K., and Olsnes, S. (1980). Diphtheria toxin entry into cells is
    facilitated by low pH. *J. Cell Biol.* 87: 828-832.

Sandvig, K., and Olsnes, S. (1981). Rapid entry of nicked diphtheria toxin
    into cells at low pH: characterization of the entry process and effects
    of low pH on the toxin molecule. *J. Cell Biol.* 256: 9068-9076.

Sandvig, K., and Olsnes, S. (1982a). Entry of the toxic proteins abrin,
    modeccin, ricin and diphtheria toxin into cells: II. Effect of pH, meta-
    bolic inhibitors and ionophores and evidence for penetration from endocy-
    tic vesicles. *J. Biol. Chem.* 257: 7504-7513.

Sandvig, K., and Olsnes, S. (1982b). Entry of the toxic proteins abrin,
    modeccin, ricin, and diphtheria toxin into cells: I. Requirement for cal-
    cium. *J. Biol. Chem.* 257: 7495-7503.

Sandvig, K., Olsnes, S., and Pihl, A. (1976). Kinetics of binding of the
    toxic lectins abrin and ricin to surface receptors on human cells. *J.
    Biol. Chem.* 251: 3977-3984.

Sandvig, K., Olsnes, S. and Pihl, A. (1979). Inhibitory effect of ammonium
    chloride and chloroquine on the entry of the toxic lectin modeccin into
    HeLa cells. *Biochem. Biophys. Res.* 90: 648-655.

Sandvig, K., Olsnes, S., Petersen, O. W., and van Deurs, B. (1987).
    Acidification of the cytosol inhibits endocytosis from coated pits: evidence
    for an alternative pathway of endocytosis. *J. Cell Biol.* 105: 679-689.

Shirakawa, O., Kuno, T., and Tanaka, C. (1983). The glycoprotein nature
    of solubilized muscarinic acetylcholine receptors from bovine cerebral cor-
    tex. *Biochem. Biophys. Res.* 115: 814-821.

Simmons, B. M., Stahl, P. D., and Russel, J. H. (1986). Mannose receptor-
    mediated uptake of ricin toxin and ricin A-chain by macrophages: multiple
    intracellular pathways for A-chain translocation. *J. Biol. Chem.* 261:
    7912-7920.

Skilleter, D. N., and Foxwell, B. M. J. (1986). Selective uptake of ricin
    A-chain by hepatic non-parenchymal cells in vitro: importance of man-
    nose oligosaccharides in the toxin. *FEBS Lett.* 192: 344-348.

Streit, W. J., Schulte, B. A., Balentine, J. D., and Spicer, S. S. (1985).
    Histochemical localization of galactose-containing glycoconjugates in sen-
    sory neurons and their processes in the central and peripheral nervous
    system of the rat. *J. Histochem. Cytochem.* 33: 1042-1052.

Strocchi, P., Novello, F., Mantanaro, N., and Stirpe, F. (1979). Effect
    of intraventricularly injected ricin on protein synthesis in rat brain.
    Neurochem. Res. 4: 259-268.

van Deurs, B., Pedersen, L. R., Sudan, A., Olsnes, S., and Sandvig, K. (1985). Receptor-mediated endocytosis of a ricin-colloidal gold conjugate in Vero cells: intracellular routing to vacuolar and tubulo-vesicular portions of the endosomal system. *Exp. Cell Res. Commun. 159*:287-304.

van Deurs, B., Tonnessen, T. I., Petersen, O. W., Sandvig, K., and Olsnes, S. (1986). Routing of internalized ricin and ricin conjugates to the Golgi complex. *J. Biol. Chem. 102*:37-47.

van Deurs, B., Petersen, O. W., Olsnes, S., and Sandvig, K. (1987). Delivery of internalized ricin from endosomes to cisternal Golgi elements is a discontinuous, temperature-sensitive process. *Exp. Cell Res. 171*: 137-152.

van Deurs, B., Sandvig, K., Petersen, O. W., Olsnes, S., Simons, K., and Griffiths, G. (1988). Estimation of the amount of internalized ricin that reaches the trans Golgi network. *J. Cell Biol. 106*:253-267.

Wall, J. T., Cusick, C. G., Migani-Wall, S. A., and Wiley, R. G. (1988). Cortical organization after treatment of a peripheral nerve with ricin: an evaluation of the relationship between sensory neuron death and cortical adjustments after nerve injury. *J. Comp. Neurol. 277*:578-592.

Wei, C. H., Koh, C., Pfuderer, P., and Einstein, J. R. (1975). Purification, properties, and crystallographic data for a principal nontoxic lectin from seeds of *Abrus precatorius*. *J. Biol. Chem. 250*:4790-4795.

Wiesenfeld-Hallin, Z., Nennesmo, I., and Kristensson, K. (1987). Autotomy in rats after nerve seciton compared with nerve degeneration following intraneural injection of *Ricinus communis* agglutinin I. *Pain 30*:93-102.

Wileman, T., Harding, C., and Stahl, P. (1985). Receptor-mediated endocytosis. *Biochem. J. 232*:1-14.

Wiley, R. G. (1985). Effects of retorgradely transported ricin on vagal neurons: time course of ricin transport, inhibition of neuronal protein synthesis and morphological changes. *Abs. Soc. Neurosci. 11*:440.

Wiley, R. G., and Oeltmann, T. N. (1986). Anatomically selective nerve ablation using intraneural ricin injection. *J. Neurosci. Methods 17*:43-53.

Wiley, R. G., and Oeltmann, T. N. (1989). Anti-ricin antibody protects against systemic toxicity without affecting suicide transmport. *J. Neurosci. Methods 27*:203-209.

Wiley, R. G., and Stirpe, F. (1987). Neuronotoxicity of axonally transported toxic lectins, abrin, modeccin and volkensin in rat peripheral nervous system. *Neuropathol. Appl. Neurobiol. 13*:39-53.

Wiley, R. G., and Stirpe, F. (1988). Modeccin and volkensin but not abrin are effective suicide transport agents in rat CNS. *Brain Res. 438*:145-154.

Wiley, R. G., Blessing, W. W., and Reis, D. J. (1982). Suicide transport: destruction of neurons by retrograde transport of ricin, abrin, and modeccin. *Science 216*:889-890.

Wiley, R. G., Talman, W. T., and Reis, D. J. (1983). Ricin transport distinguishes between central and peripheral neurons. *Brain Res. 269*:357-360.

Wiley, R. G., Donohue-Rolfe, A., and Keusch, G. T. (1985). Axonally transported *Shigella* cytotoxin is neuronotoxic. *J. Neuropathol. Exp. Neurol. 44*:496-506.

Yamamoto, T., Iwasaki, Y., and Konno, H. (1983). Retrograde axoplasmic transport of toxic lectins is useful for transganglionic tracings of the peripheral nerve. *Brain Res. 274*:325-328.

Yamamoto, T., Iwasaki, Y., and Konno, H. (1984). Experimental sensory ganglionectomy by way of suicide axoplasmic transport. *J. Neurosurg. 60*:108-114.

Yamamoto, T., Iwasaki, Y., Konno, H., and Kudo, H. (1985). Primary degeneration of motor neurons by toxic lectins conveyed from the peripheral nerve. *J. Neurol. Sci. 70*:327-337.

Yamamoto, T., Iwasaki, Y., Konno, H., and Kudo, H. (1986). Glial bundle formation in spinal roots following experimental neuronopathy. *Ann. Neurol. 20*:267-271.

Youle, R. J., and Colombatti, M. (1987). Hybridoma cells containing intracellular anti-ricin antibodies show ricin meets secretory antibody before entering the cytosol. *J. Biol. Chem. 262*:4676-4682.

Youle, R. J., and Huang, A. H. C. (1976). Protein bodies from the endosperm of castor beans: subfractionation, protein components, lectins, and changes during germination. *Plant Physiol. 58*:703-709.

Zentz, C., Frenoy, J.-P., and Bourrillon, R. (1978). Binding of galactose and lactose to ricin: equilibrium studies. *Biochem. Biophys. Acta 536*:18-26.

13

Plant Terpenoids as Pesticides

Stephen O. Duke

Southern Weed Science Laboratory, Agricultural Research Service, USDA, Stoneville, Mississippi

I. INTRODUCTION

The vast reservoir of secondary compounds produced by higher plants have only relatively recently begun to be exploited for pest control purposes (Cutler, 1988; Duke, 1986, 1989; Duke and Lydon, 1987). The most successful examples of the use of these compounds as pesticides are from the terpenoids. Examples of past successes in utilizing terpenoids as pesticides and terpenoid compounds with future potential are discussed in this review. No previous review has specifically covered this topic, although more specific reviews of the pesticidal use of terpenoids from the genus *Artemisia* (Duke et al., 1988; Sherif et al., 1987), of terpenoids as plant germination and growth inhibitors (Fischer, 1986), and of the biological activities of sesquiterpenoid lactones (Rodriquez et al., 1976; Stevens, 1984) and clerodane diterpenoids (Sarma, 1987) are available. More general reviews on secondary compounds of plants as potential pesticides (Lydon and Duke, 1989; Duke, 1986, 1989) and on terpenoids for agrochemical use (Elakovich, 1988) have been written.

In this review we concentrate on identified chemical compounds. Although there is much literature on pesticidal effects of essential oils and other mixtures of terpenoids or terpenoids with other natural products [e.g., Grainage and Ahmed (1988)], this information is very difficult to interpret. This review is not an exhaustive survey of all available examples of pesticidal activity of plant-produced terpenoid pesticides, but we try to give an ample sampling of the literature to provide the reader with an appreciation of the diversity and potential of this immense, barely tapped resource.

II. BIOLOGICAL SIGNIFICANCE AND RATIONALE

A. Biosynthetic Site

Many of the products of the terpenoid pathway (Fig. 1) are required for normal plant growth and development (e.g., carotenoids, phytol, certain hormones). However, many of the secondary products used by the plants for defense are highly phytotoxic and must be sequestered from the cytoplasm. Since many of them are highly insoluble in water, they cannot be stored easily in the vacuole as are many phenolic phytotoxins. Therefore, they are often found in greatest concentrations in epidermal glands of higher plants [e.g., Ascensão and Pais (1987), Cappelletti et al. (1986), and Eisner et al. (1987)] and nonliving resin canals. Although other secondary compounds (e.g., flavonoids and quinones) are found in epidermal trichomes and glands, terpenoids are the most commonly occurring metabolites in these structures (Kelsey et al., 1984). In some plant species, as much as 35% of the leaf surface can be covered with terpenoid-containing glands (Kelsey and Shafizadeh, 1980). These are good sites for protection from pathogens and herbivores. In many woody species, terpenoids are also localized in nonliving resin canals. This localization apparently provides protection against wood-boring insects and wood-colonizing fungi.

B. Chemical Diversity

Terpenoids arise from terpenoid pathway intermediates produced by condensation of five-carbon isoprenoid units (prenylation), beginning with isopentanyl-pyrophosphate (Fig. 1). Those arising from geranylpyrophosphate (10C), farnesylpyrophosphate (15C), and geranylgeranylpyrophosphate (20C) are termed monoterpenes, sesquiterpenes, and diterpenes, respectively. Two sesquiterpenes or two diterpenes can be condensed to form triterpenes (30C) or tetraterpenes (40C). Obviously, the number of possible permutations increases as the size of the molecule grows, and this generally holds true for the diversity of compounds from each category found in plants. For instance,

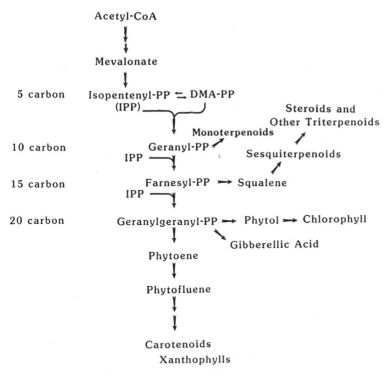

FIGURE 1 Terpenoid pathway in plants.

several hundred monoterpenes from plants have been described, whereas thousands of sesquiterpenoids are known. The diversity of plant-derived monoterpenes has been reviewed by Schütte (1984). Some terpenoids from plants contain covalently bound chlorine (Engvild, 1986), especially certain sesquiterpenoid lactones from the Asteraceae. Some of these compounds may be artifacts of isolation and analysis.

Hemiterpenoids (5C compounds) are not necessarily products of the terpenoid pathway and some are probably derived from leucine (Robinson, 1980). They will not be covered, nor will this review cover prenylated compounds that are not products of the terpenoid pathway, such as prenylated indoles [e.g., Adeoye et al. (1986)].

C. Chemical Ecology and Rationale for Pesticidal Function

The myriad of secondary compounds that plants produce are the result of coevolution of hundreds of thousands of plant species with each other and with an even greater number of pathogen and herbivore species. Because the interactions are often adversative, natural selection pressure has often been for compounds that negatively affect the other species. Since higher plants are sessile, they have fewer options than animals do when dealing with competitors, herbivores, or pathogens. Hence chemical warfare may be a more likely response for a plant than for an animal. Still, the true function

of many secondary compounds of plants is unknown. This is probably so because of multiple functions and because many of these compounds do not act
alone.

The biochemical origin of secondary compounds is varied, with compounds
occasionally being derived from more than one pathway. The pathways that
produce secondary compounds with the greatest structural diversity of secondary compounds are the shikimate and terpenoid pathways. Both pathways
produce thousands of complex heterocyclic compounds and often the biochemical origin is difficult to determine from the structure alone. Although the
terpenoid pathway produces secondary compounds from basic terpenoids built
by condensation of five carbon isoprenoid units (Fig. 1), the number of
carbons in many secondary terpenoids is not divisible by five because of metabolic conversions far removed from the basic terpenoid pathway.

III. COMMERCIAL AND POTENTIAL PESTICIDES

A. Herbicides

Inhibition of plant growth and production of phytotoxic symptoms by certain
plants and their residues is a well-established phenomenon. In searching
for potential herbicides from plants, screening of compounds known to function in plant-plant interactions is a logical strategy. All plants produce secondary compounds that are phytotoxic to some degree. However, in only a
relatively few cases has it been established that particular compounds (allelochemicals) provide the producing species with a competitive advantage over
other species that are less tolerant to the compounds. Only a few allelochemicals have been actively pursued as herbicides, and in these cases, the natural
compound has been modified.

Table 1 provides a sampling of the effects of plant terpenoids on seed
germination of various species. Of the hundreds of known plant-derived monoterpenes, camphor, 1,8-cineole, and pulegone (Fig. 2) are among the more
phytotoxic compounds. Asplund (1968) found that most monoterpenes stimulate germination at low concentrations and inhibit it at higher concentrations.
He found those with a ketone functional group to be the most phytotoxic. Although some of the thousands of characterized plant sesquiterpenoids are
among the more active natural phytotoxins, some, such as cnicin (Kelsey and
Locken, 1987), are only very weakly phytotoxic at concentrations above 1
mM. Fischer and Quijano (1985) found several sesquiterpenoid lactones to
have little effect on germination of seeds of 12 plant species.

Generally, terpenoids are more potent as growth inhibitors than as germination inhibitors. Many sesquiterpenoids have been identified as plant growth
inhibitors. The sesquiterpenoid lactones (over 2000 have been identified)
generally are more phytotoxic than other sesquiterpenoids. Artemisinin (Fig.
2), an antimalarial sesquiterpenoid lactone, is a potent plant growth inhibitor
(Duke et al., 1987) (Table 2). The sesquiterpenoids ambrosin and a dihy-
dropsilostachyin strongly inhibited growth of cress and lettuce seedlings
(Goldsby and Burke, 1987). Sequeira et al. (1968) found the sesquiterpenoid dilactone vernolepin to reduce wheat coleoptile longitudinal growth by
66% at a concentration of 37.5 µg/mL (about 100 µM). Most diterpenes have
been found to be relatively nonphytotoxic. Beyer et al. (1987) found several

TABLE 1 Survey of Plant Terpenoids and Their Effects on Seed Germination

Compound	Concentration[a] (μM)	Test organism	Effect (% inhibition)	Reference
Borneol	470	Lettuce	50	Reynolds (1987)
	s.a.	Madia sativa	100	Halligan (1975)
	s.s.	Lettuce	97	Fischer et al. (1988)
	21	Radish	50	Asplund (1968)
Calein A	50	Palmer amaranth	25	Fischer and Quaijano (1985)
Camphor	180	Lettuce	50	McCahon et al. (1973)
	3.3	Radish	50	Asplund (1968)
	s.a.	Madia sativa	100	Halligan (1975)
	s.s.	Lettuce	63	Fischer et al. (1988)
Carvone	s.s.	Lettuce	100	Fischer et al. (1988)
1,8-Cineole	78	Radish	50	Asplund (1968)
	s.s.	Madia sativa	100	Halligan (1975)
Citral	115	Lettuce	50	Reynolds (1987)

TABLE 1 (continued)

Compound	Concentration[a] (μm)	Test organism	Effect (% inhibition)	Reference
Citronellol	160	Lettuce	50	Reynolds (1987)
p-Cymene	51	Radish	50	Asplund (1968)
Ilicic acid	4000	Velvetleaf	73	Spencer et al. (1984)
Limonene	45	Radish	50	Asplund (1968)
Menthane-3,8-diol	1162	Lettuce	90	Nishimura et al. (1982)
Myrtenal	s.s.	Lettuce	81	Fischer et al. (1988)
α-Pinene	30	Radish	50	Asplund (1968)
Piperitone	75	Lettuce	50	Reynolds (1987)
Pulegone	1.5	Radish	50	Asplund (1968)
Terpinen-4-ol	140	Lettuce	50	Reynolds (1987)
Tujone	22	Lettuce	50	Reynolds (1987)
Trimethylformyl-cyclohexadienyl angelate	4000	Velvetleaf	79	Spencer (1986)

[a] s.a., Saturated atmosphere; s.s., saturated solution.

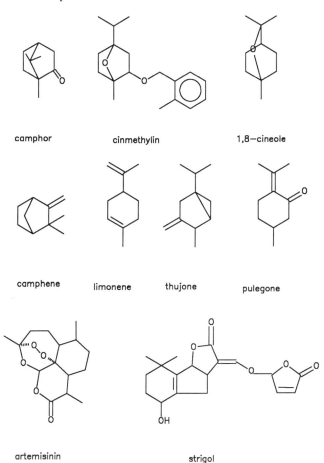

camphor   cinmethylin   1,8–cineole

camphene   limonene   thujone   pulegone

artemisinin   strigol

FIGURE 2 Structures of some phytotoxic terpenoids from plants.

diterpene sphenolobane derivatives from a liverwort to be relatively nontoxic
to rice seedlings. Podolactone E, a diterpenelactone, is an effective chlorophyll synthesis inhibitor (Miller et al., 1984). Duvatriene-diol diterpenoids
from tobacco leaf surfaces are phytotoxic to barnyard grass, with less than
0.5 mM concentrations reducing growth by more than 50% (Lawson et al., 1988).

Muller and Muller (1964) found 1,8-cineole to be one of the important phytotoxic terpenoids produced by several highly allelopathic desert shrubs.
Cinmethylin (Fig. 2) is a synthetic heribicide for grassy weeds that is structurally related to 1,8-cineole (Grayson et al., 1987). It is the only herbicide
under development that appears to have been derived from a terpene. It is
a growth inhibitor that stops meristematic growth (El-Deek and Hess, 1986).
It has low mammalian toxicity and shows no tendency to accumulate in the
environment.

The only other terpenoid-derived herbicide to be developed was chlorinated camphene (Fig. 2) (sold as Toxaphene or Camphechlor). Developed as
an insecticide, this mixture of almost 200 permutations of chlorinated camphene

TABLE 2 Survey of Plant Terpenoids and Their Effects on Seedling Radicle Growth

Compound	Concentration[a] (μM)	Test organism	Inhibition (%)	Reference
Achillin	100	Cucumber	35	McCahon et al. (1973)
Artemisinen	33	Lettuce, pigweed, purslane, and velvetleaf	50	Duke et al. (1987)
Axivalin	1000	Velvetleaf	>90	Spencer et al. (1984)
Camphor	s.a.	Barley	90	Heisey and Delwiche (1984)
1,8-Cineole	s.a.	Barley	25	Heisey and Delwiche (1984)
Cnicin	ca. 700	Lettuce	82	Kelsey and Locken (1987)
		Spotted knapweed	40	Kelsey and Locken (1987)
Conferin	1000	Achyranthes aspera	90	Amo and Anaya (1978)
	1000	Bidens pilosa	95	Amo and Anaya (1978)
	1000	Crusea calocephala	95	Amo and Anaya (1978)

Compound	Concentration	Species		Reference
Cumambrin B	1000	*Ambrosia cumanensis*	70	Amo and Anaya (1978)
	1000	*Bidens pilosa*	70	Amo and Anaya (1978)
	1000	*Crusea calocephala*	90	Amo and Anaya (1978)
Centaurepensin	200	Lettuce	50	Stevens and Merrill (1985)
Geraniol	2000	Pigweed	100	Rizvi and Rizvi (1987)
β-Pinene	s.a.	Pigweed	100	AlSaadawi et al. (1985)
Piquerol A	300	*Lepidium virginicum*	63	Gonzalez et al. (1981)
	300	*Bidens serrulata*	74	Gonzalez et al. (1981)
Repin	200	Lettuce	40	Stevens and Merrill (1985)
Solstitiolide	200	Lettuce	50	Stevens and Merrill (1985)
Terpinen-4-ol	s.a.	Barley	45	Heisey and Delwiche (1984)
Viscidulin-C	100	Cucumber	30	McCahon et al. (1973)

[a] s.a., Saturated atmosphere.

had limited use as a herbicide for control of sicklepod (*Cassia obtusifolia*) in soybeans (Sherman et al., 1983) before it was removed from the market for toxicological reasons. Although the active insecticidal principles were determined (see below), the phytotoxic principle(s) were never identified. Had the active principle been discovered, it might have been toxicologically safe.

Cotton produces a sesquiterpenoid derivative, strigol (Fig. 2), which is a powerful germination stimulant of certain parasitic weeds (e.g., *Striga* sp.). Field application of strigol results in germination of the tiny seeds of these parasitic species at times and in places in which the seedlings will not survive (Hsiao et al., 1981). Extensive research is being conducted to find efficacious analogs that will be less costly to synthesize than strigol (Pepperman et al., 1987). Four sesquiterpenoid lactones (confertiflorin, parthenin, desacetyl-confertiflorin, and dihydroparthenolide), which share structural features of the lactone rings of strigol, stimulated germination of witchweed (Fischer et al., 1989). Dihydroparthenolide had activity comparable to that of strigol.

Little is known of the mechanism of action of terpenoid phytotoxins. The monoterpene 1,8-cineole inhibits respiration (Muller et al., 1969; Lorber and Muller, 1980). Grandiol and homograndiol are photosystem II (PS II) electron transport inhibitors (Yoshida et al., 1988). Grandiol was about an order of magnitude less active than commercial herbicides that inhibit PS II, whereas homograndiol was almost as active as the commercial products. The growth-inhibiting activity of some sesquiterpenoid lactones is accompanied by stimulation of respiration (McCahon et al., 1973). The podolactones, a group of diterpenedilactones, are growth regulators. However, podolactone E is a potent greening inhibitor that blocks chlorophyll biosynthesis by inhibiting δ-aminolevulinic acid synthesis at low concentrations (Milelr et al., 1984).

Sesquiterpenoid lactones with an α-methylene/λ-lactone moiety can react with nucleophilic groups of biological molecules. A probable reaction is with the thiol group of proteins (Fig. 3). Often, small molecules with thiol groups (e.g., cysteine or reduced glutathione) can inactivate these allelochemicals, however, this is not always the case (Fischer and Quijano, 1985; Duke et al., 1988). The sesquiterpenoid lactone artemisinin apparently inhibits plant synthesis of putrecine (J. M. DiTomaso and S. O. Duke, unpublished) as it does in red blood cells infected with *Plasmodium* (Whaun et al., 1985).

Synergism between terpenoids in causing phytotoxicity has been documented. For example, Fischer et al. (1988) found that ursolic acid, a waxy triterpenoid that is found in the cuticle of leaves and fruits of many species acts synergistically with phytotoxic terpenoids. It reduces the volatility of more phytotoxic terpenoids, increases solubility of other terpenoids by its

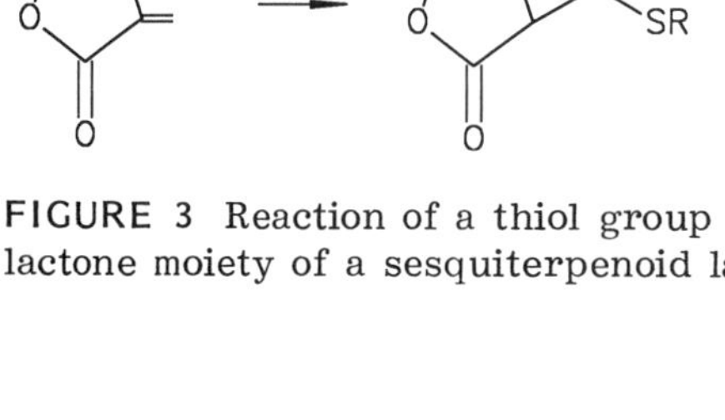

FIGURE 3 Reaction of a thiol group of a protein (R) with the α-methylene/λ-lactone moiety of a sesquiterpenoid lactone.

detergent action, and facilitates absorption of terpenoids by its adjuvant-like action.

Plants have been much more successfully exploited as sources of pesticides for pests other than weeds. This is probably due to several factors. The selection pressure caused by pathogens and herbivores has probably been more acute and intense than that caused by plant competitors. A plant species can effectively compete with plant foes in many ways other than by poisoning them with phytotoxins that might be autotoxic. Pathogens and herbivores have many potential physiological and biochemical sties of action for pesticides that plants do not share. A compound that affects one of these sites is not likely to be autotoxic. Thus the chemical option is generally a more attractive option in responding to a herbivore or pathogen that can rapidly devour or invade the plant than it is in responding to a plant competitor.

B. Insecticides and Modifiers of Insect Behavior

Plant terpenoids have been utilized more successfully as insecticides than as herbicides. Table 3 provides a sampling of the insecticidal activity of a variety of plant terpenoids. The most successful utilization of plant terpenoids for insecticidal use has been the pyrethroids. The insecticidal properties of the dried flowers of *Chrysanthemum roseum* and *Chrysanthemum carneum* were known for many years in Asia. The pyrethroids, one of the most successful insecticide classes, were derived form the *Chrysanthemum* terpenoids, the pyrethrins. The natural pyrethrins (Fig. 4) are a group of six mixed (the number of carbons is not divisible by 5) terpenoid esters observed only in the genus *Chrysanthemum* (Green et al., 1987). Since the chemical identification of the insecticidal pyrethroids from plants, many synthetic analogs have been patented and commercialized successfully (Briggs et al., 1983). These synthetic compounds have been manipulated to improve stability, toxicology, selectivity, and efficacy. The commercial productions of natural pyrethrins for pesticidal use is declining because of the less expensive and more efficacious synthetic pyrethrins.

Toxaphene, the polychlorinated product of camphene (Fig. 2), is a mixture of almost 200 compounds, many of which are polyclorobornanes. Several specific forms of chlorinated camphene were found to be much more insecticidal than others (Casida and Lawrence, 1985; Saleh and Casida, 1979). At one time during the 1970s, Toxaphene was the leading insecticide in the United States in terms of sales volume (Green et al., 1987). However, it was removed from the market because of toxicological concerns.

Ryania, the insecticidal powdered stem wood of *Ryania specisa*, contains an alkloidal diterpene, ryanodine (Fig. 4), that is the active principle (Casida et al., 1987). Ryania has been used for about 40 years as a commercial insecticide. It is one of the most potent naturally occurring insecticides against lepidopteran larvae. It controls European corn borer at only about 16 g/acre and improved preparations are effective against codling moth larvae at 3 to 4 g/acre. Rather than killing the larvae rapidly, it causes "flaccid paralysis." Ryanodine poisons muscles by binding at the Ca^{2+}-activated open state of the channel involved in the release of contractile Ca^{2+} from the sarcoplasmic reticulum, resulting in the uncoupling of the electrical signal of the transverse tubule from the Ca^{2+}-release mechanism of the sarcoplasmic reticulum (Casida et al., 1987).

TABLE 3 Insecticidal and Insect Growth-Inhibiting Properties of Plant-Derived Terpenoids

Compound	Test organism	Dose/treatment	Effect (% inhibition)	Reference
Acetylnimbandiol	H. virescens	4.4 ppm in diet	50	Klocke (1987)
Azadirachtin	Heliothus zea	0.7 ppm in diet	50	Klocke (1987)
	H. virescens	0.07 ppm in diet	50	Klocke (1987)
Argophyllin-B	H. electellum	1% in diet	100 mort.	Rogers et al. (1987)
Budlein-A	H. electellum	1% in diet	100 mort.	Rogers et al. (1987)
Camphor	H. virescens	0.5% in diet	50	Miles et al. (1985)
Caryophyllene	H. virescens	500 ppm in diet	30 GR	Gunasena et al. (1988)
Caryophyllene epoxide	Atta cephalotes	1 mM in diet	>90 mort.	Howard et al. (1988)
Cedrelone	H. zea	8 ppm in diet	50	Klocke (1987)
Desacetyleupasserin	Spondoptera evidania	1% in diet	100	Gershenzon et al. (1985)
	H. electellum	1% in diet	100 mort.	Rogers et al. (1987)
Himachalol	Callosobruchus analis	0.56 µmol[a]	98 mort.	Singh and Agarwal (1988)
Nerolidol	Atta cephalotes	1 mM in diet	ca. 90 mort.	Howard et al. (1988)
Telfairene	Culex pipiens	10 ppm solution	100 mort.	Watanabe et al (1989)
Zingiberene	Leptinotarsa decemlineatea	15 µg/insect	50 mort.	Carter et al. (1989)

[a]Per insect.

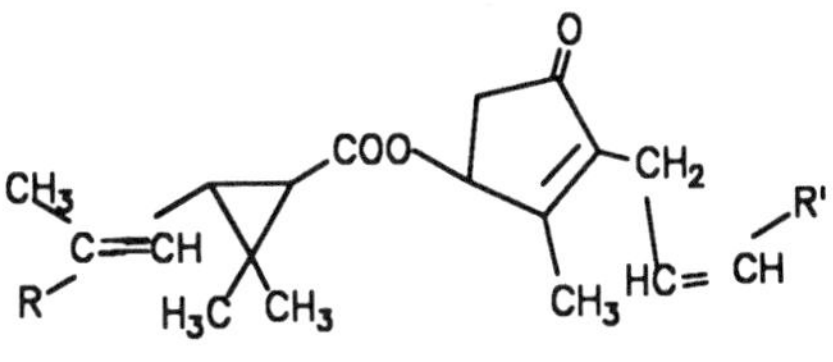

R = CH$_3$ R' = CH=CH$_2$ Pyrethrin I

R = CH$_3$OCO   R' = CH=CH$_2$ Pyrethrin II

R = CH$_3$ R' = CH$_3$ Cinerin I

R = CH$_3$OCO   R' = CH$_3$ Cinerin II

R = CH$_3$ R' = CH$_2$CH$_3$ Jasmolin I

R = CH$_3$OCO   R' = CH$_2$CH$_3$ Jasmolin II

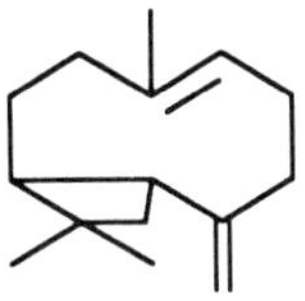

caryophyllene

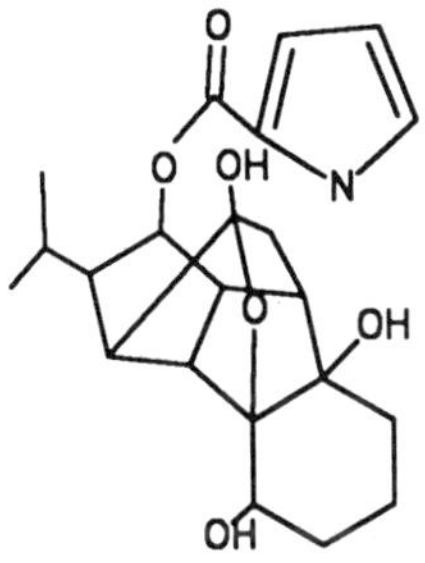

ryanodine

FIGURE 4 Structures of some insecticidal terpenoids from plants.

Because of the volatility of many plant terpenoids, they have become important cues for certain behavior of insects. They can act as repellents, attractants, oviposition cues, and antifeedants. Many plant terpenoids are strong insect repellents (Jacobson, 1966). Oil of camphor and citronella were used commercially in insect repellents during the first third of the twentieth century (Rice, 1983). Eucalyptus oil, which contains at least 70 to 85% 1,8-cineole, and other high 1,8-cineole oils are used as or in insect repellents (Klocke et al., 1987). Pure 1,8-cineole repels many insects, including mosquitoes (Klocke et al., 1987) and the American cockroach (Scriven and Meloan, 1984). Hwang et al. (1985) found several monoterpenoids from *Artemisia* species to be excellent mosquito repellents, with terpenen-4-ol being most effective.

Conversely, many terpenoids are insect attractants. Attractants can be used to lure insects to insecticides or to mask repellent properties of insecticides. They may also be used to lure beneficial insects to desired habitats. Essential oils of plants usually contain both attractants and repellents and the effect of a constituent can vary considerably between insect species. For instance, three terpenoid components of Scots pine steam distillate were attractants to the *Hylobius abietis*, a highly destructive weevil, and other components were repellent to the weevil (Selander et al., 1974). Geraniol (Fig. 5), the most basic monoterpene, will repel houseflies while attracting honeybees (Brattsten, 1983). Thus certain terpenoids might have dual utility as attractants to beneficial insects and repellents of certain insect pests. Plant terpenes are often the metabolic precursors of pheromones synthesized by insects. For example, myrcene (Fig. 5), a common constitutent of conifer resins, is is converted to the pheromones ipisidienol and ipsenol by beetles of the genus *Ips* that attack pine trees (Hughes, 1974).

    The bitter-tasting sesquiterpenoids are often antifeedants. The sesquiterpenoid caryophyllene is an aphid repellent (Gregory et al., 1986), and the epoxide of this compound inhibits *Heliothis virescens* larval growth by 60% when incorporated at a 5 mM concentration into the diet (Stipanovic et al., 1986). Caryophyllene and several other terpenoids had antifeedant activ-

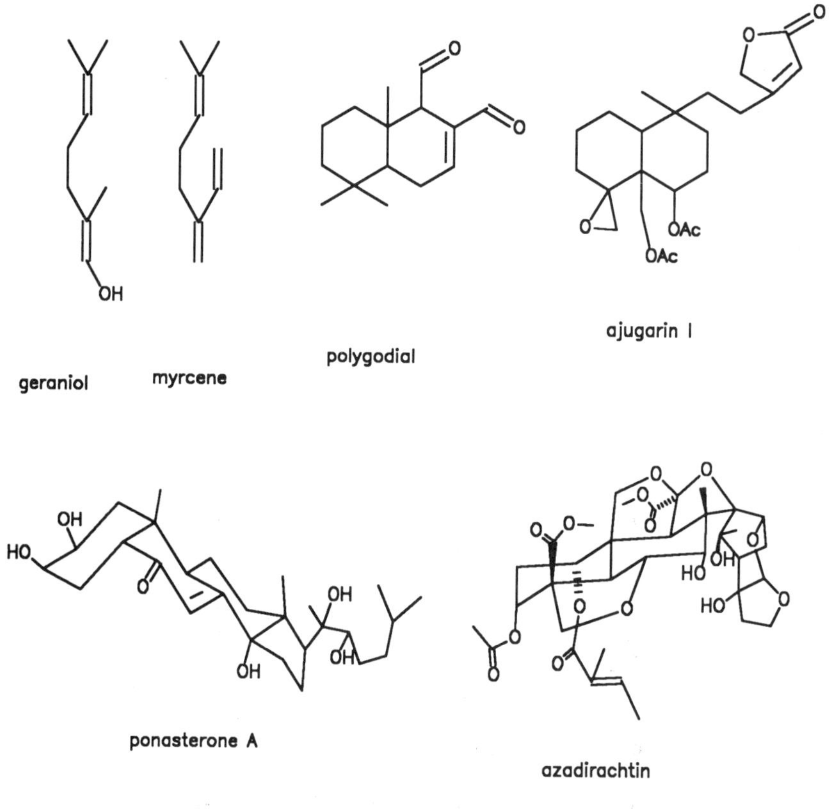

geraniol   myrcene   polygodial   ajugarin I

ponasterone A   azadirachtin

FIGURE 5 Structures of some insect behavior-modifying and development-modifying terpenoids from plants.

ity against cabbage butterfly larvae (Yano, 1987). Sesquiterpenoid and diterpenoid compounds from wild sunflower have acted as antifeedants to several
insect species (Gershenzon et al., 1985). Some plant-derived steroids are
among the most potent insect antifeedants (Kubo and Matsumoto, 1985) and
many plant-derived diterpenoids have insect antifeedant and growth-inhibiting
properties (Cooper-Driver and Le Quesne, 1987).

Terpenoid antifeedants are gaining increasing attention as pesticides.
The dipterpenoids ferruginol and manool are strong antifeedant compounds
to subterranean termites, providing protection to bald cypress (Scheffrahn et
al., 1988). Neem seed oil, containing the tetranorterpene, azadirachhtin (Fig.
5), is a potent antifeedant against a large number of insect species, in both
the larval and adult stages (Saxena, 1987). Polygodial (Fig. 5), a diterpenoid from water pepper (*Polygonium hydropiper*), increased yield of barley
by 36% due to its antifeedant effects on the aphid *Rhopalsoiphum padi* (Pickett
et al., 1987). Three treatments of 50 g/ha were used. The same investigators found ajugarin I (Fig. 5), a diterpenoid from *Ajuga remota*, to be highly
effective antifeedant against diamondback moth (*Plutella xylostella*) larvae in
laboratory studies.

Several plant-derived steroids (phytoecdysones) are close analogs of the
insect molting (ecdysis) hormone ecdysterone (Kubo and Klocke, 1986). By
preventing molting these compounds are potent insecticides. An example,
ponasterone A (Fig. 5), from the conifer *Podocarpus gracilior* is lethal to a
wide range of insect species. Another ecdysis-inhibiting terpenoid is the
tetranortriterpenoid azadirachtin from neem (*Azadirachta indica*) and china-
berry (*Melia azedarach*) trees (Kubo and Klocke, 1986). Neem tree extracts
and powders of neem tree constituents have long been known to be insecticidal, fungicidal, and nematicidal (Jacobson, 1986). Several other terpenoids
related to azadirachtin are found in the active crude extracts of neem and
could enhance the insecticidal potency. Azadiractin is not toxic or mutagenic,
but the complex structure makes azadiractin economically impossible to synthesize for pesticidal use. Insecticidal formulations of ethanol extracts of neem
tree seeds for nonfood crop use, however, are being considered for approval
in the United States.

Many terpenoids can reduce insect damage by adversely altering insect
behavior (Seigler, 1983). Insect damage may be controlled by locomotor ex-
citants, biting or piercing suppressants, oviposition deterrents, or by disruption of mating behavior.

Plant-produced terpenoid juvenile hormone mimics are effective insecticides (Bowers, 1985; Brattsten, 1983). More than a dozen plant-derived mono-
and sesquiterpenoids have been described to have insect-sterilizing effects
as juvenile hormone analogs.

Insects have evolved defenses against plant terpenoids. The mixed-function oxidases of insects that can rapidly metabolize some plant terpenoids are
induced in some insects by certain terpenoids (Brattsten et al., 1977). Simpler terpenoids (monoterpenes) may be detoxified by insects more easily than
more complex terpenoids (Yu, 1987).

C. Fungicides

A sampling of the antifungal properties of a variety of plant terpenoids is
provided in Table 4. The essential oils of many plants are highly effective

TABLE 4 Fungicidal Properties of Plant-Derived Terpenoids

Compound	Test organism	Dose[a]	Effect (% inhibition)	Reference
Camphor	Aspergillis niger	4 mM	ED$_{50}$, 2.7 mM	Moleyar and Narasimham (1987)
Carene	Boletus variegatus	s.a.	86	Melin and Krupa (1971)
	Ceratocytis pilifera	s.a.	64	Cobb et al. (1968)
p-Cymene	Trichoderma virida	s.a.	90	DeGroot (1972)
Geraniol	Alternaria solani	2 mM	93	Rizvi and Rizvi (1987)
Hemigossypol	Verticillium dahliae	100 µM	75	Stipanovic et al. (1988)
Desoxyhemi- gossypol	V. dahliae	60 µM	100	Stipanovic et al. (1988)
Limonene	Lenzites saepiaria	s.a.	95	Stipanovic et al. (1988)
	Boletus variegatus	s.a.	85	Melin and Krupa (1971)
	Trichoderma virida	s.a.	83	DeGroot (1972)
Myrcene	Ceratocystis pilifera	s.a.	68	Cobb et al. (1968)
	Trichoderma virida	s.a.	81	DeGroot (1972)
Pinene	Boletus variegatus	s.a.	86	Melin and Krupa (1971)
	Ceratocystis pilifera	s.a.	72	Cobb et al. (1968)
	Trichoderma virida	s.a.	84	DeGroot (1972)
Sclareol	Uromyces appendiculatus	s.a.	80	Bailey et al. (1975)
Terpinolene	Boletus variegatus	s.a.	77	Melin and Krupa (1971)
	Rhizopogon roseolus	s.a.	65	Melin and Krupa (1971)

[a] s.a., Saturated atmosphere.

antimicrobial and/or antifungal agents [e.g., Maiti et al. (1985), Singh et al. (1980), and Moleyar and Narasimham (1987)]. The biological activity of the saponins (glycosides of steroid alcohols) or of certain triterpenoids has been known for hundreds of years (Robinson, 1980). Certain saponins (glycosides of hederagenin, bayogenin, and medicagenic acid) have been demonstrated to have fungicidal activity at low (7.5 to 25 ppm) concentrations (Marston et al., 1988). Furthermore, several terpenoids have established functions as phytoalexins. For instance, synthesis of the sesquiterpenoid desoxyhemigossypol (Fig. 6) is elicited by *Verticillium dahliae* in cotton, and this compound is highly toxic to the elicitor (Table 4) (Stipanovic et al., 1988). Potato has an arsenal of antifungal sesquiterpenoid phytoalexins, composed of rishitin and lubimin (Fig. 6) and their derivatives as well as solavetivone (Murai, 1987). Solavetivone, lubimin, and rishitin reduce germ-tube growth of *Phytophthora infestans* by 50% at 0.3, 0.4, and 0.3 mM, respectively. There is no phytotoxity to potato at these concentrations.

Few studies have been conducted with intact plants to determine the efficacy of terpenoids in preventing damage by fungal phytopathogens. In one such study, an epimeric mixture of the diterpenes sclareol and 13-episclareol completely prevented certain rust diseases of beans when applied as a foliar spray at a concentration of 100 ppm (Bailey et al., 1975).

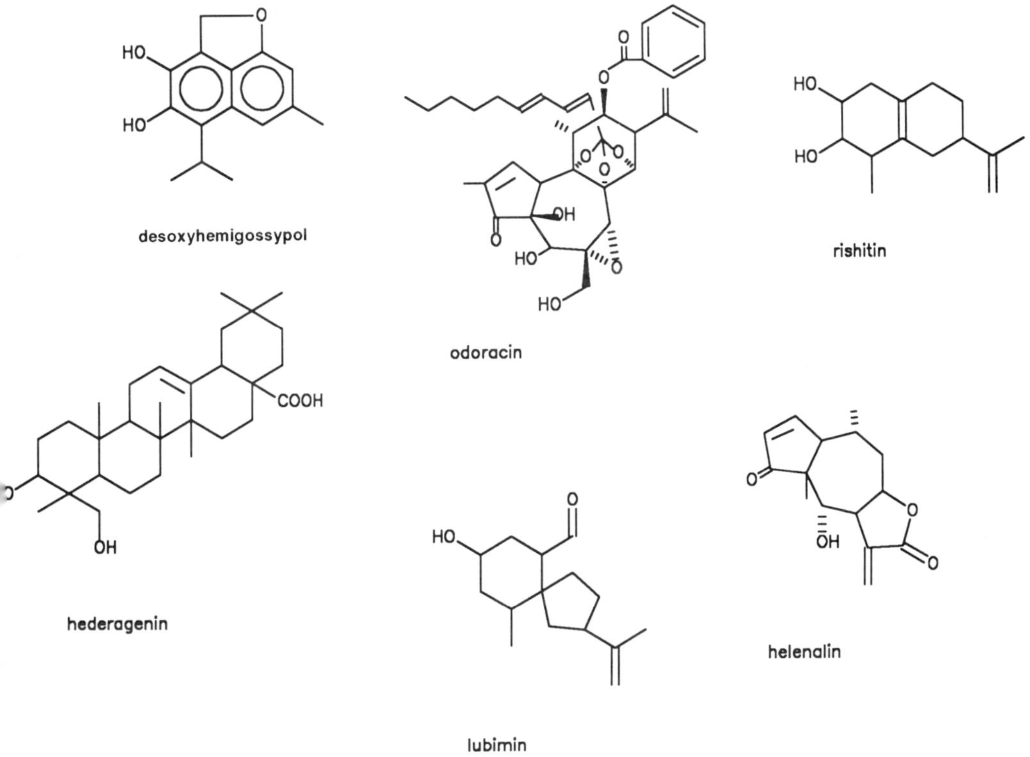

desoxyhemigossypol

odoracin

rishitin

hederagenin

lubimin

helenalin

FIGURE 6 Structures of some terpenoids from plants with fungicidal, nematicidal, molluscidal, and rodenticidal properties.

Little is known of the mode of action of antifungal terpenoids. Moleyar and Narasimham (1987) concluded that camphor and the essential oil citral exerted their toxicity through nonspecific membrane effects.

D. Molluscicides, Nematicides, and Rodenticides

Glycosides of the saponins hederagenin (Fig. 6), bayogenin, and medicagenic acid are both fungicidal and molluscicidal at concentrations of 7.5 to 25 ppm (Marston et al., 1988). At 25 ppm, a saponin mixture of dodonosides A and B caused complete mortality to snails (Wagner et al., 1987). The diterpene derivatives odoracin (Fig. 6) and odracin from the roots of sweet daphne (*Daphne odora*) have significant nematacidal activity against rice white-tip nematode (Munakata, 1983). They gave 70 to 96% mortality at 1 ppm.

Many terpenoids are toxic to mammals [cf. Rodriguez et al. (1976)] and therefore could be used as poisons for rodents. For instance, certain sesquiterpenoid lactones are responsible for the toxicity of several weeds to livestock (Herz, 1978). Helenalin (Fig. 6) from sneezeweed (*Helenium microcephalum* DC) is one of the more acutely toxic sesquiterpenoids, with an oral median lethal dose of 150 mg/kg for mice (Witsel et al., 1976). The bitter taste of many sesquiterpenoids to mammals might be a disadvantage in using these compounds as rodenticides. The mechanism of action of some sesquiterpenoid lactones in mammalian toxicity may be related to the ability of the α,β-unsaturated λ-lactone moiety to interact with sulfhydryl groups, because the sulfhydryl-protecting compound mercaptan, cysteine, can protect hamsters from poisoning (Ivie et al., 1975). However, little has been done about determining the acute toxicity of individual terpenoid compounds to rodents.

IV. PROBLEMS IN DEVELOPMENT OF TERPENOIDS AS PESTICIDES

A. Discovery

Many of the available phytotoxicity data on suspected herbicidal allelochemicals are on the effects of compounds on germination of small-seeded species [e.g., Powell and Spencer (1988)]. This is an easy assay, requiring only small amounts of test compound. However, few commercial herbicides will inhibit germination, although they will delay it. Bioassays of effects on growth, development, and photosynthesis are much better for screening for potential herbicidal utility. The volatility of most terpenoids further complicates the bioassay of many terpenoids. The effects of a saturated atmosphere of a compound on a target organism is not likely to provide a good estimate of the potential of that compound as a pesticide in the field. Unfortunately, there are relatively few published data that provide meaningful indications of the pesticidal potential of terpenoids, especially as herbicides.

Considering the probability of plant secondary products being involved in plant-pest interactions, the strategy of randomly isolating, identifying, and bioassaying these compounds may be an effective method of pesticide discovery. Biologically active compounds from plants will often have activity against organisms with which the producing plant does not have to cope. For example, the polyhalogenated terpenoids of the red alga *Plocamium telfairiae* are excellent mosquito larvicides (Watanabe et al., 1989). Most of the terpenoids described in the natural products, pharmacological, and chemical ecology literature have not been screened for pesticidal activity. This is due partly to the very small amounts of these compounds that have been available for screening.

The discovery process for natural pesticides is more complicated than that for synthetic pesticides because of the difficulties in isolation and structural identification. The degree of purification conducted initially is a variable for which there is no general rule. Furthermore, secondary compounds are generally isolated in relatively small amounts compared to the amounts of synthesized chemicals available for screening for pesticide activity. Therefore, bioassays requiring very small amounts of material will be helpful in screening terpenoids from plants. Numerous published methods for assaying small amounts of compounds for pesticidal and biological activities are available in the allelochemical and natural product literature. At some point in the discovery process, structural identification is a requirement. This step can be quite difficult for some natural products. Finally, synthesis of the compound and analogs must be considered. This can be much more difficult than identification. Despite these difficulties, modern instrumental analysis and improved methods are reducing the difficulty, cost, and time involved in each of the steps above.

B. Development

Few pesticides that are found to be highly efficaceous in preliminary testing are ever brought to market. Many factors must be considered in the decision to develop and market a pesticide. An early consideration is the patentability of the compound. As with any synthetic compound, a patent search must also be done for natural compounds. Prior publication of the pesticidal properties of a compound could cause patent problems. Compared to synthetic compounds, there is a plethora of published information on the biological activity of natural products. For this reason, patenting synthetic analogs with no mention of the natural source of the chemical family might be safer than patenting the natural product in some situations.

The toxicological and environmental properties of the compound must also be considered. Simply because a compound is a natural product does not ensure that it is safe. Some of the most toxic mammalian poisons known are natural products, and many of these are plant products. Introduction of levels of toxic natrual compounds into the environment above those found in nature could cause adverse effects. However, evidence is strong that natural products generally have a much shorter half-life in the environment than do synthetic pesticides. In fact, the relatively short environmental persistence of natural products may be a problem (e.g., natural pyrethroids) because most pesticides must have some residual activity in order to be effective. Few studies have examined the environmental persistence of terpenoids in soils. In one such study, Picman (1987) found a sesquiterpene lactone to disappear completely from soil within 90 days. As with pyrethroids, chemical modification can increase persistence.

After promising biological activity is discovered, extraction of larger amounts of the compound for more extensive bioassays can be considered.

Also, analogs of the compound should be made by chemical alteration of the compound and/or chemical synthesis. Structural manipulation could lead to improved activity and toxicological properties, altered environmental effects, or discovery of an active compound that can be economically synthesized. This has been the case with several natural compounds that have been used as templates for commercial pesticides (e.g., pyrethroids).

Before a decision is made to produce a natural pesticide for commercial use, the most cost-effective means of production must be found. Although this is a crucial question in considering the development of any pesticide, it is even more complex and critical with natural products. Historically, preparations of crude natural product mixtures have been used as pesticides. However, the potential problems in clearing a complex mixture of many biologically active compounds for use by the public may be prohibitive in today's regulatory climate. Thus the question that will most probably be considered is whether the pure compound should be produced by biosynthesis and purification or by traditional chemical synthesis.

Before considering any other factors, there are two advantages to the pesticide industry of synthetic production of products. Industry has invested heavily in personnel and facilities for chemical synthesis of pesticides. Changing this approach to biosynthetic methods may be difficult for personnel trained in more traditional industrial synthesis. Second, in addition to patents for use, patents for chemical synthesis often further protect the investment that a company makes in development of a pesticide. Some pesticidal terpenoids can be effeciently synthesized [e.g., Ley (1987)].

However, many terpenoids are simply too structurally complicated to be economically synthesized. Even so, more economically synthesized analogs with adequate or even superior biological activity may tip the balance toward industrial synthesis. For instance, considerable effort has gone into simplifying the synethsis of strigol (Pepperman and Blanchard, 1985; Brooks et al., 1985). Strigol is also an example of a terpenoid herbicide for which considerable structure-activity information is available (Vail et al., 1985; Pepperman et al., 1987). Unfortunately, most structure-activity studies to maximize the biological activity of natural compounds have not met with success [e.g., Powell and Spencer (1988) and Pepperman et al. (1987)]. If chemical synthesis is not feasible, biosynthesis must be considered. There are a growing number of biosynthetic options.

The simplest method is to extract the compound from field-grown plants. In a recent study, large-scale extraction of polygodial from water pepper (*Polygonum hydropiper*) with liquid CO_2 was accomplished (Pickett et al., 1987). To optimize production, the species and the variety of that species that produce the highest levels of the compound must be selected and grown under conditions that will optimize their biosynthetic capacity to produce the compound. Genetically manipulating the producing plants by classical or biotechnological methods could also increase production. Production of terpenoids by plants can be enhanced markedly by growth regulators, stress, or sublethal levels of herbicides. For instance, photobleaching diphenylether herbicides such as acifluorfen can increase artemisinin production by annual wormwood by at least twofold (Bryson and Croom, 1988), and it can increase the production of certain other terpenoids even more in some crop species (Kömives and Casida, 1983).

Another alternative is to produce the compound in tissue or cell culture. With these methods, cell lines that produce higher levels of the compound can be rapidly selected. However, genetic stability of such traits has been a problem in cell culture production of secondary products. Cells that produce and accumulate massive amounts of possibly autotoxic secondary compounds are obviously at a metabolic disadvantage and are thus selected against under many cell or tissue culture conditions. A technique, such as an immobilized cell column, that continuously removes secondary products can increase production by decreasing feedback inhibition of synthesis, reducing autotoxicity, and possibly increasing genetic stability. Other culture methods that optimize production can also be utilized. For instance, supplying inexpensively synthesized metabolic precursors can greatly enhance biosynthesis of many secondary products. Also, plant growth regulators, elicitors, and metabolic blockers can be used to increase production. Genetic engineering and biotechnology may allow for the production of plant-derived secondary products by gene transfer to microorganisms and production by fermentation. This concept is attractive because of the existing fermentation technology for production of secondary products. However, it may be prohibitively difficult for complex secondary products in which several genes control the conversion of several complex intermediates to the desired product.

Genetic engineering might also be used to insert genetic information for production of plant-produced pesticides from one plant species to another to provide protection from pests. However, such transgenic manipulation of the complex secondary metabolism of a higher plant will probably be extremely difficult. A simpler alternative might be to infect plant-colonizing microbes with the desired genetic machinery to produce the natural pesticide, as has been done with bacteria-produced insecticides.

V. CONCLUSIONS

The many thousands of terpenoid compounds produced by plants are a largely untapped potential resource of new pesticides and templates for new pesticide chemistries. Few of these compounds have been tested for any pesticidal activity and even fewer have been adequately screened for a broad range of pesticidal activities. Considering the success of the pyrethroids, the potential for discovery of useful pesticides from other plant terpenoids appears great. Plant-produced terpenoids are more likely to be effective against herbivores and plant pathogens than against weeds. Still, effective and selective herbicides have been developed from native plant terpenoids. Advances in molecular biology and biotechnology may soon give us the option of building terpenoid pesticide synthesis into crop plants and of industrial production of plant secondary compounds, including terpenoids, for pesticidal use.

REFERENCES

Adeoye, A. O., Oguntimein, B. O., Clark, A. M., and Hufford, C. D. (1986). 3-Dimethylallylindole: an antibacterial and antifungal metabolite from *Monodora tenuifolia*. *J. Nat. Prod.* 49:534-537.

AlSaadawi, I. S., Arif, M. B., and AlRubeaa, A. J. (1985). Allelopathic effects of *Citrus aurantium* L.: II. Isolation, characterization, and biological activities of phytotoxins. *J. Chem. Ecol. 11*:1527-1534.

Amo, S., del, and Anaya, A. L. (1978). Effect of some sesquiterpenoid lactones on the growth of certain secondary tropical species. *J. Chem. Ecol. 4*:303-313.

Ascensão, L., and Pais, M. S. S. (1987). Glandular trichomes of *Artemisia campestris* (ssp. *maritima*): ontogeny and histochemistry of the secretory product. *Bot. Gaz. 148*:221-227.

Asplund, R. O. (1968). Monoterpenes: relationship between structure and inhibition of germination. *Phytochemistry 7*:1995-1997.

Bailey, J. A., Carter, G. A., Burden, R. S., and Wain, R. L. (1975). Control of rust diseases by diterpenes from *Nicotiana glutinosa*. *Nature* (Lond.) *255*:328-329.

Beyer, J., Becker, H., Toyota, M., and Asakawa, Y. (1987). Diterpenoids with a novel skeleton from the liverwort *Anastrophyllum minutum*. *Phytochemistry 26*:1085-1089.

Bowers, W. W. (1985). Phytochemical disruption of insect development and behavior. *Am. Chem. Soc. Symp. Ser. 276*:225-236.

Brattsten, L. B. (1983). Cytochrome P-450 involvement in the interactions between plant terpenes and insect herbivores. *Am. Chem. Soc. Symp. Ser. 208*:173-195.

Brattsten, L. B., Wilkinson, C. F., and Eisner, T. (1977). Herbivore-plant interactions: mixed-function oxidases and secondary plant substances. *Science 196*:1349-1352.

Briggs, G. C., Elliott, M., and Janes, N. F. (1983). Present status and future prospects for synthetic phyrethroids. In *Pesticide Chemistry— Human Welfare and the Environment*, Vol. 2, *Natural Products*, J. Miyamoto and P. C. Kearney (Eds.). Pergamon Press, Oxford, pp. 157-164.

Brooks, D. W., Kennedy, E., and Bevinakatti, H. S. (1985). Strigol: total synthesis and preparation of analogs. *Am. Chem. Soc. Symp. Ser. 268*: 437-444.

Bryson, C. T., and Croom, E. M., Jr. (1988). Herbicide crop production systems for annual wormwood. *Proc. Miss. Acad. Sci. 33*:5.

Cappelletti, E. M., Caniato, R., and Appendino, G. (1986). Localization of the cytotoxic hydroperoxyeudesmanolides in *Artemisia umbelliformis*. *Biochem. Syst. Ecol. 14*:183-199.

Carter, C. D., Sacalis, J. N., and Gianfagna, T. J. (1989). Zingiberene and resistance to Colorado potato beetle in *Lycopersicon hirsutum* f. *hirsutum*. *J. Agric. Food Chem. 37*:206-210.

Casida, J. E., and Lawrence, L. J. (1985). Structure-activity correlations for interactions of bicyclophosphorous esters and some polychlorocycloalkane and pyrethroid insecticides with the brain-specific *t*-butylbicyclophosphorothionate receptor. *Environ. Health Perspect. 61*:123-132.

Casida, J. E., Pessah, I. N., Seifert, J., and Waterhouse, A. L. (1987). Ryania insecticide: chemistry, biochemistry and toxicology. In *Pesticide Science and Biotechnology*, R. Greenlaugh and T. R. Roberts (Eds.). Blackwell Scientific, Oxford, pp. 177-182.

Cobb, F. W., Krstic, M., Zavarin, E., and Barber, H. W. (1968). Inhibitory effects of volatile oleoresin components on *Fomes annosus* and four *ceratoscystis* species. *Phytotopathology* 58:1327-1335.

Cooper-Driver, G. A., and Le Quesne, P. W. (1987). Diterpenoids as insect antifeedants with growth inhibitors: role in *Solidago* species. *Am. Chem. Soc. Symp. Ser.* 330:534-550.

Cutler, H. G. (1988). Natural products and their potential in agriculture. *Am. Chem. Soc. Symp. Ser.* 380:1-22.

DeGroot, R. C. (1972). Growth of wood-habiting fungi in the saturated atmospheres of monoterpenoids. *Mycologia* 64:862-870.

Duke, S. O. (1986). Naturally-occurring chemical compounds as herbicides. *Rev. Weed Sci.* 2:15-44.

Duke, S. O. (1990). Natural pesticides from plants. In *New Crops*, J. Janick and E. Simon (Eds.). Timber Press, Portland, pp. 511-517.

Duke, S. O., and Lydon, J. (1987). Herbicides from natural compounds. *Weed Technol.* 1:122-128.

Duke, S. O., Vaughn, K. C., Croom, E. M., Jr., and Elsohly, H. N. (1987). Artemisinin, a constituent of annual wormwood (*Artemisia annua*), is a selective phytotoxin. *Weed Sci.* 35:499-505.

Duke, S. O., Paul, R. N., and Lee, S. M. (1988). Terpenoids from the genus *Artemisia* as potential herbicides. *Am. Chem. Soc. Symp. Ser.* 380:318-334.

Eisner, T., Eisner, M., and Meinwald, J. (1987). Technique for visualization of epidermal glandular structures in plants. *J. Chem. Ecol.* 13:943-946.

Elakovich, S. D. (1988). Terpenoids as models for new agrochemicals. *Am. Chem. Soc. Symp. Ser.* 380:250-261.

El-Deek, M. H., and Hess, F. D. (1986). Inhibited mitotic entry is the cause of growth inhibition by cinmethylin. *Weed Sci.* 34:684-688.

Engvild, K. C. (1986). Chlorine-containing natural compounds in higher plants. *Phytochemistry* 25:781-791.

Fischer, N. H. (1986). The function of mono and sesquiterpenes as plant germination and growth regulators. In *The Science of Allelopathy*, A. R. Putnam and C.-S. Tang (Eds.). Wiley-Interscience, New York, pp. 203-218.

Fischer, N. H., and Quijano, L. (1985). Allelopathic agents from common weeds: *Amaranthus palmeri*, *Ambrosia artemisiifolia*, and related weeds. *Am. Chem. Soc. Symp. Ser.* 268:133-147.

Fischer, N. H., Tanrisever, N., and Williamson, G. B. (1988). Allelopathy in the Florida scrub community as a model for natural herbicide actions. *Am. Chem. Soc. Symp. Ser.* 380:233-249.

Fischer, N. H., Weidenhamer, J. D., and Bradow, J. M. (1989). Dihydro-parthenolide and other sesquiterpene lactones stimulate witchweed germination. *Phytochemistry* 28:2315-2317.

Gershenzon, J., Rossiter, M., Mabry, T. J., Rogers, C. E., Blust, M. H., and Hopkins, T. L. (1985). Insect antifeedant terpenoids in wild sunflower: a possible source of resistance to the sunflower moth. *Am. Chem. Soc. Symp. Ser.* 276:433-446.

Goldsby, G., and Burke, B. A. (1987). Sesquiterpene lactones and a sesquiterpene diol from Jamaican *Ambrosia peruviana*. *Phytochemistry* 26:1059-1063.

Gonzalez de la Parra, M., Anaya, A. L., Espinosa, F., Jimenez, F., and Castillo, R. (1981). Allelopathic potential of *Piqueria trinerva* (Compositae) and piquerols A and B. *J. Chem. Ecol.* 7:509-515.

Grainage, M., and Ahmed, S. (1988). *Handbook of Plants with Pest-Control Properties*, Wiley-Interscience, New York.

Grayson, B. T., Williams, K. S., Freehauf, P. A., Pease, R. R., Ziesel, W. T., Sereno, R. L., and Reinsfelder, R. E. (1987). The physical and chemical properties of the herbicide cinmethylin (SD 95481). *Pestic. Sci. 21*:143-153.

Gregory, P., Tingey, W. M., Ave, D. A., and Bouthyette, P. Y. (1986). Potato glandular trichomes: a physicochemical defence mechanism against insects. *Am. Chem. Soc. Symp. Ser. 296*:160-167.

Green, M. B., Hartley, G. S., and West, T. F. (1987). *Chemicals for Crop Improvement and Pest Management*, 3rd ed. Pergamon Press, Oxford, pp. 78, 79, 105-117.

Gunasena, G. H., Vinson, S. B., Williams, H. J., and Stipanovic, R. D. (1988). Effects of caryophyllene, caryophyllene oxide, and their interaction with gossypol on the growth and development of *Heloithis virescens* (F.) (Lepidoptera: Noctuidae). *J. Econ. Entomol. 81*:93-97.

Halligan, J. P. (1975). Toxic terpenes from *Artemisia californica*. *Ecology 56*:999-1003.

Heisey, R. M., and Delwiche, C. D. (1984). Phytotoxic volatiles from *Trichostema lanceolatum* (Labiatae). *Am. J. Bot. 71*:821-828.

Herz, W. (1978). Sesquiterpene lactones from livestock poisons. In *Effects of Poisonous Plants on Livestock*, K. R. van Kampen and L. F. James (Eds.). Academic Press, New York, pp. 487-497.

Howard, J. J., Cazin, J., Jr., and Wiemer, D. F. (1988). Toxicity of terpenoid deterrents to the leafcutting ant *Atta cephalotes* and its mutualistic fungus. *J. Chem. Ecol. 14*:59-69.

Hsiao, A. I., Worsham, A. D., and Moreland, D. E. (1981). Regulation of witchweed (*Striga asiatica*) conditioning and germination. *Weed Sci. 29*:101-104.

Hughes, P. R. (1974). Myrcene: a precursor of pheromones in *Ips* beetles. *J. Insect Physiol. 20*:1271-1275.

Hwang, Y.-S., Wu, K.-H., Kumamoto, J., Axelrod, H., and Mulla, M. S. (1985). Isolation and identification of mosquito repellants from *Artemisia vulgaris*. *J. Chem. Ecol. 51*:1297-1306.

Ivie, G. W., Witzel, D. A., Herz, W., Kannan, R., Norman, J. O., Rushing, D. D., Johnson, J. H., Rowe, L. D., and Veech, J. A. (1975). Hymenovin: major toxic constituent of western bitterweed (*Hymenoxys oderata* DC). *J. Agric. Food Chem. 23*:841-845.

Jacobson, M. (1966). Chemical insect attractants and repellants. *Annu. Rev. Entomol. 11*:403-422.

Jacobson, M. (1986). The neem tree: natural resistance par excellence. *Am. Chem. Soc. Symp. Ser. 296*:220-232.

Kelsey, R. G., and Locken, L. J. (1987). Phytotoxic properties of cnicin, a sesquiterpene lactone from *Centaurea maculosa* (spotted knapweed). *J. Chem. Ecol. 13*:19-33.

Kelsey, R. G., and Shafizadeh, F. (1980). Glandular trichomes and sesquiterpene lactones of *Artemisia nova* (Asteraceae). *Biochem. Syst. Ecol. 8*:371-377.

Kelsey, R. G., Reynolds, G. W., and Rodriguez, E. (1984). The chemistry of biologically active constituents secreted and stored in plant glandular trichomes. In *Biology and Chemistry of Trichomes*, E. Rodriguez, P. L. Healey, and I. Mehta (Eds.). Plenum Press, New York, pp. 187-241.

Klocke, J. A. (1987). Natural plant compounds useful in insect control. *Am. Chem. Soc. Symp. Ser. 330*: 396-415.

Klocke, J. A., Darlington, M. V., and Balandrin, M. F. (1987). 1,8-Cineole (Eucalyptol), a mosquito feeding and ovipositional repellent from volatile oil of *Hemizonia fitchii* (Asteraceae). *J. Chem. Ecol. 13*: 2131-2141.

Kömives, T., and Casida, J. E. (1983). Acifluorfen increases the leaf content of phytoalexins and stress metabolites in several crops. *J. Agric. Food Chem. 31*: 751-755.

Kubo, I., and Klocke, J. (1986). Insect ecdysis inhibitors. *Am. Chem. Soc. Symp. Ser. 296*: 206-219.

Kubo, I., and Matsumoto, T. (1985). Potent insect antifeedants from the African medicinal plant *Bersama abyssinica*. *Am. Chem. Soc. Symp. Ser. 276*: 183-200.

Lawson, D. R., Danehower, D. A., Shilling, D. G., Menetrez, M. L., and Spurr, H. W., Jr. (1988). Allelochemical properties of *Nicotiana tabacum* leaf surface compounds. *Am. Chem. Soc. Symp. Ser. 380*: 363-377.

Ley, S. V. (1987). Synthesis of insect antifeedants. In *Pesticide Science and Biotechnology*, R. Greenlaugh and T. R. Roberts (Eds.). Blackwell Scientific, Oxford, pp. 25-34.

Lorber, P., and Muller, W. H. (1980). Volatile growth inhibitors produced in *Salvia leucophylla*—effects on metabolic activity in mitochondrial suspensions. *Comp. Physiol. Ecol. 5*: 68-75.

Lydon, J., and Duke, S. O. (1989). The potential of pesticides from plants. In *Herbs, Spices, and Medicinal Plants: Recent Advances in Botany, Horticulture and Pharmacology*, L. E. Craker and J. E. Simon (Eds.). Oryx Press, Phoenix, Az., pp. 1-41.

Maiti, D., Kole, C. R., and Sen, C. (1985). Antimicrobial efficacy of some essential oils. *J. Plant Dis. Prot. 92*: 64-68.

Marston, A., Gafner, F., Dossaji, S. F., and Hostettmann, K. (1988). Fungicidal and molluscicidal saponins from *Dolichos killimandscharicus*. *Phytochemistry 27*: 1325-1326.

McCahon, C. B., Kelsey, R. G., Sheridan, R. P., and Shafizadeh, F. (1973). Physiological effects of compounds extracted from safebrush. *Bull. Toreey Bot. Club 100*: 23-28.

Melin, E., and Krupa, S. (1971). Studies on ectomycorrhizae of pine: II. Growth inhibition of mycorrhizal fungi by volatile organic constituents of *Pinus silvestrus* (Scots pine) roots. *Physiol. Plant. 25*: 337-340.

Miles, D. H., Hankinson, B. L., and Randle, S. A. (1985). Insect antifeedants from the Peruvian plant *Alchornea triplinervia*. *Am. Chem. Soc. Symp. Ser. 276*: 469-476.

Miller, G. W., Sasse, J. M., Lovelace, C. J., and Rowan, K. S. (1984). Effects of podolactone-type inhibitors and abscisic acid on chlorophyll biosynthesis in barley leaves. *Plant Cell Physiol. 25*: 635-642.

Moleyar, V., and Narasimham, P. (1987). Mode of antifungal action of essential oil components citral and camphor. *Indian J. Exp. Biol. 25*: 781-784.

Muller, W. H., and Muller, C. H. (1964). Voltaile growth inhibitors pro-
    duced by *Salvia* species. *Bull. Torrey Bot. Club 91*: 327-330.
Muller, W. H., Lorber, P., Haley, B., and Johnson, K. (1969). Volatile
    growth inhibitors produced by *Salvia leucophylla*: effect on oxygen up-
    take by mitochondrial suspensions. *Bull. Torrey Bot. Club 96*: 89-96.
Munakata, K. (1983). Nematocidal natural products. In *Natural Products
    for Innovative Pest Management*, D. L. Whitehead and W. S. Bowers (Eds.).
    Pergamon Press, Oxford, pp. 299-309.
Murai, A. (1987). Phytoalexin chemistry and action. In *Pesticide Science
    and Biotechnology*, R. Greenlaugh and T. R. Roberts (Eds.). Blackwell
    Scientific, Oxford, pp. 81-88.
Nishimura, H., Kaku, K., Nakamura, T., Fukazawa, Y., and Mizutani, J.
    (1982). Allelopathic substances (±)-*p*-methane-3,8-diols isolated from
    Eucalyptus citriodora Hook. *Agric. Biol. Chem. 46*: 319-320.
Pepperman, A. B., Jr., and Blanchard, E. J. (1985). Improvements in the
    synthesis of strigol and its analogs. *Am. Chem. Soc. Symp. Ser. 268*:
    415-425.
Pepperman, A. B., Dailey, O. D., and Vail, S. L. (1987). Biological activ-
    ity of strigol, its precursors, and its analogs. *Am. Chem. Soc. Symp.
    Ser. 355*: 445-461.
Pickett, J. A., Dawson, G. W., Griffiths, D. C., Hassanali, A., Merritt,
    L. A., Mudd, A., Smith, M. C., Wadhams, L. J., Woodcock, C. M., and
    Zhong-Ning, Z. (1987). Development of plant-derived antifeedants for
    crop protection. In *Pesticide Science and Biotechnology*, R. Greenlaugh
    and T. R. Roberts (Eds.). Blackwell Scientific, Oxford, pp. 125-128.
Picman, A. K. (1987). Persistance and disappearance of the sesquiterpene
    lactone isoalantolactone in soils. *Biochem. Syst. Ecol. 15*: 361-364.
Powell, R. G., and Spencer, G. F. (1988). Phytochemical inhibitors of vel-
    vetleaf (*Abutilon theophrastii*) germination as models for new biorational
    herbicides. *Am. Chem. Soc. Symp. Ser. 380*: 211-232.
Reynolds, T. (1987). Comparative effect of alicyclic compounds and qui-
    nones on inhibition of lettuce fruit germination. *Ann. Bot. (Lond.) 60*:
    215-223.
Rice, E. L. (1983). *Pest Control with Nature's Chemicals*. University of
    Oklahoma Press, Norman, pp. 122-123.
Rizvi, S. J. H., and Rizvi, V. (1987). Improving crop productivity in
    India: role of allelochemicals. *Am. Chem. Soc. Symp. Ser. 330*: 69-75.
Robinson, T. (1980). *The Organic Constituents of Higher Plants*. 4th ed.
    Cordus Press, North Amherst, Mass.
Rodriguez, E., Tower, G. H. N., and Mitchell, J. C. (1976). Biological
    activities of sesquiterpene lactones. *Phytochemistry 15*: 1573-1580.
Rogers, C. E., Gershenzon, J., Ohno, N., Mabry, T. J., Stipanovic, R.
    D., and Kreitner, G. L. (1987). Terpenes of wild sunflowers (*Heli-
    anthus*): an effective mechanism against seed predation by larvae of the
    sunflower moth, *Homoeosoma electellum* (Lepidoptera: Pyralidae). *Forum
    Environ. Biol. 16*: 586-592.
Saleh, M. A., and Casida, J. E. (1979). Toxaphene composition, structure-
    toxicity relations and metabolism. In *Advances in Pesticide Science*, Part
    3, H. Geissbühler (Ed.). Pergamon Press, Oxford.
Sarma, A. S. (1987). Clerodane diterpenoids and related natural products:
    biological properties and synthetic studies. *J. Sci. Ind. Res. 46*: 492-504.

Saxena, R. C. (1987). Neem seed oil—a potential antifeedant against insect pest of rice. In *Pesticide Science and Biotechnology*, R. Greenlaugh and T. R. Roberts (Eds.). Blackwell Scientific, Oxford, pp. 139-144.

Scheffrahn, R. H., Hsu, R.-C., Su, N.-Y., Huffman, J. B., Midland, S. L., and Sims, J. J. (1988). Allelochemical resistance of bald cypress, *Taxodium distichum*, heartwood to the subterranean termite, *Coptotermes formaosanus*. *J. Chem. Ecol. 14*:765-776.

Schütte, H.-R. (1984). Secondary plant substances: monoterpenes. *Prog. Bot. 46*:119-139.

Scriven, R., and Meloan, C. E. (1984). Determining the active component in 1,3,3-trimethyl-2-oxabicyclo[2,2,2]octane (cineole) that repels the American cockroach, *Periplaneta americana*. *Ohio J. Sci. 84*:85-88.

Seigler, D. S. (1983). Role of lipids in plant resistance to insects. *Am. Chem. Soc. Symp. Ser. 208*:303-327.

Selander, J., Kalo, P., Kangus, E., and Perttunen, V. (1974). Olfactory behaviour of *Hylobius abietes* L. (Col., Curculionidae): I. Response to several terpenoid fractions isolated from Scots pine phloem. *Ann. Entomol. Fenn. 40*:109-115.

Sequeira, L., Hemingway, R. J., and Kupchan, S. M. (1968). Vernolepin: a new, reversible plant growth inhibitor. *Science 161*:789-790.

Sherif, A., Hall, R. G., and El-Amamy, M. (1987). Drugs, insecticides and other agents from *Artemisia*. *Med. Hypotheses 23*:187-193.

Sherman, M. E., Thompson, L., and Wilkinson, R. E. (1983). Sicklepod (*Cassia obtusifolia*) management in soybeans (*Glycine max*). *Weed Sci. 31*:622-627.

Singh, D., and Agarwal, S. K. (1988). Himachalol and β-himachalene: insecticidal principles of himalayan cedarwood oil. *J. Chem. Ecol. 14*:1145-1151.

Singh, A. K., Dikshit, A., Sharma, S. N., and Dixit, S. N. (1980). Fungitoxic activity of some essential oils. *Econ. Bot. 34*:186-190.

Spencer, G. G. (1986). The effects of a terpene aldehyde-ester from *Eryngium paniculatum* and analogs on velvetleaf germination. *J. Nat. Prod. 49*:924-926.

Spencer, G. F., Wolf, R. B., and Weisleder, D. (1984). Germination and growth inhibitory sesquiterpenes from *Ira axillaris* seeds. *J. Nat. Prod. 47*:730-732.

Stevens, K. L. (1984). Biological activity and chemistry of sesquiterpene lactones. In *Isopentenoids in Plants*, W. D. Nes, G. Fuller, and L. S. Tsai (Eds.). Marcel Dekker, New York, pp. 65-80.

Stevens, K. L., and Merrill, G. B. (1985). Sesquiterpene lactones and allelchemicals from *Centaurea* species. *Am. Chem. Soc. Symp. Ser. 268*:83-98.

Stipanovic, R. D., Williams, H. J., and Smith, L. A. (1986). Cotton terpenoid inhibition of *Heliothus virescens* development. *Am. Chem. Soc. Symp. Ser. 296*:79-94.

Stipanovic, R. D., Mace, M. E., Altman, D. W., and Bell, A. A. (1988). Chemical and anatomical response in *Gossypium* spp. challenged by *Verticillium dahliae*. *Am. Chem. Soc. Symp. Ser. 380*:262-272.

Vail, S. L., Dailey, O. D., Connick, W. J., and Pepperman, A. B. (1985). Strigol syntheses and related structure-activity-bioactivity studies.

Am. Chem. Soc. Symp. Ser. 268:445-456.

Wagner, H., Ludwig, C., Grotjahn, L., and Khan, M. S. Y. (1987). Biologically active saponins from *Dodonaea viscosa*. *Phytochemistry 26*:697-701.

Watanabe, K., Miyakado, M., Ohno, N., Okada, A., Yanagi, K., and Koichi, M. (1989). A polyhalogenated monoterpene from the red alga, *Plocamium telefairiae*. *Phytochemistry 28*:77-78.

Whaun, J., Brown, N., Milhous, W., Lambros, C., Scoville, J., Lin, A., and Klayman, D. (1985). Qinghaosu, a potent antimalarial, perturbs polyamine metabolism in human malaria cultures. In *Polyamines: Basic and Clinical Aspects*, K. Imahori, F. Suzuki, O. Suzuki, and U. Bachrach (Eds.). VNU Science Press, Utrecht, pp. 301-310.

Witsel, D. A., Ivie, G. W., and Dollahite, J. W. (1976). Mammalian toxicity of helenalin, the toxic principle of *Helenium microcephalum* DC (smallhead sneezeweed). *Am. J. Vet. Res. 37*:859-861.

Yano, K. (1987). Minor components from growing buds of *Artemesia capillaris* that act as insect antifeedants. *J. Agric. Food Chem. 35*:889-891.

Yoshida, S., Asami, T., Kawano, T., Yoneyama, K., Crow, W. D., Paton, D. M., and Takahashi, N. (1988). Photosynthetic inhibitors in *Eucalyptus grandis*. *Phytochemistry 27*:1943-1946.

Yu, S. J. (1987). Microsomal oxidation of allelochemicals in generalist (*Spodoptera frugiperda*) and semispecialist (*Anticarsia gemmatalis*) insects. *J. Chem. Ecol. 13*:423-436.

14

Poisoning of Livestock by *Lantana* Plants

Michael A. Pass

University of Queensland, St. Lucia, Queensland, Australia

I. INTRODUCTION

Lantana camara L. is a plant native to central America and Africa. It has
become distributed throughout many tropical and subtropical regions of the
world. It is toxic to ruminants and poisoning has been reported from Australia, India, New Zealand, South Africa, and the Americas (Black and Carter,
1985; de Aluja, 1970; Kellerman and Coetzer, 1985; Seawright, 1963; Sharma
et al., 1981). Most concerns about poisoning have been expressed from Australia and India, where losses to the livestock industries are of considerable
economic importance (Culvenor, 1985; Sharma et al., 1981). It has been estimated that cattle deaths from lantana poisoning in Queensland amount to about
$0.5m each year, and considerably higher losses occur due to morbidity in
nonfatally poisoned animals (Culvenor, 1985).

Research over the past 10 to 15 years has improved our knowledge of
this disease to a point where we now understand many of the factors responsible for its development. There have also been improvements in the methods
for treating lantana-poisoned animals, and some progress has been made toward preventing the disease. This review will present the current understanding of lantana poisoning.

II. THE PLANT

Full descriptions of the plant have been given by Everist (1981) and Smith
and Smith (1982). About 150 species of the genus *Lantana* occur, and of
these, the main toxic ones are classified as belonging to the group *Lantana
camara* (Everist, 1981). Twenty-nine taxa of *L. camara* have been identified
in Australia and at least 15 are known to be toxic to livestock (Table 1) (Smith
and Smith, 1982). Lantana grows as a bush up to 3 m high (Fig. 1) and it
can become an impenetrable thicket. It proliferates readily in cleared land,
inhibiting agricultural pursuits.

III. THE TOXINS

Lantana plants contain a wide range of triterpenoid compounds, some of which
are toxic to animals (Hart et al., 1976). The toxic triterpene acids are present in the leaves of the plant (Sharma et al., 1980). Seawright and Hrdlicka
(1977) demonstrated that lantadenes A and B (Fig. 2) are responsible for the
clinical and pathological signs of lantana poisoning. They are toxic when
given either orally or intravenously (Seawright and Hrdlicka, 1977; Pass et
al., 1979b; Pass, unpublished data).

Although lantadenes A and B appear to be the major toxins involved in
clinical poisoning, other toxic triterpene acids are also present but usually
in small quantities. Reduced lantadene A, icterogenin, and dihydrolantadene
A (Fig. 2) have been detected and they are toxic (Seawright and Hrdlicka,
1977; Brown, 1968; Pass, unpublished data). The clinical disease caused
by all of these pentacyclic triterpene acids is the same.

TABLE 1 Taxa of *Lantana camara* in Australia and Their Toxicity

Toxic	Nontoxic	Unknown toxicity
Helidon white	Common pink	Smith's snowflake
Coolum pink	Townsville prickly orange	Mr. Berryman pink
Bundaberg large-flowered pink	Bundaberg small-flowered pink	Spiny orange-centered pink
Small-flowered red-centered pink		Hawaiian pink
Mackay red-centered pink		Broad-edged pink-edged red
Rockhampton red-centered pink		Pale Stafford red
Pink Minnie Basil		Oblong red
Prosperpine pink-edged red		Chelsea gem
Balnagowan pink-edged red		Hawaiian orange red
Common pink-edged red		Orange Minnie Basil
Stafford red		Rockhampton large-flowered orange
Round red		
Large-flowered orange		
True orange		
Townsville red-centered pink		

Source: Smith and Smith (1982).

IV. THE DISEASE

A. Occurrence and Species Susceptibility

All domestic ruminants grazing lantana-infested areas are potentially susceptible to poisoning. Toxicity is not cumulative but occurs when a sufficient
amount of toxic plant is consumed in one feed. Commonly, this happens when
hungry stock are introduced into a lantana-infested paddock or at times when
other food is scarce. There is anecdotal evidence that stock endemic to a
lantana-infested area will avoid toxic plants (Seawright, 1982), but this has
not been substantiated scientifically.

Not all species are susceptible to poisoning and there are also differences
in susceptibility to the various lantana triterpene acids. It is generally considered that adult ruminants are susceptible to poisoning by lantadene A,

FIGURE 1 *Lantana camara* growing at St. Lucia, Queensland. The inset shows a typical lantana flower.

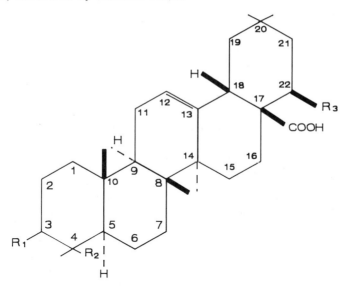

	R_1	R_2	R_3
lantadene A	=O	$-CH_3$	
reduced lantadene A	$-OH$	$-CH_3$	
icterogenin	=O	$-CH_2OH$	
lantadene B	=O	$-CH_3$	
dihydrolantadene A	=O	$-CH_3$	

FIGURE 2 Some toxic pentacyclic triterpene acids of *Lantana camara*.

lantadene B, reduced lantadene A, icterogenin, and dihydrolantadene A. This
has been shown to be the case in experimental studies in sheep (Brown, 1968;
Seawright and Hrdlicka, 1977; Pass et al., 1979b; Pass, unpublished data)
and it is assumed that cattle and goats are similarly susceptible. Horses and
rats are not susceptible to lantadene A poisoning (Pass, unpublished data).
Guinea pigs are susceptible to poisoning by lantadene A and reduced lantadene A (Seawright, 1965; Sharma et al., 1980). Although rats are resistant
to the toxic effects of the 3-oxo compounds, female rats are susceptible to
intoxication by reduced lantadene A (Pass et al., 1979a). Male rats are resistant to reduced lantadene A poisoning, and this appears to be testosterone
dependent in that castrated male rats can be intoxicated by the triterpene
acid (Pass et al., 1979a, 1985b). Neonatal calves and lambs appear to be resistant to poisoning by lantadene A (Seawright, 1965; Pass, unpublished
data), but it is not known if they can be intoxicated by reduced lantadene A.

The reasons for differences in susceptibility to poisoning are not fully
understood. In the case of reduced lantadene A, a correlation between susceptibility and the type of metabolites synthesized by the liver has been demonstrated (Pass et al., 1985a), and it could be that the pattern of hepatic
metabolism of lantana toxins determines if an animal is resistant or susceptible
to poisoning (see Section V.B).

B. Clinical Signs

The most prominent clinical sign of lantana poisoning is photosensitization,
which occurs secondary to liver injury. Photosensitive dermatitis begins within 1 to 2 days of poisoning, causing the animals to become restless and seek
shade. As the disease progresses, large areas of skin can become necrotic
and slough from the animal. Jaundice is usually prominent within 2 to 3 days
and is manifest as yellowing of the sclera and other mucous membranes. The
urine also becomes yellow. The retained bilirubin is mainly of the conjugated
type (Pass et al., 1978b).

Affected animals become inappetent within 24 h of ingestion of the plant
and ruminal motility decreases within a few hours (Dhillon and Paul, 1971;
McSweeney and Pass, 1983a; Seawright, 1963). Constipation is common, although transient diarrhea occurs in some animals (Seawright, 1982). Progressive dehydration occurs over the course of the disease and a mild metabolic
acidosis develops (McSweeney and Pass, 1983b).

The most severely poisoned animals die within 2 days of poisoning, but
usually, death occurs 1 to 3 weeks after poisoning. Less severely affected
animals recover without any apparent long-term consequences. Some animals
show a biphasic course of intoxication (McSweeney and Pass, 1983a; Pass and
Stewart, 1984). In these cases the initial phase of illness reaches a peak in
3 to 4 days and recovery is then evident. However, within a few days a second phase of liver injury develops which can, in some cases, be fatal.

C. Pathology

The pathology of lantana poisoning has been well described (Seawright, 1964;
Seawright and Allen, 1972). The essential features include generalized jaundice and dehydration of the carcass. The liver is firm, enlarged, and yellow-

ish in color, and the gallbladder is commonly grossly distended with pale-colored bile. The ruminal contents tend to be somewhat desiccated and dry, and poorly formed fecal pellets are found in the colon. The kidneys are often swollen and pale to yellow in color.

The major histological changes are seen in the liver and kidneys (Seawright, 1964; Seawright and Allen, 1972). Enlargement and feathery degeneration of hepatocytes occurs. Bile-stained deposits will be present in some cells. Necrosis of some individual hepatocytes may be seen and biliary ductular hyperplasia is common. In very severe cases there may be more extensive hepatic necrosis.

Vacuolar degeneration of renal tubular cells is common. Formation of hyaline and leucocyte casts and mild interstitial inflammation may also occur in the kidneys (Seawright and Allen, 1972).

V. MECHANISM OF LANTANA POISONING

A. Absorption of Toxins from the Digestive Tract

Four features concerned with the absorption of the lantana triterpene acids and which are important in determining the initiation and progression of poisoning have been identified. First, it has been demonstrated that only a small proportion of the ingested dose of toxins is absorbed. This is evident from a comparison of the toxicity of lantadene A given orally and intravenously. The oral toxic dose of lantadene A for sheep is about 60 mg/kg, whereas 1 to 3 mg/kg of the triterpene acid is toxic by the intravenous route (Pass et al., 1979b; Seawright and Hrdlicka, 1977). If lantadene A is given intravenously to sheep at doses higher than 3 mg/kg, hepatic necrosis rather than the typical cholestatic lesion of lantana poisoning occurs (Pass et al., 1979b). Similar observations have been made on the intravenous toxicity of icterogenin (Brown, 1968).

Second, continuous absorption of the toxins is necessary for the disease to be maintained over a long period of time. Two pieces of evidence support this concept. If lantadene A is given intravenously at 1 mg/kg, only very mild cholestasis occurs, but if this dose is given twice daily for several days, the typical cholestatic lesion of lantana poisoning occurs (Pass et al., 1979b). Furthermore, if the rumen of a poisoned animal is emptied of its contents, the animal rapidly recovers from the intoxication (McSweeney and Pass, 1982).

Third, the development of ruminal stasis causes large amounts of toxins to be retained in the rumen. Ruminal stasis was originally attributed to paralysis of the intestinal muscle caused by a direct action of the triterpene acids on the intestinal muscle. This effect was demonstrated in vitro on the duodenum (Rimington et al., 1937). However, it was later demonstrated that paralysis of intestinal muscle does not occur in vivo during lantana poisoning (Pass and Heath, 1978). It has now been shown that ruminal paralysis is a result of inappetence combined with reflex inhibition due to activation of an hepatoruminal reflex (McSweeney and Pass, 1983a). It appears that injury to the liver initiates a reflex which slows ruminal motility. Ruminal stasis occurs 4 to 6 h after toxic lantana is ingested, which is approximately the time at which liver injury is first evident (McSweeney and Pass, 1983a; Pass et al., 1978a). The onset of ruminal stasis is associated with a decrease in the flow of stomach contents into the duodenum (Pass et al., 1981b). It has been shown that the contents of the static rumen are highly toxic, and if transferred into the rumen of a normal animal, lantana poisoning occurs (McSweeney and Pass, 1982).

The fourth important feature of the absorption of lantana toxins is that absorption of the toxins from the static rumen is responsible for maintaining the intoxication. In a series of experiments in sheep, in which intestinal cannulae were used to isolate individual regions of the intestine, it was shown that although absorption occurred most rapidly from the small intestine, absorption occurred from all regions of the digestive tract (Pass et al., 1981b). Absorption from the rumen alone, though, was sufficient to cause intoxication.

After absorption the toxins appear to be transferred to the liver in the portal blood. This has been inferred from experiments in which intestinal lymph was drained from sheep that had been given lantana. Drainage of lymph did not prevent intoxication (Pass et al., 1981b). Furthermore, when the lymph from the intoxicated animal was pumped into normal sheep, the recipients did not develop lantana poisoning.

B. Metabolism of the Toxins

Although ruminal microbes are capable of metabolizing a wide variety of plant compounds, it appears that at least in the case of lantadene A, ruminal metabolism of the triterpene acid does not occur (Lamberton, personal communication).

The limited studies that have been done on the hepatic metabolsim of reduced lantadene A indicate that the species differences in susceptibility to lantana toxins could be due to differences in hepatic metabolism and that the injury to liver cells might be due to the action of metabolites rather than of the parent compounds. A correlation has been found between susceptibility to intoxication by reduced lantadene A and the type of metabolites of the triterpene acid synthesized by the liver (Pass et al., 1985a). Sheep and female rats, which are susceptible to intoxication by reduced lantadene A, synthesize one major metabolite. The structure of it is unknown, although recent studies indicate that it is reduced lantadene A with some small change at C_2 or C_3 (Pass, unpublished data). Female rats also synthesize a glucuronide of reduced lantadene A, probably the 3-glucuronide, which accounts for approximately 30% of the two major metabolites.

Male rats, which are resistant to reduced lantadene A poisoning, synthesize a different metabolite and its structure is unknown (Pass et al., 1985a). Periodically, female rats become resistant to reduced lantadene A poisoning and these resistant female rats synthesize similar metabolites to the male rats (Pass et al., 1985a).

The metabolism of the 3-oxo compounds lantadenes A and B has not been studied, but perhaps differences in metabolism of these compounds might also account for differences in susceptibility to intoxication by lantana plants. Further support for the idea that poisoning is related to synthesis of specific metabolites comes from the finding that metabolites of reduced lantadene A but not the parent compound have been detected in bile canalicular membranes isolated from intoxicated rats (Pass and Goosem, 1982; Pass et al., 1985a). The bile canalicular membrane appears to be the site of primary injury in the hepatocytes (see Section V.C).

C. Liver Injury

Lantana toxins cause intrahepatic cholestasis characterized by inhibition of bile secretion without widespread necrosis of liver cells (Seawright, 1964; Seawright and Allen, 1972; Pass et al., 1976, 1979a). Bile is secreted by the hepatocytes and the bile ductular cells. Secretion by hepatocytes is stimulated largely by the transport of bile salts into the bile canaliculi and the ductular secretion is stimulated by the gastrointestinal hormone secretion (Caple and Heath, 1975). The lantana toxins inhibit hepatocytic bile secretion but not bile ductular secretion, as shown by decreased bile salt secretion but retention of the response to secretin in lantana-poisoned animals (Pass et al., 1976).

Changes in many hepatocyte organelles have been reported in lantana-poisoned animals, including changes in the bile canalicular membranes, lysosomes, mitochondria, and smooth endoplasmic reticulum (Pass et al., 1978a, 1981a; Sharma and Dawra, 1984; Sharma et al., 1982a,b, 1983). The current evidence indicates that injury to bile canalicular membranes could be the initial hepatocyte lesion. In sheep poisoned with lantana, structural damage to these membranes, characterized by deterioration of microvilli, is evident within 6 h of ingestion of the plant (Pass et al., 1978a). Associated with the structural damage is loss of Mg^{2+} ATPase activity from the membranes (Pass et al., 1978b). Similarly, in rats intoxicated with reduced lantadena A, a decrease in the activities of the enzymes Mg^{2+} ATPase and 5'-nucleotidase on the bile canalicular membranes is detectable within 4 to 6 h of dosing with the triterpene acid (Pass et al., 1981a). Bile canalicular injury also occurs in guinea pigs with lantana poisoning (Sharma and Dawra, 1984). In sheep and rats, the bile canalicular changes are detectable before there is a significant rise in the plasma bilirubin levels, indicating that these changes could be the factor that initiates cholestasis (Pass, 1977; Pass et al., 1981a).

It has been suggested that damage to the bile canalicular membranes results from the interaction of metabolites of the lantana toxins with components of the membranes (Pass and Goosem, 1983). In the case of reduced lantadene A, only metabolites of the triterpene were detected in bile canalicular membranes of intoxicated rats (Pass and Goosem, 1982; Pass et al., 1985a). The metabolites appeared to be firmly bound to the membranes in that they were not removed by the repeated washing that occurred during preparation of the membranes. Little is known about the nature of the metabolite-membrane interaction. ^{13}C-nuclear magnetic resonance (NMR) spectra of bile canalicular membranes isolated from intoxicated rat livers indicated possible changes in the mobility of phospholipids in the membranes (Pass and Goosem, 1983).

Changes in other hepatocyte organelles also occur. These include changes in the smooth endoplasmic reticulum, lysosomes, mitochondria, and cytosolic enzymes (Pass et al., 1978a; Sharma et al., 1982a,b, 1983). It has not been determined if these changes are due to the direct action of the lantana toxins or their metabolites, or if they are secondary effects of cholestasis.

D. Kidney Injury

Chronic cases of lantana poisoning often develop elevated blood urea nitrogen levels and death has been attributed to renal failure (Seawright, 1963). Renal tubular degeneration and necrosis have been reported in lantana-

poisoned ruminants (Seawright, 1964; Seawright and Allen, 1972) and similar
changes have been observed in rats intoxicated with reduced lantadene A
(Pass et al., 1979a). Despite the renal injury being an important part of the
pathogenesis of lantana poisoning, nothing is known about its mechanism.

E. Consequences of Liver Injury

The important consequences of intrahepatic cholestasis are photosensitization,
jaundice, and ruminal stasis. Photosensitization has been attributed to the
retention of phylloerythrin, which is normally excreted in bile (Rimington
and Quin, 1934). Jaundice is due to the failure to excrete bilirubin, the
final metabolite of haemoglobin. The retention of bilirubin is due to inhibition
of bile secretion and not due to the failure to metabolize bilirubin. Ruminal
stasis is in part a direct result of liver injury, which activates an inhibitory
hepatoruminal reflex (McSweeney and Pass, 1983a) (see Section V.A).

F. Summary of the Pathophysiology of Lantana Poisoning

The available evidence suggests the following scheme to explain the development of lantana poisoning. Following consumption of the plant the toxins are
absorbed from the rumen and small intestine. They are transported in the
portal blood to the liver, where they are taken up into the hepatocytes. The
toxins are metabolized and the metabolites are transported to the bile canalicular membranes for secretion into bile. The metabolites damage the bile canalicular membranes, thus inhibiting bile secretion. The onset of liver injury
initiates the hepatoruminal reflex, causing ruminal stasis and retention of
lantana toxins. Continuous absorption of the toxins from the rumen maintains
the liver injury. Jaundice and photosensitization result from the inability
of the liver to excrete bilirubin and plant pigments, respectively.

VI. TREATMENT OF LANTANA POISONING

The key feature of the pathogenesis of lantana poisoning that has been used
to develop an effective treatment is the understanding that the development
of ruminal stasis and subsequent continuous absorption of toxins from the
rumen is responsible for maintaining the liver injury. If absorption is inhibited, animals recover from poisoning. This has been demonstrated in experiments in which recovery occurred after ruminal contents were removed from
lantana-poisoned sheep and replaced with normal ruminal contents (McSweeney
and Pass, 1982).

In practice the most convenient way of inhibiting absorption of toxins
is to administer relatively large quantities of powdered activated charcoal orally to adsorb the toxins. It has been shown that the effective dose of charcoal is about 500 g for a sheep and 2 to 2.5 kg for an adult cow (Pass and
Stewart, 1984). The charcoal should be given in a large volume of electrolyte
solution, 4 L per sheep and 20 L per cow. The fluid is helpful in rehydrating
the animal and in stimulating ruminal motility to mix the charcoal with the toxic
ruminal contents (McSweeney and Pass, 1982; Pass and Stewart, 1984). Recovery is usually rapid following such treatment as evidenced by the decline

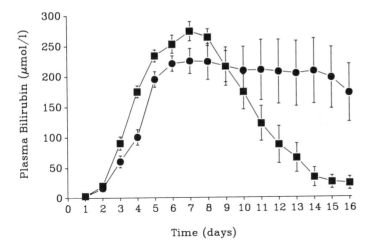

Time (days)

FIGURE 3 Effect on plasma bilirubin (mean ± SEM) of dosing lantana-poisoned
sheep orally with 500 g of activated charcoal. Eighteen sheep were dosed
with toxic lantana on day 1. Ten of the sheep (■) were given activated charcoal on day 6 and the remaining eight sheep (●) were left untreated.

in plasma bilirubin levels as cholestasis regresses (Fig. 3). Other adsorbents
may also be effective, but they have not yet been tested.

Treatments aimed at purging the animal without inhibiting absorption
should be avoided as they enhance toxicity. This has been demonstrated experimentally by giving large quantities of fluid orally to poisoned animals.
In these experiments the plasma bilirubin levels increased after treatment
and the animals died (Pass and Stewart, 1984).

Symptomatic treatment for dehydration and photosensitization is required
in addition to treatment preventing absorption of toxins. Additional fluid
therapy should be given if indicated. Animals should be housed in the shade
and antihistamines and antibiotics may be indicated to reduce the severity
of photosensitization and secondary bacterial infections.

VII. PREVENTION OF LANTANA POISONING

A. Control of the Plant

The methods used for eradication and control of lantana plants include physical removal of the plant, application of herbicides, and biological control using
lantana-eating insects (Bartholomew and Armstrong, 1978; Willson, 1979).
It has been recommended that the bulk of lantana should be burned or bull-
dozed and then the pasture sown with a shade-tolerant grass and a climbing
legume. Lantana regrowth should then be spot sprayed with an appropriate
herbicide, such as 2,4-D amine or D.P.60 (Bartholomew and Armstrong, 1978).
Annual reburning may be required for a year or two. A variety of lantana-
eating insects have been released, but they have only been partially effective
in controlling lantana in Australia (Willson, 1979).

B. Animal Management

As yet there are no specific therapeutic measures available for preventing lantana poisoning. Prevention depends on avoiding situations that predispose animals to eating large quantities of lantana in one feed. Hungry stock should not be given access to large quantities of lantana, and supplementary feeding of hay can be used to reduce the intake of lantana when other foods are scarce.

C. Future Prospects

Some advances have been made toward developing a vaccine against the lantana toxins. Sheep and cattle inoculated with protein conjugates of lantadenes A and B developed antibodies against the triterpene acids (Stewart et al., 1988). The antibodies appeared to be protective, in that vaccinated animals developed a lesser degree of cholestasis than unvaccinated animals when challenged with toxic lantana. Synthesis of more highly immunogenic conjugates and improved vaccination procedures offer the potential for protecting animals against lantana poisoning.

The relationship between susceptibility to intoxication and metabolism of the lantana toxins (Pass et al., 1985a) also offers promise for developing a method for protecting animals against lantana poisoning. If a means for altering the pathways of hepatic metabolism can be developed protection could be induced in susceptible animals. Future developments in molecular biology and a better understanding of the mechanisms of induciton and inhibition of hepatic enzyme systems may provide the basis for such a method.

VIII. CONCLUSIONS

Poisoning of ruminants by lantana plants is an important disease in many tropical and subtropical countries. The disease is characterized by intrahepatic cholestasis induced by hepatic metabolites of the triterpene acids lantadenes A and B. The liver injury leads to jaundice and photosensitization. The disease is maintained by continuous absorption of toxins from the rumen, the motility of which is severely reduced as a result of activation of an hepato-ruminal reflex by hepatic injury. Poisoned animals can be treated successfully by orally administering an adsorbent agent such as activated charcoal to reduce absorption of toxins from the rumen. No specific method of prevention is available at present. Prevention depends on eliminating lantana plants from the environment and animal management to reduce the intake of toxic plants.

REFERENCES

Bartholomew, B. L., and Armstrong, T. R. (1978). A new look at lantana control. *Queensl. Agric. J. 104*:339-344.

Black, H., and Carter, R. G. (1985). Lantana poisoning of cattle and sheep in New Zealand. *N.Z. Vet. J. 33*:136-137.

Brown, J. J. M. (1968). The chemical pathology of ovine icteric states: 3. Icterogenin induced cholestasis. *J. S. Afr. Vet. Med. Assoc. 39*:35-48.

Caple, I. W., and Heath, T. J. (1975). Biliary and pancreatic secretions in sheep: their regulation and roles. In *Proceedings of the Fourth International Symposium on Ruminant Physiology*, I. W. McDonald and A. C. I. Warner (Eds.). The University of New England Publishing Unit, Armidale, Australia, pp. 91-100.

Culvenor, C. C. J. (1985). Economic loss due to poisonous plants in Australia. In *Plant Toxicology*, A. A. Seawright, M. P. Hegarty, L. F. James, and R. F. Keeler (Eds.). Queensland Poisonous Plants Committee, Yeerongpilly, Australia, pp. 3-13.

de Aluja, A. S. (1970). *Lantana camara* poisoning in cattle in Mexico. *Vet. Rec. 86*: 628.

Dhillon, K. S., and Paul, B. S. (1971). Clinical studies of *Lantana camara* (L.) poisoning in buffalo calves, with special reference to its effects on rumen motility. *Indian J. Anim. Sci. 41*: 945-948.

Everist, S. L. (1981). *Poisonous Plants of Australia*. Angus & Robertson, London, pp. 738-747.

Hart, N. K., Lamberton, L. A., Sioumis, A. A., and Suares, H. (1976). New triterpenes of *Lantana camara*: a comparative study of several taxa. *Aust. J. Chem. 29*: 655-671.

Kellerman, T. S., and Coetzer, J. A. W. (1985). Hepatogenous photosensitivity diseases in South Africa. *Onderstepoort J. Vet. Res. 52*: 157-173.

McSweeney, C. S., and Pass, M. A. (1982). Treatment of experimentally induced lantana poisoning in sheep. *J. Appl. Toxicol. 2*: 11-15.

McSweeney, C. S., and Pass, M. A. (1983a). The mechanism of ruminal stasis in lantana-poisoned sheep. *Q. J. Exp. Physiol. 68*: 301-313.

McSweeney, C. S., and Pass, M. A. (1983b). Effect of lantana on the extracellular fluid of sheep. *Vet. Hum. Toxicol. 25*: 330-334.

Pass, M. A. (1977). The effect of lantana on the enterohepatic circulation of sheep. Ph.D. thesis, University of Queensland, St. Lucia, Australia.

Pass, M. A., and Goosem, M. W. (1982). Observation of metabolites of reduced lantadene A in bile canalicular membranes of rats with triterpene-induced cholestasis. *Chem.-Biol. Interact. 40*: 375-378.

Pass, M. A., and Goosem, M. W. (1983). Bile canalicular injury in lantana poisoning. *Toxicon Suppl. 3*: 337-340.

Pass, M. A., and Heath, T. J. (1978). The effect of *Lantana camara* on intestinal motility in sheep. *J. Comp. Pathol. 88*: 149-156.

Pass, M. A., and Stewart, C. (1984). Administration of activated charcoal for the treatment of lantana poisoning of sheep and cattle. *J. Appl. Toxicol. 4*: 267-269.

Pass, M. A., Seawright, A. A., and Heath, T. (1976). Effect of ingestion of *Lantana camara* L. on bile formation in sheep. *Biochem. Pharmacol. 25*: 2101-2102.

Pass, M. A., Gemmell, R. T., and Heath, T. J. (1978a). Effect of lantana on the ultrastructure of the liver of sheep. *Toxicol. Appl. Pharmacol. 43*: 589-596.

Pass, M. A., Seawright, A. A., Health, T. J., and Gemmell, R. T. (1978b). Lantana poisoning: a cholestatic disease of cattle and sheep. In *Effects of Poisonous Plants on Livestock*, R. F. Keeler, K. R. Van Kampen, and L. F. James (Eds.). Academic Press, New York, pp. 229-237.

Pass, M. A., Findlay, L., Pugh, M. W., and Seawright, A. A. (1979a). Toxicity of reduced lantadene A (22β-angeloyloxyoleanolic acid) in the rat. *Toxicol. Appl. Pharmacol.* *51*:515-521.

Pass, M. A., Seawright, A. A., Lamberton, J. A., and Heath, T. J. (1979b). Lantadene A toxicity in sheep: a model for cholestasis. *Pathology 11*:89-94.

Pass, M. A., Pugh, M. W., and Findlay, L. (1981a). Studies on the mechanism of toxicity of reduced lantadene A in rats. *Biochem. Pharmacol.* *30*:1433-1437.

Pass, M. A., McSweeney, C. S., and Reynoldson, J. A. (1981b). Absorption of the toxins of *Lantana camara* L. from the digestive system of sheep. *J. Appl. Toxicol.* *1*:38-42.

Pass, M. A., Goosem, M. W., and Pollitt, S. (1985a). A relationship between hepatic metabolism of reduced lantadene A and its toxicity in rats and sheep. *Comp. Biochem. Physiol.* *C82*:457-461.

Pass, M. A., Pollitt, S., Goosem, M. W., and McSweeney, C. S. (1985b). The pathogenesis of lantana poisoning. In *Plant Toxicology*, A. A. Seawright, M. P. Hegarty, L. F. James, and R. F. Keeler (Eds.). Queensland Poisonous Plants Committee, Yeerongpilly, Australia, pp. 487-494.

Rimington, C., and Quin, J. I. (1934). Studies on the photosensitisation of animals in South Africa: VII. The nature of the photosensitising agent in Geeldikop. *Onderstepoort J. Vet. Sci. Anim. Ind.* *3*:137-157.

Rimington, C., Quin, J. I., and Roets, G. C. S. (1937). Studies on the photosensitisation of animals in South Africa: X. The icterogenic factor in Geeldikkop: isolation of active principles from *Lippia rehmanni* pears. *Onderstepoort J. Vet. Sci. Anim. Ind.* *9*:225-255.

Seawright, A. A. (1963). Studies on experimental intoxication of sheep with *Lantana camara*. *Aust. Vet. J.* *39*:340-344.

Seawright, A. A. (1964). Studies on the pathology of experimental lantana (*Lantana camara* L.) poisoning of sheep. *Pathol. Vet.* *1*:504-529.

Seawright, A. A. (1965). Toxicity for the guinea pig of an extract of *Lantana camara*. *J. Comp. Pathol.* *75*:215-221.

Seawright, A. A. (1982). *Animal Health in Australia*, Vol. 2, *Chemical and Plant Poisons*. Australian Government Publishing Service, Canberra, pp. 55-57.

Seawright, A. A., and Allen, J. G. (1972). Pathology of the liver and kidney in lantana poisoning of cattle. *Aust. Vet. J.* *48*:323-331.

Seawright, A. A., and Hrdlicka, J. (1977). The oral toxicity for sheep of triterpene acids isolated from *Lantana camara*. *Aust. Vet. J.* *53*:230-235.

Sharma, O. P., and Dawra, R. K. (1984). Effect of lantana toxicity on canalicular plasma membrane of guinea pig liver. *Chem.-Biol. Interact.* *49*:369-374.

Sharma, O. P., Makkar, H. P. S., Pal, R. N., and Negi, S. S. (1980). Lantadene A content and toxicity of the lantana plant (*Lantana camara*, Linn.) to guinea pigs. *Toxicon 18*:485-488.

Sharma, O. P., Makkar, H. P. S., Dawra, R. K., and Negi, S. S. (1981). A review of the toxicity of *Lantana camara* (Linn) in animals. *Clin. Toxicol.* *18*:1077-1094.

Sharma, O. P., Makkar, H. S. P., and Dawra, R. K. (1982a). Biochemical effects of the plant *Lantana camara* on guinea pig liver mitochondria. *Toxicon 20*:783-786.

Sharma, O. P., Makkar, H. S. P., and Dawra, R. K. (1982b). Biochemical changes in hepatic microsomes of guinea-pig under lantana toxicity. *Xeno-biotica 12*: 265-269.

Sharma, O. P., Makkar, H. S. P., and Dawra, R. K. (1983). Effect of lantana toxicity on lysosomal and cytosol enzymes in guinea pig liver. *Toxicol. Lett. 16*: 41-45.

Smith, L. S., and Smith, D. A. (1982). The naturalised *Lantana camara* complex in eastern Australia. *Queensl. Bot. Bull.* No. 1.

Stewart, C., Lamberton, J. A., Fairclough, R. J., and Pass, M. A. (1988). Vaccination as a possible means of preventing lantana poisoning. *Aust. Vet. J. 65*: 349-352.

Willson, B. W. (1979). Biological control of lantana in Queensland, Tech. Bull. Queensland Department of Lands, Brisbane, Australia.

15

Role of Phenol Glycosides in Plant-Herbivore Interactions

Paul B. Reichardt and Thomas P. Clausen

University of Alaska, Fairbanks, Fairbanks, Alaska

John P. Bryant

Institute of Arctic Biology, University of Alaska, Fairbanks, Fairbanks, Alaska

I. INTRODUCTION

Probably more than any other class of metabolites, phenol glycosides are characteristic of the higher plants. In the 150 years since their discovery, over
4000 of these substances have been characterized (Harborne, 1988), and they
appear to be present in virtually all vascular plants (Pridham, 1965a). Considerable interest has arisen in their function in plants, and beginning with
Errara in 1886 (Hopkinson, 1969), speculation has centered on their role in
plant-herbivore interactions. In this chapter we describe our present understanding of the chemistry and biological properties of these compounds and
assess their ecological effects.

II. STRUCTURAL TYPES

The term "phenol glycoside" has been used for over a century, but agreement
over its exact meaning has been elusive. Some chemists include glycosylated
flavonoids in this group, while others delineate between "flavonoid glycosides"
and "phenol glycosides." Similarly, there has been little agreement on whether C-glycosides should be included. In this chapter the definition is taken
in its broadest sense: a compound containing both phenolic and carbohydrate
moieties.

A. Aglycones

The aglycones (noncarbohydrate portions) of phenol glycosides include representatives from the major biosynthetic pathways to phenols in plants. For
the most part they are "C_6-C_3" compounds, "acetate-extended C_6-C_3" compounds, and flavonoids (Geissman and Crout, 1969).

B. Carbohydrates

The most common monosaccharide units in phenol glycosides are L-arabinose,
L-rhamnose, D-xylose, D-galactose, D-glucose, and D-mannose. Monosaccharides less frequently found are D-apiose, D-allose, D-galacturonic acid,
and D-glucuronic acid (Harborne and Williams, 1982).

  The glycosyl portions of phenol glycosides are most commonly mono-, di-,
or trisaccharides. Although many of the theoretical permutations of the monosaccharides are known, there are some significant generalities. For example,
by far the most common monosaccharide residue is D-glucosyl; and apiose,
while commonly occurring in a disaccharide with glucose, has rarely been found
as a monosaccharide (Ranganathan et al., 1980).

Two somewhat subtle structural features of glycosides are ring and anomeric isomerism. Monosaccharides in phenol glycosides are normally found
in the pyranose form. However, occasional exceptions such as L-arabinose
in the furanose form have been reported (Harborne and Williams, 1982). The
configuration of the anomeric carbon has usually been assumed to be alpha
for arabinosides and rhamnosides and beta for xylosides, galactosides, glucosides, and glucuronides; but exceptions are known (Harborne and Williams,
1982). With the advent of nuclear magnetic resonance (NMR) methods for
establishing glycoside structure, more definitive assignments of stereochemistry are common in contemporary reports.

C. Glycoside Linkage to Aglycone

The final feature of structural variety in phenol glycosides is the nature of
the linkage between the glycoside and aglycone. The most common glycoside
linkage is to a phenolic or alcoholic oxygen, although linkage to carboxyl oxygen is also known. In addition, a number of *C*-glycosides have been reported
(Haynes, 1965; Chopin et al., 1982).

III. ISOLATION

A. Extraction

Traditionally, phenol glycosides have been extracted form plant material by
hot polar solvents, often followed by lead subacetate treatment or partitioning
of the phenol glycosides into a more lipophilic solvent. However, these procedures were found to produce artifacts (Steele et al., 1969; Thieme, 1965a),
and the standard procedure gradually changed to room-temperature extractions with no other treatment before separation of the mixture [e.g., Burger
et al. (1987), Potterat et al. (1988), and Rakotovao et al. (1988)]. Recently,
however, it has become clear that even these procedures can produce artifacts. Although no consensus has emerged for a single protocol, it appears
that treatment of plant material before extraction (Lindroth and Pajutee, 1987;
Mattes et al., 1987; Clausen et al., 1989a), the nature of the extracting solvent
(Lindroth and Pajutee, 1987), and the presence or absence of water in the
extraction media (Mattes et al., 1987; Clausen et al., 1989a) are important
factors in producing artifacts.

B. Chromatography

Column chromatography has been the most widely used method for initial separation of phenol glycoside mixtures (Hostettmann and Hostettmann, 1982).
A wide variety of supports have been employed, the most popular being poly-
amide (Siewek et al., 1984), LH-20 (Takeda and Fatope, 1988; Joseph et al.,
1988; Rakotovao et al., 1988; Burger et al., (1987), and silica gel (Takeda
and Fatope, 1988) and ion-exchange resins (Joseph et al., 1988). Modern
descendents of gravity column chromatography are, however, beginning to
replace traditional chromatography. Flash chromatography using both silica
gel (Strauss et al., 1987; Lindroth et al., 1987a; Clausen et al., 1989a) and
reversed-phase (Mattes et al., 1987; Clausen et al., 1989a) supports has been

used, as has low-pressure liquid chromatography (Strauss et al., 1987; Potterat et al., 1988).

Final purification of individual compounds has often involved tedious recrystallization. However, current practice is tending toward utilization of more sophisticated chromatographic techniques for this purpose. High-performance liquid chromatography (HPLC) (Sticher et al., 1981; Eldridge, 1982; Casteele et al., 1982), droplet countercurrent chromatography (Strauss et al., 1987; Potterat et al., 1988), and preparative thin-layer chromatography (Burger et al., 1987; Joseph et al., 1988; Lindroth et al., 1987a) have all recently been employed in final purifications.

IV. CHARACTERIZATION

A. Determination of Molecular Formula

Until recently, direct determination of molecular formulas of phenol glycosides has been difficult and, in many cases, impossible. Although formulas of some phenol glycosides have been determined by combustion analysis, the results are often complicated by the difficulty in obtaining rigorously pure substances and the hygroscopic nature of many phenol glycosides (Harborne, 1964; Takeda and Fatope, 1988).

Mass spectrometry has provided an alternative way of obtaining this information. Pearl and Darling (1968) have analyzed mass spectra of acetylated phenol glycosides for information on molecular weights and identities of both aglycone and glycosyl groups. Modern soft ionization techniques allow direct analysis of underivatized phenol glycosides and provide information from which structural details (e.g., aglycone structure, monosaccharide sequence of polyglycosides) can be deduced (Mabry and Ulubelen, 1980; Hostettmann and Marston, 1986; Domon and Hostettmann, 1985; Itokawa et al., 1982).

B. Hydrolysis

Hydrolysis plays an important role in structure determination of phenol glycosides. It has traditionally been used to differentiate between *C*-glycosides, which cannot be hydrolyzed, and *O*-glycosides, which can (Harborne, 1965). For *O*-glycosides, hydrolysis is especially valuable in cases where the aglycone portion is structurally complex. Although hydrolysis is, at times, problematical because of unstable aglycones or glycosides, which are difficult to hydrolyze, a variety of methods have been employed for this transformation. Acid and base have both been used to cleave glycoside bonds (Pridham, 1965b; Markham and Porter, 1975; Takeda and Fatope, 1988). Enzymatic hydrolysis is also commonly used (Pridham, 1965b; Markham and Porter, 1975; Harborne and Williams, 1982; Ravn and Brimer, 1988) and has the added advantage of providing structural information about the nature of the saccharide unit because of the specificities of the enzymes for particular carbohydrates (Harborne, 1964). Selective enzymatic hydrolysis can also be employed to determine the sequence of sugars in complex glycosides (Karl et al., 1980, 1981).

C. NMR Spectroscopy

In recent years NMR spectroscopy has become the most valuable technique available for structure elucidation of phenol glycosides. Several compilations of both ^{13}C and ^{1}H data for phenol glycosides (Markham et al., 1982; Markham and Ternai, 1976; Cussans and Huckerby, 1975; Dommisse et al., 1986) and carbohydrates (Breitmaier and Voelter, 1987; Bock and Thogersen, 1982) allow assignment of many structures by analogy if one is careful to allow for some rather dramatic solvent effects on chemical shift. More detailed analyses of spectra are possible based on the effects of glycosylation on ^{13}C chemical shifts (Markham and Ternai, 1976; Dommisse et al., 1986; Caussans and Huckerby, 1975), correlations between relaxation times of glycosidic protons and distance from the aglycone (Bock and Thogersen, 1982; Guinaudeau et al., 1981), the relationships between structural connectivities and the nuclear Overhauser effect (Bock and Thogersen, 1982; Steynberb et al., 1988), and heteronuclear two-dimensional spectra (Bock and Thogersen, 1982; Burger et al., 1987; Kessler et al., 1986).

D. Ultraviolet Spectrophotometry

Ultraviolet (UV) spectrophotometry has been particularly useful for structure determination of phenols. In addition to the usual information about aromatic systems, details about the substitution patterns of phenols and the sites of glycosylation can be elucidated from spectra of phenol glycosides to which a variety of "shift reagents" have been added (Markham, 1982; Mabry et al., 1970).

V. ANALYSIS

Both qualitative and quantitative analyses of phenol glycosides are normally carried out by chromatographic techniques. The oldest methods are paper (Pridham, 1959) and thin-layer (Audette et al., 1966) chromatography coupled with spray reagents for detection. Although these methods do not have the resolution capabilities of more recent ones, they remain useful qualitative procedures because of their simplicity and favorable economics.

The vast majority of such analyses, however, are now carried out by HPLC. The most common procedure utilizes a reversed-phase column and a UV detector (e.g., Daigle and Conkerton, 1982; Casteele et al., 1982; and Lindroth and Pajutee, 1987). However, enhanced selectivity and sensitivity is often available with postcolumn derivatization (Dalgaard and Nordholm, 1983; Hostettmann et al., 1984). Coupling of separation with rudimentary characterization is possible by utilizing a diode-array UV detector (Meier and Sticher, 1986; Siewek and Galensa, 1984), and it appears that this is becoming the analytical method of choice.

Gas chromatographic analysis of silylated phenol glycosides is also possible (Julkunen-Tiitto, 1985). Although thermal instabilities of some analytes limit the utility of this method, it does obviate the interference problem posed in HPLC methods by tannins (high-molecular-weight polar metabolites which often are poorly resolved by HPLC).

VI. DISTRIBUTION

Phenolic glycosides have been found in nearly every higher plant that has been investigated (Pridham, 1965a). However, the distributions of individual compounds vary dramatically. Phenol glycosides such as rutin and cyanidin-3-glucoside are found widely distributed in nature (Harborne, 1964). On the other hand, the limited distribution of individual glycosides within genera such as *Populus* (Pearl and Darling, 1977) and *Salix* (Julkunen-Tiitto, 1985) have been used as taxonomic markers. Finally, there are many examples of phenol glycosides which have been found in only a single species.

The individual phenol glycosides within a particular plant are not uniform-ly distributed. Quantitative differences in phenol glycoside content between sexes of willow have been noted (Thieme, 1965b). Although some phenol gly-cosides may be found in every part of a plant, the distribution of individual phenol glycosides is tissue specific (Harborne, 1964; Palo, 1984; Herrmann, 1988). Furthermore, there seems to be a rather complex relationship between amounts of free aglycone and phenol glycoside. For example, glycosides (rather than free aglycones) are more common in all plant parts other than woody tissue (Harborne, 1964), and waxes and exudates of leaves and flowers usually contain free aglycones which correspond to phenol glycosides found in cell vacuoles of the presumed source tissue (Wollenweber and Dietz, 1981).

Finally, it is important to note that phenol glycoside distribution within a plant is dynamic. In the *Populus* genus, for example, dramatic seasonal, diurnal, and age-dependent variations in glycoside content have been noted (Thieme, 1965c; Pawlowska, 1976; Lindroth et al., 1987b).

VII. METABOLISM

A. Biosynthesis

Biosynthesis of phenol glycosides in plants usually consists of two distinct stages: biosynthesis of aglycones followed by glycosylation (Heller, 1986; Pridham, 1965a,b; Conn, 1964). The construction of aglycones usually fol-lows the widely recognized routes to shikimate and shikimate/acetate-derived phenols (Torssell, 1983; Heller, 1986; Conn, 1964). The free aglycones are then glycosylated by a variety of enzymes which seem to be rather substrate specific (Conn, 1964; Heller, 1986). However, the glycosylation ability of plants is such that many free phenols administered to plants are rapidly con-verted to phenol glycosides (Miller, 1940; Pridham and Saltmarsh, 1963), sug-gesting the presence of general glycosidases which are not involved in the biosynthesis of normal plant metabolites.

B. Catabolism

Phenol glycosides are rapidly catabolized by a variety of organisms, including mammals (Hackett, 1986; Griffiths, 1982), insects (Ahmad et al., 1986; Bratt-sten, 1988; Lindroth, 1988), and microbes (Zhanaeva et al., 1980). It appears that the most common initial step in catabolism is hydrolysis of the glycoside due to the widespread distribution of glycosidases, especially β-glucosidase (Goodwin, 1976; Ahmad et al., 1986). The free aglycone is then further cata-bolized according to one of a variety of phenol-degrading pathways (Williams, 1964; Hackett, 1986; Griffiths, 1982).

To assess the ecological significance of catabolism of phenol glycosides, two aspects of these transformations must be considered. First, it is clear that in at least some cases glycoside hydrolysis by mammals (Hackett, 1986; Griffiths and Barrow, 1972) and insects (Kukor and Martin, 1983; Ahmad et al., 1986) involves the action of symbiotic microbes. Second, the glycoside hydrolysis to produce free phenols is the reverse of glycosylation, which is one of the most common pathways herbivores utilize to handle ingested free phenols (Brattsten, 1988; Hackett, 1986; Ahmad et al., 1986; Pridham, 1965a).

VIII. BIOLOGICAL PROPERTIES

A. Taste

Bitter taste has been associated with phenol glycosides for over a century, beginning with the discoveries that both phlorizin (= phloridzin) from apple trees and naringin from grapefruit have bitter tastes. Perhaps because of the long history of this association, ecologists have often considered the bitterness of phenol glycosides to be an important factor in their possible roles in mediating plant-herbivore interactions.

In fact, bitterness is known not to be a ubiquitous property of phenol glycosides (Horowitz, 1964, 1986). Perhaps the best-studied set of compounds are the phenol glycosides of grapefruit and their analogs. Grapefruit contains a set of eight flavanone glycosides, four of which are bitter neohesperidosides and four of which are tasteless rutinosides (Horowitz and Gentili, 1961). Thus the displacement of the point of attachment of α-L-rhamnose to β-D-glucose (from O-2 to O-6) converts bitter substances to tasteless ones. Synthetic analogs with rhamnose attached at O-3 and O-4 of the glucose residue also have greatly attenuated bitterness (Konishi et al., 1983). Bitterness is also a function of aglycone structure. Flavone, chalcone, and dihydrochalcone analogs of bitter grapefruit flavanone glycosides have tastes that range from slightly bitter to tasteless to sweet (Konishi et al., 1983; Horowitz, 1986). In fact, neohesperidin dihydrochalcone is intensely sweet and has official clearance in several countries to be used as a dietary sweetener (Horowitz, 1986). Stereochemical features of aglycone structure also affect taste, with the (2S) isomer of naringin reportedly more bitter than the (2R) isomer (Gaffield et al., 1975).

Much less work has been done on taste-structure relationships of non-flavonoid glycosides. However, at least some of these substances [e.g., salicin (Markham, 1971) and ferulic acid sucrose esters (Shoyama et al., 1987)] have been reported to be bitter.

In summary, it is clear that individual phenol glycosides have tastes ranging from bitter to tasteless to intensely sweet. The taste of a given phenol glycoside is closely tied to structure (in ways which are only partially understood at present), and there is a genetic factor in the sensitivity of individuals to bitterness of these substances (Horowitz, 1986). Thus although *many* phenol glycosides are bitter, one cannot presume that *any* phenol glycoside is bitter.

B. Toxicity

Antimicrobial activities of many phenol glycosides have been recorded in the literature, and only a sampling of the findings most pertinent to the present purposes will be given here. Phlorizin is known for its biological properties and is an example of a phenol glycoside with a rather broad range of anti-fungal and antibacterial effects (Cody, 1986). Rutin's ability to inactivate potato virus X (Selway, 1986) is an example of the ability of phenol glyco-sides to protect plants against pathogens. A series of caffeic acid sugar es-ters have been found to be active against *Staphylococcus aureus* and *Esch-erichia coli* (Ravn and Brimer, 1988; Kitagawa et al., 1987), two microbes of significance in human health and ecology. Hedin and Waage (1986) have screened 21 glycosides against two pathogens (*Pseudomonas maltophilia* and *Enterobacter cloacae*) from the guts of (*Heliothus zea* and *Heliothus virescens* and found many of them to be inhibitory. An interesting synergistic effect has been described for the antibacterial activities of quercetin, rutin, and isorham-netin-3-rutinoside against a *Propionibacterium* (Kimura and Yamada, 1984).

Several studies have dealt with structure-antimicrobial activity relation-ships. Hedin and Waage (1986) found that for the flavonoids, glycosylation at O-3 enhances activity and that glycosylation at O-7 attenuates it. A series of flavones, O-glycosides, and C-glycosides have been investigated for their abilities to inhibit mycelial growth and asexual reproduction of *Phytophthora parasitica* and *Colletotrichum musae* (Ravise and Chopin, 1981; Ravise et al., 1980). Generally, aglycones had greater activity than corresponding O-gly-cosides, but C-glycosides were more effective than corresponding aglycones.

There is little evidence for direct toxic effects of phenol glycosides on organisms other than microbes. Arbutin is toxic to brine shrimp (Meyer et al., 1982). Lindroth et al. (1988) have reported that salicortin and tremula-cin, but not salicin and tremuloidin, are toxic to fourth instar larvae of the tiger swallowtail butterfly. These two glycosides also caused gut lesions in southern armyworm larvae but did not reduce survival. Rutin, however, caused severe gut lesions and did reduce larval survival (Lindroth and Peter-son, 1988).

Although various phenol glycosides have properties [e.g., ability to che-late metals, destroy vitamins, and inhibit enzymes (Elliger et al., 1980, and Isman and Duffey, 1982)] that pose potential dangers to organisms and are potential latent sources of toxic phenols (Pridham, 1965a; Palo, 1984) after the action of glycosidases, acute toxicity to insects or mammals does not seem to be a general property of these substances. However, as pointed out by Lindroth (1988), the chronic effects of these substances may pose a threat to heribvores.

C. Pharmacology

There are reports of a variety of pharmacological properties of phenol glyco-sides. Matsubara et al. (1983, 1985) screened over 40 flavonoid glycosides from citrus peels and discovered a number of compounds with hypertensive activity. Matsumoto and Sei (1987) reported a flavone glycoside from ginkgo leaves with potential as a cardiovascular agent. The simple phenol glycoside gastrodin may have potential in treating epilepsy (Chai et al., 1983), and it has been found to have a variety of effects on cultured heart cells of neo-natal rats (Huang et al., 1986). Naringin is a reversible inhibitor of smooth muscle contractions induced by acetylcholine and prostaglandins (Macander, 1986). Flavonoid glycosides have the ability to attenuate certain diabetic com-

plications, and some of the structure-activity relationships for the nature
and position of attachment of the carbohydrate are known (Varma, 1986).
Rutin and hyperoside have pharmacological properties, including antihepato-
toxic properties and the ability to decrease capillary permeability (Lukic
and Gorunovic, 1979). Phlorizin (= phloridzin) affects urinary excretion of
glucose and the transport of glucose across cell membranes, causing the phenomenon known as "phloridzin diabetes" in animals (Ramwell et al., 1964).

D. Enzymatic Effects

Phenol glycosides are known to affect activities of a number of enzymes, and
some with potential ecological relevance are briefly treated here. Salicin is a
moderate inhibitor of β-glycosidases from a variety of insects (Spencer, 1988).
Apigenin-7-gentiobioside and several other flavone glycosides inhibit xanthine
oxidase (Sakushima et al., 1985). The effects of flavonoids on aldose reductase have been investigated in some detail (Varma, 1986; Varma and Kinoshita,
1976; Shimizu et al., 1984) because of the relationship between this enzyme
and diabetic cataracts. Although no simple pattern is perceptible in Varma's
data, Shimizu et al. found that the inhibitory ability is generally flavones >
flavonols > flavanones and monoglycosides > aglycones. Iodothyronine deiodinase (Koehrle et al., 1986) and cyclic nucleotide phosphorodiesterases (Beretz
et al., 1986) are inhibited by a variety of flavonoids, and in both cases aglycones are more active than corresponding glycosides. Finally, lipoxygenase
(an enzyme involved in arachidonic acid metabolism) is inhibited by a variety
of flavonoid glycosides (Michel et al., 1986; Welton et al., 1986) and caffeic
acid sugar esters (Murota and Koshihara, 1985; Kimura et al., 1987).

IX. ECOLOGICAL SIGNIFICANCE

A. Insect Herbivores

Several plant phenol glycosides have been identified as attractants or stimulants for herbivores. In some cases (Doskotch et al., 1973; Zielske et al.,
1972; Nielsen et al., 1979) individual phytochemicals which have restricted
distribution in plants are responsible for attracting insect herbivores. In
other cases, simple mixtures of rare flavonoid glycosides stimulate leaf probing by several insects (Kim et al., 1985; Matsuda and Matsuo, 1985; Besson
et al., 1985). However, common glycosides can also play a role in plant-insect
interactions. Mixtures of quercetin, quercetin-7-O-glucoside, and quercetin-
3-O-glucoside are stimulants for the boll weevil (Hedin et al., 1968). Synergistic effects between phenol glycosides and some unidentified plant metabolites serve as oviposition stimulants for papilionoid butterflies (Honda, 1986;
Nishida et al., 1987). Similarly, a mixture of chlorogenic acid and luteolin-
7-O-(6'-O-malonyl)-β-D-glucopyranoside isolated from carrot foliage serves
as an oviposition stimulant for the black swallowtail butterfly, even though
neither pure compound was active when tested alone (Feeny et al., 1988).
An example of the specificity of a response elicited by a unique mixture of
phenol glycosides has been provided by Tahavanainen et al. (1985a), who
demonstrated that four leaf beetle species select their favored host plants
(*Salix* spp.) based on phenol glycoside content. Furthermore, when forced

to shift host plant, the insects selected the alternate host with phenol glycoside content closest to that of the preferred host.

Another method for herbivores' exploitation of plant phenol glycosides
has also been described. Several species of oligophagous chrysomelid beetles
prefer as hosts willow species that have high levels of salicin (Rowell-Rahier,
1984; Pasteels et al., 1983; Smiley et al., 1985), and one beetle utilizes a sali-
cortin-containing willow (Rowell-Rahier et al., 1987). The insects do not
use the phenol glycosides as feeding cues; rather, they metabolize them to
salicaldehyde, a defensive chemical used by the insects (Pasteels et al., 1983),
and glucose, which serves as a significant source of energy (Rowell-Rahier
and Pasteels, 1986). Furthermore, the protection afforded by this defense
can be passed on to eggs (Pasteels et al., 1986).

Other studies have demonstrated that plant phenol glycosides can have
adverse effects on insect herbivores. Rutin (Elliger et al., 1980) and several
other flavonoids (Pratt and Wender, 1959; Shaver and Lukefahr, 1969; Elliger et al., 1980; Isman and Duffey, 1982) adversely affect larvae of the tobacco budworm, the cotton bollworm, the pink bollworm, and the greenbug.
However, effects of these substances are limited to certain life stages of the
larvae (Isman and Duffey, 1982) and do not extend to all insects (McFarlane
and Distler, 1982).

One component of cotton's defense against insects is the ability of some
of its phenol glycosides to inhibit larval growth (Chan et al., 1978; Hedin
et al., 1981, 1983a,b). Although the biochemical bases for these effects are
not yet known, four of these compounds are active against microbes found
in the guts of the cotton bollworm and the tobacco hornworm (Waage and Hedin,
1984).

Perhaps the most thoroughly investigated case of plant chemical defense
against insects based on phenol glycosides is in quaking aspen (*Populus tremuloides*). In one set of investigations, Lindroth et al. (1988) have shown
that of the four phenol glycosides in aspen foliage (salicin, tremuloiden, salicortin, and tremulacin), the latter two adversely affect the performance of
larvae of the swallowtail butterfly. Two subspecies (*Papilio glaucus canadensis* and *P. glaucus glaucus*) show significant differences in their abilities to
tolerate these chemicals with the subspecies (*P. canadensis*) which uses aspen
as a normal host being less sensitive to the effects of salicortin and tremulacin. Neither the mechanism for these effects nor the biochemical reasons for
the different sensitivities of the subspecies are fully known; but Lindroth
has presented evidence for synergistic effects in mixtures of salicortin and
tremulacin (Lindroth et al., 1988) that both insects rapidly metabolize both
chemicals (Lindroth et al., 1988), and that a mixture of the two phenol glycosides induces β-glucosidase activity in *P. glaucus glaucus* but not in *P.
glaucus canadensis* (Lindroth, 1988). He proposes that *P. glaucus canadensis*
has adapted to salicortin and tremulacin by decreasing the hydrolysis of the
β-glucoside to the presumably more toxic aglycone and by rapidly hydrolyzing
the carboxylic acid ester to innocuous metabolites. A separate study (Bryant
et al., 1987; Clausen et al., 1989b) has revealed that the phenol glycosides
of aspen have similar effects on larvae of the great aspen tortrix [*Choristoneura conflictana* (Walker)]. Their investigation has focused on metabolic
changes in the phenol glycoside content of the plant during herbivory. In
crushed aspen leaves, salicortin and tremulacin are transformed into salicin

and tremuloidin (respectively) and 6-hydroxycyclohexenone (6-HCH), a reactive substance that adversely affects the larvae (Clausen et al., 1989b).
Furthermore, damaging foliage on intact plants causes increases in concentrations of salicortin and tremulacin, a situation that could lead to even higher
levels of 6-HCH in damaged foliage. Taken together, these studies have identified aspen phenol glycosides which are harmful to insect herbivores and
have pointed out the importance of metabolic transformations of these compounds in the plant-insect interaction. What is not clear at this point is ex-
actly how transformations of phenol glycosides both in the plant and the insects contribute to the plant's ability to defend itself and to the insects' ability to overcome the defense.

Although the studies reviewed above represent only a limited beginning
of attempts to understand the role of phenol glycosides in plant-insect interactions, two general points emerge. The first is that the chemicals or mixtures mediating a given interaction are quite specific. That is, there appears
to be no general role that can be ascribed to phenol glycosides as a class,
but there are individual phenol glycosides that play important roles in specific cases. Second, metabolic transformation is a key aspect of the way in
which phenol glycosides influence plant-insect interactions.

B. Mammalian Herbivores

Although relatively little is known about the roles played by phenol glycosides in plant-insect interactions, even less is known about the importance
of these compounds in plant-mammal interactions. Until recently the only
direct evidence of a phenol glycoside playing any role in a mammalian herbivore's dietary choice came from the studies of Markham (1971) and Edwards
(1978). They demonstrated that opossums avoid *Populus* and *Salix* species
which contain high levels of salicin and its derivatives and ascribed the aver-
sion to the bitter taste of phenol glycosides. However, this proposal has
never been tested by bioassays of purified chemicals.

Tahavanainen et al. (1985b) reported a similar negative correlation between palatabilities of several *Salix* species to the mountain hare (*Lepus timi-
dus*) and concentrations of uncharacterized [but see Julkunen-Tiitto (1985)]
phenol glycosides. However, they extended this relationship beyond a simple
correlation by demonstrating that phenol glycoside-containing extracts of the
plants were unpalatable to hares.

A third study has suggested a less direct role for phenol glycosides in
the defense of balsam poplar (*Populus balsamifera*) against snowshoe hares
(*Lepus americanus*). Although phenol glycoside-containing extracts of balsam
poplar twigs were palatable to hares, the two major phenol glycosides of this
plant (salicortin and trichocarpin) apparently do contribute to its unpalatability. In a fashion nearly identical to that described above for aspen, salicortin is transformed into 6-HCH (unpalatable to hares) when poplar internodes
are damaged. Similarly, disruption of twig tissue causes conversion of trichocarpin into trichocarpigenin (Mattes et al., 1987), a highly unpalatable substance with a peppery taste (Reichardt et al., 1988). While the production
of these unpalatable substances from phenol glycosides during herbivory merely augments a more static defense of poplar twigs against hares (Reichardt

et al., 1988; Mattes, 1986), it again illustrates the ecological implications of the biochemical lability of phenol glycosides.

X. CONCLUSIONS

Recent advances in the procedures for identifying and analyzing phenol glyco-sides have presented the opportunity to define the ecological roles of these compounds in much more detail than was possible even a decade ago. The emerging picture is not yet fully focused, but some general outlines are evi-dent. We now have a relatively large body of information about the diverse biological effects of these compounds. Placing these effects in an ecological context has been, and will continue to be, difficult for at least two reasons. First, the effects ascribed to phenol glycosides are generally not immediate, readily apparent, nor acute. Second, phenol glycosides are readily trans-formed into other metabolites by nearly all types of biota; and there are a myriad of metabolic outcomes with potential ecological significance (Reichardt et al., 1988). Thus the ecological ramifications of an herbivore ingesting a phenol glycoside may not be readily apparent; and when effects are noted, they may not be the direct result of phenol glycosides. The relationships between structure, metabolic transformations, biological effects, and ecologi-cal significance are not simple ones (nor are they easy to study), but they are fascinating and probably hold the secrets to understanding the ecological roles of plant phenol glycosides.

REFERENCES

Ahmad, S., Brattsten, L. B., Mullin, C. A., and Yu, S. J. (1986). Enzymes involved in the metabolism of plant allelochemicals. In *Molecular Mecha-nisms in Insect-Plant Associations*, L. B. Brattsten and S. Ahmad (Eds.). Plenum Press, New York, pp. 73-151.

Audette, R. C. S., Blunden, G., Steele, J. W., and Wong, S. C. (1966). Thin-layer chromatography of phenolic glycosides and its use as a screen-ing procedure for the genus *Salix*. *J. Chromatogr.* 25:367-372.

Beretz, A., Anton, R., and Cazenave, J. (1986). The effects of flavonoids on cyclic nucleotide phosphodiesterases. In *Plant Flavonoids in Biology and Medicine*: *I. Biochemical, Pharmacological, and Structure-Activity Relationships*, V. Cody, E. Middleton, Jr., and J. B. Harborne (Eds.). Alan R. Liss, New York, pp. 281-297.

Besson, E., Dellamonica, G., Chopin, J. Markham, K. R., Kim, K., Koh, H. S., and Fukami, H. (1985). C-Glycosylflavones from *Oryza sativa*. *Phytochemistry* 24:1061-1064.

Bock, K., and Thogersen, H. (1982). Nuclear magnetic resonance spectro-scopy in the study of mono- and oligosaccharides. *Annu. Rev. NMR Spectrosc.* 13:1-57.

Brattsten, L. B. (1988). Enzymic adaptions in leaf-feeding insects to host-plant allelochemicals. *J. Chem. Ecol.* 14:1919-1939.

Breitmaier, E., and Voelter, W. (1987). *Carbon-13 NMR Spectroscopy: High*

Resolution Methods and Applications in Organic and Biochemistry, 3rd ed. VCH Publishers, New York.

Bryant, J. P., Clausen, T. P., Reichardt, P. B., McCarthy, M. C., and Werner, R. A. (1987). Effect of nitrogen fertilization upon the secondary chemistry and nutritional value of quaking aspen (*Populus tremuloides* Michx.) leaves for the large aspen tortrix (*Choristoneura conflictana* (Walker)). *Oecologia* (*Berl.*) 73:513-517.

Burger, J. F. W., Brandt, E. V., and Ferreira, D. (1987). Iridoid and phenolic glycosides from *Harpagophytum procumbens*. *Phytochemistry* 26:1453-1457.

Casteele, K. V., Greiger, H., and VanSumere, C. F. (1982). Separation of flavonoids by reversed-phase high performance liquid chromatography. *J. Chromatogr.* 240:81-94.

Chai, H., Zeng, H., Xie, Y., Xu, J., and Chen, A. (1983). Preliminary observations on the effect of synthetic gastrodin against epilepsy in rabbits induced by coriaria lactone. *Sichuan Yixueyan Xuebao* 14:288-292. *Chem. Abstr.* (1983) 99:187624r.

Chan, B. G., Waiss, A. C., Binder, R. G., and Ellinger, C. A. (1978). Inhibition of lepidopterous larval growth by cotton constituents. *Entomol. Exp. Appl.* 24:94-100.

Chopin, J., Bouillant, M. L., and Besson, E. (1982). *C*-Glycosylflavonoids. In *The Flavonoids: Advances in Research*, J. B. Harborne and T. J. Mabry (Eds.). Chapman & Hall, London, pp. 449-504.

Clausen, T. P., Reichardt, P. B., Evans, T., and Bryant, J. P. (1989a). A simple method for the isolation of salicortin, tremulacin and tremuloidin from quaking aspen (*Populus tremuloides*). *J. Nat. Prod.* 52:207-209.

Clausen, T. P., Reichardt, P. B., Bryant, J. P., Werner, R. A., Post, K., and Frisby, K. (1989b). A chemical model for short-term induction in quaking aspen (*Populus tremuloides*) foliage against herbivores. *J. Chem. Ecol.* 15:2335-2346.

Cody, V. (1986). Crystal structure of phlorizin and its interactions in the deiodinase active-site model. In *Plant Flavonoids in Biology and Medicine: I. Biochemical, Pharmacological, and Structure–Activity Relationships*, V. Cody, E. Middleton, Jr., and J. B. Harborne (Eds.). Alan R. Liss, New York, pp. 383-386.

Conn, E. E. (1964). Enzymology of phenolic biosynthesis. In *Biochemistry of Phenolic Compounds*, J. B. Harborne (Ed.). Academic Press, New York, pp. 399-435.

Cussans, N. J., and Huckerby, T. N. (1975). Carbon-13 NMR spectroscopy of heterocyclic compounds: IV. A 20 MHz study of chemical shifts and carbon-proton coupling constants in a series of hydroxy, methoxy and glucosyl coumarins. *Tetrahedron* 31:2719-2726.

Daigle, D. J., and Conkerton, E. J. (1982). High-performance liquid chromatography of 34 selected flavonoids. *J. Chromatogr.* 240:202-205.

Dalgaard, L., and Nordholm, L. (1983). Enzymatic post-column cleavage and electrochemical detection of glycosides separated by high-performance liquid chromatography. *J. Chromatogr.* 265:183-192.

Dommisse, R. A., Van Hoff, L., and Vlietinck, A. J. (1986). Structural analyses of phenolic glucosides from Salicaceae by NMR spectroscopy. *Phytochemistry* 25:1201-1204.

Domon, B., and Hostettmann, K. (1985). Mass spectroscopic studies of underivatized polyphenolic glycosides. *Phytochemistry* 24:575-580.

Doskotch, R. W., Mikhail, A. A., and Chatterji, S. K. (1973). Structure of the water-soluble feeding stimulant for *Scolytus multistriatus*: a revision. *Phytochemistry* 12:1153-1155.

Edwards, W. R. N. (1978). Effect of salicin content on palatability of *Populus* foliage to opossum (*Trichosurus vulpecula*). *N.Z. J. Sci.* 21:103-106.

Eldridge, A. C. (1982). High-performance liquid chromatography separation of soybean isoflavones and their glycosides. *J. Chromatogr.* 234:494-496.

Elliger, C. A., Chan, B. C., and Waiss, A. C., Jr. (1980). Flavonoids as larval growth inhibitors: structural factors governing toxicity. *Naturwissenschaften* 67:358-360.

Feeny, P., Sachdev, K., Rosenberry, L., and Carter, M. (1988). Luteolin-7-*O*-(6″-*O*-malonyl)-β-D-glucoside and *trans*-chlorogenic acid: oviposition stimulants for the black swallowtail butterfly. *Phytochemistry* 27:3439-3448.

Gaffield, W., Lundin, R. E., Gentili, B., and Horowitz, R. M. (1975). C-2 stereochemistry of naringin and its relationship to taste and biosynthesis in maturing grapefruit. *Bioorg. Chem.* 4:259-269.

Geissman, T. A., and Crout, D. H. G. (1969). *Organic Chemistry of Secondary Plant Metabolism*. Freeman, Cooper, San Francisco.

Goodwin, B. L. (1976). *Handbook of Intermediary Metabolism of Aromatic Compounds*. Chapman & Hall, London, pp. 103-109.

Griffiths, L. A. (1982). Mammalian metabolism of flavonoids. In *The Flavonoids: Advances in Research*, J. B. Harborne and T. J. Mabry (Eds.). Chapman & Hall, London, pp. 681-718.

Griffiths, L. A., and Barrow, A. (1972). Metabolism of flavonoid compounds in germ-free rats. *Biochem. J.* 130:1161-1162.

Guinaudeau, H., Seligmann, O., Wagner, H., and Neszmelyi, A. (1981). Faralatroside and fatatroside, two flavonol triglycosides from *Colubrina faralaotra*. *Phytochemistry* 20:1113-1116.

Hackett, A. M. (1986). The metabolism of flavonoid compounds in mammals. In *Plant Flavonoids in Biology and Medicine: I. Biochemical, Pharmacological, and Structure-Activity Relationships*, V. Cody, E. Middleton, Jr., and J. B. Harborne (Eds.). Alan R. Liss, New York, pp. 177-194.

Harborne, J. B. (1964). Phenol glycosides and their natural distribution. In *Biochemistry of Phenolic Compounds*, J. B. Harborne (Ed.). Academic Press, New York, pp. 129-169.

Harborne, J. B. (1965). Plant polyphenols: XIV. Characterization of flavonoid glycosides by acidic and enzymic hydrolyses. *Phytochemistry* 4:107-120.

Harborne, J. B. (1988). Flavonoids in the environment: structure-activity relationships. In *Plant Flavonoids in Biology and Medicine II*, V. Cody, E. Middleton, Jr., J. B. Harborne, and A. Beretz (Eds.). Alan R. Liss, New York, pp. 17-27.

Harborne, J. B., and Williams, C. A. (1982). Flavone and flavonol glycosides. In *The Flavonoids: Advances in Research*, J. B. Harborne and

T. J. Mabry (Eds.). Chapman & Hall, London, pp. 261-312.

Haynes, L. J. (1965). Naturally occurring C-glycosyl compounds. In *Advances in Carbohydrate Chemistry*, M. L. Wolfram (Ed.). Academic Press, New York, pp. 357-369.

Hedin, P. A., and Waage, S. K. (1986). Roles of flavonoids in plant resistance to insects. In *Plant Flavonoids in Biology and Medicine: I. Biochemical, Pharmacological, and Structure-Activity Relationships*, V. Cody, E. Middleton, Jr., and J. B. Harborne (Eds.). Alan R. Liss, New York, pp. 87-100.

Hedin, P. A., Miles, L. R., Thompson, A. C., and Minyard, J. P. (1968). Constituents of a cotton bud: formulation of a boll weevil stimulant mixture. *J. Agric. Food Chem. 16*:505-513.

Hedin, P. A., Collum, D. H., White, W. H., Parrott, W. L., Lane, H. C., and Jenkins, J. N. (1981). The chemical basis for resistance in cotton to *Heliothis* insects. In *Proceedings International Conference on Regulation of Insect Development and Behavior*. Wroclaw Technical University Press, Wroclaw, Poland, p. 1071. *Chem. Abstr.* (1983) *98*:211508h.

Hedin, P. A., Jenkins, J. N., Collum, D. H., White, W. H., and Parrott, W. L. (1983a). Mutliple factors in cotton contributing to resistance to the tobacco budworm, *Heliothis virescens*. *Amer. Chem. Soc. Symp. Ser. 208*:347-365.

Hedin, P. A., Jenkins, J. N., Collum, D. H., White, W. H., Parrott, W. L., and MacGown, M. W. (1983b). Cyanidin-3-β-glucoside, a newly recognized basis for resistance in cotton to the tobacco budworm *Heliothis virescens* (Lepidoptera: Noctuidae). *Experientia 39*:799-801.

Heller, W. (1986). Flavonoid biosynthesis: an overview. In *Plant Flavonoids in Biology and Medicine: I. Biochemical, Pharmacological, and Structure-Activity Relationships*, V. Cody, E. Middletone, Jr., and J. B. Harborne (Eds.). Alan R. Liss, New York, pp. 25-42.

Herrmann, K. (1988). On the occurrence of flavonol and flavone glycosides in vegetables. *Z. Lebensm.-Unters. Forsch. 186*:1-5.

Honda, K. (1986). Flavanone glycosides as oviposition stimulants in a papilionoid butterfly, *Papilio protenor*. *J. Chem. Ecol. 12*:1999-2010.

Hopkinson, S. M. (1969). The chemistry and biochemistry of phenolic glycosides. *Quart. Rev. (Lond.) 23*:98-124.

Horowitz, R. M. (1964). Relations between the taste and structure of some phenolic glycosides. In *Biochemistry of Phenolic Compounds*, J. B. Harborne (Ed.). Academic Press, New York, pp. 545-571.

Horowitz, R. M. (1986). Taste effects of flavonoids. In *Plant Flavonoids in Biology and Medicine: I. Biochemical, Pharmacological, and Structure-Activity Relationships*, V. Cody, E. Middleton, Jr., and J. B. Harborne (Eds.). Alan R. Liss, New York, pp. 163-175.

Horowitz, R. M., and Gentili, B. (1961). Phenolic glycosides of grapefruit: a relation between bitterness and structure. *Arch. Biochem. Biophys. 92*:191-192.

Hostettmann, K., and Hostettmann, M. (1982). Isolation techniques for flavonoids. In *The Flavonoids: Advances in Research*, J. B. Harborne and T. J. Mabry (Eds.). Chapman & Hall, London, pp. 1-18.

Hostettmann, K., and Marston, A. (1986). Isolation, purification, and characterization of flavonoids. In *Plant Flavonoids in Biology and Medicine*:

I. Biochemical, Pharmacological, and Structure-Activity Relationships, V. Cody, E. Middleton, Jr., and J. B. Harborne (Eds.). Alan R. Liss, New York, pp. 43-51.

Hostettmann, K., Domon, B., Schaufelberger, D., and Hostettmann, M. (1984). On line high-performance liquid chromatography: ultraviolet-visible spectroscopy of phenolic compounds in plant extracts using post-column derivatization. *J. Chromatogr.* *283*:137-147.

Huang, X., Xiao, Y., and Lei, P. (1986). Effect of synthetic gastrodin on the beating of cultured heart cell of neonatal rat and histochemical changes. *Zhongyao Tongbao* *11*:307-309. *Chem. Abstr.* (1986) *105*:54326r.

Isman, M. B., and Duffey, S. S. (1982). Toxicity of tomato phenolic compounds to the fruitworm. *Heliothis zea*. *Entomol. Exp. Appl.* *31*:370-376.

Itokawa, H., Oshida, Y., Ikuta, A., and Shida, Y. (1982). Ion beam electron impact, chemical ionization and negative ion chemical ionization of flavonoid glycosides. *Chem. Lett.* *1*:49-52.

Joseph, H., Glage, J., Moulis, C., Fouraste, I., and Stanislas, E. (1988). O-Methoxylated C-glycosylflavones from *Justicia pectoralis*. *J. Nat. Prod.* *51*:804-805.

Julkunen-Tiitto, R. (1985). Chemotaxonomical screening of phenolic glycosides in northern willow twigs by capillary gas chromatography. *J. Chromatogr.* *324*:129-139.

Karl, C., Pedersen, P. A., and Müller, G. (1980). A new acylated glycoside from *Phyllitis scolopendrum*. *Z. Naturforsch.* *C35*:826.

Karl, C., Müller, G., and Pedersen, P. A. (1981). Flavonoids in the flowers of *Primula officinalis*. *Planta Med.* *41*:96-99.

Kessler, H., Bermel, W., Griesinger, C., and Kolar, C. (1986). NMR spectroscopic structure elucidation of glycopeptides with the COLOC technique. *Angew. Chem. Int. Ed. Engl.* *25*:342-343.

Kim, M., Koh, H., and Fukami, H. (1985). Isolation of C-glycosylflavones as probing stimulants for planthoppers in rice plants. *J. Chem. Ecol.* *11*:441-452.

Kimura, M., and Yamada, H. (1984). Interaction in the antibacterial activity of flavonoids from *Sophora japonica* L. to *Propionibacterium*. *Yakugaku Zasshi* *104*:340-346. *Chem. Abstr.* (1984). *101*:51606p.

Kimura, Y., Okuda, H., Nishibe, S., and Arichi, S. (1987). Effects of caffeolglycosides on arachidonate metabolism in leukocytes. *Planta Med.* *53*:148-153.

Kitagawa, S., Nishibe, S., and Baba, H. (1987). Studies on the Chinese crude drug "Forsythiae Fructus": VIII. On isolation of phenylpropanoid glycosides from fruits of *Forsythic koreana* and their antibacterial activity. *Yakugaku Zasshi* *107*:274-278. (*Chem. Abstr.* (1987) *107*:46141c.)

Koehrle, J., Auf'mkolk, M., Spanka, M., Irmscher, K., Cody, V., and Hesch, R. (1986). Iodothyronine deiodinase is inhibited by plant flavonoids. In *Plant Flavonoids in Biology and Medicine: I. Biochemical, Pharmacological, and Structure-Activity Relationships*, V. Cody, E. Middleton, Jr., and J. B. Harborne (Eds.). Alan R. Liss, New York, pp. 359-371.

Konishi, F., Esaki, S., and Kamiya, S. (1983). Synthesis and taste of flavanone and dihydrochalcone glycosides containing 3-O-α-L-rhamnopyrano-syl-D-glucopyranose or 4-O-α-L-rhamnopyranosyl-D-glucopyanose in the sugar moiety. *Agric. Biol. Chem.* *47*:265-274.

Kukor, J. J., and Martin, M. M. (1983). Acquisition of digestive enzymes by siricid woodwasps from their fungal symbiont. *Science* 220:1161-1163.

Lindroth, R. L. (1988). Hydrolysis of phenolic glycosides by midgut β-glucosidases in *Papilio glaucus* subspecies. *Insect Biochem.* 18:789-792.

Lindroth, R. L., and Pajutee, M. S. (1987). Chemical analysis of phenolic glycosides: art, facts and artifacts. *Oecologia (Berl.)* 74:144-148.

Lindroth, R. L., and Peterson, S. S. (1988). Effects of plant phenols on performance of southern armyworm larvae. *Oecologia (Berl.)* 75:185-189.

Lindroth, R. L., Hsia, M. T. S., and Scriber, J. M. (1987a). Characterization of phenolic glycosides from quaking aspen. *Biochem. Syst. Ecol.* 15:677-680.

Lindroth, R. L., Hsia, M. T. S., and Scriber, J. M. (1987b). Seasonal patterns in the phytochemistry of three *Populus* species. *Biochem. Syst. Ecol.* 15:681-686.

Lindroth, R. L., Scriber, J. M., and Hsia, M. T. S. (1988). Chemical ecology of the tiger swallowtail: mediation of host use by phenolic glycosides. *Ecology* 69:814-822.

Lukic, P., and Gorunovic, M. (1979). Significance of bioflavonoid drugs in modern therapy. *Arch. Farm.* 29:247-257. *Chem. Abstr.* (1980). *93*:164273n.

Mabry, T. J., and Ulubelen, A. (1980). *Biochemical Applications of Mass Spectrometry—First Supplementary Volume*, G. R. Waller and O. C. Desmer (Eds.). Wiley, New York, pp. 1132-1158.

Mabry, T. J., Markham, K. R., and Thomas, M. B. (1970). *The Systematic Identification of Flavonoids*, Springer, New York.

Macander, P. J. (1986). Flavonoids affect acetylcholine, prostaglandin E_2, and antigen-mediated smooth muscle contraction. In *Plant Flavonoids in Biology and Medicine: I. Biochemical, Pharmacological, and Structure-Activity Relationships*, V. Cody, E. Middleton, Jr., and J. B. Harborne (Eds.). Alan R. Liss, New York, pp. 489-492.

Markham, K. R. (1971). A chemotaxonomic approach to the food selection of opossum resistant willows and poplars for use in soil conservation. *N.Z. J. Sci.* 14:179-186.

Markham, K. R. (1982). *Techniques of Flavonoid Identification*. Academic Press, London.

Markham, K. R., and Porter, L. J. (1975). Evidence of biosynthetic simplicity in the flavonoid chemistry of the Ricciaceae. *Phytochemistry* 14:119-201.

Markham, K. R., and Ternai, B. (1976). ^{13}C NMR of flavonoids: II. Flavonoids other than flavone and flavonol aglycones. *Tetrahedron* 32:2607-2612.

Markham, K. R., Chari, V. M., and Mabry, T. J. (1982). Carbon-13 NMR spectroscopy of flavonoids. In *The Flavonoids: Advances in Research*, J. B. Harborne and T. J. Mabry (Eds.). Chapman & Hall, London, pp. 19-134.

Matsubara, Y., Kumamoto, H., Iizuka, Y., Murakami, T., Okamoto, K., Miyake, H., and Yoki, K. (1983). The structure and physiological activity of flavonoid glycosides in four citrus fruits peel. *Tennen Yuki Kagobutsu Toronkai Koen Yoshishu* 26:142-149. *Chem. Abstr.* (1984) *101*:12057r.

Matsubara, Y., Kumamoto, H., Iizuka, Y., Murakami, T., Okamoto, K., Miyake, H., and Yoki, K. (1985). Structure and hypotensive effect of flavonoid glycosides in *Citrus unshio* peelings. *Agric. Biol. Chem. 49*: 904-914.

Matsuda, K., and Matsuo, H. (1985). A flavonoid, luteolin-7-glucoside, as well as salicin and populin stimulating the feeding of leaf beetles on salicaceous plants. *Appl. Entomol. Zool. 20*: 305-313.

Matsumoto, T., and Sei, T. (1987). Isolation of a flavone glycoside from ginkgo leaves for use as a cardiovascular agent. Eur. Pat. Appl. EP 237,066(Cl. C07H17/07). *Chem. Abstr.* (1988). *108*: 19396d.

Mattes, B. J. (1986). A qualitative and quantitative phytochemical analysis of *P. balsamifera* in relation to mammalian herbivory. M.S. thesis, University of Alaska, Fairbanks.

Mattes, B. J., Clausen, T. P., and Reichardt, P. B. (1987). Volatile constituents of balsam poplar: the phenol glycoside connection. *Phytochemistry 26*: 1361-1366.

McFarlane, J. E., and Distler, M. H. W. (1982). The effect of rutin on growth, fecundity and food utilization in *Acheta domesticus* L. *J. Insect Physiol. 28*: 85-88.

Meier, B., and Sticher, O. (1986). The use of high speed spectrophotometric detector (diode-array) in the HPLC-analysis of medicinal plants. *Pharm. Ind. 48*: 87-91.

Meyer, B. N., Ferrigne, N. R., Putnam, J. E., Jacobsen, L. B., Nichols, D. E., and McLaughlin, J. L. (1982). Brine shrimp: a convenient general bioassay for active plant constituents. *Planta Med. 45*: 31-34.

Michel, F., Mercklein, L., and Rey, R. (1986). Comparative effects of some flavonoids on cyclo-oxygenase and lipoxygenase activities in different all systems or subfractions. *Stud. Org. Chem. 23*: 389-401. *Chem. Abstr.* (1986) *105*: 145681u.

Miller, L. P. (1940). Induced formation of β-gentiobiosides in gladiolus corms and tomato plants treated with chemicals. *Science 92*: 42-43.

Murota, S., and Koshihara, Y. (1985). New lipoxygenase inhibitors isolated from Chinese plants: development of new anti-allergic drugs. *Drugs Exp. Clin. Res. 11*: 641-644.

Nielsen, J. K., Larsen, L. M., and Sorenson, H. (1979). Host plant selection of the horseradish flea beetle *Phyllotreta armoraciae* (Coleoptera: Chrysomelidae): identification of two flavonol glycosides stimulating feeding in combination with glucosinolates. *Int. Exp. Appl. 26*: 40-48.

Nishida, R., Ohsugi, T., Kokubo, S., and Fukami, H. (1987). Oviposition stimulants of a Citrus-feeding swallowtail butterfly, *Papilio xuthus* L. *Experientia 43*: 342-344.

Palo, R. T. (1984). Distribution of birch (*Betula* spp.), willow (*Salix* spp.), and poplar (*Populus* spp.) secondary metabolites and their potential role as chemical defense against herbivores. *J. Chem. Ecol. 10*: 499-520.

Pasteels, J. M., Rowell-Rahier, M., Braekman, J. C., and Dupont, A. (1983). Salicin from host plant as the precursor of salicaldehyde in defensive secretion of chrysomeline larvae. *Physiol. Entomol. 8*: 307-314.

Pasteels, J. M., Daloze, D., and Rowell-Rahier, M. (1986). Chemical defense in chrysomelid eggs and neonate larvae. *Physiol. Entomol. 11*: 29-37.

Pawlowska, L. (1976). Quantitative daily changes of flavonol glycosides in the leaves of *Betula humilis*. *Acta Soc. Bot. Pol. 45*: 395-400.

Pearl, I. A., and Darling, S. F. (1968). Mass spectroscopy as an aid for determining structures of natural glycosides. *Phytochemistry 7*: 831-837.

Pearl, I. A., and Darling, S. F. (1977). Studies on the leaves of the family Salicaceae: 17. Hot-water extractives of the leaves of *Populus hetero-phylla*. *J. Agric. Food Chem. 25*: 730-740.

Potterat, O., Msonthi, J. D., and Hostettmann, K. (1988). Four iridoid glucosides and a phenylpropanoid glycoside from *Sesamum angolense*. *Phytochemistry 27*: 2677-2679.

Pratt, C., and Wender, S. H. (1959). Identification of rutin and isoquercitin in cottonseed. *J. Am. Oil Chem. Soc. 36*: 392-394.

Pridham, J. B. (1959). Paper electrophoresis and paper chromatography of phenolic compounds. *J. Chromatogr. 2*: 605-611.

Pridham, J. B. (1965a). Low molecular weight phenols in higher plants. *Annu. Rev. Plant Physiol. 16*: 13-36.

Pridham, J. B. (1965b). Phenol-carbohydrate derivatives in higher plants. In *Advances in Carbohydrate Chemistry*, M. L. Wolfram (Ed.). Academic Press, New York, pp. 371-408.

Pridham, J. B., and Saltmarsh, M. J. (1963). The biosynthesis of phenolic glucosides in plants. *Biochem. J. 87*: 218-224.

Rakotovao, M., Voirin, B., Bayet, C., Favre-Bonvin, J., and Andriansi-ferana, M. (1988). 3'-O-β-Xylosyltricetin, a novel flavone glycoside from *Trema humbertii*. *Phytochemistry 27*: 2655-2656.

Ramwell, P. W., Sherratt, H. S. A., and Leonard, B. E. (1964). The physiology and pharmacology of phenolic compounds in animals. In *Biochemistry of Phenolic Compounds*, J. B. Harborne (Ed.). Academic Press, New York, pp. 457-510.

Ranganathan, R. M., Nagarajan, S., Mabry, T. J., Yong-Long, L., and Neuman, P. (1980). 6-Hydroxyluteolin-7-O-apioside from *Lepidagathis christata*. *Phytochemistry 19*: 2505-2506.

Ravise, A., and Chopin, J. (1981). Effect of structure of phenolic compounds on the inhibition of the growth of *Phytophthora parasitica* and the activity of parasitogenic enzymes: V. Flavones, O- and C-glycosides. *Phytopathol. Z. 100*: 257-269.

Ravise, A., Kirkiachrian, B. S., Chopin, J., and Krinesch, G. (1980). Phenolic compounds and structural analogs of phytoalexins: influence of structure and substituents on the in vitro inhibition of micromycetes and some lytic enzymes. *Ann. Phytopathol. 12*: 335-336.

Ravn, H., and Brimer, L. (1988). Structure and antibacterial activity of plantamajoside, a caffeic acid sugar ester from *Plantago major* subsp. *major*. *Phytochemistry 27*: 3433-3437.

Reichardt, P. B., Clausen, T. P., and Bryant, J. P. (1988). Phenol glycosides in plant defense against herbivores. *Amer. Chem. Soc. Symp. Ser. 380*: 130-142.

Rowell-Rahier, M. (1984). The presence or absence of phenolglycosides in *Salix* (Salicaceae) leaves and the level of dietary specialization of some their herbivorous insects. *Oecologia (Berl.) 62*: 26-30.

Rowell-Rahier, M., and Pasteels, J. M. (1986). Economics of chemical defense in Chrysomelinae. *J. Chem. Ecol. 12*: 1189-1203.

Rowell-Rahier, M., Soetens, P., and Pasteels, J. M. (1987). Influence of phenolglucosides on the distribution of herbivores on willow. In *Insects-Plants*, V. Labeyrie, G. Fabres, and D. Lachaise (Eds.). Dr. W. Junk Publishers, Hingham, Mass., pp. 91-95.

Sakushima, A., Hisada, S., and Nishibe, S. (1985). Studies on the constituents of Apocynacease plants: a new flavonol glycoside and other compounds from the leaves of *Anodenderon affine*. *Shoyakugaku Zasshi 39*: 118-122. *Chem. Abstr.* (1986) *104*:74870w.

Selway, J. W. T. (1986). Antiviral activity of flavones and flavans. In *Plant Flavonoids in Biology and Medicine*: *I. Biochemical, Pharmacological, and Structure-Activity Relationships*, V. Cody, E. Middleton, Jr., and J. B. Harborne (Eds.). Alan R. Liss, New York, pp. 521-536.

Shaver, T. N., and Lukefahr, M. J. (1969). Effect of flavonoid pigments and gossypol on growth and development of the bollworm, tobacco budworm and pink bollworm. *J. Econ. Entomol. 62*:643-646.

Shimizu, M., Ito, T., Terashima, S., Hayashi, T., Arisawa, M., Morita, N., Kurokawa, S., Ito, K., and Hashimoto, Y. (1984). Inhibition of lens aldose reductase by flavonoids. *Phytochemistry 23*:1885-1888.

Shoyama, Y., Hatano, K., Nishioka, I., and Yamagishi, T. (1987). Phenolic glycosides from *Lilium longiflorum*. *Phytochemistry 26*:2965-2968.

Siewek, F., and Galensa, R. (1984). High-performance liquid chromatographic determination of the degree of glycosidation of flavonols by use of ultraviolet-diode array detector. *J. Chromatogr. 294*:385-389.

Siewek, F., Galensa, R., and Herrmann, K. (1984). Detection of adulteration of black currant products by red currants by HPLC determination. *Z. Lebensm.-Unters. Forsch. 179*:315-321.

Smiley, J. T., Horn, J. M., and Rank, N. E. (1985). Ecological effects of salicin at three trophic levels: new problems from old adaptations. *Science 229*:649-651.

Spencer, K. C. (1988). Glycosides: the interface between plant secondary and insect primary metabolism. *Amer. Chem. Soc. Symp. Ser. 380*:403-416.

Steele, J. W., Bolan, M., and Audette, R. C. S. (1969). Phytochemistry of the Salicaceae: II. The effect of extraction procedures on the apparent free phenolic glycoside content of *Salix* species. *J. Chromatogr. 40*: 370-376.

Steynberb, J. P., Brandt, E. V., Burger, J. F. W., Bezuidenhoudt, B. C. B., and Ferreira, D. (1988). Stilbene glycosides from *Guibourtia coleosperma*: determination of glycosidic connectivities by homonuclear nuclear Overhauser effect difference spectroscopy. *J. Chem. Soc. Perkin Trans. I.* 37-41.

Sticher, O., Egloff, C., and Bettschart, A. (1981). Isolierung und quantitative Bestimmung von Phenolglyckoideden aus *Salix*-species. *Planta Med. 42*:126-128.

Strauss, C. R., Gooley, P. R., Wilson, B., and Williams, P. J. (1987). Application of droplet countercurrent chromatography to the analysis of conjugated forms fo terpenoids, phenols and other constituents of grape juice. *J. Agric. Food Chem. 35*:519-524.

Tahavanainen, J., Julkunen-Tiitto, R., and Kettunen, J. (1985a). Phenolic glycosides govern the food selection pattern of willow-feeding leaf beetles.

Oecologia (Berl.) 67:52-56.

Tahavanainen, J., Helle, E., Julkunen-Tiitto, R., and Lavola, A. (1985b). Phenolic compounds of willow bark as deterrents against feeding by mountain hare. *Oecologia (Berl.)* 65:319-323.

Takeda, Y., and Fatope, M. O. (1988). New phenolic glucosides from *Lawsonia inermis*. *J. Nat. Prod.* 51:725-729.

Thieme, H. (1965a). Die Phenolglycoside der Salicaceen. *Planta Med.* 13: 431-438.

Thieme, H. (1965b). Die Phenolglykosidespektren und der Glykosidgehalt der mitteldeutchen *Salix* Arten. *Pharmazie* 20:570-574.

Thieme, H. (1965c). Die Phenolglykoside der Salicaceen: Untersuchungen über jahr-zeitlich bedingten Veränderungen der Glykosidkonzentrationen: über die Abhängigkeit des Glykosidgehalt von der Togezeit und von alter Pflanzenorgane. *Pharmazie* 20:688-691.

Torssell, K. B. G. (1983). *Natural Product Chemistry: A Mechanistic and Biosynthetic Approach to Secondary Metabolism*. Wiley, New York, pp. 58-166.

Varma, S. D. (1986). Inhibition of aldose reductase by flavonoids: possible attenuation of diabetic complications. In *Plant Flavonoids in Biology and Medicine: I. Biochemical, Pharmacological, and Structure-Activity Relationships*, V. Cody, E. Middleton, Jr., and J. B. Harborne (Eds.). Alan R. Liss, New York, pp. 343-358.

Varma, S. D., and Kinoshita, J. H. (1976). Inhibition of lens aldose reductase by flavonoids: their possible role in the prevention of diabetic cataracts. *Biochem. Pharmacol.* 25:2505-2513.

Waage, S. K., and Hedin, P. A. (1984). Biologically-active flavonoids from *Gossypium arboreum*. *Phytochemistry* 23:2509-2511.

Welton, A. F., Tobias, L. D., Fiedler-Nagy, C., Anderson, W., Hope, W., Meyers, K., and Coffey, J. W. (1986). Effect of flavonoids on arachidonic acid metabolism. In *Plant Flavonoids in Biology and Medicine: I. Biochemical, Pharmacological, and Structure-Activity Relationships*, V. Cody, E. Middleton, Jr., and J. B. Harborne (Eds.). Alan R. Liss, New York, pp. 231-242.

Williams, R. T. (1964). Metabolism of phenolics in animals. In *Biochemistry of Phenolic Compounds*, J. B. Harborne (Ed.). Academic Press, New York, pp. 205-248.

Wollenweber, E., and Dietz, V. H. (1981). Occurrence and distribution of free flavonoid aglycones in plants. *Phytochemistry* 20:869-932.

Zhanaeva, T. A., Minaeva, Y. G., and Zaprometov, M. N. (1980). Flavonol-cleaving enzymes of *Bupleurum aureum*. *Fiziol. Biokhim. Kul't. Rast.* 12:625-631. *Chem. Abstr.* (1981) 94:79079e.

Zielske, A. G., Simons, J. N., and Silverstein, R. M. (1972). A flavone feeding stimulant in alligatorweed. *Phytochemistry* 11:393-396.

16

Cassia-Induced Myopathy

Loyd D. Rowe

Agricultural Research Service, U.S. Department of Agriculture, College Station, Texas

I. INTRODUCTION

The genus *Cassia* (Leguminosae) is a large and diverse assemblage of annual and perennial herbs, shrubs, woody vines, and trees found in the tropics and subtropics, particularly tropical America (Correll and Johnston, 1970). Certain species of *Cassia* are known to have medicinal value. Use of the drug senna (the dried leaflets of *C. acutifolia* Delile or *C. angustifolia* Vahl) as a cathartic in humans seems to antedate the historical record (Claus, 1961). Various species of *Cassia* have been employed as folk remedies for a variety of human health disorders (Watt and Breyer-Brandwijk, 1962; Burlage, 1968; Selvaraj and Chander, 1978; Kang, 1981; Assi, 1983). The roasted seeds of *C. foetida* and *C. occidentalis* have been used as coffee substitutes and adulterants (Claus, 1961). In Sudan, the leaves of *C. obtusifolia* L. are fermented to produce "Kawal," which is eaten by some Sudanese or used as a spice (Suliman et al., 1987).

Three species, *C. occidentalis*, *C. obtusifolia*, and *C. roemeriana*, are known to produce myopathy in farm animals as a result of being grazed or by contamination of feed by foliage or seeds (Bailey, 1985). The focus of this chapter is on these poisonous members of the genus and the toxic injury of skeletal and cardiac muscle (myopathy) that these plants induce.

II. *CASSIA OCCIDENTALIS* L.

Cassia occidentalis (coffee senna, styptic-weed) is a widely distributed annual weed in the tropics and subtropics of both the New and Old Worlds. This unpleasant-scented annual (August to November in the southeastern United States) attains heights of 1.1 to 1.8 m. The leaves are alternate and compound with lanceolate leaflets in four to six pairs. Two to five yellow or yellow-orange flowers that wilt by midday are mixed with bracts in a short raceme. The fruit of this legume is slender and erect (7.5 to 12 cm in length) and at maturity contains many dull brown, ovoid, somewhat flattened seeds up to 4.8 mm long (Correll and Johnston, 1970; Ajilvsgi, 1979).

In the United States, *C. occidentalis* is distributed from eastern Texas east and north to Florida, Virginia, and Kansas (Hulbert and Oehme, 1968). It is found in pastures, around corrals, and in other areas of rich soil (Schmitz and Denton, 1977). The plant grows in abundance in the sandy soil of the coastal plans of the southeastern United States, where it is common in cultivated fields of corn, grain sorghum, and soybeans (Colvin et al., 1986). In Australia, *C. occidentalis* is widely distributed in tropical areas of Queensland, the Northern Territory, and Western Australia (Rogers et al., 1979).

Despite much earlier reports of the toxicity of *C. occidentalis* seed to horses (Brocq-Rousseau and Bruere, 1925; Moussu, 1925), awareness of the myotoxicity of this plant stems from investigations of outbreaks of degenerative myopathy in cattle in the Gulf Coast region of Texas beginning in 1959. Initial feeding trials demonstrated that the plant is toxic to cattle, sheep, goats, and rabbits (Dollahite et al., 1964; Dollahite and Henson, 1965; Henson and Dollahite, 1966).

Reports of poisoning due to consumption of the plant by animals while grazing have thus far involved only cattle of the southeastern United States (Dollahite et al., 1964; Henson et al., 1965; Pierce and O'Hara, 1967; Neal and Plummer, 1967; Mercer et al., 1967) and Queensland, Australia (Rogers et al., 1979). Other reports of spontaneous poisoning involve cattle, horses (Brocq-Rousseau and Bruere, 1925; Moussu, 1925; De Barros, 1988, personal com-munication), or pigs (Colvin et al., 1986; Martins et al., 1986) and resulted from the accidental or imprudent feeding of grain contaminated by *C. occidentalis* seeds.

A. Cattle

1. *Conditions of Poisoning*

C. *occidentalis* poisoning in grazing cattle in the southeastern United States has a definite seasonal incidence. The condition is seen in the fall or early winter during the first few days following the first killing frost of the year. The plant is not usually attractive to cattle prior to that time, but may be grazed intensely following a killing freeze. Poisoned cattle may be in good nutritional condition and grazing pastures of fair to good nutritional value. The disorder is commonly seen in cattle 1 to 2 years of age, but animals of any age may be affected. Poisoning may be limited to one or two animals in a herd, or up to more than one-half of the herd may be affected (Henson et al., 1965; Pierce and O'Hara, 1967).

2. *Clinical Syndromes*

Spontaneous poisoning by C. *occidentalis* in cattle is of subacute or, less often, acute form (Pierce and O'Hara, 1967). Chronic poisoning has been produced experimentally (Mercer et al., 1967; O'Hara et al., 1969), but this form of toxicosis occurs rarely, if at all, under natrual conditions. Although there is much individual variation in the amount of plant material required to produce fatal poisoning (Mercer et al., 1967), an inverse linear relationship between survival time and daily dose rate for calves fed C. *occidentalis* beans has been demonstrated (O'Hara et al., 1969). The leaves, stems, and particularly the seeds are toxic. Fresh plant material, made up of leaves, stem, and beans fed at daily dosages of 0.3 to 1.6% of body weight for 7 to 14 days, has been fatal to calves (Dollahite et al., 1964). The dried, ground beans fed at 0.25 to 1.5% of body weight were lethal in 4 to 18 days; however, a daily dosage of 0.05% body weight produced chronic toxicosis and death over a period of 120 days (O'Hara et al., 1969).

Although diarrhea may be observed 2 to 4 days after initial ingestion of the plant (Pierce and O'Hara, 1967), the first clinical signs usually reported in spontenaeous cases of poisoning develop in 5 to 7 days and appear to result from degeneration and necrosis of skeletal muscle leading to weak, ataxic, myoglobinuric, and eventually recumbent animals that remain alert ("alert-downers") and retain some appetite until a few hours before death. Recumbency may last 1 to 7 days or longer. During the 24 h preceding death, there is anorexia, tachycardia, and labored respiration. Virtually all animals that become recumbent die (Henson et al., 1965; Pierce and O'Hara, 1967; O'Hara et al., 1969; Rogers et al., 1979). Serum creatine kinase (CK) and aspartate transaminase (AST) activities are consistently and often markedly elevated (Henson et al., 1965; Reagor and Ray, 1975).

The less frequently occurring acute form of the disease is characterized by diarrhea, dehydration, rapidly progressing weakness, and sudden death after only 2 to 3 days of illness. Myoglobinuria may not be seen, and an extended period of recumbency does not occur (Pierce and O'Hara, 1967).

Some aspects of the experimentally induced syndrome differ form the natrual disease. The first signs of poisoning observed in field cases are usually abnormalities of gait, weakness, and recumbency. In experimentally induced poisoning, a mild transient, initial phase consisting of anorexia, lethargy, and mild diarrhea precedes a second phase in which clinical signs attributable

to muscle dysfunction are seen. Another difference is the absence of an extended period of recumbency in experimental poisoning where prostration usually occurs less than 24 h before death and may be preceded by anorexia,
inactivity, dehydration, muscle tremors, stiffness, alteration in gait, and
a recurrence of diarrhea. Clinical signs of experimentally induced chronic
poisoning are similar to those of the subacute disease, but this form of the
disease is marked by periods of remission and exacerbation (Henson et al.,
1965; Mercer et al., 1967; O'Hara et al., 1969; O'Hara and Pierce, 1974a).

3. Pathology

Diffuse pallor or pale strippling of the heavy appendicular muscles, especially those of the upper pelvic limbs, is the only consistent gross lesion;
however, some cases may be without obvious gross lesions despite a period
of recumbency before death. The stippled form of muscle lesion has apparently not been reported in other degenerative myopathies. Diffuse pallor
may be so severe as to give affected muscles an almost ivory appearance (Fig.
1). Most or all of the muscles of the hindlimbs may show pallor in severe
cases; less severe cases may show pallor in only one or two muscles. Adjacent
muscles may appear pale and normal, respectively. Both pale and normal-
appearing areas may blend together in a single muscle. Hindlimb muscles
frequently affected include the m. pectineus, m. semimembranosus, m. semitendinosus, m. adductor, m. sartorius, m. quadriceps femoris, and m. biceps
femoris. Forelimb muscles frequently affected are the m. triceps branchii,
m. biceps brachii, and the m. extensor carpi radialis.

Pale streaks beneath the serosal surface of the myocardium are sometimes
seen on the ventricles, but this change is not prominent. Subepicardial hemorrhages may be observed, especially when poisoning is acute. Dark red, red-
brown, or port-wine urine (myoglobinuria) may be found in the bladder of
cattle that die early in the disease; however, those that die after 3 to 4 days
of recumbency often have normal-appearing urine. Discoloration of the kidneys as in equine azoturia is absent. Catarrhal inflammation of the abomasum
and small intesting is common (Henson et al., 1965; Pierce and O'Hara, 1967;
O'Hara et al., 1969).

Macroscopic lesions often observed in experimentally induced poisoning,
but not reported for spontaneous poisoning, include pale swollen and friable
livers with pale yellow or white spots located centrally in lobules, pericardial
and pleural effusions, and pulmonary congestion and edema (O'Hara et al.,
1969; Rogers et al., 1979). The myocardium of a chronically poisoned calf
that died after 117 days of dosing was very pale and reduced in mass (O'Hara
et al., 1969).

The predominant change seen microscopically is degeneration of sarcoplasm of skeletal muscle fibers. This is present to some degree in all poisoned
calves that live for more than 7 days after initial ingestion of C. occidentalis.
The most severe microscopic change is seen in muscles that show the greatest
pallor grossly, but these changes can be found much more widely distributed
than indicated by pallor visible macroscopically. Usually, heavy muscles of
support and locomotion, especially those of the hind limb, show microscopic
lesions of some degree. Some muscles may escape serious damage and show
few or no microscopic lesions even when most other muscles are affected. Within a single muscle, degenerated fibers and normal fibers may be found side by

FIGURE 1 Pale muscles of a cow poisoned by *Cassia* sp. The very pale semi-tendinosus muscle (center) is flanked by pale biceps femoris (left) and normal-appearing muscle (right). (Courtesy of Dr. J. W. Dollahite.)

side; although in severely damaged muscle, almost all fibers are affected to some degree. Similarly, single fibers may have affected and normal portions (Henson et al., 1965; Pierce and O'Hara, 1967). Viewed microscopically, the sarcoplasm of damaged muscle cells appears as fragmented, amorphous clumps or strands (Fig. 2). The sarcolemmal sheath remains intact in some fibers, but in others it, and the sarcolemmal nuclei, appear necrotic (Henson et al., 1965; Henson and Dollahite, 1966). Attempted regeneration of injured muscle fibers, as evidenced by proliferation of muscle nuclei, occurs during the second week after poisoning (Pierce and O'Hara, 1967). Calcification is not an usual feature of the muscle lesion of this disease (Henson et al., 1965).

Microscopic changes in pale stippled muscle were found to be identical to those in diffusely pale lesions (Rogers et al., 1979). Mercer et al. (1967) reported an increase of approximately 25% in collagen of skeletal muscle from a recovered, chronically poisoned cow compared with sections from the same location in a control calf.

Microscopic changes in liver, when present, were mild to moderate in severity and did not necessarily parallel the degree of damage in skeletal muscle. Lesions in liver reported by various workers include congestion, fatty change, generalized vacuolation and swelling of parenchymal cells, and focal

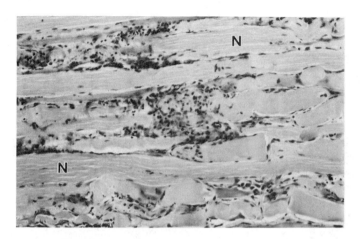

FIGURE 2 Photomicrograph of skeletal muscle from a goat fed *Cassia roemeri-ana* (0.5% of body weight daily for 23 days). Fragmented fibers consisting of amorphous clumps of necrotic sarcoplasm invaded by neutrophils, macrophages, and proliferating sarcolemmal nuclei are seen among normal fibers (N). Hematoxylin and eosin stain: ×200.

areas of hepatocellular necrosis accompanied by neutrophil infiltration. In some cases, changes were seen primarily in the central portion of the hepatic lobules around central veins and in others, as scattered foci elsewhere in the lobule (Henson et al., 1965; Mercer et al., 1967; Rogers et al., 1979).

Microscopic changes of cardiac muscle similar to those described for skeletal muscle have been reported; however, such lesions are frequently absent and, when present, are much less extensive than in skeletal muscle. Affected cardiac fibers have been described as being reduced in size and having acidophilic, dense sarcoplasm and small, dark (pyknotic) nuclei (Henson et al., 1965; Pierce and O'Hara, 1967). Various degrees of a more subtle change have been reported in all myocardial fibers of experimentally poisoned calves from which heart muscle specimens were obtained immediately after animals became recumbent. In formalin-fixed, paraffin-embedded, hematoxylin/eosin-stained sections of affected myocardium, this change appeared as small indistinct vacuoles arranged in rows between myofibrils that, when numberous, gave muscle fibers a foamy, fenestrated appearance. These vacuoles were shown by electron microscopy to consist of swollen mitochondria, and it was concluded that mitochondrial degeneration was the primary structural alteration in the myocardium of calves poisoned with *C. occidentalis* (Read et al., 1968).

B. Poultry

Several reports, involving experimental administration of *C. occidentalis* seed to chickens, cite the known toxicity of the plant to other species and the potential for inclusion of grain contaminated with *C. occidentalis* seed in poultry feeds as the impetus for their studies (Simpson et al., 1971; Torres et al., 1971; Butolo et al., 1972).

Simpson et al. (1971) fed a commercial broiler-type diet containing 0, 0.5, 1.0, 2.0, or 4.0% ground *C. occidentalis* seed to 7-day-old chicks for 21 days. Mortality was 0, 2.5, 2.5, 5.0, and 65%, respectively. Body weight and feed intake for birds fed 2.0 or 4.0% seed were significantly lower than for birds fed rations containing 0, 0.5, or 1.0% seed. Ataxia or partial paralysis was observed in most fatally affected birds fed rations containing 2.0 or 4.0% seed, and the semitendinosus muscle of these birds was pale and edematous at necropsy. Microscopic changes in semitendinosus muscle of these chicks were similar to those reported for *Cassia*-poisoned cattle and consisted of focal swelling, fragmentation, and necrosis of myofibrils accompanied by swelling and proliferation of sarcolemmal nuclei. Ultrastructural changes are determined only for semitendinosus muscle of chicks fed 2% seeds and sacrificed 21 days later. The changes observed, although more advanced and largely involving myofibrils, included mitochondrial swelling as reported in bovine myocardium by Read et al. (1968).

The administration of aqueous extracts of *C. occidentalis* seed to 7-day-old chicks at daily dosages (in terms of whole seed) of 0.5 to 2% of body weight resulted in loss of body weight, weakness, diarrhea, dropping wings, reluctance to stand or move about, ruffled feathers, hypothermia, recumbency, unresponsiveness, and death. Depletion of skeletal muscle mass (especially the pectoral muscles) was the first gross change observed followed by the development of paleness in the myocardium. These changes were followed by development of pallor in the muscles of the proximal portion of the leg. Light- and electron microscopic examination of tissues of these birds revealed myodegeneration in both skeletal and cardiac muscle similar to that seen in poisoned cattle; however, no microscopic lesion was found in pectoralis muscle despite the presence of typical degenerative changes in leg muscle of the same individual (Hebert et al., 1983; Graziano et al., 1983).

Butolo et al. (1972) investigated the effects of feeding a ration containing 0.3% pulverized *C. occidentalis* seed to layers for 8 months beginning at age day 1. Percent mortality, feed intake, and body weight were not significantly different form controls during the study. Weekly laying rates for seed-fed layers were 94 to 103% (average 100.2%) of controls except during two 4-week periods immediately following introduction of freshly collected *C. occidentalis* seed into the ration. Laying rate for seed-fed layers during these two periods was 20 to 44% (average 33.8%) that of controls. The authors suggested that an unstable factor in fresh seed may have been responsible for the observed decline in egg production. This hypothesis is consistent with the observation that endosperm of *C. occidentalis* seed that was stored at room temperature for 6 weeks was significantly less potent in rabbits than was fresh endosperm (O'Hara and Pierce, 1974a).

C. Swine

Colvin et al. (1986) reported accidental poisoning of swine by seeds of *C. occidentalis* that resulted from the use of contaminated grain sorghum in the ration. Signs of intoxication included decreased weight gains, a gaunt appearance, apparent muscular weakness, ataxia, difficulty in standing, inability to rise from recumbency or right from lateral recumbency, paddling, and death. This progression of signs began 21 days after introduction of the contaminated diet and reached greatest severity on days 42 to 56. No change was observed in serum activity of CK or AST in these animals, indicating that no significant damage to striated muscle (or other tissues containing these enzymes) had taken place. Consistent macroscopic lesions in the tissues of these animals were absent, and muscle pallor was not observed. Microscopic examination of tissue specimens revealed significant evidence of myopathy only in the diaphragm. The experimental feeding of a diet containing 1% seed to swine produced results comparable to those seen in the accidental case. Serum biochemical (CK and AST), gross, and microscopic evidence indicative of skeletal or cardiac muscle damage in pigs experimentally fed 2% or 4% seed was not observed. Unusual features of this case report and study are (1) the uniform absence of myopathy in muscles of the limbs of affected pigs, despite prolonged exposure to *Cassia* seed, and clinical signs of ataxia, muscular weakness, and recumbency; and (2) the presence of myopathy of the diaphragm and necrosis of acinar cells of the pancreas.

   Martins et al. (1986) reported poisoning and death in 420 of 1200 pigs in one incident and 39 of 800 pigs in a second incident involving the feeding of corn contaminated with "large amounts" of *C. occidentalis* seed. Clinical signs included anorexia, apathy, ataxia, diarrhea, vomiting, dyspnea, lateral recumbency, and death 8 to 12 days after ingestion of contaminated feed began. Areas of pallor in skeletal and cardiac muscle and enlargement of the liver were observed at necropsy. Microscopic examination revealed degeneration of skeletal and cardiac muscle and vacuolizaiton of hepatocytes. The condition was reproduced experimentally by feeding a ration containing 10 or 20% *C. occidentalis* seed.

D. Horses

The toxic nature of *C. occidentalis* was first reported in 1925 by French workers following incidents of intoxication of horses fed oats mixed with the seeds of this plant (Brocq-Rousseau and Bruere, 1925; Moussu, 1925). On the fifth day following consumption of the contaminated oats, the horses developed muscular trembling, enteritis, anuria, paralysis, and death. The only other incident involving spontaneous poisoning of horses by *Cassia* sp. known to the author is a large outbreak of myopathy in cattle and horses in Brazil following consumption of sorghum containing 10% *C. occidentalis* seed (De Barros, 1988, personal communication).

   Martin et al. (1981) investigated the toxicity of a single oral dose of ground *C. occidentalis* seeds in three Shetland ponies. Seeds given at the rate of 0.10% of body weight produced no sign of illness, and changes in serum biochemistry were limited to a small, transient rise in CK activity. Seeds given at the rate of 0.20% of body weight to a second pony produced no effect until day 5, on which the animal showed depression, anorexia, and posterior ataxia prior to death. Serum biochemical changes included a two- to threefold elevation of CK, lactic dehydrogenase (LDH), and alkaline phosphatase activity and a 6.6-fold elevation of AST. Lesions observed at necropsy included icterus, "nutmeg liver," and congestion of the renal cortex. No gross lesion of muscle was seen, and no myoglobin was detected in urine. Microscopic lesions in tissues of this pony included segmental necrosis of occasional skeletal muscle fibers, focal necrosis of the renal tubular epithelium, and centrilobular hepatic necrosis; no microscopic lesion was evident in myocardium. A third pony given seeds at 0.33% of body weight displayed depression and anorexia 40 h after treatment and died 10 h later. No characteristic lesions were seen in tissues of this animal at necropsy.

E. Other Species

1. Goats and Sheep

Feeding trials in Texas (Dollahite et al., 1964; Dollahite and Henson, 1965) and Sudan (Suliman et al., 1982; Suliman and Shommein, 1986) have demonstrated the toxicity of the leaves, beans, and seeds of C. occidentalis to goats. The Texas trial involved only one goat, and the few details known include the plant part fed (beans), dosage (1.0% of body weight daily for 5 days, then 2.0% of body weight for 2 days), survival time (7 days), and the absence of pale muscle lesions at necropsy. In the African trials, daily feeding of seeds of C. occidentalis to goats at 0.5% of body weight was fatal in 9 to 10 days; seeds fed at one-half this rate or leaves fed at the same rate were fatal in 17 to 20 days. Clinical signs of toxicosis were similar to those observed in experimentally poisoned cattle and consisted of dullness, diarrhea, inappetence, loss of weight, shivering, muscle tremors, staggering gait, dyspenea, and recumbency. Gross and microscopic observations on tissues of these animals revealed pulmonary edema, marked hydrothroax, myocardial hemorrhage and focal degeneration, hepatic congestion and lipidosis, focal necrosis of hepatocytes, and renal congestion and degeneration. Neither macroscopic nor microscopic evidence of skeletal muscle damage was found. Similar results were reported in goats fed C. senna (El Sayed et al., 1983) and goats and sheep fed C. italica (Galal et al., 1985).

Sheep were fatally poisoned by the experimental administration of the various parts of green or dried C. occidentalis at dosages ranging from 1.4% of body weight for 3 days to 0.3% of body weight for 29 days. Clinical signs were similar to those reported for calves; however, like goats, no myoglobinuria of poallor of skeletal muscle was observed (Dollahite et al., 1964; Dollahite and Henson, 1965).

2. Rabbits

Early feeding trials demonstrated that intoxication of rabbits by C. occidentalis foliage or seeds requires substantially higher dosage than for calves, and muscle pallor is not a prominent feature of the disease (Dollahite et al., 1964; Dollahite and Henson, 1965).

Rabbits poisoned by daily oral administration of the endosperm of C. occidentalis seed displayed depression, lethargy, and anorexia as early signs of toxicosis. As death approached, some rabbits displayed marked lethargy, tachypnea, tachycardia, low venous pressure, and prostration. Other fatally affected rabbits were found dead without previous indication of terminal illness. Myocardial pallor or yellowing and dilatation of atria and ventricles were seen at necropsy. Enlarged livers contained uniformly distributed pale spots associated with the hepatic venous system. Pulmonary congestion and edema were infrequent, and gross pallor of skeletal muscles was not seen. Microscopic changes were indicative of a primary degenerative cardiomyopathy characterized by mitochondrial degeneration, lipid accumulation, myofibrillar degeneration, myocytolysis, and relatively minor reparative changes. Microscopic changes in liver were moderate to severe centrilobular venous congestion accompanied by a corresponding level of hepatocellular degeneration or necrosis. Generalized skeletal myopathy was found in only 1 and degeneration of isolated skeletal muscle fibers was present in only 4 of 34 poisoned rabbits. Despite the near absence of skeletal myopathy, cardiac lesions in *C. occidentalis* poisoned rabbits were consistent with those of poisoned cattle, and the rabbit appears to be a suitable model for study of the bovine disease (O'Hara and Pierce, 1974a).

III. *CASSIA OBTUSIFOLIA* L.

Cassia obtusifolia (sicklepod, West Indian senna) is a malodorous weed originating from tropical America. The annual herb (July to September in the southeastern United States) reaches heights to 1.5 m and has two to three pairs of round-tipped leaflets. Flowers are one to three in number on a short axillary peduncle with pedicels to 2 cm (3.6 cm in fruit). The yellow 0.8- to 1.5-cm petals wilt by midday. The pods are linear, up to 20 cm in length, gently curved downward, and contain numerous shiny, dark-brown seeds approximately 0.5 cm in length. This plant has been confused with a very similar Old World species, *Cassia tora* L., which has shorter pedicels that do not exceed 1.0 cm in flowers or 1.5 cm in fruit. *C. obtusifolia* is found on sandy soils from eastern Texas, east and north to Florida, Pennsylvania, Indiana, Missouri, and Kansas, south through the American tropics, and in the Old World (Wills and Irwin, 1961; Correll and Johnston, 1970). Along the coastal plain of the southeastern United States, *C. obtusifolia* (often with *C. occidentalis*) is prevalent in pastures and becomes well established in fields of corn, sorghum, millet, or soybeans. Crops from these fields may be contaminated with the seeds of these weeds, creating a potential for their inclusion in feeds for livestock and poultry. Samples of corn taken from the bottom of freight cars have been found to contain as much as 40% *C. obtusifolia* seed (Page et al., 1977; Nicholson et al., 1985).

A. Cattle

Poisoning of cattle by *C. obtusifolia* occurs from southeastern Texas to Florida during July-October and is associated with ingestion of substantial quantities of *C. obtusifolia* foliage. Clinical and pathologic aspects of the toxicosis appear to be identical to those induced in cattle by *C. occidentalis*. In three separate dairy herds, 3 to 15 cows developed fatal toxicosis following daily feeding of an estimated 12 to 25 lb of immature or mature *C. obtusifolia* foliage (in greenchop corn or greenchop sorghum hybrid forage) per cow for 4 to 12 days. In two herds, milk production dropped by 33% within 2 days after feeding of the contaminated greenchop began and remained at that level for 7 to 14 days after replacing the contaminated greenchop with wholesome feed (Nicholson et al., 1977; McCormack adn Neisler, 1980; Nicholson et al., 1985).

Cattle usually avoid this plant when grazing; however, spontaneous, fatal poisoning due to grazing of this plant has been reported. Voluntary consumption of fatal quantities is usually seen in yearling animals having access to large quantities of the plant, especially if other, more desirable forage is lacking. Mild signs of poisoning were reported in cattle fed *C. obtusifolia*-contaminated corn silage; however, the relative toxicity of fresh foliage versus that subjected to ensiling is unknown (Nicholson et al., 1985).

In contrast to *C. occidentalis*, the seeds of *C. obtusifolia* are considered to be of low toxicity (Mercer et al., 1967; Schmitz and Denton, 1977). This view is supported by the results of a study in which calves consumed seeds of *C. obtusifolia* at dosages (up to 0.57% of body weight daily for 15 days) that could be expected to produce toxicosis and death if seeds of *C. occidentalis* had been used. This resulted only in intermittent feed refusal, decreased feed consumption, intermittent diarrhea, and decreased weight gain. No change in serum activity of CK, AST, or LDH was observed, indicating the absence of damage to striated muscle, liver, or other tissues that release these enzymes upon injury. Histological examination revealed no evidence of muscle damage. The calves of this study typically picked over the ration in an attempt to avoid consuming the seeds. It was concluded that the clinical effects observed were probably due to unpalatability rather than to direct toxicity of the seeds (Putnam et al., 1988).

B. Poultry

Interest in the effects of *C. obtusifolia* seed consumption by chickens arose in the mid-1970s following field observations suggesting that rations contaminated by seeds were responsible for severe reductions in egg production. Since that time, several investigators have examined the toxicity of *C. obtusifolia* seed to chickens by feeding rations containing 1.5 to 30% ground seed for periods of 2 to 8 weeks (Charles, 1976; Page et al., 1977; Hebert and Flory, 1983; Flunker et al., 1988). These experiments demonstrated that inclusion of ground seed in the ration at a minimum level of 2 to 6% may result in a significant reduction of feed intake that is due, at least in part, to reduced palatability rather than toxicity of the seed-containing ration. Depressed feed intake was followed by a dose-related reduction in growth and feed efficiency in broiler chicks and depressed egg production and egg quality in layers. No appreciable effect on mortality was observed. Of these studies, only one (Page et al., 1977) reported evidence of myopathy (pallor of leg and breast muscle); however, histological details of the lesion were not presented or discussed.

In an attempt to induce myopathy in chicks by feeding ground *C. obtusifolia* seed (3 to 30% of the ration for 16 to 23 days) or oral administration of an aqueous extract of the seed, Hebert and Flory (1983) were uanble to produce gross or microscopic evidence of skeletal or cardiac myopathy in treated birds despite their ability to do so in chicks with similarly prepared extracts of *C. occidentalis* seed (Hebert et al., 1983).

C. Rabbits

Early workers reported an absence of muscle lesions in fatally poisoned rabbits fed only green leaves and stems or green beans of *C. occidentalis* (Dollahite et al., 1964; Dollahite and Henson, 1965). O'Hara and Pierce (1974a) demonstrated that intoxication of rabbits by the seed of *C. occidentalis* differed from the disease in cattle in that, in rabbits, there is more severe car-

diomyopathy and negligible skeletal myopathy. In contrast, the feeding of
leaves and stems of C. obtusifolia to rabbits as their sole source of food for
16 to 23 days produced a syndrome that resembled that of C. occidentalis or
C. obtusifolia-poisoned cattle. Dark-colored urine, involuntary recumbency,
very pale muscles in the hindlimbs, pale streaking of the heart muscle, and
markedly high elevations of serum CK activity were seen. Segmental degeneration of up to 50% of muscle fibers with sarcolemmal membranes and nuclei remaining visible was observed in leg muscles (Nicholson et al., 1985).

IV. *CASSIA ROEMERIANA* SCHEELE

Cassia roemeriana (twin-leaf senna, two-leaved senna) is a common, drought-
hardy, herbaceous perennial of hillsides, open woods, and flats on limestone
soils of central Texas west and south to New Mexico, Coahuila, and Nuevo
Leon. The plant arises form a woody root to attain a height of 30 to 50 cm.
The orange-yellow flowers (1.9 to 2.5 cm in diameter) appear in April and
May, frequently again in September, and sometimes intermittently throughout
the summer. Each leaf has a pair of leaflets 3 to 6 cm long and 7 to 12 mm
wide. *Cassia roemeriana* and *C. lindheimeriana* are the commonest cassias of
central and western Texas. The latter has been reported to be poisonous
to sheep based on a single experimental trial, but this plant has caused little,
if any, poisoning of livestock (Boughton and Hardy, 1939; Correll and Johnston, 1970).
    Beginning in 1974, an illness of cattle was observed during March through
June at various locations from central Texas to eastern New Mexico that was
identical (except for geographic location and season) to spontaneous *C. occidentalis* or *C. obtusifolia* poisoning. Exposure to *C. roemeriana* was a common
finding in these cases leading to a suspicion that this plant was the cause
of the condition (J. C. Reagor, personal communication). Field observations
of sick and dying sheep that had eaten this plant had previously suggested
that it was toxic (Dollahite, 1978). The plant is not usually attractive to livestock but may be consumed in drought conditions when more desirable forage
is absent.
    Experimentally induced poisoning of calves and goats with the dried leaves,
stems, and beans of *C. roemeriana* resulted in (1) hepatopathic poisoning
characterized by a short survival time (4 to 8 days), moderate to severe hepatic congestion, hepatocellular damage, and little or no evidence of injury
to skeletal muscle, or (2) myopathic poisoning characterized by a longer period
of survival, mild to severe lesions of skeletal myopathy, and mild hepatocellular injury. Morphologic evidence of cardiac injury was lacking in animals affected with either syndrome. The minimum dosage resulting in hepatopathic
poisoning was 1.0% of body weight daily for 3 days for calves and 5 days for
goats. The minimum dosage producing myopathic poisoning was 1.0% of body
weight daily for 6 days for calves and 0.5% daily for 10 to 16 days for goats.
Development of the hepatopathic form of the disease appeared to be related
to both individual susceptibility and a high rate of *C. roemeriana* administration. The myopathic form of the disease in calves appeared to be identical
to experimentally induced bovine *C. occidentalis* poisoning and was therefore
compatible with the spontaneous condition observed in cattle exposed to *C.*

roemeriana in the field. Myopathic poisoning in goats of this study differed from that observed in calves in that the syndrome developed more slowly and neither myoglobinuria or diarrhea were seen (Rowe et al., 1987).

V. TOXIC CONSTITUENTS

Several investigators have reported the identification of toxic materials from *C. occidentalis* (Moussu, 1925; Puleo, 1966; Kim, 1970; Kim et al., 1972; Hebert et al., 1983); however, the identity of the component(s) responsible for myodegeneration of striated muscle remain(s) unknown. Like many members of the genus, *C. occidentalis* contains anthraquinone compounds that have strong cathartic action (Selvaraj and Chander, 1978). These compounds are considered to be responsible for the diarrhea observed in animals following ingestion of *Cassia* sp. foliage or seed (Rowe et al., 1987). The roots and seeds of *C. occidentalis* have been reported to contain 1.9% free and 4.5% total anthraquinones, including physcion, chrysophanol, rhein, and aloe-emodin. Similar compounds isolated from *C. obtusifolia* are gluco-obtusifolin and gluco-aurantio-obtusin (Selvaraj and Chander, 1978). Graziano et al. (1983) noted similarities in solubility and biochemical effects on mitochondrial function between rhein and the unidentified myotoxic component(s) in extracts of *C. occidentalis* seed, but experimental evidence of involvement of rhein or related compounds in the myotoxicity of *Cassia* sp. has not been demonstrated.

Using the chicken to detect myotoxic activity, Hebert et al. (1983) found that organic solvents ranging in polarity from methanol to benzene were ineffective in removing the toxic from *C. occidentalis* seed. The toxin was removed successfully by aqueous 25 mM sodium bicarbonate; however, myotoxic activity remained associated with particulate matter in the extract. The addition of surfactant (Triton X-100) moved the toxin from the particulate to the aqueous phase. Further isolation and characterization of the toxin have not been reported.

VI. PATHOGENESIS

Myocardial failure has been shown to be the cause of death in calves and rabbits poisoned by *C. occidentalis* (Read et al., 1968; O'Hara et al., 1969; O'Hara and Pierce, 1974a,b). Pathologic findings reported for poisoning of animals by other species of *Cassia* are, in most cases, consistent with this view. Light-microscopic and ultrastructural studies indicated that mitochondrial degeneration (leading to swelling, loss of matrix, disruption of the inner membrane, and collapse of the organelle) was an early lesion in myocardium of poisoned calves and rabbits, suggesting that mitochondria are the primary target of the myotoxic component(s) of *C. occidentalis* (Read et al., 1968; O'Hara and Pierce, 1974a). Biochemical studies with mitochondria isolated from the myocardium of poisoned rabbits indicated that the basic biochemical defect was uncoupling of oxidative phosphorylation, leading to depression of energy production by the organelle. Without energy derived from oxidative phosphorylation, ionic gradients are not maintained, resulting in mitochondrial swelling and the other mitrochondrial changes observed. Declining mitochondrial respiratory function would progressively deprive the myocardium of energy [adenosine triphosphate (ATP)] and induce a state functionally similar to ischemia, leading to the myofibrillar degeneration seen microscopically and cardiac failure seen clinically. Hepatic lesions observed in experimentally poisoned animals were considered to be secondary to passive venous congestion of the liver resulting from inadequate cardiac function (Read et al., 1968; O'Hara and Pierce, 1974a,b). The potential presence of a direct hepatotoxic action in *Cassia* sp. poisoning has been mentioned by several authors (O'Hara and Pierce, 1974a, Rowe et al., 1987), more because the possibility could not be excluded than in response to a need to explain the origin of the hepatic lesions. Even the purely hepatopathic syndrome described in goats by Rowe et al. (1987) is compatible with acute failure of cardiac function (Cohen and Kaplan, 1978).

The pathologic changes in skeletal muscle of poisoned animals have not been studied as extensively as those in cardiac muscle; however, ultrastructural changes in semitendinosus muscle of poisoned chicks appear to be similar to those for myocardium (Simpson et al., 1971; Hebert et al., 1983). The variable presence or anatomical location of myopathy between different species of animals poisoned by the same species of *Cassia* or between animals of the same species poisoned by different species of *Cassia* is not presently understood. It appears that *Cassia* myotoxin(s) can produce damage to cardiac and skeletal muscle at different rates under various circumstances. Daily dosage of plant material, individual susceptibility, species of animal, level of physical exercise, and variation in plant composition are factors that may modify this response (O'Hara and Pierce, 1974a; Rowe et al., 1987).

REFERENCES

Ajilvsgi, G. (1979). *Wild Flowers of the Big Thicket: East Texas and Western Louisiana.* Texas A & M University Press, College Station.

Assi, L. W. (1983). Some medicinal properties of *Cassia occidentalis* L. (Caesalpiniaceae) in the lower Ivory Coast. *Bothalia 14*:617-620.

Bailey, E. M. (1985). Myopathies associated with *Cassia* spp. In *Plant Toxicology*, A. A. Seawright, M. P. Hegarty, L. F. Janes, and R. F. Keeler (Eds.). Queensland Poisonous Plants Committee, Yeerongpilly, Australia, pp. 395-400.

Boughton, I. B., and Hardy, W. T. (1939). Feeding trials of suspected plants. *Tex. Agric. Exp. Stn. Annu. Rep.*, College Station.

Brocq-Rousseau, B. P., and Bruere, P. (1925). Accidents mortels sur des cheveaux due a la graine de *Cassia occidentalis* L. *C. R. Soc. Biol. 92*: 555-557. [Cited by Kim (1970), O'Hara and Pierce (1974a), and Martin et al. (1981).].

Burlage, H. M. (1968). *Index of Plants of Texas with Reputed Medicinal and Poisonous Properties.* H. M. Burlage, Austin, Tex., pp. 99-100.

Butolo, J. E., Torres, W. L. N., Nakano, M., Saliba, A. Am., Grecchi, R., Bottino, J. A., and Ysey, T. (1972). Intoxication in layers (*Gallus domesticus*) caused by *Cassia occidentalis* L. *Proc. 2nd World Cong. Anim. Feeding*, Madrid, pp. 647-653.

Charles, O. W. (1976). Coffee weed toxicity in animals. *Proc. G. Nutr. Conf. Feed Ind.*, pp. 67-76.

Claus, E. P. (1961). *Pharmacognosy*. Lea & Febiger, Philadelphia.

Cohen, J. A., and Kaplan, M. M. (1978). Left-sided heart failure presenting as hepatitis. *Gastroenterology* 74:583-587.

Colvin, B. M., Harrison, L. R., Sangster, L. T., and Gosser, H. S. (1986). *Cassia occidentalis* toxicosis in growing pigs. *J. Am. Vet. Med. Assoc.* 189:423-426.

Correll, D. S., and Johnston, M. E. (1979). *Manual of the Vascular Plants of Texas*. Texas Research Foundation, Renner.

Dollahite, J. W. (1978). Research and observations on toxic plants in Texas 1932-1972. *Tex. Agric. Exp. Stn. Tech. Rep.* No. 78-1.

Dollahite, J. W., and Henson, J. B. (1965). Toxic plants as the etiologic agent of myopathies in animals. *Am. J. Vet. Res.* 26:749-752.

Dollahite, J. W., Henson, J. B., and Householder, G. T. (1964). Coffee senna (*Cassia occidentalis*) poisoning in animals. *Tex. Agric. Exp. Stn. Prog. Rep.* No. 2318.

El Sayed, N. Y., Abdelbari, E. M., Mahmoud, O. M., and Adam, S. E. I. (1983). The toxicity of *Cassia senna* to Nubian goats. *Vet. Q.* 5:80-85.

Flunker, L. K., Damron, B. L., Wilson, H. R., and Sundlof, S. F. (1988). *Cassia obtusifolia* seed in the diets of White Leghorn hens. *Poult. Sci.* 67(Suppl. 1):15 (abstract).

Galal, M., Adam, S. E. I., Maglad, M. A., and Wasfi, I. A. (1985). The effects of *Cassia italica* on goats and sheep. *Acta Vet. (Belgr.)* 35:163-174.

Graziano, M. J., Flory, W., Seger, C. L., and Hebert, C. D. (1983). Effects of a *Cassia occidentalis* extract in the domestic chicken (*Gallus domesticus*). *Am. J. Vet. Res.* 44:1238-1244.

Hebert, C. D., and Flory, W. (1983). Determination of the oral toxicity of *Cassia obtusifolia* seeds in chickens. *Vet. Hum. Toxicol.* 25:164-166.

Hebert, C. D., Flory, W., Seger, C., and Blanchard, R. E. (1983). Preliminary isolation of a myodegenerative toxic principle from *Cassia occidentalis*. *Am. J. Vet. Res.* 44:1370-1374.

Henson, J. B., and Dollahite, J. W. (1966). Toxic myodegeneration in calves produced by experimental *Cassia occidentalis* intoxication. *Am. J. Vet. Res.* 27:947-949.

Henson, J. B., Dollahite, J. W., Bridges, C. H., and Rao, R. R. (1965). Myodegeneration in cattle grazing *Cassia* species. *J. Am. Vet. Med. Assoc.* 147:142-145.

Hulbert, L. C., and Oehme, F. W. (1968). *Plants Poisonous to Livestock*. Kansas State Unviersity, Manhattan.

Kang, L. C. (1981). The ringworm shrub. *Nature Malaysiana* 6:24-25.

Kim, H. L. (1970). A study of the toxic constituents of the seeds of *Cassia occidentalis* L. and the fruits of *Karwinskia humboldtiana* Zucc. Dissertation, Texas A & M University, College Station.

Kim, H. L., Camp, B. J., Grigsby, R. D. (1972). Isolation of *N*-methylmorpholine from the seeds of *Cassia occidentalis* L. (coffee senna). *Agric. Food Chem.* 19:198-199.

Martin, B. W., Terry, M. K., Bridges, C. H., and Bailey, E. M. (1981). Toxicity of *Cassia occidentalis* in the horse. *Vet. Hum. Toxicol.* 23:416-417.

Martins, E., Martins, V. M., Riet-Correa, F., Soncini, R. A., and Paraboni, S. B. (1986). *Cassia occidentalis* (Leguminosae) poisoning in swine. *Pesqui. Vet. Bras.* *6*: 35-38.

McCormack, J. E., and Neisler, W. E. (1980). *Cassia obtusifolia* (sicklepod) toxicity in a dairy herd. *Vet. Med. Sm. Anim. Clin.* *75*: 1849-1851.

Mercer, H. D., Neal, F. C., Himes, J. A., and Edds, G. T. (1967). *Cassia occidentalis* toxicosis in cattle. *J. Am. Vet. Med. Assoc.* *151*: 735-741.

Moussu, R. (1925). L'intoxication par les grains de *Cassia occidentalis* L. est due a une tox-albumine. *C. R. Soc. Biol.* *92*: 862-863. [Cited by Kim (1970), O'Hara and Pierce (1974a), and Martin et al. (1981).]

Neal, F. C., and Plummer, C. B. (1967). *Cassia occidentalis* poisoning in cattle. *Fla. Agric. Exp. Stn. Annu. Rep.* 207.

Nicholson, S. S., Thornton, J. T., and Rimes, A. J. (1977). Toxic myopathy in dairy cattle caused by *Cassia obtusifolia* in greenchop. *Bovine Pract.* *12*: 120.

Nicholson, S. S., Flory, W., and Ruhr, L. P. (1985). Sicklepod poisoning in cattle: A new development. *La. Agric.* *29*: 18-19.

O'Hara, P. J., and Pierce, K. R. (1974a). A toxic cardiomyopathy caused by *Cassia occidentalis*: I. Morphological studies in poisoned rabbits. *Vet. Pathol.* *11*: 97-109.

O'Hara, P. J., and Pierce, K. R. (1974b). A toxic cardiomyopathy caused by *Cassia occidentalis*: II. Biochemical studies in poisoned rabbits. *Vet. Pathol.* *11*: 110-124.

O'Hara, P. J., Pierce, K. R., and Read, W. K. (1969). Degenerative myopathy associated with ingestion of *Cassia occidentalis* L.: Clinical and pathological features of the experimentally induced disease. *Am. J. Vet. Res.* *30*: 2173-2180.

Page, R. K., Vazey, S., Charles, O. W., and Hollifield, T. (1977). Effects on feed consumption and egg production of coffee bean seed (*Cassia obtusifolia*) fed to White Leghorn hens. *Avian Dis.* *21*: 90-96.

Pierce, K. R., and O'Hara, P. J. (1967). Toxic myopathy in Texas cattle. *Southwest. Vet.* *20*: 179-184.

Puleo, L. E. (1966). Isolation of an alkaloid from *Cassia occidentalis*. Thesis, Texas A & M University, College Station.

Putnam, M. R., Boosinger, T., Spano, J., Wright, J., Wiggins, A., and D'Andrea, G. (1988). Evaluation of *Cassia obtusifolia* (sicklepod) seed consumption in Holstein calves. *Vet. Hum. Toxicol.* *30*: 316-318.

Read, W. K., Pierce, K. R., and O'Hara, P. J. (1968). Ultrastructural lesions of an acute toxic cardiomyopathy of cattle. *Lab. Invest.* *18*: 227-231.

Reagor, J. C., and Ray, A. C. (1975). The identification of plant poisoning in animals. *Proc. Annu. Meet. Am. Assoc. Vet. Lab. Diagn.* *18*: 433-444.

Rogers, R. J., Gibson, J, and Reichman, K. G. (1979). The toxicity of *Cassia occidentalis* for cattle. *Aust. Vet. J.* *55*: 408-412.

Rowe, L. D., Corrier, D. E., Reagor, J. C., and Jones, L. P. (1987). Experimentally induced *Cassia roemeriana* poisoning in cattle and goats. *Am. J. Vet. Res.* *48*: 992-997.

Schmitz, D. G., and Denton, J. H. (1977). Senna bean toxicity in cattle. *Southwest. Vet.* *30*: 165-170.

Selvaraj, Y., and Chander, M. S. (1978). Senna—its chemistry, and pharmaceutical value. *J. Indian Inst. Sci.* *60*:179-196.

Simpson, C. F., Damron, B. L., and Harms, R. H. (1971). Toxic myopathy of chicks fed *Cassia occidentalis* seeds. *Avian Dis.* *15*:284-290.

Suliman, H. B., and Shommein, A. M. (1986). Toxic effects of the roasted and unroasted beans of *Cassia occidentalis* in goats. *Vet. Hum. Toxicol.* *28*:6-11.

Suliman, H. B., Wasfi, A. I., and Adam, S. E. I. (1982). The toxicity of *Cassia occidentalis* to goats. *Vet. Hum. Toxicol.* *24*:326-329.

Suliman, H. B., Shommein, A. M., and Shaddad, S. A. (1987). The pathological and biochemical effects of feeding fermented leaves of *Cassia obtusifolia* "Kawal" to broiler chicks. *Avian Pathol.* *16*:43-49.

Torres, W. L. N., Nakano, M., Nobre, D., and Momose, N. (1971). Poisoning of poultry caused by *Cassia occidentalis* L. *Biologico* *37*:204-208.

Watt, J. M., and Breyer-Brandwijk, M. G. (1962). *The Medicinal and Poisonous Plants of Southern and Eastern Africa*, 2nd ed. E & S Livingstone, Edinburgh.

Wills, M. M., and Irwin, H. S. (1961). *Roadside Flowers of Texas*. University of Texas Press, Austin.

17

Position of Perilla Ketone Metabolism by Lung Cytochromes P450: Evidence for the Mechanism of Bioactivation Through Design of an In Vivo Inhibitor of Toxicity

John E. Garst

Primate Research Institute, New Mexico State University, Holloman Air Force Base, New Mexico

William C. Wilson

Arthropod-Borne Animal Diseases Research Laboratory, Agricultural Research Service, USDA, Laramie, Wyoming

I. INTRODUCTION

Serious pulmonary damage can arise in many animal species from a variety of naturally occurring five-membered heterocycles. But the greatest acute risk seems associated with those bearing 3-substituents (Garst and Wilson, 1981; Garst et al., 1985; Kerr and Linnabary, 1989; Wilson et al., 1990). For example, in susceptible species, acute and often lethal pulmonary edema quickly arises from ingestion of foodstuffs containing the furans 4-ipomeanol [1-(3-furyl)-4-hydroxypentan-1-one] and perilla ketone ([1]) [1-(3-furyl)-4-methylpentan-1-one]. 4-Ipomeanol is one of several constituents in moldy sweet potatoes (Wilson et al., 1978). Perilla ketone ([1]) and related unsaturated derivatives are constituents of the mint plant *Perilla frutescens* (Garst and Wilson, 1984). Similar toxicity results when animals consume large quantities of the 3-substituted indole, tryptophan, although this amino acid must first be transformed to 3-methylindole (3MI) (Nocerini et al., 1984, 1985a,b).

Bioactivation of either the furan or the indole by pulmonary cytochromes P450 is required for the toxicity of these substances. The inhibitor, piperonyl butoxide, decreases covalent binding by both 3-substituted furan and indole (Boyd, 1975; Bray and Carlson, 1979). Furthermore, species susceptibility to [1] depends in large part on the gross lung cytochrome P450 content (Garst et al., 1985). In both cases formation of a reactive metabolite seems rate limiting to toxicity (Garst et al., 1985; Nocerini et al., 1984, 1985a,b). For 3-substituted furans the evidence suggests a butenedialdehyde reactive metabolite (Ravindranath et al., 1984), while a methylene imine is the suspect reactive metabolite from 3MI (Huijzer et al., 1987).

The mechanism(s) for the critical enzymatic bioactivation is (are) still not well understood, but structure-activity relationships (SAR) have been useful in understanding them. Unpublished studies by Garst have discovered that 1-(3-furyl)-4-methylpentane, in which a methylene group replaces the carbonyl group of [1], and 1-(phenyl)-4-methylpentan-1-one, the phenyl congener of [1], are nearly 100 times less toxic than [1]. Similar results were obtained by Boyd for the phenyl congener of 4-ipomeanol (Boyd, 1975). These findings clearly indicate that both the furan and the adjacent carbonyl groups are required for maximum toxicity. They are also interesting because α, β-unsaturated ketones, in general, and 3-furyl ketones, in particular, are quite susceptible to nucleophiles such as amines (van der Plas, 1973), hydroxyl ion (Takagi and Ueda, 1971), and even Grignard reagents (Lutz and Reveley, 1941). Moreover, preliminary SAR found a 0.99 correlation between furan lethality and a ^{13}C-nuclear magnetic resonance (NMR) shift at position 5, with electron-withdrawing 3-substituents considerably enhancing toxicity (Garst and Wilson, 1981). Although limited to lethality data without enzyme measurements per se, evidence for nucleophilic attack on the furan was indicated by a positive slope of the ^{13}C-derived "biological" Hammett plot. While a nucleophilic mechanism strongly discounts attack at furan position 4, limitations of the Hammett approach could not differentiate between involvement of position 2 or 5 (Garst and Wilson, 1981). Thus a separate investigation was undertaken to ascertain the effect of such substituents on this cytochromes P450 reactive metabolite-mediated toxicity.

II. POSITION OF METABOLISM

Some time ago preliminary studies suggested low toxicity for 2,5-dimethyl perilla ketone. In newer work this compound has been reexamined, although insufficient compound was obtained for exhaustive determinations (Wilson et al., submitted). The 48-h LD_{50} value of 2238 µmol/kg (see Table 1) was computed via probit extrapolation from three higher dosages. However, a dosage of [2] as high as 2775 µmol/kg [intraperitoneally (IP)] was without microscopic evidence of lung toxicity or lethality in the male Notre Dame strain Swiss

TABLE 1　LD$_{50}$ Values for Four 3-Substituted Furans

Compound[a]	Observed	
	LD$_{50}$[b]	Ratio[c]
[1]	30 ± 1.8[d]	1
[2]	2238 ± 1242	74.6
[3]	193 ± 15	6.3
[4]	8806 ± 3455	293.4

[a]Number corresponds to compounds: [1], 1-(3-furyl)-4-methylpentan-1-one; [2], 1-(2,5-dimethyl-3-furyl)-4-methylpentan-1-one; [3], 1-(2-methyl-3-furyl)-4-methylpentan-1-one; [4], 1-(5-methyl-3-furyl)-4-methylpentan-1-one.
[b]The 48-h LD$_{50}$ (μmol/kg) of Notre Dame Swiss mice after a single IP dose.
[c]Ratio calculated by dividing the observed 48-h LD$_{50}$ (μmol/kg) of the congener by that for [1].
[d]Literature value (Garst et al., 1985).

mouse. At the even higher dosages actually causing death, alveolar hemorrhage and kidney tubule degenerative changes were observed in mice treated with [2]. From these limited data, obtained under the same conditions as with [1], it is clear that [2] is considerably less toxic than [1]. The low toxicity of [2] when compared to [1] supports the view that enzymatic attack occurs on the furan ring at either ring position 2 or 5. To ascertain independently which of these positions is attacked by the enzyme, 1-(2-methyl-3-furyl)-4-methylpentan-1-one ([3]) and 1-(5-methyl-3-furyl)-4-methylpentan-1-one ([4]) were synthesized and their acute toxicities were compared in the mouse (Wilson et al., submitted).

The toxicities of the monomethyl 3-furyl ketones [3] and [4] are very different from each other and from [2] (Table 1). Pulmonary edema results

1	R$_1$ = —H	R$_2$ = —H
2	R$_1$ = —CH$_3$	R$_2$ = —CH$_3$
3	R$_1$ = —H	R$_2$ = —CH$_3$
4	R$_1$ = —CH$_3$	R$_2$ = —H

from IP administration of the 2-methyl-3-furyl ketone ([3]), although the acute 48-h LD_{50} is only sixfold greater (less toxic) than that for the parent compound [1]. Microscopic examination of five mice treated with [3] also revealed thickening of the alveolar and bronchiolar epithelial walls. Mice dying after administration of the 5-methyl-3-furyl ketone [4], however, showed few signs of the extensive pulmonary edema typical of [1], but interstitial thickening and focal hyperplasia of bronchiolar epithelial cells were noted upon microscopic evaluation. Virtually nontoxic, [4] had an 48-h LD_{50} nearly 300 times greater than the 48-h LD_{50} of the parent compound (Table 1) (Wilson et al., submitted). It is interesting but of uncertain meaning that some separation of microscopic change and edema type (alveolar versus interstitial) was apparent between each monomethyl furyl ketone and perilla ketone. More extensive pathology studies would be useful, for these differences could be important in understanding the underlying toxicology.

Assuming that methyl substitution directly or indirectly affects cytochromes P450 metabolism occurring closest to the substituted position, these data strongly suggest that bioactivation involves cytochromes P450 attack at carbon 5 of the furan ring. The results obtained further confirm the suggestions of the "biological" Hammett plot and the before-mentioned chemical susceptibility of 3-furyl ketones. Only a nucleophilic attack at that position could explain the reported correlation between the position 5 ^{13}C-NMR and the acute toxicities of a variety of 3-substituted furans (Garst and Wilson, 1981). Since a free nucleophile could chemically attack either furan ring position 2 or 5, accessibility to the enzyme catalytic site may favor attack at the sterically more accessible position 5.

In the earlier studies, lethality was the endpoint. But, the toxicity of the naturally occurring air pollutant 3-methylfuran (3MF; [5]; R = CH_3), for example, has been shown to arise from the bioproduction of reactive methylbutene-dialdehyde ([6]) (R = CH_3) (Ravindranath et al., 1984). Thus a lower lethality might signify diminished product reactivity or diminished rate of formation of the postulated reactive intermediate and not necessarily an innate inability of the compound to undergo metabolism per se. Both possibilities are examined.

5   6

Diminished product reactivity is unlikely. In the cases at hand, methyl substitution on the furan ring would afford a methylketone rather than an aldehyde product from [6]. But the dramatically reduced toxicity associated with [4] is unlikely to arise from this change from an aldehyde to ketone product for several reasons. Methylbutenedialdehyde ([6]; R = CH_3) reacts exceedingly rapidly with tissue macromolecules (Burka, National Institute of Environmental Health Sciences, personal communication). Ravindranath and Boyd (1985) found that acetylacrolein, the methyl ketone congener of [6] but with R = H, "is extremely reactive and binds rapidly with tissue macromolecules." So little effect on reactivity is apparent between a dialdehyde and a monoaldehyde, monomethyl ketone-substituted olefin. An acyl rather than methyl substitutent in the reactive metabolite could increase the product reactivity, but given its already high reactivity, this increased reactivity may not be apparent. Although the change from aldehyde to methyl ketone (as would occur with either products from [3] or [4]) could diminish product reactivity, such a change is also unlikely to be apparent. Findings with [3], which presumably would form a methyl ketone, aldehyde reactive metabolite, indicate that [3] is over 10 times as toxic as 3-methylfuran and only slightly less potent than perilla ketone [1]. Consequently, decreased olefin product reactivity seems quite unlikely to explain why [4] is so much less toxic than [3].

It is possible, however, that a diminished rate of formation of these olefin intermediates could occur because of methyl substitution. The methyl group could alter ring oxidation and lead to hydroperoxide or methyl oxidation products. In that regard, hydroperoxides formed by chemical treatment of 2-methylfuran or 2,5-dimethylfuran with H_2O_2 seem to be comparatively stable (Milas et al., 1954; Seebach, 1963). A similar hydroperoxide [8] was reported as a metabolite of methfuroxam [7], a fungicide (Mitchell and Paulson, 1982). If these hydroperoxides or hydroxylated methyl groups, for

7 → 8

example, are formed with [3] or [4], the methyl substituents could block toxicity yet not necessarily prevent enzymatic attack. *But regardless of what metabolite is formed from the methylated furans, the dramatic alteration of toxicity by the methyl substituent, such as is apparent here between [3] and [4], necessarily confirms the side of enzymatic attack on the 3-substituted furan.* When no methyl group is present (as in [1]), these data implicate attack at furan carbon atom 5 of perilla ketone ([1]).

III. EFFECTS OF METHYL-SUBSTITUTED PERILLA KETONE ANALOGS ON IN VIVO PERILLA KETONE TOXICITY

To further understand the considerable range of toxicity for [2], [3], and [4] in mice compared to [1], the effects of pretreatment with these compounds on the toxicity of [1] were examined (Wilson et al., submitted). Control challenge doses of [1] at 30 (LD_{50}) and 60 µmol/kg ($2LD_{50}$) resulted in 60% and 100% mortality, respectively (Fig. 1). Administration (IP) of [2] at the low pretreatment dosage (0.55 mmol/kg) 1 h before treatment with a LD_{50} dose of [1] seemed to reduce toxicity, but that reduction was not statistically valid. At the higher pretreatment dosage of [2] (1.1 mmol/kg), an LD_{50} challenge with [1] afforded clearly diminished toxicity, but at a dosage twice the LD_{50}, no reduction was evident. An abrupt enhancement of toxicity was seen with [1] given at the highest pretreatment dosage of [2] (Fig. 1). Doubling the

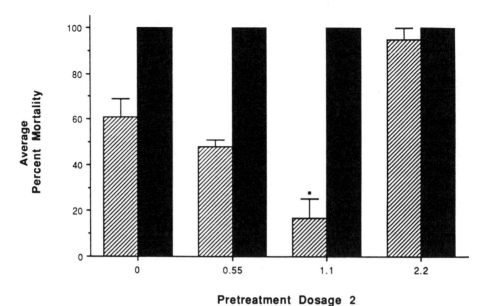

Pretreatment Dosage 2

FIGURE 1 Effect of pretreatment (IP) with 1-(2,5-dimethyl-3-furyl)-4-methyl-pentan-1-one ([2]) 1 h before challenge dosages (IP) with 1-(3-furyl)-4-methylpentan-1-one [(1)]; striped boxes indicate a 30-μmol/kg (LD$_{50}$) challenge dosage, solid boxes indicate a 60-μmol/kg (2LD$_{50}$) challenge dosage, and dots above bars indicate a significant difference from the control group (P = 0.05).

dosage of [2] revealed no protection against any dosage of [1] administered. For control purposes, IP administration of [2] alone caused no lethality at doses as high as 1.6 mmol/kg. Also, pulmonary edema was not evident in the mice that died at the highest pretreatment dosage of [2]. Thus it seems that [2] may incompletely protect against the pulmonary bioactivation of [1] up to the 1.1-mmol/kg dosage, but that a higher dosage reverses this protection (see Wilson et al. submitted).

The protection evident with [2] was greatly clarified by similar studies with the monomethylated-3-furyl ketones. Under the same pretreatment conditions as those used for [2], a significant decrease in the toxicity of [1] was evident in mice pretreated with the 5-methyl-3-furyl ketone [4] (Fig. 2). Protection by [4] seems to increase with pretreatment dosage at either challenge dosage but appears to reach a plateau affording 80 to 90% protection. Furthermore, that protection was eliminated when [4] was administered IP 1 h after instead of before IP administration of [1] (Fig. 3). These results are not surprising; the maximum covalent binding of [1] occurs within 1 to 2 h (Dutcher and Boyd, 1982). Protection by [4] persists for up to 2 days, although it does decrease during this time (Fig. 3). In contrast to [4], however, the 2-methyl derivative [3] did not protect against the toxicity of [1] (Fig. 4). Also, as anticipated, pretreatment with [1] had an additive effect on the toxicity of the challenge dosage of [1] (Fig. 5). In retrospect, the

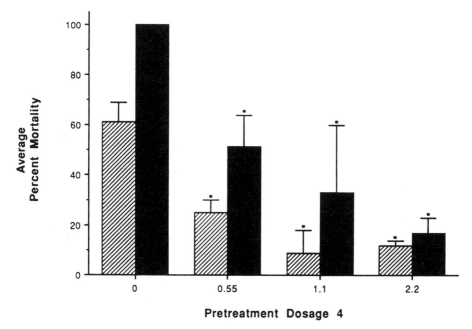

FIGURE 2 Effect of pretreatment (IP) with 1-(5-methyl-3-furyl)-4-methyl-pentan-1-one ([4]) 1 h before challenge dosages (IP) with 1-(3-furyl)-4-methylpentan-1-one ([1]); striped boxes indicate a 30-μmol/kg (LD_{50}) challenge dosage, solid boxes indicate 60-μmol/kg ($2LD_{50}$) challenge dosage, and dots above bars indicate a significant difference from control group ($P = 0.05$).

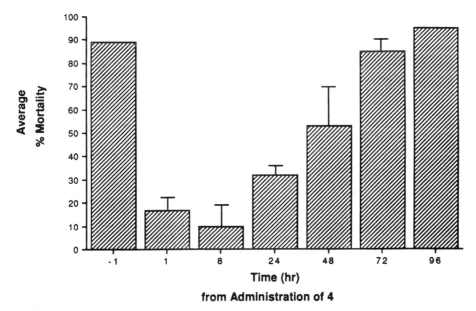

FIGURE 3 Effect of time on 1-(5-methyl-3-furyl)-4-methylpentan-1-one ([4]; 2.22 mmol/kg) protection against the toxicity (IP) with 1-(3-furyl)-4-methyl-pentan-1-one ([1]; 60 μmol/kg, $2LD_{50}$).

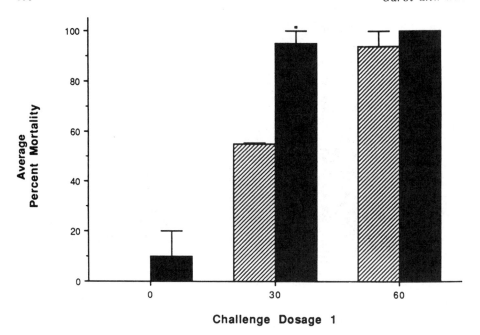

FIGURE 4 Effect of pretreatment (IP) with 1-(2-methyl-3-furyl)-4-methyl-
pentan-1-one ([3]) 1 h before challenge dosages (IP) with 1-(3-furyl)-4-
methylpentan-1-one ([1]); striped boxes indicate DMSO + [2] control pretreatment, solid boxes indicate [3] pretreatment dosage, and dots above bars indicate significant differences from the control group ($P = 0.05$).

dose-dependent protection, followed at the highest pretreatment dosage by
enhancement of the toxicity of [1] suggests that results with [2] reflect an
average of the independent effects of [3] and [4].

IV. MECHANISTIC ASPECTS AND RELEVANCE

Given their considerable similarity in structure and their parallel animal toxicology, it at first seems reasonable that the 3-substituted furans and indoles
have the same mechanism of bioactivation. Indeed, there are many mechanistic similarities between them. Burka and Boyd (1985) have considered hypothetical mechanisms for furan bioactivation. They first discuss epoxide
hydratase inhibitor studies that discount furan epoxide formation. They then
relate unpublished observations that thiols, such as dithiothreitol and cyste-
amine, decrease covalent binding 80 to 90% and that the radical trapping phenols, such as propyl gallate or 2,6-di-*t*-butyl-4-carboxyphenol, have a similar effect. Although they mention the evidence supporting ferrous superoxide nucleophilic attack (Garst and Wilson, 1981), they overlook it in favor
of a radical bioactivation mechanism, although no products suggesting free-
radical mechanisms have ever been isolated.

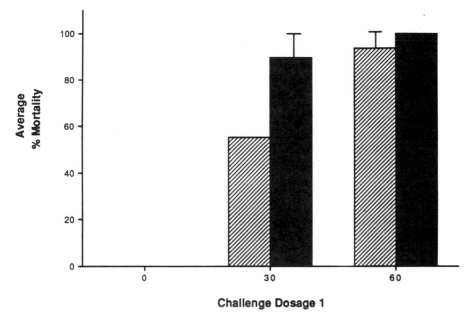

FIGURE 5 Effect of pretreatment (IP) with 1-(3-furyl)-4-methylpentan-1-one [1]; 18 μmol/kg) 1 h before challenge dosage (IP) with the same compound striped boxes indicate DMSO + [2] control pretreatment, solid boxes indicate [1] pretreatment dosage,.

3MI is converted by metabolism into an electrophilic methylene imine (Nocerini et al., 1985a). As with the furans, this metabolism product is not directly suggestive of an epoxide intermediate. Neither is it suggestive of a free-radical bioactivation, but Nocerini et al. (1985a) have proposed such a mechanism, on the strength of a spin-trapped metabolite found by Kubow et al. (1984). In the bioactivation proposal of Nocerini et al. (1985a), a first electron abstraction forms a radical cation on nitrogen, then a hydrogen atom abstraction affords a reactive methylene imine product; this product is believed responsible for tissue alkylation. Formation of the reactive methylene imine product is clearly the rate-limiting step to toxicity, as evidenced by a large deuterium isotope effect with 3-(trideuteromethyl)indole (Huijzer et al., 1987).

Various precedents support the proposed stepwise, radical cation oxidation mechanism for 3MI offered by Nocerini et al. (1985a). Among these are the alkyl cleavage and dihydropyridine aromatization of a 4-alkyl-1,4-dihydropyridine after formation first of a nitrogen radical cation (Ortiz de Montellano, 1986). Ring opening of cyclopropylamines via a nitrogen radical cation is further evidence for the possibility of discrete electron transfer steps in cytochrome P450 reactions with nitrogenous substrates (Ortiz de Montellano, 1986).

But the analogies for amines undergoing oxidation to radical cations is not extendable to the oxygen counterparts. Ortiz de Montellano (1986) finds carbon hydroxylation, as evidenced by a large deuterium isotope effect during

O-dealkylation of 7-ethyoxycoumarin, instead of oxygen atom oxidation. Nitrogen oxidation, as evidenced by a low isotope effect, often occurs instead of
carbon oxidation when nitrogen is present. Unlike oxygen systems the "N-
and S-dealkylations are initiated by oxidation of the heteroatom to the corresponding radical cation." Elsewhere he indicates that this arises because
of the uniquely lower reactivity caused by the greater "electronegativity of
oxygen." Consequently, the metabolism of these furans could differ considerably from their corresponding indole congeners, despite numerous analogies
between their toxicology.

    In organic chemistry, position of attack, product, and evidence as to
mechanism are sufficient to allow proposal of a mechanism for reaction. In
the case of these 3-substituted furans, the available evidence now enables a
specific nonradical (e.g., concerted) mechanism to be proposed for metabolism of the 3-substituted furans. In view of the general evidence implicating
attack on carbon rather than on oxygen (Ortiz de Montellano, 1986), the pathway in Scheme 1 for 3-substituted furans is also consistent with least-hindered
cytochrome P450-mediated nucleophilic attack at furan carbon 5 evidently by
a ferrous superoxide (ferric peroxide di-) anion. While the actual product
of perilla ketone (PK) metabolism is unknown [and is unlikely to be as neatly
established as was that for the carbonyl-less 3MF by Ravindranath et al.
(1984)], this mechanism affords a substituted butenedialdehyde product and,
in concerted fashion, restores the ferric form of cytochrome P450.

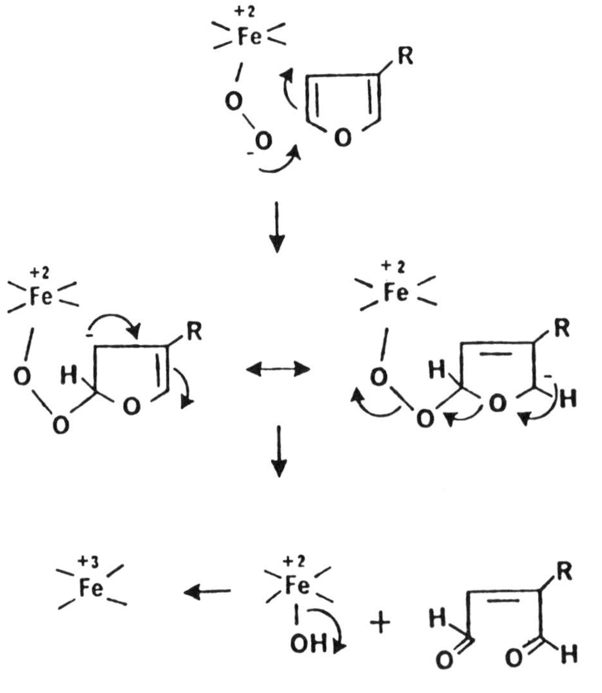

SCHEME 1 Proposed pathway for the in vivo pulmonary cytochrome P450 metabolism of the often-lung-toxic 3-substituted furans.

Other evidence in strong support of the nucleophilic process for 3-substituted furans is the high velocity of covalent binding (.e.g, metabolism). Covalent binding by 4-ipomeanol (Boyd, 1975) and perilla ketone (Dutcher and Boyd, 1982) are complete in 1 to 2 h. This rate compares similarly to the rate of carbon tetrachloride metabolism, which clearly involves formation of the trichloromethyl radical (Recknagel et al., 1977). Such exceedingly fast rates from a notoriously sluggish enzyme system would be consistent with utilization of a first-formed ferrous superoxide intermediate. Such an intermediate could arise at least transiently from addition of the second electron to the ferrous ion-oxygen adduct. This is known to exist in the cytochrome P450 cycle (Ortiz de Montellano, 1986). Free-radical reactions of such a intermediate would be obvious; the nucleophilicity of this purported superoxide species has also been discussed (Garst and Wilson, 1981). Consequently, its abstraction of a chlorine atom from carbon tetrachloride could initiate a trichloromethyl radical-based toxicology while forming hypochlorite and reforming the ferric form of the enzyme. Alternatively, its nucleophilic attack on 3-substituted furans would give the "Hammett plot" and be consistent with the known susceptibility of these compounds to nucleophiles (Garst and Wilson, 1981). However, any breakdown of a ferrous superoxide species to a perferryl ion or stepwise electron transfer would be a far slower process; the rates of covalent binding would necessarily reflect this. 3MI metabolism is clearly slower in view of the deuterium isotope effect, but 3MI is difficult to compare to the furans. The toxicity of the 2-isomer of perilla ketone is much less than that of perilla ketone (unpublished data). Moreover, structure-toxicity studies show little difference in lethality, as the electronegativity of the 2-furyl substituent is increased in contrast to the 3-substituted counterparts (Garst, unpublished data). Interestingly, 2-furyl ketones are not as susceptible to nucleophilic reactions as are the 3-furyl ketones. No comparable data are yet available concerning rates of covalent binding by 2-furyl isoamyl ketone, but if its rate is markedly lower, it would clearly suggest the possibility of a different mechanism. Perhaps the ferrous superoxide intermediate must decompose to the perferryl ion before the electrophile can react with the 2-substituted furan. Perferryl ion-mediated attack on a 2-substituted furan has been suggested by Kobayashi et al. (1987), although they simply assumed its intermediacy. The nucleophilic bioactivation by cytochrome(s) P450 hypothesized here for 3-substituted furans will be more fully discussed in several future papers. In those papers the preliminary correlations between substituted furan toxicity and log P or ^{13}C-NMR data (Garst and Wilson, 1981) will be presented more thoroughly and extended.

The proposal for a concerted mechanism of 3-substituted furan oxidation contrasts distinctly with that proposed by Nocerini et al. (1985a) for 3MI. This raises questions concerning their mechanism. Those questions center around two issues. First, many chemicals can undergo free-radical reactions; finding protection by trapping agents or even a spin-trapped metabolite may or may not be relevant to the main biological process. This problem is especially true for lung, which is rich in oxygen, but it can arise in any tissue. Lung, for example, has an active glutathione peroxidase (GP) enzyme system, which catalyzes the oxidation of glutathione to its disulfide while reducing lipid hydroperoxides to an alcohol and water (Scheme 2) (Wendel, 1985). The disulfide is reduced back to GSH by other enzymes; consequently, GSH is not

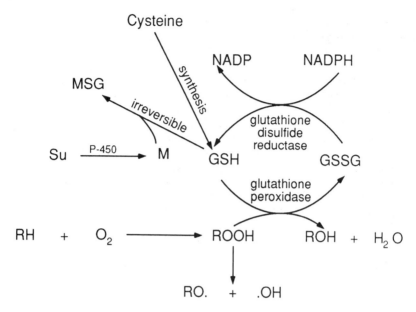

SCHEME 2 Irreversible addition of glutathione (GSH) to reactive metabolite
(M) depletes GSH stores forming MSG, eliminates GSH substrate for glutathione
peroxidase, and results in an abundance of lipid hydroperoxides, homolysis
of which forms free radicals and can lead to numerous free-radical reactions.

irreversibly lost. But clearly, free radicals should abound when lung is challenged with a reactive metabolite that irreversibly depletes glutathione (GSH),
as do both 3MI (Nocerini et al., 1985b) and 4-ipomeanol (Burka and Boyd,
1985), through the respective reactive metabolite. This loss of GSH would
deprive GP of substrate, which in turn will prevent enzymatic reduction of
lipid peroxides and will invariably lead to the accumulation of destructive free
radicals formed by homolytic reactions (Scheme 2). As a result, it is under-
standable that radicals are formed, can be trapped, and even that exogenous
thiols and radical-trapping agents can protect against covalent binding or
toxicity. Consequently, while radical formation may be involved in the toxicity of either 3-substituted heterocycle, it is arguably unrelated to the mechanism of their bioactivation. That this is a real concern has been demonstrated
in less-oxygenated liver by studies with N-hydroxy-2-acetylaminofluorene.
This substance is not oxidized to the nitroxide radical by liver microsomes
in a NADPH-dependent reaction, but is oxidized to that radical by lipid peroxide (Ortiz de Montellano, 1986). It so happens that 3MI has been established as an effective antioxidant (Adams et al., 1987). Adams et al. indicate
that this ability may arise by lipid peroxidation-mediated formation of a nitro-
gen-centered radical of sufficient stability to stop lipid peroxidation reactions.
Consequently, the suggested 3MI-derived radicals may have no real involvement in the cytochrome P450-mediated process.
    The second factor casting doubt on the Nocerini et al. mechanism is re-
vealed in Scheme 3. This scheme indicates that the same nucleophilic process,
this time occurring at the unsubstituted 2-position of 3MI, could, in concerted

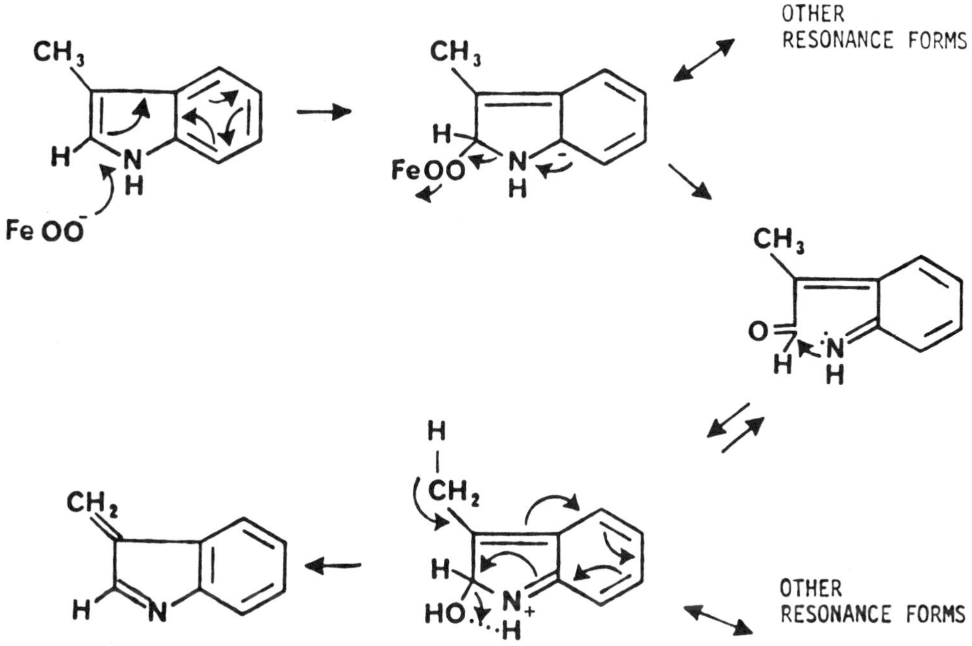

SCHEME 3 Possible pathway for the in vivo pulmonary cytochrome P450 trans-formation of lung toxic 3-methylindole to its methylene imine metabolite.

fashion, afford an unconjugated benzenoid product and simultaneously restore the ferric form of the cytochromes P450 enzyme. Examination of Scheme 3 also reveals that a slow proton abstraction from the 3-methyl group of 3MI (after the nucleophilic addition) would enable benzene ring rearomatization to produce the observed methylene imine product. Such would be consistent with the deuterium isotope effect. The energy lost and the resultant stability reduction, if benzene rearomatization cannot occur (as is the case with indole), could explain why indole toxicity differs; it produces a massive hemolysis and with little evident lung damage (Hammond and Carlson, 1980), in contrast to furan and 3-methylfuran (Garst and Wilson, 1981).

These questions and the possibility that the same concerted, mechanistic process could account for products of two related but different substrates (Schemes 1 and 3) should be evidence of caution regarding acceptance of any mechanism for metabolism of 3MI without more evidence. Indeed, the same caution should be invoked for the furan mechanisms, for the data may suggest different mechanisms, even between 2- and 3-furyl ketones.

V. APPLICATIONS AND RAMIFICATIONS

This work may have application to pyrroles in addition to 3-substituted furans and indoles. Aromatic five-membered pyrrole metabolites of the pyrrolizidine alkaloids are suspected of mediating the considerable toxicological damage associated with these widespread plant constituents. Although some of this damage involves direct nucleophilic alkylation, other evidence suggests that aldehyde ring-opened pyrrole metabolites may be of greater toxicological significance than previously believed (Segall et al., 1985). Even though the exact metabolism mechanisms may differ with substrate, since pyrroles may be aromatized by cytochromes P450, the possibility that [4] may obviate 3MI, 3-substituted furan, and also pyrrolizidine alkaloid-induced damage must be explored. That [4] actually protects via inhibiting the bioactivating cytochrome P450-metabolizing enzyme requires further investigation, but the possibility of that and of isozyme selective inhibition makes such investigations more important, for they could provide a valuable tool and perhaps even a useful therapeutic agent.

Besides discovery of a possible protective agent, this work has other ramifications. This work also affects current considerations concerning LD_{50} values. Such values mathematically reflect hundreds of complex processes that can lead to death in animals. They have been criticized by several quarters (Kaufman and Cohen, 1987) and a law was proposed that threatened to ban LD_{50} determinations in Cambridge, Massachusetts (Shulman, 1989) before being defeated (Holden, 1989). This is quite unfortunate and a disservice to science. These values can be exceedingly useful; this is especially so when deuterium isotope effects or structure-activity comparisons are being evaluated. But the problem with most such numbers is that we often do not know how to interpret them properly. Wilson et al. (1990) have examined various aralkyl and alkyl 3-substituted furyl ketones and compared their LD_{50} values to the simple 3-furyl alkyl ketones examined by Garst and Wilson (1981). They found some predictability of lethality for these ketones using the results already discovered for the simple ketones. But by no means were the results of Wilson et al (1990) predictable to the extent necessary either to obviate the use of animals or to rationalize computer modeling studies even with an animal-derived data base. So efforts to calculate the LD_{50} are clearly premature, although studies like that herein can improve our understanding of these numbers. "History clearly demonstrates that as a science develops, it moves progressively from descriptive to quantitative phases . . . . Discouragement of use and abandonment of the LD_{50} to satisfy animal concerns, political decrees, or even popularism will ensure that toxicology abandons its most desirable potential achievement—namely the future ability to afford quantitative predictability of acute lethality . . ." first, and with that, other adverse effects (Garst, 1987).

ACKNOWLEDGMENTS

A portion of the work described in this review was performed when both authors were in the Department of Animal Sciences at the University of Illinois in Urbana. This work was supported in part by the U.S. government (NIEHS 02193) and the University of Illinois (Project 20-323 of the Agricultural Experiment Station). The authors also wish to thank Professor Joseph Simon (Department of Veterinary Pathobiology, College of Veterinary Medicine, University of Illinois) for his assistance and pathology support and knowledge support for WCW from the National Research Award (5 T 32 ES 07001). The authors also thank Pam Durfee for help in preparing the manuscript.

REFERENCES

Adams, J. D., Jr., Heins, M. C., and Yost, G. S. (1987). 3-Methylindole inhibits lipid peroxidation. *Biochem. Biophys. Res. Commun.* 149:73-78.

Boyd, M. R. (1975). Isolation, characterization and studies of the mechanism of action of lung-toxic furans produced in mold-damaged sweet potatoes (*Ipomea batatas*). Ph.D. thesis, Vanderbilt University, Nashville, Tenn., p. 157.

Bray, T. M., and Carlson, J. R. (1979). Role of mixed-function oxidase in 3-methylindole-induced acute pulmonary edema in goats. *Am. J. Vet. Res.* 40:1268-1272.

Burka, L. T., and Boyd, M. R. (1985). Furans. In *Bioactivation of Foreign Compounds*, M. W. Anders (Ed.). Academic Press, New York, pp. 243-257.

Dutcher, J. S., and Boyd, M. R. (1982). Studies of the in vivo metabolic activation and covalent binding of the lung toxic furan derivative perilla ketone. In *Microsomes: Drug Oxidations, Drug Toxicity*, R. Sato and R. Kato (Eds.). Japan Scientific Societies Press, Tokyo, pp. 557-558.

Garst, J. E. (1987). A letter on "The clinical relevance of the LD_{50}." *Vet. Hum. Toxicol.* 29:160.

Garst, J. E., and Wilson, B. J. (1981). Preliminary evidence supporting iron peroxide intermediates and nucleophilic addition in the lung cytochrome P-450-catalyzed bioactivation and toxicity of 3-substituted furans. In *Oxygen and Oxy Radicals in Chemistry and Biology*, M. A. J. Rodgers and E. L. Powers (Eds.). Academic Press, New York, pp. 507-520.

Garst, J. E., and Wilson, B. J. (1984). Synthesis and analysis of various 3-furyl ketones from *Perilla frutescens*. *J. Agric. Food Chem.* 32:1083-1087.

Garst, J. E., Wilson, W. C., Kristensen, N. C., Harrison, P. C., Corbin, J. E., Simon, J., Philpot, R. M., and Szabo, J. R. (1985). Species susceptibility to the pulmonary toxicity of 3-furyl isoamyl ketone (perilla ketone): in vivo support for involvement of the lung monooxygenase system. *J. Anim. Sci.* 60:248-257.

Hammond, A. C., and Carlson, J. R. (1980). Indole toxicity in cattle. *Vet. Rec.* 107:344-346.

Holden, C. (1989). Cambridge to oversee animal research. *Science* 244:1253.

Huijzer, J. C., Adams, J. D., Jr., and Yost, G. S. (1987). Decreased pneumotoxicity of deuterated 3-methylindole: bioactivation requires methyl C-H bond breakage. *Toxicol. Appl. Pharmacol.* 90:60-68.

Kaufman, S. R., and Cohen, M. J. (1987). The clinical relevance of the LD_{50}. *Vet. Hum. Toxicol.* 29:39-41.

Kerr, L. A., and Linnabary, R. D. (1989). A review of interstitial pneumonia in cattle. *Vet. Hum. Toxicol.* 31:247-254.

Kobayashi, T., Sugihara, J., and Harigaya, S. (1987). Mechanism of metabolic cleavage of a furan ring. *Drug Metab. Dispos.* 15:877-881.

Kubow, S., Janzen, E. G., and Bray, T. M. (1984). Spin-trapping of free radicals formed during in vitro and in vivo metabolism of 3-methylindole. *J. Biol. Chem.* 259:4447-4456.

Lutz, R. E., and Reveley, W. G. (1941). 1,4-Addition of methylmagnesium iodide to a α,β-unsaturated ketone system involving the double bond of an β-aroylfuran nucleus and ring cleavage of the resulting vinyl allyl ether system. *J. Am. Chem. Soc.* 63:3178-3180.

Milas, N. A., Peeler, R. L., Jr., and Mageli, O. L. (1954). Organic peroxides: XIX. α-Hydroperoxy-ethers and related peroxides. *J. Am. Chem. Soc. 76*: 2322-2325.

Mitchell, A. D., and Paulson, G. D. (1982). Metabolism of methfuroxam (2,4,5-trimethyl-N-phenyl-3-furancarboxamide) in the rat and isolated rat hepatocytes. *Pestic. Biochem. Physiol. 18*: 57-68.

Nocerini, M. R., Carlson, J. R., and Yost, G. S. (1984). Electrophilic metabolites of 3-methylindole as toxic intermediates in pulmonary edema. *Xenobiotica 14*: 561-564.

Nocerini, M. R., Yost, G. S., Carlson, J. R., Liberato, D. J., and Breeze, R. G. (1985a). Structure of the glutathione adduct of activated 3-methylindole indicates that an imine methide is the electrophile intermediate. *Drug Metab. Dispos. 13*: 690-694.

Nocerini, M. R., Carlson, J. R., and Yost, G. S. (1985b). Glutathione adduct formation with microsomally activated metabolites of the pulmonary alkylating and cytotoxic agent 3-methylindole. *Toxicol. Appl. Pharmacol. 81*: 75-84.

Ortiz de Montellano, P. R. (1986). Oxygen activation and transfer. In *Cytochrome P-450 Structure, Mechanism, and Biochemistry*, P. R. Ortiz de Montellano (Ed.). Plenum Press, New York, pp. 217-271.

Ravindranath, V., and Boyd, M. R. (1985). Metabolic activation of 2-methylfuran by rat microsomal systems. *Toxicol. Appl. Pharmacol. 78*: 370-376.

Ravindranath, V., Burka, L. T., and Boyd, M. R. (1984). Reactive metabolites from the bioactivation of toxic methylfurans. *Science 224*: 884-886.

Recknagel, R. O., Glende, E. A., Jr., and Hruszkewycz, A. M. (1977). Chemical mechanisms in carbon tetrachloride toxicity. In *Free Radicals in Biology*, Vol. 3, W. A. Pryor (Ed.). Academic Press, New York, pp. 97-132.

Seebach, D. (1963). Die Reaktion von 2,5-dimethyl Furan mit Wasserstoffperoxyd. *Chem. Ber. 96*: 2712-2722.

Segall, H. J., Wilson, D. W., Dallas, J. L., and Haddon, W. F. (1985). Trans-4-hydroxy-2-hexenal: a reactive metabolite from the macrocyclic pyrrolizidine alkaloid senecionine. *Science 229*: 472.

Shulman, S. (1989). Municipal law on its way. *Nature 338*: 534.

Takagi, K., and Ueda, T. (1971). Etude de la réactivite d'oxo-4 tetrahydro-4,5,6,7 benzofurannes: I. Accès aux puru [2,3-c]-acrididnes par condensation de l'isatine et de l'acide anthranilique. *Chem. Pharmac. Bull. 19*: 1218-1222.

van der Plas, H. C. (1973). *Ring Transformations of Heterocycles*, Vol. 1. Academic Press, New York, p. 190.

Wendel, A. (1985). Glutathione peroxidase. In *Enzymatic Basis of Detoxication*, W. A. Jakoby (Ed.). Academic Press, New York, pp. 333-353.

Wilson, B. J., Garst, J. E., Linnabary, R. D., and Doster, A. R. (1978). Pulmonary toxicity of naturally occurring 3-substituted furans. In *Effects of Poisonous Plants on Livestock*, R. E. Keeler, K. R. Van Kampen, and L. F. James (Eds.). Academic Press, New York, pp. 311-323.

Wilson, W. C., Simon, J., and Garst, J. E. Design of an in vivo inhibitor of perilla ketone toxicity: implied position of perilla ketone metabolism by lung cytochromes P-450. *J. Anim. Sci.* (submitted).

Wilson, W. C., Simon, J., and Garst, J. E. (1990). The effects of selected bulky substituents on the pulmonary toxicity of 3-furyl ketones in mice. *J. Anim. Sci. 68*: 1072-1076.

II
NATURE AND TOXICITY OF FUNGAL TOXINS

18

Phomopsins: Antimicrotubule Mycotoxins

John A. Edgar

Commonwealth Scientific and Industrial Research Organisation, Parkville, Victoria, Australia

I. INTRODUCTION

A disease of animals, now called lupinosis, was first investigated more than 100 years ago in central Europe following outbreaks among sheep. The disease posed a serious threat to a thriving sheep-farming industry in eastern Germany and a determined effort was made to establish its etiology (Hackbarth, 1961; Marasa, 1974). Lupins had been introduced into German agriculture in 1841 and had rapidly become a popular and useful feed for sheep as well as being used as a green manure plant for increasing soil fertility in poor-quality, sandy soils. They were being widely used to feed sheep in the areas affected by lupinosis, and an association of the disease with this legume was established by feeding lupins or extracts of toxic lupins to experimental animals and reproducing the signs observed in the field.

Lupinosis, a hepatotoxicity, was recognized by the early investigators as being distinct from lupin poisoning caused by the quinolizidine alkaloids of *Lupinus* spp. (Liebscher, 1880), and an extractable, toxic product ("icterogen"), believed to be produced by fungi found growing on the lupins, was considered to be the likely cause of the disease, although this was not established unequivocally (Zurn, 1879; Kuhn, 1880). The mycotoxin hypothesis was accepted and supported by some later investigators (Brash, 1943); however, despite evidence that lupin alkaloids do not produce the liver damage characteristic of lupinosis, the view that they were the cause of lupinosis persisted in the scientific literature until quite recently. The mistaken belief that lupinosis ceased in Europe following the introduction of low-alkaloid lupin varieties in the 1930s was part of the evidence cited to support an alkaloid etiology for the disease (Hackbarth, 1961).

Following severe outbreaks of lupinosis in Western Australia beginning around 1950, and its appearance a short time later in South Africa, a new period of research into the cause of the disease was initiated. Gardiner (1966) was able to induce toxicity in nontoxic lupin roughage by spraying it with a mixed, aqueous suspension of fungi isolated from toxic lupins, thus firmly establishing lupinosis as a mycotoxicosis. The fungal species responsible for the disease was identified by Van Warmelo et al. (1970) as *Phomopsis leptostromiformis* (Kuhn) Bubak ex Lind, a species given the name *Cryptosporium leptostromiforme* by Kuhn and recognized by him as being frequently associated with toxic lupins (Kuhn, 1880). The same species (under the synonym *Phomopsis rossiana* Sacc.) was also being investigated independently by Gardiner (Gardiner, 1966; Gardiner and Petterson, 1972) as a likely source of the lupinosis toxin (Marasas, 1974). The clinical and histological indicators of lupinosis have been reviewed extensively by Gardiner (1967a) and Marasas (1974) and more recently by Mortimer and Ronaldson (1983) and Peterson (1986). They will not be dealt with in any detail here.

Functional failure of the liver is the main cause of death from lupinosis, and the commonly observed clinical signs of the disease result from liver damage. Inappetence is the most sensitive clinical indicator of the disease, and this is accompanied by listlessness and jaundice. The main lesions are in the liver, which in acute poisoning, is enlarged, bright yellow, and fatty but becomes small, nodular, and cirrhotic after prolonged exposure to the lupinosis toxins (Gardiner, 1967a; Peterson, 1986). Mitotic arrest and karyomegaly are the most visually striking indicators of the extensive structural damage suffered by the liver of animals exposed to the toxins (Peterson, 1986).

Sheep, cattle, horses, pigs, goats, rabbits, dogs, mice, ducklings, guinea pigs, donkeys, chickens, and rats have all been found to be susceptible to lupinosis (Gardiner, 1967a; Marasas, 1974; Mortimer and Ronaldson, 1983; Allen, 1986). The field disease has, however, occurred mainly in sheep, the species currently most exposed to *Phomopsis*-infected lupins. Natural outbreaks have also been reported in horses (Gardiner and Seddon, 1966), cattle (Gardiner, 1967b), goats, donkeys (Allen, 1986), and pigs (Marczewski, 1955). All mammalian species are likely to be affected to some extent by the toxins, which have been shown to be potent antimicrotubule agents (see below). Given the conserved nature of microtubule structure, the toxins may eventually be found to affect a wide spectrum of species even beyond the animal kingdom.

II. ISOLATION OF TOXINS

The early German investigators were able to obtain extracts of toxic lupins which, on administration to experimental animals, produced lupinosis. They found the toxin to be extracted by aqueous alkali and, after further purification, to have the properties of a proteinaceous substance. Their success in determining the nature of the disease (now confirmed as a mycotoxicosis) and the chemical nature of the agents that cause it (modified hexapeptides—see below) is, in retrospect, a tribute to their scientific skills.

Contemporary efforts aimed at isolation of the lupinosis toxins began with the work of Petterson and Parr (1970), who used aqueous methanol to extract the toxin from field samples of toxic lupins. They demonstrated, using a bioassay based on the antimitotic effect of the toxin on mouse cells in vivo (Gardiner, 1967c), that the toxin could be extracted into butanol from aqueous solution at pH 3.5 and was reextractable from butanol by water at pH 8. These partitioning properties, color reactions, and other tests led them to conclude that the toxin had phenolic and/or other acidic groups.

A crystalline mixture of two toxins (phomopsin A and phomopsin B) was subsequently isolated from cultures of *P. leptostromiformis* grown on lupin seeds (Culvenor et al., 1977). The isolation of the toxins was aided by the use of a modified version of the mouse liver cell bioassay developed by Gardiner and Petterson (1972) and by a nursling rat assay developed by Peterson (1978). Ovine kidney, bovine kidney, and mouse mastocytoma cell assays were also employed in developing the isolation methods (Culvenor et al., 1977).

The toxins produced by fungal cultures were extracted into methanol, and a crude mixture containing the toxins was isolated from this initial extract using the pH-dependent butanol-solubility properties of the toxins. The crude toxin mixture was further purified by extraction of the toxins from an aqueous potassium chloride solution with tetrahydrofuran (THF). The THF-soluble toxins were then dissolved in water and adsorbed onto macroreticular polystyrene resin (XAD-2). Washing the resin with water and 1:1 aqueous methanol removed impurities, and the purified toxin mixture was then desorbed with methanol. The 4:1 mixture of phomopsins A and B obtained in this way subsequently crystallized from aqueous THF-ethanol-methanol solution on storage at 4°C.

The solubility properties of the toxins in butanol and THF, their relative insolubility in most other common organic solvents, and their adsorption from aqueous solution by XAD and desorption by methanol remain the main fractionation procedures used to purify the toxins from *Phomopsis* cultures and field samples of infected lupins. Other purification techniques that have been employed include high-voltage paper electrophoresis (HVPE), preparative thin-layer chromatography (TLC), countercurrent distribution, and column chromatography on Sephadex LH-20 and diethylaminoethyl (DEAE)-cellulose (Culvenor et al., 1977, 1989; Hancock et al., 1986). These and preparative high-performance liquid chromatography (HPLC), which has proved to be an effective means of isolating the individual toxins, are discussed below.

III. CHEMICAL STRUCTURE AND PROPERTIES

Details of final stages in the structural elucidation and absolute configuration of phomopsin A [1], the main mycotoxin isolated from cultures of *P. leptostromiformis*, are reported by Culvenor et al. (1989). Phomopsin B [2] lacks the chlorine atom but appears to be otherwise identical to phomopsin A (Edgar

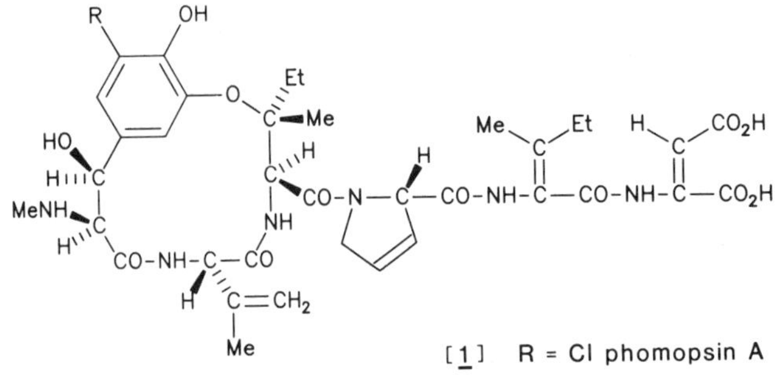

[1] R = Cl phomopsin A

[2] R = H phomopsin B

et al., 1986). They are linear hexapeptides containing 3,4-didehydro-L-proline, *E*-2,3-didehydroisoleucine, *E*-2,3-didehydroaspartic acid, 3,4-didehydro-L-valine, *N*-methyl-3-(3-chloro-4,5-dihydroxyphenyl)serine [*N*-methyl-3-(4,5-dihydroxyphenyl)serine in the case of phomopsin B], and 3-hydroxy-L-isoleucine. The phomopsins incorporate a 13-membered ring formed by an ether bridge linking the 5-hydroxy group of the phenylserine unit with the 3-hydroxyisoleucine unit. In this regard, they resemble the cyclopeptide alkaloids found in the plant family Rhamnaceae and some other families. The cyclopeptide alkaloids are, however, tetra- or pentapeptides and the peptide chain is connected through the amino group of the 3-(hydroxyphenyl-serine unit rather than the carboxyl as in the phomopsins.

Initial attempts to determine the structure of phomopsin A [1] by x-ray crystallography met with little success and the structure was largely established by chemical degradation, nuclear magnetic resonance (NMR), fast-atom-bombardment mass spectrometry (FABMS), and gas chromatography/mass spectrometry (GC/MS) studies (Culvenor et al., 1983; Edgar et al., 1985, 1986; Edgar, 1985; Edgar and Culvenor, 1985). This work led to the postulation of a macrocyclic hexapeptide structure [3] which lacked the ether bridge and in which the didehydroaspartic acid α-carboxyl was linked via an amide bond to the *N*-methylamino group of the phenylserine unit (Culvenor et al., 1983). This was later revised, based on FABMS data, to a linear structure [4] in which the phenylserine-didehydroaspartic acid link was eliminated

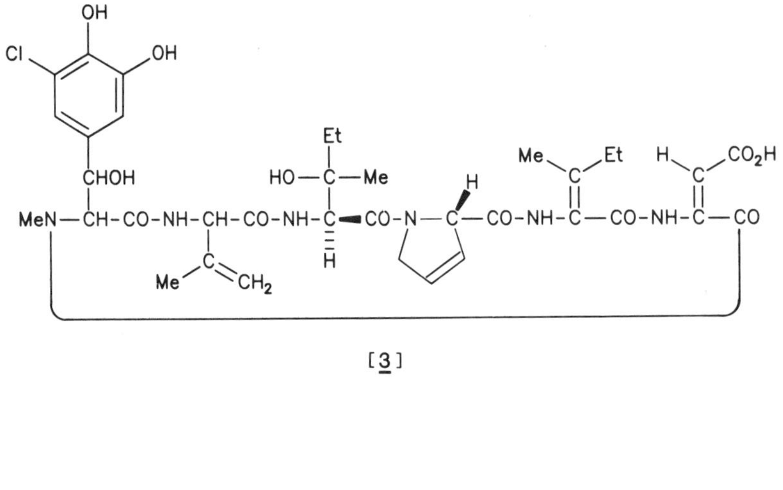

[3]

[**4**]

(Edgar et al., 1986). A recent, successful crystallographic analysis (Mackay et al., 1986) has now confirmed the amino acid composition and sequence, completed details of stereochemistry, and revealed the presence of the ether bridge which forms the macrocyclic ring. The molecular weight and elemental composition ($C_{35}H_{45}ClN_6O_{12}$) of phomopsin A [1] were determined by the positive ion, FABMS (Fig. 1a). The $[M + H]^+$ ions of the chlorine-containing molecule are seen at m/z 789/791 with $[M + Na]^+$ and $[M + K]^+$ ions at m/z 811/813 and m/z 827/829, respectively. Negative ion FABMS gives $[M - H]^-$ ions at m/z 787/789 (Fig. 1b).

Under FAB conditions, the relative intensities of the molecular ion cluster are slightly distorted from the theoretical distribution expected from the natural abundance of the isotopes present (Edgar et al., 1986). This is apparently due to hydrogen addition occurring under the FABMS conditions. The positive and negative ion FAB spectra of phomopsin A also shows prominent ions formed by replacement of the aromatic chlorine by hydrogen. These reduction phenomena have been observed previously in the FAB spectra of other halogen-containing phenolic and polyunsaturated molecules (Sethi et al., 1984; Gale et al., 1986; Chandler et al., 1988). The toxin is not amenable to conventional electron impact or chemical ionization mass spectrometry, and under field desorption(FD) and rapid-desorption electron impact conditions (i.e., rapidly heating the sample on the FD probe in the electron beam) the highest mass ions observed are at m/z 771/773, corresponding to $[M + H - H_2O]^+$ (Frahn et al., 1983).

In the early stages of the chemical investigation of phomopsin A it was found that it could be hydrolyzed in 24 h with dilute HCl at room temperature to a basic product, subsequently identified as phomopsinamine A [5], and 1 mol of oxalacetic acid. More vigorous hydrolysis conditions (concentrated HCl at room temperature) generated, as well as oxalacetic acid, an aromatic, chlorine-containing molecule ($C_7H_5O_3Cl$), approximately 2 mol of NH_3, and about 0.25 mol of methylamine (Frahn et al., 1983). These data became interpretable only with additional information on the unusual amino acids that form the toxin molecule.

The presence of amino acids in phomopsin A was suggested by ^{13}C-NMR data showing seven carbonyl carbon and four methine carbon signals and by the demonstration that radiolabeled amino acids (L-[U-^{14}C]isoleucine, L-[U-^{14}C]valine, L-[U-^{14}C]proline, and L-[U-^{14}C]phenylalanine) are incorporated into the toxin produced in liquid culture (Payne, 1983; Payne et al., 1985).

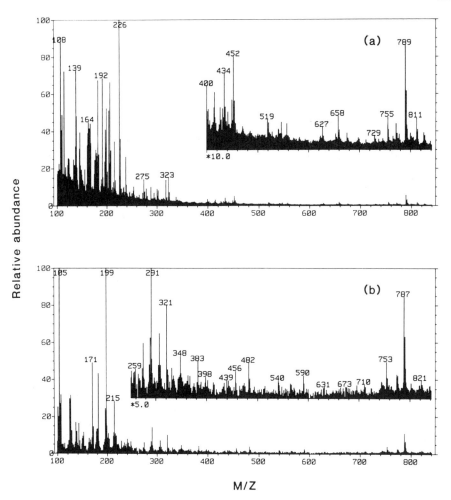

FIGURE 1 Fast-atom-bombardment mass spectra of phomopsin A [1]: (a) positive-ion spectrum; (b) negative-ion spectrum.

Hydrolysis of the toxin using typical protein hydrolysis conditions (6 M HCl, 110°C, 20 h) gave a mixture of amino acids that were identified by capillary GC/MS as their N-trifluoroacetyl n-butyl ester derivatives (Edgar et al., 1985). Glycine (0.36), sarcosine (0.11), 3,4-didehydro-valine (0.08), valine (0.18), two didehydroisoleucines (0.20, 0.44), and 3,4-didehydroproline (1) were detected in the hydrolysate, the figures in parentheses indicating the relative amount of each amino acid (Edgar et al., 1985). Only the didehydroproline was produced in sufficient yield to justify consideration as a component of the toxin, although it too was possibly an artifact (e.g., produced by dehydration of a hydroxyproline moiety during hydrolysis). The others were considered to be degradation products, indicating the presence of modified amino acids such as hydroxy and didehydro amino acids which would be unstable to the acid hydrolysis conditions employed. The latter are converted

[**5**] R = Cl phomopsinamine A

[**6**] R = H phomopsinamine B

to α-keto acids and ammonia on acid hydrolysis, while hydroxy amino acids are likely to be dehydrated to unsaturated amino acids or undergo other changes.

Sodium borohydride reduction of phomopsin A was used to convert 2,3-didehydroamino acids present to stable DL-amino acids and subsequent hydrolysis yielded two amino acids in addition to those seen prior to reduction. These were identified as aspartic acid and a 1:1 mixture of isoleucine and alloisoleucine. They were present in amounts equal to that of 3,4-didehydroproline and indicated the presence of 2,3-didehydroaspartic acid and 2,3-didehydroisoleucine in phomopsin A (Edgar et al., 1985), the former being the source of the oxalacetic acid and 1 mol of ammonia seen on hydrolysis of phomopsin A and the latter generating a second mole of ammonia and, theoretically, 2-keto-3-methylpentanoic acid, which was not detected. It was anticipated that catalytic hydrogenation of phomopsin A would convert the 2,3-didehydroamino acids into DL-amino acids and that 3,4-didehydroamino acids such as the putative 3,4-didehydroproline unit would be converted into acid-stable, saturated amino acids, the latter retaining their chirality at the α-carbon and thus providing stereochemical information on the phomopsin A molecule.

Hydrogenation of phomopsin A using a platinum catalyst at room temperature and pressure resulted in the uptake of eight hydrogen atoms ($[M + H]^+$, m/z 797; $[M - H]^-$, m/z 795) (Fig. 2), indicating the presence of four easily reduced double bonds in the phomopsin A molecule. Acid hydrolysis of the hydrogenation product ("octahydrophomopsin A") gave DL-aspartic acid, DL-isoleucine, L-proline, and DL-valine in the ratio 1:1:1:1. Also present in the hydrolysate were the two dehydrosioleucines seen in the hydrolysis of phomopsin A, but the glycine and sarcosine seen previously were not detected. DL-aspartic acid, DL-isoleucine, and L-proline were the expected products of 2,3-didehydroaspartic acid, 2,3-didehydrosioleucine, and 3,4-didehydroproline, the latter thus being confirmed as a component of the phomopsin A molecule and shown to have the L configuration. The formation of DL-isoleucine and the absence of DL-alloisoleucine established that the 2,3-didehydroisoleucine is in the E configuration. The presence of DL-valine, which had not been seen after borohydride reduction, indicated that 3,4-didehydrovaline was also a likely constituent of the phomopsin A molecule, but this required further confirmation. The apparent racemization of 3,4-didehydrovaline was unexpected, although it could have been promoted during adsorption on the

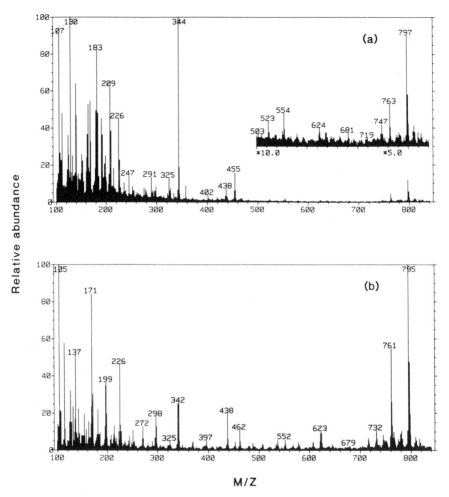

FIGURE 2 Fast-atom-bombardment mass spectra of "octahydrophomopsin A":
(a) positive-ion spectrum; (b) negative-ion spectrum.

catalytic surface prior to hydrogenation. The apparent instability of this
amino acid during acid hydrolysis of phomopsin A [only a trace was detected
in the hydrolysate along with a larger amount of valine (see above)] was also
unexpected. In this regard it is noteworthy that a report on the synthesis
of 3,4-didehydrovaline, involving a final acid hydrolysis step carried out
under conditions similar to those used to degrade phomopsin A, does not record any instability of the amino acid to these conditions (Baldwin et al., 1977).

The two didehydroisoleucines detected in the hydrolysate of phomopsin
A and its reduction products were apparently derived by an elimination process, such as dehydration of a hydroxyisoleucine, under the acid conditions
of hydrolysis. On catalytic hydrogenation of the hydrolysate mixtures, the
didehydroisoleucines were converted to L-isoleucine, thus establishing the
L configuration for this unit. Phomopsinamine A [5], produced with oxalace-

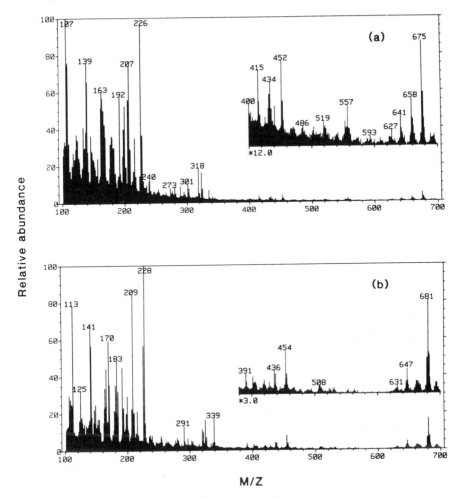

FIGURE 3 Positive-ion fast-atom-bombardment mass spectra of (a) phomopsinamine A [5] and (b) "hexahydrophomopsinamine A."

tic acid by hydrolysis of phomopsin A under mild acid conditions, was shown by FABMS to have a molecular weight of 674 ([M + H]$^+$, m/z 675) (Fig. 3a) and to be converted to a hexahydro derivative on catalytic hydrogenation ([M + H]$^+$, m/z 681) (Fig. 3b) which on acid hydrolysis yielded the same amino acids seen on hydrolysis of octahydrophomopsin A except for DL-aspartic acid, which, as expected, was not detected. The results of amino acid analysis of phomopsin A, phomopsinamine A, and their reduction products thus provided evidence of 3,4-didehydro-L-proline, 3,4-didehydrovaline, hydroxy-L-isoleucine, E-2,3-didehydroisoleucine, and 2,3-didehydroaspartic acid in phomopsin A.

The nature of the remaining aromatic amino acid unit was suggested by the incorporation of L-[U^{14}C]phenylalanine into phomopsin A grown in liquid culture (Payne, 1983) and identification of the chlorine-containing, aromatic degradation product generated by concentrated HCl hydrolysis of phomopsin A. The mass spectrum of the dimethyl ether and ditrimethylsilyl ether derivatives of the latter compound suggested that it was a chlorodihydroxybenzaldehyde. The substitution pattern was indicated by the high-field NMR data recorded for phomopsin A (see below) and comparison with an authentic sample confirmed it to be 3-chloro-4,5-dihydroxybenzaldehyde. Such a product could be generated by a retro-aldol fission of a substituted 3-phenylserine unit biosynthetically derived form phenylalanine. The other product of this cleavage was apparently the sarcosine found in acid hydrolysates of phomopsin A.

An alternative acid degradation pathway for the putative N-methyl-3-(3-chloro-4,5-phenyl)serine unit (i.e., dehydration to a 2,3-didehydro amino cid prior to hydrolysis) produces methylamine and 3-chloro-4,5-dihydroxyphenylpyruvic acid. The former had been identified as a product of acid hydolysis of phomopsin A (Frahn et al., 1983), while a product considered to be the latter was also detected in acid hydrolysates of the toxin by GC/MS as its tetra-TMS derivative (M^+, m/z 518) (Edgar et al., 1986). Thus N-methyl-3-(3-chloro-4,5-dihydroxyphenyl)serine was indicated as the remaining amino acid unit of phomopsin A, and this was further substantiated by NMR data (see below).

The glycine generated during acid hydrolysis of phomopsin A has been shown to be a degradation product of the 3,4-didehydrovaline unit (Culvenor et al., 1989). It apparently arises by Markovnikov addition of water across the double bond, followed by a retro-aldol reaction to give glycine and acetone. This was established by detection of acetone, the other product of the retro-aldol reaction, in the products of acid hydrolysis and by radiolabeling studies in which phomopsin A labeled with L-[U-^{14}C]valine (Payne, 1983) gave radiolabeled glycine on hydrolysis (Edgar et al., 1986).

The presence of the six amino acids in phomopsin A, identified as described above, was confirmed by extensive resolution-enhanced 500-MHz ^{1}H-NMR and ^{13}C-NMR data (Culvenor et al., 1989). The ^{1}H chemical shifts, coupling constants, and proton-proton connectivity pattern of phomopsin A in [^{2}H$_6$]dimethylsulfoxide are reproted by Culvenor et al. (1989). Complete assignment of the ^{13}C resonances was also achieved (Culvenor et al., 1989) and long-range ^{13}C,^{1}H connectivity studies provided independent evidence of the amino acid composition of phomopsin A.

As well as confirming the amino acids identified by hydrolysis and hydrogenation, the long-range ^{13}C,^{1}H connectivity data established, in particular, the N-methyl group as a constituent of the phenylserine unit and the 3-chloro-4,5-dihydroxy substitution pattern of the aromatic ring. These data also provided amino acid sequence information which showed two partial sequences: N-methyl-3-(3-chloro-4,5-dihydroxyphenyl)serine/3,4-didehydrovaline/3-hydroxyisoleucine and 3,4-didehydroproline/2,3-didehydroisoleucine/2,3-didehydroaspartic acid.

In a preliminary communication (Culvenor et al., 1983), the presence of the sequence 2,3-didehydroaspartic/N-methyl-3-(3-chloro-4,5-dihydroxyphenyl)serine was also postulated. This incorrect linking of the previously deduced partial sequences appeared to be indicated by the presence of a two-bond (^{13}C,^{1}H) coupling in the carbon resonance of the HNCH$_3$ methyl group of phomopsinamine A [5]. The corresponding resonance in the ^{13}C spectrum

of phomopsin A shows no such coupling, and it was concluded that formation
of phomopsinamine A [5], by loss of the 2,3-didehydroaspartic acid unit as
oxalacetic acid, resulted in the appearance of the $NHCH_3$ group. The absence
of a two-bond (^{13}C,^1H) coupling in the ^{13}C spectrum of phomopsin A [1] is
now readily explained by the formation of a zwitterion involving the tautomer-
ism-stabilized monoanion of the 2,3-didehydroaspartic acid unit and the protonated N-methyl nitrogen atom (see below). This misinterpretation, however,
led to the postulation of the macrocyclic structure [3] for phomopsin A in
which the 3-hydroxyisoleucine/3,4-didehydroproline sequence was also proposed to accommodate the cyclic structure indicated by the empirical formula
(Culvenor et al., 1983).

The structure [3] did not accommodate chemical evidence suggesting that
one of the phenolic hydroxyl groups was unavailable in phomopsin A (Edgar
et al., 1985). Thus it was known that if phomopsin A is methylated with diazomethane, hydrolyzed, and the hydrolysate trimethylsilylated, a monomethyl-
mono-TMS derivative of 3-chloro-4,5-dihydroxybenzaldehyde is formed. This
indicated that one phenolic group in phomopsin A was available for reaction
with diazomethane and that the second become available for derivatization only
after hydrolysis. It was also shown that phomopsin A fails to complex with
borate buffer (Edgar et al., 1985) and therefore cannot have free ortho phenolic hydroxyl groups, as shown in [3]. The structure [3] was made even
more untenable by a detailed investigation of the FAB spectra of phomopsin
A and its derivatives, which showed that no link existed between the N-methyl-
3-(3-chloro-4,5-dihydroxyphenyl)serine and the 2,3-didehydroaspartic acid
units and that these units form the amino and carboxy termini, respectively,
of a linear peptide with the sequence N-methyl-3-(3-chloro-4,5-dihydroxy-
phenyl)serine/3,4-didehydrovaline/3-hdyroxy-L-isoleucine/3,4-didehydr-L-
proline/E-2,3-didehydroisoleucine/E-2,3-didehydroaspartic acid (Edgar et
al., 1986). This led to a tentative revision of the structure to a linear hexapeptide [4] which, however, still failed to accommodate the chemical evidence
showing the unavailability of one of the phenolic hydroxyl groups and also
required the highest mass ions in the positive-ion FAB spectrum, at m/z 789/
791, to be $[M + H - H_2O]^+$ rather than $[M + H]^+$ ions (Edgar et al., 1986).

The final structure [1], which accounts for all the chemical and physical
properties of phomopsin A, was revealed by x-ray diffraction data (Mackay
et al., 1986). This showed that an ether bridge is present, replacing the
5-hydroxyl group of the substituted phenylserine unit and the hydroxyl group
of the 3-hydroxyisoleucine unit. With prior knowledge that the 3-hydroxy-
isoleucine and 3,4-didehydroproline units have the L-configruation, the x-ray
data enabled the absolute configuration to be determined as depicted in [1]:
that is, 22E, 25E, 3R, 4S, 7S, 10S, 11S, and 19S (Culvenor et al., 1989).

Phomopsin A [1] forms prismatic crystals from ethanol-methanol-water
which analyze for $\overline{2}(C_{36}H_{45}ClN_6O_{12}) \cdot 5H_2O$. The two molecules present in
the unit cell have different conformations, and determination of the structure
of phomopsin A by x-ray crystallography was not straightforward, due mainly
to difficulties in locating the site of one of the chlorine atoms in the asymmetric
unit (Mackay et al., 1986). It was located only after molecular fragments,
representing about 40% of the scattering matter, were included in the analysis.

The two conformations represented in the crystal are shown in Fig. 4.
The principal difference between them involves the orientation of the aromatic

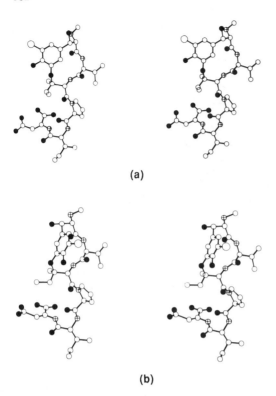

(a)

(b)

FIGURE 4 The two conformations of phomopsin A [1] present in crystals (Mackay et al., 1986): (a) molecule A; (b) molecule B.

ring. In one molecule (A) the phenyl ring lies roughly in the plane of the macrocyclic ring, while in the other (B) it has rotated about 137° along the axis of its points of attachment to the macrocyclic ring, in effect closing over on the macrocyclic ring. The three amino acids not involved in the macrocyclic system form a side chain having a similar conformation in both molecules. They are not fully extended but exhibit a turn at the 2,3-didehydroisoleucine unit. The two molecules are oriented in the crystal so that the 2,3-didehydroaspartate monoanion of one is adjacent to the protonated amino group of the phenylserine moiety in the other to form electrostatic zwitterionic centers. Seven other intermolecular hydrogen bonds are also involved in holding the two molecules together (Culvenor et al., 1989).

The stablized monoanion formed by the 2,3-didehydroaspartic acid, in which a hydrogen-bonded proton is held symmetrically between the two carboxyl groups, is analogous to the maleate monoanion and remains unprotonated even at pH 2 (maleic acid, pK_a 1.92). Thus phomopsin A retains its zwitterionic character even at very low pH. This accounts for its low cationic mobility on paper electrophoresis at pH 2 (Frahn et al., 1983; Hancock et al., 1986), a characteristic initially interpreted as indicating the presence of a very weakly basic group which was incompletely protonated even at low pH (Frahn et al., 1983). The hydrogen-bonded proton of the anion resonates at very low

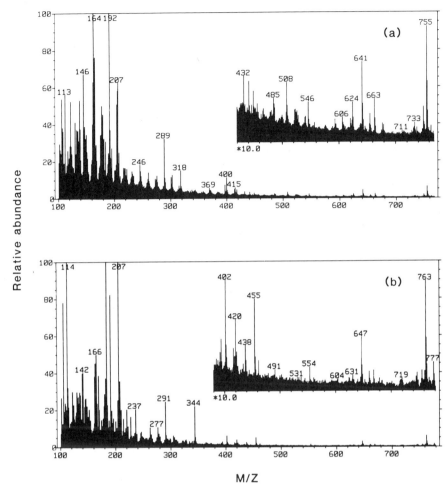

FIGURE 5 Positive-ion fast-atom-bombardment mass spectra of (a) phomopsin B and (b) "octahydrophomopsin B."

field, δH 18.96 ppm (maleate monoanion, 20.1 ppm) and is a characteristic feature of the ^{1}H-NMR spectrum of phomopsin A.

The structure of phomopsin B [2] has been deduced from its FAB mass spectrum (Fig. 5a) and by chemical comparison with phomopsin A (Edgar et al., 1986); thus it has a molecular weight of 754 and a FABMS fragmentation pattern paralleling that of phomopsin A [1]. It is converted into an octahydro derivative on hydrogenation (Fig. 5b) and is hydrolyzed to phomopsin-amine B [6] by dilute HCl, both of which give mass spectra exhibiting the expected [M + H][+] and amino acid sequence ions (Edgar et al., 1986). Hydrolysis and amino acid analysis of phomopsin B [2] and octahydrophomopsin B by GC/MS using a chiral-phase capillary column, has established the L configuration for the hydroxyisoleucine and 3,4-didehydroproline units and the E configuration of the 2,3-didehydroisoleucine (Edgar, unpublished results).

Other aspects of phomopsin B stereochemistry have not been established but are assumed to be the same as in phomopsin A [1].

As well as their conversion to phomopsinamines A [5] and B [6] by dilute acid, phomopsins A [1] and B [2] are easily converted into monomethyl esters by dilute methanolic HCl (Frahn et al., 1983). The nature of these derivatives and their deuteromethyl analogs has been established by FABMS (Edgar et al., 1986). Phomopsin A also undergoes a rapid and complete structural change on exposure to mercuric salts (Frahn et al., 1983). The product has a FAB mass spectrum identical to that of phomopsin A, but unlike phomopsin A, it has significant cationic mobility at acid pHs and its ^{1}H NMR lacks the resonance attributed to the 2,3-didehydroaspartic monoanion proton at δH 18.96 ppm. With current knowledge of the structure of phomopsin A, this evidence is interpreted as conversion of the E-2,3-didehydroaspartic acid to the Z configuration.

The use of HPLC to detect and quantitate phomopsins A and B in field samples of *Phomopsis*-infected lupin stubble has indicated the presence of other possible mycotoxins of the phomopsin type which may contribute to lupinosis. One of these, "phomopsin C," has been isolated in a crude form and is reported to produce mitotic disturbances in hepatocytes of nursling rats (Allen, 1986; Allen and Hancock, 1989). The chemical nature of phomopsin C has not yet been determined, but preliminary data have shown that the isolated material is, in fact, a mixture of two chlorine-containing components. They show FABMS $[M + H]^+$ ions at m/z 710/712 and 724-726 (phomopsin A $[M + H]^+$, m/z 789/791) (Edgar and Cockrum, unpublished results) and hydrogenation converts the mixture into two products which lack chlorine and have $[M + H]^+$ ions at m/z 680 and 694, thus indicating the presence of two double bonds and an easily hydrogenolized chlorine atom (Edgar and Cockrum, unpublished results).

IV. BIOLOGICAL ACTIVITY

An important mechanism by which the phomopsins exert their toxic effects is by binding to tubulin and preventing formation of microtubules (Tonsing et al., 1984; Lacey et al., 1987; Peterson, 1986). The toxins, and certain of their derivatives, have been shown to bind at or near the site of vinblastine binding, and like vinblastine and its competitive inhibitor maytansine, they also enhance the binding of the classical antimicrotubule agent, colchicine (Lacey et al., 1987). The phomopsins differ from other compounds capable of binding to tubulin by being remarkably tissue specific, exerting their effects in vivo primarily in liver parenchymal cells.

The presence of abnormal mitotic cells in the liver of animals suffering from lupinosis is a long-recognized characteristic of the disease (Gardiner, 1967a). The similarity of this effect with the mitotic arrest produced by colchicine (Papadimitriou et al., 1974; Peterson and Lanigan, 1976; Peterson, 1978) led to a comparative study which concluded that, as for colchicine, the primary target of the phomopsins is the microtubular system which forms the mitotic spindle in dividing cells (Petterson et al., 1979).

Using immunofluorescence microscopy with tubulin-specific antibodies, Tonsing et al. (1984) showed that treating several cell lines (human HeLa cells, monkey CV_1 and BSC_1 cells, mouse 3T3 cells, rat kangaroo PtK_2 cells, and primary rat hepatocytes) in tissue culture with phomopsin A leads to destruction of microtubules in interphase cells as well as producing metaphase arrest. While microtubules in all cell lines tested were affected by phomopsin A in tissue culture, primary hepatocytes were found to be more sensitive than others, mirroring the situation found in lupinosis. Tonsing et al. (1984) also showed that phomopsin A inhibits, in a time- and concentration-dependent manner, the in vitro polymerization of purified pig brain tubulin and causes the depolymerization of preformed microtubules.

In vitro studies of the effect of phomopsin A [1], phomopsinamine A [5], octahydrophomopsin A, and phomopsin B [2] have shown that they all markedly inhibited both the rate and extent of polymerization of sheep brain tubulin (Lacey et al., 1987). Phomopsin A [1], phomopsinamine A [5], and octahydrophomopsin A were shown to be 30-fold more potent than colchicine, and equipotent with vinblastine, in inhibiting both the rate and extent of tubulin polymerization, while phomopsin B [2] was even more potent, thus establishing that the phomopsins are among the most effective antimicrotubule agents known. Like vinblastine and maytansine, the phomopsins increase the ability of tubulin to bind colchicine. This effect plateaus at about 0.5 µm for each of the phomopsins tested, with a 150 to 175% enhancement of colchicine binding compared to an enhancement of 169% for maytansine at 2 µM and 140% for vinblastine at 1.5 µM (Lacey et al., 1987). The phomopsins were also shown to inhibit the binding of radiolabeled vinblastine to tubulin, with phomopsinamine A and phomopsin B being the most effective. Thus it was concluded by Lacey et al. (1987) that these toxins are extremely potent antimicrotubule agents which probably bind to tubulin at or near the vinblastine binding site.

The effect of the phomopsins on microtubule assembly accounts for many of the symptoms of lupinosis (Peterson, 1986). As well as its involvement in formation of the mitotic spindle, the microtubular system is involved in intracellular transport (e.g., of lipids) (Dustin, 1984). Both processes are interfered with in the liver of lupinosis-poisoned animals, giving rise to the fatty liver and the colchicinelike metaphase arrest of hepatocytes which characterize the disease. Other manifestations (e.g., the nodular and cirrhotic liver seen in the chronic disease) are the expected consequences of hepatic damage and regeneration. The clinical symptoms of the disease—jaundice, ascites, photosensitization, lethargy and coma, and possibly inappetence—can all be related to the resulting functional failure of the liver (Peterson, 1986).

Less clearly associated with the action of the phomopsins as microtubule toxins is their carcinogenicity (Peterson, 1986, 1990). In a 2-year experiment with rats given low daily doses (30 µg/kg) of the toxins for the first 17 weeks, Peterson found a total cancer incidence of 13%. Three of 37 animals developed malignant hepatic cell tumors and another 2 had malignant biliary tumors. At least 60% of the rats developed benign biliary fibrocystic adenomas, some of which were large enough to put the animal's survival at risk. These results and the chromosomal aberrations (chromatid and isochromatid deletions and chromatid exchange) induced by the phomopsins (Brown and Bick, 1986) may indicate direct interaction of the phomopsins with DNA (Peterson, 1986).

An aspect requiring further investigation is the peculiar susceptibility of the liver in the intact animal and hepatocytes in cell culture to the effects of the phomopsins. This specificity is in marked contrast with the effects of colchicine in vivo (Peterson, 1986). Colchicine causes relatively indiscriminate metaphase arrest in mitotically active tissues, and even in the liver, after an initially similar response to that seen with the phomopsins, it produces a quite different pattern of cell death and regeneration (Peterson, 1986). This may reflect a specific mechanism favoring the transport of the phomopsins into hepatocytes, a specificity for hepatocyte tubulin, or as suggested by Peterson (1986), conversion of the phomopsins into a highly reactive form in the liver, which augments the damage done by the antimicrotubular action of the toxins and is responsible for the effects of lupinosis not readily explained on the basis of reversible tubulin binding alone.

The structural requirements for the toxicity and antimicrotubule action of the phomopsins have not been fully determined. Phomopsinamine A [5] has been shown to prevent polymerization of tubulin in vitro as effectively as phomopsin A (Lacey et al., 1987) and also to display the same degree of toxicity in the nursling rat assay developed by Peterson (1978). Thus the 2,3-didehydroaspartic acid unit does not appear to be important for the antimicrotubule activity or for producing typical antimitotic activity in the livers of young rats. "Octahydrophomopsin A," a mixture of isomers in which both D and L configurations are present in the constituent aspartic acid, isoleucine, and valine units, also retains the antimicrotubule and antimitotic activity of the parent toxin (Lacey et al., 1987; Peterson and Edgar, unpublished results). The retention of full biological activity by such a mixture is hard to reconcile with the concept of a highly defined "pocket" binding site. It is possible that one or a limited number of the octahydrophomopsin isomers have increased activity relative to the parent toxin or that the concept of the phomopsins binding in a "pocket" in the tubulin molecule is incorrect (see below). The structural feature that is perhaps least disturbed by hydrogenation and which also remains intact in phomopsinamine A [5] is the macrocyclic ring, and it seems likely that the biological activity of the phomopsins resides in that system.

The binding of antibiotics of the vancomycin group to cell wall analogs terminating in -D-Ala-D-Ala may provide a model of the binding of the phomopsins to tubulin. The vancomycins (e.g., vancomycin and ristocetin A) bear a noticeable resemblance to the phomopsins. They are linear heptapeptides which contain macrocyclic ring systems formed by ether bridges between aromatic amino acids in the peptide chain (Williams, 1984). The binding of the vancomycins to -D-Ala-D-Ala involves formation of hydrogen bonds between NH and CO groups of the antibiotics and the -D-Ala-D-Ala chain and the binding of the carboxylate anion of the cell wall analog to the protonated amino groups at the N terminus of the antibiotics. These electrostatic interactions take place in a hydrophobic environment of low dielectric constant formed as a cleft between two aromatic rings in ristocetin A and, in the case of vancomycin, between an aromatic ring and an N-methylleucine $CH_2CH(CH_3)2$ group (Williams, 1984). A parallel interaction appears to be possible between the phomopsins and a specific linear amino acid sequence in tubulin. Thus the terminal N-methylamino group fo the phomopsins could be involved in salt formation with a carboxyl group of tubulin, and NH and CO groups of the two peptide chains could form hydrogen bonds as in the -D-Ala-D-Ala/vancomycin interaction.

The two low-energy conformations of phomopsin A present in the crystal (Fig. 4) suggest the possibility of a two-step trapping mechanism in which the

"open" A form of the mycotoxin molecule initially interacts with the appropriate linear amino acid sequence of tubulin. Subsequent rotation of the aromatic ring to approximate the "closed" B conformation then traps the peptide
chain, and some of the hydrogen-bonding interactions between it and the phomopsin, in a vancomycinlike hydrophobic cleft formed, for example, between
the aromatic ring and ethyl group of the hydroxyisoleucine on one side and
the aliphatic side chains of the didehydrovaline, didehydroproline, and dide-
hydroisoleucine residues on the other. It is also noteworthy that the phomopsins are unique among antimicrotubule toxins in being polypeptides, and as
such, they could be close structural mimics of endogenous peptides involved
in the modulation of microtubule assembly and disassembly.

V. DETECTION

Methods of detecting and quantitating the phomopsins have recently been reviewed by Hancock et al. (1986). Early work on lupinosis made use of the
characteristic antimitotic effect on liver parenchymal cells of mice as a means
of detecting the toxins (Gardiner, 1967c; Gardiner and Petterson, 1972). Attempts were later made to convert this activity into a reliable quantitative
measure of the toxins in lupin extracts and fractions (Culvenor et al., 1977).
These culminated in the nursling rat bioassay developed by Peterson (1978),
which can be performed using relatively crude extracts. It is currently the
favored in vivo assay for the toxins.

   The Peterson assay involves rats 15 ± 1 days old weighing 25 ± 5 g. Groups
of five are injected (1 mL per 100 g of body weight) intraperitoneally with
serial doubling dilutions of the putative toxin solutions and killed 18 h later.
Strained liver sections are then examined for abnormal mitoses. Twenty microscopic fields (×630), distributed over the sections taken from each animal,
are examined until a maximum of five abnormal mitoses are counted. The results are recorded in terms of how many fields need to be examined to give
five abnormal mitoses and, if five are not seen, the number of abnormal mitoses
counted in the 20 fields examined from each animal. The toxin titer is defined
as the reciprocal of the highest dilution giving a group mean of five abnormal
mitoses in fewer than 20 microscopic fields. This figure is converted to toxin
content by means of a calibration curve generated with an authentic toxin
reference standard (Peterson, 1978; Petterson et al., 1985).

   At dilutions covering the assay endpoint, the mitotic abnormality which
predominates is characterized by scattered chromosomes. These abnormal
cells are readily recognized, enabling a rapid assessment of the sections to
be made. Other types of abnormal mitotic figures, most prominent at higher
phomopsin concentrations, still occur, however, and these are also counted.
The endpoint of the assay has been found to correspond with a phomopsin
A concentration of about 0.3 µg/mL (Peterson, 1978) and to be about the same
for both hooded and Wistar-derived strains of rat (Peterson et al., 1985).

   In vitro assays, based on the effects of the toxins on cells growing in
culture, were developed to assist in the isolation of the phomopsins from toxic
lupins and *P. leptostromiformis* cultures (Petterson and Coackley, 1973; Culvenor et al., 1977). These lack the specificity, sensitivity, and reproducibility displayed by the nursling rat assay and by recently developed chemical

and immunochemical methods of phomopsin analysis (see below) and are there-fore no longer used.

Once phomopsins A and B were isolated and shown to be the principal toxins produce by *P. leptostromiformis*, physicochemical methods of analysis were developed. Methods that have been used include high-voltage paper electrophoresis (HVPE) (Culvenor et al., 1977; Lanigan et al., 1979), thin-layer chromatography (TLC) (Culvenor et al., 1977; Hancock et al., 1986), and high-performance liquid chromatography (HPLC) (Hancock et al., 1986, 1987). Detection of the phomopsins on chromatograms and HVPE pherograms is by ultraviolet (UV) light absorption and color reaction with spray reagents (Table 1) (Frahn et al., 1983; Hancock et al., 1986) and by UV detection in the case of HPLC.

The UV spectra of phomopsins A and B show an absorption maximum at 286 nm ($\Sigma = 1.6 \times 10^4$ in methanol), and absorption measurement at this wave-length has been used to quantify the toxins in relatively pure samples as well as to detect and quantify them in mixtures following separation by TLC, HVPE, and HPLC (Culvenor et al., 1977; Hancock et al., 1986, 1987). The presence of other UV-absorbing material in lupin extracts and *Phomopsis* cultures can, however, seriously interfere with UV detection, and assays using this method require a number of purification steps to reduce the level of interfering sub-stances (Hancock et al., 1987). Scanning and diode array UV detectors for HPLC, which provide full UV spectra, give added certainty to the identifica-tion and the homogeneity of HPLC peaks at the retention times of the phomop-sins and also facilitates detection of their degradation products (Fig. 6).

TABLE 1 Spray Reagents for Detecting the Phomopsins

Spray reagent	Color reaction	Detection limit (μg)
$KMnO_4/CrO_3/H_2SO_4$[a]	Yellow spots on pink background changing to white spots on brown background	1
$KMnO_4/MnSO_4/H_2SO_4$[b]	White spots on brown background	1
10% $Ce(SO_4)_2$ in H_3PO_4 (diluted 1:5 with CH_3OH)[c]	Yellow spots turning pink	5
Diazotized sulfonilic reagent[c]	Orange spots on pale yellow background	5
Diazotized p-nitanaline reagent[c]	Orange spots on pale yellow background	2
Ferric chloride-ferri-cyanide reagent[c]	Blue spots on yellow-green back-ground	2

[a] Frahn and Mills (1959).
[b] Mills (1978).
[c] Hathway (1969).
Source: Hancock et al. (1986).

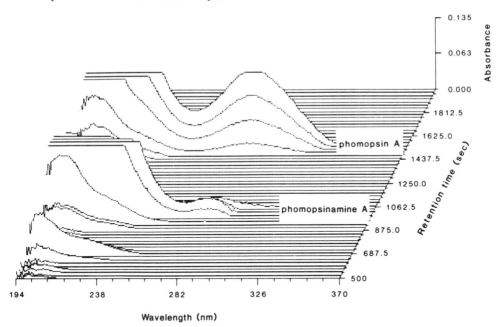

FIGURE 6 Three-dimensional HPLC chromatogram, obtained using a scanning UV detector, of a mixture containing phomopsin A [1] and its hydrolysis product, phomopsinamine A [5].

Phomopsinamine A [5], for example, shows greatly reduced absorption at 286 nm (Fig. 6), and since it retains the toxicity of the parent mycotoxin and is a readily formed breakdown product of phomopsin A, detection based on absorptivity at 286 nm alone can lead to an underestimation of the toxicity of samples in which it occurs (Cockrum and Edgar, unpublished results).

An extraction procedure and HPLC assay method for the analysis of phomopsins in lupin seed and stubble has been reported (Hancock et al., 1986, 1987). One sample a day, or four samples in 2 days, can be analyzed by this method. After correction for an extraction efficiency of 64%, the assay is reported to have a detection limit of 200 µg of phomopsin A per kilogram of lupin seed and 500 µg of the mycotoxin per kilogram of lupin stubble. This sensitivity is adequate for assessing the likely toxicity of these materials to sheep, where a daily intake of 12 µg of phomopsin A per kilogram of sheep for 16 weeks has been shown to cause no obvious toxic effects (Peterson et al., 1987); however, it falls short of the requirement for ensuring the safety of lupin products for human consumption. In the latter case a limit of 5 µg of phomopsin A per kilogram of lupin flour has been set in Australia (National Health and Medical Research Council, 1987). Solvent systems that have been used for TLC of the phomopsins on silica gel plates are shown in Table 2. A solvent system that provides good resolution with a short running time is tetrahydrofuran:methanol (1:1) (Hancock et al., 1986).

The HVPE system used for the phomopsins is that described by Frahn and Mills (1959). Phomopsin A is reported to have a mobility of 5.7 to 5.9

TABLE 2 TLC Solvent Systems for the Phomopsin Mycotoxins on
Silica Gel Plates

	R_f	
Solvent	Phomopsin A	Phomopsin B
Tetrahydrofuran:methanol (1:1)	0.65	0.51
n-Butanol:acetic acid:water (4:1:1)	0.49	0.41
Methanol:isopropanol:acetic acid (20:30:1)	0.30	0.18

Source: Hancock et al. (1986).

cm/h per kilovolt, while phomopsin B has a mobility of 4.5 to 4.8 cm/h per
kilovolt at pH 9.2 (Lanigan et al., 1979; Hancock et al., 1986). The electrophoretic mobilities of the phomopsins at different pH values provide useful
characterizing data (Frahn et al., 1983; Hancock et al., 1986). Their anionic
mobilities in alkaline electrolytes is high, reflecting the presence of three
acidic centers, while their cationic mobility is extremely low above pH 2 due
to the high acidity of the 2,3-didehydroaspartic acid anion, which remains
unprotonated at this pH. A phomopsin enzyme immunoassay with the sensitivity, specificity, and speed required for quality control of lupin products for
human consumption has been developed in the author's laboratory, where it
is also being used to determine the wider occurrence of these toxins in other
Phomopsis species, especially those associated with items of human diet.

VI. CONTROL OF LUPINOSIS

Epidemiological studies (Neil et al., 1960; Gardiner, 1964, 1967a; Allen et
al., 1985) have led to the development of animal management practices to reduce the incidence of lupinosis. Recommendations include regular and close
observation of animals in order to detect early signs of lupinosis in the more
susceptible animals, reduced stocking rates (30 sheep per hectare), provision
of alternative feed, grazing of stubble immediately after harvest, removal
of stock after summer rains of 8 mm or more, rotational grazing of animals
on lupin and nonlupin pastures, and a recommendation that hungry and pregnant animals should not be exposed to lupin stubble.
     It is acknowledged that an animal management approach is successful only
when stubbles are of low or moderate toxicity (Allen, 1986) and agronomic
practices have therefore also been investigated as a means of reducing the
incidence of lupinosis. Of these, the making of lupin hay (Allen et al., 1978;
Allen and Wood, 1979; Morcombe et al., 1986; Allen, 1986), the planting of
mixed lupin and oat crops (Morcombe et al., 1987), and the treatment of stubble with alkali (Allen et al., 1986) have proved to be at least partially effective in reducing the incidence of lupinosis (Allen, 1986).

Prospects for the long-term control of lupinosis and of preventing contamination of lupin seed with the phomopsins rest with the development of *Phomopsis*-resistant varieties of cultivated sweet lupins. A breeding program to produce resistant varieties of *Lupinus angustifolius* L. has resulted in the production of plants which, in the field, show a significant reduction in the severity of symptoms of lupin stem blight caused by *P. leptostromiformis*, and stubbles of the resistant breeding lines produced no signs of lupinosis in sheep after 48 days grazing, while sheep exposed to *Phomopsis* susceptible cultivars developed lupinosis within 15 to 20 days (Cowling et al., 1986).

While the resistant plants showed reduced lesion numbers and a reduction in the overall level of colonization, lesion size and rate of colonization were reported not to be greatly reduced relative to susceptible varieties. However, some of the resistant lines appeared to exhibit low toxicity despite relatively high frequency of isolation of *P. leptostromiformis*, suggesting that the resistant lines may directly or indirectly prevent toxin production by the fungus (Cowling et al., 1986, 1988; Allen and Cowling, 1986).

Phomopsis-resistant cultivars can be expected, in the long term, to provide a means of reducing the incidence of lupinosis among animals grazing postharvest lupin stubbles and also to reduce the level of contamination of lupin seeds by the phomopsins. Prevention of lupinosis in animals grazing natural stands of self-sown lupins will, however, require another type of solution to be developed. One approach that is showing good prospects is vaccination (Payne, Than, and Edgar, unpublished results) and a combination of vaccination with the planting of resistant lupin varieties may eventually make lupinosis a curiosity of the past.

REFERENCES

Allen, J. G. (1986). Lupinosis: a review. In *Proceedings of the Fourth International Lupin Conference*. Western Australian Department of Agriculture, South Perth, pp. 173-187.

Allen, J. G., and Cowling, W. A. (1986). Preventing lupinosis with phomopsis-resistant lupins. *J. Agric. West. Aust.* 27:89-90.

Allen, J. G., and Hancock, G. R. (1989). Evidence that phomopsins A and B are not the only toxic metabolites produced by *Phomopsis leptostromiformis*. *J. Appl. Toxicol.* 9:83-90.

Allen, J. G., and Wood, P. McR. (1979). The prevention of lupinosis by making lupin hay. *Aust. Vet. J.* 55:38-39.

Allen, J. G., Wood, P. McR., and O'Donnel, F. M. (1978). Control of ovine lupinosis: experiments on the making of lupin hay. *Aust. Vet. J.* 54:19-22.

Allen, J. G., Wood, P. McR., Croker, K. P., Cowling, W. A., and Sawkins, D. N. (1985). The prevention of lupinosis in sheep. In *Plant Toxicology*, A. A. Seawright, M. P. Hegarty, L. F. James, and R. F. Keeler (Eds.). Queensland Poisonous Plants Committee, Yeerongpilly, Australia, pp. 80-88.

Allen, J. G., Croker, K. P., Hancock, G. R., and Southey, I. N. (1986). Control of ovine lupinosis: the treatment of lupin stubble material with alkali. *Aust. Vet. J.* 63:350-352.

Baldwin, J. E., Haber, S. B., Hoskins, C., and Kruse, L. I. (1977). Synthesis of β,γ-unsaturated amino acids. *J. Org. Chem.* 42:1239-1241.

Brash, A. G. (1943). Lupin poisoning of sheep. *N.Z. J. Agric.* 67:83-84.

Brown, J. K., and Bick, Y. A. E. (1986). Comparison of cellular effects of phomopsin and colcemid in Chinese hamster cells in vitro. *Cytobios* 79-91.

Chandler, C. J., Brownlee, R. T. C., Hook, R. J., Phillips, D. R., Reiss, J. A., and Edgar, J. A. (1988). Fast atom bombardment mass spectrometry of some anthracycline and bisanthracycline derivatives. *Biomed. Environ. Mass Spectrom.* 17:21-25.

Cowling, W. A., Wood, P. McR., Allen, J. G., Gladstones, J. S., and Hamblin, J. (1986). Effects of genetic resistance on *Phomopsis* incidence and potential stem and seed toxicity. In *Proceedings of the Fourth International Lupin Conference.* Western Australian Department of Agriculture, South Perth, pp. 230-239.

Cowling, W. A., Allen, J. G., and Wood, P. McR. (1988). Resistance to *Phomopsis* stem blight reduces the lupinosis toxicity of narrow-leafed lupin stems. *Aust. J. Exp. Agric.* 28:195-202.

Culvenor, C. C. J., Beck, A. B., Clarke, M., Cockrum, P. A., Edgar, J. A., Frahn, J. L., Jago, M. V., Lanigan, G. W., Payne, A. L., Peterson, J. E., Petterson, D. S., Smith, L. W., and White, R. R. (1977). Isolation of toxic metabolites of *Phomopsis leptostromiformis* responsible for lupinosis. *Aust. J. Biol. Sci.* 30:269-277.

Culvenor, C. C. J., Cockrum, P. A., Edgar, J. A., Frahn, J. L., Gorst-Allman, C. P., Jones, A. J., Marasas, W. F. O., Murray, K. E., Steyn, P. S., Vleggaar, R., and Wessels, P. L. (1983). Structure elucidation of phomopsin A, a novel cyclic hexapeptide mycotoxin produced by *Phomopsis leptostromiformis*. *J. Chem. Soc., Chem. Commun.* 1259-1262.

Culvenor, C. C. J., Edgar, J. A., MacKay, M. F., Gorst-Allman, C. P., Marasas, W. F. O., Steyn, P. S., Vleggaar, R., and Wessels, P. L. (1989). Structure elucidation and absolute configuration of phomopsin A, a hexapeptide mycotoxin produced by *Phomopsis leptostromiformis*. *Tetrahedron* 45:2351-2372.

Dustin, P. (1984). *Microtubules*, 2nd ed. Springer-Verlag, Berlin.

Edgar, J. A. (1985). Phomopsin A: structure and properties of a mycotoxin produced by *Phomopsis leptostromiformis*. In *Natural Products Chemistry 1984*, R. I. Zalewski and J. J. Skolik (Eds.). Elsevier, Amsterdam, pp. 85-94.

Edgar, J. A., and Culvenor, C. C. J. (1985). Aspects of the structure of phomopsin A, the mycotoxin causing lupinosis. In *Plant Toxicology*, A. A. Seawright, M. P. Hegarty, L. F. James, and R. F. Keeler (Eds.). Queensland Poisonous Plants Committee, Yeerongpilly, Australia, pp. 589-595.

Edgar, J. A., Culvenor, C. C. J., Frahn, J. L., Jones, A. J., Gorst-Allman, C. P., Marasa, W. F. O., Steyn, P. S., Vleggaar, R., and Wessels, P. L. (1985). The structure of phomopsin A, a mycotoxin produced by *Phomopsis leptostromiformis* (Kuhn) Bubak ex Lind. In *Trichothecenes and Other Mycotoxins*, J. Lacey (Ed.). Wiley, Chichester, West Sussex, England, pp. 317-324.

Edgar, J. A., Frahn, J. L., Cockrum, P. A., and Culvenor, C. C. J. (1986). Lupinosis: the chemistry and biochemistry of the phomopsins. In *Mycotoxins and Phycotoxins*, P. S. Steyn and R. Vleggaar (Eds.). Elsevier, Amsterdam, pp. 169-184.

Frahn, J. L., and Mills, J. A. (1959). Paper ionophoresis of carbohydrates. *Aust. J. Chem.* 12:65-89.

Frahn, J. L., Jago, M. V., Culvenor, C. C. J., Edgar, J. A., and Jones, A. J. (1983). The chemical and biological properties of phomopsin. *Toxicon Suppl.* 3:149-152.

Gale, P. J., Bentz, B. L., Chait, B. T., Field, F. H., and Cotter, R. J. (1986). Reduction in liquid secondary ion mass spectrometry: comparison of the fission fragment and liquid secondary ion mass spectra of organic dyes. *Anal. Chem.* 58:1070-1076.

Gardiner, M. R. (1964). Recent advances in lupinosis research. *J. Agric. Est. Aust.* 5:890-897.

Gardiner, M. R. (1967a). Lupinosis. *Adv. Vet. Sci.* 11:85-138.

Gardiner, M. R. (1967b). Cattle lupinosis: a clinical and pathological study. *J. Comp. Pathol.* 77:63-69.

Gardiner, M. R. (1967c). Liver cell abnormalities induced in mice by the fungal toxin causing lupinosis. *J. Pathol. Bacteriol.* 94:452-455.

Gardiner, M. R., and Petterson, D. S. (1972). Pathogenesis of mouse lupinosis induced by a fungus (*Cytospora* spp.) growing on dead lupins. *J. Comp. Pathol.* 82:5-13.

Gardiner, M. R., and Seddon, H. D. (1966). Equine lupinosis. *Aust. Vet. J.* 42:242-244.

Hackbarth, J. (1961). Lupinosis in the light of old and new evidence. *J. Aust. Inst. Agric. Sci.* 27:61-67.

Hancock, G. R., Petterson, D. S., and Edgar, J. A. (1986). Laboratory detection of phomopsins. In *Proceedings of the Fourth International Lupin Conference*. Western Australian Department of Agriculture, South Perth, pp. 209-219.

Hancock, G. R., Vogel, P., and Petterson, D. S. (1987). A high performance liquid chromatographic assay for the mycotoxin phomopsin A in lupin stubble. *Aust. J. Exp. Agric.* 27:73-76.

Hathway, D. E. (1969). Plant phenols and tannins. In *Chromatographic and Electrophoretic Techniques*, I. Smith (Ed.). Heinemann, London, pp. 390-436.

Kuhn, J. (1880). Die Schmarotzerpilze der Lupinenpflanze und die bekämpfung der Lupinenkrankheit der Schafe. *Ber. Landw. Inst. Univ. Halle* 2:115-128. [Cited by Hackbarth (1961) and Gardiner (1967a).]

Lacey, E., Edgar, J. A., and Culvenor, C. C. J. (1987). Interaction of phomopsin A and related compounds with purified sheep brain tubulin. *Biochem. Pharmacol.* 36:2133-2138.

Lanigan, G. W., Payne, A. L., Smith, L. W., Wood, P. McR., and Petterson, D. S. (1979). Phomopsin A production by *Phomopsis leptostromiformis* in liquid media. *Appl. Environ. Microbiol.* 37:289-292.

Liebscher, G. (1880). Beitrag zur Klarlegung der Frage nach den Ursachen der Lupinenkrankheit der Schafe. *Ber. Landw. Inst. Univ. Halle* 2:53-114. [Cited by Marasas (1974).]

Mackay, M. F., van Donkelaar, A., and Culvenor, C. C. J. (1986). The x-ray structure of phomopsin A, a hexapeptide mycotoxin. *J. Chem. Soc. Chem. Commun.* 1219-1221.

Marasas, W. F. O. (1974). *Phomopsis leptostromiformis*. In *Mycotoxins*, I. F. H. Purchase (Ed.). Elsevier, Amsterdam, pp. 111-127.

Marczewski, H. (1955). Przypadek masowego zatrucia swin lubinem gorzkim. *Med. Weter.* 22:738. [Cited in *Veterinary Bulletin* (Commonwealth Bureau of Animal Health) 26:293 (1956).]

Mills, J. A. (1978). A versatile spray reagent. *Aust. J. Chem.* 31:435-437.

Morcombe, P. W., Ryan, W. J., and Allen, J. G. (1986). Sandplain lupins (*Lupinus cosentinii*) as a summer feed for yearling steers. *Aust. J. Exp. Agric.* 26:13-18.

Morcombe, P. W., Croker, K. P., and Allen, J. G. (1987). Liver damage and the live-weight changes in Merino wether weaners grazing mixed crops of oats and sweet narrow-leafed lupins. *Aust. J. Exp. Agric.* 27:19-25.

Mortimer, P. H., and Ronaldson, J. W. (1983). Fungal-toxin-induced photosensitization. In *Plant and Fungal Toxins*, R. F. Keeler and A. T. Tu (Eds.). Marcel Dekker, New York, pp. 361-419.

National Health and Medical Research Council. (1987). *Food Standards Code 1987*. Australian Government Publishing Service, Canberra.

Neil, H. G., Toms, W. J., and Ralph, C. M. (1960). A survey of the incidence of lupinosis in sheep in the Dandaragan district in 1959. *J. Agric. West. Aust.* 1:565-572.

Papadimitriou, J. M., Bradshaw, R. D., Petterson, D. S., and Gardiner, M. R. (1974). A histological, histochemical and biochemical study of the effect of the toxin of lupinosis on murine liver. *J. Pathol.* 112:43-53.

Payne, A. L. (1983). Biosynthesis of radiolabeled phomopsin by *Phomopsis leptostromiformis*. *Appl. Environ. Microbiol.* 45:389-392.

Payne, A. L., Edgar, J. A., Frahn, J. L., and Culvenor, C. C. J. (1985). Biosynthetic studies on phomopsin A. In *Trichothecenes and Other Mycotoxins*, J. Lacey (Ed.). Wiley, Chichester, West Sussex, England, pp. 281-287.

Peterson, J. E. (1978). *Phomopsis leptostromiformis* toxicity (lupinosis) in nursling rats. *J. Comp. Pathol.* 88:191-203.

Peterson, J. E. (1986). The toxicity of phomopsin. In *Proceedings of the Fourth International Lupin Conference*. Western Australian Department of Agriculture, South Perth, pp. 199-208.

Peterson, J. E. (1990). Biliary hyperplasia and carcinogenesis in chronic liver damage induced in rats by phomopsin. *Pathology* (in press).

Peterson, J. E., and Lanigan, G. W. (1976). Effects of *Phomopsis rossiana* toxin on the cell cycle and on the pathogenesis of lupinosis in mice. *J. Comp. Pathol.* 86:293-306.

Peterson, J. E., Jago, M. V., Payne, A. L., and Stewart, P. L. (1987). The toxicity of phomopsin for sheep. *Aust. Vet. J.* 64:293-298.

Petterson, D. S., and Coackley, W. (1973). Changes in cell cultures produced by toxic lupin extracts. *Aust. J. Exp. Biol. Med. Sci.* 51:513-520.

Petterson, D. S., and Parr, W. H. (1970). Investigations into a hepatotoxin in lupin roughage. *Res. Vet. Sci.* 11:282-285.

Petterson, D. S., Howlett, R. M., Robertson, T. A., and Papadimitriou, J. M. (1979). Alteration in cell division, morphology and motility induced by the toxic principle of lupinosis. *Aust. J. Exp. Biol. Med. Sci. 57*:211-223.

Petterson, D. S., Peterson, J. E., Smith, L. W., Wood, P. McR., and Culvenor, C. C. J. (1985). Bioassay of the contamination of lupin seed by the mycotoxin phomopsin. *Aust. J. Exp. Agric. 25*:434-439.

Sethi, S. K., Nelson, C. C., and McCloskey, J. A. (1984). Dehalogenation reactions in fast atom bombardment mass spectrometry. *Anal. Chem. 56*: 1975-1977.

Tonsing, E. M., Steyn, P. S., Osborn, M., and Weber, K. (1984). Phomopsin A, the causative agent of lupinosis, interacts with microtubules in vivo and in vitro. *Eur. J. Cell Biol. 35*:156-164.

van Warmelo, K. T., Marasas, W. F. O., Adelaar, T. F., Kellerman, T. S., van Rensburg, I. B. J., and Minne, J. A. (1970). Experimental evidence that lupinosis of sheep is a mycotoxicosis caused by the fungus, *Phomopsis leptostromiformis* (Kuhn) Bubak, *J. S. Afr. Vet. Med. Assoc. 41*: 235-247.

Williams, D. H. (1984). Structural studies on some antibiotics of the vancomycin group, and on the antibiotic-receptor complexes, by ^{1}H NMR. *Acc. Chem. Res. 17*:364-369.

Zurn, F. A. (1879). Massenerkrankung von Schafen durch den Genuss befallener Lupinen. *Vortr. Thierarzte 7*:251-277. [Cited by Gardiner (1967a).]

19

Phytotoxins from Fungi Attacking Weedy Plants

Gary A. Strobel, Doug Kenfield,[*] and Greg Bunkers

Montana State University, Bozeman, Montana

Fumio Sugawara

Institute of Physical and Chemical Research, Riken, Wako-shi, Saitama, Japan

I. INTRODUCTION

Sometimes plant pathogens, especially fungi and bacteria, are capable of inducing symptoms of disease in their respective host(s) by virtue of the phytotoxins that they produce (Strobel, 1982). These compounds vary dramatically in size and also the chemical class to which they belong (e.g., peptides, terpenoids, macrolides, glycosides, phenolics, glycopeptides, and others). The

---

[*]*Current affiliation*: Kendolynn, Columbia Falls, Montana

phytotoxins also vary in host specificity, ranging from the identical host specificity of the pathogen to having no specificity whatever. Traditionally, most
investigators have been concerned with the isolation, characterization, and
mode of action of phytotoxins from plant pathogens of crop plants. Sometimes,
these phytotoxins have proven useful as tools for screening plants for toxin
insensitivity (disease resistance) and as probes of normal physiological plant
function.

Virtually all land plants are hosts to a score or more of phytopathogens.
Some of these plants are herbs, weed species, ornamentals, tropical species,
forest types, or important land cover forms. Generally, the disease-causing
fungi and bacteria of the vast majority of the plants in these groups have
not been examined for their ability to produce phytotoxins. Potentially, there
is a reservoir of novel biologically important substances awaiting discovery
in these organisms.

Over the past 8 years we have examined for toxin production a few select
fungal pathogens causing disease on some important weedy plants. Our rationale has been that the identification of such phytotoxins may prove useful
as new probes of plant function, at the same time serving the chemical industry with new models for herbicides since pathogens have had millenia to co-
evolve with their hosts and devise biochemical strategies to kill them or influence their gross physiology (Strobel, 1982; Cutler, 1986; Duke, 1986a,b;
Strobel et al., 1987).

In this chapter we discuss several examples of novel phytotoxins from
pathogens attacking weedy plants that have been isolated and characterized.
Host specificity of the compounds and other biochemical and physiological aspects of their activity are presented.

II. PATHOGEN ACQUISITION AND CULTURING

In some cases, fungal and bacterial pathogens of weedy plants have found
their way into various private and public culture collections in the world and
one has only to identify the host, the disease, and the causal organisms in
order to eventually acquire the pathogen from the holder. On the other hand,
many pathogens of weed species have yet to be isolated and identified. The
standard techniques used in phytopathological research can be used to isolate
the causal organism and ultimately show its relationship to the disease.

Once obtained in pure culture, the organism is placed in a defined liquid
medium under shaking and stationary conditions. A simple puncture-wound
leaf assay is used to guide phytotoxin production in the medium over a time
course of about 3 weeks. Sometimes, however, a simple aqueous extract of
1 to 2 g of the host plant is needed to stimulate the production of phytotoxins
by the pathogen. As a general rule it is advisable to keep the addition of
various concoctions to the medium at a minimum since these substances only
add difficulty to the phytotoxin purification process.

Phytotoxin isolation proceeds according to some of the general methods
used for the isolation of natural products from any source. One has only to
rid the medium of the pathogen, reduce the volume of the medium by flash
evaporation, and begin organic solvent extraction procedures. Flash chromatography, preparative thin-layer chromatography, and high-pressure liquid

chromatography are common techniques used for toxin isolation. This generalized procedure, however, will exclude proteins that may have phytotoxic activity, since solvent extraction will inactivate them. Characterization of the
phytotoxin is done by various spectroscopic means and ideally structural determination is considered complete after the compound is crystallized and its
x-ray structure determined.

III. EREMOPHILANES

Eremophilanes are bicyclic sesquiterpenoids. Over 200 examples of this group
have been characterized in higher plants (Pinder, 1977). One, capsidiol,
is a potent phytoalexin produced by pepper (Stillman et al., 1981). Numerous
eremophilanes have been found in fungi as well. These include phomenone
(*Phoma exigua*), phaseolinone (*Macrophomina phaseolina*), sporogen AO-1
(*Aspergillus oryzae*), and PR-toxin (*Penicillium roqueforti*) (Riche et al.,
1974; Dhar et al., 1982; Tanaka et al., 1984; Wei et al., 1975). Phomenone
and phaseolinone cause necroses in dicots. Sporogen AO-1 seems to be involved in the physiology of sporulation in *A. oryzae*. PR-toxin is a dangerous mycotoxin produced by the fermentive agent of blue cheese when it is
cultured on corn (*Zea mays* L.) kernels.

   Eremophilanes with phytotoxic properties were isolated from *Bipolaris
cynodontis*, a fungal pathogen of Bermudagrass [*Cynodon dactylon* (L.) Pers.]
(Sugawara et al., 1985b). This pathogen makes two eremophilanes—bipolaroxin
and its reduced analog, dihydrobipolaroxin. Bipolaroxin shows some host
selectivity. It causes lesions on Bermudagrass at 38 M, while a concentration
of 0.7 mM is required to produce detectable symptoms on wild oats (*Avena
fatua* L.), sugarcane (*Saccharum officinarum* L.), and corn. Dihydrobipolaroxin lacks the aldehyde moiety and is totally inactive.

   Drechslera gigantea, a relatively obscure pathogen of Bermudagrass and
quackgrass (*Agropyron repens* L. Beauv.), produces phytoactive compounds.
Organic extracts of culture filtrates contain numerous (at least 13) eremophilanes, many of which have novel structures. The basic structure of eremophilanes from *D. gigantea* includes a rigid bicyclic system with a keto group
at C8, unsaturation at C9-C10, a hydroxyl at C3, and cis methyl groups at
C4 and C5 (Fig. 1). Biogenic variability occurs via hydroxylation, epoxidation, and dehydration at C6 through C13. Hydroxylation at C1 occurs in one
compound. Organic synthesis of eremophilanes has been accomplished (Bohlman and Otto, 1982; Pinder, 1977).

   Our interest in this class of compounds was piqued by the observation
that when dicots were tested for sensitivity, a necrotic reaction developed
(Kenfield, et al., 1989b). When tested on monocots, however, phomenone,
petasol, and gigantenone evoked green islands, localized areas of chlorophyll
retention in senescing tissues. Cucumber (*Cucumis sativus* L.) was a notable
exception because this dicot developed green islands. Pumpkin (*Cucumis
pepo* L.), a close relative of cucumber, followed the norm and became necrotic. Further studies revealed that like cytokinin-induced green islands, ere-
mophilane-induced green islands retained their photosynthetic ability. Eremophilanes differ from cytokinins, however, by inducing a localized delay
of senescence which does not act as a metabolic sink. Furthermore, they are

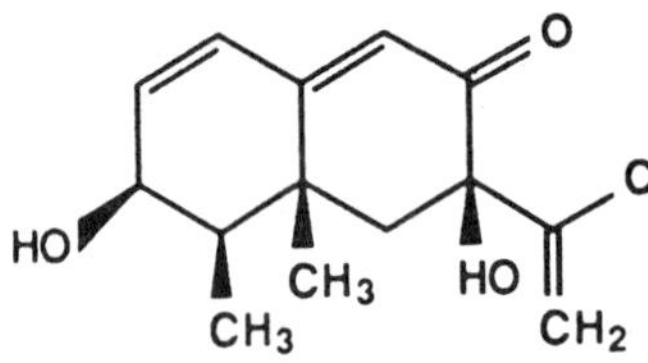

BIPOLAROXIN

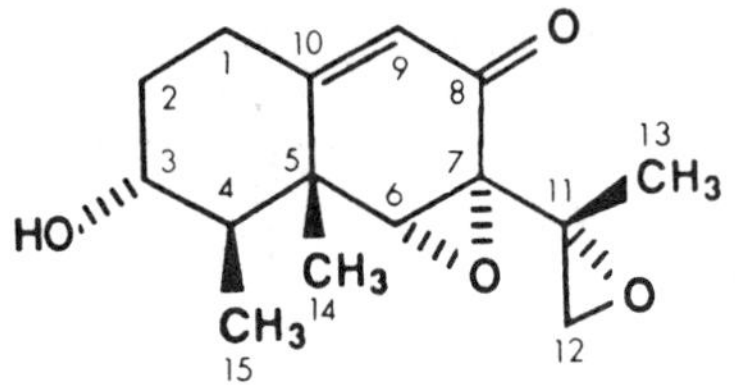

GIGANTENONE 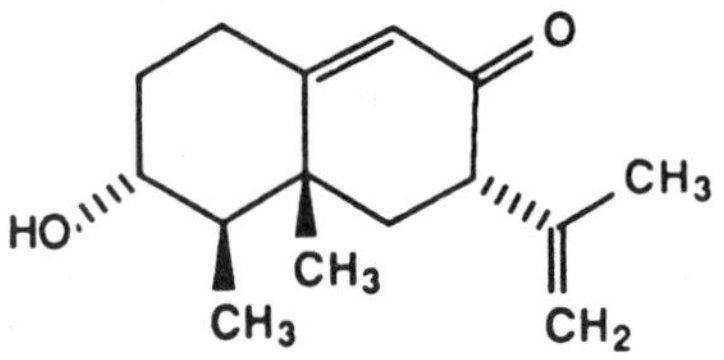   **PETASOL**

FIGURE 1 Chemical structure of eremophilanes.

nearly as effective as cycloheximide in inhibiting in vitro and in vivo protein synthesis, making their mode of action dramatically different from the cyto-kinins (Bunkers, 1989). In addition, they fail to induce synthesis of chloro-phyll in etiolated tissue from both monocots and dicots. Gigantenone and peta-sol, the two most interesting eremophilanes from *D. gigantea*, simulate auxin-like activity in their ability to stimulate rhizogenesis in cuttings of mung beans [*Vigna radiata* (L.) Wilczek]. In tissue culture, these compounds promote rooting of calli of common sunflower (*Helianthus annus* L.). When tested on explants of asparagus (*Asparagus officinalis* L.), a monocot, no effect on rhizogenesis was noted but shoots were larger and more branched than con-trols.

The mixed phytohormone-like response of plant tissue to these eremophil-anes offers another tool to explore bioregulation of important physiological processes ranging from senescence to rhizogenesis. In addition, the differ-ential response of monocots and dicots has implications in agriculture for selec-tive herbicidal as well as growth-promotive effects. Currently, we are ad-dressing the fate of these interesting chemicals once they enter the plant. Preliminary evidence using radiolabeled petasol indicates that it is converted to a very polar, water-soluble product within 12 h after application (Bunkers, 1989). The bioactivity of this conversion product is unknown, but it fails to elicit green islands when extracted from treated leaves and reapplied to fresh tissue. Chemically, it appears to contain the petasol moiety. Finally, we wish to stress that gigantenone and its chemical relatives join zinniol and polyhydroxamates as the only pathogen-produced compounds chemically iden-tified known to cause green islands (Atking and Neilands, 1972; Robeson and

Strobel, 1984). Numerous researchers have ascribed this activity in higher plants to purein-based "cytokininlike" compounds, but the chemistry support- ing this speculation is incomplete (Dekhuijzen, 1976). More attention should be addressed to the possible involvement of eremophilanes and their lactone derivatives in the normal physiological functions of plants.

IV. OPHIOBOLINS

A second group of terpenes recognized as phytotoxins are the ophiobolins, a group of sesterterpenoids. Ophiobolin A is the original and most widely studied member of this group, and more than 20 biogenic analogs are now known. Ophiobolins have been implicated in two of the most significant epi- phytotics of recent times: the Bengal rice famine of 1943 and the Southern corn leaf blight epidemic in the United States in 1972 (Strobel et al., 1988). In both diseases, the pathogen was a *Drechslera* sp. (with telemorph in the genus *Cochliobolus*) known to produce a contingent of ophiobolins. *D. maydis*, the etiological agent of southern corn leaf blight, has been shown to produce ophiobolin A, 6-epiophiobolin A, 25-hydroxyophiobolin I, 3-anhydro-6-epio- phiobolin A, ophiobolin I, and the previously known ophiobolin C (Fig. 2) (Sugawara et al., 1987).

6-Epiophiobolin-A, which differs from ophiobolin A only in the orientation of the proton on C6, can selectively inhibit CO_2 fixation in corn bearing Tms (Texas male sterile) cytoplasm at concentrations three orders of magnitude be- low that required for the same effect in corn bearing normal cytoplasm (Suga- wara et al., 1987). Ophiobolin A is not discriminating in its toxicity toward these two germplasms of corn. Thus, in corn, 6-epiophiobolin-A is cultivar selective, showing that the most subtle of chemical changes can alter dramati- cally the bioactivity of a molecule. This notion of host specificity has to be tempered, however, because of the following example. *D. heveae* is a patho- gen of the rubber tree (*Hevea brasiliensis*) (Willd. ex A. Juss.) Mull-Arg., a relative of such noxious weedy euphorbs as leafy spurge (*Euphorbia esula* L.) and wild poinsettia (*Euphorbia heterophylla* L.). In an attempt to find euphorb-specific toxins, we analyzed metabolites of this fungus and found that it, too, produces a complement of ophiobolins including ophiobolin A and 6-epiophiobolin-A. Although 6-epiophiobolin-A was the most toxic, all the ophiobolins examined were phytotoxic to a variety of grasses and dicots (Strobel et al., 1988). Depending on the diversity of the cropping system, then, a phytotoxin could be considered both as host specific and broadly toxic—biological activities that are exploitable in an applied sense.

D. sorghicola, a pathogen of Johnsongrass, produces all the ophiobolins found in *D. maydis* except ophiobolin-C and 6-epianhydro-ophiobolin-A (Suga- wara et al., 1987). *D. oryzae*, causative agent of brown spot on rice, also produces the contingent of ophiobolins found in *D. maydis*. In addition, sev- eral novel ophiobolins occur, including ophiobolin J, which showed modest host selectivity on rice varieties (Sugawara et al., 1988a). The genetic com- patibilities of all three *Cochliobolus* spp. should make these fungi amenable to mating experiments and subsequent assessment of ophiobolin production correlated with pathogenicity.

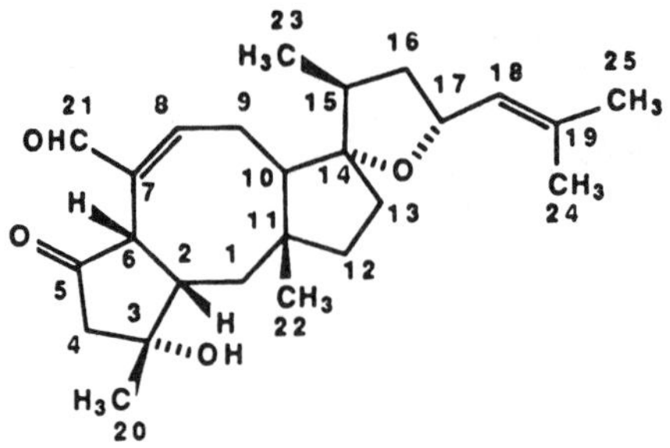

OPHIOBOLIN A

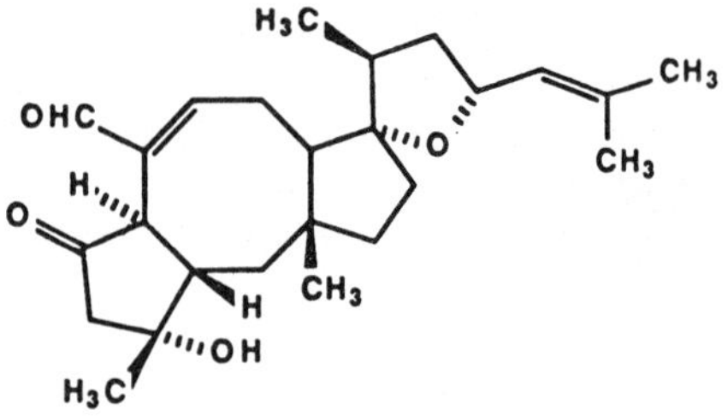

6-EPIOPHIOBOLIN A

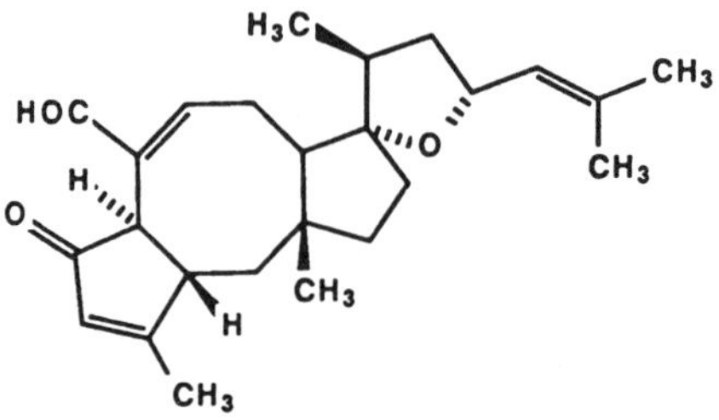

3-ANHYDRO-6-EPIOPHIOBOLIN A

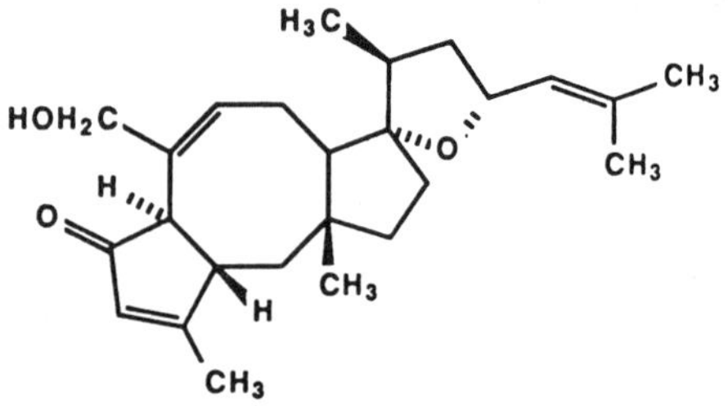

OPHIOBOLIN I

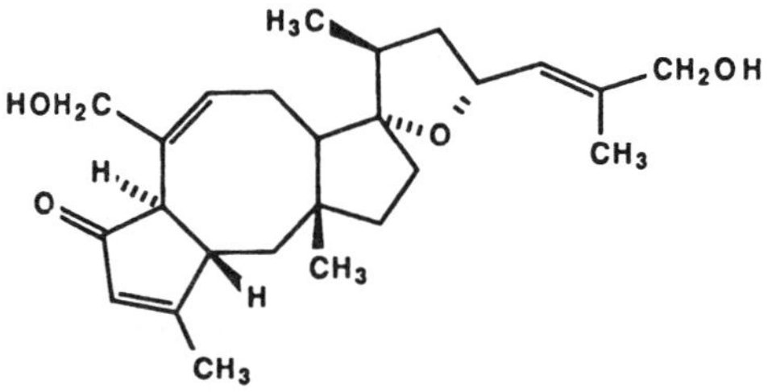

25-HYDROXYOPHIOBOLIN I

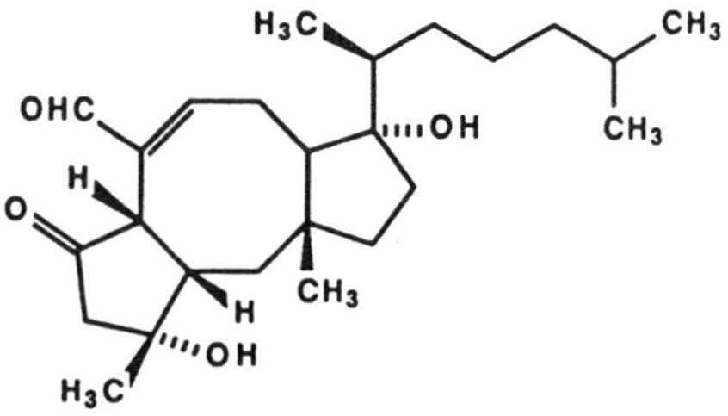

OPHIOBOLIN B

FIGURE 2 Chemical structure of ophiobolins.

V. CURVULINS

Curvulin is a cyclic polyketide produced by numerous fungi. Its chemistry had been worked out in the late 1960s, but nothing was known of its biological activity. Curvulin was isolated from *D. indica*, a pathogen of common purslane (*Portulaca oleraceae* L.) and spiny amaranth (*Amaranthus spinosus* L.), and the structure confirmed by x-ray crystallography (Kenfield et al., 1989b). A related compound, *O*-methylcurvulinic acid, was also obtained (Fig. 3). At nanomolar amounts, curvulin was somewhat selective toward purslane and spiny amaranth. As the concentration increased, curvulin became more broadly toxic. *O*-Methylcurvulinic acid, the methylated free acid of curvulin, was generally toxic, although a few plants were insensitive. A dozen analogs of curvulin are known from various fungi, offering excellent prospects for assessing structure-activity relationships of these ketides. Also, curvulin is readily synthesized by organic methods, making it amenable to structure-activity manipulations.

VI. DE-*O*-METHYLDIAPORTHIN

D. siccans is a pathogen of perennial ryegrass (*Lolium perenne* L.) and oats (*Avena sativa* L.), with the telemorph being *Pyrenophora lolii* (Lam, 1984). Toxic extracts from this fungus contained de-*O*-methyldiaporthin (Fig. 3), a novel isocoumarin (Hallock et al., 1988). The toxin is selective and effective when applied in nanomolar amounts to abaxial surfaces of leaves. De-*O*-methyldiaporthin is notable because very few coumarins have been characterized in fungi. Indeed, much of the literature on coumarins stresses their role

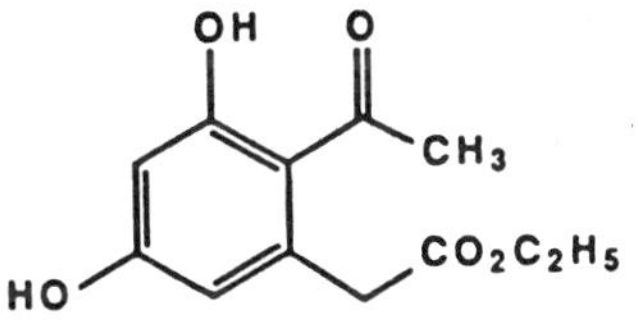

CURVULIN

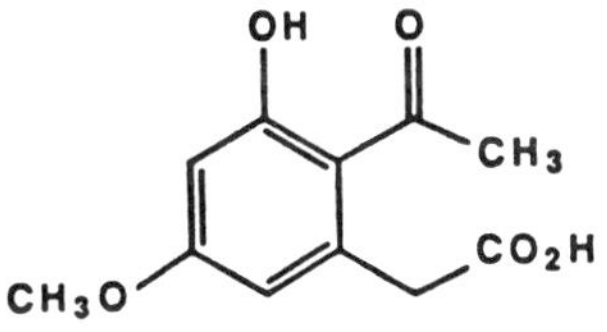

MONO-O-METHYLCURVULINIC ACID

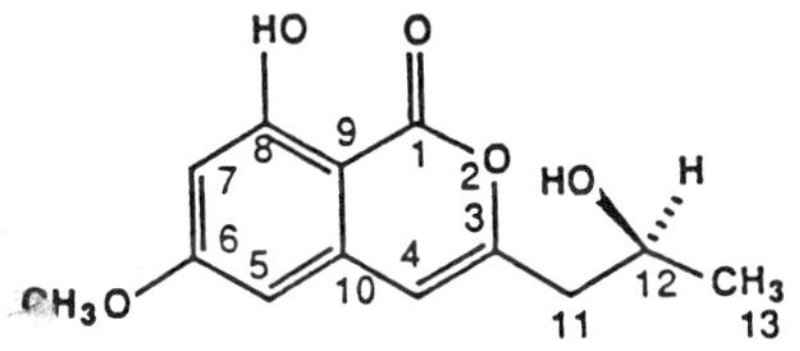

DE-O-METHYLDIAPORTHIN

FIGURE 3 Chemical structure of curvulins and de-*O*-methyldiaporthin.

as phytoalexins, antifungal compounds from higher plants (Murray et al., 1982; Tietjen et al., 1983), and as allelopathic compounds (Duke, 1986a).

VII. RESORCYLIDES

Resorcylides were first discovered in an unidentified *Penicillium* sp. (Oyama et al., 1978). Two isomers, cis and trans, were identified which differed in the stereochemistry of the α, β unsaturation adjacent to the ketone group. The cis isomer is relatively inactive; however, trans-resorcylide is cytotoxic, antimicrobial, and inhibits growth of roots of rice seedlings at concentrations approaching 1 ppm. These two isomers and the saturated analog have been identified in extracts of *D. phlei* (Hallock, 1988). The trans isomer caused necrosis on corn and crabgrass (*Digitaria sanguinalis*) at 0.06 µg per leaf. At 2 g per leaf, timothy (*Phleum pratense*), wild poinsettia, and sunflower (*Helianthus annua*) were also very sensitive. The cis isomer was inactive at 1 µg per leaf. The saturated resorcylide fell midway between the two and retained activity at 0.5 µg per leaf. Again, modest chemical alterations affect the bioactivity of these compounds and demonstrate the potential for developing important herbicides form these toxins.

VIII. TRITICONES

Triticones are novel toxins containing a rare spirocyclic γ-lactam moiety (Sugawara et al., 1988b). These compounds have been found in *D. tritici-repentis*, which causes tan spot on wheat (*Triticum aestivum* L.) and in *Curvularia clavata*, a pathogen of turfgrasses. Currently, eight triticones are known. Only triticones A and B, which have an exocyclic double bond adjacent to a ketone, are toxic. Triticone A (Fig. 4) causes necroses on numerous plants, kills protoplasts of wheat, and inhibits esterase activity and CO_2 fixation in wheat (Berglund et al., 1988). Weedy species that are sensitive include common lambsquarters (*Chenopodium album* L.), redroot pigweed (*Amaranthus retro-*

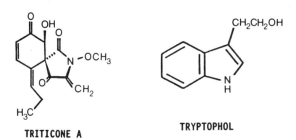

TRITICONE A

TRYPTOPHOL

FIGURE 4   Chemical structure of triticone A and tryptophol.

flexus L.), leafy spurge, and dandelion (*Taraxacum officinale* Weber). When tested on isolated chloroplasts of wheat, oats, or spinach, it inhibits photo-synthetic electron transport (PS-ETS) (Kenfield et al., 1988). However, with purified ferredoxin-oxidoreductase, the terminal enzyme in PS-ETS, it is stimulatory. Another seeming paradox is that triticone A quenches prote-ase activity in the fungus that produces it. Neither β-glucosidase nor ester-ase activity in this fungus are affected. In the test tube, triticone A reacts stoichiometrically with cysteine in less than 1 min. This affinity for sulfhy-dryl groups is thought to be responsible for some of its biological activity—a premise reinforced by the ability of triticone A to inhibit ficin, a known sulf-hydryl protease. Thus, when assaying tissue or organelles, triticone A ap-pears to be nonselectively toxic. At the molecular level, however, it is selec-tive and has great potential as an analytical tool for studying active sties on enzymes and site-specific sensitivity in multicomponent systems such as PS-ETS.

IX. AMINO ACID DERIVATIVES

A. Tryptophol

Tryptophol (Fig. 4) is a major metabolite in culture filtrates of *D. nodulosum*, a pathogen of goose grass [*Eleusine indica* (L.) Gaerth.] (Sugawara and Stro-bel, 1987). At a concentration of 0.6 mM, tryptophol is selectively toxic to young leaves of goose grass. As the concentration is increased to 6 mM, selec-tivity is lost and tryptophol is toxic to many grasses and dicots.

B. Diketopiperazines

Exserohilum holmi is a pathogen on crowsfootgrass (*Dactyloctenium aegyptium*), an annual weedy grass of the Old World tropics. This fungus makes two novel diketopiperazines and a *p*-bromobenzoate derivative was made of one, exsero-hilone. It was crystallized and its structure determined by x-ray crytallo-graphy (Sugawara et al., 1985a).

Dihydroexserohilone also produced by *E. holmi* was determined by spectro-scopic analyses. Both compounds showed nonselective toxicity toward several plant species at 10^{-4} and 10^{-5} M. These phytotoxins produced necrotic le-sions surrounded by reddish-brown borders.

Maculosin is a fascinating cyclic dipeptide belonging to the chemical class of diketopiperazines. A number of these compounds were discovered from an isolate of *Alternaria alternata* cultured from diseased spotted knapweed (*Centaurea maculosa* Lam.) (Stierle et al., 1988). Numerous, nontoxic diketo-piperazines were identified, but one, cyclo(L-Pro-L-Tyr) (= maculosin-1), caused necrotic lesions on spotted knapweed at 10 M. Even at 1 mM, maculo-sin-1 did not affect 19 other grasses and dicots that were tested or other *Centaurea* spp. This makes maculosin-1 the first phytotoxin produced by a pathogen of weeds that shows such a high degree of host specificity—a pleas-ant surprise because the genetic diversity of weeds has been considered to preclude the occurrence of host specificity (Dinoor and Eshed, 1984). Macu-losin-1 has been synthesized from t-BOC-L-proline and the methyl ester of L-tyrosine. The synthetic product retains the host specificity of the natural compound.

X. DISCUSSION

Results of studies on pathogens of weed species have shown phytotoxicology to be rich in novel structures and intriguing bioactivity. Even previously known chemicals such as curvulin have tremendous impact on the biology of the interacting organisms. The future of this field is exciting, especially in associations where one eukaryote—a fungus—produces toxins that regulate or kill another eukaryote—a higher plant. The chemistry of the attack must be finely tuned or the pathogen may become autotoxic. These are examples of pathogenic associations that offer tremendous potential to the searcher of natural products for use as selective herbicides.

Numerous inferences can be drawn from the results listed above. First, it generally appears that toxins are usually found as groups of related analogs which usually encompass a range of biological activities. Most likely, these "phytotoxins" are biosynthetic intermediates which play some role in microbial physiology. Their activity as phytotoxins could be serendipitous for the natural-products researchers, or they could have been selected because of some environmental advantage they offer the producing organism. Regardless, a disciplined analysis of extracts of pathogens, especially those involved with dramatic or unusual symptoms, will usually yield a number of interesting, potentially useful compounds. A good example is the study on *A. alternata* from knapweed (*Centaurea* spp.). Isolates of *A. alternata* usually produce an abundance of known phytotoxins such as tenuazonic acid and perylene quinones (Stierle et al., 1988). Because the researcher pursued necrogenic activity still present in fractions not containing these compounds, a host-specific toxin was discovered. In contrast to the better known, more complex toxins produced by this fungus, maculosin can be synthesized readily, adding a further dimension to its commercial interest. The same is true of curvulin and its analogs.

A second general conclusion is that even when studying toxins from pathogens of crops, candidate herbicides can be discovered. The cultivar-specific 6-epiophiobolin-A has a broad range of activity when one looks outside the microcosm of the *D. maydis*-corn interaction. This observation can be tied to a general strategy for development of crops resistant to specific herbicides, such as the current attempts to make important crops resistant to glyphosate (*N*-phosphonomethyl glycine). Unlike resistance to the synthetic herbicides, resistance to naturally occurring toxins is already present in many germplasms. This resistance may be exploited more easily by traditional breeding approaches or bioengineering (wide hybridization or transposon mutagenesis), thus circumventing problems inherent in effecting expression of prokaryotic genes in higher plants. A further extension of this strategy devolves from our observations that toxin production by pathogens is often regulated by chemicals produced in the host. Biosynthesis of toxins usually declines the longer a pathogen is cultured on artificial media. Addition of tissue or extracts from the host causes the pathogen to revert to a highly toxicogenic state. In a cropping system such as corn where Johnsongrass is a problem, incorporation of resistance in corn to ophiobolins could serve two purposes: (1) to maintain high yields in the presence of a dangerous pathogen, and (2) to allow the crop to serve as an inoculum source for toxicogenic pathogens which would help control the weed. The genetic compatibility of *D. sorghicola* and *D.*

maydis should allow for development of cross-infective pathogens which produce these potentially useful chemicals, thus precluding problems of synthesizing such organically complex phytotoxins. Admittedly, these strategies are speculative but very feasible given the technical expertise available today. The major point is that they represent a biorational approach to agricultural problems based on fundamental knowledge of the pertinent molecular biology. Such approaches can be both profitable and environmentally sound.

In conclusion, recent studies have uncovered novel and previously known phytotoxins which should elicit a broad-ranged interest as potential herbicides. Curvulin and maculosin-1 are readily synthesized and represent both nonselective and extremely selective possibilities for direct application. More complex organics such as the eremophilanes, resorcylides, triticones, and ophiobolins are useful both as tools for understanding biochemical and physiological processes in plants and as selective, biorational agrichemicals.

ACKNOWLEDGMENTS

The majority of the work reported herein was supported, in part, by NSF grant DMB-8607347 to J. Clardy, Cornell University, and G. Strobel, Montana State University. Help from the Montana Agricultural Experiment Station and the Montana Department of Agriculture, Noxious Weed Trust Fund, is also appreciated.

REFERENCES

Atkin, C. L., and Neilands, J. B. (1972). Leaf infectious: siderochromes (natural polyhydroxymates) mimic the "green island" effect. *Science 176*: 300-301.

Berglund, D., Strobel, S., Sugawara, F., and Strobel, G. (1988). Flow cytometry as a method for assaying the biological activity of phytotoxins. *Plant Sci. 56*:183-188.

Bohlman, F., and Otto, W. (1982). Synthese des Isopetasols. *Liebigs Ann. Chem.* 186-190.

Bunkers, G. (1989). Ph.D. thesis, Montana State University, Bozeman.

Cutler, H. G. (1986). Isolating, characterizing, and screening mycotoxins for herbicidal activity. In *The Science of Allelopathy*, A. R. Putnam and C. S. Tang (Eds.). Wiley-Interscience, New York, pp. 147-170.

Dekhuijzen, H. M. (1976). Endogenous cytokinins in healthy and diseased plants. In *Encyclopedia of Plant Physiology, New SEries*, Vol. 4, *Physiological Plant Pathology*, R. Heitefuss and P. H. Williams (Eds.). Springer-Verlag, New York, pp. 538-540.

Dhar, T. K., Siddiqui, K., and Ali, E. (1982). Structure of phaseolinone, a novel phytotoxin from *Macrophomina phaseolina. Tetrahedron Lett. 23*:5459-5462.

Dinoor, A., and Eshed, N. (1984). The role and importance of pathogens in natural plant communities. *Annu. Rev. Phytopathol. 22*:443-466.

Duke, S. O. (1986a). Microbially produced phytotoxins as herbicides—a perspective. In *The Science of Allelopathy*, A. R. Putnam and C. S.

Tang (Eds.). Wiley-Interscience, New York, pp. 287-304.

Duke, S. O. (1986b). Naturally occurring chemical compounds as herbicides. *Rev. Weed Sci.* 2:15-44.

Hallock, Y. (1988). Ph.D. thesis, Cornell University, Ithaca, N.Y.

Hallock, Y., Clardy, J., Kenfield, D., and Strobel, G. (1988). De-O-methyl-diaporthin, a new phytotoxin from *Drechslera siccans*. *Phytochemistry* 27:3123-3125.

Kenfield, D. S., Strobel, S., Sugawara, F., Berglund, D., and Strobel, G. A. (1988). Triticone A, a novel bioactive lactam with potential as a molecular probe. *Biochem. Biophys. Res. Commun.* 157:174-182.

Kenfield, D. S., Bunkers, G., Wu, Y.-H., Strobel, G. A., Sugawara, F., Hallock, Y., and Clardy, J. (1989a). Gigantenone—a novel phytohormone mimic. *Experientia* (in press).

Kenfield, D. S., Hallock, Y. F., Clardy, J., and Strobel, G. A. (1989b). Curvulin and O-methylcurvulinic acid: phytotoxic metabolites of *Drechslera indica* which cause necroses on purslane and spiny amaranth. *Plant Sci.* 60:123-127.

Lam, A. (1984). *Drechslera siccans* from ryegrass fields in England and Wales. *Trans. Br. Mycol. Soc.* 83:305-311.

Murray, R. D. H., Mendez, J., and Brown, A. A. (Eds.). (1982). *The Natural Coumarins: Occurrence, Chemistry, and Biochemistry.* Wiley, Chichester, West Sussex, England.

Oyama, H., Sassa, T., and Ikeda, M. (1978). Structures of new plant growth inhibitors, *trans*- and *cis*-resorcylides. *Agric. Biol. Chem.* 42: 2408-2409.

Pinder, A. R. (1977). The chemistry of the eremophilane and related sesquiterpenes. *Fortschr. Chem. Org. Naturst.* 34:81-186.

Riche, C., Pascard-Billy, C., Devys, M., Gaudemer, A., and Barbier, M. (1974). Structure crystalline et moléculaire de la phomenone, phytoxine produite par le champignon *Phoma exigua* var. *non-oxydabilis*. *Tetrahedron Lett.* 32:2765-2766.

Robeson, D. J., and Strobel, G. (1984). Zinniol induces chlorophyll retention in barley leaves: the selective action of a non-host-specific phytotoxin. *Phytochemistry* 23:1597-1599.

Stierle, A., Cardellina, J. H., II, and Strobel, G. (1988). Maculosin, a host-specific phytotoxin for spotted knapweed from *Alternaria alternata*. *Proc. Natl. Acad. Sci. USA* 85:8008-8011.

Stillman, M. J., Stothers, J. B., and Stoessl, A. (1981). Capsidiol and 1-epicapsidiol: absolute configuration, nmr, and optical spectra of the dibenzoates. *Can. J. Chem.* 59:2303-2305.

Strobel, G. (1982). Phytotoxins. *Annu. Rev. Biochem.* 51:309-333.

Strobel, G. A., Sugawara, F., and Clardy, J. (1987). Phytotoxins from plant pathogens of weedy plasnt. *Am. Chem. Soc. Symp. Ser.* 330:516-523.

Strobel, G., Kenfield, D., and Sugawara, F. (1988). The incredible fungal genus—*Drechslera* and its phytotoxic ophiobolins. *Phytoparasitica* 16: 145-152.

Sugawara, D., Sugawara, F., Strobel, G. A., Yali Fu, He Cun-Heng, and Clardy, J. (1985a). Exserohilone: A novel phytotoxin produced by *Exserohilum holmii*. *J. Org. Chem.* 50:5631-5633.

Sugawara, F., and Strobel, G. A. (1987). Tryptophol, a phytotoxin produced by *Drechslera nodulosum*. *Phytochemistry 26*: 1349-1351.

Sugawara, F., Strobel, G., Fisher, L. E., Van Duyne, G. D., and Clardy, J. (1985b). Bipolaroxin, a selective phytotoxin produced by *Bipolaris cynodontis*. *Proc. Natl. Acad. Sci. USA 82*: 8291-8294.

Sugawara, F., Strobel, G., Strange, R., Siedow, J., Van Dyne, G. D., and Clardy, J. (1987). Phytotoxins from the pathogenic fungi *Drechslera maydis* and *Drechslera sorghicola*. *Proc. Natl. Acad. Sci. USA 84*: 3081-3085.

Sugawara, F., Takahashi, N., Strobel, G., Yun, C. H., Gray, G., Fu, Y., and Clardy, J. (1988a). Some new phytotoxic ophiobolins produced by *Drechslera oryzae*. *J. Org. Chem. 53*: 2170-2172.

Sugawara, F., Samsoedin, R., Takahashi, N., Liu, H., Fu, Y., Clardy, J., Strobel, S., Berglund, D. L., and Strobel, G. (1988b). Triticones, novel spirocyclic lactam compounds isolated from the plant pathogenic fungus, *Drechslera tritici-repentis*. *J. Am. Chem. Soc. 110*: 4086.

Tanaka, S., Wada, K., Marumo, S., and Hattori, H. (1984). Structure of sporogen AO-1, a sporogenic substance. *Tetrahedron Lett. 25*: 5907-5910.

Tietjen, K. G., Hunkler, D., and Matern, U. (1983). Differential response of cultured parsley cells to elicitors from two nonpathogenic strains of fungi: I. Identification of induced products as coumarin derivatives. *Eur. J. Biochem. 131*: 409-413.

Wei, R., Schnoes, H. K., Hart, P. A., and Strong, F. M. (1975). The sturcture of PR-toxin, a mycotoxin from *Penicillium roqueforti*. *Tetrahedron 31*: 109-114.

20

Phytotoxins of Microbial Origin

Horace G. Cutler

Richard B. Russell Center, Agricultural Research Service, USDA, Athens, Georgia

I. INTRODUCTION

In earlier reviews we have commented about the structural diversity of biologically active natural products from microorganisms and the broad range of activities, from growth promotion to inhibition, and the fact that very minor changes in structure can significantly alter the expression of selectivity and activity (Cutler, 1984, 1985, 1987, 1988a,b). These statements also hold true for phytotoxins of microbial origin; and as the search for biodegradable secondary metabolites for industrial use becomes more focused, the evidence of natural elaboration by microorganisms within chemical classes becomes staggering. It is clear that microorganisms can mutate specific molecules with facility, doing in very short periods of time that which takes the synthetic chemist weeks. This is seen in biotransformation exercises, where molecules are fed to organisms that neatly produce phytotoxic metabolites for further use. During the course of this chapter we examine specific phytotoxins, their congeners, and in certain cases, their biotransformed products in the context of their specific activity on plants.

II. TOXINS

A. Specific Toxins

1. AK Toxins I and II

Certain toxins have been delineated as such, usually in conjunction with their source of origin, for example, AK toxins I and II (Fig. 1). While we have discussed others in detail (Cutler, 1985, 1987, 1988a; Edwards et al., 1988), we now turn our attention to the AK toxins, which are host-specific toxins produced by the causal organism of black spot disease of Japanese pear. *Alternaria alternata* (formerly, *A. kikuchiana*) attacks susceptible cultivars, affecting both leaves and fruit, and induces necrosis. Susceptible cultivars include *Pyrus serotina* Rehder var. *culta*, cvs. Chojuro, Kikusui, and Kosui. A single droplet of culture filtrate is sufficient to induce necrosis in susceptible cultivars (Nakashima et al., 1982, 1985), indicating that only a small amount of each toxin is necessary for necrotic induction. In fact, this may be as little as one molecule per active site per cell (discussions with S. Nishimura). Since the threshold dose of AK toxin I is 5×10^{-9} M (0.0024 μg/mL) and that of AK toxin II is 10^{-7} M, the actual number of molecules applied to the test site may be ascertained by using Avogadro's number. Examination of the structures for both toxins reveals that each contains the amino acid phenylalanine: AK toxin I possessing the N-acetyl-β-methyl phenylalanine and AK toxin II the N-acetyl-β-demethyl moiety. Thus the former is characterized as 8-[(2'S,3'S)-2'-acetylamino-3'-methyl-3'-phenylpropionyloxy](8R,9S)-9,10-epoxy-9-methyl-deca(2E,4Z,6E)-trienoic acid and the latter as its 3'-demethyl derivative (Nakashima et al., 1985). At least two thoughts come to mind concerning the chemistry of the AK toxins. The first is the 9,10-epoxy-9-methyl-decatrienoic acid fragment, which is hauntingly familiar in the 2-amino-8-oxy-9,10-epoxydecanoic acid residue of the Cyl-1 and Cyl-2 toxins from *Cylindrocladium scoparium*, which causes sheath net blotch in rice (*Oryza sativa* L.) (Hirota et al., 1973a,b; Takayama et al., 1984); and the second is that the toxins are simple amino acid derivatives reminding one of the herbicide N-(phosphonomethyl) glycine.

2. AF Toxins I, II, and III

The AF toxins appear to be related to the AK toxins and are also metabolites of the fungus *Alternaria alternata*, but this particular strain is a strawberry pathotype and is pathogenic to only one strawberry cultivar, Morika-16, producing *Alternaria* black spot disease. However, the Japanese pear cultivar Nijisseiki is also susceptible to this strawberry pathotype. To date, AF toxins I, II, and III have been isolated and I induces necrosis in Morika-15 strawberry and Nijisseiki pear, while II affects only pear, and III affects both strawberry and pear. The structures of AF toxins I and III are yet to be clarified, and AF toxin II consists of a mixture of three stereoisomers (Nakatsuka et al., 1986). Each stereoisomer contains the 9,10-epoxy-9-methyl decatrienoic acid residue observed in the AF toxins and, more specifically, AF

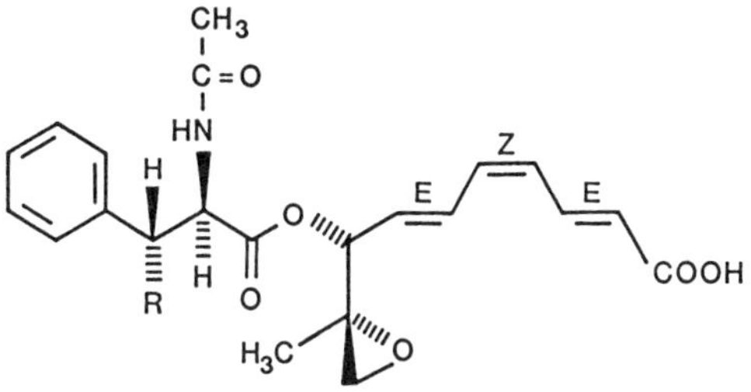

	R
AK Toxin I	CH₃
AK Toxin II	H

(Alternaria alternata)

FIGURE 1 AK toxins I and II.

toxin IIb contains the E,Z,E conformation noted in both AF toxins. Furthermore, both AF toxin IIa, with the Z,E,E conformation, and AF toxin IIc, with the E,E,E conformation, are toxic to strawberry, whereas AF toxin IIb is not (Fig. 2). A comparison of both sets of toxins suggest that derivatives of the 9,10-epoxy structure are interesting candidates for the production of selective phytotoxins. Indeed, the isomeric mixture of AF toxin II induced toxicity in Japanese pear at 10 ng/mL, although no damage was induced in strawberry at this concentration (Nakatsuka et al., 1986).

3. AV Toxins C, D, and E

A new disease emerged in Japan, in 1978, on mulberry (*Morus alba* L.) and quickly spread to 24 other genera. The pathogen, identified as *Acrospermum viticola* Ikata, causes zonate leaf spot in mulberry and has been found in all parts of the tropical and subtropical zones of the world (Takahashi and Teramine, 1984, 1986). Subsequently, cultures of *A. viticola* have yielded AV toxins C and D, while AV toxin E has been isolated from diseased mulberry leaves (Fig. 3). While the biological data presented are skimpy, these phytotoxins were active at about 10 μg/mL when leaves were soaked with solutions (Kinjo et al., 1987). As might be expected from analyzing the chemical structure, all the compounds are either red, or brown-yellow, because of the number of conjugations. It is also anticipated that further reports will be forthcoming on these toxins because there presumably exist AV toxins A and B.

4. FRT-A and FRT-B Toxins

Another class of specific toxins, which contain an epoxide ring as part of an epoxy-diketone system, are the fruit rot toxins (FRTs) A and B (Fig. 4) isolated from the fungus *Botryosphaeria berengeriana* (sexual stage of *Macrophoma* sp.). The pathogen causes apple fruit rot and appears to be quite widespread in northern Japan. During the isolation of the toxins it was observed that they occurred in a ratio of 3:1 (for A:B), and in the final steps of purification they were separated at the ratio of 130:40 mg (Sassa

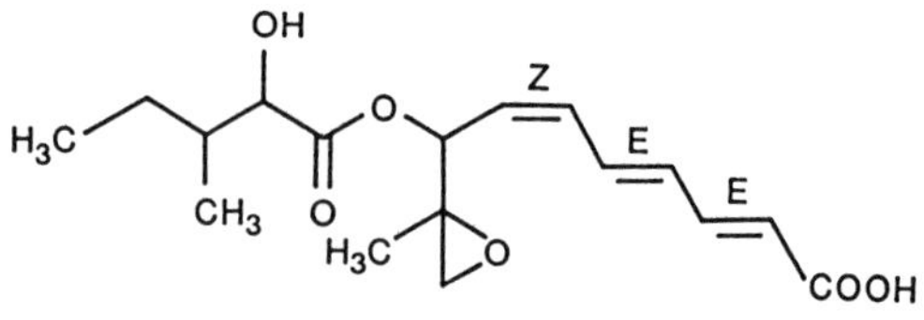

AF Toxin II a

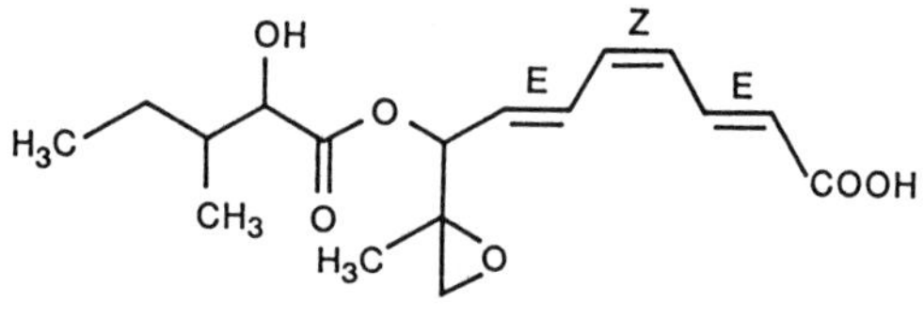

AF Toxin II b

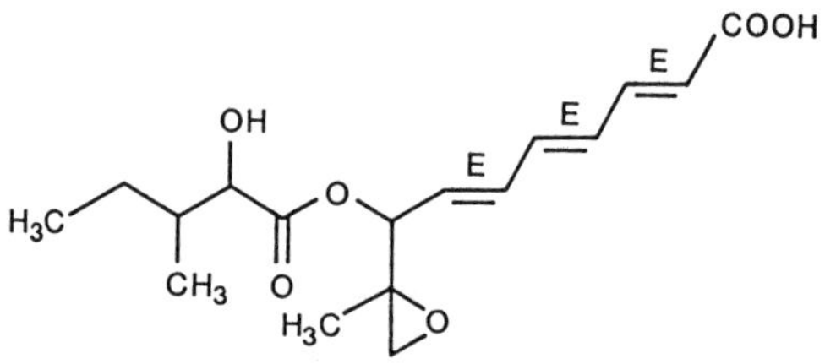

AF Toxin II c

(Alternaria alternata)

FIGURE 2 AF toxins IIa, b, and c.

and Onuma, 1983). As might be anticipated, the major difference between the two molecules is the *sec*-butyl group in A and the *iso*-butyl group in B, and there was a concomitant difference in biological activity when the toxins were applied to susceptible apple varieties (Sassa and Onuma, 1983). Toxin A induced necrotic lesions within a few hours when 5 µL, containing 1 µg, was applied to fruit surfaces, although lower concentrations of 0.16 to 0.32 µg of toxin A produced necrotic lesions when apples were observed after 1 day. The specific activity of toxin A was higher than that of toxin B, although no absolute values were given, and the relative amounts of necrosis were dependent on the apple variety so that, in order of sensitivity, the responses were Golden Delicious > Sekaiichi > Fuji > Starking Delicious. The responses with the toxins paralleled those obtained with the pathogen in the different apple cultivars (Sassa and Onuma, 1983). Surprisingly, FRT-B is identical to the antibiotic flavipucine, a metabolite of the fungus *Aspergillus flavipes* (Findlay and Radics, 1972), and it is probable that *Botryosphaeria berengeriana* uses the material for a double purpose: first, as an antibiotic to control competing organisms, and second, as a cytotoxic agent. Under

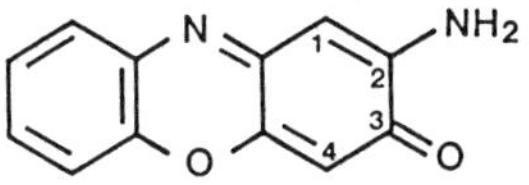

AV - Toxin C

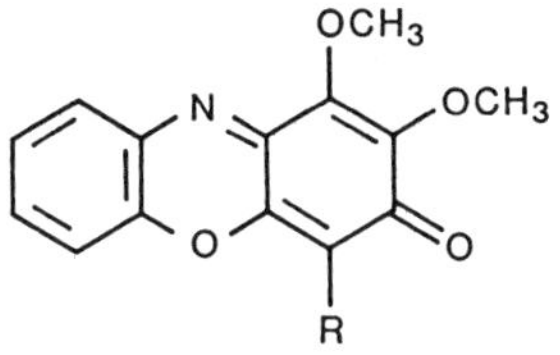

	R
R	
AV - Toxin D	R = H
AV - Toxin E	R = OCH3

(Acrospermum viticola)

FIGURE 3 AV toxins C, D and E.

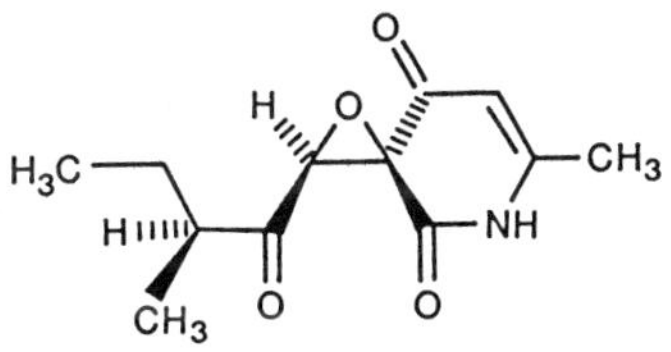

FRUIT ROT TOXIN A

(Botryosphaeria berengeriana)

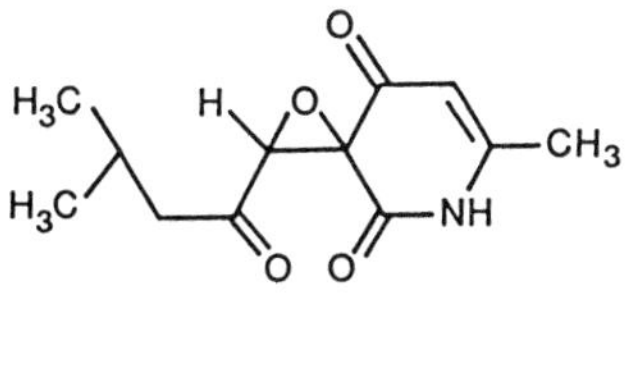

FRUIT ROT TOXIN B

(Botryosphaeria berengeriana)

FLAVIPUCINE

(Aspergillus flavipes)

FIGURE 4 Fruit rot toxins A and B and flavipucine.

certain circumstances the molecule is fairly reactive and it has been suggested
that FRT-A may react with sulfhydryl groups to give glyoxal derivatives,
which, in turn, may have biological activity (Sassa, 1983). The epoxy function was easily opened by treatment with thiophenol to yield a number of products (Sassa, 1983), and this observation led to a series of experiments with
FRT-A in the presence of other nucleophiles, photochemical decomposition
under fluorescent light, and the metabolism in situ in cv. Mutsu apple in the
dark. The products obtained from each regimen were tested in cv. Mutsu
apples. Of least importance was the photodecomposition product 3-formyl-4-
hydroxy-6-methyl-2-pyridone (Fig. 5), which was only slightly active. But
FRT-A induced lesions with 0.16 µg, *sec*-butylglyoxal with 10 µg, and the
thioacetal of *sec*-butylglyoxal (Fig. 6) with 0.32 µg. The 2-pyridone derivative of FRT-A (Fig. 7) does not appear to have been tested (Sassa et al.,
1987).

B. General Toxins

1. Macrophorins A, B, C, and D

Other phytotoxic metabolites have been isolated from the *Macrophoma*
fruit rot of apple organism (*Botryosphaeria berengeriana*), which are also
epoxides. These are the terpene-linked cyclohexenone epoxides, macrophorin
A, B, C (Sassa and Yoshikoshi, 1983), and D (Sassa and Nukina, 1984) (Fig.
8). Macrophorin D differs from the other three in that it is a β-hydroxy-
β-methylglutaric acid conjugate of macrophorin A. These metabolites are only
weakly phytotoxic to apple leaves (D was not tested), but their uniqueness
is their antibiotic activity. For example, macrophorin A was active against
Staphylococcus aureus (minimum inhibitory concentration, 25 ppm) and *Tricho-
phyton* spp. (MIC 6.2 to 25 ppm). Furthermore, macrophorin A and D were
potent self-inhibitors at 5 to 10 and 20 to 40 µg/disk, respectively, in bioassays, while B was effective at 200 µg and C at >800 µg/disk.

2. Alternaria Toxins

The genus *Alternaria* has provided a number of toxins and novel natural
products, some of which have highly selective herbicidal and phytotoxic properties (Cutler, 1988a). Among them are those obtained from *Alternaria solani*,
which as the species name implies, attacks solanaceous plants, including tomato and potato, wherein it produces early blight. Some exacting work has
been accomplished in isolating natural products from *A. solani*, especially
the discoveries of altersolanol A and a number of anthraquinones (Stoessl,

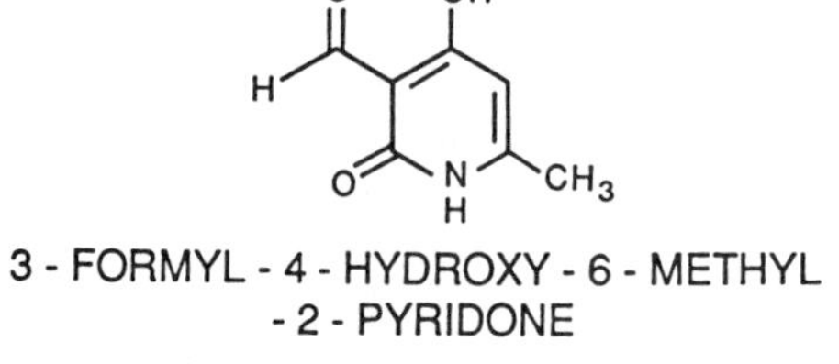

3 - FORMYL - 4 - HYDROXY - 6 - METHYL
        - 2 - PYRIDONE

FIGURE 5   3-Formyl-4-hydroxy-6-methyl-2-pyridone.

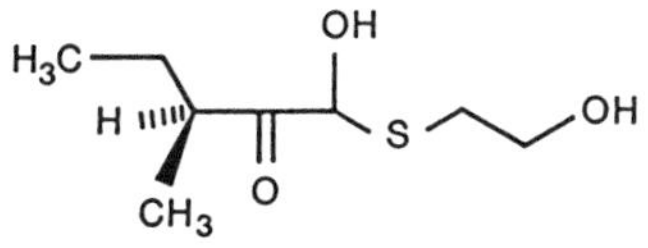

THIOACETAL OF SEC - BUTYLGLYOXAL

FIGURE 6 Thioacetal of *sec*-butylglyoxal.

1967, 1969), but none of these appeared to be the phytotoxic principle. Later work showed that there were at least two toxic materials that were specific toxins for potato, *Solanum tuberosum* cv. Russet Burbank (clone 420), and tomato, *Lycopersicon esculentum* cv. Early Hi Crimson, although lesions in treated tomato plants remained relatively small (<0.8 cm). Indeed, other test plants gave either no response or very minor lesions: for example, *Petroselinum crispum* (none), *Nicotiana tabacum* (small), *Brassica oleracea* var. *capitata* (small), *Citrullus vulgaris* (small), *Solanum integrifolium* (none), *Apium graveolens* (none), *Raphanus sativus* (none), *Solanum dulcamara* (small), *Carthamus tintorius* (small), and *Cucumis anguria* (small) (Matern et al., 1978). The identities of the toxins were not released at the time that Matern's work was published, but later, the structures for three phytotoxic metabolites, solanapyrones A, B, and C (Fig. 9), were reported (Ichihara et al., 1983). Of these solanapyrone A induced leaf necrosis in potato when applied at 100 µg per 100 µL, but data concerning the remaining two metabolites were not given. The authors did point out the structural similarity of the solanapyrones to the betaenones, which possess phytotoxic properties, and compactin (Fig. 10), a metabolite from *Penicillium* and *Monascus* species (Endo et al., 1976; Endo, 1979) which has both hypocholesterolemic properties and is now used in derivatized form to control blood serum cholesterol in humans and which has been shown to inhibit the growth of tobacco callus tissue (2.5 µM compactin inhibited callus yield by 50%), suggesting that it may be used as a growth retardant or herbicide (Hashizume et al., 1983). Later, a further phytotoxin was characterized from *A. solani* and named zinnolide (Ichihara et al., 1985) (Fig. 11), although it was structurally unrelated to the solanapyrones. It was, however, related to zinniol (Fig. 12), a metabolite that had been isolated from the phytopathogenic fungus *Alternaria zinniae* (Starratt, 1968). Zinnolide was bioassayed against lettuce seedlings, where it produced a 34.5% inhibition of hypocotyl growth and 22% root growth inhibition at concentrations of 100 ppm. A footnote to the *A. solani* toxin history is that in 1987

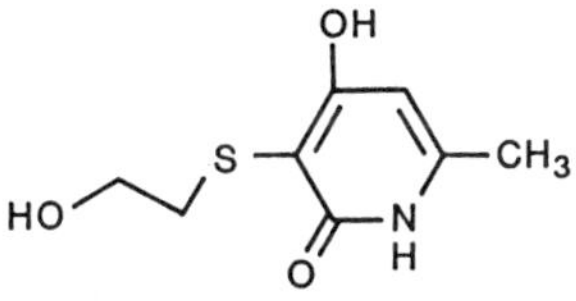

FRUIT TOXIN A, 2 - PYRIDONE DERIVATIVE

FIGURE 7 Fruit toxin A, 2-pyridone derivative.

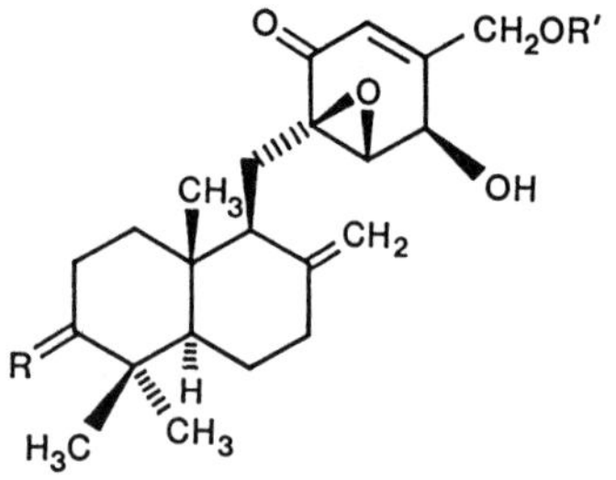

	R	R'
MACROPHORIN A	H_2	H
MACROPHORIN B	O	H
MACROPHORIN C	OH H	H
MACROPHORIN D	H_2	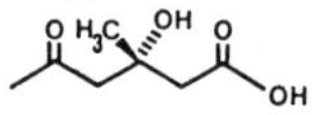

(Botryophaeria berengeriana)

FIGURE 8   Macrophorins A , B , C , and D.

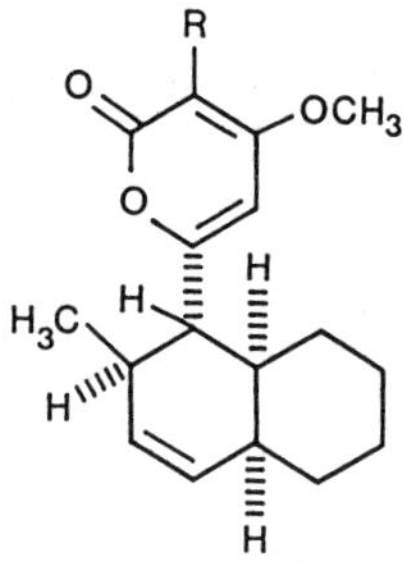

	R
SOLANAPYRONE A	CHO
SOLANAPYRONE B	CH₂OH

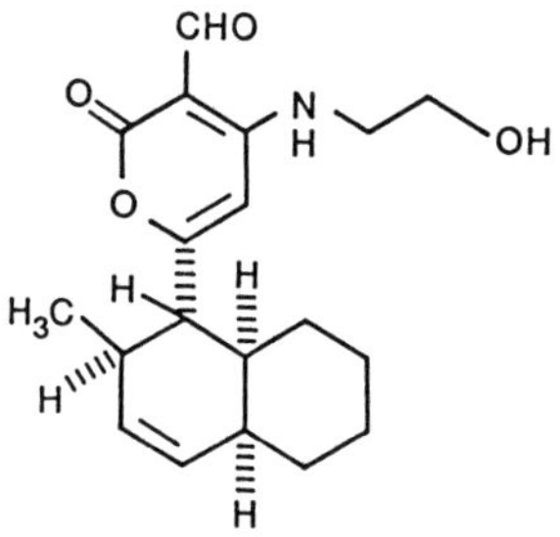

SOLANAPYRONE C

(Alternaria solani)

FIGURE 9   Solanapyrones A , B , and C.

418

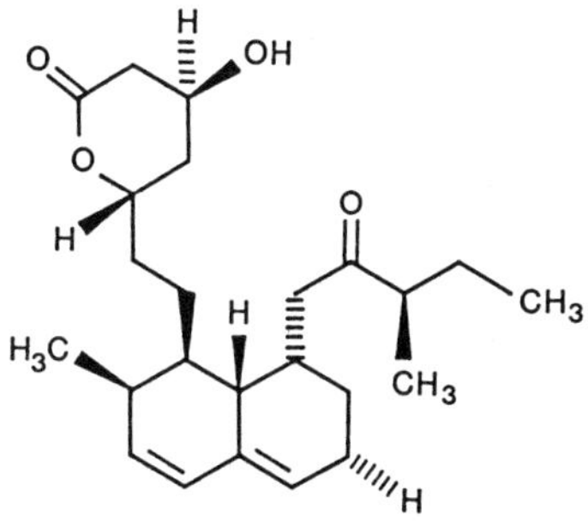

COMPACTIN

(Penicillium brevicompactum)

(Penicillium cyclopium)

FIGURE 10 Compactin.

(Ichihara et al., 1987) the synthesis of (±)solanapyrone A was accomplished. Doubtless more synthetic elaborations of these molecules will follow, as they must for many other biologically active natural products, to produce biodegradable agricultural products and to screen for resistant cultivars in tissue culture.

3. *Fusarium Toxins*

The fusaria also produce many phytotoxins, which have been covered in previous reviews (Cutler, 1984, 1985). However, there are a series of related compounds from the fusaria and other organisms that appear to play a major role in pathogenesis of fungi. Among these are the naphthazarines from *Fusarium martiella* and *Neocosmospora vasinfecta*. Both organisms cause root and stem rot of peas, *Pisum sativum*, and in examination of the cultivar Kelvedon Wonder a sequence of events was noted. Immediately following infection, only marticin and isomarticin (Fig. 13) can be extracted from pea tissue, and it is these two compounds that are phytotoxic, their mechanisms of action being, first, the decarboxylation of α-keto acids, and second, the

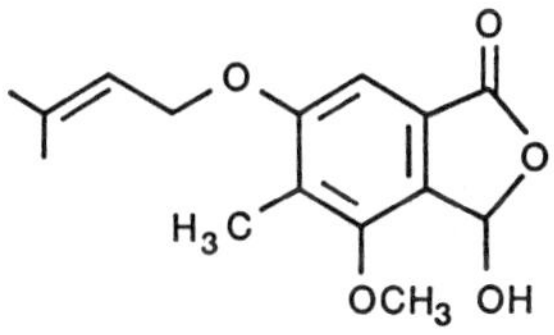

ZINNOLIDE

(Alternaria solani)

FIGURE 11 Zinnolide.

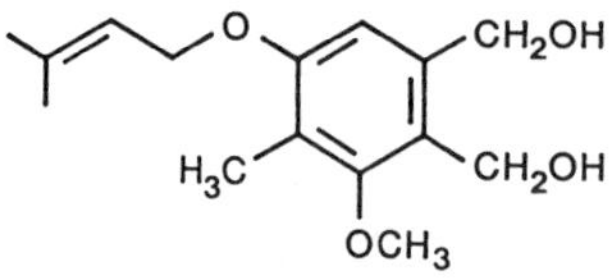

ZINNIOL

(Alternaria zinniae)

FIGURE 12 Zinniol.

inhibition of glutamine synthetase, thereby disrupting amino acid metabolism. During the course of the disease cycle, other events take place, including the altering of cell wall permeability in leaf tissue and the production of other pigments that range from being relatively phytotoxic to relatively nonphytotoxic. These include fusarubin (Fig. 14), novarubin (which lacks the aromatic CH_2OH group of fusarubin), javanicin (Fig. 15), and nor-javanicin (which lacks the CH_3 functional group of javanicin). Their relative toxicities are, respectively, 40, 35, 60, and 90 μg/g when tested on tomato shoot cuttings (Kern, 1978). In contrast, novarubin and nor-javanicin are quite active as fungicides against *Botrytis allii* (5 and 10 μg/mL, respectively), whereas the remainder of the compounds, including the marticins, require >500 μg/mL. By the time the infection has run its course in peas, only the marticins and fusarubin can be extracted from the tissues. Therefore, it appears that the marticins are synthesized more quickly than the other metabolites and they are also transported with greater ease (Kern, 1978). Javanicin and fusarubin 8-O-methyl derivatives are also produced by the fungus *Fusarium moniliforme*, which is a major parasite of grasses throughout the tropics and subtropics (Steyn et al., 1979). In addition to these metabolites, the 8-O-methyl derivatives of bostrycoidin and solaniol have been isolated, but in all cases they were not evaluated for phytotoxic properties and the only mention of biological activity was that of bostrycoidin, which strongly inhibited the growth of the tubercle bacillus in vitro (Steyn et al., 1979). A more recent study

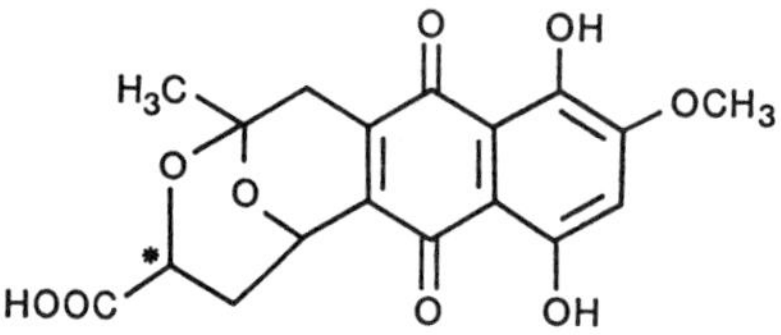

MARTICIN

*ISOMARTICIN

(Fusarium Martii)

(Necosmospora vasinfecta)

FIGURE 13 Marticin and isomarticin.

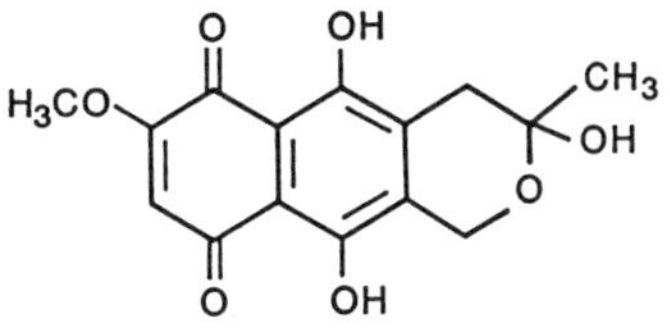

FUSARUBIN

(Fusarium solani)

FIGURE 14 Fusarubin.

has turned up some conflicting data relative to the phytotoxic action of 8-O-methyljavanicin isolated from *Fusarium solani*. At 10 ppm the metabolite suppressed the elongation of lettuce seedlings hypocotyls, although root growth remained normal. Higher concentrations of 100 ppm inhibited the growth of both hypocotyls and roots and at 500 ppm, necrosis occurred. However, rice seedlings treated with 8-O-methyljavanicin (Fig. 16) reacted quite differently to lettuce. At 100 ppm, the second leaf sheaths were promoted about 12%, while at 30 to 300 ppm the response was not as great (Kimura et al., 1981).

Again, fusarubin, javanicin, and anhydrofusarubin appear to play a role in the etiology of another disease, blight of citrus, which affects most of the citrus plantings in Florida. *Fusarium solani* was obtained from the fibrous roots of citrus trees exhibiting blight symptoms, cultured in liquid medium, and extracted with ethyl acetate to finally yield fusarubin, javanicin, and anhydrofusarubin. These compounds, when tested against germinating White Icicle radish seed, inhibited root growth and demonstrated that fusarubin was the most inhibitory (99%) and anhydrofusarubin the least (14%). Fusarubin was also the most toxic to the growth of rough lemon roots when tested on germinating seed (Baker et al., 1981). Recently, a new naphthoquinone, fusarubionic acid (Fig. 17), has been isolated from the fungus *Nectria haematococca* (imperfect stage, *F. solani*) but apparently it has not been tested for biological activity (Parisot et al., 1988).

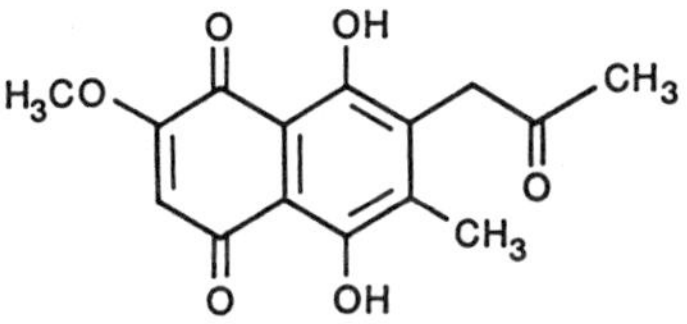

JAVANICIN

(Fusarium solani)

FIGURE 15 Javanicin.

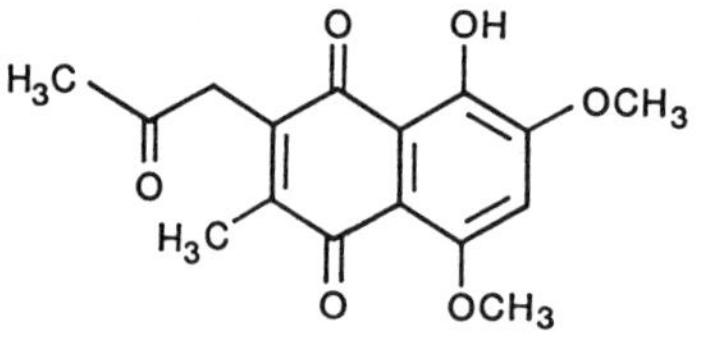

8 - 0 - METHYLJAVANICIN

(Fusarium solani)

(Fusarium moniliforme)

FIGURE 16   8-O-Methyljavanicin.

C.   Toxins Possessing Herbicidal Properties

Because of the public perception, and accumulating data that support the
effect of many hard pesticides on the environment, there has been increased
interest in specific microbial natural products that control noxious plants.
One of the first compounds isolated in this regard was bipolaroxin (Fig. 18)
from the fungus *Bipolaris cynodontis*, which is a pathogen of Bermudagrass
(*Cynodon dactylon* L.). The metabolite was phytotoxic to Bermudagrass and
Johnsongrass (*Sorghum halepense*) at concentrations of 0.038 mM, but at concentrations of 0.38 mM it also affected sugarcane (*Saccharum officinarum*)
and goosegrass (*Eleusine indica*). At 0.76 mM both corn (*Zea mays*) and wild
oat (*Avena fatua*) were affected, and at the highest rate, 3.8 mM, fescue
(*Festuca* sp.) was controlled, but neither pigweed (*Amaranthus arvense*) nor
sunflower (*Helianthus annuus*) were killed. Neither were any symptoms observed on wheat (*Triticum aestivum*), barley (*Hordeum vulgare*), or cotton
(*Gossypium hirsutum*) (Sugawara et al., 1985). A second metabolite, dihydrobipolaroxin, was also isolated in conjunction with bipolaroxin and that compound, in which the terminal aldehyde of bipolaroxin had been reduced to
the alcohol, was inactive. Thus the aldehyde is necessary for biological activity and a possible mechanism of action has been postulated (Schneider and
Nakanishi, 1983) for these types of compounds, wherein a nucleophile conjugates to the enal function to give a 1,3-diol cleavage and, at the same time,
genesis of acrolein, which is phytotoxic, and an α-diketone, which may also

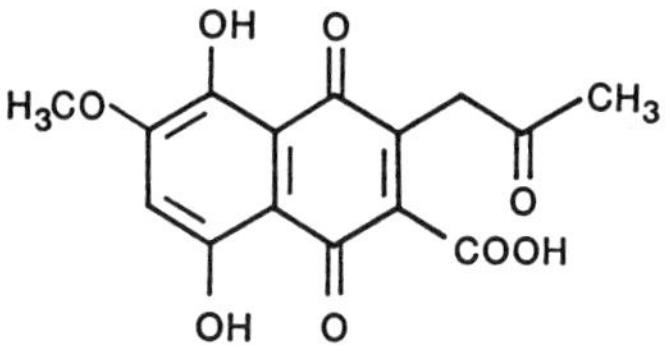

FUSARUBIONIC ACID

(Fusarium solani)

FIGURE 17 Fusarubionic acid.

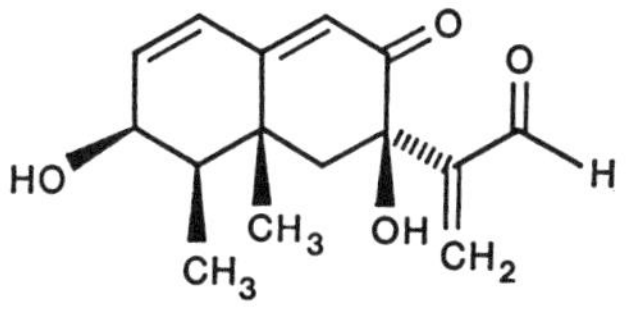

BIPOLAROXIN

(Bipolaris cynodontis)

FIGURE 18 Bipolaroxin.

be toxic. It is unlikely that such a reaction occurs with dihydrobipolaroxin
(Sugawara et al., 1985).

The discovery of bipolaroxin led to the synthesis of a monocyclic analog
of the B-ring (Lidert et al., 1988) because, as we have just noted, the arrangement of certain functions on that ring may be the key to biological activity.
The synthetic 6-hydroxy-6-(2'propenal)-4,4-dimethyl-2-cyclohexen-1-one
(Fig. 19), when applied as a 0.5% solution, was only moderately phytotoxic
to velvet leaf (*Arbutilon theophrasti*) and pigweed (*Amaranthus albus*), both
broadleaved weeds, but no effects were obtained on grasses. It was, however,
active against rice blast fungus (*Pyricularia oryzae*) and completely inhibited
that organism when added to suspension cultures at 5 ppm. But more important, synthesis and biological testing indicated that the specificity of bipolaroxin depends on more than the functionality and conformation of the B-
ring.

Stemphylium botryosum is a fungus whose many pathovars affect horti-
cultural crops from which specific phytotoxins have been isolated. A case in
point is stemphyloxin I (not to be confused with the stemphyltoxins, which
are perylenequinones), from *S. botryosum* pv. *lycopersici*, a foliage blight
disease of tomato (Fig. 20). The metabolite, a multifunctionalized β-ketoalde-
hyde *trans*-decalin, was unlike any phytotoxin, structurally, until the discovery of the betaenones. When the compound is applied to leaf surfaces by
puncturing the epidermis and adding a few microliters of various concentrations in solution (10 to 250 μg/mL), necrotic lesions appear within 14 h. The
most sensitive plant is tomato and the least is barley (*Hordeum sativum*).

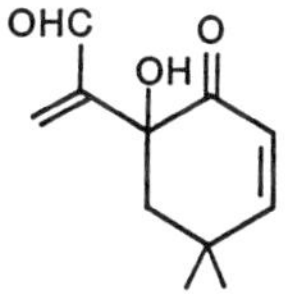

6 - HYDROXY - 6 - (2' PROPENAL) - 4,4 -
DIMETHYL - 2 - CYCLOHEXEN - 1 - ONE

FIGURE 19 6-Hydroxy-6-(2'propenal)-4,4-dimethyl-2-cyclohexene-1-one.

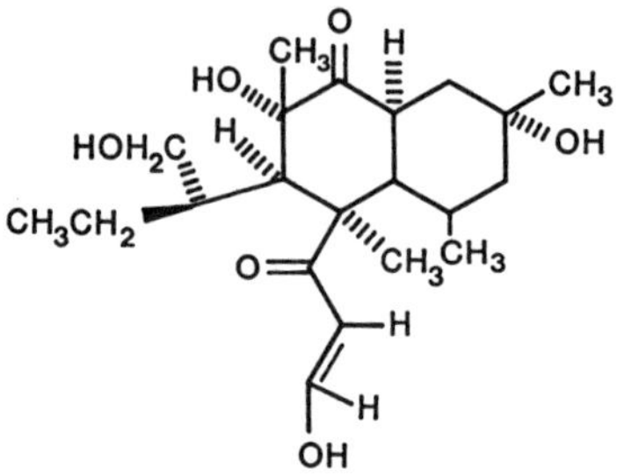

STEMPHYLOXIN I

(Stemphylium botryosum)

FIGURE 20 Stemphyloxin I.

More refined bioassays include the incorporation of ^{14}C-labeled amino acids into protein, and when white or green tomato cell suspension are used, there is complete inhibition of amino acid incorporation with 1 μM of stemphyloxin (Barash et al., 1983). The production of stemphyloxin is regulated by the amount of [Fe^{3+}] in the culture medium, and to ensure optimum yield, [Fe^{3+}] must be added to the substrate. It is possible that the metabolite interacts with [Fe^{3+}] in the plant and that the chlorosis observed in infected plants is due to an iron deficiency.

Stemphylium botryosum pv. *lactucum* is responsible for losses in lettuce and the probable phytotoxin involved in the death has, after some controversy, been established as stemphylin $C_{16}H_{16}O_8$ (Fig. 21) (not, as previously reported, $C_{17}H_{22}O_9$). The natural product is highly conjugated and, therefore, orange. But it is identical to the compound altersolanol A (Stoessl, 1967). When 5-μL droplets of 100 ppm solution of stemphylin were applied to lettuce leaves (*Lactuca sativa* cv. Trocadero) obtained from 3-week-old seedlings, and kept in a moist chamber, characteristic necrotic lesions appeared within 16 h. Unfortunately, 40 mg/kg caused death in mice (Assante and Nasini, 1987), making its practical use as an antibiotic or agrochemical doubtful.

The genus *Botrytis* is starting to yield some structurally interesting metabolites. Among these are O-methyldihydrobotrydial and deacetyl-O-methyl-

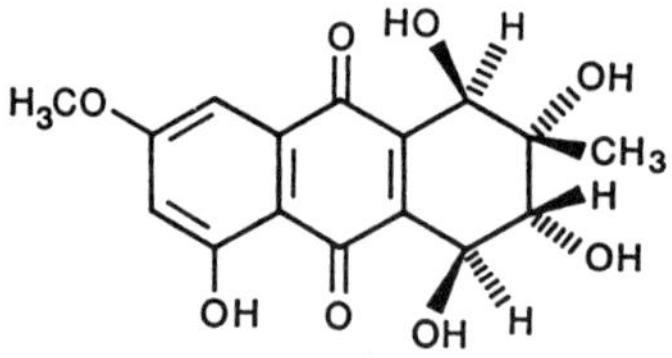

STEMPHYLIN = ALTERSOLANOL A

(Stemphylium botryosum)

FIGURE 21 Stemphylin = altersolanol A.

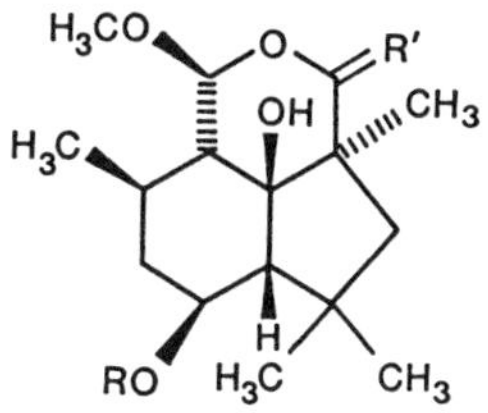

	R	R'
O-METHYLDIHYDROBOTRYDIAL	Ac	H$_2$
DEACETYL-O-METHYLDIHYDROBOTRYDIALONE	H	O

FIGURE 22 O-Methyldihydrobotrydial and deacetyl-O-methyldihydrobotrydialone.

dihydrobotrydial and deacetyl-O-methyldihydrobotrydialone (Fig. 22) from the fungus *Botrytis squamosa*. Biological tests with the former on lettuce seedlings produced odd results. For example, 10-ppm treatments inhibited hypocotyl elongation by 70%, while root growth was proportionately stimulated with concentrations that ranged from 3 to 100 ppm, so that at 100 ppm, root growth increased 70% relative to controls. The deacetyl derivative inhibited hypocotyls 50% even at 300 ppm, while there was little significant effect on root growth in concentration ranges from 1 to 1000 ppm (Kimura et al., 1988). Again, it is interesting to note that relatively minor structural changes in biologically natural products effect major changes in both selectivity and specific activity. We have already reviewed those phytotoxins that are structurally related, including botrydienal (*Botryotinia squamosa*), dehydrobotrydienal (*B. squamosa*), and deacetyldihydrobotrydial (*B. squamosa*, *Botrytis squamosa*)(Cutler, 1988a). The reader is reminded that all the metabolites were active against turnip seedlings and that the amount of metabolite necessary to give a 50% inhibition was 10 µg/mL for botrydienal, 40 µg/mL for dehydrobotrydienal, and 1 mg/mL for deacetyldihydrobotrydial (Kimata et al., 1985).

The phytotoxin prehelminthosporol has recently come under scrutiny again. In 1982 it was reported that prehelminthosporol, isolated from the fungus *Drechslera sorokiana*, was active in a number of plant systems (Cutler et al., 1982). The metabolite significantly inhibited wheat coleoptile extension at 10^{-3} and 10^{-4}, although it promoted growth at 10^{-5} M. In addition, it induced selective responses in greenhouse-grown plants. Corn (*Zea mays* L., cv. Norfolk Market White) plants exhibited stem collapse and general necrosis when treated with prehelminthosporol at 10^{-2} M within 24 h, while bean (*Phaseolus vulgaris* L., cv. Black Valentine) plants treated with the same concentration responded with bending of the pulvinus within 24 h so that leaf blades were either vertical or completely inverted. On the other hand, tobacco plants gave no response. Prehelminthosporol and dihydroprehelminthosporol (Fig. 23) have been isolated from a species of *Bipolaris* known to be a pathogen of Johnsongrass (see above). (The genus has gone through some nomenclature changes in the past decade, so that *Helminthosporium sativum* = *Drechslera sorokiana* = *Bipolaris sorokiana*.) These two products have been tested against sorghum (*Sorghum bicolor*) and Johnsongrass (*Sorghum halepense*) and

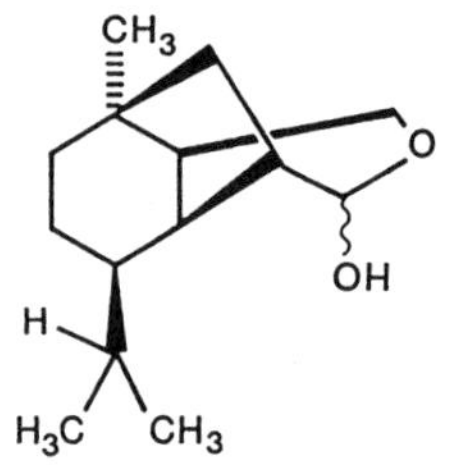

PREHELMINTHOSPOROL
(Drechslera sorokiana)
(Bipolaris sp.)

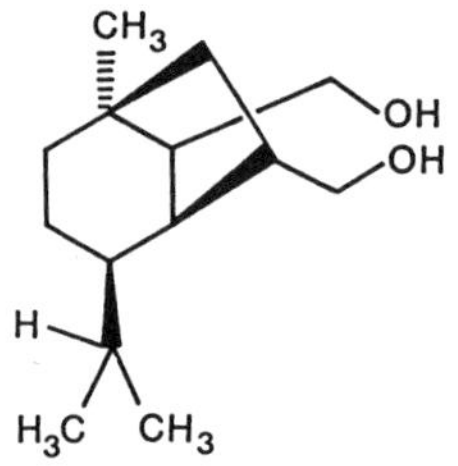

DIHYDROPREHELMINTHOSPOROL
(Bipolaris sp.)

FIGURE 23 Prehelminthosporol and dihydroprehelminthosporol.

prehelminthosporol is more active than dihydroprehelminthosporol. Prehelminthosporol is slightly toxic when applied to leaves at 2.5 µg per 5-µL droplet moderately toxic at 5 µg and extremely toxic at 12.5 and 25 µg per 5-µL
droplet. Dihydroprehelminthosporol is only slightly toxic at 5 µg, very toxic
at 12.5 µg, and extremely toxic at 25 µg per 5-µL droplet (Pena-Rodriguez
et al., 1988). Prehelminthosporol remains a candidate for agricultural development because of the relatively low toxicity. Doses up to 450 mg/kg in 1-day-
old chicks produced no visible effects (Cutler et al., 1982). Furthermore, it
is a simple molecule with a functional group available for synthetic derivatization.

D. Biotransformations of Natural Products

Simple molecules are especially tempting to synthetic organic chemists for structural alteration, but there has occurred, during the decade, the elaboration
of natural products not by classical synthesis but by biotransformations mediated through microorganisms. Such is the case with (-)-carvone, which was
biotransformed to (-)-cis-carveol or (-)-trans-carveol by Streptomyces, A-5-1,
and Nocardia, 1-3-11 (Noma, 1980). Now a further transformation has been
made starting with (-)-cis-carveol to produce a novel bicyclic monoterpene,
(4R,6R)-(+)-6,8-oxidomenth-1-en-9-ol (Fig. 24), in the presence of Strepto-

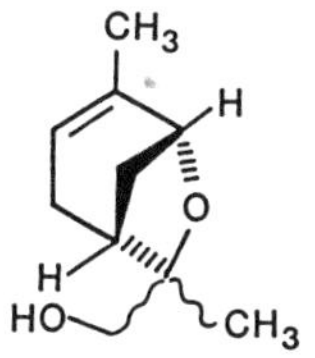

(4R, 6R) - (+) - 6,8 - OXIDOMENTH - 1-EN - 9 - oL

FIGURE 24 (4*R*,6*R*)-(+)-6,8-Oxidomenth-1-en-9-ol.

myces bottropensis (Noma et al., 1982). The product, a colorless oil, was
dissolved in acetone to give a 200-ppm solution, and 2 mL of this was applied
to a 6-cm-diameter filter paper and allowed to dry. The impregnated filter
paper was placed in a petri dish to which 2 mL of Tween 80 aqueous solution
was added along with 50 lettuce seeds (*Lactuca sativa* L., cv. Wayahead) and
there followed incubation at 22°C for 24 and 48 h. Within 24 h, 97% of seed
germination was inhibited, but this dropped to 52% in 48 h, although whether
this was due to breakdown of the metabolite or to measuring root growth inhibition relative to controls, because germination may have taken place, (Noma
et al., 1982) was not noted. A further development was the biotransformation
of (-)-*cis*-carveol to produce the novel metabolite (+)-bottrospicatol (Fig. 25)
(Nishimura et al., 1983) and this compound was very active against lettuce
seed germination at concentrations between 50 and 100 ppm (about 40 and
80%, respectively) with complete inhibition at 200 ppm. These results have
prompted the authors to speculate that (+)-bottrospicatol may be an important
lead compound for the exploration of new herbicides. In contrast, (-)-isobot-
trospicatol is not active even at 500 ppm, while (-)-carvone is only weakly
inhibitory to germinating seeds and seedlings of garden cress (*Lepidium sativum*, green foxtail (*Setaria viridis*), green amaranth (*Amaranthus retroflexus*), barnyard grass (*Echinochloa crus-galli*), and lettuce (*Lactuca sativa*)
(Nishimura et al., 1982). The metabolic pathways for the production of bottrospicatols from (-)-*cis*-carveol by *Streptomyces bottropensis* SY-2-1 and
S. ikutamanensis have now been elucidated in some detail (Noma and Nishimura,
1987), and this is an important step if gene splicing is planned for a number
of obvious reasons. *S. bottropensis* SY-2-1 transformed (-)-*cis*-carveol primarily to (+)-bottrospicatol [(4*R*,6*R*,8*R*)-(+)-6,8-oxidomenth-1-en-9-ol] with

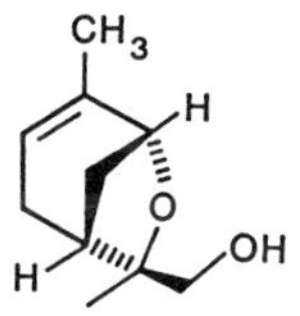

(+) - BOTTROSPICATOL
(<u>Streptomyces bottropensis</u>)

FIGURE 25 (+)-Bottrospicatol.

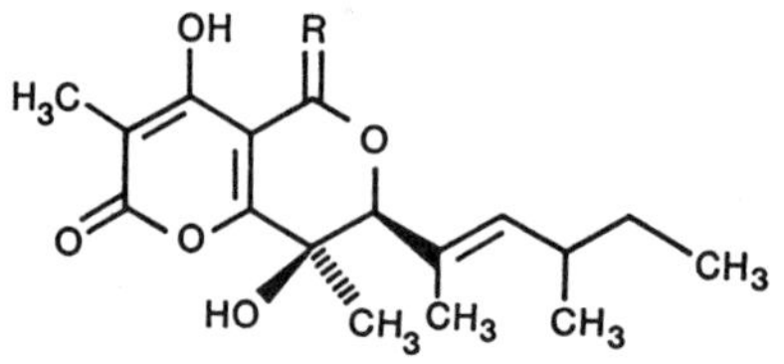

NEOVASININ, R = H$_2$
NEOVASINONE, R = O
(Neocosmospora vasinfecta)

FIGURE 26 Neovasinin and neovasinone.

(+)-isobottrospicatol [(4R,6R,8S<)-(+)-6,8-oxidomenth-1-en-9-ol] as a minor
metabolite. But (+)-*cis*-carveol was transformed by the same microbe SY-2-1
to (-)-isobottrospicatol as the major component, and (-)-bottrospicatol as
the minor one. *S. ikutamanensis* metabolized the *cis*-carveols in an almost
identical manner, indicating that the species difference was less important
than the stereochemistry of the starting compound. The biotransformation
product (+)-bottrospicatol was the most inhibitory of the four isomers to germinating lettuce seed, but in bioassays using germinating alfalfa seed (*Medi-
cago sativa*) at 50 to 500 ppm, both (+)-isobottrospicatol and (-)-isobottrospica-
tol were more active than (+)-bottrospicatol in inhibiting germination. None
of the isomers was active against garden cress (*Lepidium sativum*).

E. Miscellaneous Natural Products and Toxins

A number of miscellaneous compounds that warrant further investigation have
been isolated from microorganisms, and some of these are now considered.
Neocosmospora vasinfecta is a pathogen that causes fruit rot and root rot in
several plant species. Two metabolites, one trivially named neovasinin,
2H,5H-pyrano[4,3-6]pyran-2-one, the other neovasinone, 2H,5H-pyrano[4,3-
b]pyran-2,5-dione (Fig. 26), have been isolated and purified from the fungus
(Nakajima et al., 1987a,b). Neovasinin inhibited root growth of germinating
lettuce 50% at 300 ppm, while neovasinone, which has a ketone feature as opposed to the two extra protons of neovasinin at C14, stimulated root growth
with as little as 3 ppm and as much as 70% with 100 ppm. Neither did increasing the concentration to 300 ppm cause inhibition. The authors state that
the ketone carbonyl forms a chelate with the hydroxyl group at C3, and this,
in some fashion, plays an integral role in stimulating lettuce root growth (Nakajima et al., 1987a). Whatever the mode of action, it is intriguing that two
protons can so alter the activity of a natural product, but this is repeated
many times in structure-activity comparisons.

   Another member of the genus, *Neocosmospora tenuicristata*, has been
reported to produce a metabolite that inhibits the growth of etiolated wheat
coleoptiles (*Triticum aestivum* L., cv. Wakeland) 100 and 44% at 10^{-3} and 10^{-4}
M, respectively. The metabolite, monorden (Fig. 27), did not inhibit the
growth of greenhouse-grown bean and tobacco plants but did induce slight
necrosis in corn plants (*Zea mays* L., cv. Norfolk Market White) 1 week follow-

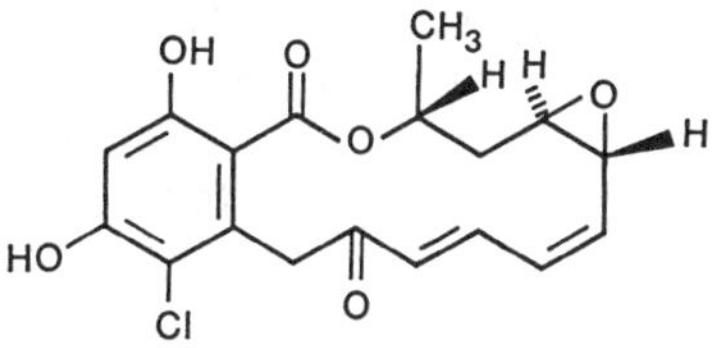

MONORDEN
(Neocosmospora tenuicristata)
(Monosporium bonorden)
(Monocillium nordinii)
(Cylindrocarpon radicicola)
(Penicillium luteoaurantium)

FIGURE 27 Monorden.

ing treatment with 10^{-2} M solutions (Cutler et al., 1987). The compound was also inhibitory to the gram-positive bacterium *Bacillus subtilis* at 500 μg per disk, in assays, and against *B. cereus* at 50, 250, and 500 μg per disk. The metabolite has also been isolated from *Cylindrocarpon radicicola*, hence the other trivial name, radicicolin (Evans and White, 1966).

For well over 12 years, the metabolite coronatine (Fig. 28) and its congeners have been the objects of close study. Coronatine was first described as a product of the bacterium *Pseudomonas coronafaciens* pv. *atropurpurea*, which induced chlorosis on the leaves of Italian ryegrass, although it also caused potato cells to expand at 1×10^{-7} M (Ichihara et al., 1977). Later, it was isolated from the liquid culture of *P. glycinea* and induced chlorosis in bean and soybean leaves (Mitchell and Young, 1978). An intensive survey of assorted *Pseudomonas* species revealed that 5 of 5 *P. syringae* pv. *atropurpurea* strains produced coronatine, 5 of 6 *P. syringae* pv. *glycinea* strains also produced coronatine, while none of the *P. syringae* pv. *maculicola* accessions produced any of the metabolite and 3 of 12 strains of *P. syringae* pv.

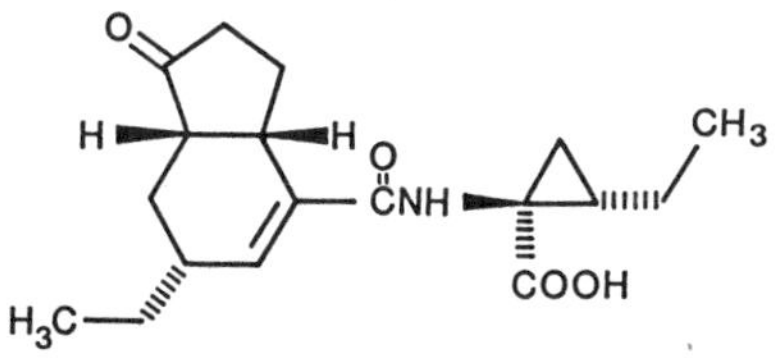

CORONATINE

(Pseudomonas coronafaciens pv. atropurpurea)
(Pseudomonas syringae pv. atropurpurea)
(pv. glycinea)

FIGURE 28 Coronatine.

morsprunorum produced only small quantities coronatine (Mitchell, 1982). Two years later, liquid cultures of *P. syringae* pv. *atropurpurea* gave not only coronatine but two further novel metabolites, *N*-coronafacoyl-L-valine and coronafacic acid (Fig. 29). Only *N*-coronafacoyl-L-valine was toxic in bean bioassays (Mitchell, 1984). *P. syringae* pv. *glycinea* produced the phytotoxin norcoronatine (Fig. 30) in liquid culture and was reported a year later (Mitchell, 1985). A final communication concerning the presence of *N*-coronafacoyl-L-isoleucine and *N*-coronafacoyl-L-alloisoleucine (Fig. 30) in the same organism indicates that they were purified as a mixture occurring in approximately 2:1 ratio and together they possessed chlorosis-inducing activity (Mitchell and Young, 1985). Both compounds may contribute to the biosynthesis of coronatine. But whether they act independently, in concert, or synergistically to produce the symptoms of the disease has yet to be determined. The parent molecule is relatively simple, has a number of functional groups, and is an ideal candidate for either synthetic elaboration or biotransformation by a suitable microorganism.

The cytochalasins are a biologically active group of natural products whose properties have been reviewed in some detail (Cutler et al., 1986), but new congeners are being discovered with surprising regularity although not all appear to have been evaluated for biological activity. One that has is pyrichalasin H (Fig. 31) from the fungus *Pyricularia grisea*. It strongly inhibited the growth of rice (*Oryza sativa* L., cv. Sasanishiki) seedlings at 1.9×10^{-6} M and it also caused curling of the shoots. It should be emphasized that both roots and shoots were inhibited (Nukina, 1987). In tests with etiolated wheat coleoptiles (*Triticum aestivum* L., cv. Wakeland), inhibition was identical at 10^{-3}, 10^{-4}, and 10^{-5} M (42%, respectively) and sections had the characteristic banana shape and curvature associated with the responses obtained with all

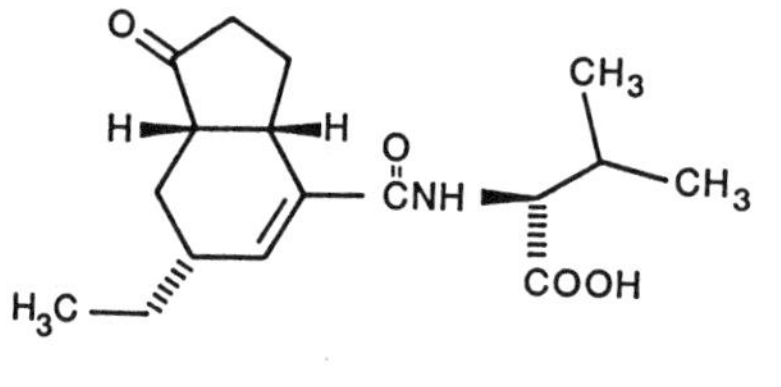

N - CORONAFACOYL - L - VALINE
(*P. syringae* pv. atropurpurea)

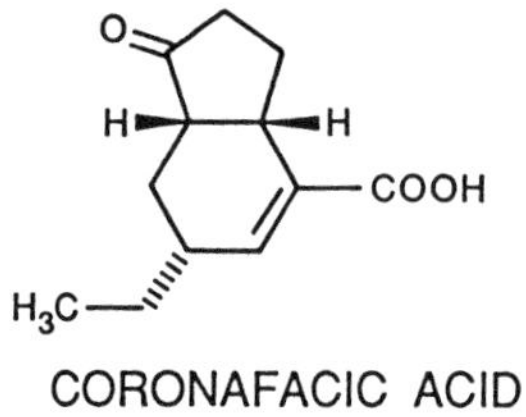

CORONAFACIC ACID

FIGURE 29 *N*-Coronafacoyl-L-valine and coronafacic acid.

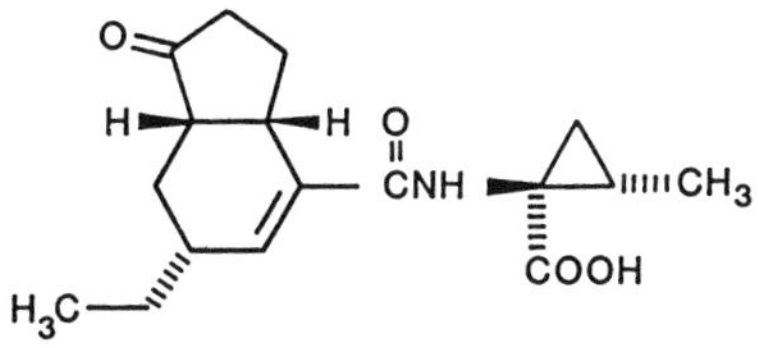

NORCORONATINE

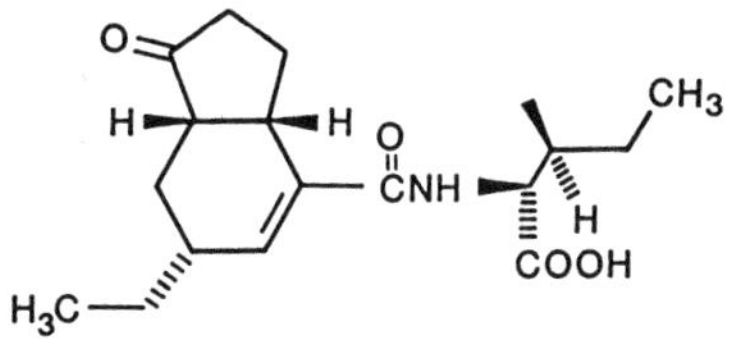

N - CORONAFACOYL - L - ISOLEUCINE

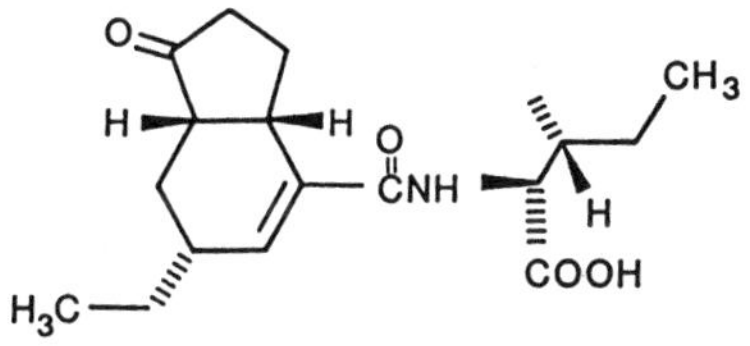

N - CORONAFACOYL - L - ALLOISOLEUCINE
(<u>Pseudomonas syringae</u> pv. <u>glycinea</u>)

FIGURE 30 Norcoronatine, *N*-coronafacoyl-L-isoleucine, and *N*-coronafacoyl-L-alloisoleucine.

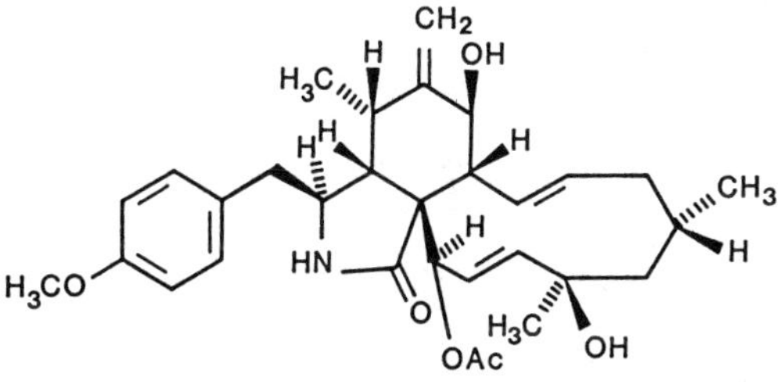

PYRICHALASIN H

(<u>Pyricularia grisea</u>)

FIGURE 31 Pyrichalasin H.

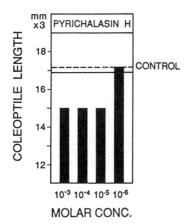

FIGURE 32 Effects of pyrichalasin H on etiolated wheat coleoptiles (*Triticum aestivum* L., cv. Wakeland). Initial length of coleoptiles (×3) = 12 mm. Control, dashed line; below solid line, significant inhibition (*P* <0.01).

previously tested cytochalasins (Fig. 32). The probable reason for all treatments being equally inhibited is one of solubility. Pyrichalasin H is relatively insoluble in polar solvents (acetone in water). As a class of compounds, the cytochalasins are quite cytotoxic, inhibit cellular extension in higher plants and, in some instances, control flowering in plants (Wells et al., 1976). As a group, they offer some potential as agricultural chemicals.

The plant growth regulating molecule indole-3-acetic acid has played an important role in plant physiology for about 75 years, and for most of us, it has been our first introduction to the world of plant hormones. While the indole alkaloids are well known in pharmacy as potent biologically active natural products (e.g., ergotamine and LSD), there have been a few instances within the past 5 years where indoles have been isolated from microorganisms that possess phytotoxic, as opposed to plant stimulatory, properties. In 1987, tryptophol (Fig. 33), indole-3-ethanol, was isolated from *Drechslera nodulosum* (formerly, *Helminthosporium nodulosum*), a pathogen of goosegrass (*Eleusine indica* L.). At concentrations of 6.2×10^{-3} M, tryptophol was toxic to goosegrass 10 weeks after treatment and killed crabgrass (*Digitaria ischaemum*), foxtail (*Alopercurus aequalis*), barnyard grass (*Echinochloa crus-galli*), signal grass (*Brachiaria* sp.), and lambsquarters (*Chenopodium album*). Grain

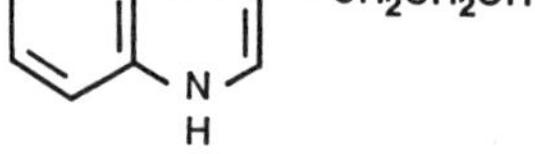

TRYPTOPHOL
(Drechslera nodulosum)

FIGURE 33 Tryptophol.

sorghum (*Sorghum vulgare*), barley (*Hordeum vulgare*), bluegrass (*Poa annua*), and Canada thistle (*Cirsium arvense*) had symptoms of flecking or necrotic spotting. At the lower concentration of 6.2×10^{-4} M, goosegrass was dead after 4 weeks (Sugawara and Strobel, 1987). Tryptophol is derived from tryptophane which is converted to tryptamine, and following the action of the enzyme monoamine oxidase, the next product is indoleacetaldehyde. Ultimately, indoleacetaldehyde is converted, by aldehyde reductase, to tryptophol. Tryptophol has been reported in the systemic fungus *Balansia epichloë*, which is an endophyte of grasses (Porter et al., 1985).

Another set of indoles that may be promising as selective phytotoxins are the structures harman and norharman (Fig. 34) from *Nocardia* sp. Knowledge of their structure is not new and one of the first references is 70 years old (Perkin and Robinson, 1919), concerning the nature of harman. But as is so often the case, much of the earlier natural product work appears to have been conducted primarily to determine structure without much concern about activity against plant species. If there was an effort to determine biological activity, it was generally limited to pharmaceutical evaluations. Consequently, much valuable time has been lost in the search for biodegradable agricultural chemicals. Be that as it may, both harman and norharman are known to inhibit monoamine oxidase activity (Ho et al., 1968) and both have been shown to inhibit the growth of rice (*Oryza sativa* L., cv. Nihonbare) and lettuce (*Lactuca sativa*, cv. Great Lakes 366) seedlings. Harman reduced rice root growth 10% at 100 ppm and lettuce roots by 50% at 40 ppm (Yomosa et al., 1987). Norharman inhibited rice roots 20% at 100 ppm and lettuce 50% at 20 ppm. As seen in previous examples, the structure-activity relationship is attractive because the two compounds differ only by the replacement of a proton by a methyl function, and vice versa.

Not all phytotoxic metabolites of microbial origin are simple structures. To the contrary, many are complex and some are symmetrically complex. Such is our concluding example of a phytotoxic molecule, secalonic acid A (Fig. 35), a highly potent plant toxin from liquid cultures of *Pyrenochaeta terrestris*. *P. terrestris* is the etiological agent of pink root disease of onion (*P. terrestris* is itself highly pigmented and occurs on sugarcane that had been fired, cut, and left laying in the field more than 48 h—the bright pink to red organism is highly visible on the fire-blackened stems from a distance.) Secalonic acid A markedly inhibited stem growth in onion (*Allium cepa*, cv. Early Lockyer) seedlings 94% at 10^{-5} M, 68% at 10^{-6} M, 40% at 10^{-7} M, 32% at 10^{-8} M, and 4% at 10^{-9} M. The toxin was equally as potent in tests against radish

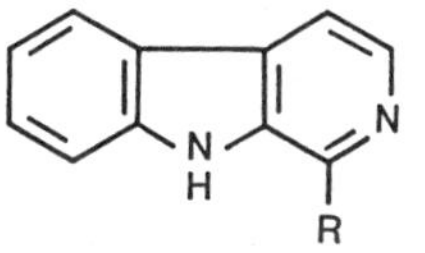

	R
HARMAN	CH$_3$
NORHARMAN	H

FIGURE 34 Harman and norharman.

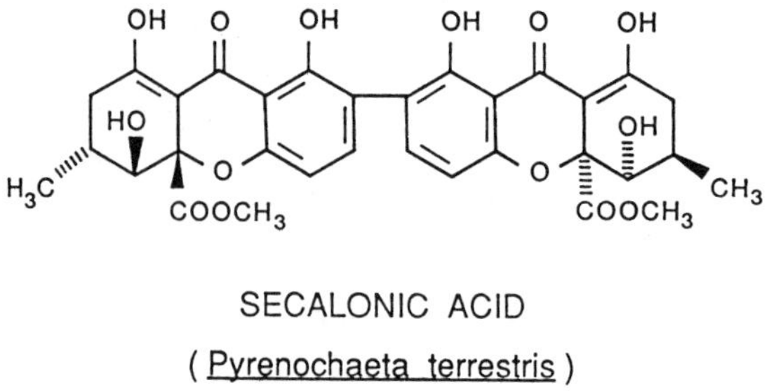

SECALONIC ACID

(<u>Pyrenochaeta terrestris</u>)

FIGURE 35 Secalonic acid.

(*Raphanus sativus*) and pepper (*Capsicum annuum*) (Steffens and Robeson,
1987). The polyfunctional groups of secalonic acid A are ideal for derivatization to make models for structure-activity correlations.

III. CONCLUSIONS

It seems probable that there are many natural product phytotoxins yet to be
discovered in microorganisms, and those discoveries may serve two interre-
lated purposes: (1) the use of natural products as biodegradable agricultural
chemicals, and (2) the use of these templates for synthetic elaboration to alter
selectivity and, if necessary, specific activity, without deleting the biodegradable properties. Finally, if significant gene splicing is to be accomplished,
the characteristics of secondary metabolites must be absolutely known to serve
minimally as gene benchmarks, and the metabolic pathways by which these
important natural products are derived must be elucidated. Microorganisms
have an uncanny way of suppressing genetic expression without deleting it.
Consequently, much interdisciplinary work remains to be done.

ACKNOWLEDGMENT

The author thanks Dr. M. Nukina, Department of Agricultural Chemistry,
Yamagata University, Tsuruoka, Japan, for the generous sample of pyrichalasin H.

REFERENCES

Assante, G., and Nasini, G. (1987). Identity of the phytotoxin stemphylin
    from *Stemphylium botryosum* with altersolanol A. *Phytochemistry 26*:
    703-705.
Baker, R. A., Tatum, J. H., and Nemec, S., Jr. (1981). Toxin production
    by *Fusarium solani* from fibrous roots of blight-diseased citrus. *Phyto-
    pathology 71*: 951-954.
Barash, I., Manulis, S., Kashman, Y., Springer, J. P., Chen, M. H. M.,
    Clardy, J., and Strobel, G. A. (1983). Crystallization and x-ray anal-

ysis of *Stemphylium botryosum*. *Science* 220:1065-1066.

Cutler, H. G. (1984). Biologically active natural products from fungi: templates for tomorrow's pesticides. *Am. Chem. Soc. Symp. Ser.* 257:153-170.

Cutler, H. G. (1985). A personal perspective of Japanese research on biologically active natural products from fungi. In *Proceedings of the Twelfth Annual Meeting of the Plant Growth Regulator Society of America*, A. R. Cooke (Ed.). Plant Growth Regulator Society of America, pp. 160-174.

Cutler, H. G. (1987). Japanese contributions to the development of allelochemicals. *Am. Chem. Soc. Symp. Ser.* 330:23-38.

Cutler, H. G. (1988a). Unusual plant-growth regulators from microorganisms. *Crt. Rev. Plant Sci.* 6:323-342.

Cutler, H. G. (1988b). Natural products and their potential in agriculture. *Am. Chem. Soc. Symp. Ser.* 380:1-22.

Cutler, H. G., Crumley, F. G., Cox, R. H., Davis, E. E., Harper, J. L., Cole, R. J., and Sumner, D. R. (1982). Prehelminthosporol and prehelminthosporol acetate: plant growth regulating properties. *J. Agric. Food Chem.* 30:658-662.

Cutler, H. G., Wells, J. M., and Cole, R. J. (1986). Effects of cytochalasins in prokaryotic systems and in plants. In *Recent Advances in Cytochalasins*, G. S. Pendse (Ed.). Balodyan Press, Shukrawar Peth, Pune-411002, India, Chapt. IV, pp. 83-111.

Cutler, H. G., Arrendale, R. F., Springer, J. P., Cole, P. D., Roberts, R. G., and Hanlin, R. T. (1987). Monorden from a novel source, *Neocosmospora tenuicristata*: stereochemistry and plant growth regulatory properties. *Agric. Biol. Chem.* 51:3331-3338.

Edwards, J. V., Dailey, O. D., Jr., Bland, J. M., and Cutler, H. G. (1988). Approaches to structure-function relationships for naturally occurring cyclic peptides: a study of tentoxins. *Am. Chem. Soc. Symp. Ser.* 380:35-56.

Endo, A. (1979). Monacolin K, a new hypocholesterolemic agent produced by a *Monascus* species. *J. Antibiot.* 32:852-854.

Endo, A., Kuroda, M., and Tsujita, T. (1976). ML-236A, ML-236B, and ML-236C, new inhibitors of cholesterogenesis produced by *Penicillium citrinum*. *J. Antibiot.* 29:1346.

Evans, G., and While, N. H. (1966). Radicicolin and radicicol, two new antibiotics produced by *Cyclindrocarpon radicicola*. *Trans. Br. Mycol. Soc.* 49:563-576.

Findlay, J. A., and Radics, L. (1972). Flavipucine [3'-isovaleryl-6-methylpyridine-3-spiro-2'-oxiran-2(1H),-4(3H)-dione], an antibiotic from *Aspergillus flavipes*. *J. Chem. Soc. Perkin Trans. I*, 16:2071-2074.

Hashizume, T., Matsubara, S., and Endo, A. (1983). Compactin (ML-236B) as a new growth inhibitor of plant callus. *Agric. Biol. Chem.* 47:1401-1403.

Hirota, A., Suzuki, A., Suzuki, H., and Tamura, S. (1973a). Isolation and biological activity of cyl-2, a metabolite of *Cylindrocladium scoparium*. *Agric. Biol. Chem.* 37:643-647.

Hirota, A., Suzuki, A., Aizawa, K., and Tamura, S. (1973b). Structure of cyl-2, a novel cyclotetrapeptide from *Cylindrocladium scoparium*. *Agric. Biol. Chem.* 37:955-956.

Ho, B. T., McIssac, W. M., Walker, K. E., and Estevez, V. (1968). Inhibitors of monoamine oxidase: inference of methyl substitution on the inhibitory activity of β-carbolines. *J. Pharm. Sci.* 57: 269-274.

Ichihara, A., Shiraishi, K., Sato, H., Sakamura, S., Nishiyama, K., Sakai, R., Furusaki, A., and Matsumoto, T. (1977). The structure of coronatine. *J. Am. Chem. Soc.* 99: 636-637.

Ichihara, A., Tazaki, H., and Sakamura, S. (1983). Solanapyrones A, B and C, phytotoxic metabolites from the fungus *Alternaria solani*. *Tetrahedron Lett.* 24: 5373-5376.

Ichihara, A., Tazaki, H., and Sakamura, S. (1985). The structure of zinnolide, a new phytotoxin from *Alternaria solani*. *Agric. Biol. Chem.* 49: 2811-2812.

Ichihara, A., Miki, M., Tazaki, H., and Sakamura, S. (1987). Synthesis of (±)-solanapyrone A. *Tetrahedron Lett.* 28: 1175-1178.

Kern, H. (1978). Les naphthazarines des *Fusarium*. *Ann. Phytopathol.* 10: 327-345.

Kimata, T., Natsume, M., and Marumo, S. (1985). Botrydienal, a new phytotoxin, and its related metabolites, dehydrobotrydienal and deacetyldihydrobotrydial produced by *Botryotinia squamosa*. *Tetrahedron Lett.* 26: 2097-2100.

Kimura, Y., Hamasaki, T., and Nakajima, H. (1981). Isolation, identification and biological activities of 8-O-methyljavanicin produced by *Fusarium solani*. *Agric. Biol. Chem.* 45: 2653-2654.

Kimura, Y., Fujioka, H., Nakajima, H., Hamasaki, T., and Isogai, A. (1988). Isolation and structures of O-methyldihydrobotrydial and deacetyl-O-methyldihydrobotrydialone produced by *Botrytis squamosa*. *Agric. Biol. Chem.* 52: 1845-1847.

Kinjo, J.-E., Yokomizo, K., Awata, Y., Shibata, M., Nohara, T., Teramine, T., and Takahashi, K. (1987). Structures of phytotoxins, AV-toxins C, D and E, produced by zonate leaf spot fungus of mulberry. *Tetrahedron Lett.* 28: 3697-3698.

Lidert, Z., Williams, S. F., and Holmes, A. B. (1988). Synthesis of a monocyclic analogue of bipolaroxin, a phytotoxin of fungal origin. *Tetrahedron Lett.* 29: 1347-1350.

Matern, U., Strobel, S., and Shepard, J. (1978). Reaction to phytotoxins in a potato population derived from mesophyll protoplasts. *Proc. Natl. Acad. Sci. USA* 75: 4935-4939.

Mitchell, R. E. (1982). Coronatine production by some phytopathogenic pseudomonads. *Physiol. Plant Pathol.* 20: 83-89.

Mitchell, R. E. (1984). A naturally-occurring structural analogue of the phytotoxin coronatine. *Phytochemistry* 23: 791-793.

Mitchell, R. E. (1985). Norcoronatine and N-coronafacoyl-L-valine, phytotoxic analogues of coronatine produced by a strain of *Pseudomonas syringae* pv. *glycinea*. *Phytochemistry* 24: 1485-1487.

Mitchell, R. E., and Young, H. (1978). Identification of chlorosis-inducing toxin of *Pseudomonas glycinea* as coronatine. *Phytochemistry* 17: 2028-2029.

Mitchell, R. E., and Young, H. (1985). N-Coronafacoyl-L-isoleucine and N-coronafacoyl-L-alloisoleucine, potential biosynthetic intermediates of phytotoxin coronatine. *Phytochemistry* 24: 2716-2728.

Nakajima, H., Nishimura, K., Hamasaki, T., Kimura, Yl, and Udagawa, S.-I. (1987a). Structure of neovasinin, a new metabolite produced by the fungus, *Neocosmospora vasinfecta* E.F. Smith and its biological activity to lettuce seedlings. *Agric. Biol. Chem. 51*:2831-2833.

Nakajima, H., Nishimura, K., Hamasaki, T., Kimura, Yl, Yokota, T., and Udagawa, S.-I. (1987b). Structure of neovasinone, a new α-pyrone plant growth regulator produced by the fungus, *Neocosmospora vasinfecta* E.F. Smith. *Agric. Biol. Chem. 51*:1221-1224.

Nakashima, T., Ueno, T., and Fukami, H. (1982). Structure elucidation of AK toxins host specific phytotoxic metabolites produced by *Alternaria kikuchiana* Tanaka. *Tetrahedron Lett. 23*:4469-4472.

Nakashima, T., Ueno, T., Fukami, H., Taga, T., Masuda, H., Osaki, K., Otani, H., Kohmoto, K., and Nishimura, S. (1985). Isolation and structures of AK-toxin I and II, host-specific phytotoxic metabolites produced by *Alternaria alternata* Japanese pear pathotype. *Agric. Biol. Chem. 49*:807-815.

Nakatsuka, S.-I., Ueda, K., Goto, T., Yamamoto, M., Nishimura, S., and Kohmoto, K. (1986). Structure of AF-toxin II, one of the host-specific toxins produced by *Alternaria alternata* strawberry pathotype. *Tetrahedron Lett. 27*:2752-2756.

Nishimura, H., Kaku, K., Nakamura, T., Fukazawa, T., and Mizutani, J. (1982). Allelopathic substances, (±)-p-menthane-3,8-diols isolated from *Eucalyptus citriodora* Hook. *Agric. Biol. Chem. 46*:319-320.

Nishimura, H., Hiramoto, S., Mizutani, J., Noma, T., Furusaki, A., and Matsumoto, T. (1983). Structure and biological activity of bottrospicatol, a novel monoterpene produced by microbial transformation of (-)-*cis* carveol. *Agric. Biol. Chem. 47*:2697-2699.

Noma, Y., and Nishimura, H. (1987). Bottrospicatols, novel monoterpenes produced on conversion of (-)- and (+)-*cis*-carveol by *Streptomyces*. *Agric. Biol. Chem. 51*:1845-1849.

Noma, Y., Nishimura, H., Hiramoto, S., Iwami, M., and Tatsumi, C. (1982). A new compound (4R,6R)-(+)-6,8-oxidomenth-1-en-9-ol produced by microbial conversion of (-)-*cis*-carveol. *Agric. Biol. Chem. 46*:2871-2872.

Nukina, M. (1987). Pyrichalasin H., a new phytotoxic metabolite belonging to the cytochalasans from *Pyricularia grisea* (Cooke) Saccardo. *Agric. Biol. Chem. 51*:2625-2628.

Parisot, D., Devys, M., and Barbier, M. (1988). Fusarubionic acid, a new naphthoquinone from the fungus *Nectria haematococca*. *Phytochemistry 27*:3002-3004.

Pena-Rodriquez, L. M., Armingeon, N. A., and Chilton, W. S. (1988). Toxins from weed pathogens: I. Phytotoxins from a *Bipolaris* pathogen of Johnson grass. *J. Nat. Prod. 51*:821-828.

Perkin, W. H., and Robinson, R. (1919). Harman and harmaline. *J. Chem. Soc. 115*:967-972.

Porter, J. K., Bacon, C. W., Cutler, H. G., Arrendale, R. F., and Robbins, J. D. (1985). In vitro auxin productions by *Balansia epichloë*. *Phytochemistry 24*:1429-1431.

Sassa, T. (1983). Structure and absolute configuration of *Macrophoma* fruit rot toxin A. *Agric. Biol. Chem. 47*:1417-1418.

Sassa, T., and Nukina, M. (1984). Macrophorin D, a new self-growth in-
    hibitor of the casual fungus of *Macrophoma* fruit rot of apple. *Agric.
    Biol. Chem. 48*:1923-1925.
Sassa, T., and Onuma, Y. (1983). Isolation and identification of fruit rot
    toxins from the fungus-caused *Macrophoma* fruit rot of apple. *Agric.
    Biol. Chem. 47*:1155-1157.
Sassa, T., and Yoshikoshi, H. (1983). New terpene-linked cyclohexenone
    epoxides, macrophorin A, B and C, produced by the fungus caused
    Macrophoma fruit rot of apple. *Agric. Biol. Chem. 47*:187-189.
Sassa, T., Uchie, K., Kato, H., and Onuma, Y. (1987). Decomposition of
    fruit rot toxin A, a host-selective phytotoxin from *Botryosphaeria beren-
    geriana. Agric. Biol. Chem. 51*:271-272.
Schneider, J. A., and Nakanishi, K. (1983). A new class of sweet potato
    phytoalexins. *J. Chem. Soc. Chem. Commun.* 353-355.
Starratt, A. N. (1968). Zinniol: a major metabolite of *Alternaria zinnae.
    Can. J. Chem. 46*:767-770.
Steffens, J. C., and Robeson, D. J. (1987). Secalonic acid A, a vivotoxin
    in pink root-infected onion. *Phytochemistry 26*:1599-1602.
Steyn, P. S., Wessels, P. L., and Marasas, W. F. O. (1979). Pigments from
    Fusarium moniliforme Sheldon: structure and ^{13}C nuclear magnetic reso-
    nance assignments of an azaanthraquinone and three naphthoquinones.
    Tetrahedron 35:1551-1555.
Stoessl, A. (1967). Altersolanol A, a novel tetrahydroanthraquinone. *J.
    Chem. Soc. Chem. Commun.* 307-308.
Stoessl, A. (1969). Some metabolites of *Alternaria solani. Can. J. Chem.
    47*:767-776.
Sugawara, F., and Strobel, G. A. (1987). Tryptophol, a phytotoxic pro-
    duced by *Drechslera nodulosum. Phytochemistry 26*:1349-1351.
Sugawara, F., Strobel, G., Fisher, L. E., Van Duyne, G. D., and Clardy,
    J. (1985). Bipolaroxin, a selective phytotoxin produced by *Bipolaris
    cynodontis. Proc. Natl. Acad. Sci. USA 82*:8291-8294.
Takahashi, K., and Teramine, T. (1984). Taxonomy studies on the perfect
    stage of *Gonatopharamium mori* (Sawada) Deighton (= *Acrospermum* Tode
    ex. FR), the fungus causing mulberry ring spot disease. *Ann. Phyto-
    pathol. Soc. Jpn. 50*:413.
Takahashi, K., and Teramine, T. (1986). Zonate leaft spot of mulberry,
    with special reference to the life-cycle and taxonomy of casual fungus
    Gonatophragmium mori. Ann. Phytopathol. Soc. Jpn. 52:404-412.
Takayama, S., Isogai, A., Nakata, M., Suzuki, H., and Suzuki, A. (1984).
    Structure of cyl-1, a novel cyclotetrapeptide from *Cylindrocladium sco-
    parium. Agric. Biol. Chem. 48*:839-842.
Wells, J. M., Cutler, H. G., and Cole, R. J. (1976). Toxicity and plant
    growth regulator effects of cytochalasin H isolated from *Phomopsis* sp.
    Can. J. Microbiol. 22:1137-1143.
Yomosa, K., Hirota, A., Sakai, H., and Isogai, A. (1987). Isolation of har-
    man and norharman from *Nocardia* sp. and their inhibitory activity of
    plant seedlings. *Agric. Biol. Chem. 51*:921-922.

21

Fungal Elicitors of Plant Phytoalexins

Jack D. Paxton

University of Illinois at Urbana-Champaign, Urbana, Illinois

I. INTRODUCTION

A legitimate question might be "Why a chapter on fungal elicitors of plant phytoalexins in a handbook on natural toxins?" The answer is that phytoalexins (natural plant antibiotics) are toxic to plant cells as well as to microorganisms, so their elicitors, which cause phytoalexins to accumulate in plant cells, may cause these cells to self-destruct and die in the process of accumulating phytoalexins. As you will see, fungal toxins can be phytoalexin elicitors as well. In fact, it is hard to draw a distinction between fungal toxins and fungal phytoalexin elicitors, since these elicitors are detected by their ability to elicit the accumulation of toxic compounds (phytoalexins) in plant cells.

II. THEORY

A. Elicitors

The accumulation of phytoalexins in plants can be evoked by biologic or nonbiologic treatment. Examples of nonbiologic treatments that lead to the accumulation of phytoalexins are treatment with ultraviolet light, salts of heavy metals, and freezing of tissues. Elicitors are compounds that are capable of evoking the accumulation of phytoalexins in plants. For the purpose of this chapter, elicitors are defined as compounds of biological origin that stimulate the production and accumulation of phytoalexins in plants. Biologic elicitors can be divided into endogenous elicitors, such as fragments of pectin molecules from plant cell walls, and exogenous elicitors, such as carbohydrate, fatty acid, glycoprotein, and/or protein molecules, which are capable of stimulating plant cells to accumulate phytoalexins. These endogenous elicitors are presumably from fungal cell walls. In this chapter I will confine the discussion to recent work on fungal biological elicitors of phytoalexins.

The rapid accumulation of phytoalexins seems to be closely associated with a plant disease resistance response termed hypersensitive resistance. Hypersensitive resistance (HR) refers to the rapid death of plant cells around an infection site, which generally leads to necrosis visible to the naked eye. Elicitors, molecules of microbial origin, can trigger symptoms characteristic of the hypersensitive response in plants.

Elicitors of plant phytoalexins have been known and studied for quite some time. The first elicitor carefully studied was a peptide from *Monilinia fructicola* (Cruickshank and Perrin, 1968). Since that discovery, several elicitors of several different chemical types have been described, including peptides, extracellular glycoconjugates, enzymes, glucans, chitosan, and fatty acids.

Fungal elicitors of plant phytoalexins have the potential of becoming a new class of plant protectants and herbicides. Progress has been made to chemically characterize them and to study further their application to agriculture.

The diverse fungal compounds that elicit phytoalexin production in plants and their parts are well characterized in some cases. Fungal pectinases also have been implicated in phytoalexin elicitation. These enzymes appear to elicit phytoalexin production by releasing pectic fragments from the cell walls of plants. These fragments then are recognized by the plant in some way that leads to phytoalexin accumulation. Another area of interest, similar to current animal research, is the transduction of the elicitor's signal to the plant nucleus for directed processing of nucleic acids.

Templeton and Lamb (1988) reviewed bean defense gene activation by elicitors and reported that this begins in less than 5 min after elicitor treatment. This is clearly a rapid response, implying that few biochemical steps exist between elicitor recognition and the initiation of defense gene transcription.

They also observe that little is known about how plants recognize pathogens and elicitors or how this recognition is signaled to the plant nucleus. Significant differences in the Michaelis constant, for phenylalanine, of phenylalanine ammonia lyase were observed, and elicitor treatment of bean tissue preferentially induced the two phenylalanine ammonia lyase isozymes with the lowest K_m (greatest affinity for phenylalanine). This suggests a metabolic priority for the phenylpropanoid pathway in stressed bean tissue. Their studies also show that hydroxyproline-rich glycoprotein synthesis transcripts differ in their elicitation. A wound-induced hydroxyproline-rich glycoprotein synthesis transcript 4.1 was 300 base pairs smaller than that which accumulated in response to elicitor (Templeton and Lamb, 1988).

It is important to keep in mind that several environmental effects can have a strong impact on elicitor activity. For instance, Stäb and Ebel (1987) demonstrated the effects of Ca ion on phytoalexin accumulation. They showed that Ca^{2+} is important for soybean cells to respond to a *Phytophthora megasperma* f. sp. *glycinea* glucan elicitor, and removal of extracellular Ca^{2+} by treatment with ethylene glycol bis(β-aminoethyl ether)-N,N'-tetraacetic acid followed by washing the cells with Ca-free culture medium abolished elicitor-mediated phytoalexin accumulation. This suppression was largely reversed on readdition of Ca^{2+}. La^{3+} at 30 μmol/L was even more effective in inhibition of glyceollin accumulation than in its inhibition of phenylalanine ammonia lyase or chalcone synthease in soybean tissue. They suggested that the glucan elicitor from *P. megasperma* f. sp. *glycinea* causes changes in metabolic fluxes across the plasma membrane of soybean cells, and these changes are important in stimulation of phytoalexin accumulation. Only 300 μM Ca^{2+} is needed for normal elicitor response by soybean tissue.

B. Phytoalexins

Phytoalexins are low-molecular-weight antimicrobial compounds that are both synthesized by and accumulated in plants after exposure to microorganisms (Paxton, 1981). Several lines of evidence suggest that these compounds have an important role in plant disease and pest resistance. Although it is not possible to demonstrate production of a single phytoalexin by all species within a plant family, there is a systematic relationship in the distribution of classes of phytoalexins among higher plants.

Phytoalexins from a large number of different plants have been chemically characterized. Phytoalexins have been found in the isoflavanoid, sesquiterpenoid, diterpenoid, polyacetylene, phenanthrene, and stilbene families of secondary plant products. These can be taxonomically categorized into isoflavanoid-derived pterocarpan compounds characteristic of the Leguminosae, sesquiterpenoid compounds characteristic of the Solanaceae, phenanthrene compounds characteristic of the Orchidaceae, and acetylenic compounds characteristic of the Compositae. Examples of phytoalexins are shown in Fig. 1.

Biosynthesis of these phytoalexins involves a number of common pathways. The isoflavanoids are synthesized by a combination of precursors from the shikimate, acetate-malonate, and acetate-mevalonate pathways. Sesquiterpenes and furanoterpenes are synthesized via the acetate-mevalonate pathway. Polyketides such as 6-methoxymellein from carrot are synthesized by the acetate-malonate pathway.

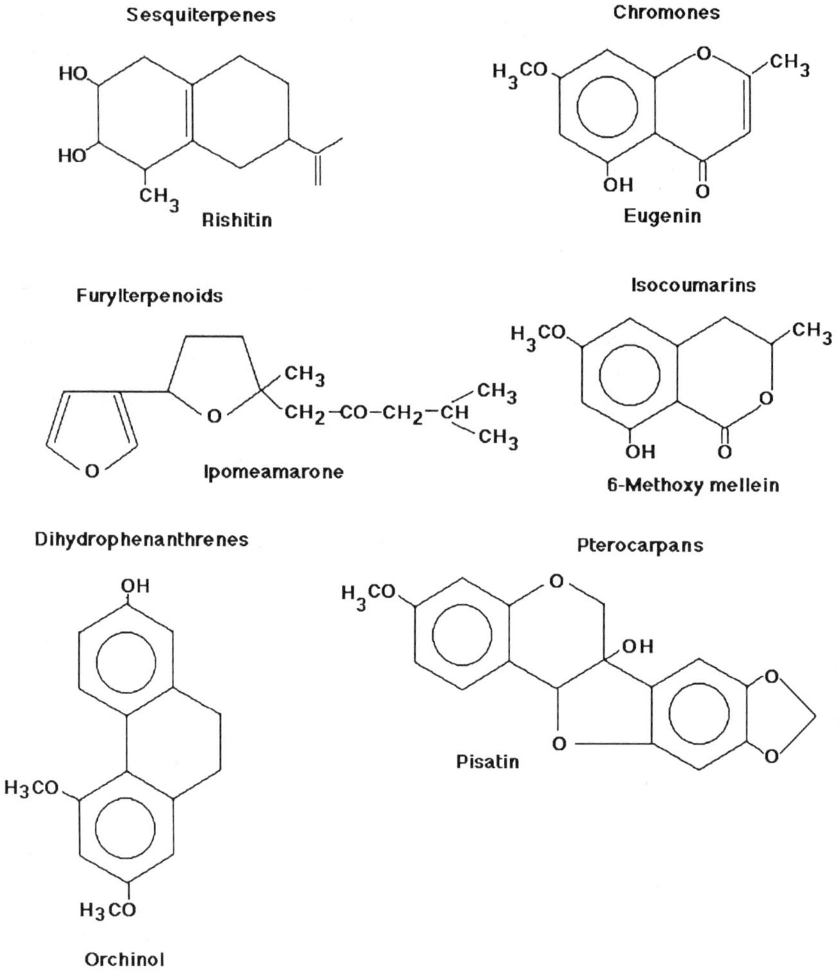

FIGURE 1 Phytoalexins.

Glyceollin is a phytoalexin of soybeans that occurs as a series of isomers first chemically characterized by Lyne et al. (1976). The most common iso-mers are shown in Fig. 2. It is not unusual for plants to produce a series of active isomers and chemically related phytoalexins.

It should be clear that in examining phytoalexin accumulation we are look-ing only at a part of a complex defense response of plants to microorganisms and other threats to the plant's integrity. It is probable that phytoalexin accumulation is an integral part of symptom development in plants, especially as it bears on the often observed hypersensitive response associated closely with plant disease resistance. Since phytoalexins are antibiotics, they inhibit plant cells as well as microorganisms and probably are involved in the cell death associated with plant disease resistance and the hypersensitive re-sponse.

Furylacetylenes

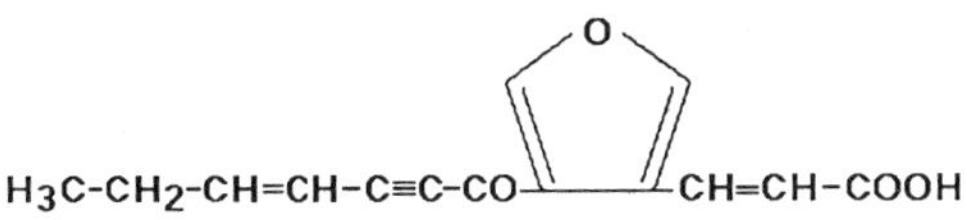

H₃C-CH₂-CH=CH-C≡C-CO—CH=CH-COOH

Wyrone Acid

Psoralens

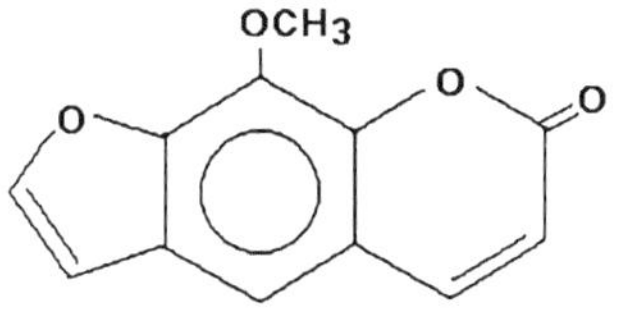

Xanthotoxin

Polyacetylenes

$H_2COH-CHOH-CH=CH-(C\equiv C)_3-CH=CH-CH_3$

Safynol

FIGURE 1 (continued)

Why might elicitors be useful? Paxton (1973) suggested some time ago that compounds produced by *P. megasperma* f. sp. *glycinea* might be useful in disease control. These compounds, from fungal culture media, can stimulate a soybean or other plant to accumulate phytoalexins, which can protect the plant from subsequent invasion by pathogens.

The plant accumulates phytoalexins to prevent colonization by potential pathogens. The elicitor is a signal that emanates from the pathogen, which the plant can perceive and respond to by producing phytoalexins, among other responses. This phenomenon, if used wisely by scientists and agriculturists, holds the potential to be very useful in agriculture as a way of protecting plants from disease, producing desirable compounds for subsequent use, and sometimes, eliminating, selectively, unwanted plant species (weeds).

The use of these elicitors in agriculture holds exciting promise. Since phytoalexins have an important role in plant disease and pest resistance, their controlled elicitation could be used to stimulate natural disease and pest resistance without the use of environmentally damaging compounds. The toxicity of phytoalexins toward the producing plant might also be used to create a new class of herbicides, elicitors that cause the plant to self-destruct.

Another potential use for elicitors is suggested by the work of Cline and Coscia (1988), who stimulated the production of sanguinarine (an alkaloid useful in fighting dental plaque buildup) in cell suspension cultures of *Papaver*. For example, they were able to get a 500-fold increase in sanguinarine accumulation (to a content of 10% of dry weight) by eliciting *Papaver bracteatum* cell suspension cultures with elicitor preparations made from mycelia of *Dendryphion penicillatum* or conidia of *Verticillium dahliae*. This procedure obviously could be applied to many other systems producing useful compounds,

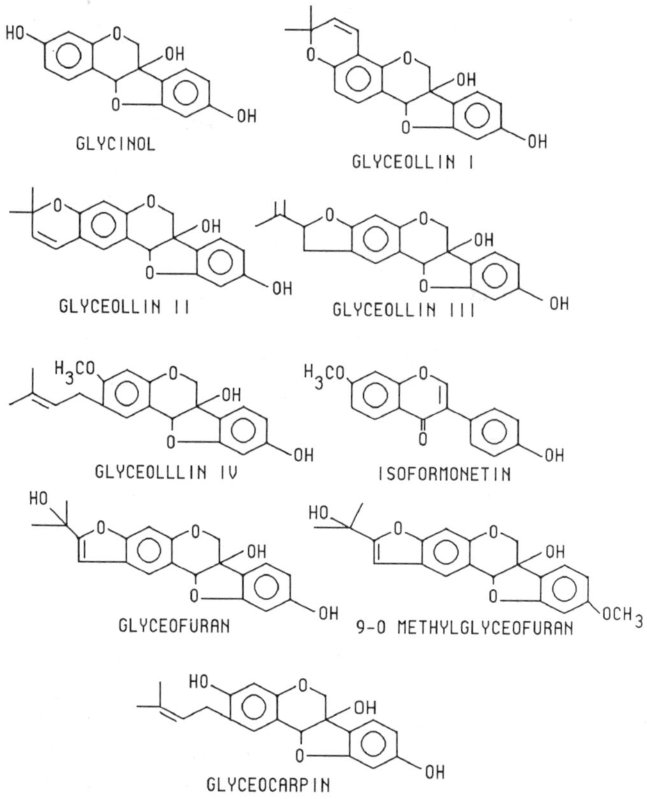

FIGURE 2 Phytoalexin isomers from soybean.

either to elicit their production or to stimulate even greater production than that found at present.

Many of the elicitors studied are carbohydrates. It is well known that carbohydrates carry "recognizable information." An example of specific recognition, of subtle changes in surface carbohydrates, is that of the human blood group antigens. Microorganisms "recognition" is being studied in several plant-microorganism interactions. Some specific examples of elicitor involvement in plant disease responses follow.

III. SPECIFIC EXAMPLES OF ELICITORS

A. *Monilinia fructicola*

Elicitors were first discovered by Cruickshank and Perrin (1968). They found that when grown on a semisynthetic broth with glucose as the primary carbon source, *Monilinia fructicola* produces a water-soluble peptide. This peptide was named monilicolin A, found to have a molecular weight of about 7900 daltons and to contain 20 common amino acids, with lysine at its N-terminus and alanine at its C-terminus. When tested at 10 ppm on germinated wheat seeds, the endocarp of peas, and broad beans, or the fungi *Monilinia fructicola* and *Colletotrichum lindemuthianum*, it showed no readily observable effect. Interestingly, however, at concentrations as low as 20 ppb, it could elicit a significant accumulation of phaseollin in bean endocarp tissue. Monilicolin A has an ED_{50} of 70 ppb, which is about 8×10^{-9} M. It is of special interest that this peptide did not elicit the phytoalexins pisatin from treated peas or viciatin, now known as wyerone acid, from treated broad beans.

Since monilicolin A is effective in eliciting the phytoalexin phaseollin in garden beans but not in eliciting related phytoalexins in pea or broad bean, this suggests a specific activity that could be useful in a herbicide.

B. *Phytophthora parasitica* var. *nicotianae*

Farmer and Helgeson (1987) found that at the early stages of rapid growth, the most abundant extracellular protein produced by *P. parasitica* var. *nicotianae* is a potent elicitor of the phytoalexin capsidiol in tobacco callus cultures. This protein elicitor has a molecular weight of 46 kilodaltons (kD) and a pI of 4.67. It is a glycoprotein with 1.8% glucose, 1.6% mannose, and 0.5% galactose. As little as 20 ng (4.3×10^{-13} mol) elicits the accumulation of capsidiol in tobacco. Pretreatment of this protein with either pronase or boiling destroyed the elicitor activity. Periodate treatment, however, did not affect its elicitor activity, suggesting that the protein component is the active part. Western blotting experiments with monospecific antibodies raised to the protein showed that it was present in infected tobacco plants. Capsidiol appeared rather abruptly in cultures 10 to 12 h after they were treated with this elicitor. They found β-1,4-endoxylanase activity associated with this protein, but it is not known whether this activity is responsible for elicitation or is a contaminant.

C. *Phytophthora megasperma* f. sp. *glycinea*

The best characterized elicitor at present is from the acid hydrolyzed cell walls of the oomycete *P. megasperma* f. sp. *glycinea*. The smallest active, and potentially the most useful fragment of this elicitor is a heptaglucan with specific structural requirements.

Frank and Paxton (1971) were the first to recognize and partially characterize compounds *P. megasperma* f. sp. *glycinea* cultures release, which are capable of inducing phytoalexin production in soybean plants. This elicitor appeared to be a glycoprotein with a molecular weight of about 10 kD. They developed a cut-cotyledon bioassay for this elicitor that has been widely used in subsequent elicitor studies. Elicitor activity also was found in extracts of *Venturia inaequalis*, *Rhizoctonia solani*, *Diplodia zeae*, and *Helminthosporium turcicum*, suggesting that elicitors of phytoalexin production are common in fungi. They also suggested that plants may have the ability to stimulate the production of these elicitors by fungi.

In one of the first studies looking for specific elicitors, which would partially explain race specificity in fungal pathogens, Keen (1975) presented evidence that culture filtrates of race 1 of *P. megasperma* f. sp. *glycinea* contained compounds that differed in some respects from race 3 of this fungus. Although he was not able to purify and identify this specific elicitor, he speculated that absence of this elicitor may be involved in the difference between race 1 and race 3 of this fungus.

Surface glycoproteins on *P. megasperma* f. sp. *glycinea* were suggested to play the role of race-specific phytoalexin elicitors by Keen and Legrand (1980). Isolated cell walls of *P. megasperma* f. sp. *glycinea* were extracted with 0.1 N NaOH at 0°C. The high-molecular-weight glycoproteins in this extract elicited glyceollin accumulation in a race-specific fashion. That is, the elicitor would evoke substantial phytoalexin accumulation only in cultivars which were resistant to races that produced the elicitor. The glycoprotein contained only glucose and mannose as sugars, and while its activity was diminished by boiling or pronase treatment, the elicitor activity was destroyed by periodate treatment. This suggests that the carbohydrate portions are important for elicitor activity. As they point out, this observation is clouded by considerable variation in replicates, a high concentration requirement for activity, and a lack of total specificity similar to races of this pathogen. This work remains to be confirmed but provides an interesting lead toward finding a useful class of compound.

In a series of papers, Ayers et al. (1976a,b) explored the composition of elicitors released by autoclaving purified *P. megasperma* f. sp. *glycinea* cell walls. They found at least four fractions, with varying composition and activity in elicitation of defense responses, from soybean cotyledons. They suggested that the elicitor activity of each fraction resides in the 3- and 3,6-highly branched glucan component of the fraction. They also suggested that the mannosyl residues, which represent about 1% of the undegraded glucan, are likely to participate in the active site of this molecule.

Bonhoff and Grisebach (1988) found that laminarin and polytran N (a glucan) are more effective elicitors of glyceollin, in soybean roots, than the acid-hydrolyzed glucan elicitor isolated from *P. megasperma* f. sp. *glycinea* by Sharp and coworkers (1984). Figure 3 shows the structure of the acid-hydrolyzed elicitor, which has been synthesized. Interestingly, on cut soybean cotyledons, the reverse was true in that laminarin was less effective in eliciting glyceollin accumulation.

When Bonhoff and Grisebach (1988) pretreated soybean roots with laminarin, they increased the resistance of seedlings against *P. megasperma* f. sp. *gly-*

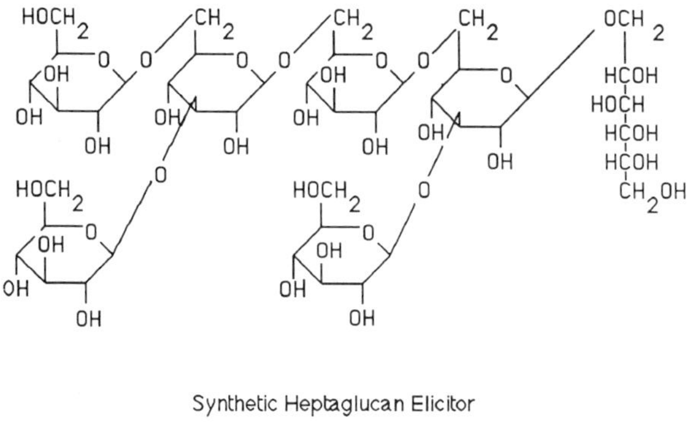

Synthetic Heptaglucan Elicitor

FIGURE 3 Elicitor from *P. megasperma* f. sp. *glycinea*.

cinea. When added with the laminarin, digitonin further increased the elicitation of glyceollin accumulation in intact roots. Soybean roots deposit callose when treated with digitonin but not when treated with various glucans.

An interesting observation by Yoshikawa, Matama, and Masago (1981) was that soybean tissues contain an enzyme which released elicitor from *P. megasperma* f. sp. *glycinea* cell walls. This suggests a role for such enzymes in "recognition" of potential pathogens when they come in contact with soybean tissue, by releasing fragments that are free to diffuse to binding sites on the cell. At a recent Congress of Plant Pathology in Kyoto, Japan, Yoshikawa reported, informally, that he has succeeded in releasing very active elicitor fragments from the cell walls of *P. megasperma* f. sp. *glycinea* with a β-1, 3-endoglucanase. These fragments are larger than the acid-hydrolyzed fragments studied by Sharp et al. (1984) and are reportedly 10 to 100 times more active in elicitation of glyceollin in soybeans.

Schmidt and Ebel (1987), expanding on earlier work by Yoshikawa, Keen, and Wang, found high-affinity elicitor binding sites on plasma membranes from soybean roots. The apparent K_d value for the β-glucan elicitor binding is about 2×10^{-7} M and the maximum number of binding sites is 0.5 pmol per milligram of protein. Only branched chain β-glucan polysaccharides could effectively compete for this membrane binding. These stringent structural requirements for competitive binding suggest that these sites are where elicitor binding occurs in whole soybean cells.

Transformation of this signal into gene activation is an area receiving attention now. Chappell et al. (1984) saw a rapid induction of ethylene biosynthesis in cultured parsley cells that had been treated with *P. megasperma* f. sp. *glycinea* elicitor. Ethylene production is thought to be a common response of plant cells to stresses, such as pathogen attack. Parsley cell cultures respond by production of ethylene within 1 h of treatment with this elicitor. Hauffe et al. (1986) showed that cultured parsley cells respond to this same elicitor by producing *S*-adenosyl-L-methionine:bergaptol and *S*-adenosyl-L-methionine:xanthotoxol *O*-methyltransferases. Kuhn et al. (1984) demonstrated that treatment of parsley cells with the *P. megasperma* f. sp. *glycinea* elicitor induced phenylalanine ammonia lyase and 4-coumarate:CoA ligase mRNAs. Farmer (1985) found that 5 µg/mL of *P. megasperma* f. sp. *glycinea* elicitor suppressed lignin accumulation in treated soybean suspension cultures. Therefore, phenolics normally polymerized into lignin were probably diverted into glyceollin and other compounds. This also suggests that elicitor recognition is a common phenomenon in triggering various defense responses in plants.

Race-specific molecules that protect soybeans from *P. megasperma* f. sp. *glycinea* were found by Wade and Albersheim (1979). These appeared to be glycoproteins found in the incompatible races of the pathogen but not the compatible races. Introduction of this glycoprotein fraction into wounds 90 min before subsequent inoculation was sufficient to protect soybean plants. Subsequent work by Desjardins et al. (1982) indicated that glycoprotein fractions from both compatible and incompatible races of *P. megasperma* f. sp. *glycinea* could protect soybean plants from subsequent infection by this fungus. Variability in the bioassay unfortunately prevented further purification and identification of these components.

Ziegler and Pontzen (1982) found an extracellular invertase in *P. megasperma* f. sp. *glycinea* capable of inhibiting glucan-elicited glyceollin accumulation in soybeans. This glycoprotein suppressor was active at 0.3 to 10 µg/ mL and race specific (i.e., the invertase would inhibit elicitation of glyceollin accumulation only on soybean cultivars that could be attacked by the race that was the source of the invertase). This work has not been confirmed and remains an area worth exploring. The study of soybean *Phytophthora* root rot has led to a better understanding of how plants can recognize pathogens (by their elicitors) and what they do after a pathogen is recognized (produce phytoalexins).

D. *Colletotrichum lindemuthianum*

Elicitor-active preparations from the α-race of the fungal pathogen *Colletotrichum lindemuthianum* stimulated the accumulation of products characteristic of lipid peroxidation in treated bean tissues. Bean suspension cells treated with these elicitors accumulated a "lipofuscin-like pigment." The accumulation of this pigment, about 6 h after treatment, coincided with the onset of visible browning and production of the bean phytoalexins kievitone, phaseollin, and phaseollinisoflavan. Generators of activated oxygen species, such as xanthine: xanthine oxidase and Fe:ethylenediamine di-*o*-hydroxyphenylacetic acid, also triggered phytoalexin accumulation. These researchers suggest that generation of active oxygen species may be involved in lipid peroxidation triggered by elicitors (Rogers et al., 1988).

Tepper and Anderson (1986) found an elicitor from the α-race of *C. lindemuthianum*, which showed selective elicitor activity on bean cultivars resistant to this race. The elicitor, which was 17% galactose, 38% glucose, and 45% mannose, has a molecular weight of approximately 60 kD. It resembles a galactoglucomannan elicitor released from *P. megasperma* f. sp. *glycinea* hyphae.

Maha and Dixon (1987) found that many galactose- and mannose-rich polysaccharide fractions from a culture filtrate of *C. lindemuthianum* showed elicitor activity. Elicitation was measured by the ability to induce phenylpropanoid pathway biosynthetic enzymes in cell suspension cultures of bean. Some of these uncharacterized fractions exhibited differential effects on the induction of phenylalanine ammonia lyase, chalcone synthase, and chalcone isomerase activities. However, only a highly mannose-rich fraction was a potent elicitor of all three enzymes. These heterogeneous fractions are probably related structurally and the protein part is not necessary for elicitor activity.

They suggest further that either more than one type of elicitor molecule may be necessary to induce the total of effects observed in a multicomponent resistance response, or different molecules may exist, with the potential to elicit differential responses.

Cramer et al. (1985) showed that an elicitor from *C. lindemuthianum* induces the de novo synthesis of mRNAs encoding chalcone synthase, phenylalanine ammonia lyase, and chalcone isomerase. These three enzymes of phenylpropanoid metabolism are involved in the synthesis of isoflavanoid-derived phytoalexins and are part of an extensive shift in the pattern of mRNA synthesis. These specific changes in gene expression occur at an early stage in the plant defense response.

Griffiths and Anderson (1987) found that *C. lindemuthianum* β-race culture filtrates at 10 ng of glucose equivalent per milliliter rapidly killed twice as many Great Northern bean protoplasts as the α-race culture filtrates.

This is surprising since infection of Great Northern bean tissue by the α-race conidia resulted in small lesions, whereas the β-race conidia caused the formation of even smaller lesions. They also warn that bean mesophyll protoplasts did not give this differential response, suggesting that protoplasts should be isoalted from cells that normally would be challenged by the pathogen.

E. *Cladosporium fulvum*

De Wit and Spikeman (1982) found that intercellular fluids of compatible race-cultivar interactions of *Cladosporium fulvum* and tomato contained race- and cultivar-specific elicitors. These elicitors induced chlorosis and necrosis specifically in resistant but not in susceptible plants. Elicitors of necrosis could also be obtained from this fungus when it was grown on synthetic media or on intercellular fluids of healthy tomato cultivars. However, these elicitors were nonspecific (i.e., they induced necrosis in all cultivars of tomato, irrespective of the resistance genes the tomato plant contained).

These elicitors induced phytoalexin accumulation, callose deposition, host cell necrosis, and ion leakage in tomato leaf tissue and also induced ion leakage in isolated tomato mesophyll cells. The intercellular fluids from tomato leaves inoculated with races of *C. fulvum* (other than race 2) were vacuum infiltrated into tomato leaves. Cultivars carrying the resistance gene *Cf* 2 reacted more quickly and generally more intensely than cultivars carrying the resistance genes *Cf* 4 or *Cf* 5. This chlorosis- and necrosis-inducing activity was present only in intercellular fluids obtained from compatible interactions. Intercellular fluids obtained from incompatible interactions did not contain chlorosis- or necrosis-inducing activity.

These specific elicitors were produced by the intercellularly growing fungus. Since callose deposition, necrosis, and phytoalexin accumulation are specifically induced in incompatible interaction between *C. fulvum* and tomato, it appears that specific elicitors for these responses are involved.

These specific elicitors might be used to identify tomato cultivars, used as herbicides on specific and unwanted tomato cultivars, and possibly used as protectants for desirable tomato cultivars. Since they are extractable from tomato leaves, they are not irreversibly bound to receptors in tomato cell walls. This activity was detectable 6 to 8 days after inoculation and reached a maximum 10 to 14 days after inoculation.

Toma and de Wit (1988) have now characterized the peptide elicitor, a putative product of the avirulence gene *A* 9 of *C. fulvum*, which specifically induces necrosis in tomato cultivars containing resistance gene *Cf* 9. This peptide contains 27 amino acids and has a molecular weight of 3049 daltons. It has been sequenced and has the following arrangement of amino acids, starting with the N terminus: Tyr-Cys-Asn-Ser-Ser-Cys-Thr-Arg-Ala-Phe-Asp-Cys-Leu-Gly-Gln-Cys-Gly-Arg-Cys-Asp-Phe-His-Lys-Leu-Gln-Cys-Val.

F. *Fusarium solani*

Chitosan, a β-1,4-linked glucosamine polymer, is a partial degradation product of chitin. Chitin is found in the cell walls of most insects and many higher fungi. Chitosan is formed by deacylation of chitin, and in this process undoubtedly some of the chitosan is cleaved into smaller pieces.

Pearce and Ride (1982) found that chitin and related compounds acted as elicitors of lignification in wounded wheat leaves. Hadwiger et al. (1981) detected chitosan along the surface of the macroconidium, within the fungal cell wall, and in the protoplasm of *Fusarium solani* fungal cells in infected pea plants, using immunochemical labeling with antichitosan antisera. Kendra and Hadwiger (1984) found that the antifungal and pisatin-inducing abilities of chitosan oligomers increased as the polymer size increased. No antifungal activity was shown by the monomer and dimer units of chitosan and these induced little phytoalexin in pea. A sharp increase in antifungal activity, and pisatin elicitation, was noted for the hexamer unit. The maximal antifungal and elicitor activity was found in the heptamer and larger chitosan polymers. These completely inhibited *F. solani* growth at 4 to 8 μg/mL and had maximal activity as elicitors of pisatin at this concentration as well. According to Kendra and Hadwiger, acetylation of the amine group is associated with the loss of antifungal and elicitor activities.

Loschke et al. (1983) found that induction of phenylalanine ammonia lyase and other specific proteins in pea, by chitosan, resembled the proteins induced by pathogens, actinomycin D, and 260-nm ultraviolet light. This suggests that these responses were similar to the authentic "resistance response" of the pea plant. More recently, Kendra and Hadwiger (1987) reported that no correlation was found between disease resistance and host cell death and membrane leakage in the interactions between bean endocarp tissue and *F. solani* f. sp. *pisi* or *F. solani* f. sp. *phaseolli*. Furthermore, changes in conductivity due to release of electrolytes from damaged plant tissue after fungal inoculation or chitosan treatment did not correlate with disease resistance.

G. *Helminthosporium victoriae*

Mayama et al. (1986) found that the well-known toxin victorin was an efficient elicitor of the oat phytoalexins, avenalumins, in near-isogenic oat cultivars containing the *Pc-2* allele for crown rust resistance and not the *pc-2* recessive allele, which would condition susceptibility. Victorin gave maximal phytoalexin elicitation at 10 pg/mL.

Helminthosporium victoriae was relatively insensitive to growth inhibition in vitro by the avenalumins. In contrast, the crown rust fungus was very sensitive to growth inhibition in vitro by the avenalumins.

It is interesting to speculate that the symptoms of victoria blight of oats are partly caused by this elicitation of phytoalexins by the toxin and not just victorin alone. The *Pc* gene is known to confer sensitivity to victoria blight at the same time that it confers resistance to crown rust.

H. *Phytophthora infestans*

Doke et al. (1980) found that germinating cystospores of *Phytophthora infestans* race 1,2,3,4 released substances that suppressed rishitin accumulation and the hypersensitive reaction of potato tuber tissue to an incompatible race of the fungus. These suppressors were partially characterized as water-soluble nonanionic glucans containing β-1,3 linkages. The nonanionic glucan from race 4 was less active as a suppressor. Glucose was the only sugar found after acid hydrolysis of the glucan. The β-1,3 linkage was established by

the observation that treating the glucan with laminarinase released glucose
from more than 85% of the suppressor. Doke and Tomiyama (1980) reported
that β-1,3 glucan molecules of 17 to 23 glucose units from *P. infestans* suppressed phytoalexin accumulation in an anticipated race-specific manner in
potato.

Bostock et al. (1986) found that arachidonic acid elicited sesquiterpene
phytoalexin accumulation and a number of other reactions characteristic of
the hypersensitive response in potato tubers. Furthermore, they separated
the stimulation of lignin formation, ethylene and ethane production caused
by unsaturated fatty acids in general, from the rather specific stimulation
of sesquiterpenoid phytoalexin production and protection of potato tissue from
infection by compatible races of *P. infestans*.

A β-glucan, extracted from the mycelium of *P. infestans*, stimulated arachidonic acid elicitation of phytoalexin accumulation. These glucans are inactive as elicitors of phytoalexin accumulation but dramatically enhance arachidonic acid's ability to elicit phytoalexin accumulation (Preisig and Kuć, 1986).

Both arachidonic and eicosapentaenoic acids are fatty acids that occur
as acyl esters in the membrane and storage lipids of *P. infestans* zoospores
and mycelium. These two acids can elicit phytoalexin accumulation in potato,
and their elicitor activity is dramatically enhanced by soluble glucans also
found in the cell walls of this fungus. However, the glucans show no elicitor
activity by themselves. If applied prior to inoculation, arachidonic and eicosapentaenoic acid also protect potato tuber tissue from colonization by a compatible race of *P. infestans*.

Bloch et al. (1984) found that arachidonic and eicosapentaenoic acids could
elicit phytoalexin accumulation in potato and pepper fruit but not in sweet
potato, broad bean, french bean, pea, soybean, tobacco, tomato, carrot,
or parsnip. This suggests the use of these elicitors as herbicides where some
solanaceous weeds, such as nightshade in soybeans, might be selectively eliminated.

I. *Puccinia graminis*

A glycoprotein elicitor of the lignification response in wheat leaves was isolated by Kogel et al. (1985) from the germ-tube walls of wheat stem rust (*Puc-
cinia graminis* f. sp. *tritici*). The approximate molecular weight of the active
compound is 100 kD and it is composed mainly of glucose plus 30% protein.
Pronase did not destroy the elicitor activity, whereas periodate did, and this
supports the notion that the carbohydrate moiety bears the active part of
this molecule.

J. *Verticillium albo-atrum*

Woodward and Pegg (1986) found that culture filtrates and cell walls of *Verticillium albo-atrum*, a tomato pathogen, elicited the accumulation of the tomato
phytoalexin rishitin. High levels of rishitin were induced in both susceptible
and resistant isolines of tomato by a low-molecular-weight glucan, containing
β-1,3 linkages, which was produced in 14-day-old cultures of *V. albo-atrum*.
Since this elicitor has a molecular weight of less than 1800 daltons, it may
lend itself to easy application to plants. They suggest that polysaccharides

alone might be responsible for the activity since elicitor quantities were unaffected by deproteinizing treatments. Glucose was the only compound detected in hydrolysates of elicitor-active fractions, so the elicitor may consist
of approximately six glucose units.

K. Endogenous Elicitors

Endogenous elicitors are compounds that either exist preformed in the plant
or are fragments of preformed compounds, and can elicit phytoalexin accumulation by the plant. The best known of these compounds is pectin or its fragments. Pectin fragments can elicit phytoalexins in plants and even potentiate
the activity of other elicitors. This suggests that damage to a plant cell wall
may activate defense responses, including enhanced phytoalexin accumulation.
Many plant pathogens produce various enzymes capable of degrading pectin,
presumably as a source of nutrients, and these enzymes are good elicitors
of phytoalexin accumulation. Stekoll and West (1978) obtained evidence for
the presence, in culture filtrates of young *Rhizopus stolonifer* cultures, of
both high- and low-molecular-weight elicitors. These stimulated the production of the phytoalexin casbene in cell-free extracts of castor bean seedlings.
This high-molecular-weight elicitor is a glycoprotein enzyme, endopolygalacturonase, with a hydrolytic mode of cleavage. The low-molecular-weight elicitors appear to be pectin fragments released from the culture medium by the
action of the endopolygalacturonase.

Hahn et al. (1981) found that soybean cell walls also have an endogenous
elicitor, a fragment of a pectic polysaccharide, probably from the middle
lamella. Elicitor activity also was found in tobacco cell walls and in a rhamno-
galacturonan II fraction from cultured sycamore cells.

Research by Robertsen (1986) showed that pectin fragments are capable
of eliciting production of ligninlike compounds in cucumber hypocotyls. The
most active of the oligosaccharides showed elicitor activity when diluted to a
concentration of 800 ng of uronic acid units per milliliter and was composed
of 11 galacturonosyl units. Very large galacturonic acid polymers or small
polymers with a degree of polymerization of less than seven showed little or
no activity.

Of further interest is the observation by Davis et al. (1985) that the
decagalacturonide released from citrus polygalacturonic acid by endopolygalacturonic acid lyase, increased the elicitor activity of a hexa-β-glucosyl glucitol, released from *P. megasperma* f. sp. *glycinea* cell walls by acid hydrolysis,
by as much as 35-fold. This stimulation occurred at 22 μg of decagalacturonide per milliliter. This effect is synergistic in that the decagalacturonide
conferred more than an additive increase in response to the elicitor. It should
be noted, however, that dilute acetate, formate, or propionate buffer increased
the elicitor activity of the hexa-β-glucosyl glucitol 30- to 60-fold! This stimulation, possibly due to damage to the soybean cells by sodium acetate, remains
to be investigated.

Davis et al. (1986) studied the elicitation of glyceollin accumulation in
soybean cotyledons by an α-1,4-D-endopolygalacturonic acid lyase from *Er-
winia carotovora*. They found the major, if not only component with the highest specific elicitor activity was a decasaccharide of α-1,4-D-galactosyluronic
acid that contained the expected 4-deoxy-β-L-5-threohexopyranos-4-enylu-

ronic acid at the nonreducing terminus. This compound showed a maximum elicitor activity at 5 μg per cotyledon (32 μM) and is identical to an elicitor released from soybean cell walls by this lyase.

IV. CONCLUSIONS

Future research. One disconcerting aspect of most of the elicitors studied so far is the lack of confirmed specificity in phytoalexin elicitation similar to host specificity of the pathogen. Specificity, as shown by the pathogens that produce the elicitors, would be one of the more useful properties of these compounds. Specific elicitors would allow rather precise targeting of plants to be protected or killed.

Some work suggesting that this is possible has been reported. De Wit and Spikeman (1982) were able to purify and characterize a glycoprotein from the intercellular fluids of tomato tissue infected by *Cladosporium fulvum*. This glycoprotein elicited necrosis characteristic of an incompatible interaction (resistance) as early as 7 h after treatment of tissue normally resistant to the particular race of this pathogen that produced the elicitor. Cultivars of tomato susceptible to that eliciting race did not give this reaction.

Work by Keen and others has suggested the presence of these elusive specific elicitors in *P. megasperma* f. sp. *glycinea*. They appear to be glycoproteins, but they have not been chemically characterized or their identity confirmed.

Crop protection. Cross protection of plants against disease has been demonstrated several times. This protection is effected by first inoculating plants with a nonpathogenic microorganism. After a period of time, ranging up to several days, inoculation with a normally pathogenic microorganism will not cause disease. This phenomenon is akin to the vaccination of humans with the cowpox virus to protect them from smallpox.

The use of elicitors of phytoalexin production in plants as protectants of these plants was first suggested by Paxton (1973). Several companies have become interested in applying this knowledge to create a new type of "fungicide" that uses the plant's own defense mechanisms to protect it from disease. These compounds, which often are relatively stable polysaccharides or glycoproteins, would be welcome additions to the plant pathologist's arsenal to protect plants. Unlike most of the other fungicides, these compounds generally would have low impact on the environment and nontarget organisms.

As protectants, these compounds would need to be formulated to remain on the surface of the plant until such time as the plant is wounded or pathogens or insects introduce the compound into the cell during attack. For use as herbicides, they would need to be formulated to enter the plant immediately after application to the plant.

Suppressors of phytoalexin production. Suppressors are of interest in studying the virulence of fungal pathogens and may have an important role in the ability of a pathogen to attack its host rapidly. Conceivable, they could have a role as herbicides [e.g., suppression of nightshade (*Solanum nigrum*) in other crops] since they might increase the aggressiveness of natural pathogens on these plants. Specific suppressors could prove useful as very selective herbicides, but once again, their chemical characterization remains to be completed.

Present interest. The immediate commercial application of this information in plant protection is suggested by an interest several companies have expressed in developing carbohydrates for applications in medical science. Bicarb AB of Lund Sweden and Chembiomed of Edmonton, Canada, are two such companies engaged in the research, development, and marketing of biologically active carbohydrates. Carbohydrates International AB of Arlov, Sweden (a subsidiary of Volvo AB), is also looking for novel ways to synthesize complicated carbohydrates found in human membranes.

IGENE Biotechnology of Columbia, Maryland recently developed a chitin nematicide, CladoSan, which has been used in nematode control. Other companies are looking into the production of chitin for disease control and the utilization of large masses of crab shells, which are now waste but predominantly chitin.

Elicitors contained in plant, animal and microorganism cell walls are important signals of the presence of microorganisms in the plant, and regulators of plant cell defense activities, including accumulation of phytoalexins against invading insects, bacteria and fungi. The application of our knowledge of elicitors and fungicide formulation could benefit from immediate attention. Understanding how these molecules function in plant disease and pest resistance might significantly improve our lives.

ACKNOWLEDGMENT

Certain aspects of the research work presented in this report were supported in part by the Illinois Agricultural Experiment Station.

REFERENCES

Ayers, A. R., Ebel, J., Valent, B., and Albersheim, P. (1976a). Host-pathogen interactions: X. Fractionation and biological activity of an elicitor isolated from the mycelium walls of *Phytophthora megasperma* var. *sojae. Plant Physiol.* 57:760-765.

Ayers, A. R., Valent, B., Ebel, J., and Albersheim, P. (1976b). Host-pathogen interactions: XI. Composition and structure of wall-released elicitor fractions. *Plant Physiol.* 57:766-774.

Bloch, C. B., de Wit, P. J. G. M., and Kuć, J. (1984). Elicitation of phytoalexins by arachidonic and eicosapentaenoic acids: a host survey. *Physiol. Plant Pathol.* 25:199-208.

Bonhoff, A., and Grisebach, H. (1988). Elicitor-induced accumulation of glyceollin and callose in soybean roots and localized resistance against *Phytophthora megasperma* f. sp. *glycinea. Plant Sci.* 54:203-209.

Bostock, R. M., Schaeffer, D. A, and Hammerschmidt, R. (1986). Comparison of elicitor activities of arachidonic acid, fatty acids and glucans from *Phytophthora infestans* in hypersensitivity expression in potato tubers. *Physiol. Mol. Plant Pathol.* 29:349-360.

Chappell, J., Hahlbrock, K., and Boller, T. (1984). Rapid induction of ethylene biosynthesis in cultured parsley cells by fungal elicitor and its relationship to the induction of phenylalanine ammonia-lyase. *Planta 161:* 475-480.

Cline, S. D., and Coscia, C. J. (1988). Stimulation of sanguinarine production by combined fungal elicitation and hormonal deprivation in cell suspension cultures of *Papaver bracteatum*. *Plant Physiol.* 86:161-165.

Cramer, C. L., Ryder, T. B., Bell, J. N., and Lamb, C. J. (1985). Rapid switching of plant gene expression induced by fungal elicitors. *Science* 227:1240-1242.

Cruickshank, I. A. M., and Perrin, D. R. (1968). The isolation and partial characterization of monilicolin A, a polypeptide with phaseollin-inducing activity from *Monilinia fructicola*. *Life Sci.* 7:449-458.

Davis, K. R., Darvill, A. G., and Albersheim, P. (1985). Several biotic and abiotic elicitors act synergistically in the induction of phytoalexin accumulation in soybean. *Plant Mol. Biol.* 6:23-32.

Davis, K. R., Darvill, A. G., Albersheim, P., and Dell, A. (1986). Host-pathogen interactions: XXIX. Oligogalacturonides released from sodium polypectate by endopolygalacturonic acid lyase are elicitors of phytoalexins in soybean. *Plant Physiol.* 80:568-577.

Desjardins, A., Ross, L. M., Spellman, M. W., Darvill, A. G., and Albersheim, P. (1982). Host-pathogen interactions: XX. Biological variation in the proteciton of soybeans from infection by *Phytophthora megasperma* f. sp. *Glycinea*. *Plant Physiol.* 69:1046-1050.

de Wit, P. J. G. M., and Spikeman, G. (1982). Evidence for the occurrence of race and cultivar-specific elicitors of necrosis in intercellular fluids of compatible interactions of *Cladosporium fulvum* and tomato. *Physiol. Plant Pathol.* 21:1-11.

Doke, N., and Tomiyama, K. (1980). Suppression of the hypersensitive response of potato tuber protoplasts to hyphal wall components by water soluble glucans isolated from *Phytophthora infestans*. *Physiol. Plant Pathol.* 16:177-186.

Doke, N., Garas, N. A., and Kuć, J. (1980). Effect on host hypersensitivity of suppressors released during the germination of *Phytophthora infestans* cystospores. *Phytopathology* 70:35-39.

Farmer, E. (1985). Effects of fungal elicitor on lignin biosynthesis in cell suspension cultures of soybean. *Plant Physiol.* 78:338-342.

Farmer, E. E., and Helgeson, J. P. (1987). An extracellular protein from *Phytophthora parasitica* var. *nicotianae* is associated with stress metabolite accumulation in tobacco callus. *Plant Physiol.* 85:338-342.

Frank, J. A., and Paxton, J. D. (1971). An inducer of soybean phytoalexin and its role in the resistance of soybeans to *Phytophthora* rot. *Phytopathology* 61:954-958.

Griffiths, H. M., and Anderson, A. J. (1987). Response of *Phaseolus vulgaris* protoplasts to chemical components of fungal origin. *Can. J. Bot.* 65:63-68.

Hadwiger, L. A., Beckman, J. M., and Adams, J. M. (1981). Localization of fungal components in the pea—*Fusarium* interaction detected immunochemically with antifungal and antifungal cell wall antisera. *Plant Physiol.* 67:170-175.

Hahn, M. G., Darvill, A. G., and Albersheim, P. (1981). Host-pathogen interactions: XIX. The endogenous elicitor, a fragment of a plant cell wall polysaccharide that elicits phytoalexin accumulation in soybeans. *Plant Physiol.* 68:1161-1169.

Hauffe, K. D., Hahlbrock, K., and Scheel, D. (1986). Elicitor-stimulated furanocoumarin biosynthesis in cultured parsley cells: S-adenosyl-L-methionine:bergaptol and S-adenosyl-L-methionine:xanthotoxol O-methyltransferases. Z. Naturforsch. C41:228-239.

Keen, N. T. (1975). Specific elicitors of plant phytoalexin production: determinants of race specificity in pathogens? Science 187:74-75.

Keen, N. T., and LeGrand, M. (1980). Surface glycoproteins: evidence that they may function as the race specific phytoalexin elicitors of Phytophthora megasperma f. sp. glycinea. Physiol. Plant Pathol. 17:175-192.

Kendra, D., and Hadwiger, L. A. (1984). Characterization of the smallest chitosan oligomer that is maximally antifungal to Fusarium solani and elicits pisatin formation in Pisum sativum. Exp. Mycol. 8:276-281.

Kendra, D., and Hadwiger, L. A. (1987). Cell death and membrane leakage not associated with the induction of disease resistance in peas by chitosan. Phytopathology 77:100-106.

Kogel, K.-H., Heck, B., Kogel, G., Moerschbacher, B., and Reisener, H.-J. (1985). A fungal elicitor of the resistance response in wheat. Z. Naturforsch. C40:743-744.

Kuhn, D., Chappell, J., Boudet, A., and Hahlbrock, K. (1984). Induction of phenylalanine ammonia-lyase and 4-coumarate:CoA ligase mRNAs in cultured plant cells by UV light or fungal elicitor. Proc. Natl. Acad. Sci. USA 81:1102-1106.

Loschke, D. C., Hadwiger, L. A., and Wagoner, W. (1983). Comparison of mRNA populations coding for phenylalanine ammonia lyase and other peptides form pea tissue treated with biotic and abiotic phytoalexin inducers. Physiol. Plant Pathol. 23:163-173.

Lyne, R. L., Mulheirn, L. J., and Leworthy, D. P. (1976). New pterocarpinoid phytoalexins of soybean. J. Chem. Soc. Chem. Commun. 1976:497-498.

Maha, A. M. S. H., and Dixon, R. A. (1987). Fractionation and properties of elicitors of the phenylpropanoid pathway from culture filtrates of Colletotrichum lindemuthianum. Physiol. Mol. Plant Pathol. 31:91-103.

Mayama, S., Tani, T., Ueno, T., Midland, S. L., Sims, J. J., and Keen, N. T. (1986). The purification of victorin and its phytoalexin elicitor activity in oat leaves. Physiol. Mol. Plant Pathol. 29:1-18.

Paxton, J. D. (1973). Plants' "self" recognition may aid disease control. Ill. Res. 15:13.

Paxton, J. D. (1981). Phytoalexins-A working redefinition. Phytopathology Z. 101:106-109.

Pearce, R. B., and Ride, J. P. (1982). Chitin and related compounds as elicitors of the lignification response in wounded wheat leaves. Physiol. Plant Pathol. 20:119-123.

Preisig, C. L., and Kuć, J. A. (1985). Arachidonic acid-related elicitors of the hypersensitive response in potato and enhancement of their activities by glucans from Phytophthora infestans (Mont.) deBary. Arch. Biochem. Biophys. 239:379-389.

Robertsen, B. (1986). Elicitors of the production of lignin-like compounds in cucumber hypocotyls. Physiol. Mol. Plant Pathol. 28:137-148.

Rogers, K. R., Albert, F., and Anderson, A. J. (1988). Lipid peroxidation is a consequence of elicitor activity. Plant Physiol. 86:547-553.

Schmidt, W., and Ebel, J. (1987). Specific binding of a fungal glucan phytoalexin elicitor to membrane fractions from soybean *Glycine max*. *Proc. Natl. Acad. Sci. USA 84*: 4117-4121.

Sharp, J. K., Albersheim, P., Ossowski, P., Pilotti, A., Garegg, P., and Lindberg, B. (1984). Comparison of the structures and elicitor activities of a synthetic and mycelial-wall-derived hexa (β-D-glucopyranosyl)-D-glucitol. *J. Biol. Chem. 259*: 11341-11345.

Stäb, M., and Ebel, J. (1987). Effects of Ca on phytoalexin induction by fungal elicitor in soybean cells. *Arch. Biochem. Biophys. 257*: 416-423.

Stekoll, M., and West, C. A. (1978). Purification and properties of an elicitor of castor bean phytoalexin from culture filtrates of the fungus *Rhizopus stolonifer*. *Plant Physiol. 61*: 38-45.

Templeton, M. D., and Lamb, C. J. (1988). Elicitors and defense gene activation. *Plant Cell Environ. 11*: 395-401.

Tepper, C., and Anderson, A. J. (1986). Two cultivars of bean display a differential response to extracellular components from *Colletotrichum lindemuthianum*. *Physiol. Mol. Plant Pathol. 29*: 411-420.

Toma, I. M. J., and de Wit, P. J. G. M. (1988). Purification and primary structure of a necrosis-inducing peptide from the apoplastic fluids of tomato infected with *Cladosporium fulvum* (syn. *Fulvia fulva*). *Physiol. Plant Pathol. 33*: 59-67.

Wade, M., and Albersheim, P. (1979). Race-specific molecules that protect soybeans from *Phytophthora megasperma* var. *sojae*. *Proc. Natl. Acad. Sci. USA 76*: 4433-4437.

Woodward, S., and Pegg, G. F. (1986). Rishitin accumulation elicited in resistant and susceptible isolines of tomato by mycelial extracts and filtrates from cultures of *Verticillium albo-atrum*. *Physiol. Mol. Plant Pathol. 29*: 337-347.

Yoshikawa, M., Matama, M., and Masago, H. (1981). Release of a soluble phytoalexin elicitor from mycelial walls of *Phytophthora megasperma* var. *sojae* by soybean tissues. *Plant Physiol. 67*: 1032-1035.

Ziegler, E., and Pontzen, R. (1982). Specific inhibition of glucan-elicited glyceollin accumulation in soybeans by an extracellular mannan-glycoprotein of *Phytophthora megasperma* f. sp. *glycinea*. *Physiol. Plant Pathol. 20*: 321-331.

22

Cyclic Peptide Hepatotoxins from Cyanobacteria

Val Richard Beasley, Randall A. Lovell, Andrew M. Dahlem,* Wanda M. Haschek, and Stephen B. Hooser

University of Illinois at Urbana-Champaign, Urbana, Illinois

Current affiliation: Eli Lilly, Inc., Indianapolis, Indiana

I. INTRODUCTION

Cyanobacteria (blue-green algae) are unicellular or microscopically filamentous organisms, which rely on photosynthesis for energy and have a cell wall similar to those of gram-negative bacteria. The organisms occur in waters of varied organic and ionic composition and salinity, ranging from fresh, through brackish, and marine, to hypersaline (Fogg et al., 1973). Conditions which promote formation of dense blooms of cyanobacteria include (1) ample sunlight, (2) moderate to high nutrient concentrations (notably phosphorus, ammonia, and nitrate) which may arise from household, industrial, or agricultural pollution, (3) water temperatures of 15 to 30°C (Ringelberg and Baard, 1988), and (4) a pH > 6 (Skulberg et al., 1984). However, factors which trigger algal toxin formation are not precisely known. Ingestion of wind-concentrated blooms has often been associated with the deaths of livestock, waterfowl, and dogs. Hepatotoxicoses and neurotoxicoses are the most common syndromes caused by ingestion of these blooms.

To the authors' knowledge, blue-green algae toxicosis was first reported by Francis (1878) in Australia. Despite his identification of *Nodularia spumigena* and current knowledge of its ability to produce a hepatotoxin, Francis made no mention of hepatic lesions. Thus, the nature of the toxin(s) involved remains speculative. The first known algal toxicosis in North America occurred in 1882-1884 near Waterville, Minnesota. *Gloeotrichia echinulata* was implicated as the cause of deaths in cattle, horses, and hogs (Arthur, 1882 and 1891; Porter, 1886).

Various cyanobacteria may produce hepatotoxins, neurotoxins, endotoxins, skin irritants, allergens, and/or tumor promoters. Moreover, *Microcystis* spp. have been associated with each type of syndrome listed apart from skin irritation (Fitch et al., 1934; Evans, 1936; Heise, 1949; Stewart et al., 1950; O'Donoghue and Wilton, 1951; Moore, 1977; Carmichael, 1982; Carmichael, 1988; Falconer and Buckley, 1989). However, prior to the mid-1950s, it was often implied that "algae poisoning" was caused by a single toxin and authors often failed to differentiate the toxic syndromes. Assessments of many of the early reports are difficult because of (1) failure to examine tissues for gross and histologic lesions, (2) collection of algae days after deaths occurred, (3) the presence of multiple cyanobacterial species in algal blooms, (4) changes in nomenclature, (5) toxin instability, (6) failure to lyse cells before parenteral dosing, and (7) the capability of some species to produce more than one type of toxin.

A. Differentiation of Hepatotoxicoses

Data in the early literature on survival time, lesions, and clinical signs were used to differentiate between the probable involvement of the two major classes of cyanobacterial toxins, neurotoxins and hepatotoxins. Although for the balance of this chapter we have made an effort to discuss the literature only in regard to algal hepatotoxins, in studies involving evaluations of cell materials or extracts, the concurrent involvement of additional toxins cannot be ruled out.

B. Initial Reports of Algal Hepatotoxicosis

Wheeler et al. (1942) provided the first definitive documentation of *M. aeruginosa*-associated hepatotoxicosis. They observed that fresh algae given ip or sc to mice at 0.25 ml caused death in 16-36 hr, while lysed algae given sc at 0.025 ml was lethal in 40-90 min. Their description of mice that died less than 3 hr after sc dosing is consistent with recent reports. The following is their report. "Mice behaved normally for half an hour . . . Then they had periods of apathy alternating with restlessness . . . During this interval the ears and tails became chalky white . . ." (upon) "postmortem . . . there was no bleeding on cutting through the skin or abdominal wall . . . the liver was enormously dilated and dark . . . and the visceral circulation no more in evidence than the peripheral, except that the engorged liver bled profusely when incised." Finally, these workers found that toxin could be adsorbed to charcoal, but it survived the equivalent of common water purification processes (alum coagulation, chlorination and filtration).

Ashworth and Mason (1946) described lesion development in livers of rats after a lethal or sublethal ip dose of an extract from *M. aeruginosa*. Fifteen min post-dosing, hepatocytes were swollen and their "outlines" less prominent. By 4 hr, hepatic injury was maximal and consisted of marked centrilobular necrosis with complete dissociation of liver cords and hepatocyte debris free in the blood of sinusoids. In survivors at 24-48 hr, the lobular architecture was largely restored and blood in the sinusoids greatly reduced as compared to earlier stages. Two to 3 days after a maximal sublethal dose, however, the liver was reduced in size by one-third, and it was soft, mottled, and dull yellow. Five days after a maximal sublethal dose, livers had returned to near normal, except hepatocytes, which were swollen and had very granular cytoplasm and enlarged hyperchromatic nuclei. Numerous mitotic figures were present. Also reported were milder degeneration and necrosis in the kidney and heart.

The animals were more tolerant of a subsequent dose of the same algal extract. Four weeks after a sublethal dose, the liver was normal on microscopic examination. Acute death was attributed to shock and circulatory collapse and delayed death to hepatic insufficiency, renal failure, and generalized cellular damage. Finally, the authors recognized similarities in the chemical properties of, and lesions caused by, the cyanobacterial toxin and the thermostable toxin of the mushroom, *Amanita phalloides*.

II. CYANOBACTERIAL HEPATOTOXINS

A. Distribution Among Cyanobacteria

Two species of cyanobacteria involved in many case reports on deaths in animals are *M. aeruginosa* (Fig. 1[a]) and *N. spumigena* (Fig. 1[b]). *M. aeruginosa* and other members of this genus produce a family of monocyclic heptapeptide compounds termed microcystins (MCs; at one time referred to as "fast
death factor"). Strains of *N. spumigena* produce nodularin, a structurally
and toxicologically similar monocyclic pentapeptide (Rinehart et al., 1988).
The genera *Oscillatoria, Anabaena, Gomphosphaeria,* and *Aphanizomenon* also
have the ability to produce hepatotoxins but the hazard posed by these organisms is less apparent (Carmichael, 1988; Berg et al., 1986). *Microcystis*
and *Gomphosphaeria* are unicellular genera which reproduce by binary fission
and belong to the subgroup Chroococcales. *Anabaena, Nodularia,* and *Aphanizomenon* are unbranched, (microscopically) filamentous genera with heterocysts, and belong to the subgroup Nostocacean. *Oscillatoria* is a filamentous
blue-green algae without heterocysts which belongs to the subgroup Oscilla-
torian (Fogg et al., 1973). Thus, the ability to produce hepatotoxins is widely distributed in subgroups of cyanobacteria and is not exclusively related
to heterocyst formation, means of reproduction, or unicellular vs filamentous
morphology.

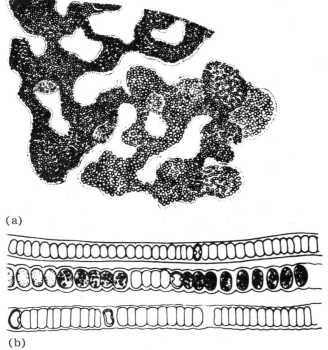

(a)

(b)

FIGURE 1 Line drawings of (a) a low power view of naturally occurring masses
of thousands of *Microcystis aeruginosa* cells; and (b) a high power view of
Nodularia spumigena (with permission from the Wm. C. Brown Publishing Co.).

Berg et al. (1986) found that 30 of 51 eutrophic Scandinavian lakes contained hepatotoxic cyanobacterial blooms; and 54 of 82 waterbloom samples contained greater than 1 mouse unit (MU) of hepatotoxic compound/g of freeze-dried algae. The three most toxic genera were *Microcystis*, *Nodularia*, and *Oscillatoria*. Four of 21 samples containing *M. aeruginosa* had 8000 MU/g; nine contained 1000 or more MU/g; and 17 had greater than 500 MU/g. The one *N. spumigena* sample contained 2000 MU/g. The most toxic sample of *O. agardhii* had 1000 MU/g and only 11 of 24 contained ⩾ 500 MU/g. The one sample of *O. rubescens* contained 1000 MU/g. Seven of 13 *Anabaena flos-aquae* samples were hepatotoxic, but the most potent one had only 500 MU/g. Two of seven *Aphanizomenon flos-aquae* samples and two of three *Gomphosphaeria* spp. were hepatotoxic, but none exceeded 40 MU/g. Thus, upon further study, hepatotoxic strains of widely varying potency are likely to be encountered.

B. Structural Determinations

Partial structures of peptide toxins from algae have only recently been reported (Elleman et al., 1978; Botes et al., 1982a,b, 1984, 1985; Krishnamurthy et al., 1985, 1986a,b, 1989; Kusumi et al., 1987a,b; Painuly et al., 1988; Santikarn et al., 1983; Williams, 1983). The MCs are monocyclic and composed of the D-amino acids, alanine, erythro-β-methylaspartic acid, and glutamic acid; two variable L-amino acids with combinations known to include leucine and alanine (LA), leucine and arginine (LR), tyrosine and arginine (YR), tyrosine and alanine (YA), tyrosine and methionine (YM), or arginine and arginine (RR); and the two unusual amino acids, N-methyl dehydroalanine, and 3-amino-9-methoxy-10-phenyl-2,6,8-trimethyl-deca-4,6-dienoic acid (termed ADDA) (Fig. 2). The stereochemistry of ADDA has recently been completed and assigned as 2S,3S,8S,9S, completing the absolute structure of MCLR (Rinehart et al., 1988). Desmethyl derivatives have also been described (Krishnamurthy et al., 1989).

The structure of nodularin, from a New Zealand bloom and laboratory strain of *N. spumigena*, has recently been elucidated and assigned as the cyclic compound D-glutamic acid, N-methyl-Z-dehydrobutyrine, D-erythro-β-methylaspartic acid, L-arginine, and ADDA (Carmichael et al., 1988; Eriksson et al., 1988; Rinehart et al., 1988) (Fig. 2).

III. SPECIES OVERVIEWS

A. Humans

"Palm Island mystery disease" is a hepatitis-like illness in Australian aboriginal islanders which has been associated with water supply contamination by cyanobacteria (Byth, 1980). The syndrome developed in 3 phases (1) a hepatitis phase for 2 days, (2) a lethargic phase of 1 to 2 days, and (3) a diarrhea phase for 5 days (Bourke and Hawes, 1983). The tropical cyanobacterium, *Cylindrospermopsis raciborskii*, was isolated from domestic water supplies after the disease outbreak and later cultured. Extracts given ip to mice were hepatotoxic and caused varying degrees of injury to the kidneys, lungs, and adrenal glands (Hawkins et al., 1985). To the authors' knowledge, however, no human deaths have been directly attributed to toxic cyanobacteria.

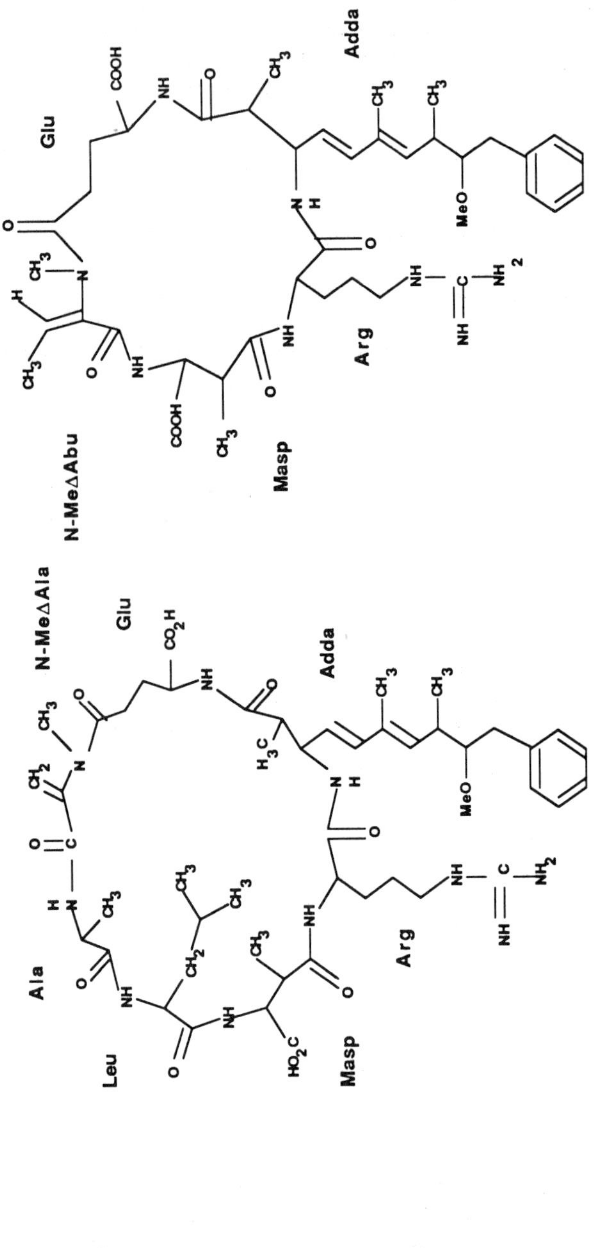

FIGURE 2 The proposed structures of microcystin-LR (MCLR) and nodularin (NL). (Courtesy of A. Kore.)

The consistency, odor, and appearance of waterblooms are probably sufficiently repugnant to prevent most people from ingesting a lethal dose of bloom
material (Gorham, 1964).

B. Nonhuman Primates

The authors are aware of only one report of algal hepatotoxicosis in non-human
primates (Tustin et al., 1973). Severe hepatic damage occurred when suspensions of lyophilized *M. toxica* were given intragastrically to vervet monkeys
(*Cercopithecus aethiops*) at 100, 200, or 500 mg/kg/wk. A monkey given 500
mg/kg/wk died after 4 doses, one given 200 mg/kg/wk died after 3 doses,
two given 200 mg/kg/wk died after 12 doses, and one given 100 mg/kg/wk
died after 24 doses. Death reportedly occurred with few, if any, prodromal
signs. Monkeys which died after 3 to 4 doses had panlobular necrosis with
hemorrhage superimposed on lesions resembling subacute hepatitis. Subacute
changes included inter- and intralobular connective tissue proliferation with
leucocytic infiltration and, sometimes, bile duct formation. In two monkeys
(200 mg/kg/wk) that died after 12 doses, lesions included centrilobular and
midzonal necrosis and degeneration, loss of the normal plate-like arrangement
of hepatocytes, sinusoidal dilatation or compression, and a paucity of central
veins. Many hepatocytes were pleomorphic and the number of binucleate cells
was increased. A monkey that died on day 172 had a few foci of hyperplastic
hepatocytes. A biopsy taken on day 198 from a surviving animal showed nodular regeneration and small groups of hepatocytes in an acinar-like pattern.

C. Dogs

1. Toxicity

Dogs may be poisoned by hepatotoxic cyanobacterial blooms (Steyn, 1945;
Dillenberg and Dehnel, 1960; Senior, 1960; Kalbe and Thiess, 1964; Lindstrom,
1976; Edler et al., 1985). Two reports involve the deaths of at least 30 dogs
associated with a waterbloom in the summer of 1959, in which *Microcystis* and
Anabaena were the predominant cyanobacteria (Senior, 1960; Dillenberg and
Dehnel, 1960). Edler et al. (1985) reported on 9 dogs that ingested *N. spumigena* in the Baltic Sea. Three were euthanatized 1, 5, and 12 days after
exposure, and six died on postexposure days 1, 2, 5, 6, 8, and 15.

2. Clinical Signs

In the incident involving the 30 or so dogs, the animals displayed signs
of abdominal discomfort soon after exposure. They lay down, began retching
with convulsive movements, and soon had foam at the mouth and then developed diarrhea. Within 30-60 min, the dogs could not rise and did not respond
to fondling or to food or water. Death followed a short period of dyspnea
interrupted by convulsions (Senior, 1960; Dillenberg and Dehnel, 1960). In
the report by Edler et al. (1985), all of the dogs developed clinical signs within 1 day of exposure. Depression, vomiting, diarrhea, icterus, weakness,
secretions from the eyes and mouth, dehydration, uremia, anorexia, ataxia,
and coma were noted.

3. Lesions

Gross lesions in the *M. aeruginosa*-exposed dogs included swelling and mottling of the liver, hemorrhagic enteritis, and pulmonary edema. Greenish flecks of algae were observed on the small intestinal mucosae (Senior, 1960; Dillenberg and Dehnel, 1960). In the case of *N. spumigena* exposure, the most common lesions were icterus, widespread hemorrhage, an enlarged, firm liver, and pulmonary edema (Edler et al., 1985). On microscopic examination, centrilobular hepatocyte necrosis and degeneration were observed. Tubular nephrosis, ulcerative gastritis, and focal myocardial necrosis with subendo-cardial hemorrhage were less often seen.

D. Cattle

1. Toxicity, Clinical Signs, Lesions

Clinical signs in cattle following exposure to blooms of hepatotoxic cyano-bacteria are presented in Table 1. In cases where initial access of cattle to hepatotoxic blooms was clearly established, deaths usually occurred 12 to 60 hr after exposure. In calves given bloom material intraruminally, survival times were from 9 to 28 hr (Konst et al., 1965; Stowe et al., 1981; Galey et al., 1987). Lethal intraruminal doses were (1) 3.8 l of pond water in 91 kg calves (Stowe et al., 1981), (2) 9.6 g/kg of lyophilized *M. aeruginosa* (mouse ip LD_{100} = 80 mg/kg) in water in an 86.8 kg calf, (3) 32.0 g/kg of lyophilized *M. aeruginosa* (mouse ip LD_{100} = 160 mg/kg) in a 78.2 kg calf (Konst et al., 1965), and (4) 8 l of wet bloom material (equivalent to 2 g of dried *M. aeru-ginosa* cells/kg) given in two doses 1 hr apart to a 125 kg calf (mouse ip LD_{100} of lyophilized bloom = 15 mg/kg) (Galey et al., 1987). Lesions are list-ed in Table 2(a,b).

2. Clinical Pathologic Parameters

Aspartate amino transferase (AST; SGOT) was the biochemistry param-eter most consistently reported as altered in suspected cyanobacterial hepato-toxicoses of cattle, and activities were still mildly elevated (approximately 2× normal) 5 to 7 days after exposure in clinically affected survivors (Galey et al., 1987; Stowe et al., 1981). Increases in serum alkaline phosphatase (AP), gamma glutamyl transferase (GGT), creatine phosphokinase (CPK), arginase, lactate dehydrogenase (LDH), and/or total bilirubin were also re-ported (Stowe et al., 1981; Galey et al., 1987). A doubling of prothrombin time (PT) and a decrease of 40% or more from predose values in red blood cell count (RBC) and hemoglobin concentration (Hb) occurred in a calf that survived 28 hr after intraruminal administration of lyophilized *M. aeruginosa* (Konst et al., 1965). Mild to moderate hypocalcemia occurred in *M. aeru-ginosa*-exposed lactating dairy cows (Galey et al., 1987). Early hypergly-cemia may be followed by terminal hypoglycemia (Galey et al., 1987).

3. Therapy

Two 91 kg Holstein calves intraruminally given 3.8 l of *M. aeruginosa*-contaminated pond water followed within an hour by activated charcoal made uneventful recoveries, whereas calves intraruminally given 3.8 l of the same

TABLE 1 Clinical Signs from 13 Reports of Apparent or Confirmed
Spontaneous Cyanobacterial Hepatotoxicoses in Cattle

Clinical sign	No. of times reported	Clinical sign	No. of times reported
Death	12	Pale mucous membranes	3
Recumbency/weakness	9	Algae on skin/hair	3
Diarrhea[a]	8	Weight loss	3
Tachypnea/dyspnea	7	Nausea/abdominal pain	3
Trembling	6	Hypersalivation	3
Photosensitization	6	Tachycardia	3
Reduced milk	4	Icterus	2
Aberrant behavior[b]	4	Anorexia	3
Ataxia	3		

Source: From Steyn (1945); Brandenburg and Shigley (1947); MacDonald
(1960); Dillenberg and Dehnel (1960); Senior (1960); Konst et al. (1965);
Skulberg (1979); Zin and Edwards (1979); Reynolds (1980); Stowe et al.
(1981); Kerr et al. (1987); Galey et al. (1987).
[a]Includes hemorrhagic or severe enteritis.
[b]Includes mental derangement, aggressiveness and hyperexcitability, noise
would exacerbate the abberrant behavior, opisthotonus, eyes rolled back.

pond water but not given charcoal became progressively weaker, collapsed,
convulsed and died within 24 hr (Stowe et al., 1981).

E. Sheep

1. Toxicity and Clinical Signs

Sheep are also susceptible to toxicosis following oral/intraruminal dosing
with hepatotoxic cyanobacteria. Wethers given 2 l doses of *N. spumigena*
"at 12 hr intervals," died within 72 hr of the initial dose, after 2 to 4 doses
(Main et al., 1977). After fasting, a 2-month-old lamb was given 16 g/kg
of lyophilized *M. aeruginosa* (ip LD_{100} in mice = 80 mg/kg). The lamb died
18 to 19 hr postdosing (Konst et al., 1965). Six of seven 6-month-old lambs
died 18 to 24 hr after administration of 0.4 to 1.0 l of *M. aeruginosa* bloom
material, which was equivalent to 1070-1840 mg of dried algae/kg (ip LD_{100}
in mice = 19 mg/kg). Two sheep given a minimum lethal dose of 1040 to 1050
mg of dried algae/kg died at 41 to 48.5 hr postdosing. However, up to 90%
of the lethal dose could be given to sheep without measurable effect (Jackson
et al., 1984). Recumbency, weakness and death were the most commonly documented signs in reports involving sheep. Tachypnea/dyspnea, depression,
and less frequently pyrexia, tachycardia, and tremors were described. Reported less often were "algae" on the forelimbs, signs suggestive of abdominal

TABLE 2a Gross Lesions Documented in Four Reports of Suspected or Confirmed Cyanobacterial Hepatotoxicoses in Cattle[a]

Gross finding	No. of reports
Liver enlarged, congested, mottled or friable	4
Enteritis/hemorrhage in GI tract	3
Marked distention of the gall bladder and edema of adjacent tissue	2
Anemia	1
Serosanguinous fluid in peritoneal and pleural cavities	1
Enlarged mesenteric lymph nodes	1
Algae in digestive tract	1
Pale kidneys	1

TABLE 2b Histologic Lesions Documented in Four Reports of Suspected or Confirmed Cyanobacterial Hepatotoxicoses in cattle[a]

Histologic finding	No. of reports
Diffuse/centrilobular hepatocyte degeneration, necrosis and/or disassociation	4
Large amounts of hemosiderin in the liver	3
Toxic tubular nephritis[b]	3
Petechial hemorrhages in the gastrointestinal tract	3
Proliferation of fibrous tissue in the portal areas (liver)	1
Serosal edema in the gall bladder	1
Edematous lymph nodes[c]	1

[a]From Galey et al. (1987); Stowe et al. (1981); Konst et al. (1965); and MacDonald (1960).
[b]Includes glomerular tufts which were swollen and devoid of blood; proteinaceous material in glomerular spaces; swelling and granular appearance to the convoluted tubular epithelium; and moderate, subacute, multifocal interstitial nephritis.
[c]RBCs and a mixed population of inflammatory cells were present in the sinuses.

pain, hypersalivation, ruminal atony, bloat, anorexia, ataxia, opisthotonus, tetanic convulsions, pale mucous membranes, and photosensitization.

2. Clinical Pathologic Findings

Leukopenia occurred in two wethers given *N. spumigena*, and one developed increased plasma ornithine carbamyl transferase activity (Main et al., 1977). The white blood cell count (WBC) of *M. aeruginosa*-dosed sheep increased from a predose mean of 8,800 to 11,300 cells/μl prior to death, largely due to increases in segmented and immature neutrophils (Jackson et al., 1984; McInnes et al., 1983). Marked changes occurred in PT, activated partial thromboplastin time (PTT), thrombin clotting time and platelet count of lethally dosed sheep, ranging from a 60% decrease in platelets to a 4.5-fold increase in PT.

Marked increases in serum activities of aspartate amino transferase (AST) glutamate dehydrogenase (GDH), and LDH occurred in sheep given a lethal dose, or toxic but sublethal dose of dried *M. aeruginosa* cells intraruminally (Jackson et al., 1984; McInnes et al., 1983). In lethally dosed sheep after 9 to 12 hr, GDH, AST, and AP rapidly increased; and GDH and AST reached 100 times the predose values. AP reached 2.5 to 4 times the predose value. In the toxic/sublethal group, maximal AST and GDH were reached at 2 days, with a return to the normal range by day 6; LDH peaked on day 3 and was still above normal on day 6. Increases in direct and indirect serum bilirubin occurred in sheep in the lethal and toxic/sublethal dose groups. Total bilirubin concentrations in the toxic-sublethal dose group were greatest at 48 hr and returned to predose values by 144 hr. Serum glucose in the toxic-sublethal dose groups remained in the normal range, but in the lethal dose group, it was decreased to extremely low concentrations before death.

3. Lesions

Commonly documented gorss lesions in sheep were (1) enlargement, congestion, pallor and mottling of the liver, (2) abundant straw-colored fluid in the thoracic and abdominal cavities, and (3) widespread petechial and ecchymotic hemorrhages (Konst et al., 1965; McBarron and May, 1966; Main et al., 1977; Jackson et al., 1984). On microscopic examination, the most consistent lesions included extensive hepatic necrosis, with variable centrilobular hemorrhage and some sparing of periportal hepatocytes. Bile duct hyperplasia, neutrophilic infiltration of bile ducts, and swollen Kupffer cells were reported less often. Generally mild lesions occurred in the kidney (congestion, protein in "glomerular spaces," and cloudy swelling of cortical tubular epithelium), lungs (edema, hyperemia, interstitial pneumonia, and thickening of the alveolar wall), and heart (subepicardial hemorrhage with slight swelling and loss of cross striations in myocardial fibers).

F. Rabbits

1. Toxicity

Following a fast, 10 rabbits were given suspensions of dried *M. aeruginosa* intragastrically at 20 to 160 times the mouse ip LD$_{100}$ (80 mg/kg) (Konst et al., 1965). Nine died, eight from 1.2 to 5 hr of dosing; the tenth rabbit died at 30 hr. Lethal intragastric doses of a thick algal bloom of *M. toxica* ranged from 35 to 100 ml/kg, and rabbits often died within 4 hr (Louw and Smit, 1950). Rabbits previously given sublethal doses were markedly resistant to a subsequent exposure.

2. Clinical Signs

Signs in acute cases included dyspnea, restlessness, anemia, progressive paralysis, coma, and death; and in chronic cases listlessness, loss of condition, and ascites (Louw and Smit, 1950). The time before the onset of signs ranged from 0.8 to 3 hr in rabbits that died less than 5 hr after dosing, and the onset was at 6 hr postdosing in the rabbit which died at 30 hr (Konst et al., 1965). Dyspnea and tachycardia were early signs. Muscle tremors were perceptible by palpation. Pallor developed concurrently with paresis, which affected the neck, hind and later the front legs, and progressed to a nearly complete loss of muscle tone. Terminally, bradypnea, gasping, marked tachycardia, and spasmodic contractions of the hind legs were seen.

3. Lesions

Acute toxicosis was manifested by hepatic congestion and hemorrhage, ascites, splenic enlargement, and hyperemia of the kidneys, sometimes with mild nephrosis. There was severe hepatic necrosis, hemorrhage, and fatty degeneration. In less acute toxicosis, hepatocyte necrosis, fatty degeneration, regeneration, and cirrhosis were noted. In chronic cases, lesions consisted primarily of cirrhosis and ascites (Louw and Smit, 1950). In the report by Konst et al. (1965), hepatic, cardiac, and renal lesions were not distinguishable from those described below for mice, except the glomerular spaces of rabbits sometimes contained proteinaceous material, the lungs were bloodless, and there was serosanguinous fluid in the peritoneal cavity.

G. Guinea Pigs

1. Toxicity

Wheeler et al. (1942) observed no toxic effects in guinea pigs given 4 ml of fresh *M. aeruginosa* by gavage, although 2 ml ip was lethal in 24 hr. However, when Konst et al. (1965) dosed eight guinea pigs (0.5 to 0.7 kg) intragastrically with freeze-dried *M. aeruginosa* at 1.6, 2.4, 3.2, 6.4, and 12.8 g/kg following a fast, one given 1.6 g/kg (20 times the mouse ip LD_{100}) survived and all the other animals died 8 to 12 hr postdosing. There was no indication of shorter survival time with increasing dosage. Guinea pigs also died after intragastric administration of 5 ml of water containing *N. spumigena*. Although, when the bloom material was given after a few more days of storage, no ill effects were observed (Main et al., 1977).

2. Clinical Signs and Lesions

The onset of clinical signs in guinea pigs was at 0.3 to 1 hr following parenteral dosing and 3 to 5 hr after oral dosing. Signs and lesions were much like those in mice (see below), except guinea pigs experienced rapidly progressing paresis more often than the mice (Konst et al., 1965).

H. Rats

1. Toxicity

Parenteral doses. In 6-week-old rats, the LD_{50} of an extract of dried *M. aeruginosa* given ip was equivalent to 67.4 mg of dry cells/kg (Oishi and Watanabe, 1986). In rats given MCLR intraarterially, a 72 hr LD_{50} was 50 µg/kg and survival time at the LD_{50} averaged 30.4 hr (LeClaire et al., 1988). In male rats given MCLR ip at up to 80 µg/kg, and females given 40 µg/kg, no clinical signs and no gross or microscopic lesions were observed (Hooser et al., 1989a). However, at doses of 80 to 400 µg/kg, all clinically affected animals died and had similar lesions irrespective of sex or dose.

Intragastric or intraintestinal doses. When rats were dosed by gavage with 5 mg of MCLR/kg or with suspensions of lyophilized cells in amounts equivalent to 12 mg of MCLR/kg, no signs of toxicosis were apparent. However, when given via an isolated jejunal or ileal loop, MCLR at 5.0 mg/kg caused increased liver weight and lesions typical of acute cyanobacterial hepatotoxicosis (Dahlem et al., 1989).

2. Survival Time as a Function of Dose

In establishing an LD_{50} (50 µg/kg) for MCLR in rats dosed ip, a dose response was apparent in survival times. Rats that survived more than 40 hr appeared to recover completely. Rats given 400 µg/kg or more, died at approximately 2 hr, while those at 50 to 400 µg/kg survived for variable periods (Theiss and Carmichael, 1986). Similarly, rats dosed ip with 4 times the MLD_{100} of an aqueous extract of lyophilized *O. agardhii* died in 2 to 4 hr. With lower doses, survival times were 24 to 48 hr (Berg and Soli, 1985a). In rats given MCLR ip at less than 240 µg/kg, survival times were 20 to 32 hr. In rats given doses of 400 to 1200 µg/kg, death occurred at 6 to 8 hr (Hooser et al., 1989a).

3. Influence of Fasting on Susceptibility

A 25 hr LD_{50} of MCLR for rats that had been fed and dosed ip was 122 µg/kg and for rats that had fasted 72 µg/kg. At 100, 150, and 200 µg/kg, median times to death were 31.9, 18.2, and 11.2 hr for fed animals and 1.8, 1.7, and 1.5 hr for fasted animals. Rats given a sublethal dose (50 µg/kg) of MCLR were rechallenged 72 hr later with a "lethal" dose of toxin (200 µg/kg). Five of the 10 originally fasted rats survived a second dose of toxin, while only one of the 10 fed rats survived (Miura et al., 1988).

4. Clinical Signs

Rats given lyophilized *M. aeruginosa* cells ip experienced a latent period of 10 to 15 min, followed by incoordination, paralysis, pallor, lethargy, labored respiration, and a coma-like state before death at 30 to 200 min postdosing (Berg et al., 1987). Rats given MCLR ip were lethargic and had a ruffled fur coat, which began several hr after toxin administration and increased in severity until death (Hooser et al., 1989a).

5. Effects on Blood Pressures

When anesthetized rats were dosed with MCLR intraarterially, arterial blood pressure decreased slowly to values indicative of shock (40 to 50 mm Hg) and continued to decline until death. However, there were no changes either in the jugular or hepatic portal pressures (Theiss et al., 1988). In another report, blood pressure of rats given lethal doses of MC (50 to 200 mg/kg) declined by over 50% within 45 min (Ostensvik et al., 1981). When rats were given lethal doses, intravenously, of an extract of *O. agardhii*, systolic and diastolic blood pressures increased immediately after dosing. This was followed by a gradual decrease to normal values after 20 min, and a decline until death occurred at 90 to 120 min (Berg and Soli, 1985b).

6. Clinical Pathologic Findings

In rats given sublethal intraarterial doses of MCLR, arterial lactic acid concentration, an indicator of anaerobic metabolism, increased concurrently with reductions in arterial blood pressure. Hemoglobinuria was tentatively attributed to intrahepatic hemorrhage (Theiss and Carmichael, 1986). A lethal ip dose of hepatotoxin(s) from *Anabaena* and *Microcystis* caused reduced white blood cell (WBC) and platelet counts, but packed cell volume (PCV) remained constant (Jones and Carmichael, 1984).

Serum iditol dehydrogenase activities of rats proved to be a sensitive index of hepatic injury, increasing as early as 0.5 hr after a lethal intraarterial dose of MCLR. Serum alanine amino transferase (ALT) activity also increased (LeClaire et al., 1988). When rats were given an extract of *O. agardhii* ip, plasma AST and ALT activities as well as bile acid concentrations increased 10- to 20-fold from 30 to 90 min postdosing, but AP or GGT were not yet significantly increased (Berg and Soli, 1985a). Blood glucose increased 2- to 3-fold. Relative liver weights increased from 3.5 to 4.0%, to 7.0 to 7.5% of body weight within 90 min of toxin administration. With longer survival times, lesser increases in relative liver weights were seen. However, when survival times exceeded 24 hr, plasma AST and ALT increased 100 to 200 times and AP and GGT 5 to 10 times the predose values. Also, at 24 hr, blood glucose was markedly reduced (0 to 5 mmol/l) in comparison to control animals (9 to 12 mmol/l). When Hooser et al. (1989a) gave rats MCLR ip at 160 µg/kg, marked increases were noted in the activities of ALT and ALP, as well as in total bilirubin. Moderate elevations in BUN and creatinine, and a 67% decrease in blood glucose also occurred.

7. Lesions

In a time-course study (Theiss et al., 1988), rats were given an extract of *M. aeruginosa* ip which was lethal by 90 to 150 min postdosing. Most were killed at 20 to 60 min, although one died at 90 min. Lesions were noted only in the liver and lungs. The lungs were mildly edematous. Microscopically, hepatic lesions included centrilobular to panlobular hemorrhagic necrosis, acute congestion, swollen hepatocytes with homogeneous eosinophilic cytoplasm, enlarged nuclei with evenly dispersed chromatin, and central veins and disrupted sinusoids containing erythrocytes admixed with amorphous globular eosinophilic debirs or intact cells thought to represent degenerative hepatocytes. Pulmonary vessels contained amorphous, globular eosinophilic material, not distinctly attached to endothelial cells, with an appearance suggestive of degenerating hepatocytes and debris from the liver. PTAH staining of sections indicated an absence of fibrin in these deposits. Thus, the debris was thought to consist of emboli from the liver. Hepatic lesions and emboli were noted at 20 min postdosing. The liver lesions were moderately severe, but the emboli were mild to minimal. Due to their small size and low numbers, the emboli were not thought to be life-threatening. In a time-course study of rats, using ip doses of MCLR that would generally result in survival times of 8 hr or longer a number of things were observed, (1) hepatocyte rounding and necrosis (Fig. 3a), (2) intact hepatocytes and hepatic debris in central veins (Fig. 3b), and (3) hepatocytes which had formed emboli and passed into pulmonary vessels (Fig. 4) (Hooser et al., 1989a). Also, finely granular eosinophilic deposits were present in glomerular capillaries, and there was vacuolization of renal cortical tubular epithelial cells.

8. Therapy

Rats given MCLR via an isolated ileal loop had marked increases in liver size, whereas rats similarly dosed with toxin followed by the anion exchange resin cholestyramine, were largely unaffected (Dahlem et al., 1989b). Cholestyramine was also highly effective in binding MCLR in vitro. Superactivated charcoal both adsorbed MCLR in vitro and, when given after MCLR via an isolated ileal loop, reduced the increase in liver weights in rats (Dahlem et al., 1989). However, on an equal weight basis, superactivated charcoal was somewhat less effective than cholestyramine both in vitro and in vivo.

I. Mice

1. Toxicity

Mouse bioassays. Mice dosed ip are often used to assess cyanobacterial toxicity. Responses to hepatotoxic extracts usually include: (1) a latent period of 15 to 30 min, (2) death in 40 to 200 min, (3) a pale carcass and blood engorged liver, and (4) liver weights of 8 to 10.5% of body weight.

Theory regarding "slow death factor." Although Gorham (1960) held that a "slow death factor" was possibly produced by bacteria which may contaminate hepatotoxic cyanobacteria, Henning and Kohl (1981) observed no signs of poisoning in mice given large doses of bacteria isolated from a *Microcystis* strain. In the authors' view, a more plausible cause for the "slow death" may be either delayed release of hepatotoxin(s) from undisrupted algal colonies, or administration of a minimally lethal dose.

Role of gender and pregnancy. Generally, sex-related differences in susceptibility to algal peptide hepatotoxins are minimal. However, with repeated ingestion of an extract of *M. aeruginosa* in drinking water, male mice were more susceptible than females (Falconer et al., 1988). Also, pregnant mice (LD_{100} = 160 mg/kg) were more tolerant of hepatotoxins given ip than mice that were not pregnant (LD_{100} = 80 mg/kg) (Konst et al., 1965).

Influence of age. Neonatal mice dosed ip with extracts of *M. aeruginosa* did not display clinical signs or hepatic lesions. Treated mice did not die until they were approximately 20 days old (Foxall and Sasner, 1981). Like-

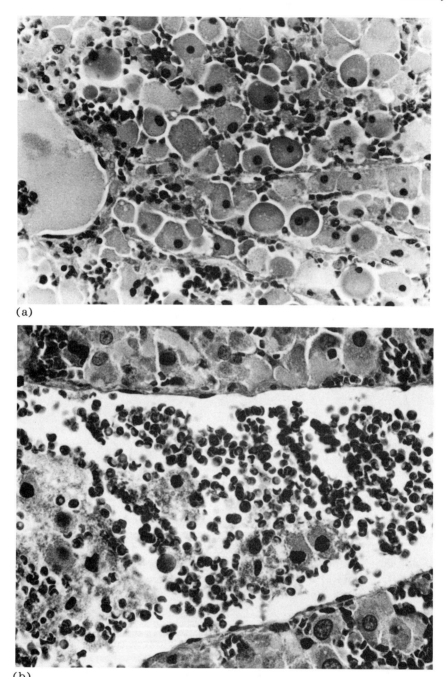

(a)

(b)
FIGURE 3 Liver from rats injected ip with microcystin-LR at 160 µg/kg. HE
(a) Centrilobular hepatocyte degeneration, disassociation, and rounding with
hemorrhage, 6 hr postdosing; ×500. (b) Hepatocytes in central vein at 1
hr postdosing, ×500 (from Hooser et al., 1989a; with permission).

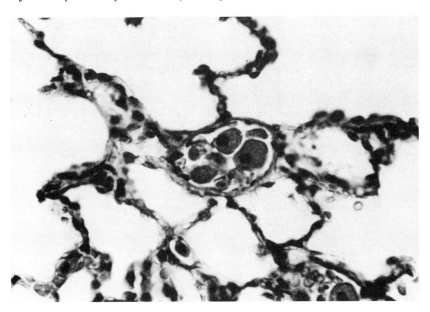

FIGURE 4 Lung from rat injected ip with microcystin-LR at 160 µg/kg.
Pulmonary vessel contains intact hepatocytes and erythrocytes. Six hours
postdosing, HE ×500.

wise, MCLR did not cause acute (under 2 hr) deaths in 1- or 2-week-old mice
but was lethal to over two-thirds of 3-week-old mice (Adams et al., 1985).

Effects of repeated parenteral dosing. A steep dose-response curve was
found in the lethal responses of mice given MCLR ip. The LD_{50} was 32.5 µg/
kg, the approximate LD_0 max was 25 µg/kg, and the approximate LD_{100} min
was 40 µg/kg. Mice were more likely to survive a "consistently lethal" ip
dose of MCLR when it was given 2 to 3 days following a previous dose which
had been lethal to a minority of the exposed animals (Lovell et al., 1989).
Mechanisms for increased tolerance to MCs after a previous exposure to an
acutely toxic dose might include (1) decreased or slower uptake of toxin by
the damaged liver, and (2) less severe acute hemorrhage into the already
distended liver.

Elleman et al. (1978) dosed mice ip daily for 6 wk with toxin from *M. aeruginosa* at 0.25 to 0.75 of an LD_{100} (70 µg/kg ip). Eleven of 16 given 0.75
of the LD_{100} died. Deaths began the day after the initial dose and continued
until the third week. Five of 14 mice given 0.50 of the LD_{100} also died during
the fourth and fifth week, whereas none of the mice at 0.25 of the LD_{100} died.

Oral toxicity and enhancement of toxicity due to fasting. Severe hepatic
destruction and death occurred in mice within 4 to 6 hr of an oral dose of
extract of *M. aeruginosa* or naturally contaminated water (Stowe et al., 1981).
Oishi and Watanabe (1986) found an oral LD_{50} of an extract of *M. aeruginosa*
in mice to be near the equivalent of 30 mg of dried cells/kg. However, it
is unknown whether the mice in these studies fasted.

Konst et al. (1965) and Heaney (1971) found that mice that fasted for 18 to 24 hr before intragastric/oral dosing of suspensions of hepatotoxic algae died at approximately 40 times the ip LD_{100} min. When 21 mice were given suspensions of dried *M. aeruginosa* at 40, 80, or 160 times the ip LD_{100} (80 mg/kg), 15 died within 4 hr, and the other six died within 18 hr. Higher doses did not markedly decrease survival times. In contrast, using mice that were fed, Reynolds (1980), Wheeler et al. (1942), McBarron and May (1966), Dillenberg and Dehnel (1960), Dahlem, Hassan, and Beasley (unpublished data), and Watanabe and Oishi (1982) were unable to induce toxicosis with bloom material after oral or intragastric exposure, despite evidence of toxicity after parenteral dosing.

Clinical signs in mice after intragastric dosing. Beginning 0.5 to 1.5 hr after intragastric administration of a suspension of dried *M. aeruginosa* mice displayed ruffled coats, tachypnea, and hyperpnea. Later, tremors of muscles of the head and neck, convulsive jumping movements, periods of hyperexcitability and inactivity, and generalized pallor were observed. Paresis, especially of the hind limbs, sometimes developed rapidly. The animals became weak and eventually motionless. Before death respiration was slow and labored, and occasionally "bicycling movements" of the hind legs occurred (Konst et al., 1965).

Effects after a single or repeated feeding of concentrated algae. The day after fasted mice were fed their ration plus a *M. aeruginosa* paste, the animals were subdued with hunched backs and raised fur. On day 3, the mice were hunched and immobile; but on day 4, they seemed to have recovered. When mice were each fed smaller doses for 3 days, most died on day 4; but one mouse showed no signs of distress for the twelve day observation period (Heaney, 1971).

Although most mice survived 23 days of exposure to a hepatotoxic extract of *M. aeruginosa* when given as the sole source of water, severe toxicosis (with euthanasia before death) occurred as early as day 13 (Falconer et al., 1988). Weight loss was noted in this study, and when the extract was given for up to 57 wk, body weights were reduced. Also, males were somewhat more sensitive than females, and a degree of resistance developed over time.

2. Physiologic Effects

Tachycardia, hypothermia and a fall in blood pressure occurred in mice dosed sc or ip with a lethal dose of an extract of *M. aeruginosa* (equivalent to 3 mg of dried algae/mouse) (Mason and Wheeler, 1942). In mice given a lethal ip dose of an extract from *M. aeruginosa*, R-wave voltage gradually decreased and ST-segments were depressed (Oishi and Watanabe, 1986). Twenty minutes postdosing, tachycardia developed; and bradycardia with atrial fibrillation occurred terminally. Toxicosis in mice elicited the production of hydrolysis products of vasoactive mediators shown to play a role in other shock syndromes, including 6-keto-prostaglandin $F_{1\alpha}$, and thromboxane B_2. There was no increase in vascular permeability as indicated by leakage of ^{125}I-labeled albumin before the onset of hemorrhage (Adams et al., 1988).

3. Clinical Pathologic Findings

No significant changes in whole-blood clotting time, euglobulin lysis time, PT, PTT, or fibrinogen concentration were detected in 8- to 12-week-old mice administered a lethal dose of MCLR. Platelet counts, however, decreased more than 75% from 30 to 45 min after dosing (Slatkin et al., 1983). In MCLR-dosed mice, platelets accumulate in the damaged liver (Adams et al., 1988). Thrombocytopenia developed within 1 hr of MCLR administration in 1-week-old (0.49×10^6), 2-week-old (0.21×10^6), and 3-week-old (0.06×10^6 platelets/μl) mice (controls had $1.09\text{-}1.25 \times 10^6$ platelets/μl) (Adams et al., 1985). Thus, the increased sensitivity to MCLR associated with age is correlated with the severity of the thrombocytopenia.

AST and ALT activities of mice were markedly increased and β glucuronidase activity was decreased within 30 min of an ip dose of MCLR at 100 μg/kg. In mice given a lethal ip dose (5 times the LD_{100}) of toxin from *M. aeruginosa*, AST and LDH activities, liver weight, and blood content of the liver were increased by 74.6-, 14.1-, 1.64-, and 8.15-fold, respectively, within 45 min of dosing (Falconer et al., 1981). Within 50 min of dosing with toxin from *N. spumigena* at 92 μg/kg, activities of AST, ALT, and LDH, as well as glucose, and liver weight increased to 2.3, 3.4, 2.9, 2.0, and 1.8 times control values, respectively. Sublethal doses of toxin caused significant changes in in enzyme activity and glucose concentration only when more than 90% of the LD_{50} was given (Runnegar et al., 1988).

Hyperglycemia and reductions in serum total protein, PCV, Hb, and RBC occurred in mice given a lethal sc or ip dose of an extract of *M. aeruginosa* (equivalent to 3 mg of dried algae/mouse) (Mason and Wheeler, 1942). In mice given an extract of *M. aeruginosa* as their drinking water from 23 days to 57 weeks, there were dose (concentration) related elevations in serum ALT, which were more severe in males than females and which declined over time despite continued exposure (Falconer et al., 1988).

4. Lesions

Intragastric and ip dosing. Livers of mice given freeze-dried *M. aeruginosa* were enlarged and hyperemic, and blood oozed freely from the cut surface (Konst et al., 1965). The livers were often mottled with hemorrhage bordered by yellow-brown degeneration, and when death was delayed, such areas of degeneration were more extensive. There were traces of blood in the ingesta of the upper gastrointestinal tract, and the intestinal mucosa was slightly hyperemic. On microscopic examination, liver lobules were uniformly affected. Centrilobular hepatocytes were necrotic or replaced by a pool of blood. Periportally, the cord structure was retained, but hepatocytes were degenerative. Myocardial fibers were slightly swollen with a loss of cross-striations. Glomerular tufts were swollen and devoid of blood, and the epithelium of the convoluted tubules was swollen and granular.

In a recent report, mice given purified MCLR ip had lesions limited to the liver and kidneys (Hooser et al., 1989a). Hepatic lesions evident on light microscopy were similar to those previously described, whereas kidney lesions consisted of dilation of renal cortical tubules and the presence of eosinophilic to fibrillar material in many tubular lumens. Similar material was sometimes present in Bowman's space and glomerular capillaries.

In mice given an extract of M. *aeruginosa* as their source of water for up to 23 days, liver lesions included progressive hepatocyte injury over time, with necrosis, leukocyte infiltration, and fibrosis (Falconer et al., 1988). Brain size at 5 days postpartum was smaller than average in approximately 10% of the offspring of chronically exposed dams.

Multiple ip doses. In mice given MCLR at an approximate LD_{100} minimum, fractional liver weights were increased by 50 to 64%, and kidney weights by 20 to 32% (Lovell et al., 1989). However, when mice survived 2 doses of MCLR (a dose lethal to a minority of mice followed by a "consistently lethal" dose), lesions were compatible with a rapidly regenerative process in the liver. Such mice had marked disorganization of the centrilobular and midzonal architecture. Irregularly shaped areas that formerly had contained central veins were filled with erythrocytes. Hepatocytes were often elongated with a "streaming" cyto-plasm and there was an increase in mitotic figures.

Mice repeatedly given 0.25 to 0.75 of the single dose LD_{100} developed dose-related signs and lesions (Elleman et al., 1978). Lesions in mice that died within 2 to 3 days of starting daily ip doses at 0.75 of the LD_{100} were much like those in animals which died after one dose. When killed at 1 wk, gross lesions were present only in mice given 0.75 of the LD_{100}, and they consisted of pale livers with a fine lobular surface pattern without hemorrhage. On each successive week, hepatic changes became more obvious. Livers were progressively enlarged to 7 to 10% of body weight (controls averaged 5.3%) and were pale with surface dimpling. At 0.50 and 0.75 of the LD_{100}, severe-ly affected mice had marked weight loss, and some had subcutaneous edema and mild icterus. There was progressive and generalized hepatocyte degen-eration, with scattered necrosis accompanied by fibrosis and mononuclear cell infiltration. Milder lesions and an increase in hepatocyte mitotic figures oc-curred at 0.25 of the LD_{100}/day.

5. Therapy

Survival times and overall survival rates of 8-week-old mice given an ex-tract from M. *aeruginosa* at 15, 18, or 21.6 mg/kg were slightly improved in response to coadministration of phenoxybenzamine at 5 mg/kg (Oishi and Watanabe, 1986). Mice given M. *aeruginosa*-contaminated water orally died within 4 to 6 hr, whereas those given the same water plus activated charcoal or plus charcoal and mineral oil survived (Stowe et al., 1981). However, in mice given the algae-contaminated water, adrenocortical steroids (time of administration not specified) were of no apparent benefit. These results with steroid treatment are in contrast to those obtained by pretreatment of animals with hydrocortisone, as discussed below.

6. Prevention

When one part *Clostridium botulinum* type A antiserum plus one part of type B antiserum were mixed with two parts of lysed M. *aeruginosa* and given ip to mice, the animals died within 2 hr (McBarron and May, 1966). Attempts to protect mice against extracts containing algal hepatotoxins by simultaneous administration of 1.3 mg of atropine also failed. Moreover, a sublethal dose (0.013 mg) of physostigmine combined with a sublethal dose of hepatotoxin did not cause synergistic toxicity in mice (Wheeler et al., 1942). Also, the

lethality of MCLR was not affected by (1) streptokinase at doses that shortened the euglobulin lysis time to about 50% of normal, (2) Malayan pit viper venom
at doses that produced sustained noncoagulability of blood in vitro, (3) heparin, warfarin, or acetylsalicylic acid in doses up to 10% of the LD_{50} (Slatkin
et al., 1983), or (4) leukopenia, or leukopenia and thrombocytopenia induced
by prior X-irradiation (Adams et al., 1985).

Pretreatment with hydrocortisone ip at 5 mg/mouse did not prevent MCLR
(100 µg/kg iv)-induced thrombocytopenia or death, but 12.5 mg/mouse one
hr before MCLR prevented thrombocytopenia and death in 33 of 35 mice (Adams
et al., 1985). The hepatotoxic chemical, carbon tetrachloride, given 24 hr before MCLR administration also prevented preacute deaths, but delayed deaths
frequently occurred for 2 to 3 days after toxin administration (Adams et al.,
1985). In contrast, pretreatment of mice with SKF-525A or cobaltous chloride,
to inhibit MFO activity, did not alter the acute toxicity of MCLR. The authors
concluded that CCl_4 protected the toxin-treated mice by inhibition or destruction of hepatic MFOs, but this was not reconciled with the SKF-525A and
$CoCl_2$ results.

J. Other Mammals

After cats were given a lethal ip or sc dose of an extract from *M. aeruginosa*,
there was a latent period of 2 to 3 hr, followed by pallor, hypotension, tachycardia, hypothermia, hyperglycemia, and terminal marked reductions in PCV,
Hb, RBC, and serum total protein. Death followed respiratory failure and
gross lesions included a markedly congested liver (Mason and Wheeler, 1942).

Swine are also sensitive to MCLR whether given orally in bloom material
or as purified toxin iv (Lovell, Holmes, Hooser, and Beasley, unpublished
data). Swine experienced hepatic necrosis with acute intrahepatic hemorrhage
and shock. A rapid decline in hepatic and later renal perfusion were seen.
Pigs surviving several hours, terminally developed marked hypoglycemia and
sometimes hyperkalemia.

The death of a white rhinoceros was also associated with a bloom of *M.
aeruginosa* (Soll and Williams, 1985). Lesions included severe hepatic enlargement, hemorrhage, and necrosis as well as numerous subcutaneous and
subserosal hemorrhages. Based on circumstantial evidence, deaths of horses
(Steyn, 1945; Senior, 1960; Dillenberg and Dehnel, 1960) and deer (Brandenburg and Shigley, 1947) have also been associated with ingestion of apparently hepatotoxic "waterblooms."

K. Birds

1. Toxicity and Clinical Signs

Steyn (1945) and Dillenberg and Dehnel (1960) reported deaths of turkeys,
ducks, and geese following exposure to *Microcystis*-containing blooms. Brandenburg and Shigley (1947) obtained algal samples 2 wk after an episode of
photosensitization and death in cattle and fed the material or gave it ip to
old hens. Clinical signs, began 10 min after feeding and included restlessness, blinking of the eyes, and repeated swallowing with upward jerking of
the head. Frequent defecation was noted in all algae-exposed birds. The

ip-dosed birds displayed terminal clonic spasms. At high ip doses, survival time was 60 to 90 min.

In chickens, oral LD_{50}s of extracts of lyophilized M. aeruginosa bloom material were equivalent to 1295 to 1643 mg dried algae/kg. The ip LD_{50} was the equivalent of 13 mg of dried algae/kg in chickens, which may be compared to 19 mg/kg in mice (Jackson et al., 1986). Most deaths occurred by 10 hr, with a few continuing to die until approximately 24 hr.

When, following a fast, immature chickens were intragastrically given lyophilized suspensions of M. aeruginosa, 16 g/kg was consistently lethal (Konst et al., 1965). For 5 to 6 hr after treatment, all birds were normal in behavior or only slightly quieter than usual. Death occurred within 25 hr of a lethal dose. A limited number, observed during the last hour prior to death, displayed marked somnolence and severe paresis. The susceptibility of chickens was similar to that of ruminants. Ducks were similarly given 2.2 or 16 g of the dried algae/kg. Doses retained by the ducks were often reduced due to regurgitation or profuse defecation. Ducks seemed to be comparatively resistant, apparently via mechanisms in addition to evacuation of the digestive tract since they not only survived the highest oral dose of 16 g/kg, but the ip LD_{100} was at least four-fold that of mice, guinea pigs, and rabbits.

2. Lesions

Dillenberg and Dehnel (1960) described hepatic congestion and enlargement, pulmonary edema, mild enteritis and colonies of Microcystis and Anabaena on the intestinal mucosae of a goose from a field case. In intragastrically dosed birds (Konst et al., 1965), the principal gross lesions occurred in the liver, but petechial hemorrhages, in the heart, renal congestion, and serosanguinous fluid in body cavities and the pericardial sac were also noted. In contrast to mammals, the degenerative and necrotic hepatocytes were diffusely distributed throughout the lobule in livers of birds. Chickens given lethal doses of lyophilized M. aeruginosa had massive hepatocyte necrosis without sparing of any of the hepatocytes and with bile ductule hyperplasia, which became more evident if the birds lived to near 24 hr (Jackson et al., 1986). Pulmonary lesions included eosinophilic deposits in the capillaries and edema. Necrosis of lymphocytes occurred in the bursa and spleen. Birds that survived 24 hr without appearing to be near death had scattered necrosis of hepatocytes with an increased number of mitotic figures, hyperplasia of bile ductule epithelium, and hypertrophy of the hepatic sinusoidal epithelium.

L. Other Species

Although one report based on circumstantial evidence suggests that fish are susceptible to cyanobacterial hepatotoxicosis (Steyn, 1945), a strain of M. aeruginosa known to produce MCLR was nontoxic to rainbow trout (Salmo gairdneri) even when the fish were immersed in a culture for 10 days (Phillips et al., 1985). In contrast, trout given sonicated algae ip at 30 to 40 mg dry wt/kg died 12 to 36 hr later and exhibited foci of massive hepatic necrosis. Another report indicates that not only teleosts but also adult frogs and tadpoles, crayfish, cladocerans, bacteria, green algae (Chlorella), and yeast (Saccharomyces cerevisiae) were unaffected by partially purified aqueous extracts of *M. aeruginosa* when evaluated after immersion, ip administration, or growth assay (Foxall and Sasner, 1981).

IV. ULTRASTRUCTURAL LESIONS AND MECHANISMS OF ACTION

A. Ultrastructural Lesions

Scanning and transmission electron microscopy (SEM and TEM) have been used to evaluate hepatic ultrastructure of mice, sheep, and rats given algal extracts or purified toxin. When sheep died 23 to 48 hr after being given *M. aeruginosa* cells, TEM showed centrilobular hepatic necrosis with vacuolation, aggregation of endoplasmic reticulum, peripheral displacement of organelles, swollen mitochondria, and "leached" nuclei with "obvious chromatin strands" (Jackson et al., 1984).

When mice were given a lethal dose of crude extract of *M. aeruginosa* (one of only two reports known in which hepatic lesions progressed from periportal to centrilobular), SEM and TEM revealed a breakdown of sinusoidal endothelium within 15 min of dosing, which was sometimes associated with adjacent hepatocyte damage. At 60 min, the sinusoidal endothelium was not visible in most areas, and erythrocytes were adjacent to hepatocytes. Hepatocyte mitochondria survived "better than the nucleus and endoplasmic reticulum" (Falconer et al., 1981). When mice were given a sublethal (10 μg/kg) or lethal (100 μg/kg) dose of MCLR and examined using TEM, the hepatocyte changes described included vesiculation and degranulation of the rough endoplasmic reticulum, mitochondrial swelling, and in addition at 100 μg/kg, an increase in intracytoplasmic membrane whorls (Dabholkar and Carmichael, 1987).

In a study in which rats were given a lethal (160 μg/kg) dose of MCLR ip and killed at 5, 10, 20, 30, or 60 min, lesions at 10 min postdosing consisted of mild widening of intercellular spaces between hepatocytes (Hooser et al., 1990). At 20 min, there was marked separation of hepatocytes, and hepatocyte plasma membranes were often markedly invaginated, which in cross section appeared as variably sized cytoplasmic vacuoles. There was also a loss of microvilli along the sinusoidal face. In areas with severe hepatocyte lesions, sinusoidal endothelial fenestrae were widened. In addition, at 30 min, there was marked widening of the space of Disse and blunting of microvilli in bile canaliculi, although nearby tight junctions were intact. At 60 min, centrilobular areas had necrotic hepatocytes, a loss of endothelium, and free-floating organelles were intermingled with erythrocytes and platelets. Pulmonary and renal emboli consisted of intact hepatocytes and hepatocyte debris, which are believed to account for the nonfibrinous "atypical pulmonary thrombi" reported by other researchers.

B. Morphologic Changes and Enzyme Release In Vitro

Dose-dependent morphologic changes, visible by light microscopy, were present in rat hepatocytes in suspension as early as 5 min after addition of MCLR. Numerous, large, plasma membrane blebs were present in 12% of hepatocytes after 20 min of exposure to MCLR at 0.01 μg/ml, while virtually all of the hepatocytes had blebs when similarly exposed to 0.1 μg/ml. Nevertheless,

at all doses, hepatocytes continued to exclude Trypan blue and there was
no significant release of AST after 100 min of incubation (Runnegar et al.,
1981). Thus, although rapid deformation of hepatocyte plasma membranes
takes place, membrane leakage and cell death do not occur after nearly 2 hr
of exposure to the toxin. However, upon prolonged (3 hr) exposure to extracts of *M. aeruginosa*, rat hepatocytes released elevated amounts of LDH
(Berg and Aune, 1987).

C. Effects on Other Cultured Cell Types

MCLR has been incubated with rat hepatic sinusoidal endothelial cells (Hooser
et al., 1989b; Solow et al., 1989), Kupffer cells (Hooser et al., 1989b), thy-
mocytes, mammary alveolar cells, fibroblasts, and red blood cells (Falconer
and Runnegar, 1987), but morphologic changes were not seen in any of these
cell lines at concentrations that caused rapid deformation of hepatocytes. Also,
neither bovine pulmonary artery endothelial cells nor mouse peritoneal macrophages were injured following incubation with MCLR in vitro (Adams et al.,
1988). The results of these studies using cell types other than hepatocytes
are in agreement with the hypothesis (see section V below) that the MCs are
primarily hepatotoxic because they are transported into hepatocytes via specific bile acid carrier(s).

D. Effects on Actin Polymerization

It is probable that cyanobacterial cyclic peptides induce hepatocyte plasma
membrane blebbing via cytoskeletal (actin, intermediate filaments, and/or
microtubule) alterations. Effects of incubation with an MC (not specified)
on the polymerization state of hepatocyte actin (unpolymerized = monomeric
or G-actin vs polymerized = filamentous or F-actin) were measured with the
DNase assay for monomeric actin. MC did not cause any change in the polymerization state of actin. This was in contrast to the effect of phalloidin which
caused hepatocyte monomeric actin to decrease to less than 1% (i.e., more
than 99% was in the filamentous form) (Runnegar and Falconer, 1986). However, recent evidence has demonstrated marked alterations in the organization
of actin filaments in MCLR exposed cultured rat hepatocytes. The actin filaments (Fig. 5) initially condense to form thick rays which extend to the tips
of toxin-induced plasma membrane blebs (Fig. 6a) and later collapse into a
dense mass in the central portion of the cell (Fig. 6b) (Hooser, et al., 1989b).

E. Influence of Calcium

Exposure of hepatocytes to MCYM was followed by an increase in phosphory-
lase-a activity and hepatocyte blebbing in a time- and dose-dependent manner.
This occurred even in a Ca^{2+}-free medium suggesting that, if the change was
calcium related, the increase in blebbing was due to intracellular Ca^{2+} release
(Runnegar et al., 1987).

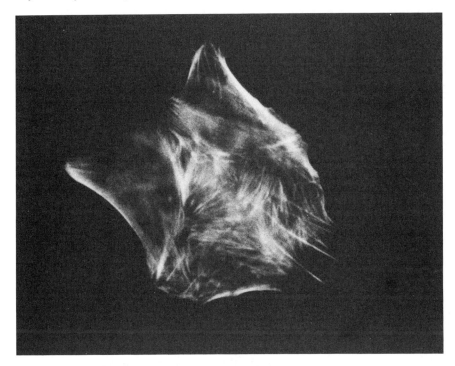

FIGURE 5 Actin filaments in a control, 72-hr cultured hepatocyte, fixed and stained with rhodamine phalloidin. RP ×500.

V. FATE

A. Stability in Acid and Digestive Enzymes

Studies in our laboratory indicate that MCLR is stable at pHs anticipated in the stomachs of monogastrics, as well as in pepsin, trypsin, and chymotrypsin (Dahlem, Hassan and Beasley, unpublished data).

B. Role of Bile Acid Carriers

When hepatocytes in vitro were preincubated with the bile acids deoxycholate and cholate or with either of two noncompetitive inhibitors of hepatocyte bile acid carriers, rifampicin or bromosulfophthalein, algal hepatotoxin-induced hepatocyte deformation was reduced. Also, increasing the concentrations of the inhibitors decreased the percentages of deformed hepatocytes (Runnegar et al., 1981). In addition, the resistance of neonatal animals to MCs (Foxall and Sasner, 1981) might result from a relative lack of bile acid carriers. Thus, it seems likely that the toxins enter hepatocytes via bile acid carriers, which may explain their hepatospecificity.

The ileum also has cells which actively transport bile acids (Hofmann, 1983); however, the multispecific bile acid transporters located in hepatocytes are distinct from the bile acid transporters which occur in the intestine. Thus, phalloidin is transported by multispecific carriers into hepatocytes, but is

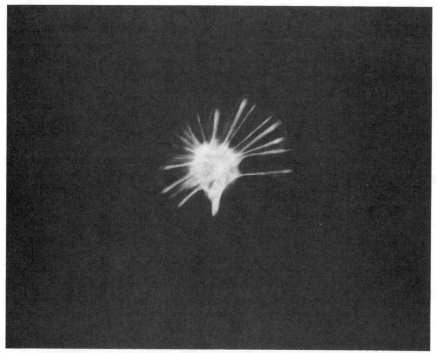

(a)

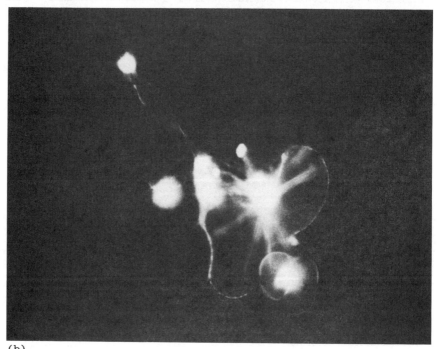

(b)

FIGURE 6 Microcystin-LR (10 µg/ml) treated hepatocytes. RP ×500. (a)
Actin is aggregating beneath the plasma membrane with thickened actin filaments extending out to the tips of the blebs. Seventy-two-hour culture, 3
hr postdosing. (b) Most of the intracellular actin has aggregated centrally
and there is extensive blebbing of the plasma membranes. Seventy-two-hour
culture, 6 hr postdosing.

poorly transported by those located in the ileum (Weiland et al., 1984). In rats dosed via isolated intestinal loops, the ileum, with its much smaller surface area but larger population of bile acid carriers, appeared to be a more efficient site of uptake of MCLR than the jejunum (Dahlem et al., 1989). Therefore, ileal uptake of MCs may be quite important. If this is the case, it will be important to determine the reason(s) why lesions are not also seen in mucosal cells of the ileum.

C. Studies using Radiolabeled Toxins

Radiolabeled algal peptide hepatotoxins have been produced biosynthetically (Brooks and Codd, 1987) and synthetically (Runnegar et al., 1986; Falconer et al., 1986). The biosynthetic method utilized ^{14}C labeled bicarbonate to produce toxin of low specific activity, which was subsequently given ip to mice. It was reported that 70% of the radiolabel was in the liver after only 1 min and 90% was present in the liver at 3 hr. Radioactivity was also present in the kidneys, urine, and lungs of the toxin-treated animals.

The synthetic method involved incorporation of ^{125}I, probably into the tyrosine residue of MCYR, to produce toxin of rather high specific activity which was purified and given ip to mice or iv to rats. Although ^{125}I in MCYR is a nonisotopic label, the iodinated toxin was still taken up by the liver and it remained hepatotoxic. However, iodination will not work for many of the MCs or for nodularin since they do not contain tyrosine.

In our laboratory we recently synthesized ^3H-dihydroMCLR using a method which could be adapted for several MCs or for nodularin. The dihydro compound retained potent, hepatospecific toxicity (Dahlem et al., 1990). When given ip to mice, sublethal doses were more completely taken up by the liver than lethal doses. In sublethally dosed mice, over 50% of the radiolabel was still present in the liver at 72 hr after dosing. Elimination was primarily via the feces (Dahlem, Rinehart, and Beasley, unpublished data).

VI. ANALYTICAL CHEMISTRY AND DIAGNOSIS

At present, diagnoses of blue-green algae poisoning are generally based on a history of ingestion of a "waterbloom" containing large amounts of a cyanobacterial species known to synthesize hepatotoxin(s) (algae observed in water and/or gastrointestinal contents), compatible clinical signs, clinical pathologic effects and lesions, and bioassays utilizing laboratory animals (Beasley et al., 1989). Since toxin-producing cells are morphologically indistinguishable from nontoxic cells (Ecker et al., 1981), it is highly desirable to employ standardized methods for direct analysis of algal toxins.

A. Isolation, Purification, and Detection

Previous methods for isolation and partial purification of toxic peptides from lyophilized cyanobacteria have utilized organic extraction followed by size exclusion chromatography (Botes et al., 1982a,b; Elleman et al., 1978; Kungsuwan et al., 1987; Toerien et al., 1976). Most currently used methods (Brooks et al., 1986; Brooks and Codd, 1986; Krishnamurthy et al., 1986a;

Siegelman et al., 1984) involve solvent extraction, adsorption onto octadecyl-silane (ODS) columns, gel filtration column chromatography, and reversed phase high performance liquid chromatography (HPLC). All of these methods rely on detection by mouse bioassay and/or ultraviolet light (UV) absorption. The conjugated diene located in the ADDA group gives the toxins a UV absorbance maximum near 238 nm. These methods have been used to produce quantities of toxin with relatively high purity from field material and laboratory cultures; however, the lack of specificity of the detection methods have occasionally permitted contamination of purified toxin by non-UV-absorbing impurities.

Reversed phase HPLC has been used to quantify toxins from lyophilized cells (Siegelman et al., 1984; Brooks and Codd, 1986). Although effective most reported methods are tedious and contain steps not needed for rapid analysis of cells, and/or they are incapable of separating certain commonly encountered MCs (Harada et al., 1988a,b). One HPLC method utilizes extraction methods similar to those previously described, but liquid chromatographic separations in the protocol rely upon weak anion exchange columns instead of ODS (Gathercole and Thiel, 1987). This method does not save time, but it is capable of separating all of the MCs tested. Another method does save time over the above mentioned ones; however, it was unclear whether it will separate the MCs, and it requires an expensive HPLC column (Meriluoto and Eriksson, 1988).

Recently a less time-consuming method for purification of peptide toxins from lyophilized cyanobacteria was described. It relied upon extraction using aqueous acetic acid and ODS reversed phase silica gel, thin layer chromatography (TLC) with UV and iodine vapor detections, and silica gel chromatography and HPLC separations with detection at 238 nm. Confirmation of purity utilized TLC and mass spectrometry (MS) (Harada et al., 1988b). In a subsequent paper, similar methods (excluding MS) were refined for the analysis of cyanobacterial peptide hepatotoxins (Harada et al., 1988a).

B. Trace Level Analysis

Trace level analysis for MCs has been achieved using monoclonal antibodies (Kfir et al., 1986a,b). To stimulate differentiation of antibody-producing cells, mice were injected ip with complexes consisting of MC, muramyl dipeptide, and polylysine. Cells were derived for the production of monoclonal antibodies that proved specific for the MCs and antibodies were produced for screening of drinking water for trace levels of toxin. No analytical methods of any type are yet available for detection of nonradiolabeled cyanobacterial peptides in exposed animals.

VII. CONCLUSIONS

Cyanobacterial cyclic peptide hepatotoxins are remarkably potent compounds which seem to use bile acid carriers for entry into hepatocytes and perhaps for absorption from the intestine. Intracellularly, the toxins cause disorganization of the actin filaments of the cytoskeleton without altering the polymerization state of actin. This may be the cause of hepatocyte rounding and ne-

crosis, as well as the associated destruction of sinusoidal endothelium, which
are followed by intrahepatic hemorrhage. Thresholds exist such that doses
lower than 10% of a lethal dose seem unlikely to have significant effects on
exposed animals.

Virtually all species of mammals and birds are susceptible to the cyanobacterial peptide toxins when exposed parenterally, and, to a lesser but often
very significant degree, orally. Reasons why animals are more tolerant of
oral than parenteral doses remain to be elucidated. They do not appear to
be a function of detoxification via acid hydrolysis, or degradation by pepsin,
trypsin, or chymotrypsin. Fasting causes increased susceptibility to the
toxins. However, other factors which influence the oral toxicity of these organisms have not been well characterized. Humans are unlikely to ingest cyano-
bacteria-contaminated water on purpose. However, because the toxins are
likely to survive customary water purification processes, there is cause for
concern for human health when "waterblooms" occur in sources of potable
water.

Slatkin et al. (1983) suggested that toxicosis induced by MCLR was mediated via atypical pulmonary thrombi which result in pulmonary congestion,
right heart failure, and centrilobular hepatic necrosis. However, Theiss and
Carmichael (1986) and Hooser et al. (1988) have since reported that the lung
lesions are not life-threatening and are caused by emboli from the liver. Also,
Theiss et al. (1988) found no changes in central venous or portal venous pressures following MCLR administration in rats. If obstruction of flow through
the lungs was responsible for hepatic lesions, then a backup of blood should
result in increased pulmonary artery, central venous, and portal venous pressures. The increase in liver weight of mice given lyophilized *M. aeruginosa*
could account for a 36% reduction in circulating blood volume (Sasner et al.,
1984). Relying upon similar evidence, several groups have concluded that
the cause of acute death in algal hepatotoxin dosed animals is usually hemorrhagic shock (Ostensvik et al., 1981; Runnegar and Falconer, 1982; Sasner
et al., 1984; Theiss and Carmichael, 1986; Theiss et al., 1988; Hooser et al.,
1989a). Animals that live for 12 to 96 hr may die acutely from the combined
effects of hemorrhagic shock and acute liver failure. With repeated exposure
at near acutely toxic doses, animals may develop cirrhosis and/or chronic
liver failure.

Species differences include the tendency for mice to die more rapidly than
other species, the relatively high tolerance of orally exposed ducks, the widespread hepatocellular damage in birds vs centrilobular damage in mammals,
and the relative resistance of some species of fish. Neonates and animals with
prior liver damage are more tolerant of the toxins, perhaps via reduced uptake by hepatocytes.

Tentative diagnoses of cyanobacterial hepatotoxicoses rely upon (1) a
history of exposure to hepatotoxic blue-green algae, and (2) liver damage
originating centrilobularly (in mammals), with intrahepatic hemorrhage and/or
acute liver failure. Although mouse bioassays must still be used for confirmation in most settings, hepatocytes in culture or suspension should soon
replace this method; and these should be superceded by analytical detection
of the toxins.

Therapy for exposed animals should include (1) measures to remove algae
from the digestive tract, (2) cholestyramine or superactivated charcoal to

bind the toxin, and (3) if no diarrhea or shock is present, an osmotic or saline cathartic to hasten evacuation from the gut. Supportive care is empirical at this time and may include intravenous fluids, blood transfusions, corticosteroids, and glucose solutions as needed. Restriction from sunlight if photosensitization is encountered (grazing animals), and nutritional therapy including a low fat, high quality protein diet, and supplementation with B-vitamins are recommended.

REFERENCES

Adams, W. H., Stoner, R. D., Adams, D. G., Slatkin, D. N., and Siegelman, H. W. (1985). Pathophysiologic effects of a toxic peptide from *Microcystis aeruginosa*. *Toxicon 23*: 441-447.

Adams, W. H., Stone, J. P., Sylvester, B., Stoner, R. D., Slatkin, D. N., Tempel, N. R., and Siegelman, H. W. (1988). Pathophysiology of cyanoginosin-LR: In vivo and in vitro studies. *Tox. Appl. Pharm. 96*: 248-257.

Arthur, J. C. (1880-1882). Some algae of Minnesota supposed to be poisonous. *Bull. Minn. Acad. Natur. Sci. 2*: 1-12.

Arthur, J. C. (1883-1891). Second report on some algae of Minnesota supposed to be poisonous. *Bull. Minn. Acad. Natur. Sci. 3*: 97-103.

Ashworth, C. T., and Mason, M. F. (1946). Observations on the pathological changes produced by a toxic substance present in blue-green algae (*Microcystis aeruginosa*). *Am. J. Path. 22*: 369-383.

Beasley, V. R., Dahlem, A. M., Cook, W. M., Valentine, W. M., Lovell, R. A., Hooser, S. B., Harada, K.-I., Suzuki, M., and Carmichael, W. W. (1989). Diagnostic and clinically important aspects of cyanobacterial (blue-green algal) toxicosis. *J. Vet. Diagn. Invest. 1*: 359-365.

Berg, K., and Aune, T. (1987). Freshly prepared rat hepatocytes used in screening the toxicity of blue-green algal blooms. *J. Tox. Environ. Health 20*: 187-197.

Berg, K., Carmichael, W. W., Skulberg, O. M. Benestad, C., and Underdal, B. (1987). Investigation of a toxic water-bloom of *Microcystis aeruginosa* (Cyanophycaea) in Lake Akersvatn, Norway. *Hydrobiologia 14*: 97-103.

Berg, K., and Soli, N. E. (1985a). Toxicity studies with the blue-green alga *Oscillatoria agardhii* from two eutrophic Norwegian lakes. *Acta Vet. Scand. 26*: 363-373.

Berg, K., and Soli, N. E. (1985b). Effects of *Oscillatoria agardhii* toxins on blood pressure and isolated organ preparations. *Acta Vet. Scand. 26*: 374-384.

Berg, K., Skulberg, O. M., Skulberg, R., Underdal, B., and Willen, T. (1986). Observations of toxic blue-green algae (cyanobacteria) in some Scandinavian lakes. *Acta Vet. Scand. 27*: 440-452.

Botes, D. P., Kruger, H., and Viljoen, C. C. (1982a). Isolation and characterization of four toxins from the blue-green alga, *Microcystis aeruginosa*. *Toxicon 20*: 945-954.

Botes, D. P., Tuinman, A. A., Wessels, P. L., Viljoen, C. C. Kruger, H., Williams, D. H., Santikarn, S., Smith, R. J., and Hammond, S. J. (1984).

The structure of cyanoginosin-LA, a cyclic peptide from the cyanobacterium *Microcystis aeruginosa*. *J. Chem. Soc. Perkin Trans. I.* pp. 2311-2318.

Botes, D. P., Viljoen, C. C., Kruger, H., Wessels, P. L., and Williams, D. H. (1982b). Configuration assignments of the amino acid residues and the presence of N-methyldehydroalanine in the toxins from the blue-green alga, *Microcystis aeruginosa*. *Toxicon* 20:1037-1042.

Botes, D. P., Wessels, P. L., Kruger, H., Runnegar, M. T. C., Santikarn, S., Smith, R. J., Barna, J. C. J., and Williams, D. H. (1985). Structural studies on cyanoginosins-LR, -YR, -YA, and -YM, peptide toxins from *Microcystis aeruginosa*. *J. Chem. Soc. Perkin Trans. I.* pp. 2747-2748.

Bourke, A. T. C., and Hawes, R. B. (1983). Freshwater cyanobacteria (blue-green algae) and human health. *Med. J. Aust.* 1:491-492.

Brandenburg, T. O., and Shigley, F. M. (1947). "Water bloom" as a cause of poisoning in livestock in North Dakota. *J. Am. Vet. Med. Assoc.* 110:384-385.

Brooks, W. P., and Codd, G. A. (1986). Extraction and purification of toxic peptides from natural blooms and laboratory isolates of the cyanobacterium *Microcystis aeruginosa*. *Letters Appl. Micro.* 2:1-3.

Brooks, W. P., and Codd, G. A. (1987). Distribution of *Microcystis aeruginosa* peptide toxin and interactions with toxic microsomes. *Pharmacol. Toxicol.* 60:248-257.

Brooks, W. P., Bell, S. G., and Codd, G. A. (1986). Production, purification, and properties of *Microcystis* toxins. *British Phycological Society* 21:327.

Byth, S. (1980). Palm Island Mystery Disease. *Med. J. Aust.* 2:40-42.

Carmichael, W. W. (1982). Chemical and toxicological studies of the toxic freshwater cyanobacteria *Microcystis aeruginosa*, *Anabaena flos-aquae* and *Aphanizomenon flos-aquae*. *S. Afr. J. Sci.* 78:367-372.

Carmichael, W. W. (1988). Toxins of freshwater algae. In *Handbook of Natural Toxins, Vol. 3: Marine Toxins and Venoms*, A. T. Tu (ed.), Marcel Dekker, New York, NY, pp. 121-147.

Carmichael, W. W., Eschedor, G. M., Patterson, G. M. L., and Moore, R. E. (1988). Toxicity and partial structure of a hepatotoxic peptide produced by the cyanobacterium *Nodularia spumigena* Mertens emend. L575 from New Zealand. *Appl. Environ. Microbiol.* 54:2257-2263.

Dabholkar, A. S., and Carmichael, W. W. (1987). Ultrastructural changes in the mouse liver induced by hepatotoxin from the freshwater cyanobacterium *Microcystis aeruginosa* strain 7820. *Toxicon* 25:285-292.

Dahlem, A. M., Beasley, V. R., Hooser, S. B., Harada, K.-I., Matsuura, K., Suzuki, M., Rinehart, K. L., Harvis, C. A., and Carmichael, W. W. (1990). The structure/toxicity relationship of dehydro amino acids in microcystin-LR and nodularin, two monocyclic peptide hepatotoxins from cyanobacteria. *Chem. Res. Toxicol.* (in press).

Dahlem, A. M., Hassan, A. S., Swanson, S. P., Carmichael, W. W., and Beasley, V. R. (1989). A model system for studying the bioavailability of intestinally administered microcystin-LR, a hepatotoxic peptide from the cyanobacterium *Microcystis aeruginosa*. *Pharmacol. Toxicol.* 64:177-181.

Dillenberg, H. O., and Dehnel, M. K. (1960). Toxic waterbloom in Saskatchewan, 1959. *Canad. Med. Assoc. J. 83*:1151-1154.

Ecker, M. M., Foxall, T. L., and Sasner, J. J., Jr. (1981). Morphology of toxic versus non-toxic strains of *Aphanizomenon flos-aquae*. In *The Water Environment: Algal Toxins and Health*, W. W. Carmichael (ed.), Plenum Press, New York, pp. 113-126.

Edler, L., Ferno, S., Lind, M. G., Lundberg, R., and Nilsson, P. O. (1985). Mortality of dogs associated with a bloom of the cyanobacterium *Nodularia spumigena* in the Baltic Sea. *Ophelia 24*:103-109.

Elleman, T. C., Falconer, I. R., Jackson, A. R. B., and Runnegar, M. T. (1978). Isolation, characterization and pathology of the toxin from a *Microcystis aeruginosa* (= *Anacystis cyanea*) bloom. *Aust. J. Biol. Sci. 31*:208-218.

Eriksson, J. E., Meriluoto, J. A. O., Kujari, H. P., Österlund, K., Fagerlund, K., and Hällbom, L. (1988). Preliminary characterization of a toxin isolated from the cyanobacterium *Nodularia spumigena*. *Toxicon 26*:161-166.

Evans, W. M. (1936). Report of investigations of cattle poisoning around Payne Lake, Jefferson County, New York. *Cornell Vet. 26*:337-341.

Falconer, I. R., and Buckley, T. H. (1989). Tumour promotion by *Microcystis* sp., a blue-green alga occurring in water supplies. *Med. J. Aust. 150*: 351.

Falconer, I. R., Jackson, A. R. B., Langley, J., and Runnegar, M. T. (1981). Liver pathology in mice in poisoning by the blue-green alga *Microcystis aeruginosa*. *Aust. J. Biol. Sci. 34*:179-187.

Falconer, I. R., Buckley, T., and Runnegar, M. T. C. (1986). Biological half-life, organ distribution and excretion of ^{125}I-labeled toxic peptide from the blue-green alga *Microcystis aeruginosa*. *Aust. J. Biol. Sci. 39*:17-21.

Falconer, I. R., Smith, J. V., Jackson, A. R. B., Jones, A., and Runnegar, M. T. C. (1988). Oral toxicity of a bloom of the cyanobacterium *Microcystis aeruginosa* administered to mice over periods up to 1 year. *J. Tox. Environ. Health. 24*:291-305.

Fitch, C. P., Bishop, L. M., and Boyd, W. L. (1934). "Water bloom" as a cause of poisoning in domestic animals. *Cornell Vet. 24*:30-39.

Fogg, G. E., Stewart, W. D. P., Fay, P., and Walsby, A. E. (1973). *The Blue-Green Algae*. Academic Press, New York.

Foxall, T. L., and Sasner, J. J. (1981). Effects of a hepatic toxin from the cyanophyte *Microcystis aeruginosa*. In *The Water Environment: Algal Toxins and Health*, W. W. Carmichael (ed.), Plenum Press, New York, pp. 365-387.

Francis, G. (1878). Poisonous Australian lake. *Nature 18*:11-12.

Galey, F. D., Beasley, V. R., Carmichael, W. W., Kleppe, G., Hooser, S. B., and Haschek, W. M. (1987). Blue-green algae (*Microcystis aeruginosa*) hepatotoxicosis in dairy cows. *Am. J. Vet. Res. 48*:1415-1420.

Gathercole, P. S., and Theil, P. B. (1987). Liquid chromatographic determination of the cyanoginosins, toxins, produced by the cyanobacterium (*Microcystis aeruginosa*). *J. Chromatogr. 408*: 435-440.

Gorham, P. R. (1960). Toxic waterblooms of blue-green algae. *Canad. Vet. J. 1*:235-245.

Gorham, P. R. (1964). Toxic algae as a public health hazard. *J. Am. Water Works Assoc.* 56:1481-1488.

Harada, K.-I., Matsuura, K., Suzuki, M., Oka, H., Watanabe, M. F., Oishi, S., Dahlem, A. M., Beasley, V. R., and Carmichael, W. W. (1988a). Analysis and purification of toxic peptides from cyanobacteria by reversed-phase high-performance liquid chromatography. *J. Chromatogr.* 448:275-283.

Harada, K.-I., Suzuki, M., Dahlem, A. M., Beasley, V. R., Carmichael, W. W., and Rinehart, K. L. (1988b). Improved method for purification of toxic peptides produced by cyanobacteria. *Toxicon* 26:433-439.

Hawkins, P. R., Runnegar, M. T., and Jackson, A. R. B. (1985). Severe hepatotoxicity caused by the tropical cyanobacterium (blue-green alga) *Cylindrospermosis raciborskii* (Woloszynska) Seenya and Subba Raju isolated from a domestic water supply reservoir. *Appl. Environ. Micro.* 50:1292-1295.

Heaney, S. I. (1971). The toxicity of *Microcystis aeruginosa* Kutz from some English reservoirs. *Water Treat. Exam.* 20:235-244.

Heise, H. A. (1949). Symptoms of hay fever caused by algae. *J. Allergy* 20:383-385.

Henning, M., and Kohl, J. G. (1981). Toxic blue-green algae water bloom found in some lakes in the German Democratic Republic. *Int. Revue. ges Hydrobiol.* 66:553-561.

Hofmann, A. F. (1983). The enterohepatic circulation of bile acids in health and disease. In *Gastrointestinal Disease*, M. H. Sleisenger and J. S. Fordtran (eds.), W. B. Saunders Co., Philadelphia, PA, pp. 115-134.

Hooser, S. B., Basgall, E. J., Beasley, V. R., and Haschek, W. M. (1988). Sequential ultrastructural hepatic, pulmonary and renal changes due to *Microcystis aeruginosa*. *The Toxicologist* 8:219.

Hooser, S. B., Beasley, V. R., Basgall, E. J., Carmichael, W. W., and Haschek, W. M. (1990). Microcystin LR-induced ultrastructural changes in rats. *Vet. Path.* 27:9-15.

Hooser, S. B., Beasley, V. R., Lovell, R. A., Carmichael, W. W., and Hascheck, W. M. (1989a). Toxicity of microcystin-LR, a cyclic heptapeptide hepatotoxin from *Microcystis aeruginosa*, to rats and mice. *Vet. Path.* 26:246-252.

Hooser, S. B., Waite, L. L., Beasley, V. R., Carmichael, W. W., Kuhlenschmidt, M. S., and Haschek, W. M. (1989b). *Toxicon* 27:50-51.

Jackson, A. R. B., McInnes, A., Falconer, I. R., and Runnegar, M. T. C. (1984). Clinical and pathological changes in sheep experimentally poisoned by the blue-green alga *Microcystis aeruginosa*. *Vet. Path.* 21:102-113.

Jackson, A. R. B., Runnegar, M. T. C., Cumming, R. B., and Brunner, J. F. (1986). Experimental acute intoxication of young layer and broiler chickens with the cyanobacterium (blue-green alga) *Microcystis aeruginosa*. *Avian Path.* 15:741-748.

Jones, C. L. A., and Carmichael, W. W. (1984). Comparison of hepatotoxins from the cyanobacteria *Anabaena flos-aquae* and *Microcystis aeruginosa*. *FASEB J.* 43:579.

Kalbe, L., and Thiess, D. (1964). Entenmassensterben durch *Nodularia*-Wasserblute am Kleinen Jasmunder Bodden auf Rugen. *Archiv. fur Experimentelle Veterinarmedizin* 18:535-555.

Kerr, L. A., McCoy, C. P., and Eaves, D. (1987). Blue-green algae toxicosis in five dairy cows. *J. Am. Vet. Med. Assoc.* *191*:829-830.

Kfir, R., Johannsen, E., and Botes, D. P. (1986a). Monoclonal antibody specific for cyanoginosin-LA: preparation and characterization. *Toxicon* *24*:543-552.

Kfir, R., Johannsen, E., and Botes, D. P. (1986b). Preparation of anti-cyanoginosin-LA monoclonal antibody. In *Mycotoxins and Phycotoxins, Bioactive Molecules*, I., P. S. Steyn and R. S. Vleggaar (eds.). Elsevier, Amsterdam, pp. 377-385.

Konst, H., McKercher, P. D., Gorham, P. R., Robertson, A., and Howell, J. (1965). Symptoms and pathology produced by toxic *Microcystis aeruginosa* NRC-1 in laboratory and domestic aniamls. *Canad. J. Comp. Med. Vet. Sci.* *29*:221-229.

Krishnamurthy, T., Carmichael, W. W., and Sarver, E. W. (1986a). Toxic peptides from freshwater cyanobacteria (blue-green algae). I. Isolation, purification and characterization of peptides from *Microcystis aeruginosa* and *Anabaena flos-aquae*. *Toxicon* *24*:865-873.

Krishnamurthy, T., Szafraniec, L., Hunt, D. F., Shabanowitz, J., Yates, J., Hauer, C. R., Carmichael, W. W., Skulberg, O., Codd, G. A., and Missler, S. (1989). Structural characterization of toxic cyclic peptides from blue-green algae by tandem mass spectrometry. *Proc. Natl. Acad. Sci.* *86*:770-774.

Krishnamurthy, T., Szafraniec, L., Sarver, E. W., Hunt, D. F. Missler, S., and Carmichael, W. W. (1985). Amino acid sequencing of Norwegian freshwater blue-green algal (*Microcystis aeruginosa*) peptide by FAB-MS/MS technique. Fifth Int. Conf. Secondary Ion Mass Spectroscopy—V. Washington, D.C., Sept. 29-Oct. 4, 1985.

Krishnamurthy, T., Szafraniec, L., Sarver, E. W., Hunt, D. F. Shanbanowitz, J., Carmichael, W. W., Missler, S., Skulberg, O., and Codd, G. (1986b). Amino acid analysis of freshwater blue-green algal toxic peptides by fast atom bombardment tandem mass spectrometric techniques. Proc. 34th Ann. Conf. on Mass Spec. and Allied Topics. Cincinnati, Ohio, pp. 93-94.

Kungsuwan, A., Noguchi, T., Watanabe, M. F., Matsunaga, S., Watabe, S., and Hashimoto, K. (1987). Isolation of two toxins from the blue-green alga *Microcystis aeruginosa*. *Nippon Suisan Gak-Kaishi* *53*:2051-2054.

Kusumi, T., Ooi, T., Watanabe, M., and Kakisawa, H. (1987a). Structure of cyanoviridin RR, a toxin from the cyanobacterium (blue-green alga) *Microcystis viridis*. Proc. of the 29th Symposium on the Chemistry of Natural Products. Sapporo, Japan, pp. 536-543.

Kusumi, T., Ooi, T., Watanabe, M., Takahashi, H., and Kakisawa, H. (1987b). Cyanoviridin-RR, a toxin from the cyanobacterium (blue-green alga), *Microcystis viridis*. *Tetrahedron Letters* *28*:4695-4698.

LeClaire, R. D., Lawrence, W. B., Bostian, K. A., and Mereish, K. A. (1988). Acute toxicity of microcystin-LR in the rat: a comparative dose-response study using serum chemistries and mortality as indices. *The Toxicologist* *8*:221.

Lindstrom, E. (1976). Et udbrud af algeforgiftning blandt unde. *Dansk. Vet. Tidsskr.* *59*:637-641.

Louw, P. G. J., and Smit, J. D. (1950). The active constituents of the poisonous algae, *Mycrocystis toxica* Stephens; with a note on experimental cases of algae poisoning in small animals. *S. Afr. Indust. Chem.* 4: 62-66.

Lovell, R. A., Schaeffer, D. J., Hooser, S. B., Dahlem, A. M., Haschek, W. M., Carmichael, W. W., and Beasley, V. R. (1989). Toxicity of one or two intraperitoneal doses of microcystin-LR in two strains of male mice. *J. Environ. Path., Oncol., Toxicol.* 9: 221-238.

MacDonald, D. W. (1960). Algal poisoning in beef cattle. *Can. Vet. J. 1*: 108-110.

Main, D. C., Berry, P. H., Peet, R. L., and Robertson, J. P. (1977). Sheep mortalities associated with the blue green alga *Nodularia spumigena*. *Aust. Vet. J.* 53: 578-581.

Mason, M. F., and Wheeler, R. E. (1942). Observations upon the toxicity of blue-green algae. *Am. Soc. Biol. Chem. 36th Ann. Meeting, Boston. Fed. Proc.* 1: 124.

McBarron, E. J., and May, V. M. (1966). Poisoning of sheep in New South Wales by the Blue-green alga *Anacystis cyanea* (Kuetz.) Dr. and Dail. *Aust. Vet. J.* 42: 449-453.

McInnes, A., Jackson, A. R. B., Falconer, I. R., and Runnegar, M. T. C. (1983). The clinical pathology of sheep experimentally poisoned with the blue-green alga *Microcystis aeruginosa*. *Toxicon* 3: 281-284.

Meriluoto, J. A. O., and Eriksson, J. E. (1988). Rapid analysis of peptide toxins in cyanobacteria. *J. Chromatogr.* 438: 93-99.

Miura, G. A., LeClaire, R. D., Templeton, C. B., and Pace, J. G. (1988). Enhanced hepatotoxicity of microcystin-A in fasted rats. *FASEB J.* 2: 1351.

Moore, R. E. (1977). Toxins from the blue-green algae. *Bioscience* 27: 797-802.

O'Donoghue, J. G., and Wilton, G. S. (1951). Algal poisoning in Alberta. *Canad. J. Comp. Med.* 15: 193-198.

Oishi, S., and Watanabe, M. F. (1986). Acute toxicity of *Microcystis aeruginosa* and its cardiovascular effects. *Env. Res.* 40: 518-524.

Ostensvik, O., Skulberg, O. M., and Soli, N. E. (1981). Toxicity studies with blue-green algae from Norwegian inland waters. In *The Water Environment: Algal Toxins and Health*, W. W. Carmichael (ed.), Plenum Press, New York, pp. 315-324.

Painuly, P., Perez, R., Fukai, T., and Shimizu, Y. (1988). The structure of a cyclic peptide toxin, cyanogenosin-RR from *Microcystis aeruginosa*. *Tetrahedron Letters* 29: 11-14.

Phillips, M. J., Roberts, R. J., and Stewart, J. A. (1985). The toxicity of the cyanobacterium *Microcystis aeruginosa* to rainbow trout, *Salmo gairdneri* Richardson. *J. Fish Dis.* 8: 339-344.

Porter, E. M. (1886). *Investigation of supposed poisonous vegetation in the waters of some of the lakes of Minnesota. Fourth biennial report of Board of Regents of Univeristy of Minnesota, Supplement I*, Department of Agriculture, pp. 95-96.

Reynolds, C. S. (1980). Cattle deaths and blue-green algae: a possible instance from Cheshire, England. *J. Inst. Water Engin. Sci.* 34: 74-76.

Rinehart, K. L., Harada, K.-I., Namikoshi, M., Chen, C., Harvis, C. A., Munro, M. H. G., Blunt, J. W., Mulligan, P. E., Beasley, V. R., Dahlem,

A. M., and Carmichael, W. W. (1988). Nodularin, microcystin, and the configuration of Adda. *J. Am. Chem. Soc.* *110*:8557-8558.

Ringelberg, J., and Baard, R. (1988). Growth and decline of a population *Microcystis aeruginosa* in mesotrophic Lake Maarseveen I (The Netherlands). *Arch. Hydrobiol.* *111*:533-545.

Runnegar, M. T. C., and Falconer, I. R. (1982). The in vivo and in vitro biological effects of the peptide hepatotoxin from the blue-green alga *Microcystis aeruginosa*. *S. Afr. J. Sci.* *78*:363-366.

Runnegar, M. T. C., and Falconer, I. R. (1986). Effect of toxin from the cyanobacterium *Microcystis aeruginosa* on ultrastructural morphology and actin polymerization in isolated hepatocytes. *Toxicon 24*:109-115.

Runnegar, M. T. C., Falconer, I. R., and Silver, J. (1981). Deformation of isolated rat hepatocytes by a peptide hepatotoxin from the blue-green alga *Microcystis aeruginosa*. *Naunyn-Schmiedeberg's Arch. Pharmacol.* *317*:268-272.

Runnegar, M. T. C., Falconer, I. R., Buckley, T., and Jackson, A. R. B., (1986). Lethal potency and tissue distribution of ^{125}I-labelled toxic peptides from the blue-green alga *Microcystis aeruginosa*. *Toxicon 24*:506-509.

Runnegar, M. T. C., Andrews, J., Gerdes, R. G., and Falconer, I. R. (1987). Injury to hepatocytes induced by a peptide toxin from the cyanobacterium *Microcystis aeruginosa*. *Toxicon 25*:1235-1239.

Runnegar, M. T. C., Jackson, A. R. B., and Falconer, I. R. (1988). Toxicity of the cyanobacterium *Nodularia spumigena* Mertens. *Toxicon 26*: 143-151.

Santikarn, S., Williams, D. H., Smith, R. J., Hammond, S. J., Botes, D. P., Tuinman, A., Wessels, P. L., Viljoen, C. C., and Kruger, H. (1983). A partial structure for the toxin BE-4 from the blue-green algae, *Microcystis aeruginosa*. *J. Chem. Soc. Chem. Commun.* *12*:652-655.

Sasner, J. J., Jr., Ikawa, M., and Foxall, T. L. (1984). Studies on *Aphanizomenon* and *Microcystis* toxins. In *Seafood Toxins*, E. P. Ragelis (ed.), Am. Chem. Soc. Symp. Series 262, Washington, D.C., pp. 391-406.

Senior, V. E. (1960). Algal poisoning in Saskatchewan. *Canad. J. Comp. Med.* *24*:26-31.

Siegelman, H. W., Adams, W. H., Stoner, R. D., and Slatkin, D. N. (1984). Toxins of *Microcystis aeruginosa* their hematological and histopathological effects. In *Seafood Toxins*, E. P. Ragelis (ed.), Am. Chem. Soc. Symp. Series 262. Washington, D.C., pp. 407-413.

Skulberg, O. M. (1979). Toxic effects of blue-green algae, first case of *Microcystis*-poisoning reported from Norway. *Temarapport No. 4*, Norwegian Institute of Water Research, Oslo, pp. 1-42.

Skulberg, O. M., Codd, G. A., and Carmichael, W. W. (1984). Toxic blue-green algal blooms in Europe: a growing problem. *Ambio.* *13*:244-247.

Slatkin, D. N., Stoner, R. D., Adams, W. H., Kycia, J. H., and Siegelman, H. W. (1983). Atypical pulmonary thrombosis caused by a toxic cyanobacterial peptide. *Science 220*:1383-1385.

Soll, M. D., and Williams, M. C. (1985). Mortality of a white rhinoceros (*Ceratotherium simum*) suspected to be associated with the blue-green alga *Microcystis aeruginosa*. *J. S. Afr. Vet. Assoc.* *56*:49-51.

Solow, R., Mereish, K., Anderson, G. W. (1989). Effect of microcystin-LR on cultured rat endothelial cells. *The Toxicologist 9*: 637.

Stewart, A. G., Barnum, D. A., and Henderson, J. A. (1950). Algal poisoning in Ontario. *Canad. J. Comp. Med. 14*: 197-202.

Steyn, D. G. (1945). Poisoning of animals and human beings by algae. *S. Afr. J. Sci. 41*: 243-244.

Stowe, C. M., Abdullah, A. S., Monson, E., and Barnes, D. (1981). Blue-green algae poisoning (*Microcystis aeruginosa*) in a dairy herd. *Bovine Clinics 1*: 6-8.

Theiss, W. C., and Carmichael, W. W. (1986). Physiological effect of a peptide toxin produced by the freshwater cyanobacteria (blue-green algae) *Microcystis aeruginosa* strain 7820. In *Mycotoxins and Phycotoxins, Bioactive Molecules*, I., P. S. Steyn and R. Vleggaar (eds.). Elsevier, Amsterdam, pp. 353-364.

Theiss, W. C., Carmichael, W. W., Wyman, J., and Bruner, R. (1988). Blood pressure and hepatocellular effects of the cyclic peptide toxin produced by the freshwater cyanobacterium (blue-green alga) *Microcystis aeruginosa* strain PCC-7820. *Toxicon 26*: 603-613.

Toerien, D. F., Scott, W. E., and Pitout, M. J. (1976). *Microcystis* toxins: isolation, identification, implications. *Water S. Afr. 2*: 160-162.

Tustin, R. C., van Rensburg, S. J., and Eloff, J. N. (1973). Hepatic damage in the primate following ingestion of toxic algae. In *Liver*, Proc. Int. Liver Congress, S. J. Saunders and J. Terblanche (eds.). Pitman Medical, London, pp. 383-385.

Watanabe, M. F., and Oishi, S. (1982). Toxic substance from a natural bloom of *Microcystis aeruginosa*. *Appl. Environ. Microbiol. 43*: 819-822.

Weiland, T., Nassal, M., Kramer, W., Fricker, G., Bickel, V., and Kurz, G. (1984). Identity of hepatic membrane transport systems for bile salts, phalloidin, and anfamanide by photoaffinity labeling. *Proc. Natl. Acad. Sci. 81*: 5232-5236.

Wheeler, R. E., Lackey, J. B., and Schott, S. A. (1942). Contribution on the toxicity of algae. *Publ. Health Rep. 57*: 1695-1701.

Williams, D. B. (1983). Application of fast atom bombardment mass spectroscopy to structural problems in organic chemistry. *International J. Mass Spectroscopy and Ion Physics 53*: 37-44.

Zin, T. L., and Edwards, W. C. (1979). Toxicity of blue-green algae in livestock. *Bovine Pract. 14*: 151-153.

23

Human Poisoning by Mushrooms of the Genus *Cortinarius*

Kenneth F. Lampe[†]

Division of Drugs and Toxicology, American Medical Association, Chicago, Illinois

---

The views expressed are those of the author and do not necessarily reflect those of the American Medical Association.

[†]Deceased

I. INTRODUCTION

Widespread attention was aroused by the publication of a report of a mass mushroom poisoning with several fatalities that occurred in Poland (Grzymała, 1957) and a companion article describing the responsible species, *Cortinarius orellanus* Fries (Skirgiello and Nespiak, 1957). The unique features of the intoxication were its incredible latent period following ingestion of days to 2 weeks before signs of poisoning appeared and a symptom complex unlike any other toxic mushroom. Within a few years, similar intoxications were reported from other parts of Europe and England. Related species were identified as the cause of human and even veterinary poisonings. The toxin was isolated, its structure determined, and its synthesis accomplished. Preliminary work has been undertaken concerning its mechanism of action. Recommendations have been suggested for clinical management of the intoxicated patient. A species of *Cortinarius* containing the toxin has been identified in North America. No reports of poisoning related to that mushroom have appeared, possibly because single incidents may not be ascribed to the correct etiology since relatively little attention has been given to this intoxication in the medical literature of North America.

Despite several comprehensive reviews of *Cortinarius* poisoning appearing during this decade (Kubička, 1980; Flammer, 1982, 1985; Schumacher and Høiland, 1983; Bresinsky and Besl, 1985), information concerning the toxin is accumulating at a rate that justifies an update. It is an unusual event to have a mushroom identified as potentially lethal if it belongs to a genus that if not particularly desirable gastronomically, at least is considered edible. That such a discovery should be announced in continental Europe with its centuries-old tradition of mycophagy was particularly remarkable.

II. HISTORICAL OVERVIEW OF HUMAN POISONING

During September and October 1952, in the area about Poznań, Poland, a city just midway between Warsaw and Berlin, there was an unusual epidemic affecting 102 men and women that was characterized initially by burning and dryness of the mouth with intense thirst. Other symptoms followed and, in patients seriously affected, increased diuresis followed by oliguria or anuria. Of the 24 patients that had to be hospitalized, 11 died. Stanisław Grzymała, a public health epidemiologist for Poznań, became involved because an infectious disease etiology was presumed. It became apparent from the case histories that the only common element was the ingestion of a brownish-red mushroom some days prior to the onset of the illness. The mushroom, zasłonak rudy in Polish (literally, a veil of ginger-colored hair; similarly, orangefuchsigen Schleierling or Hautkopfes in German), was identified as *C. orellanus*, then considered edible in mushroom hunters' handbooks. Feeding the mushroom to cats established the mushroom as the cause of the nephrotoxicity. There were two lesser outbreaks, one in 1955 involving nine individuals, two of whom died, and another in 1957 involving 21, with six fatalities. Grzymała (1957, 1958, 1959b, 1965a) and Wysocki et al. (1958) published some individual case notes and a summary of the clinical findings for these events.

Onset of symptoms after mushroom ingestion was variable, but not earlier than 2 days, usually 3 or more, and, sometimes, not until day 17. The more serious cases had the more rapid onset and were related to the quantity of mushroom consumed. Toxicity seemed to be unaffected by the geographic source of the mushroom, the year of growth, the method of preparation, or by drying. Later laboratory investigations were to show that the dried mushroom retains its toxicity for at least 60 years (Rapior et al., 1988).

The frequency of symptoms for the first 132 cases of *Cortinarius orellanus* poisoning in Poland between 1952 and 1957 were tabulated by Grzymała (1959b) (Table 1). Laboratory findings were noncontributory except in the more serious cases in which the expected increase in blood urea nitrogen (BUN), creatinine, and potassium reflected the severity of renal damage. A mild leucocytosis was present in the more serious intoxications as well as an increased sedimentation rate. Once recognized as toxic, poisoning by *C. orellanus* was reported from other countries: France (Marichal et al., 1977; Brousse et al., 1981; Andary et al., 1989), Germany (Färber and Feldmeier, 1977), Switzerland (Farve et al., 1976; Leski et al., 1976), and Czechoslovakia (Bouška et al., 1979). The poisoning in Czechoslovakia by an unidentified species of *Cortinarius* reported by Středová et al. (1978) probably belongs here also.

An identical syndrome was reported following ingestion of *Cortinarius speciosissimus Kühn* and Romagn., first in Finland by Hulmi et al. (1974) and subsequently there by Harmaja (1973). Poisoning by this species was also recognized in Sweden (Holmdahl et al., 1980, 1984; Heath et al., 1980), Norway (Fauchald and Westlie, 1982; and Høiland and Schumacher, 1982), Germany (Nolte et al., 1987), Italy (Soresina and Leoni, 1978; Busnach et al., 1983), France (Traverso, 1973), and Scotland (Short et al., 1980; Azéma, 1981; Watling, 1982). The single instance of animal poisoning ascribed to this species was reported in a flock of sheep in Norway (Överås et al., 1979). The most recent report for this syndrome was a mass intoxication of one officer and 25 enlisted men in a French army survival exercise (Pats et al., 1988). Twelve of the men developed acute renal insufficiency, of whom eight required

TABLE 1 Signs and Symptoms in 132 Cases of *Cortinarius orellanus* Intoxications

Gastroenteric		Other	
Thirst	130	Headache	87
Nausea	107	Chill	77
Dry mouth	97	Loin pain	75
Emesis	93	Tinnitus	49
Abdominal pain	75	Extremity pain	42
Constipation	34	Somnolence	41
Diarrhea	28	Visual defects	29

Less frequent symptoms, in decreasing order of incidence, included agitation, rash, respiratory disturbances, digital paresthesias, pedal edema, unconsciousness, convulsions, and subicterus.

Source: After Grzymała (1959b).

management by hemodialysis. The mushroom was identified as *Cortinarius orellanoides* R. Hry.

A *Cortinarius*-like syndrome also was reported from the ingestion of *C. splendens* R. Hry. in France (Colon et al., 1981, 1982; Gérault, 1976, 1981; Finaz de Villaine, 1981) and in Switzerland (Schliessbach et al., 1983). The latent period was 3 to 13 days following ingestion, and the clinical picture was that of acute renal insufficiency. Gérault (1981) conducted some studies with samples of dried mushroom in the rat and demonstrated the appearance of interstitial nephritis with sparing of the glomerulus just as seen with *C. orellanus*. However, the primary toxins of *C. orellanus* are absent from this mushroom (Rapior et al., 1988). Although Gérault speculated that an anthroquinone pigment might be responsible, this has not been investigated.

III. CHEMISTRY OF THE TOXINS

A. Isolation of Orellanine

A crystalline material was obtained from *C. orellanus* by subjecting dried mushrooms to solvents of differing polarities in a Soxhlet extractor. The extracts were evaporated and the residue from each extraction was examined for toxicity (Grzymała, 1959a, 1959b, 1962, 1965b). A toxic residue was obtained from the methanol extract that formed pale yellow needles on recrystallization from methanol. About 1 to 1.2 g of crystals could be obtained from 100 g of dried mushroom. Grzymała, who named this material orellanine, showed that it reproduced the toxic effects of the whole mushroom in experimental animals. Its oral LD_{50} in the cat was 4.9 mg/kg, subcutaneously in the mouse was 8.3 mg/kg, and by intraperitoneal injection in the guinea pig was 8 mg/kg. Histological examination of the organs showed effects identical to those produced by the mushroom in poisoned patients. Orellanine also was shown to be a cumulative toxin administered in doses of 3 mg/kg to guinea pigs at 5-day intervals.

Grzymała also provided information on the physical properties of orellanine. The crystal conformation differed depending on the solvent from which it formed. He measured its indices of refraction, noted that it exhibited no optical activity, showed birefringence with a polarizing microscope, determined its specific gravity, and recorded its ultraviolet (UV) spectra in aqueous solution. He discovered that the crystals decomposed explosively on heating at 267 to 269°C. Quantitative solubility data were determined for a variety of solvents. He also noted the strong reducing property of the crystals for solutions of potassium permanganate, methylene blue, ferric ion in sulfuric acid, and for Tollen's, Benedict's, and Molisch reagents.

B. Structural Determination

Preparative paper chromatography showed that Grzymała's "orellanine" could be resolved into three components, which were labeled Or I, Or II, and Or III by Antkowiak and Gessner (1975). Or I and Or II were toxic to mice, but not Or III. The thermal degradation product of orellanine that had been obtained by sublimation under reduced pressure (0.01 mm at 180°C) as a yellow solid (Grzymała and Fiksiński, 1960) was found to have chromatographic properties similar to Or III. It was noted that Or I became fluorescent after UV irradiation.

By gas chromatography it was discovered that the thermal decomposition of orellanine to Or III, for which they proposed the name orelline, involved the liberation of gaseous oxygen (Antkowiak and Gessner, 1978, 1979). Catalytic hydrogenation with Adam's catalyst (plantinic oxide) of orellanine also resulted in the formation of orelline. Elemental analysis, UV, infrared (IR), and the mass spectra permitted these authors to propose 3,3',4,4'-tetrahydroxy-2,2'-bipyridyl-N,N'-dioxide as the structure for orellanine and 3,3',4,4'-tetrahydroxy-2,2'-bipyridyl for orelline (Fig. 1a and c).

The photodecomposition of orellanine (Or I) was examined by two-dimensional chromatography (Antkowiak and Gessner, 1985). A mixture of orellanine (Or I), Or II, and orelline (Or III) was resolved on a cellulose plate with a mixture of isopropranol-concentrated hydrochloric acid-water (85:22:18) as three spots: R_f 0.78 (navy blue to UV light: orellanine), R_f 0.66 (dark blue: Or II), and R_f 0.48 (light blue fluorescence, orelline). The dried chromatogram was exposed to UV irradiation (254 nm) for several minutes and then developed in the same solvent system in a direction perpendicular to the original. Orellanine once again split into three analogous spots, Or II into two, and orelline remained unchanged. Or II, identified as the mono-N-oxide, was given the name orellinine (Fig. 1b). All three substances were shown to be present in *C. orellanus*, but orellinine and orelline only in small quantities. All three were also found in *Cortinarius speciosissimus*.

Precursors for orellanine have not been sought. However, orellanine-producing mycelium has been cultured successfully (Rapior et al., 1987). The orellanine content of the mycelium was very low compared to its concentration in the fruiting body of the mushroom and extracts for analysis had to be enriched by passage over an adsorbent resin. However, mycelium culture does offer a feasible approach in the search for intermediates involved in the production of orellanine in the mushroom.

C. Synthesis of Orellanine and Orelline

Dehmlow and Schulz (1985) were the first to report the successful synthesis of orellanine and orelline. Detailed reaction conditions appeared later (Dehmlow and Schulz, 1987). Their initial attempts to form the toxin from a pre-

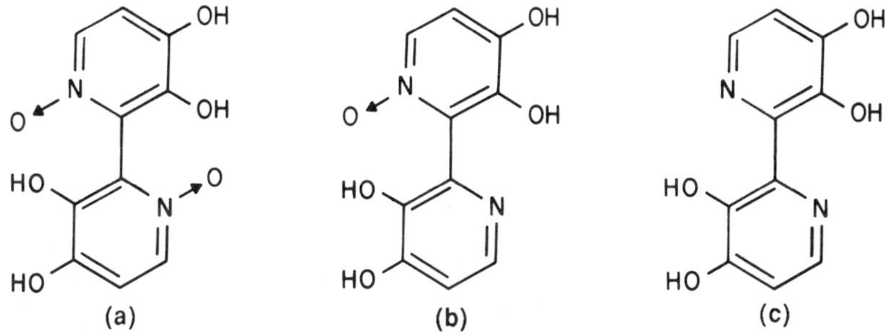

FIGURE 1 (a) Orellanine; (b) orellinine; (c) orelline.

existing bipyridyl were unsuccessful. Ultimately, they developed a 10-step process beginning with 3-aminopyridine. From this, 2-chloro-3-aminopyridine was prepared by treatment with hydrogen peroxide in concentrated hydrochloric acid. This was converted to the 3-fluoro compound by the Schiemann reaction (diazotization in the presence of fluoborate followed by thermal decomposition of the diazonium salt). The pyridyl-N-oxide was produced by oxidation with 30% hydrogen peroxide in acetic anhydride. The product was treated with 100% HNO_3 in 100% H_2SO_4 containing 10% SO_3 to give a mixture containing 42% 2-chloro-3-fluoro-4-nitropyridine-N-oxide and 2% of the 6-nitro derivative. The principal reaction product was treated with a solution of sodium in methanol. This induced a selective, stepwise substitution of the 3-fluoro, then the 4-nitro groups by methoxy groups to produce 2-chloro-3,4-dimethoxy-pyridine-N-oxide. The attempted isolation of the dimethoxy product sometimes resulted in a violent decomposition. Therefore, the authors recommended its immediate reduction with PCl_3. The resulting compound, 2-chloro-3,4-dimethoxypyridine, was coupled by stirring with nickel-(0)-triphenylphosphine complex in N,N-dimethylformamide (DMF). The 2,2'-bipyridyl could be hydrolyzed with hydrogen bromide (HBr) in acetic acid to orelline (Fig. 1c) or oxidized with hydrogen peroxide in acetic anhydride to the bipyridyl-bis-N-oxide and then hydrolyzed to yield orellanine (Fig. 1a).

Independently, Tiecco and co-workers (1986) published a synthesis of orellanine and orelline using an essentially similar approach beginning with 3-hydroxypyridine. This underwent bromination in alkaline solution to give the 2-bromo derivative. The hydroxy group was then alkylated and the resulting 2-bromo-3-methoxy pyridine was transformed to the N-oxide by reaction with m-chloroperbenzoic acid in chloroform. Treatment of this product with a mixture of concentrated sulfuric acid and fuming nitric acid yielded an approximately equimolecular mixture of the 4- and 6-nitro derivatives. Separation could be effected easily by the near insolubility of the 6-nitro derivative in water. The nitro group was converted to a methoxy group by treatment with sodium methoxide. The authors make special note in their discussion of the reaction conditions concerning the care that must be exercised to prevent the simultaneous formation of the 2,3,4-trimethoxy derivative. Deoxygenation of 2-bromo-3,4-dimethoxypyridine-N-oxide was accomplished with phosphorus tribromide. Coupling to form the 2,2'-bipyridyl was effected with the nickel-triphenylphosphine complex and zinc in DMF. The bipyridyl could then be demethylated with HBr to form orelline or oxidized with $meta$-chloroperbenzoic acid in chloroform to the N,N'-dioxide and subsequently dealkylated to orellanine. The authors also showed that orelline could be oxidized at room temperature by hydrogen peroxide to form orellanine.

Ballesteros et al. (1988) devised an improved synthesis for the 2-chloro-3-methoxy-4-nitropyridine intermediate used in the Tiecco approach for the preparation of orellanine. Commercially available 2-chloro-3-hydroxypyridine in methylene chloride, water, sodium hydroxide, and tetrabutylammonium bromide was treated with dimethyl sulfate to yield 2-chloro-3-methoxypyridine. The reaction product was oxidized with $meta$-chloroperbenzoic acid in methylene chloride to form the corresponding N-oxides, which were nitrated with a mixture of nitric and sulfuric acids to give a 50% yield of the desired 4-nitro derivative and a 30% yield of the 6-nitro isomer.

An alternative synthesis for orelline from 2-bromo-3-hydroxypyridine has been reported (Hasseberg and Gerlach, 1988). The hydroxyl group is converted to form a (2-trimethylsilyl)ethoxy-methyl ether. The product is coupled to form the corresponding 2,2'-bipyridyl by treatment with zinc and nickelous chloride in triphenylphosphine. The bipyridyl can be selectively substituted by lithium in the 4,4'-positions with butyl lithium in ether at -50°C. Oxidation to the 4,4'-diol could be accomplished by either 2-(phenylsulfonyl)-3-phenyloxaziridine or with bis(trimethylsilyl) peroxide. Acid-catalyzed hydrolysis of the silyl ether groups gave the desired orelline. These authors, however, were not able to convert orelline to orellanine by hydrogen peroxide using the procedure described by Tiecco et al. (1986).

D. Physical Properties

Since the original isolation of orellanine by Grzymala, a number of reports have been made on the physical properties of orellanine of both natural and synthetic origin and its photodecomposition products (Antkowiak and Gessner, 1979; Dehmlow and Schulz, 1985; Tiecco et al., 1986, 1987; Andary et al., 1986; Holmdahl et al., 1987; Prast et al., 1988; Richard and Ulrich, 1989). There is essential agreement between all. For consistency, all data have been taken from a single laboratory except as noted (Table 2).

The crystal structure of the complex formed during crystallization of orellanine was examined to determine the orientation of the two pyridyl rings and to search for the presence of intra- and intermolecular bonding (Cohen-Addad et al., 1987). The crystal structure is in agreement with prior studies of orellanine in solution, indicating a perpendicular configuration of the rings. There is no evidence for intramolecular hydrogen bonding. Short intermolecular OH $\cdots$ O bonds are formed. In the trifluoracetic acid complex, a very short one, of 2.45 Å, links two molecules of orellanine through their N-O groups along the *a* axis. This suggested to the authors the existence in the complex of a protonated form of orellanine, one hydrogen being shared by two *N*-oxides. The bond lengths of 1.35 to 1.37 Å are in agreement. Additional evidence has been presented against intramolecular bonding in an electron-impact (EI) mass spectra and mass-analyzed ion kinetic energy (MIKE) mass spectra study of orellanine (Richard and Ulrich, 1989). The purpose of their investigation was to determine the mode of pyrolytic decomposition of orellanine.

E. Synthesis of Orellinine

Treatment of 3,3',4,4'-tetramethoxy-2,2'-bipyridyl with a single equivalent of *meta*-perchlorobenzoic acid in chloroform at room temperature forms the mono-*N*-oxide (Tiecco et al., 1987). Dealkylation with 48% hydrobromic acid produces 3,3',4,4'-tetrahydroxy-2,2'-bipyridyl-*N*-oxide (orellinine) (Fig. 1b).

F. Detection of Orellanine in Mushrooms, Biological Fluids, and Tissues

There are different analytical requirements depending on the intended application of the result. For example, there are two specific clinical needs. If an individual discovers a child eating a wild mushroom, he may become con-

TABLE 2 Physical Properties of Orellanine and Its Derivatives

Orellanine[a]

Colorless crystals. Stable to 150-160°C. Above this temperature, decomposes slowly to give orelline. At 270-280°C, decomposes explosively to orelline. Soluble in dilute sodium hydroxide, ammonium hydroxide, and dimethyl sulfoxide, slightly soluble methanol, almost insoluble water, and most organic solvents.

^{1}H-NMR (DMSO-d_6) δ 8.25 (d, 1 H, J = 7.0 Hz), 7.15 (d, 1 H, J = 7.0 Hz), 8.8-7.8 (broad s, 2 H).

^{13}C-NMR (DMSO-d_6) δ 155.2, 150.6, 131.8, 130.1, 110.0.

Mass, *m/e* (CI) 253 (*m* + 1, 100), 237 (29), 221 (57), 204 (10), 192 (17), 164 (43), 138 (52), 137 (46), 110 (28), 108 (28), 95 (23), 71 (29), 55 (45).

UV (methanol) λ_{max} = 216 nm, 248, 279, 351.
(0.1 N NaOH)   221 (sh), 232, 290, 315.
(0.1 N HCl)   211, 262, 290.

IR (KBr) 1617 cm^{-1}, 1458, 1398, 1349, 1311, 1252, 1186, 1147, 1070, 1028, 988, 877, 836, 755.

Orelline[a]

Bright yellow crystals. Slowly decomposes >310-320°C; sublimes 180°C/0.2 mm. Soluble in DMSO; almost insoluble in most common organic solvents.

^{1}H-NMR (DMSO-d_6) δ 7.9 (d, 1 H, J = 5.5 Hz), 6.9 (d, 1 H, J = 5.5 Hz), 9.5-10.8 (broad s, 2 H).

^{13}C-NMR (DMSO-d_6) δ 155.5, 145.8, 137.2, 136.4, 111.1.

Mass, *m/e* (CI) 221 (*m* + 1, 91), 203 (100), 192 (43.5), 151 (22), 138 (45), 137 (38), 136 (30), 110 (38), 95 (45), 70 (48).

UV (methanol) λ_{max} = 216 nm, 344, 390.
(0.1 N HCl)   305, 248, 212.

IR (KBr) 1596 cm^{-1}, 1507, 1443, 1314, 1277, 1211, 1090, 973, 907, 832, 795, 775.

Orellinine[b]

Almost colorless. Stable to 160-170°C. At higher temperatures or on exposure to UV light, decomposes to orelline. Soluble in alkaline and acid solutions and DMSO. Slightly soluble methanol. Almost insoluble in water and common organic solvents.

^{1}H-NMR (DMSO-d_6) δ 9.2-8.2 broad (s, 2 H), 8.05 (d, 1 H, J = 7.0 Hz), 8.0 (d, 1 H, J = 5.5 Hz), 6.95 (d, 1 H, J = 7.0 Hz).

^{13}C-NMR (DMSO-d_6) δ 159.2, 151.8, 147.3 147.1 136.0 133.4, 131.1, 130.5, 110.8, 110.4.

Mass, *m/e* (CI) 237 (50), 221 (27), 192 (46), 164 (51), 138 (27), 137 (19), 111 (13), 95 (13), 70 (11).

UV (methanol) λ_{max} = 213 nm, 267, 342.
(0.1 N NaOH)   223, 305.
(0.1 N HCl)   209, 267, 281 (sh).

[a]Data from Tiecco et al. (1986), except IR spectra from Dehmlow and Schulz (1987).
[b]Data from Tiecco et al. 1987).

cerned that the mushroom might be toxic, so he brings one of the uneaten
mushrooms and the asymptomatic child to the emergency room. In the absence
of a consulting mycologist, the usual situation, the physician's question is:
"Does this mushroom contain *anything* that is seriously toxic such that intervention is required?" On the other hand, a patient presenting with impending renal failure and a vague history of sampling various local flora on a camp
ing trip, the question to be resolved is: "Might this be an orellanine intoxication?" Since in this instance no collection of the materials consumed is available, the answer must be sought in the blood, urine, or in biopsied renal
tissue. The answer is of interest primarily to rule out another etiology to
which there may be continuing exposure and as a limited guide to prognosis.
In either clinical situation, the answer must be obtainable by the usual hospital laboratory, in a timely fashion, and not require special apparatus, train-
ing, or unusual chemicals (including an orellanine standard). At the moment,
quantitative data would be of no value to the clinician because such data will
not influence the clinical management.

The research scientist, however, requires unequivocal identification of
the toxin, generally in the mushroom specimen but, sometimes, in the tissues
of research animals. Other than specificity, the requirements for sensitivity
or quantitative information will vary with the purpose of the research. The
development of analytical methods for the nephrotoxin in *Cortinarius* was ham-
pered by arguments concerning the number of toxins in the mushrooms and
if all their blue fluorescent components were both toxic and had identical
pathologic effects. There was a lack of appreciation of the ease of photodecomposition of orellanine and the distinction between it and orelline. Many
of these were not resolved completely until about 1988.

A quick qualitative test to be used by medical personnel for demonstrating whether an unknown mushroom contains orellanine has been suggested
(Schumacher and Høiland, 1983). The fresh or dried mushroom is crushed
in water, allowed to stand for 10 min, then filtered. The filtrate is mixed
with an equal volume of 3% ferric chloride hexahydrate dissolved in 0.5 N hydrochloric acid. If the solution turns a dark gray blue (like dilute ink), the
mushroom is presumed to contain orellanine.

A more rigorous test requires methanol-water extraction of the mushroom
under conditions in which ultraviolet light is excluded. The extract is analyzed by thin-layer chromatography on a cellulose support with a solvent composed (v/v) of *n*-butanol-acetic acid-water (3:1:1). An orellanine standard
is run simultaneously. Orellanine (R_f 0.57) and orelline (R_f 0.42) are detected by exposure of the chromatogram to UV light (366 nm). Orellanine
will appear initially as a dark spot. After exposure to ultraviolet light for
1 to 3 min it will photodecompose to produce the bluish-white fluorescence
characteristic of orelline. The detection limit is about 10 ng (Andary et al.,
1986; Rapior et al., 1988).

In an animal study, rats given *Cortinarius orellanus* orally had detectable
quantities of orellanine in the urine only during the first 24 h. In this study,
50 μL of urine was applied to a cellulose layer TLC plate. The developing
solvent was butanol-acetic acid-water (3:1:1). The presence of orellanine
was verified by a turquoise blue band at R_f 0.68 under UV exposure (Prast
and Pfaller, 1988).

Only two reports could be found of attempts to measure the toxins in patients. Blue UV-fluorescence was detected in the proximal tubules in the

kidney of a child who died as the result of *C. orellanus* poisoning. This finding was replicated in guinea pigs administered dried mushrooms, 0.9 to 1.3 g/kg (Bouška et al., 1980). In an adult patient who was hospitalized 9 days after the ingestion of *C. orellanus*, an attempt was made to detect the toxin in the blood and urine collected on the day of admission and from an extract from renal biopsies made 13 days and 6 months after the ingestion (Andary et al., 1989). The urine, after concentration, and the blood plasma, loaded directly, were passed through an Amberlite XAD column as described by these authors earlier (Rapior et al., 1987). The tissue sample was homogenized with methanol-water, centrifuged, and the supernatant passed through the column. Orellanine was sought by fluorimetry on two-dimensional cellulose thin-layer chromatograms by a method reported previously (Andary et al., 1986). As would be anticipated, no orellanine or its photodecomposition products were found in the urine. The concentration of orellanine in the plasma sample was 6 mg/L. The concentration of orellanine was 7 µg in 25 µL in the first biopsy and 24 µg in 8 µL in the second.

Orellanine can be quantified by spectrofluorimetry, excitation wavelength 396 nm, fluorescent emission at 447 nm (Prast et al., 1988). A technically more difficult approach has been described by Cantin et al. (1988) using differential pulse polarography. The authors state that they are developing a procedure to couple this detection system, which gives a linear peak current to concentration relationship between 10^{-6} and 10^{-7} M orellanine, to a high-performance liquid chromatography (HPLC) system. Another system with a detection limit of 500 pg of orellanine using reversed-phase HPLC coupled with an electrochemical detector was described by Holmdahl et al. (1987).

G. Other Proposed Toxins

Testa (1970, 1982), Gérault (1976), and Kürnsteiner and Moser (1981) conducted chromatographic investigation on *C. orellanus*. They proposed that toxins other than or in addition to orellanine were present in the mushroom and suggested that the principal toxicity resided with one or more peptides. The early recognition that chromatograms of toxic species of *Cortinarius* were associated with fluorescence also became complex with the publication of a catalog of fluorescent substances in the genus *Cortinarius* subgenus *Leprocybe* (to which *C. orellanus* belongs), showing many species to have similar fluorescent spots on their chromatograms (Gruber, 1969).

Caddy and Tebbett, of the Forensic Science Unit at the University of Strathclyde in Glasgow, Scotland, became interested following the first such poisoning in Scotland from *C. speciosissimus* reported by Short et al. (1980). Since, as they remark in their initial paper, there was a general consensus that toxicity resided with those compounds that show fluorescence when irradiated with ultraviolet light, they sought to isolate the compound that on a chromatogram of a methanolic extract from *C. speciosissimus* consistently exhibited a single bright blue fluorescence when irradiated at 254 nm (Caddy et al., 1982). The substance was isolated by preparative TLC and by column chromatography. Elemental analysis showed the presence of carbon, hydrogen, oxygen (by inference), sulfur, nitrogen, and chlorine. When treated with a neutral solution of ferric chloride there was no reaction, but with the addition of hydrochloric acid an orange color developed. Neutral ninhydrin spray was nonreactive but gave a purple color if the TLC plate was pretreated with hydrochloric acid for 2 min at 100°C. An acid hydrolysate of the isolated material was subjected to analysis by an automated amino acid analyzer, which indicated the presence of threonine, ornithine, phenylalanine, lysine, glycine, alanine, valine, isoleucine, leucine, tyrosine, and one other unidentified compound. Infrared, ultraviolet, NMR, and mass spectra were not contributory. The fluorescence spectrum showed maximum excitation at 327 nm and a maximum emission at 378 nm.

The authors screened methanol extracts of 61 of some 250 British species of *Cortinarius* by thin-layer chromatography with three different developing solvents seeking the substance they had isolated from *C. speciosissimus*. Included in the study were species from each of the seven subgenera of *Cortinarius* (Tebbett and Caddy, 1983; Tebbett et al., 1983). Extracts from 60 of these showed the presence of a single blue fluorescent spot when examined by ultraviolet light at 254 nm, at the same R_f as that of the reference material isolated from *C. speciosissimus*. There were interspecies concentration differences as reflected by differences in the intensity of fluorescence. Only *C. violaceus*, the single representative of *Cortinarius* subgenus *cortinarius* tested, did not exhibit fluorescence.

In one of their 1983 papers, the toxin was labeled cortinarin A (Tebbett and Caddy, 1983). All species containing cortinarin A contained a second, nonfluorescent substance, labeled cortinarin C. It was considered structurally related to cortinarin A, but probably not toxic. Cortinarin B, a nephrotoxic compound found only in *C. orellanus*, *C. speciosissimus*, and *C. orellanoides*, was announced later (Tebbett and Caddy, 1984a). Cortinarin B also exhibited blue fluorescence. The concentration of cortinarins in these three species is shown in Table 3. The structures of the two toxic cortinarins are shown in Fig. 2. Details of the structure studies are given by Tebbett and Caddy (1984b). All of the amino acids in these cyclic peptides are in the L-configuration except for D-threonine.

A dose of 5 mg of cortinarin A was given intraperitoneally to an unspecified number of male BKA mice. One died after 4 days. The remaining mice, sacrificed after 2 weeks, showed mild to severe kidney damage of an unspecified nature. Mice given 5 mg of cortinarin B intraperitoneally showed similar renal damage, two mice dying after 4 days. The kidneys of the poisoned mice exhibited a blue fluorescence under UV light. The material in the kidneys was extracted and its UV spectrum examined. The extract from both the cortinarin A- and cortinarin B-poisoned animals appeared to contain the sulfoxide

TABLE 3 Concentrations of Cortinarins Expressed as Percent Dry Weight Mushroom

Species	Cortinarin A	Cortinarin B	Cortinarin C
Cortinarius orellanus	0.42	0.52	0.24
Cortinarius orellanoides	0.45	0.47	0.20
Cortinarius speciosissimus	0.47	0.60	0.20

Source: After Tebbett and Caddy (1984a).

```
    ┌─Phe──HN──CH──CO─Val─Orn
    │       R      │CH₂              │
    │      ⌬───⌬                     │
Lys │      │   │  N  S               Leu
    │      ⌬───⌬  H   ＼CH₂          │
    │                       │        │
    └─Gly──Thr─OC─CH──NH──IsoLeu
                     '
```

FIGURE 2 R = OCH$_3$, cortinarin A; R = OH, cortinarin B.

of cortinarin B. The authors propose, although without additional evidence, that S-oxidation occurs prior to renal toxicity. Unfortunately, the authors conducted no tests in which cortinarin A or B was administered orally.

A thorough reinvestigation of *C. orellanus* and *C. speciosissimus* was undertaken to determine whether these mushrooms contained one or more toxins (Prast et al., 1988). Polar and apolar solvents were employed for extraction. All extracts were examined for toxicity and compared to homogenates of the whole mushroom. Two toxins were identified, orellanine and a rapidly acting toxin. The rapid-acting toxin (maximum latency, 10 h) was nonfluorescent. It was not active orally. Following intraperitoneal administration at high doses, it produced a neurotoxic response. Its chemical identity was not pursued. Other than orellanine, no fluorescent compounds, or compounds developing fluorescence by UV exposure, were discovered that exhibited a toxic action. The cyclic peptides, cortinarins A and B, described by Tebbett and Caddy could not be detected. The oral toxicity in mice for a mushroom homogenate showed exact correspondence to its orellanine content. It was concluded that the nephrotoxicity of these *Cortinarius* species is due solely to orellanine.

IV. SPECIES DISTRIBUTION OF ORELLANINE

Orellanine and its degradation products have been found only in *Cortinarius* species, subgenus *Leprocybe* section *Orellani* (Høiland, 1980; Keller-Dilitz et al., 1985; Rapior et al., 1988) (Table 4). Extraction of the dried mushrooms was conducted in the dark to avoid photodecomposition of orellanine. Rapior et al. (1988) recommend the use of methanol-water as the extraction solvent. The extracts were analyzed by thin-layer chromatography using various solvent systems. Comparison was made to a reference standard of orellanine by UV fluorescence at 366 nm. After 1 to 3 min of exposure, the dark spot corresponding to orellanine decomposed to the bluish-white fluorescence characteristic of orelline. The detection limit for orellanine was approximately 10 ng.

Rapior et al. (1988) also examined but did not find orellanine in a large number of species examined from other sections of *Leprocybe*, in subgenus *Phlegmacium*, or in species of *Dermocybe*. They discuss the possible synonymy between *C. speciosissimus* and *C. orellanoides*, but these will be considered distinct species for this review. Also considered was the anomalous position of *C. fulvaureus*.

TABLE 4 Detection of Orellanine in *Cortinarius* Species, Subgenus *Leprocybe*, Section *Orellani*

Species	Collection site	Orellanine present
C. brunneofulvus Fr. sensu Bres.	Italy	+
C. fluorescence Horak	Chile	+
C. fulvaureus R. Hry.	France	-
C. henrici Reum.	France	+
C. orellanoides R. Hry.	France	+
C. orellanus (Fr.) Fries	France	+
C. rainierensis Smith and Stuntz	U.S.A.	+
C. speciosissimus Kühn. and Romagn.	France	+

Source: After Rapior et al. (1988).

V. BIOLOGICAL ACTIVITY OF ORELLANINE

A. Toxicity and Pathophysiology

Although by early 1989 over 200 cases of human poisoning have been reported, there is little data to provide an estimate of the relationship of quantity of mushroom ingestion to the severity of poisoning. It is estimated that about 100 to 200 g of fresh *C. orellanus* may cause permanent renal failure in an adult. A number of studies have been conducted in animals with dried mushroom homogenates and with orellanine. Selected recent data are shown in Table 5, which includes Grzymała's experiments with his crystallized toxin for comparison.

In the first clinical description of human poisoning by *C. orellanus*, Grzymała noted the prolonged latency between ingestion and symptom onset, rarely 2 days, usually 3 to 17 days (Grzymała, 1959b, 1965a). The higher the quantity of mushrooms consumed, the shorter the latent period. The prolonged latent period is also seen in animals, although in this instance, measurement from administration of mushroom homogenate to death is usually recorded. In mice, for example, the administration of homogenates of dried *C. orellanus* or *C. speciosissimus*, even in doses far in excess of the LD_{100}, did not cause death earlier than 5 days (Prast et al., 1988).

Numerous studies have been made of the pathophysiology of orellanine or whole mushrooms in animals, only a few of which will be described. In all contemporary studies, the kidney has been shown to be the sole target of injury. Following a 2-g/kg dose of dried *C. orellanus* homogenate suspended in water, the first changes observed by light microscopy in the rat kidney are seen after a latent period of about 12 h (Prast and Pfaller, 1988). Vacuoles appeared within the proximal tubular cells of all segments. Cytoplasmic protrusions into the tubular lumen and irregularities in the brush border region of the proximal nephron could be seen. Electron microscopy revealed a shortening and deformation of the microvilli and enhanced vacuolization of

TABLE 5 Toxicity of Orellanine and Dried *Cortinarius* Mushroom Homogenates

Toxin	Species	Route	(ref.)	LD$_{50}$		LD$_{100}$		Remarks
Orellanine	Mouse	SC	(a)	8.3	mg/kg			Male mice
		PO	(b)	33	mg/kg	109	mg/kg	Female mice
		PO	(c)	90	mg/kg			Male mice
		IP	(b)	15	mg/kg	42	mg/kg	Male mice
		IP	(c)	12.5	mg/kg			Female mice
	Cat	PO	(a)	8.3	mg/kg			
	Guinea pig	IP	(a)	8	mg/kg			
C. orellanus	Mouse	PO	(b)	2.2	g/kg	4.57	g/kg	Containing 14 mg/g orellanine; male mice
		PO	(c)	2.1	g/kg			Containing 15-20 mg/kg orellanine; female mice
	Rat	PO	(d)	0.976	g/kg			Containing 15-20 mg/g orellanine; male rats
C. speciosissimus	Mouse	PO	(b)	3.12	g/kg	6.22	g/kg	Containing 9 mg/g orellanine; male mice

Refs.: (a) Grzymała (1962), (b) Prast et al. (1988), (c) Richard et al. (1988), (d) Prast and Pfaller (1988).

the apical cell pole in the proximal tubule. No changes were detected in the distal tubule or collecting duct. After 24 to 48 h, tissue injury was distributed over the entire cortex. Nests of prenecrotic and necrotic cells appeared in the proximal and distal tubules. Changes in the brush border, rarefaction, and deformation of the microvilli became more pronounced. The apical cell poles of the proximal tubules showed enhanced vacuolization and an increased number of lysosomal structures, dilation of the endoplasmic reticulum, and reduction in the number of ribosomes. The smooth endoplasmic reticulum sometimes appeared to form large clumps. The mitochondria were swollen and displayed disrupted cristae and sometimes flocculent densities. The changes were found only occasionally in the distal tubular epithelium and in the collecting ducts. In an earlier study seeking ultrastructural changes in the glomeruli, none could be identified (Prast et al., 1983).

These findings were similar to those of Lahtiperä et al. (1986), who administered 500 mg/kg dried *C. speciosissimus* orally to rats. Groups of rats were sacrificed at intervals of 4 h; 2, 5, and 7 days; and 2 months. The renal tissue was examined by electron microscopy. At 4 h there was a slight increase in the number of lysosomes in the epithelial cells of the cortical proximal tubules. By 2 days, the proximal tubular cells exhibited dilation of the endoplasmic reticulum, mitochondrial swelling with broken cristae, and a significant increase in lysosomes. At 5 days, all tubules examined showed cellular necrosis. A dense, fingerprintlike or lamellar nuclear structure, often surrounded by granular heterochromatin, was seen in some nuclei of the tubular cells. There was a decreased number of ribosomes in the tubular cells and swollen mitochondria with disrupted cristae. Some of the tubular cells were detached from the basal lamina. By 10 days, tubular regeneration had started. At 2 months, the most prominent feature was bundles of collagen surrounding the interstitial cells.

Both orally and intraperitoneally administered orellanine produced identical histological changes in mouse kidney with light microscopy (Richard et al., 1988). In contrast to rats, damage with minimally toxic doses in the mouse involved primarily the distal tubules of the outermost layer of the cortex (cortex corticis). The cytoplasm of the tubular epithelial cells was vacuolar and the nuclei swollen. The remainder of the cortical region, glomeruli, and proximal tubules appeared undamaged. The differences in target area observed in the mouse and the rat were not commented upon by these authors. It may reflect a different reabsorption site that is species specific.

Almost no details have been given concerning the renal damage in human intoxications beyond the description of acute interstitial nephritis with tubular necrosis but glomerular sparing. The biopsy reports of two patients with *C. speciosissimus* in Sweden describes the changes as most severe in the outer medullary region (Holmdahl et al., 1980). Raszeja (1960) described the action in the human kidney as resembling a case of mercury intoxication, which is associated with acute interstitial nephritis and destruction of the proximal tubules.

Few histochemical studies have been conducted on the affected renal tissue. Nieminen et al. (1975) examined the arginine-residue-cleaving-aminopeptidase activity and the valine-residue-cleaving-aminopeptidase activity on frozen tissue sections of rats poisoned with *C. speciosissimus*. The activities of arginine-aminopeptidase and valine-aminopeptidase were both decreased in the necrotic tubules of the cortex; however, the decrease in the activity of valine-aminopeptidase could be observed within 2 days, whereas the diminished arginine-aminopeptidase activity became evident only after 4 days. In orellanine-intoxicated rats (Prast and Pfaller, 1988) there was continuous increase in excretion of sodium, glucose, and protein. Potassium excretion was enhanced only slightly during the first 24 h but later returned to control values. The activity of γ-glutamyltranspeptidase activity in the urine was slightly decreased.

The Finnish investigators working with homogenized dry specimens of C. *speciosissimus* administered orally to rats in dose ranges below the LD_{50} noted considerable variation between animals in their sensitivity, some animals developing severe renal damage and others no damage at all (Möttönen et al., 1975; Nieminen and Pyy, 1976a). These investigations used male rats only. A new study, in which female rats were included, showed a sex difference in the distribution of damage within the kidney (Nieminen and Pyy, 1976b). Interstitial infiltrates in the medulla were comparable to those in males. The principal lesions in the females were necrotic changes in the inner cortex appearing either at the same time as the medullary infiltrates or as the sole histologic finding. Necrotic changes in the inner cortex of the male first appeared after 3 to 4 days, compared to 2 days in the female, and only in those males that also had interstitial changes in the medulla. No additional follow-up seems to have been made concerning these observations.

B. Studies on Mechanism

No satisfactory hypothesis has been accepted to explain the specificity and toxicity exhibited by orellanine. A number of studies have been conducted that at least eliminate some possible mechanisms or show avenues of approach that may prove fruitful. Since the chemical structure then proposed for orellanine resembled that of the herbicides paraquat (1,1'-dimethyl-4,4'-bipyridinium dichloride) and diquat (6,7-dihydrodipyido[1,2-a:2',1'-c]pyrazinediium dibromide), evidence was sought seeking a similar mechanism of action. Paraquat and diquat interfere with photosynthesis by inhibition of the conversion of NADP to NADPH and interfering with electron transport. Although their mechanism of toxic action in animals and humans has not been verified, it is assumed generally that the cellular reduction in NADPH content renders animal cells more sensitive to attack by lipid hyperperoxides.

Lemna minor L., duckweed, a bioassay organism used for herbicides, was adapted by floating shoots of *L. minor* on aqueous extracts of powdered, dry fruiting bodies of various *Cortinarius* species (Høiland, 1983). Some of the culture dishes were exposed to a 60-W light bulb at a distance of 50 cm; others had light excluded. Only the plants exposed to both light and the extract from C. *speciosissimus* were affected. The author suggested a redox reaction mechanism for orellanine similar to that of these herbicide models. Orellanine might act as the primary electron receptor in the photosynthetic pathway, thereby blocking the reduction of NADP.

This hypothesis was examined by another group of investigators (Richard et al., 1987, 1988; Cantin et al., 1988). Although a similar inhibition of photosynthesis could be observed with isolated chloroplasts from spinach, orellanine, unlike paraquat, was ineffective in this regard on osmotically rup-

tured chloroplasts (thylakoids). Polarographic investigation indicated that
the electrochemical reduction of orellanine and paraquat are not alike. Orellanine is reduced only with difficulty and does not form a stable radical. Neither
electrons derived from water nor from NADPH can reduce orellanine. It was
concluded that the ability of orellanine to affect photosynthesis of the intact
chloroplast did not involve interference with the electron transfer chain. In
addition, orellanine did not inhibit electron transfer in the mitochondria and
did not uncouple oxidative phosphorylation. In a recent report (Cantin et al.,
1988), the authors conclude that since cyclic voltametry showed that the reduction of orellanine is highly irreversible, the mechanism of toxicity had
to differ from paraquat, which is dependent on reoxidation for its activity.

A major effort was made to determine structure-activity relationships for
substituted pyridines at a time when its proposed structure had not been verified by synthesis (Richard et al., 1985). The quantitative structure-activity
relationship (QSAR) compared the LD_{50} expressed as moles per kilogram of
each compound administered by intraperitoneal injection to female mice. The
Hansch-Fujita equation, $\log 1/C = K_1 X + K_2 X^2 + K_3 Y + K_4 Z + K_5$, was used
to determine the relationship between the toxicity (C) and the physical parameters, hydrophobicity (X), electronic effects (Y), and steric effects (Z).
The regression coefficients are represented by K. Twenty-one compounds
were investigated. These included hydroxy- and methyl-substituted pyridines and bipyridyls and their corresponding N-oxides. Various groupings
of these comounds were compared to the compound now established as the
structure for orellanine. The results suggest that the toxic mechanism for
orellanine must be different from all other molecules in the tested series.

The compounds 2,2'- and 4,4'-dipyridyl produce kidney damage (Groce
and Kimbrough, 1982). In an initial effort to examine the mechanism of orellanine toxicity, a preliminary study was undertaken with these simpler compounds using renal cell cultures (Gstraunthaler and Prast, 1983). Two separate epithelial cell lines derived from pig kidney were employed, $LLC-PK_1$,
presumed to be of proximal tubule origin, and MDCK, presumed to be of distal tubule origin. These cultures retain the morphological properties of the
tubular epithelium, building monolayers of differentiated and polarized cells
with the formation of tight junctions. On their apical surface the cells exhibit high levels of activity of the enzymes of the brush border membrane,
γ-glutamyl-transpeptidase, alkaline phosphatase, and leucine-aminopeptidase.

This was followed by another study in which the toxicity of orellanine was
evaluated (Heufler et al., 1984). The cytotoxic ED_{50} at 24 h evaluated for
orellanine on the proximal tubule cell line was 2×10^{-4} M. No effects were
seen at 24 h on the distal tubular cell line; there were effects after 48 h (ED_{50}
$= 2 \times 10^{-3}$ M) or 72 h ($ED_{50} = 10^{-4}$ M). Changes in enzyme activity were noted.

Because of the greater specificity of orellanine for the cell culture presumably derived from the proximal tubule, an expanded investigation was
made using that cell culture exclusively (Heufler et al., 1987). The major
purpose was to examine the effect of orellanine on DNA and protein synthesis
and its effects on ATP and NADPH. Orellanine was more toxic to growing
cells than to the confluent monolayer. Within 5 h, orellanine caused a moderate decrease in the incorporation of [3H]-leucine and [3H]-thymidine. ATP
and NADPH were unaffected during the first 24 h. After 24 h, the activity
of alkaline phosphatase and lactate dehydrogenase were reduced equally. The

cell membranes retained integrity (impermeability to trypan blue) even after monolayer disruption was initiated. It will be of interest to follow future work with orellanine by this technique.

The exposure of orellanine to ultraviolet light (366 nm) causes its N-deoxidation to the nontoxic molecule orelline. This photodecomposition was examined by high-field ^{1}NMR (360 MHz) of a saturated solution of orellanine (DMSO-d_6). The authors concluded that intermediate isoxazoliniums are formed that could bind covalently to proteins leading to organ damage (Andary et al., 1986). The authors assumed a coplanar bipyridyl for orellanine, now known not to be its configuration. The proposed mechanism does not address the specificity of the toxin for the kidney.

The action of an extract of *C. speciosissimus*, partially purified by filtration to remove substances with a molecular weight greater than 10,000, on ion-induced pinocytosis of *Amoeba proteus* was investigated (Ahlmén et al., 1983). Pretreatment of the amoeba with the extract reduced the capacity of the cells to form pinocytotic channels and reduced the pinocytotic response to sodium chloride. The morphologic appearance, motility, and substrate attachment of the amoeba remained normal. The mushroom extract had no effect on potassium or UV light-induced pinocytosis. Calcium ions reduced the potency of the extract. The authors suggested that the toxin acted by interfering with calcium-dependent pinocytosis and, therefore, may act in the ischemic kidney by altering cytosolic calcium concentration.

Orellanine itself did not modify fluid-phase pinocytosis of the cellular slime mold amoeba, *Dictyostelium discoideum*, or phagocytosis by the bacterium, *Escherichia coli* (Klein et al., 1986). However, orellanine did stop cell growth in both cultures. The authors suggested that the target of the toxin is likely to be a cellular process common to both prokaryotic and eukaryotic cells. They speculated that the inhibition of pinocytosis observed by Ahlmén et al. (1983) must have been due to other molecules present in the mushroom extract and not due to the action of orellanine. The effects of various drugs on renal damage induced by *C. speciosissimus* in the rat have been determined. This rather interesting approach to the examination of the mechanism of orellanine toxicity does not appear to have been pursued since 1976.

Cyclophosphamide given as a single intraperitoneal dose of 150 mg/kg at the same time as the oral administration of an aqueous suspension of homogenized dried mushroom to the male rat prevented inflammation in the outer medullary zone (Nieminen et al., 1976a). There was a reduction also in fibrosis about the collecting tubules. Since cyclophosphamide requires about 7 to 14 days to affect the hepatic microsomal enzymes, this effect cannot be ascribed to a failure of metabolic activation of a toxin by the liver. Earlier studies (Hulmi et al., 1974) had ruled out an immunologic basis for *Cortinarius* toxicity, so the ability of cyclophosphamide to act as an immunosuppressive agent was not considered important. However, the ability of cyclophosphamide to decrease peripheral leukocyte mobilization could contribute to the diminished inflammatory response.

The effect on renal toxicity in rats by the mushroom extract was investigated after 11 days of pretreatment with phenobarbital (Nieminen, 1976b). Phenobarbital increased the tubular necrosis in the inner cortex but did not affect the tubules in the outer cortex or the degree of inflammation in the outer medullary zone. The glomeruli remained normal. The response with phenobarbital deserves repetition of the study with orellanine. It certainly is suggestive of metabolic action, perhaps in the renal tissue. It had been proposed in the literature that the observed action of phenylbutazone to reduce toxicity in animals to another mushroom, *Amanita phalloides*, might be beneficial in *Cortinarius* intoxication. The proposed mechanism in *Amanita* poisoning was a reduction of protein binding sites, thereby enhancing renal excretion of the toxin. In a companion experiment, the effect of 50- and 100-mg/kg subcutaneous doses of phenylbutazone given 1 h prior to oral administration of a *Cortinarius* mushroom extract was determined. This treatment had no effect on *Cortinarius*-induced pathology.

Finally, the influence of furosemide on mushroom-induced renal damage in female rats was explored (Nieminen et al., 1976b; Nieminen, 1976a). Co-administration of furosemide caused marked necrotic changes in the tubules of the outer cortical layer, whereas in animals receiving only the mushroom the outer cortex was clear. The authors point out the potential danger of using furosemide in human *Cortinarius* poisoning (it was employed, for example, in the patient described by Andary et al in their 1989 article in *Lancet*). The authors also make the interesting comparative observation that furosemide also increases the severity of the proximal tubular damage produced by the then-available antibiotic cephaloridine. Tune and Fravert (1980) found that this antibiotic accumulates in the proximal tubule and proposed that the drug enters the contraluminal side of the cell by passive diffusion but cannot then be actively secreted through the luminal surface since it forms a zwitterion. Probenecid, which blocks entrance through the contraluminal surface, prevents renal damage by cephaloridine. The mechanism for the increase of toxicity by the coadministration of furosemide has not been resolved. It would be of interest to puruse these observations as applied to orellanine.

VI. PROGNOSIS AND MANAGEMENT OF INTOXICATIONS

In the original report of 132 cases of intoxication by *C. orellanus* in Poland, there were 19 fatalities (Grzymala, 1959b, 1965a). Death from renal failure usually occurred in the second or third week after onset of symptoms. However, death could be delayed for some months, or in children, death could occur after only a few days. In almost all these cases, the onset of symptoms appeared within 3 to 4 days after ingestion of the mushroom. In cases of very mild intoxication, usually associated with a long latent period of 10 to 17 days, the patient did not require hospitalization. These cases were characterized by a burning dryness of the mouth with intense thirst and a moderate degree of polyuria resolving after a few days. Intermediate-onset cases are more serious, but signs and symptoms usually resolve in 3 to 4 weeks, although the dry mouth and thirst may persist longer.

There is no specific therapy. If the development of impending renal failure is recognized early, dialysis should be instituted in an attempt to permit recovery of renal function (Färber and Feldmeier, 1977; Short et al., 1980; Holmdahl et al., 1984). Since evidence in animals indicates that orellanine is no longer present in the urine after the first 24 h, there seems to be no advantage to conducting extracorporeal hemoperfusion through resin for removal of the toxin after this period, as has been suggested by Heath et al.

(1980). The same consideration probably applies as well to plasma exchange as sued by Busnach et al. (1983). Patients who do not recover adequate renal function, of course, will require permanent intermittent dialysis or renal transplant.

REFERENCES

Ahlmén, J., Holmdahl, J., Josefsson, J.-O., and Nässberger, L. (1983). Inhibition of pinocytosis by *Cortinarius speciosissimus* toxins. *Acta Pharmacol. Toxicol.* 52:238-240.

Andary, C., Rapior, S., Fruchier, A., and Privat, G. (1986). Cortinaires de la section *Orellani*: photodécomposition et hypothèse de la photo-toxicité de l'orellanine. *Cryptogram. Mycol.* 7:189-200.

Andary, C., Rapior, S., Delpech, N., and Huchard, G. (1989). Laboratory confirmation of *Cortinarius* poisoning. *Lancet* 1:213.

Antkowiak, W. Z., and Gessner, W. P. (1975). Isolation and characteristics of toxic components of *Cortinarius orellanus* Fries. *Bull. Acad. Pol. Sci., Ser. Sci. Chim.* 23:729-733.

Antkowiak, W. Z., and Gessner, W. P. (1978). Structure elucidation of orellanine. *11th IUPAC Int. Symp. Chem. Nat. Prod.* 2:45-47.

Antkowiak, W. Z., and Gessner, W. P. (1979). The structures of orellanine and orelline. *Tetrahedron Lett.* 21:1931-1934.

Antkowiak, W. Z., and Gessner, W. P. (1985). Photodecomposition of orellanine and orellinine, the fungal toxins of *Cortinarius orellanus* Fries and *Cortinarius speciosissimus*. *Experientia* 41:769-771.

Azéma, R. C. (1981). Sur des empoisonnements causes par *Cortinarius speciosissimus*. *Bull. Soc. Mycol. Fr.* 97:73-76.

Ballesteros, P., Claramunt, R. M., and Elguero, J. (1988). An improved synthesis of 2-chloro-3-methoxy-4-nitropyridine N-oxide, intermediate for the preparation of orellanine. *An. Quim. C84*:53-54.

Bouška, I., Řehánek, L., Veselský, J., and Cuřík, R. (1979). Diagnostické problémy při otravě houbou pavucincem plysovým (*Cortinarius orellanus* Fr.) s nefrotickým účinkem. *Soudni Lek.* 24(2):27-32.

Bouška, I., Řehánek, L., Motyčka, K., and Veselský, J. (1980). Průkaz UV-fluorescence ve tkáních ledviny u otravy pavucincem plysovým— *Cortinarius orellanus* Fr. *Ceska Mykol.* 34:188-190.

Bresinsky, A., and Besl, H. (1985). *Giftpilze mit einer Einführung in die Pilzbestimmung: Ein Handbuch für Apotheker, Arzte und Biologen.* Wissenschaftliche Verlagsgesellschaft, Stuttgart, West Germany, pp. 50-61.

Brousse, A., Herve, J. P., Leguy, P., Cledes, J., and Leroy, J. P. (1981). L'Intoxication par champignons de type *Cortinarius orellanus*: une cause rare d'insuffisance rénale. *Nouv. Presse Med.* 10:1940.

Busnach, G., Dal Col, A., Perrino, M. L., Surian, M., Rovati, C., Barbiano di Belgioioso, G., and Minetti, L. (1983). Plasma exchange in acute renal failure by *Cortinarius speciosissimus*. *Int. J. Artif. Organs* 6 (Suppl. 1):73-74.

Caddy, B., Kidd, C. B. M., Robertson, J., Tebbett, I. R., Tilstone, W. J., and Watling, R. (1982). *Cortinarius speciosissimus* toxins—a preliminary report. *Experientia* 38:1439-1440.

Cantin, D., Richard, J.-M., Alary, J., and Serve, D. (1988). Electrochemical study of the mushroom toxin orellanine and of related pyridine-1-oxides: I. Reduction. *Electrochim. Acta 33*:1047-1059.

Cohen-Addad, C., Richard, J.-M., and Guitel, J.-C. (1987). Structure of orellanine-trifluoracetic acid complex: evidence of a very short O-H···O hydrogen bond. *Acta Crystallogr. C43*:504-507.

Colon, S., Deteix, P., Béruard, M., Gérault, A., Finaz, A., Zech, P., and Traeger, J. (1981). Insuffisance rénale aiguë au cours d'une intoxication collective par *Cortinarius splendens*: étude anatomo-clinique. *Nephrologie 2*:199.

Colon, S., Deteix, P., Béruard, M., Gérault, A., Finaz, A., Zech, P., and Traeger, J. (1982). *Cortinarius splendens* intoxication and acute renal failure: a clinico-pathological study. *Kidney Int. 21*:121-122 (abstract).

Dehmlow, E. V., and Schulz, H.-J. (1985). Synthesis of orellanine, the lethal poison of a toadstool. *Tetrahedron Lett. 26*:4903-4906.

Dehmlow, E. V., and Schulz, H.-J. (1987). Synthesen von hydroxylierten Bipyridinen: I. Das Pilztoxin Orellanin. *Liebigs Ann. Chem.* 857-861.

Färber, D., and Feldmeier, S. (1977). Die Orellanus-Pilzvergiftung im Kindesalter. *Anasth. Prax. 13*:87-92.

Farve, H., Leski, M., Christeler, P., Vollenweider, E., and Chatelanat, F. (1976). Le *Cortinarius orellanus*: un champignon toxique provoquant une insuffisance rénale aiguë retardée. *Schweiz. Med. Wochenschr. 106*: 1097-1102.

Fauchald, P., and Westlie, L. (1982). Slørsoppforgiftning. *Tiddskr. Nor. Laegeforen. 102*:15-16.

Finaz de Villaine, A. (1981). Intoxication collective par *Cortinarius splendens*, champignon toxique responsable d'une insuffisance rénale aiguë retardée: à propos de 17 cas. Thesis (Medicine), Lyon. [Cited by Pats et al. (1988).]

Flammer, R. (1982). Das Orellanus-Syndrom: Pilzvergiftung mit Niereninsuffizienz. *Schweiz. Med. Wochenschr. 112*:1181-1184.

Flammer, R. (1985). Das Orellanussyndrom: Tubulusatrophie nach Pilzgenuss. *Schweiz. Rundsch. Med. Prax. 74*: 985-987.

Gérault, A. (1976). Les champignons supérieurs et leurs intoxications. Thesis, University of Rennes, France.

Gérault, A. (1981). Intoxication collective de type orellanine provoquée par *Cortinarius splendens* R. Hy. *Bull. Soc. Mycol. Fr. 97*:67-72.

Groce, D. F., and Kimbrough, R. D. (1982). Acute and subacute toxicity in Sherman strain rats exposed to 4,4'- and 2,2'-dipyridyl. *J. Toxicol. Environ. Health 10*: 363-372.

Gruber, I. (1969). Fluoreszierende Stoffe der *Cortinarius*-Untergattung *Leprocybe*. *Z. Pilzk. 35*:249-261.

Grzymała, S. (1957). Erfahrungen mit *Dermocybe orellana* (Fr.) in Polen: B. Massenvergiftung durch den orangefuchsigen Hautkopf. *Z. Pilzk. 23*:139-142.

Grzymała, S. (1958). Uber Vergiftungen dur den Orangefuchsigen Hautkopf *Cortinarius (Dermocybe) orellanus* Fr. *Mykol. Mitteilungsblatt 2(2)*:3-6.

Grzymała, S. (1959a). Uber den Giftsoff des orangefuchsigen Hautkopfes (*Cortinarius orellanus* Fr.): 2. Mitteilung. *Mykol. Mitt. 3(1)*:1-3.

Grzymała, S. (1959b). Zur toxischen Wirkung des orangefuschsigen Hautkopfes (*Dermocybe orellana* Fr.). *Dtsch. Z. Gerichtl. Med. 49*:91-99.

Grzymała, S. (1962). L'Isolement de l'orellanine poison du *Cortinarius orellanus* Fries et l'étude de ses effets anatomo-pathologiques. *Bull. Soc. Mycol. Fr. 78*: 394-404.

Grzymała, S. (1965a). Etude clinique des intoxications par les champignons du genre *Cortinarius orellanus* Fr. *Bull. Med. Leg. Toxicol. Med. 8*: 60-70.

Grzymała, S. (1965b). L'Experimentation par la toxine. *Bull. Med. Leg. Toxicol. Med. 8*: 73-83.

Grzymała, S., and Fiksiński, R. (1960). Zastosowanie mikroelektrofiltracji do wytracania fazy dymnej produckt w termicznego roskładu orellaniny. *Postepy Hig. Med. Dosw. 14*: 699-702.

Gstraunthaler, G., and Prast, H. (1983). Studies on the nephrotoxicity of *Cortinarius orellanus* (Fr.) Fr.: the effect of dipyridyles on renal epithelial cell-cultures. *Sydowia Ann. Mycol. 36*: 53-58.

Harmaja, H. (1973). Tappavan myrkyllisiä lajeja löydetty seitikkien suvusta (*Cortinarius*). *Sienilehti* (Finland) *2*: 6-9. [Cited by Schumacher and Høiland (1983).]

Hasseberg, H.-A., and Gerlach, H. (1988). Synthese von Orellin. *Helv. Chim. Acta 71*: 957-963.

Heath, A., Delin, K., Edén, E., Mårtensson, E., Selander, D., Wickström, I., and Ahlmén, J. (1980). Hemoperfusion with Amberlite resin in the treatment of self-poisoning. *Acta Med. Scand. 207*: 455-460.

Heufler, C., Felmayer, G., and Prast, H. (1984). Effect of the fungustoxin orellanine on renal cell-cultures. *Hoppe-Seyler's Z. Physiol. Chem. 365*: 921 (abstract).

Heufler, C., Felmayer, G., and Prast, H. (1987). Investigations on the mode of action of the fungus toxin orellanine on renal cell cultures. *Agents Actions 21*: 203-208.

Høiland, K. (1980). *Cortinarius* subgenus *Leprocybe* in Norway. *Norw. J. Bot. 27*: 101-126.

Høiland, K. (1983). Extracts of *Cortinarius speciosissimus* affecting the photosynthetic apparatus of *Lemna minor*. *Trans. Br. Mycol. Soc. 81*: 633-635.

Høiland, K., and Schumacher, T. (1982). Nyere erfaringer med spiss giftslørsopp og slørsoppforgiftninger. *Våre Nyttevekster* (Norway) *77*: 6-17. [Cited by Schumacher and Høiland (1983).]

Holmdahl, J., Ahlmén, J., Svalander, C., Eriksson, J., and Bucht, H. (1980). Renal damage after intoxication with *Cortinarius* mushrooms. In *Toxicological Aspects*, A. Kovatsis (Ed.). Technika Studio, Thessalonika, Greece, pp. 155-163.

Holmdahl, J., Mulec, H., and Ahlmén, J. (1984). Acute renal failure after intoxication with *Cortinarius* mushrooms. *Hum. Toxicol. 3*: 309-313.

Holmdahl, J., Ahlmén, J., Bergek, S., Lundberg, S., and Persson, S. Å. (1987). Isolation and nephrotoxic studies of orellanine from the mushroom *Cortinarius speciosissimus*. *Toxicon 25*: 195-199.

Hulmi, S., Sipponen, P., Forsström, J., and Vilska, J. (1974). Seitikkisienen aiheuttama vakava munuaisvaurio. *Duodecim 90*: 1044-1050.

Keller-Dilitz, H., Moser, M., and Ammirati, J. F. (1985). Orellanine and other fluorescent compounds in the genus *Cortinarius*, section *Orellani*. *Mycologia 77*: 667-673.

Klein, G., Richard, J.-M., and Satre, M. (1986). Effect of a mushroom toxin, orellanine, on the cellular slime mold *Dictyostelium discoideum* and the bacterium *Escherichia coli*. *FEMS Microbiol. Lett. 33*:19-22.

Kubička, J. (1980). Giftige Schleierlinge (Gattung *Cortinarius*). *Ceska Mykol. 34*:3-8.

Kürnsteiner, H., and Moser, M. (1981). Isolation of a lethal toxin from *Cortinarius orellanus* Fr. *Mycopathologia 74*:65-72.

Lahtiperä, S., Naukkarinen, A., and Collan, Y. (1986). Mushroom poisoning due to *Cortinarius speciosissimus*: electron microscope study in rats. *Arch. Toxicol. Suppl. 9*:315-319.

Leski, M., Favre, H., Chatelanat, F., Vollenweider, E., and Baczko, A. M. (1976). Insuffisance rénale aiguë provoquée par l'ingestion d'un champignon: *Cortinarius orellanus*. *J. Urol. Nephrol. 82*:976-981.

Marichal, J.-F., Triby, F., Wiederkehr, J.-L., and Carbiener, R. (1977). Insuffisance rénale chronique après intoxication par champignons de type *Cortinarius orellanus* Fries: deux cas d'intoxication familiale. *Nouv. Presse Med. 6*:2973-2975.

Möttönen, M., Nieminen, L., and Heikkilä, H. (1975). Damage caused by two Finnish mushrooms, *Cortinarius speciosissimus* and *Cortinarius gentilis* on the rat kidney. *Z. Naturforsch. C 30*:668-671.

Nieminen, L. (1976a). Effects of drugs on mushroom poisoning induced in the rat by *Cortinarius speciosissimus*. *Arch. Toxicol. 35*:235-238.

Nieminen, L. (1976b). *The Nephrotoxicity of Cortinarius speciosissmus Gathered in Finland: An Experimental Study in the Rat*. University of Turku, Finland, pp. 1-33.

Nieminen, L., and Pyy, K. (1976a). Individual variation in mushroom poisoning induced in the male rat by *Cortinarius speciosissimus*. *Med. Biol. 54*:156-158.

Nieminen, L., and Pyy, K. (1976b). Sex differences in renal damage induced in the rat by the Finnish mushroom, *Cortinarius speciosissimus*. *Acta Pathol. Microbiol. Scand. A 84*:222-224.

Nieminen, L., Möttönen, M., Tirri, R., and Ikonen, S. (1975). Nephrotoxicity of *Cortinarius speciosissimus*: a histological and enzyme histochemical study. *Exp. Pathol. 11*:239-246.

Nieminen, L., Pyy, K., Tirri, R., and Laurila, H. (1976a). The effect of cyclophosphamide on the experimental inflammation induced by the toxic mushroom *Cortinarius speciosissimus* in the rat kidney. *Exp. Pathol. 12*:169-173.

Nieminen, L., Pyy, K., and Hirsimäki, Y. (1976b). The effect of furosemide on the renal damage induced by toxic mushroom *Cortinarius speciosissimus* in the rat. *Br. J. Exp. Pathol. 57*:400-403.

Nolte, S., Hufschmidt, C., Steinhauer, H., Rohrbach, R., and Künzer, W. (1987). Terminale Niereninsuffizienz durch interstitielle Nephritis nach Pilzvergiftung durch *Cortinarius speciosissimus*. *Monatsschr. Kinderheilkd. 135*:280-281.

Överås, J., Ulvund, M. J., Bakkevig, S., and Eiken, R. (1979). Poisoning in sheep induced by the mushroom *Cortinarius speciosissimus*. *Acta Vet. Scand. 20*:148-150.

Pats, B., Durrand, G., Bousser, J., Beauche, A., Nicand, E., Galliez, M., Thomas, R., and Giudicelli, C. P. (1988). Toxicologie automnale lors d'un exercice de survie: à propos d'une intoxication collective par champignons du type *Cortinarius orellanoide*. *Med. Armees 16*: 231-233.

Prast, H., and Pfaller, W. (1988). Toxic properties of the mushroom *Cortinarius orellanus* (Fries): II. Impairment of renal function in rats. *Arch. Toxicol. 62*: 89-96.

Prast, H., Gstraunthaler, G., and Pfaller, W. (1983). Die Nephrotoxizität des Pilzes *Cortinarius orellanus*. *Nieren-Hochdruckkr. 12*: 359-360. [Cited by Prast and Pfaller (1988).]

Prast, H., Werner, E. R., Pfaller, W., and Moser, M. (1988). Toxic properties of the mushroom *Cortinarius orellanus*: I. Chemical characterization of the main toxin of *Cortinarius orellanus* (Fries) and *Cortinarius speciosissimus* (Kühn. & Romagn.) and acute toxicity in mice. *Arch. Toxicol. 62*: 81-88.

Rapior, S., Andary, C., and Mousain, D. (1987). *Cortinarius* section *Orellani*: isolation and culture of *Cortinarius orellanus*. *Trans. Br. Mycol. Soc. 89*: 41-44.

Rapior, S., Andary, C., and Privat, G. (1988). Chemotaxonomic study of orellanine in species of *Cortinarius* and *Dermocybe*. *Mycologia 80*: 741-747.

Raszeja, S. (1960). Niezwykły obraz zmian morfologicznych w zatruciach rzekomo jadalnymi grzybami. *Patol. Pol. 11*: 113-123.

Richard, J.-M., and Ulrich, J. (1989). Mass spectrometry of orellanine, a mushroom toxin, and of related bipyridine-*N*-oxides. *Biomed. Environ. Mass Spectrom. 18*: 1-4.

Richard, J.-M., Taillandier, G., and Benoit-Guyod, J.-L. (1985). A quantitative structure-activity relationship study on substituted pyridines as a contribution to the knowledge of the toxic effects of orellanine, a toxin from the mushroom, *Cortinarius orellanus*. *Toxicon 23*: 815-824.

Richard, J.-M., Ravanel, P., and Cantin, D. (1987). Phytotoxicity of orellanine, a mushroom toxin. *Toxicon 25*: 350-354.

Richard, J.-M., Louis, J., and Cantin, D. (1988). Nephrotoxicity of orellanine, a toxin from the mushroom *Cortinarius orellanus*. *Arch. Toxicol. 62*: 242-245.

Schliessbach, B., Hasler, S., Friedli, H. P., and Müller, U. (1983). Akute Niereninsuffizienz nach Pilzvergiftung mit *Cortinarius splendens* (Fries) oder "schöngelbem Klumpfuss" (sog. Orellanus-Syndrom). *Schweiz. Med. Wochenschr. 113*: 151-153.

Schumacher, T., and Høiland, K. (1983). Mushroom poisoning caused by species of the genus *Cortinarius* Fries. *Arch. Toxicol. 53*: 87-106.

Short, A. I. K., Watling, R., MacDonald, M. K., and Robson, J. S. (1980). Poisoning by *Cortinarius speciosissimus*. *Lancet 2*: 942-944.

Skirgiello, A., and Nespiak, A. (1957). Erfahrungen mit *Dermocybe orellana* (Fr.) in Polen: A. *Cortinarius* (*Dermocybe*) *orellanus* Fr. non Quél. —Cause d'intoxications fongiques en Pologne en 1952-55. *Z. Pilzk. 23*: 138-139.

Soresina, P., and Leoni, G. (1978). Il *Cortinarius orellanus* ed i suòi effetti tòssici. *Micol. Ital. 3*: 9-15.

Středová, M., Krautová, H., Šellenberg, P., Herink, J., and Marek, J. (1978). Otrava houbami z rodu pavučinec (*Cortinarius*). *Vnitr. Lek. 24*: 822-826.

Tebbett, I. R., and Caddy, B. (1983). Analysis of *Cortinarius* mushrooms by high-performance liquid chromatography. *J. Chromatogr.* 268:535-538.

Tebbett, I. R., and Caddy, B. (1984a). Analysis of *Cortinarius* toxins by reversed-phase high-performance liquid chromatography. *J. Chromatogr.* 283:417-420.

Tebbett, I. R., and Caddy, B. (1984b). Mushroom toxins of the genus *Cortinarius*. *Experientia* 40:441-446.

Tebbett, I. R., Kidd, C. B. M., Caddy, B., Robertson, J., and Tilstone, W. J. (1983). Toxicity of *Cortinarius* species. *Trans. Br. Mycol. Soc.* 81:636-638.

Testa, E. (1970). *Cortinarius orellanus* Fries non quélet: indàgini sulla tòssicità dei funghi del gènere *Cortinarius*. *Rass. Micol. Ticinese* (Soc. Micol. Carlo Benzoni, Chiasso) 2:89-99.

Testa, E. (1982). I principi tòssici del *Cortinarius orellanus* (Fr.) Fr. *Schweiz. Z. Pilzkd.* 60:204-208.

Tiecco, M., Tingoli, M., Testaferri, L., Chianelli, D., and Wenkert, E. (1986). Total synthesis of orellanine, the lethal toxin of *Cortinarius orellanus* Fries mushroom. *Tetrahedron* 42:1475-1485.

Tiecco, M., Tingoli, M., Testaferri, L., Chianelli, D., and Wenkert, E. (1987). Total synthesis of orellinine, a minor toxic component of the fungus *Cortinarius orellanus* Fries. *Experientia* 43:462-463.

Traverso, M. (1973). Intoxications mortelles par *Cortinarius speciosissimus*. *Bull. Trimest. Fed. Mycol. Dauphiné-Savoie* 13:9-10. [Cited by Schumacher and Høiland (1983).]

Tune, B. M., and Fravert, D. (1980). Mechanisms of cephalosporin nephrotoxicity: a comparison of cephaloridine and cephaloglycin. *Kidney Int.* 18:591-600.

Watling, R. (1982). *Cortinarius speciosissimus*: the cause of renal failure in two young men. *Mycopathologia* 79:71-78.

Wysocki, K., Ruszkowski, M., and Raszeja, S. (1958). Ciężkie toksyczne uszkodzenie nerek w przebiegu zatrucia zasłonakiem rudym (*Cortinarius orellanus*). *Pol. Tyg. Lek.* 13:1314-1317.

24

Trichothecene Mycotoxins

William B. Buck

College of Veterinary Medicine, University of Illinois at Urbana-Champaign, Urbana, Illinois

Louise-Marie Côté

Consul-Tox, Inc., Tolono, Illinois

I. INTRODUCTION

The trichothecene mycotoxins are a group of chemicals with the same basic structure, produced by various species of fungi growing on plants. The reason for their name lies in their basic chemical ring described as the tetracyclic 12,13 epoxytrichothecene skeleton (Fig. 1). This skeleton can be produced by different genera of fungi, which will add to it different side chains, thus producing the diverse trichothecenes. The known genera of fungi producing trichothecenes are *Fusarium, Myrothecium, Cephalosporium, Verticimonosporium, Stachyobotrys, Trichothecium, Trichoderma, Cylindracarpon,* and *Phomopsis* (Ueno et al., 1973; Ichinoe and Kurata, 1983; Samples et al., 1984; Marasas et al., 1984; ApSimon et al., 1986; Jarvis, 1986). The most

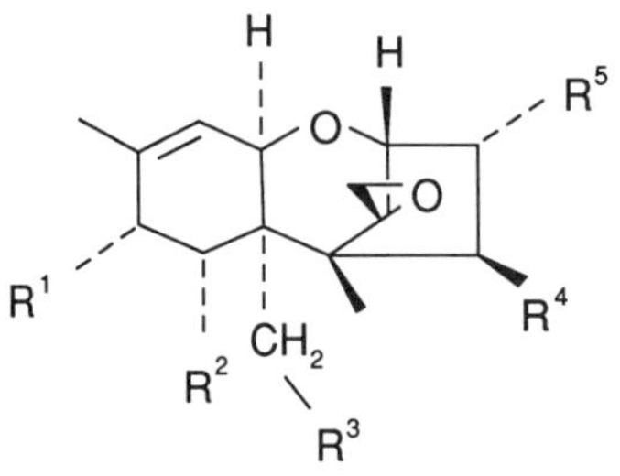

FIGURE 1 Basic ring structure of naturally occurring trichothecenes.

	R_1	R_2	R_3	R_4	R_5
T-2 Toxin	$(CH_3)_2CHCH_2COO-$	H	CH_3COO-	CH_3COO-	OH
Diacetoxyscirpenol	H	H	CH_3COO-	CH_3COO-	OH
Deoxynivalenol	O	OH	OH	H_2	OH
Nivalenol	O	OH	OH	OH	OH

important of them is the genus *Fusarium*. Although up to 100 trichothecenes have been characterized, only a few of the *Fusarium* toxins have been widely studied: deoxynivalenol (DON), diacetoxyscirpenol (DAS), nivalenol (NIV), T-2 toxin, HT-2 toxin (4-deacethyl, T-2, HT-2). These mycotoxins have affected all parts of the world because they are detected as naturally occurring contaminants of agricultural commodities. The toxicoses related to the presence of the fungi and/or the trichothecenes were characterized as fusariotoxicosis in North America, red-mold disease in the Far East, bean-hull poisoning in Japan, stachybotryotoxicosis and dendrodochiotoxicosis in Central Europe, and alimentary toxic aleukia in the Soviet Union.

II. NATURAL OCCURRENCE OF TRICHOTHECENES

In any area of the world where cereal grains, forages, or corn are grown under required weather conditions, including, but not limited to, ambient humidity, temperature, crop management, and geographical location, a genus or many genera of fungi may infect the plant. Although the appearance of fungi is not the ultimate factor in determining the presence of trichothecenes, it is the most common indicator since they are responsible for their production.

Many surveys have been conducted to determine the extent of grain contamination, especially since 1978, following the alleged use as a chemical warfare agent of a mixture of trichothecenes by the Soviet Union in Southeast Asia (Haig, 1982). The "yellow rain" incident has stimulated research to determine the extent of natural occurrence and effects of trichothecenes on plants, animals, and humans. Table 1 summarizes the worldwide natural occurrence of trichothecenes.

TABLE 1 Natural Occurrence of Trichothecenes in the World and Related Substrate

Trichothecene	Substrate	Country	References
T-2	Corn	Argentina	Cirilli (1983)
	Barley Oats	Australia	Cirilli (1983)
	Barley Corn Oats	Canada	Abramson et al. (1983) Cirilli (1983) Lauren and Greenhalgh (1987) Puls and Greenway (1976)
	Barley	Czechoslovakia	Bartos and Matyas (1982)
	Feeds/grains	Finland	Ylimaki et al., (1979)
	Beer Corn Feed Potatoes Vegetables Wheat	France	Cirilli (1983) Jemmali et al. (1978) Lafont et al. (1983) Lafont and Lafont (1977) Lafont and Lafont (1980) Payen et al. (1983) Renault et al. (1979)
	Corn Feeds/feed- stuffs Other crops Swine food Wheat	Hungary	Bata et al. (1983) Glavits et al. (1983) Sandor et al. (1984) Szathmary (1983)
	Banana Safflower Sorghum Sweet corn	India	Chakrabarti and Ghosal (1986) Ghosal et al. (1977) Ghosal et al. (1978)
	Corn Feeds/grains	Italy	Cirilli (1983)
	Feeds/grains	South Africa	Dutton and Westlake (1985)
	Rice	Sri Lanka	Cirilli (1983)
	Feedstuffs Brewer's grain	United Kingdom	Patterson (1983)
	Corn Cornstalks Feeds	United States	Cirilli (1983) Gabal et al. (1986) Hsu et al. (1972) Mirocha et al. (1976)

TABLE 1 (continued)

Trichothecene	Substrate	Country	References
			Mirocha et al. (1979)
			Stahr et al. (1978)
			Stahr et al. (1981)
			Tseng et al. (1985)
	Mixed feeds	West Germany	Barnikol et al. (1985)
	Oats		Gareis et al. (1985)
	Pig feed		Thalmann et al. (1985)
	Rye		
	Wheat		
DAS	Corn	Argentina	Cirilli (1983)
	Oats	Australia	Cirilli (1983)
	Corn	Austria	Bottalico et al. (1981)
	Barley	Canada	Cirilli (1983)
	Wheat		
	Rice	China	Cirilli (1983)
	Feeds/grains	Finland	Karppanen et al. (1985)
	Beer	France	Cirilli (1983)
	Corn		Lafont et al. (1983)
	Potatoes		Lafont and Lafont (1980)
	Wheat		Payen et al. (1983)
	Corn	Hungary	Bata et al. (1983)
	Other crops		Sandor et al. (1984)
			Szathmary (1983)
	Banana	India	Chakrabarti and Ghosal (1986)
	Safflower		Ghosal et al. (1977)
	Sweet corn		Ghosal et al. (1978)
	Feedstuffs	Italy	Cirilli (1983)
	Grains		
	Grains/feeds	South Africa	Dutton and Westlake (1985)
	Feeds	United States	Cirilli (1983)
	Wheat		Mirocha et al. (1976)
			Stahr et al. (1979)
			Stahr et al. (1983)
	Barley	West Germany	Gareis et al. (1985)
	Corn		Siegfried (1977)
	Mixed feed		Thalmann et al. (1985)
	Wheat		

TABLE 1 (continued)

Trichothecene	Substrate	Country	References
	Corn	Yugoslavia	Cirilli (1983)
DON	Corn	Argentina	Gilbert et al. (1983)
	Triticale Wheat	Australia	Moore et al. (1985) More et al. (1985) Tobin (1988)
	Corn Feed Wheat	Austria	Bottalico et al. (1981) Lew et al. (1981) Noonpudgee et al. (1986) Schweighardt and Leibetsener (1981) Schweighardt and Schuh (1981) Ueno et al. (1985) Vesonder and Ciegler (1979)
	Wheat	Bulgaria	Ueno et al. (1985)
	Bran Corn Corn foods Oat flour Rye Wheat Wheat foods	Canada	Gilbert et al. (1983) Gilbert et al. (1984) Neish et al. (1983) Scott (1984) Scott et al. (1981) Scott et al. (1982) Teich and Hamilton (1985) Trenholm et al. (1983) Trenholm et al. (1981) Vesonder and Ciegler (1979)
	Feeds Grains	Denmark	Hald and Krogh (1983)
	Foods/feeds	Egypt	Abdel Hamid (1983)
	Feeds Grains	Finland	Karppanen et al. (1985)
	Beer Corn Potatoes Wheat	France	Gilbert et al. (1983) Gilbert et al. (1984) Jemmali et al. (1978) Lafont et al. (1983) Ueno et al. (1985)
	Wheat	Greece	Ueno et al. (1985)

TABLE 1 (continued)

Trichothecene	Substrate	Country	References
	Corn	Hungary	Bata et al. (1983)
	Wheat		Sandor et al. (1984)
			Ueno et al. (1985)
	Corn	Italy	Gilbert et al. (1984)
			Visconti et al. (1984)
	Barley	Japan	Kamimura et al. (1981)
	Barley products		Kuroda et al. (1979)
	Grain food		Morooka et al. (1972)
	Wheat		Sasaki (1984)
	Wheat flour		Tanaka et al. (1985a)
			Tanaka et al. (1985b)
			Yoshizawa (1983)
	Acha	Nigeria	Gbodi et al. (1986)
	Barley	Poland	Ueno et al. (1985)
	Wheat		
	Corn	South Africa	Abdel Hamid (1983)
	Grains		Dutton and Westlake (1981)
	Feeds		Marasas et al. (1977)
			Marasas et al. (1978)
			Thiel et al. (1982b)
	Barley	South Korea	Lee et al. (1986)
	Malt		Lee et al. (1985)
	Rye		
	Barley	United Kingdom	Gilbert et al. (1984)
	Brewer's maize		Gilbert et al. (1983)
	Wheat		Osborne and Willis (1984)
			Tanaka et al. (1986)
			Ueno et al. (1985)
	Corn	United States	Abbas et al. (1986)
	cornmeal		Bennett et al. (1983)
	Cornstalks		Brumley et al. (1985)
	Feeds		Côté et al. (1984)
	Flour		Eppley et al. (1984)
	Hominy corn		Gilbert et al. (1983)
	Snack foods		Gilbert et al. (1984)
	Wheat		Hagler et al. (1984)
			Ishii et al. (1975)
			Mirocha et al. (1979)
			Mirocha et al. (1976)

TABLE 1 (continued)

Trichothecene	Substrate	Country	References
			Saito and Betchtel (1985)
			Shotwell et al. (1985)
			Stahr et al. (1979)
			Stahr et al. (1983)
			Tanaka et al. (1985a)
			Trucksess et al. (1986)
			Tseng et al. (1985)
			Vesonder and Ciegler (1979)
			Vesonder et al. (1976)
			Vesonder et al. (1978)
			Vesonder et al. (1973)
			Vesonder et al. (1979)
	Oats	USSR	Ueno et al. (1986b)
	Cereal products	West Germany	Bauer et al. (1980)
	Oats		Blaas et al. (1984)
	Wheat bran		Steinmeyer et al. (1985)
			Thalmann et al. (1985)
			Tiebach et al. (1985)
	Corn	Zambia	Marasas et al. (1978)
NIV	Corn	Austria	Ueno et al. (1985)
	Wheat		
	Wheat	Bulgaria	Ueno et al. (1985)
	Barley	Canada	Cirilli (1983)
	Corn		Lauren and Greenhalgh (1987)
	Rye		
	Wheat		
	Rice	China	Cirilli (1983)
	Wheat		Ueno et al. (1986a,b)
	Feeds/grains	Finland	Karppanen et al. (1985)
	Corn	France	Jemmali et al. (1978)
	Wheat		Ueno et al. (1985)
	Wheat	Greece	Ueno et al. (1985)
	Wheat	Hungary	Ueno et al. (1985)
	Corn	Italy	Cirilli (1983)
	Grains		
	Barley	Japan	Kamimura et al. (1981)

TABLE 1 (continued)

Trichothecene	Substrate	Country	References
	Flour Grain foods Wheat		Kuroda et al. (1979) Morooka et al. (1972) Sasaki (1984) Tanaka et al. (1985a,b) Yoshizawa (1983)
	Barley Wheat	Poland	Ueno et al. (1985)
	Corn	South Africa	Thiel et al. (1982a,b)
	Barley Malt Rye	South Korea	Lee et al. (1986) Lee et al. (1985)
	Barley Wheat	Taiwan	Ueno et al. (1986b)
	Barley Wheat	United Kingdom	Tanaka et al. (1986) Ueno et al. (1985)
	Popcorn	United States	Tanaka et al. (1985b)
	Oats	USSR	Ueno et al. (1986b)

	Barley
	Bran
	Corn flakes
	Other cereal
	  products
	Other grain
	  foods
	Wheat
		West Germany	Blaas et al. (1984)
			Steinmeyer et al. (1985)
			Tiebach et al. (1985)

	Corn	Yugoslavia	Cirilli (1983)

Sources: Tanaka et al. (1988) and Scott (1989).

III. BIOCHEMICAL MECHANISM OF ACTION

The mechanism(s) of action of trichothecene mycotoxins has recently been reviewed by Feinberg and McLaughlin (1989). Essentially, all of the toxic effects of the trichothecenes observed in yeast, mammalian cells, and in animals appear to be due to inhibition of protein synthesis. Cells dependent on a high rate of protein synthesis, such as those lining the gastrointestinal (GI) tract and lymphoid cells, seem to be the most susceptible to the trichothecenes. Secondary cellular effects of trichothecenes involve inhibition of DNA synthesis, DNA breakage (reversible), and compromised membrane integrity. However, the trichothecenes are regarded as only weakly mutagenic or carcinogenic (Hascheck, 1989), and immunosuppression and tissue necrosis are probably more important than damage to DNA.

Although the toxic effects of the trichothecenes mimic those of radiation poisoning in the GI tract and lymphoid organs (Coppock et al., 1985b), their toxic effects are much more extensive because the heart and pancreas are also target organs (Pang et al., 1986).

The simple trichothecenes, DON, T-2, and DAS, administered orally or parenterally, do not accumulate in the body of exposed mammals to any significant extent and residues are excreted within a few days after exposure (Copock et al., 1985b; Côté et al., 1986; Beasley et al., 1986; Corley et al., 1986). By contrast, elimination is significantly delayed after topical exposure to lipophilic trichothecenes (T-2, DAS), with the skin and fat apparently acting as reservoirs for the toxin (Pang et al., 1987c).

The trichothecenes are metabolized in vivo by at least four common processes: ester hydrolysis, hydroxylation, epoxide reduction, and conjugation, either in the GI tract or by the liver and other organs. Their biotransformation is relatively rapid, with plasma half-lives ranging from a few minutes to several hours, depending on the species involved and the individual toxin (Corley et al., 1985; Coppock et al., 1985b, 1987; Beasley et al., 1986). They apparently are readily absorbed from the GI tract (Swanson and Corley, 1989), although following administration of highly toxic oral doses, parent compound and metabolites (both free and glucuronide conjugated) have been found in the upper GI tract 24 h postexposure in pigs and cattle (Beasley et al., 1986). The GI flora of animals such as ruminants and rats convert trichothecenes to deepoxy metabolites, and this reaction is quite important in their detoxification (Yoshizawa et al., 1985a,b; Swanson et al., 1986,1987a,b; Côté et al., 1986; Pfeiffer et al., 1988). Although deepoxidation and conjugation are major detoxification pathways, these processes are apparently overwhelmed in view of the toxicity of trichothecenes to cattle and other species that utilize these metabolic pathways (Osweiler et al., 1981; Buening et al., 1982; Beasley, 1983; Beasley et al., 1986; Pfeiffer et al., 1988). Glucuronide conjugates of parent compounds and metabolites of trichothecenes are assumed to be less toxic than their unconjugated forms; however, there is evidence that conjugates are reabsorbed from the GI tract either intact or after being deconjugated (Corley et al., 1985; Coddington et al., 1989). Thus, despite rapid metabolism and depletion of parent toxins, the metabolic products of T-2 toxin and DAS (but not DON) are highly toxic. When lethal doses of T-2 toxin were given orally to pigs and cattle, no detectable parent toxin was found in plasma or tissues of dying animals. Similarly, when lethal doses were given intravascularly, no T-2 toxin could be detected in plasma and tissues 4 h after dosing, although the subjects died from 10 to 20 h after exposure (Beasley et al., 1986; Coppock et al., 1987). Exposure to environmental xenobiotics or drug therapies, which delay elimination of the trichothecenes or inhibit detoxification reactions, would probably result in increased toxicity.

IV. TOXICITY

The trichothecenes consist of nearly 100 distinct chemical compounds with a broad range of toxic capabilities, together with numerous toxic metabolites produced from the parent toxins by both plants and animals. The toxicity of certain trichothecenes has been investigated including DON, T-2 toxin,

DAS, nivalenol, HT-2 toxin, trichodermin, neosolaniol, verrucarins, roridins, and satratoxins (Trenholm et al., 1989). Of these, DON, T-2 toxin, DAS, and nivalenol have been associated with naturally occurring problems in livestock, other animals, and humans. In addition, these trichothecenes, particularly T-2 and DAS, have attracted considerable international attention due to their alleged use in chemical warfare as the agent "yellow rain" in southeast Asia and Afghanistan (Haig, 1982; Rosen and Rosen, 1982).

The toxicity of DON, T-2 toxin, DAS, and nivalenol in animals is presented in Table 2. Toxicity data taken from studies involving naturally contaminated feedstuffs with trichothecenes, however, may be misleading because only specific mycotoxins were identified and presumed to be the cause of feed refusal or other toxic effects (Côté et al., 1984). Other unidentified mycotoxins or their toxic metabolites probably were present. This is especially true of DON because in subsequent investigations the effect of 4.7 ppm purified compound in pig feed was not significantly different from that of control, whereas pigs on several naturally contaminated diets at a similar DON level had significantly lower feed intake and weight gain values (Foster et al., 1986). These findings account for livestock having signs of trichothecenes mycotoxicoses while consuming feeds containing less than 1.0 ppm DON and no detectable T-2 toxin or DAS (Friend et al., 1982; Côté et al., 1984).

V. CLINICAL SIGNS AND LESIONS

Trichothecene toxins have induced a wide variety of biochemical and physiologic abnormalities in most species that have been tested. These include gastrointestinal, cardiovascular, neurologic, dermatologic, immunologic, and hematologic changes. However, one of the most ubiquitous naturally occurring trichothecenes, DON, causes only transient, dose-dependent reduced feed intake (and concomitant reduced rate of body weight gain) in the more sensitive species, such as swine, rats, and mice, when present in the ration at concentrations up to 5 ppm (Côté et al., 1985; Foster et al., 1986; Trenholm et al., 1989). Vomiting has occurred in pigs on a diet containing over 15 ppm DON (Young et al., 1983), hence the synonym "vomitoxin." On the other hand, cattle did not have reduced feed intake nor other adverse effects when given a grain ration containing an average of 66 ppm DON for 5 days (Côté et al., 1986).

Other signs and lesions that have been attributed to DON contamination of feeds under natural conditions have not been reproduced with purified DON, and probably reflect the presence of toxic fungal metabolites that were not detected at the time of the problem. These include reproductive problems, increased incidence of infections, diarrhea, emesis, and death (Côté et al., 1984). No substantial lesions have been associated with oral exposure to purified DON; however, Coppock et al. (1985b) reported mild lesions in the pancreas and mesenteric lymph nodes of intravascularly dosed swine.

The clinical effects of T-2 toxin and DAS have been investigated extensively in laboratory animals and livestock, and to a lesser extent in dogs, cats, and nonhuman primates (Trenholm et al., 1989). The toxic effects of DAS have been documented in clinical trials in humans in association with its

TABLE 2 Toxicity of T-2 Toxin, DAS, DON, and NIV (mg/kg body weight) in Animals

Toxin	Species	Route	Parameter	Dosage	Reference
T-2	Mouse	IV	LD$_{50}$	4.2	Ueno (1984)
		IP	LD$_{50}$	5.2	Ueno et al. (1972)
		IP	LD$_{50}$	3.0	Bamburg and Strong (1971)
		PO	LD$_{50}$	10.5	Ueno (1984)
		SQ	LD$_{50}$	2.1	Ueno (1984)
	Newborn	SQ	LD$_{50}$	0.15	Ueno (1984)
	Rat	IV	Acute toxic	1.0	Wilson et al. (1982)
		IV	LD$_{50}$	0.9	Doebler et al. (1985)
		IP	LD$_{50}$	3.0	Kosuri et al. (1970)
		PO	LD$_{50}$	5.2	Ueno (1984)
		PO	LD$_{50}$	3.8	Kosuri et al. (1971)
		SQ	LD$_{50}$	~8.0	Bamburg (1968)
		Topical	Acute toxic	5.0	Chan and Gentry (1984)
	Guinea pig	IV	LD$_{50}$	1.1	Chan and Gentry (1984)
	Cat	SQ	LD$_{50}$	<0.5	Sato et al. (1975)
		PO	Lethal	0.08	Lutsky et al. (1978)
	Pig	IV	LD$_{50}$	1.2	Weaver et al. (1978b)
		IV	Toxic	0.6	Lorenzana et al. (1985)
		IV	Lethal	4.8	Lorenzana et al. (1985)
		PO	Chronic toxic	8.0 ppm[a]	Weaver et al. (1978a)
		PO	Chronic NE[b]	<1.0 ppm[a]	Weaver et al. (1978b)
		PO	Feed refusal	1.5 ppm[a]	Weaver et al. (1978a)
		Topical	Acute toxic	15.0	Pang et al. (1987c)
		Inhalation	Acute toxic	8.0	Pang et al. (1988)
	Calf	IV	Toxic	1.2	Beasley (1983)
		PO	Lethal	3.6	Beasley (1983)
		PO	Chronic lethal	0.1	Grove et al. (1970)

TABLE 2 (continued)

Toxin	Species	Route	Parameter	Dosage	Reference
		PO	Minimum toxic	0.16	Pier et al. (1976)
		IM	LD50	3.8	Kosuri et al. (1970)
	Horse	PO	LD50	~1.0	Ueno (1983)
	Chick embryo	Inject	Toxic	0.001 μg	Vesely et al. (1982)
		Inject	LD50	0.07 μg	Ueno et al. (1977)
	Chick	PO	LD50	5.0	Chi et al. (1977)
	Broiler	PO	Chronic toxic	4.0 ppm[a]	Chi et al. (1977)
		PO	Acute toxic	2.5	Hoerr et al. (1981)
	Hen	PO	LD50	6.3	Chi et al. (1977)
		PO	Chronic toxic	2.0 ppm[a]	Doerr et al. (1981)
	Turkey	PO	Toxic	5.0 ppm[a]	Allen et al. (1983)
	Goose	PO	Chronic lethal	25.0 ppm[a]	Puls and Greenway (1976)
	Duck	PO	Chronic lethal	20.00 ppm[a]	Hayes and Wobeser (1983)
	Trout	PO	LD50	6.1	Marasas et al. (1967)
		PO	Chronic NE[b]	400.0 ppb[a]	Marasas et al. (1967)
		PO	Chronic toxic	4.0	Marasas et al. (1969)
	Monkey	IM	Lethal	2.0	Hassler (1983)
		IM	LD50	0.65	Hassler (1983)
		IM	Toxic	0.33	Hassler (1983)
		PO	Chronic toxic	0.1	Jagadeesan (1982)
		PO	Acute lethal	0.5	Rukmini et al. (1979)
		PO	Acute toxic	0.1	Rukmini et al. (1979)
HT-2	Mouse	IP	LD50	9.0	Ueno et al. (1973)
		IP	LD50	6.5	Yoshizawa et al. (1982)
	Chick	PO	LD50	7.2	Chi et al. (1977)
	embryo	Inject	LD50	0.5 μg	Ueno (1977)

Toxin	Animal	Route	Measure	Value	Reference
DAS	Mouse	IV	LD$_{50}$	0.75	Grove and Mortimer (1969)
		IV	LD$_{50}$	10.0	Bamburg et al. (1968)
		IV	LD$_{50}$	9.0	Fromentin et al. (1980)
		IP	LD$_{50}$	23.0	Ueno et al. (1972)
		IP	LD$_{50}$	20.00	Rogers et al. (1984)
		IP	LD$_{50}$	8.0	Saito and Ohtsubo (1974)
		IP	LD$_{50}$	2.3	Ueno (1983)
		PO	LD$_{50}$	7.3	Ueno et al. (1972)
		PO	LD$_{50}$	46.00	Ueno (1983)
		PO	LD$_{50}$	15.5	Rogers et al. (1984)
		SQ	LD$_{50}$	0.17	Ueno (1983)
	Rat	IV	LD$_{50}$	1.3	Ueno (1983)
		IP	LD$_{50}$	0.75	Ueno (1983)
		PO	LD$_{50}$	7.3	Ueno (1983)
		Topical	LD$_{50}$	>10.0	Crone (1984)
	Guinea pig	PO	LD$_{50}$	2.14	Kriegleder (1981)
	Rabbit	IV	LD$_{50}$	1.0	National Research Council (1983)
	Dog	IV	LD$_{50}$	~1.1	Ueno (1983)
	Cattle	IV	Toxic	0.5	Coppock et al. (1987)
	Pig	IV	Lethal	0.5	Coppock et al. (1985a)
		IV	LD$_{50}$	0.4	Weaver et al. (1978a)
	Chick embryo	PO	LD$_{50}$	3.8	Chi and Mirocha (1978)
		Inject	LD$_{50}$	0.09 μg	Ueno et al. (1977)
DON	Mouse (M)	IP	LD$_{50}$	70.0	Yoshizawa and Morooka (1979)
	Mouse (F)	IP	LD$_{50}$	76.6	Yoshizawa and Morooka (1979)
		PO	LD$_{50}$	46.0	Yoshizawa and Morooka (1979)
		SQ	LD$_{50}$	45.0	Thompson and Wannamaker (1986)
	Pig	IV	Toxic	0.5	Coppock et al. (1985b)
		PO	NE[b]	<1.0	Schuh et al. (1982)
		PO	NE[b]	1.7 ppm[a]	Chavez (1984)

TABLE 2 (continued)

Toxin	Species	Route	Parameter	Dosage	Reference
		PO	Red. feed int.[c]	1.3 ppm[a]	Young et al. (1983)
		PO	Red. feed int.[c]	3.1 ppm[a]	Côté et al. (1985)
		PO	Red. feed int.[c]	3.6 ppm[a]	Forsyth et al. (1977)
		PO	Red. feed int.[c]	4.4 ppm[a]	Young and Vesonder (1979)
		PO	Red. feed int.[c]	5.0 ppm[a]	Schuh et al. (1982)
		PO	Feed refusal[c]	12.0 ppm[a]	Young et al. (1983)
		PO	Emetic	20.0 ppm[a]	Young et al. (1983)
		PO	Emetic	44.4 ppm[a]	Young et al. (1983)
	Dairy cow	PO	NE (5 days)[b]	66.0	Côté et al. (1986)
	Chick	PO	LD_{50}	140.0	Huff et al. (1981)
	Duck	SQ	LD_{50}	27.0	Yoshizawa and Morooka (1979)
	Mouse Newborn	SQ	LD_{50}	0.16	Ueno (1984)
	Mouse	IV	LD_{50}	6.3	Ueno (1984)
		IP	LD_{50}	4.1	Tatsuno et al. (1968)
		IP	LD_{50}	4.0	Tatsuno (1968)
		IP	LD_{50}	4.1	Ueno et al. (1973)
		IP	LD_{50}	7.4	Ryu et al. (1986)
		SQ	LD_{50}	7.2	Ryu et al. (1986)
		PO	LD_{50}	38.9	Ryu et al. (1986)
	Chick embryo	Inject	LD_{50}	4.0 µg	Ueno (1977)

[a] Concentration in the diet.
[b] NE, no effect.
[c] The reported reduced feed intake result from feeding naturally contaminated diets containing DON. Other fungal metabolites were probably present even though not mentioned.

use as an antineoplastic agent (Thigpen et al., 1981). Under natural conditions of feed contamination, these mycotoxins are usually associated with feed refusal, necrosis of skin and oral mucosa, vomiting and diarrhea, and increased incidence of bacterial and viral infections. Other effects of natural exposure have included hemorrhage and necrosis of gastrointestinal mucosa, destruction of hemopoietic tissue and lymphoid necrosis, meningeal hemorrhage, shock, and death (Weaver et al., 1978a,b).

Acute, experimental toxicoses induced by dosing pigs and other species with purified T-2 toxin or DAS resulted in emesis associated with chewing movements and excessive salivation (in species prone to vomiting). This was followed by evidence of abdominal stress with prolonged exhalation and purplish mucous membranes. Animals developed posterior paresis and lethargy. After 3 to 4 h the skin was reddened and ears and limbs were cold to the touch. Death usually occurred within 12 h, or recovery commenced. These signs are reminiscent of endotoxic shock. The shock was characterized by reductions in cardiac output and blood pressure and increased plasma concentrations of epinephrine, norepinephrine, thromboxane B_2, 6-keto PGF_{1a}, and lactate (Lorenzana et al., 1985). The sympathetic effects of toxins are probably mediated through a central nervous system mechanism (Feuerstein et al., 1989). Blood flow to the pancrease and spleen was drastically reduced, while flow to the liver, gastrointestinal tract, and adrenal glands increased (Lorenzana et al., 1985; Lundeen et al., 1986; Beasley et al., 1987).

The immunotoxicity of the trichothecenes has recently been reviewed by Taylor et al. (1989). Known acute and chronic exposures of humans and animals to T-2 toxin have been associated with increased incidence of bacterial infections and other immunologic effects (Fig. 2; Table 3). Pang et al. (1987a) observed a reduced cellular immune response, in addition to severe local dermal injury, reduced body weight gain, increased rectal temperature, and changes in hematologic and serum biochemical parameters of pigs treated topi-

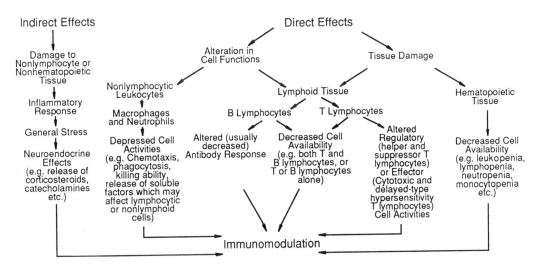

FIGURE 2 Immunomodulation effects of trichothecene exposure.

TABLE 3 Immunologic Effects Reported for T-2 Toxin

Species	Route	Dose	Effect	References
Chickens	PO	16 ppm	Increased mortality from *Salmonella*	Boonchuvit et al. (1978)
Mice, lymphocytes	In vitro	5 μg/L	Breaks in DNA	LaFarge-Frayssinet et al. (1981)
Mice	IP	3 mg/kg	Increased DNA breaks in lymphocytes	LaFarge-Frayssinet et al. (1981)
Mice	PO	0.1 mg/kg/day	Decreased resistance to *M. bovis* and decreased response to BCG vaccine	Kanai and Kondo (1984)
Calves	PO	0.1, 0.3, or 0.6 mg/kg/day	Decreased resistance to *Anaplasma* vaccine; dose-related reduction in thymic weight; lymphoid depletion	Osweiler et al. (1981), Buening et al. (1982)
Pigs	PO	5 ppm	Severe reduction in weight gain, leucopenia, reduced response to mitogens, lower titers to *Clostridium* bacterin	Rafai and Tuboly (1982)
Pigs	Topical	15 mg/kg in DMSO	Responses of enriched peripheral blood mononuclear cells to mitogens reduced up to 28 days' postexposure	Pang et al. (1987a)
Pigs	Inhalation	1.8, 2.7 mg/kg	Reduction in alveolar macrophage phagocytosis and mitogen-induced blastogenic responses of pulmonary lymphocytes	Pang et al. (1987b)

cally with T-2 toxin (15 mg/kg body weight). Pang et al. (1987b) also reported a marked reduction in alveolar macrophage phagocytosis and mitogen-induced blastogenic responses of pulmonary lymphocytes, but not peripheral blood lymphocytes, in pigs following inhalation exposure to toxic amounts of T-2 toxin.

Both T-2 toxin and DAS affect hematologic parameters in various species. In poultry, laboratory animals, dogs, and cats this is primarily a reduction in RBC and platelet counts (Gentry, 1989). Certain coagulation parameters of chickens are also sensitive to these toxins. Depressed bone marrow activity in mice, rats, and cats are reversible, and tend to return to normal even while the animals are still exposed to the toxin. Thrombocytopenia is a consistent observation after exposure to DAS and T-2 toxin in humans and rhesus monkeys. Necrosis of bone marrow hematopoietic elements and accompanying abnormal cells in the blood have been reported in pigs, dogs, and calves exposed to DAS (Coppock et al., 1989). A neutrophilia has been observed in pigs exposed to T-2 toxin (Pang et al., 1987c). Although T-2 toxin does not act as a vitamin K antagonist, the biological activities of specific coagulation factors are markedly depressed in calves, monkeys, rabbits, and guinea pigs exposed to relatively high doses of this mycotoxin (Gentry, 1989).

Morphologic changes associated with T-2 toxin or DAS toxicosis are comparable regardless of the species in question or route of exposure (i.e., oral, intravenous, or inhalation). Gross lesions consist of edema, congestion, and hemorrhage of the lymph nodes and pancreas; and congestion, hemorrhage, and sometimes necrosis of the gastrointestinal mucosa, subendocardium, adrenal glands, and meninges. Microscopically, there is often widespread degeneration and necrosis of the lymphoid tissues as well as of the surface and crypt epithelium of the gastrointestinal mucosa; and mild necrosis of pancreatic acinar cells, myocardium, bone marrow cells, adrenal cortical cells, and renal tubular epithelium. In mitotically and metabolically active tissues such as GI epithelium and lymphoid aggregates, the effects of these mycotoxins mimic radiation poisoning. As mentioned previously, however, in addition to radiomimetic lesions of the GI tract and lymphoid organs, the heart and pancreas are target organs of the trichothecenes (Pang et al., 1986; Coppock et al., 1987).

VI. DIAGNOSTIC CONSIDERATIONS

Confirmation of trichothecene toxicoses in animals and humans requires both differential clinical diagnostic efforts with the affected individual(s) and chemical analysis of body fluids and suspect feedstuffs. A large number of different trichothecenes have been reported to occur in nature. In addition, their metabolism in mammals and plants is extensive. Therefore, detection and confirmation of exposure can be difficult. A successful approach is to hydrolyze all esters from the basic trichothecene to alcohols prior to analysis (Rood et al., 1988a). This leads not only to greater sensitivity, but also reduces the total number of compounds that must be monitored during the analytical step.

Both parent compounds or the metabolites of DON, T-2 toxin, and DAS can be simultaneously identified and quantified using this hydrolysis technique. The parent T-2 and its metabolites are expressed as T-2 equivalents, while DAS and its metabolites are expressed as DAS equivalents (Rood et al., 1988a). DON is analyzed unchanged because it is an alcohol.

Thus animals that have been exposed orally to these trichothecenes are likely to have detectable concentrations of either parent toxin, metabolite(s), or conjugated parent or metabolite in their plasma, milk, urine, or feces for a period up to 72 h after exposure (Côté et al., 1986; Pfeiffer et al., 1988).

Similarly, there is evidence that T-2 toxin and DAS are metabolized in grains or feedstuffs and that certain of these metabolites are also toxic. Very seldom are either of these mycotoxins found in feeds at concentrations sufficient to cause the health effects being observed in the exposed animal(s) (Côté et al., 1984). Often, DON is the only mycotoxin detected at less than 1 ppm, yet livestock consuming the feed are manifesting health and production deficits representative of the more toxic trichothecenes. This diagnostic enigma has been answered, in part, using the hydrolysis technique of Rood et al. (1988b). Of 176 feed samples submitted to the University of Illinois Laboratories of Veterinary Diagnostic Medicine during the 6-month period December 1, 1986 to May 30, 1987, nearly half were found to contain toxic metabolites of T-2 toxin or DAS, although no detectable parent T-2 toxin nor DAS were present (Swanson et al., 1988). Similarly, moldy soybeans from the 1986 crop in Illinois, Michigan, and Iowa had no detectable T-2 toxin nor DAS. However, significant concentrations of their toxic metabolites were found using the hydrolysis technique mentioned above (Lambert et al., 1987).

In summary, if trichothecene mycotoxicosis is suspected, both animal specimens (i.e., plasma, urine, milk, feces) should be analyzed using the Rood et al. (1988a) hydrolysis screening technique and mass spectroscopy utilized for identification of the specific metabolite(s) to confirm exposure. Representative samples of feedstuffs should be analyzed using the Rood et al. (1988b) technique to determine if toxic metabolites of T-2 toxin or DAS are present, even when no parent toxin is present. A limitation of these procedures is the paucity of trichothecene metabolite analytical standards.

VII. THERAPEUTIC CONSIDERATIONS

The prevention and treatment of trichothecene toxicosis has recently been reviewed by Fricke and Poppenga (1989). Numerous classes of therapeutic agents and protocols have been evaluated: (1) GI-adsorbing agents, (2) anti-inflammatory agents, (3) antioxidants, (4) microsomal-inducing agents, (5) multiple drug therapy, and (6) miscellaneous drugs. Of these, only the first two have proven to be consistently efficacious. The most effective preventive or therapeutic protocol for trichothecene toxicosis in various species is the repeated oral administration of superactivated charcoal (SuperChar, Gulf Biosystems, Inc., Dallas, Texas; Super-A X-21, Anderson Development Co., Adrian, Michigan). The optimal dosage ranged from 0.5 to 1.0 g/kg body weight. The treatment should be repeated at 8- to 12-h intervals for three to five treatments, or until clinical signs of toxicosis disappear (Buck and Bratich, 1986a,b; Buck et al., 1986). This protocol is undoubtedly effective because the superactivated charcoal adsorbs not only parent toxins, but also metabolites, both conjugated and unconjugated, that are circulated enterohepatically (Buck et al., 1986; Corley et al., 1986; Coddington et al., 1989). For most species, the inclusion of a saline cathartic facilitates the passage of the trichothecene-adsorbed charcoal, however, this may not be true for rodents (Galey et al., 1987).

In addition to charcoal adsorption of the toxins and their metabolites in the GI tract, corticosteroids (dexamethasone, methylprednisolone), given prior to or immediately after administration of T-2 toxin, for the control of cardiovascular shock have also been beneficial (Buck et al., 1986; Poppenga et al., 1987; Wong-Pack, 1987; Fricke and Poppenga, 1989). Single doses (10 mg/kg) of corticosteroid given parenterally have proven beneficial in preventing death or prolonging survival time of laboratory animals and livestock given lethal doses of T-2 toxin; however, Wong-Pack (1987) reported that repeated doses of dexamethasone (10 mg/kg) every 5 h, beginning 1 h after administration of a lethal intravenous dose of T-2 toxin to rats provided no beneficial effect.

VIII. SUMMARY

The trichothecene mycotoxins are found worldwide in nature where cereal and feed grains are produced. In this chapter we have discussed the most prominent simple trichothecenes: DON, T-2 toxin, DAS, and nivalenol. Of these, DON has relatively low mammalian toxicity, having as its primary effect transient reduced feed intake. T-2 toxin and DAS are highly toxic, being lethal to most species following oral exposure to less than 10 mg/kg body weight. Their toxic effects mimic radiation poisoning, but are more extensive, in that the heart and pancreas are also target organs. The cardiovascular syndrome produced by these toxins resembles endotoxic shock. Confirmation of trichothecene exposure to mammals can best be made by testing biological fluids, feces, and suspect feedstuffs, hydrolyzing the parent toxins and their metabolites to their final alcohol, and detecting their derivatives using gas chromatography/mass spectroscopy. The most efficacious treatment of trichothecene toxicosis consists of repeated (8 to 12 h intervals) oral administration of superactivated charcoal to facilitate the fecal excretion of toxins and their metabolites. Parenteral administration of a high dose (10 mg/kg) of corticosteroid may lessen the shock syndrome.

REFERENCES

Abbas, H. K., Mirocha, C. J., and Tuite, J. (1986). Natural occurrence of deoxynivalenol, 15-acetyl-deoxynivalenol and zearalenone in refusal factor corn stored since 1972. *Appl. Environ. Microbiol.* 51:841-843.

Abdel Hamid, A. H. M. (1983). Occurrence of vomitoxin in Egyptian foods and feeds. *Abstract International Mycotoxin Conference I*, Cairo, Egypt, Mar. 19-24. National Research Center, Cairo and U.S. Food and Drug Administration, Washington, D.C., No. 59.

Abramson, D., Mills, J. T., and Boycott, B. R. (1983). Mycotoxins and mycoflora in animal feedstuffs in western Canada. *Can. J. Comp. Med.* 23:23-26.

Allen, N., Pegure, A., Mirocha, C., and Newman, J. (1983). Effects of *Fusarium*, T-2 toxin and F-2 on the reproduction of turkey females. *Poult. Sci.* 62:282-285.

ApSimon, J. W., Blackwell, B., Grenhalgh, R., Meier, R.-M., Miller, D., Paré, J. R. J., and Taylor, A. (1986). Secondary metabolites produced by some *Fusarium* species. In *Bioactive Molecules*, P. S. Steyns and R. Vleggar (Eds.). Elsevier, Amsterdam, pp. 125-137.

Bamburg, J. R. (1969). Mycotoxins of the trichothecene family produced by cereal mold. Ph.D. thesis, University of Wisconsin, Madison.

Bamburg, J. R., and Strong, F. M. (1971). 12,13-Epoxytrichothecenes. In *Microbial Toxins*, Vol. 7, S. Kadis, A. Ciegler, and S. J. Ajl (Eds.). Academic Press, New York, pp. 207-289.

Bamburg, J. R., Marasas, W. F. O., Riggs, N. V., Smalley, E. B., and Strong, F. M. (1968). Toxic spiro-epoxy compounds from *Fusaria* and other Hyphomycetes. *Biotechnol. Bioeng. 10*:445-455.

Barnikol, H., Thalmann, A., and Wengert, D. (1985). Hautschaden bei neugeborenen Ferkeln in Zusammenhang mit einem Fusarientoxin (T-2 toxin) und Mutterkorn. *Tieraerztl. Umsch. 40*:658-666.

Bartos, J., and Matyas, Z. (1982). Bioassays of trichothecenes in the grains. *Vet. Med. (Prague) 17*:567-574.

Bata, A., Vanyi, A., and Lasztity, R. (1983). Simultaneous detection of some fusariotoxins by gas-liquid chromatography. *J. Assoc. Off. Anal. Chem. 66*:577-581.

Bauer, J., Wermter, R., and Gedek, B. (1980). Zur Kontamination von Futtermitteln mit toxinbildenden Fusarienstammen und deren Toxinen. *Wien Tieraerztl. Monatsschr. 67*:282-288.

Beasley, V. R. (1983). The toxicokinetics and toxicodynamics of T-2 toxin in swine and cattle. Ph.D. thesis, University of Illinois, Urbana.

Beasley, V. R., Swanson, S. P., Corley, R. A., Buck, W. B., Koritz, G. D., and Burmeister, H. R. (1986). Pharmacokinetics of the trichothecene mycotoxin, T-2 toxin, in swine and cattle. *Toxicon 24*:13-23.

Beasley, V. R., Lundeen, G. R., Poppenga, R. H., and Buck, W. B. (1987). Distribution of blood flow to the gastrointestinal tract of swine during T-2 toxin-induced shock. *Fundam. Appl. Toxicol. 9*:588-594.

Bennett, G. A., Stubblefield, R. D., Shannon, G. M., and Shotwell, O. L. (1983). Gas chromatographic determination of deoxynivalenol in wheat. *J. Assoc. Off. Anal. Chem. 66*:1478-1480.

Blaas, W., Keelert, M., Steinmeyer, S., Tiebach, R., and Weber, R. (1984). Untersuchung von Cerealien auf Deoxynivalenol und Nivalenol im μg/kg-Bereich. *Z. Lebensm.-Unters. Forsch. 179*:104-108.

Boonchuvit, B., Hamilton, P. B., and Burmeister, H. R. (1975). Interaction of T-2 toxin with *Salmonella* infections of chickens. *Poult. Sci. 54*: 1693-1696.

Bottalico, A., Lerario, P., and Visconti, A. (1981). Occurrence of trichothecenes and zearalenone in preharvest *Fusarium*-infected ears of maize from some Austrian localities. *Phytopathol. Mediterr. 20*:1-6.

Brumley, W. C., Trucksess, M. W., Alder, S. H., Cohen, C. K., White, K. D., and Sphon, J. A. (1985). Negative ion chemical ionization mass spectrometry of deoxynivalenol (DON): application to identification of DON in grains and snack foods after quantitation/isolation by thin-layer chromatography. *J. Agric. Food Chem. 33*:326-330.

Buck, W. B., and Bratich, P. M. (1986a). Activated charcoal: preventing unnecessary death by poisoning. *Vet. Med. 81*:73-77.

Buck, W. B., and Bratich, P. M. (1986b). Experimental studies with activated charcoals and oils in preventing toxicoses. *Ann. Proc. Am. Assoc.
Vet. Lab. Diagn. 28:*193-200.

Buck, W. B., Lambert, R. J., Swanson, S. P., et al. (1986). *Diagnosis
and management of trichothecene toxicosis in the swine model.* Annual
Report, Contract No. DAMD 17-85-C-5224 to U.S. Army Medical Research
and Development Command, Ft. Detrick, Frederick, p. 371.

Buening, G. M., Mann, D. D., Hook, B., and Osweiler, G. D. (1982). The
effect of T-2 toxin on the bovine immune system: cellular factors. *Vet.
Immunol. Immunopathol. 3:*411-417.

Chakrabarti, D. K., and Ghosal, S. (1986). Occurrence of free and conjugated 12,13-epoxytrichothecenes and zearalenone in banana fruits infected
with *Fusarium moniliforme. Appl. Environ. Microbiol. 51:*217-219.

Chan, P., and Gentry, P. (1984). LD$_{50}$ values and serum biochemical changes
induced by T-2 toxin in rats and rabbits. *Toxicol. Appl. Pharmacol.
73:*402-410.

Chavez, E. R. (1984). Vomitoxin-contaminated wheat in pig diets: pregnant
and lactating gilts and weaners. *Can. J. Anim. Sci. 64:*717-723.

Chi, M., and Mirocha, C. (1978). Necrotic oral lesions in chickens fed diacetoxyscirpenol, T-2 toxin and crotocin. *Poult. Sci. 57:*807-808.

Chi, M., Mirocha, C., Kurtz, H., Weaver, G., Bates, F., and Shimoda, W.
(1977). Subacute toxicity of T-2 toxin in broiler chicks. *Poult. Sci.
56:*306-313.

Cirilli, G. (1983). Trichothecene problems in Italy. In *Developments in
Food Science*, Vol. 4, *Trichothecenes, Chemical, Biological and Toxicological Aspects*, Y. Ueno (Ed.). Kodansha, Tokyo and Elsevier, Amsterdam, pp. 254-258.

Coddington, K. A., Swanson, S. P., Hassan, A. S., and Buck, W. B. (1989).
Enterohepatic circulation of T-2 toxin metabolites in the rat. *Drug Metab.
Dispos.* (in press).

Coppock, R. W., Gelberg, H. B., Hoffmann, W. E., and Buck, W. B. (1985a).
The acute toxicopathy of intravenous diacetoxyscirpenol (anguidine) administration in swine. *Fundam. Appl. Toxicol. 5:*1034-1049.

Coppock, R. W., Swanson, S. P., Gelberg, H. B., Koritz, G. D., Hoffmann,
W. E., Buck, W. B., and Vesonder, R. F. (1985b). Preliminary study
of the pharmacokinetics and toxicopathy of deoxynivalenol (vomitoxin)
in swine. *Am. J. Vet. Res. 46:*165-168.

Coppock, R. W., Swanson, S. P., Gelberg, H. B., Koritz, G. D., Buck,
W. B., and Hoffmann, W. E. (1987). Pharmacokinetics of diacetoxyscirpenol in cattle and swine: effects of halothane. *Am. J. Vet. Res.
48:*691-695.

Coppock, R. W., Hoffmann, W. E., Gelberg, H. B., Bass, D., and Buck,
W. B. (1989). Hematologic changes induced by intravenous administration of diacetoxyscirpenol in pigs, dogs, and calves. *Am. J. Vet. Res.
50:*411-415.

Corley, R. A., Swanson, S. P., and Buck, W. B. (1985). Glucuronide conjugates of T-2 toxin and metabolites in swine bile and urine. *J. Agric.
Food Chem. 33:*1085-1089.

Corley, R. A., Swanson, S. P., Gullo, G. J., Johnson, L., Beasley, V. R.,
and Buck, W. B. (1986). Disposition of T-2 toxin, a trichothecene mycotoxin, in intravascularly dosed swine. *J. Agric. Food Chem. 34:*868-875.

Côté, L.-M., Reynolds, J. D., Vesonder, R. F., Buck, W. B., Swanson, S. P., Coffey, R. T., and Brown, D. C. (1984). Survey of vomitoxin-contaminated feed grains in midwestern United States, and associated health problems in swine. *J. Am. Vet. Med. Assoc. 184*:189-192.

Côté, L.-M., Beasley, V. R., Bratich, P. M., Swanson, S. P., Shivaprasad, H. L., and Buck, W. B. (1985). Sex-related reduced weight gains in growing swine fed diets containing deoxynivalenol. *J. Anim. Sci. 61*:942-950.

Côté, L.-M., Dahlem, A. M., Yoshizawa, T., Swanson, S. P., and Buck, W. B. (1986). Excretion of deoxynivalenol and its metabolite DOM-1, in milk, urine and feces of lactating dairy cows. *J. Dairy Sci. 69*:2416-2423.

Crone, H. D. (1984). *Response of rats to cutaneous dosing with trichothecene mycotoxins*, Report No. MRL-R-902, Department of Defence Publication. Defence Science and Technology Organization, Material Research Laboratories, Melbourne, Australia, p. 20.

DeNicola, D. B., Rebar, A. H., Carlton, W. W., and Yagen, B. (1978). T-2 toxin mycotoxicosis in the guinea pig. *Food Cosmet. Toxicol. 16*: 601-609.

Doebler, J., Wall, T., and Antony, A. (1985). Alterations in brain neuronal chromatin in T-2 toxin treated rats. *Fed. Proc. 44*:890.

Doerr, J., Hamilton, P., and Burmeister, H. (1981). T-2 toxicosis and blood coagulation in young chickens. *Toxicol. Appl. Pharmacol. 60*:157-162.

Dutton, M. R., and Westlake, K. (1985). Occurrence of mycotoxins in cereals and animal feedstuffs in Natal, South Africa. *J. Assoc. Off. Anal. Chem. 68*:839-861.

Eppley, R. M., Trucksess, M. W., Nesheim, S., Thorpe, C. W., Wood, G. E., and Pohland, A. E. (1984). Deoxynivalenol in winter wheat: thin layer chromatogrpahic method and survey. *J. Assoc. Off. Anal. Chem. 67*: 43-45.

Feinberg, B., and McLaughlin, C. S. (1989). Biochemical mechanisms of action of trichothecene mycotoxins. In *Trichothecene Mycotoxicosis: Pathophysiologic Effects*, V. R. Beasley (Ed.). CRC Press, Boca Raton, Fla. (in press).

Feuerstein, G., Goldstein, D. S., Ramwell, P. W., Zerbe, R. L., Lux, W. E., Faden, A. I., and Bayorh, M. A. (1985). Cardiorespiratory, sympathetic and biochemical responses to T-2 toxin in the guinea pig and rat. *J. Pharm. Exp. 232*:786-794.

Feuerstein, G., Lorenzana, R. M., and Beasley, V. R. (1989). Effects of trichothecene mycotoxins on the nervous system. In *Trichothecene Mycotoxicosis: Pathophysiologic Effects*, V. R. Beasley (Ed.). CRC Press, Boca Raton, Fla. (in press).

Forsyth, D. M., Yoshizawa, T., Morooka, N., and Tuite, J. (1977). Emetic and refusal activity of deoxynivalenol to swine. *Appl. Environ. Microbiol. 34*:547-552.

Foster, B. C., Trenholm, H. L., Friend, D. W., Thompson, B. K., and Hartin, K. (1986). Evaluation of different sources of deoxynivalenol (vomitoxin) fed to swine. *Can. J. Anim. Sci. 66*:1149-1154.

Fricke, R. F., and Poppenga, R. H. (1989). Treatment and prophylaxis for trichothecene mycotoxicosis. In *Trichothecene Mycotoxicosis:*

Pathophysiologic Effects, V. R. Beasley (Ed.). CRC Press, Boca Raton, Fla. (in press).

Friend, D. W., Trenholm, H. L., Elliot, J. I., Thompson, B. K., and Hartin, K. E. 1982). Effect of feeding vomitoxin-contaminated wheat to pigs. *Can. J. Anim. Sci. 62"*1211-1222.

Fromentin, H., Salazar-Mejicanos, S., and Mariat, F. (1980). Pouvoir pathogène de *Candida albicans* pour la souris normale ou déprimée par une mycotoxine: le diactozxiscirpenol. *Ann. Microbiol. 131B*:39.

Gabal, M. A., Awad, Y. L., Morcos, M. B., Barakat, A. M., and Malik, G. (1986). Fusariotoxicoses of farm animals and mycotoxic leucoencephalomalacia of the equine associated with the finding of trichothecenes in feedstuffs. *Vet. Hum. Toxicol. 28*:207-212.

Galey, F. D., Lambert, R. J., Busse, M., and Buck, W. B. (1987). Therapeutic efficacy of superactive charcoal in rats exposed to oral lethal doses of T-2 toxin. *Toxicon 25*:493-499.

Gareis, M., Bauer, J., and Gedek, B. (1985). Fusarientoxine in Futtermitteln: Nachweis und Vorkommen von Trichothecenen. *Tieraerztl. Prax., Suppl. 1*:8-19.

Gbodi, T. A., Nwede, N., Aliu, Y. O., and Ikediobi, C. O. (1986). The mycoflora and some mycotoxins found in Acha (*Digitaria exilis* Stapf) in Plateau State, Nigeria. *Food Chem. Toxicol. 24*:339-342.

Gentry, P. A. (1989). Effects on hemostasis and red cell production. In *Trichothecene Mycotoxicosis: Pathophysiologic Effects*, V. R. Beasley (Ed.). CRC Press, Boca Raton, Fla. (in press).

Ghosal, S., Chakrabarti, D. K., and Chaudhary, K. C. B. (1977). The occurrence of 12,13-epoxytrichothecenes in feeds of safflower infected with *Fusarium oxysporum*. *Experientia 33*:574-575.

Ghosal, S., Biswas, K., Srivastava, R. S., Chakrabarti, D. K., and Chaudhary K. C. B. (1978). Toxic substances produced by *Fusarium*: V. occurrence of zearalenone, diacetoxyscirpenol and T-2 toxin in mold corn infected with *Fusarium moniliforme* Sheld. *J. Pharm. Sci. 67*:1768-1769.

Gilbert, J., Sheperd, M. J., and Startin, J. R. (1983). A survey of the occurrence of the trichothecene mycotoxins deoxynivalenol (vomitoxin) in UK grown barley and in imported maize by combined gas chromatography/mass spectrometry. *J. Sci. Food Agric. 34*:86-92.

Gilbert, J., Sheperd, M. J., and Startin, J. R. (1984). The analysis and occurrence of *Fusarium* mycotoxins in the United Kingdom and their fate during food processing. In *Developments in Food Science*, Vol. 7, *Toxigenic Fungi—Their Toxins and Health Hazard*, H. Kurata and Y. Ueno (Eds.). Kodansha, Tokyo and Elsevier, Amsterdam, pp. 209-216.

Glavits, R., Sandor, G. S., Vanyi, A., and Gajdacs, G. (1983). Reproductive disorders caused by trichothecene mycotoxins in a large-scale pig herd. *Acta Vet. Hung. 31*:173-180.

Grove, J. F., and Mortimer, P. H. (1969). The cyotoxicity of some transformation products of diacetoxyscirpenol. *Biochem. Pharmacol. 18*:1473-1478.

Grove, G., Yater, S., Tallent, W., Ellis, J., Wolff, I., Kosure, N., and Nichols, R. (1970). Mycotoxins produced by *F. tricinctum* as possible cause of cattle disease. *J. Agric. Food Chem. 18*:734-736.

Hagler, W. M., Jr., Tyczkowka, K., and Hamilton, P. B. (1984). Simultaneous occurrence of deoxynivalenol, zearalenone and aflatoxin in 1982 scabby wheat from the midwestern United States. *Appl. Environ. Microbiol.* 47:151-154.

Haig, A. M., Jr. (1982). *Chemical warfare in southeast Asia and Afghanistan.* Congressional Special Report No. 98, report to the Congress from Secretary of State Alexander M. Haig, Jr., Mar. 22.

Hald, B., and Krogh, P. (1983). Toxicoses and natural occurrence in Denmark. In *Developments in Food Science*, Vol. 4, *Trichothecenes, Chemical, Biological and Toxicological Aspects*, Y. Ueno (Ed.). Kodansha, Tokyo and Elsevier, Amsterdam, pp. 251-253.

Hascheck, W. M. (1989). Mutagenicity and carcinogenicity of T-2 toxin. In *Trichothecene Mycotoxicosis: Pathophysiologic Effects*, V. R. Beasley (Ed.). CRC Press, Boca Raton, Fla. (in press).

Hassler, C. (1983). *Acute and Subacute Toxicology of T-2 Toxin in Monkeys: A pilot study.* U.S. Army Medical Research and Development Command, Fort Detrick, Frederick, Md.

Hayes, M., and Wobeser, G. (1983). Subacute toxic effects of dietary T-2 toxin in young mallard ducks. *Can. J. Comp. Med.* 47:180-187.

Hoerr, G., Carlton, W., and Yagen, B. (1981). Mycotoxicosis caused by a single dose of T-2 toxin or DAS in broiler chickens. *Vet. Pathol.* 18: 652-654.

Hsu, I.-C., Smalley, E. B., Strong, F. M., and Ribelin, W. E. (1972). Identification of T-2 toxin in moldy corn associated with a lethal toxicosis in dairy cattle. *Appl. Microbiol.* 24:684-690.

Huff, W. E., Doerr, J. A., Hamilton, P. B., and Vesonder, R. F. (1981). Acute toxicity of vomitoxin (deoxynivalenol) in broiler chickens. *Poult. Sci.* 60:1412-1414.

Ichinoe, M., and Kurata H. (1983). Trichothecene-producing fungi. In *Developments in Food Science*, Vol. 4, *Trichothecenes, Chemical, Biological and Toxicological Aspects*, Y. Ueno (Ed.). Kodansha, Tokyo and Elsevier, Amsterdam, pp. 83-97.

Ishii, K., Ando, Y., and Ueno, Y. (1975). Toxicological approaches to the metabolites of Fusaria: IX. Isolation of vomiting factor from moldy corn infected with *Fusarium* spp. *Chem. Pharm. Bull.* 23:2162-2164.

Jagadeesan, V. (1982). Immune studies with T-2 toxin: effect of feeding and withdrawal in monkeys. *Food Chem. Toxicol.* 20:83-87.

Jarvis, B. B. (1986). Trichothecene mycotoxins and their interactions with plants. In *Bioactive Molecules*, Vol. 1, *Mycotoxins and Phycotoxins*, P. S. Steyns and R. Vleggar (Eds.). Elsevier, Amsterdam, pp. 153-165.

Jemmali, M., Ueno, Y., Ishii, K., Frayssinet, C., and Etienne, M. (1978). Natural occurrence of trichothecenes (nivalenol, deoxynivalenol, T-2) and zearalenone in corn. *Experientia* 34:1333-1334.

Kamimura, H., Nishijima, M., Yasuda, K., Saito, K., Ibe, A., Nagayama, T., Ushiyama, H., and Naoi, Y. (1981). Simultaneous detection of several *Fusarium* mycotoxins in cereals, grains, and foodstuffs. *J. Assoc. Off. Anal. Chem.* 64:1067-1073.

Kanai, K., and Kondo, E. (1984). Decreased resistance to mycobacterial infection in mice fed a trichothecene compound (T-2 toxin). *Jpn. J. Med. Sci. biol.* 37:91-014.

Karppanen, E., Rizzo, A., Berg, S., Lindfons, B., and Aho, R. (1985). *Fusarium* mycotoxins as a problem in Finnish feeds and cereals. *J. Agric. Sci. Fin.* 57:195-206.

Kosuri, N. R., Grove, M. D., Yates, S. G., Tallent, W. H., Ellis, J. J., Wolf, I. A., and Nichols, R. .E (1970). Response of cattle to mycotoxins of *Fusarium tricinctum* isolated from corn and fescue. *J. Am. Vet. Med. Assoc.* 157:938-940.

Kriegleder, H. (1981). Morphological findings in guinea pigs after acute and subacture intoxication with diacetoxyscirpenol. *Zentralbl. Veterinaer. med. Reiche A* 28:165-175.

Kuroda, H., Mori, T., Nishioka, C., Okasaki, H., and Takagi, M. (1979). Studies on gas chromatographic determination of trichothecene mycotoxins in food. *J. Food Hyg. Soc. Jpn.* 20:137-142.

LaFarge-Frayssinet, C., DeCloitre, F., Mousset, S., Martin, M., and Frayssinet, C. (1981). Induction of DNA single strand breaks by T-2 toxin, a trichothecene metabolite of *Fusarium*. *Mutat. Res.* 88:115-123.

Lafont, P., and Lafont, J. (1977). Research and dosage of mycotoxins in human foods. *Inf. Alim.* 16:119-123.

Lafont, P., and Lafont, J. (1980). Contamination du maïs par des mycotoxines. *Bull. Acad. Vet. Fr.* 53:533-538.

Lafont, P., Giarard, T., Payen, J., Sarfati, J., and Gaillardin, M. (1983). Contamination de pommes de terre de consommation par des fusariotrichothécènes. *Microbiol. Alim. Nutr.* 1:147-152.

Lambert, R. J., Harlin, K. S., Swanson, S. P., Rood, H. D., Jr., Jacobsen, B. J., Buck, W. B., and Beasley, V. R. (1987). *Fusarium* mycotoxins in Illinois, Michigan and Iowa 1986 soybeans. *Proc. Ann. Meet. U.S. Anim. Health Assoc.* 91:305-306.

Lauren, D. R., and Greenhalgh, R. (1987). Simultaneous analysis of nivalenol and deoxynivalenol in cereals by liquid chromatography. *J. Assoc. Off. Anal. Chem.* 70:479-483.

Lee, U.-S., Jang, H.-S., Tanaka, T., Hasegawa, A., Ohm, Y.-J., and Ueno, Y. (1985). The co-existence of the *Fusarium* mycotoxins nivalenol, deoxynivalenol and zearalenone in Korean cereals harvested in 1983. *Food Addit. Contam.* 2:185-192.

Lee, U.-S., Jang, H.-S., Tanaka, T., Hasegawa, A., Ohm, Y.-J., Cho, C.-M., Sugiura, Y., and Ueno, Y. (1986). Further survey on the *Fusarium* mycotoxins in Korean cereals. *Food Addit. Contam.* 3:253-261.

Lew, H., Mullner, E., Hagerm, R., and Gregor, M. (1981). Futterungsprobleme bei Mastschweinen verursacht durch fusarientoxinhaltingen Mais. *Bodenkultur* 30:309-316.

Lorenzana, R. M., Beasley, V. R., Buck, W. B., Ghent, A. W., Lundeen, G. R., and Poppenga, R. H. (1985). Experimental T-2 toxicosis in swine: I. Changes in cardiac output, aortic mean pressure, catecholamines, 6-keto-PGF$_{1a}$, thromboxane B$_2$, and acid-base parameters. *Fundam. Appl. Toxicol.* 5:879-892.

Lundeen, G. R., Poppenga, R. H., Beasley, V. R., Buck, W. B., Tranquilli, W. J., and Lambert, R. J. (1986). Systematic distribution of blood flow during T-2 toxin induced shock in swine. *Fundam. Appl. Toxicol.* 7:309-323.

Lutsky, I., Mor, N., Yagen, B., and Joffe, A. (1978). The role of T-2 toxin in experimental ATA: a toxicity study in cats. *Toxicol. Appl. Pharmacol. 43*:111-124.

Marasas, W., Smalley, E., Gedurse, P., Bamberg, J., and Nichols, R. (1967). Acute toxicity to rainbow trout of a metabolite produced by *f. trinicinctum. Nature 214*:817-818.

Marasas, W., Bamberg, J., Smalley, E., Strong, F., Ragland, W., and Degurse, P. (1969). Toxic effects on trout, rats and mice of T-2 toxin. *Toxicol. Appl. Pharmacol. 15*:471-482.

Marasas, W. F. O., Kreik, N. P. J., van Rensburg, S. J., Steyn, M., and van Schalkwyk, G. C. (1977). Occurrence of zearalenone and deoxynivalenol, mycotoxins produced by *Fusarium graminearum* Schwabe, in maize in southern Africa. *S. Afr. J. Sci. 73*:346-349.

Marasas, W. F. O., van Rensburgh, S. J., and Mirocha, C. J. (1978). Incidence of *Fusarium* species and the mycotoxins, deoxynivalenol and zearalenone, in corn produced in esophageal cancer areas in Transkei. *J. Agric. Food Chem. 27*:1108-1112.

Marasas, W. F. O., Nelson, P. E., and Toussoun, T. A. (1986). *Toxigenic Fusarium Species: Identity and Mycotoxicology.* Pennsylvania State University Press, University Park, Pa.

Mirocha, C. J. (1983). Trichothecene mycotoxins in farm animals. In *Trichothecenes: Chemical, Biological and Toxicological Aspects*, Y. Ueno (Ed.). Elsevier, New York, pp. 177-194.

Mirocha, C. J., Pathre, S. V., Schauerhamer, B., and Christensen, C. M. (1976). Natural occurrence of *Fusarium* toxins in feedstuff. *Appl. Environ. Microbiol. 32*:553-556.

Mirocha, C. J., Schauerhamer, B., Christensen, C. M., and Kommedahl, T. (1979). Zearalenone, deoxynivalenol, and T-2 toxin associated with stalk rot in corn. *Appl. Environ. Microbiol. 38*:557-558.

Moore, C. J., Blaney, B. J., Spencer, R. A., and Dodman, R. L. (1985). Rejection by pigs of mouldy grain containing deoxynivalenol. *Aust. Vet. J. 62*:60-62.

Morooka, N., Uratsuji, N., Yoshizawa, T., and Yamamoto, H. (1972). Studies on the toxic substances in barley infected with *Fusarium* spp. *J. Food Hyg. Soc. Jpn. 13*:368-375.

National Research Council. (1983). *Protection Against Trichothecene Mycotoxins.* National Academy Press, Washington, D.C.

Neish, G. A., FArnsworth, E. R., Greenhalgh, R., and Young, J. C. (1983). Observations on the occurrence of *Fusarium* species and their toxins in corn in eastern Ontario. *Can. J. Plant Pathol. 5*:11-16.

Noonpudgee, C., Boohm, J., Abdelhamid, A. M., Leibetseder, J., and Schuh, M. (1986). Uber das Vorkommen von Desoxynivalenol (Vomitoxin, DON) in Futtermitteln fur osterreichische Nutztierbestande im Zeitraum von 1979 bis 1985. *Bodenkultur 37*:87-92.

Osborne, B. G., and Willis, K. H. (1984). Studies into the occurrence of some trichothecene mycotoxins in UK homegrown wheat and in imported wheat. *J. Sic. Food AGric. 35*:579-583.

Osweiler, G. D., Hook, B. S., Mann, D. D., Buening, G. M., and Rottinghaus, G. E. (1981). Effects of T-2 toxin in cattle. *Proc. Ann. Meet. U.S. Anim. Health Assoc. 85*:214-230.

Pace, J. G., Watts, M. R., Burrows, E. P., Dinterman, R. E., Matson, C., Hauer, E. C., and Wannemacher, R. W. (1985). Fate and distribution of ^{3}H-labeled T-2 mycotoxin in guinea pigs. *Toxicol. Appl. Pharmacol. 80*: 377-385.

Pang, V. F., Adam, J. H., Beasley, V. R., Buck, W. B., and Haschek, W. M. (1986). Myocardial and pancreatic lesions induced by T-2 toxin, a trichothecene mycotoxin, in swine. *Vet. Pathol. 23*: 310-319.

Pang, V. F., Felsburg, P. J., Beasley, V. R., Buck, W. B., and Hascheck, W. M. (1987a). The toxicity of T-2 toxin in swine following topical application: II. Effects on hematology, serum biochemistry, and immune response. *Fundam. Appl. Toxicol. 9*: 50-59.

Pang, V. F., Lambert, R. J., Felsburgh, P. J., Beasley, V. R., Buck, W. B., and Hascheck, W. M. (1987b). Experimental T-2 toxicosis in swine following inhalation exposure: effects on pulmonary and systemic immunity and morphologic changes. *Toxicol. Pathol. 15*: 308-319.

Pang, V. F., Swanson, S. P., Beasley, V. R., Buck, W. B., and Haschek, W. M. (1987c). The toxicity of T-2 toxin in swine following topical application: I. Clinical signs, pathology, and residue concentrations. *Fundam. Appl. Toxicol. 9*: 41-49.

Pang, V. F., Lambert, R. J., Felsburgh, Beasley, V. R., Buck, W. B., and Hascheck, W. M. (1988). Experimental T-2 toxicosis in swine following inhalation exposure: clinical signs and effects on hemathology serum biochemistry and immune response. *Fundam. Appl. Toxicol. 11*: 100-109.

Patterson, D. S. P. (1983). Trichothecenes: toxicoses and natural occurrence in Britain. In *Developments in Food Science*, Vol. 4, *Trichothecenes, Chemical, Biological and Toxicological Aspects*, Y. Ueno (Ed.). Kodansha, Tokyo and Elsevier, Amsterdam, pp. 259-264.

Payen, J., Girard, T., Gaillardin, M., and Lafont, P. (1983). Sur la Présence de mycotoxines dans des bières. *Microbiol. Alim. Nutr. 1*: 143-146.

Pfeiffer, R. L., Swanson, S. P., and Buck, W. B. (1988). Metabolism of T-2 toxin in rats: effects of time, dose, and route. *J. Agric. Food Chem. 36*: 1227-1232.

Pier, A., Cysewski, S., Richard, J., Baetz, A., and Mitchell, L. (1976). Experimental toxicosis in calves with aflatoxin, ochratoxin, rubratoxin and T-2 toxin. *Proc. Ann. Meet. U.S. Anim. Health Assoc. 80*: 130-148.

Poppenga, R. H., Beasley, V. R., and Buck, W. B. (1987). Assessment of potential therapies for acute T-2 toxicosis in the rat. *Toxicon 25*: 537-546.

Puls, R., and Greenway, J. A. (1976). Fusariotoxicosis from barley in British Columbia: II. Analysis and toxicity of suspected barley. *Can. J. Comp. Med. 40*: 16-19.

Rafai, P., and Tuboly, S. (1982). Effect of T-2 toxin on adrenocortical function and immune response in growing pigs. *Zentralbl. Veterinaer. med. Reiche B 29*: 558-565.

Renault, L., Goujet, M., Monin, A., Boutin, G., Palisse, M., and Alamagny, A. (1979). Suspicion de mycotoxicose provoquée par les trichothécènes chez les poulets de chair. *Bull. Acad. Vet. Fr. 52*: 181-187.

Rogers, A. E., Punyarit, P., Riengrojpitak, P., and Conner, M. W. (1984). Toxicity of anguidine in mice. *Toxicologist 4*: 12-14.

Rood, H. D., Jr., Buck, W. B., and Swanson, S. P. (1988a). Diagnostic screening method for the determination of trichothecene exposure in animals. *J. Agric. Food Chem. 36*: 74-79.

Rood, H. D., Jr., Buck, W. B., and Swanson, S. P. (1988b). Gas chromatographic screening method for T-2 toxin, diacetoxyscirpenol, deoxynivalenol, and related trichothecenes in feeds. *J. Assoc. Off. Anal. Chem. 71*: 493-498.

Rosen, R. T., and Rosen, J. D. (1982). Presence of four *Fusarium* mycotoxins and synthetic material in "yellow rain." *Biomed. Mass Spectrom. 9*: 443-450.

Saito, M., and Ohtsubo, K. (1974). Trichothecene toxins of *Fusarium* species. In *Mycotoxins*, I. F. H. Purchase (Ed.). p. 293-316.

Samples, D., Hill, D. W., Bridges, C. H., and Camp. B. J. (1984). Isolation of a mycotoxin (roridin A) from *Phomopsis* spp. *Vet. Hum. Toxicol. 26*: 21-24.

Sandor, G., Bata, A., Vanyi, A., and Kovacs, F. (1984). Complex investigation of the storage and feeding value of wet (by fermentation) preserved maize: V. Incidence of *Fusarium* toxins. *Magy. Allatorv. Lapja 39*: 733-737.

Sasaki, M. (1984). Determination of nivalenol and deoxynivalenol in wheat and shoyu. *Nippon Shoyu Kenkyusho Zasshi 10*: 183-188.

Sato, N., Ueno, Y., and Enomoto, M. (1975). Toxicological approaches to the toxic metabolite of *Fusaria*: VIII. Acute and subacute toxicities of T-2 toxin in cats. *Jpn. J. Pharmacol. 25*: 263-270.

Schuh, M., Leibetsener, J., and Glawischnig, E. (1982). Chronic effects of different levels of deoxynivalenol (vomitoxin) on weight gain, feed consumption, blood parameters, pathological as well as histopathological changes in fattening pigs. In *Proceedings of the Fifth International IUPAC Symposium on Mycotoxins and Phycotoxins*, Vienna, Austria, Sept. 1-3, W. Pfannhauser and P. B. Czedik-Eysenberg (Eds.). Austrian Chemical Society, Vienna, p.

Schweighardt, H., and Leibetsener, J. (1981). Nachweis on Mykotoxinen mittels Hochdruckflussigkeits-Chromatographie (HPLC). *Wein. Tieraerztl. Monatsschr. 68*: 302-350.

Schweighardt, H., and Schuh, M. (1981). Desoxynivalenol: ein beteutendes Trichothecen. *Ubers. Tierernahrung 9*: 11-32.

Scott, P. M. (1984). The occurrence of vomitoxin (deoxynivalenol, DON) in Canadian grains. In *Developments in Food Science*, Vol. 7, *Toxigenic Fungi—Their Toxins and Health Hazard*, H. Kurata and Y. Ueno (Eds.). Kodansha, Tokyo and Elsevier, Amsterdam, pp. 182-184.

Scott, P. M. (1989). Natural occurrence of trichothecenes. In *Trichothecene Mycotoxicosis*: *Pathophysiologic Effects*, V. R. Beasley (Ed.). CRC Press, Boca Raton, Fla. (in press).

Scott, P. M., Lau, P.-Y., and Kanhere, S. R. (1981). Gas chromatography with electron capture and mass spectrometric detection of deoxynivalenol in wheat and other grains. *J. Assoc. Off. Anal. Chem. 64*: 1364-1371.

Scott, P. M., Kanhere, S. R., and Lau, P.-Y. (1982). Methodology for trichothecenes. In *Proceedings of the Fifth International IUPAC Symposium on Mycotoxins and Phycotoxins*, Vienna, Austria, Sept. 1-3, W. Pfannhauser and P. B. Czedik-Eysenberg (Eds.). Austrian Chemical Society, Vienna, p. 44.

Shotwell, O. L., Bennett, G. A., Stubblefield, R. D., Shannon, G. M., Kwolek, W. F., and Plattner, R. D. (1985). Deoxynivalenol in hard red winter wheat: relationship between toxin levels and factors that could be used in grading. *J. Assoc. Off. Anal. Chem. 68*:954-957.

Siegfried, R. (1977). Fusariumtoxine (Trichothecentoxine) in Futtermais. *Landwirtsch. Forsch. Kongressband, Part I*, pp. 37-43.

Stahr, H. M., Ross, P. F., Hyde, W., and Obioha, W. (1978). Scirpene toxin analyses of feed associated with animal intoxication. *Appl. Spectrosc. 32*:167-174.

Stahr, H. M., Kraft, A. A., and Schuh, M. (1979). The determination of T-2 toxin, diacetoxyscirpenol, and deoxynivalenol in foods and feeds. *Appl. Spectrosc. 33*:294-297.

Stahr, H. M., Ross, P. F., and Obioha, W. (1981). Some mycotoxin levels in farm-stored corn. *J. Agric. Food Chem. 29*:207.

Stahr, H. M., Lerdal, D., Hyde, W., and Pfeiffer, R. (1983). Analysis of trichothecene mycotoxins. *Appl. Spectrosc. 37*:396-400.

Steinmeyer, S., Tiebach, R., and Weber, R. (1985). Gaschromatographische Untersuchung von Cerealien auf Deoxynivalenol uns Nivalenol nach Derivatisierung zu den Heptafluorbutyraten. *Z. Lebensm.-Unters. Forsch. 181*:198-199.

Swanson, S. P., and Corley, R. J. (1989). The distribution, metabolism and excretion of trichothecene mycotoxins. In *Trichothecene Mycotoxicosis: Pathophysiologic Effects*, V. R. Beasley (Ed.). CRC Press, Boca Raton, Fla. (in press).

Swanson, S. P., Dahlem, A. M., Rood, H. D., Jr., Côté, L.-M., and Buck, W. B. (1986). Gas chromatographic analysis of milk for deoxynivalenol and its metabolite DOM-1. *J. Assoc. Off. Anal. Chem. 69*:41-43.

Swanson, S. P., Nicolletti, J., Rood, H. D., Buck, W. B., Côté, L.-M., and Yoshizawa, T. (1987a). Metabolism of three trichothecene mycotoxins, T-2 toxin, diacetoxyscirpenol, and deoxynivalenol by bovine rumen microorganisms. *J. Chromatogr. Biomed. Appl. 414*:335-342.

Swanson, S. P., Rood, H. D., Behrens, J. C., and Sanders, P. E. (1978b). Preparation and characterization of the deepoxy trichothecenes: deepoxy HT-2, deepoxy T-2 triol, deepoxy T-2 tetraol, deepoxy 15-monoacetoxyscirpenol, and deepoxy scirpentriol. *Appl. Environ. Microbiol. 53*:2821-2826.

Swanson, S. P., Buck, W. B., Harlin, K., and Lambert, R. (1988). *Incidence of mycotoxins in feed samples submitted to the Illinois Diagnostic Laboratory.* UI NC-129 Ann. Rep. Feb.

Szathmary, C. I. (1983). Trichothecene toxicoses and natural occurrence in Hungary. In *Developments in Food Science*, Vol. 4, *Trichothecenes, Chemical, Biological and Toxicological Aspects*, Y. Ueno (Ed.). Kodansha, Tokyo and Elsevier, Amsterdam, pp. 229-250.

Tanaka, T., Hasegawa, A., Matsuki, Y., and Ueno, Y. (1985a). A survey of the occurrence of nivalenol, deoxynivalenol and zearalenone in foodstuffs and health foods in Japan. *Food Addit. Contam. 2*:259-265.

Tanaka, T., Hasegawa, A., Matsuki, Y., Ishii, K., and Ueno, Y. (1985b). Improved methodology for the simultaneous detection of the trichothecene mycotoxins deoxynivalenol and nivalenol in cereals. *Food Addit. Contam. 2*:125-137.

Tanaka, T., Hasegawa, A., Matsuki, Y., Matsui, Y., Lee, U.-S., and Ueno, Y. (1985c). Co-contamination of the

Tanaka, T., Hasegawa, A., Matsuki, Y., Matsui, Y., Lee, U.-S., and Ueno, Y. (1985c). Co-contamination of the *Fusarium* mycotoxins, nivalenol, deoxynivalenol and zearalenone, in scabby wheat grains harvested in Hokkaido. *J. Food Hyg. Soc. Jpn. 26*:519-522.

Tanaka, T., Hasegawa, A., Matsuki, Y., Lee, U.-S., and Ueno, Y. (1986). A limited survey of *Fusarium* mycotoxins, nivalenol, deoxynivalenol and zearalenone in 1984 UK harvested wheat and barley. *Food Addit. Contam. 3*:247-252.

Tanaka, T., Hasegawa, A., Yamamoto, S., Lee, U.-S., Sugiura, Y., and Ueno, Y. (1988). Worldwide contamination of cereals by the *Fusarium* mycotoxins nivalenol, deoxynivalenol and zearalenone: 1. Survey of 19 countries. *J. Agric. Food Chem. 36*:979-983.

Tatsuno, T. (1968). Toxicological research on substances from *Fusarium nivale*. *Cancer Res. 28*:2393.

Tatsuno, T., Saito, M., Enomoto, M., and Tsunoda, H. (1968). Nivalenol, a toxic principle of *Fusarium nivale*. *Chem. Pharm. Bull. 16*:2519-2520.

Taylor, M. J., Pang, V. F., and Beasley, V. R. (1989). The immunotoxicity of trichothecene mycotoxins. In *Trichothecene Mycotoxicosis: Pathophysiologic Effects*, V. R. Beasley (Ed.). CRC Press, Boca Raton, Fla. (in press).

Teich, A. H., and Hamilton, J. R. (1985). Effects of cultural practices, soil phosphorus, potassium, and pH on the incidence of *Fusarium* head blight and deoxynivalenol levels in wheat. *Appl. Environ. Microbiol. 49*:1429-1431.

Thalmann, A., Matzenauer, S., and Gruber-Schlev, S. (1985). Untersuchungen über das Vorkommen on Fusarientoxinen in Getreide. *Ber. Landwirtsch. 63*:257-272.

Thiel, P. G., Meyer, C. J., and Marasa, W. F. O. (1982a). Natural occurrence of moniliformin together with deoxynivalenol and zearalenone in Transkeian corn. *J. Agric. Food Chem. 30*:038-312.

Thiel, P. G., Marasas, W. F. O., and Meyer, C. J. (1982b). Natural occurrence of *Fusarium* toxins in maize from Transkei. In *Proceedings of the Fifth International IUPAC Symposium on Mycotoxins and Phycotoxins*, Vienna, Austria, Sept. 1-3, W. Pfannhauser and P. B. Czedik-Eysenberg (Eds.). Austrian Chemical Society, Vienna, p. 126-130.

Thigpen, J. T., Vaughn, C., and Studkey, W. J. (1981). Phase II trial of anguidine in patients with sarcomas unresponsive to prior chemotherapy: a southwest oncology group study. *Cancer Treat. Rep. 65*:881-882.

Thompson, W. L., and Wannemacher, R. W., Jr. (1986). Structure-function relationship of 12,13-epoxytrichothecene mycotoxins in cell culture: comparison to whole animal lethality. *Toxicon 24*:985-994.

Tiebach, R., Blaas, W., Kellert, M., Steinmeyer, S., and Weber, R. (1985). Confirmation of nivalenol and deoxynivalenol by on-line liquid chromatography-mass spectrometry and gas chromatography-mass spectrometry: comparison of methods. *J. Chromatogr. 318*:103-111.

Tobin, N. F. (1988). Presence of deoxynivalenol in Australian wheat and triticale—New South Wales Northern Rivers region, 1983. *Aust. J. Exp. Agric. 28*:107-110.

Trenholm, H. L., Cochrane, W. P., Cohen, H., Elliot, J. I., Farnworth, E. R., Friend, D. W., Hamilton, R. M. G., Neish, G. A., and Standish,

J. F. (1981). Survey of vomitoxin contamination of the 1980 white winter wheat crop in Ontario, Canada. *J. Am. Oil Chem. Soc. 58*: 992A-994A.

Trenholm, H. L., Cochrane, W. P., Cohen, H., Elliot, J. I., Farnworth, E. R., Friend, D. W., Hamilton, R. M. G., Standish, J. F., and Thompson, B. K. (1983). Survey of vomitoxin contamination of the 1980 Ontario white winter wheat crop: results of survey and feeding trials. *J. Assoc. Off. Anal. Chem. 66*: 92-97.

Trenholm, H. L., Friend, D. W., Hamilton, R. M. G., Prelusky, D. B., and Foster, B. C. (1989). Lethal toxicity and nonspecific effects. In *Trichothecene Mycotoxicosis: Pathophysiologic Effects*, V. R. Beasley (Ed.). CRC Press, Boca Raton, Fla. (in press).

Trucksess, M. W., Wood, M. T., and Page, S. W. (1986). Thin layer chromatographic determination of deoxynivalenol in processed grain products. *J. Assoc. Off. Anal. Chem. 69*: 35-36.

Tseng, T.-C., Yuan, G.-F., Tseng, T., Hsiao, I.-W., and Mirocha, C. J. (1985). Natural occurrence of *Fusarium* mycotoxins in grains and feeds in Taiwan. *Bot. Bull. Acad. Sin. 26*: 83-95.

Ueno, Y. (1977). Mode of action of trichothecenes. *Pure Appl. Chem. 49*: 1737-1745.

Ueno, Y. (1983). General toxicology. In *Trichothecenes: Chemical, Biological and Toxicological Aspects*, Y. Ueno (Ed.). Elsevier, New York, pp. 135-146.

Ueno, Y. (1984). Toxicological features of T-2 toxin and related trichothecenes. *Fundam. Appl. Toxicol. 4*: S124.

Ueno, Y., Ishii, K., Sakai, K., Kanaeda, S., Tsunoda, H., Tanaka, T., and Enomoto, M. (1972). Toxicological approaches to the metabolites of *Fusaria*: IV. Microbial survey of bean-hulls poisoning of horses with the isolation of toxic trichothecenes, neosolaniol and T-2 toxin of *Fusarium solani* M-1-1. *Jpn. J. Exp. Med. 42*: 187-203.

Ueno, Y., Nakajima, M., Sakai, K., Ishii, K., Sato, N., and Shimada, N. (1973). Comparative toxicology of trichothecene mycotoxins: inhibition of protein synthesis in animals. *J. Biochem. 74*: 285-296.

Ueno, Y., Lee, U.-S., Tanaka, T., Hasagawa, A., and Strzelecki, E. (1985). Natural occurrence of nivalenol and deoxynivalenol in Polish cereals. *Microbiol. Alim. Nutr. 3*: 321-326.

Ueno, Y., Tanaka, T., Hasegawa, A., Hu, C.-H., and Xu, D.-D. (1986a). Deoxynivalenol, nivalenol and zearalenone in scabby wheat from Shanghai, China. *J. Food Hyg. Soc. Jpn. 27*: 180-182.

Ueno, Y., Lee, U.-S., Tanaka, T., Hasegawa, A., and Matsuki, Y. (1986b). Examination of Chinese and U.S.S.R. cereals for the *Fusarium* mycotoxins, nivalenol, deoxynivalenol and zearalenone. *Toxicon 24*: 618-621.

Vesely, R., Vesela, D., and Jelinek, R. (1982). Nineteen mycotoxins tested on chick embryos. *Toxicol. Lett. 13*: 239-245.

Vesonder, R. F., and Ciegler, A. (1979). Natural occurrence of vomitoxin in Austrian and Canadian corn. *Eur. J. Appl. Microbiol. Biotechnol. 8*: 237-240.

Vesonder, R. F., Ciegler, A., and Jensen, A. H. (1973). Isolation of the emetic principle from *Fusarium*-infected corn. *Appl. Microbiol. 26*: 1008-1010.

Vesonder, R. F., Ciegler, A., Jensen, A. H., Rohwedder, W. K., and Weisleder, D. (1976). Co-identity of the refusal and emetic principle from *Fusarium*-infected corn. *Appl. Environ. Microbiol. 31*:280-285.

Vesonder, R. F., Ciegler, A., Rogers, R. F., Burbridge, K. A., Bothast, R. J., and Jensen, A. H. (1978). Survey of 1977 crop year preharvested corn for vomitoxin. *Appl. Environ. Microbiol. 36*:885-888.

Vesonder, R. F., Ciegler, A., Rohwedder, W. R., and Eppley, R. (1979). Re-examination of 1978 midwest corn for vomitoxin. *Toxicon 17*:658-662.

Visconti, A., Bottalico, A., Palmissano, F., and Zambonin, P. G. (1984). Differential-pulse polarography of trichothecene mycotoxins: determination of deoxynivalenol, nivalenol and fusarenon-x in maize. *Anal. Chim. Acta 159*:111-118.

Weaver, G., Kurtz, H., Mirocha, C., Bates, F., and Behrens, J. (1978a). Acute toxicity of the mycotoxin DAS in swine. *Can. Vet. J. 19*:267-271.

Weaver, G. A., Kurtz, H. J., Bates, F. Y., Chi, M. S., Mirocha, C. J., Behrens, J. C., and Robison, T. S. (1978b). Acute and chronic toxicity of T-2 mycotoxin in swine. *Vet. Rec. 103*:531-535.

Wilson, C., Everard, D., and Schoental, R. (1982). Blood pressure changes and cardiovascular lesions found in rats given T-2 toxin. *Toxicol. Lett. 10*:35-40.

Wong-Pack, R. (1987). The plasma disposition of dexamethasone in normal rats and in rats with T-2 toxicosis. M.S. thesis, University of Illinois, Urbana, p. 116.

Ylimaki, A., Kopenen, H., Hintikka, E.-L., Nummi, M., Niku-Paavola, M.-L., Ilus, T., and Enari, T.-M. (1979). *Microflora and Occurrence of Fusarium Toxins in Finnish Grain*, Publication 21, Materials and Processing Technology. Technical Research Centre of Finland, Espoo.

Yoshizawa, T. (1983). Red-mold diseases and natural occurrence in Japan. In *Developments in Food Science*, Vol. 4, *Trichothecenes, Chemical, Biological and Toxicological Aspects*, Y. Ueno (Ed.). Kodansha, Tokyo and Elsevier, Amsterdam, pp. 195-209.

Yoshizawa, T., and Hosokawa, H. (1983). Natural co-occurrence of deoxynivalenol and nivalenol, trichothecene mycotoxins, in commercial foods. *J. Food Hyg. Soc. Jpn. 24*:413-415.

Yoshizawa, T., and Morooka, N. (1979). Studies on the toxicogenic substances in the infected cereals: III. Acute toxicities of new trichothecene mycotoxins: deoxynivalenol and its monoacetate. *J. Food Hyg. Soc. Jpn. 15*:261-269.

Yoshizawa, T., Sakamoto, T., Ayano, Y., and Mitocha, C. J. (1982). 3'Hydroxy T-2 and 3'hydroxy HT-2 toxins: new metabolites of T-2 toxin, a trichothecene mycotoxin, in animals. *Agric. Biol. Chem. 46*:2613-2615.

Yoshizawa, T., Okamoto, K., Sakamoto, T., and Kuwamura, K. (1985a). In vivo metabolism of T-2 toxin, a trichothecene mycotoxin, on the formation of deepoxidation products. *Proc. Jpn. Assoc. Mycol. 21*:9-12.

Yoshizawa, T., Sakamoto, T., and Kuwamura, K. (1985b). Structures of deepoxytrichothecene metabolites from 3'-hydroxy HT-2 toxin and T-2 toxin. *Appl. Environ. Microbiol. 50*:676-679.

Young, L. G., and Vesonder, R. F. (1979). Moldy corn containing zearale-none and vomitoxin in diets of young pigs. *J. Anim. Sci. 49(Suppl. 1):* 258-262.

Young, L. G., McGirr, L., Valli, V. E., Lumsden, J. H., and Lun, A. (1983). Vomitoxin in corn fed to young pigs. *J. Anim. Sci. 57:*655-664.

III
EPIDEMIOLOGY AND RESPONSES

25

Epidemiology of Plant Poisoning in Humans

D. Jesse Wagstaff

Center for Food Safety and Applied Nutrition, U.S. Food and Drug Administration, Washington, D.C.

I. INTRODUCTION

A. Characterization of Epidemiology

Epidemiology in the strict etymological sense is the study of epidemics, but in
a broader more meaningful sense it is the science of counting cases of disease
and from those counts calculating rates, determining disease distributions in
populations, and determining conditions of disease occurrence. Most important, it is the application of this knowledge to control disease and improve
public health, which is measured by the rates at which illness and death occur
in a human population. Rates are calculated for specific causes of disease
and are used to make decisions for controlling disease.

B. Usefulness of Epidemiology in Disease Control

Usefulness of epidemiologic methods for disease control is best illustrated by
microbial diseases. Programs to collect data on disease occurrence were started nationally late in the nineteenth century. Death rates today have improved
to the extent that more lives are saved each year than there are people living
in the state of West Virginia (Wagstaff, 1986). This is due largely to control
of bacterial diseases of young children.

   A classic story of using epidemiologic methods for disease control is that
of the London physician John Snow, who calculated death rates for cholera
during a nineteenth-century epidemic and, by plotting geographic distribution of cases, discovered that the disease was associated with the drinking
of sewage-contaminated water from the Thames River (Snow, 1855). All of
this occurred before the work of Pasteur, which led to proof of the microbial
cause of the disease and the fecal-oral route of transmission.

   On the other hand, the role of products of macroscopic plants in diseases
of developed nations is not so obvious. In less developed areas of the world,
plants are used for food and drugs and for other purposes with little processing. Most of the processing that is done takes place in the home or local
village. In the United States, as in other developed nations, plant products
generally are processed at distant central locations before being distributed
for use. Legal and illegal recreational psychoactive products derived from
plants are the leading causes of preventable illness and death. Tobacco, alcohol, and cocaine injure and kill more people in the United States than all other
known etiologic agents. Tobacco and alcohol are each considered responsible
for 1.5 million years of life lost due to premature death (Amler and Eddins,
1987). Some of the harm is due to accidents, suicide, murder, and other
crimes associated with the use and distribution of these plant products. In
early 1989 the murder rate averaged more than one person per day in Washington, D.C. Most of these murders are thought to be related to cocaine. Drug
overdose and suicide add to the toll in this epidemic of human misuse of plant
products.

C. Importance of Poisoning by Plant Products

The incidence of acute plant poisoning is low; however, if chronic conditions
are also considered, plant poisoning may be a major cause of disease in the
world. Ames (1983) has estimated that our exposure to natural carcinogens,

mainly from plant sources, is 10,000 times greater than carcinogen exposure
from pesticides, industrial pollutants, and other synthetics. Plant carcinogens are found in a number of foods and species (Ames, 1983; Hirono, 1987).

D. Problems in Applying Epidemiologic Methods to Plant Poisoning

Estimates of disease rates or economic losses are all too often based on non-
factual assumptions. When these estimates are repeated or published, they
acquire credence. This oral or written publicizing does not enhance accuracy
but instead obscures matters by inhibiting people from asking critical questions. It is difficult to solve a problem through research, education, regulation, or other means if the magnitude of the problem cannot be measured.
Disease rates, whether extrapolated or counted, are based on a set of observations and assumptions, logic, and mathematical formulas. The listener or
reader should identify factors that underlie rates and ask whether those underlying factors reasonably support the decisions to be made. We should not
demand perfection, but we should ask that each item supporting a disease
rate or loss estimate is the best available. Furthermore, rates and estimates
should be adjusted when better data or better methods become available. Data
sets, particularly large data sets, are almost never perfect because of errors
of observation, recording, and transcription.

The objectives of an epidemiologic study of plant poisoning should be to
determine the distribution of the disease in a population (i.e., to define the
types of people at highest risk and to determine the underlying conditions).
Intervention efforts can then be concentrated on these particular groups to
alleviate the conditions and reduce disease incidence. The development and
use of child-proof drug containers is an example of successful intervention
for a high-risk group.

Plant poisonings are low incidence, diverse, and complex diseases. Data
sources that contain records of plant poisoning cases are themselves diverse
and complex. Major data sources are presented with their strengths and limitations, groups of people at high risk are defined, and future activities are
discussed. Emphasis is on vascular plants; the fungi are covered in Chapter
23.

II. DEFINITIONS

A. Importance of Definitions

Definitions are critical. Even a seemingly slight variation of criteria can pro-
foundly affect calculation of a disease rate. Results and conclusions are affected by study of objectives, definitions, and experimental design. Measurement of the total negative effect of a given factor on a human population is
difficult. This is also true for animal populations (Nielsen, 1978,1988) and
is particularly difficult for uncommon diseases such as acute plant poisoning.

1. Mortality Rate

Effects on a population are measured as rates. A death rate or mortality
is usually calculated as the number of deaths per unit of population per unit

of time. The unit of population is selected to make the numerator (i.e., the number of cases) a small number. The unit of population is often 100,000, but it could be 1 million or more and at the other end it could be as low as 1000. The most common time period is 1 year. Annual national mortality data are published yearly by the National Center for Health Statistics (NCHS). For example, in 1975 the death rate for diabetes mellitus was 16.5 per 100,000 population (U.S. Department of Health, Education, and Welfare, 1979).

2. Morbidity Rate

Morbidity is the rate for illness. The terms *illness, sickness,* and *disease* are used interchangeably here and are not limited to infectious disease. Incidence is the morbidity rate computed as the number of cases of disease per unit of population per unit of time. On the other hand, prevalence is the number of cases of disease per unit of population at a point in time. Other more general terms, such as *occurrence,* are sometimes used for incomplete data, but it is necessary to use well-defined terms and formulas in order to understand the data.

B. Data Types Needed

Before a rate can be computed, two types of data are needed: the count and characterization of the population, and the number of cases of the disease of interest. The count and characterization of the U.S. population is provided by the U.S. Bureau of Census from the national decennial census. Estimates for intercensal years are provided from samples and mathematical extrapolations. The general census at the beginning of each decade gives a count of people in the United States by age, race, sex, geographic location, and a number of other demographic factors. In addition, during a decade, other censuses are taken of various socioeconomic aspects of our society (e.g., agriculture and employment). The population census is the basis for probability sampling and is the denominator for calculation of morbidity and mortality rates.

C. Criteria for Case Selection

Criteria for including and excluding cases to be counted in a study are critical. Diagnosis of cases is one issue and classification of diseases is another. Medical personnel sometimes have difficulty in diagnosing plant poisoning. Emergency medicine health care professionals at a large urban teaching center could identify only 17% of common houseplants and could correctly identify only 13% of them as being toxic or nontoxic. Females scored better than males (Harchelroad et al., 1988). In a similar study, less than 10% of common local berries were correctly identified and their potential toxicity was even less well known (Scalise et al., 1988). Even if a case is correctly diagnosed as a plant poisoning at one stage in medical record keeping (as in an emergency room), the diagnosis may change, usually to something less specific at a later stage, as when a patient is admitted from an emergency room to a hospital.

There are a number of different schemes for defining and classifying diseases and causes of death, the most common being the International Classification of Disease (ICD). The first edition of ICD was presented in 1893

(World Health Organization, 1977). Since then revisions have been published almost every decade. The present revision is the ninth (ICD-9), which was published by the World Health Organization of the United Nations (1977). ICD has been adapted or modified for particular purposes in different countries; therefore, the exact revision and modification should be stated every time an ICD code (e.g., ICD-9CM) is used or referenced (Public Health Service, 1980). ICD provides numeric codes for causes of death, types of disease, and medical procedures. The basic set of codes consists of three-digit numbers ranging from 001 to 999. This set is further divided by adding one or more digits after a decimal point (e.g., one of the ICD-9 codes used for plant poisoning is 988.2). Supplementary sets of codes are prefixed with an alphabetical character. The set of interest here is for external causes (e.g., E865.4 is used for some plant poisonings).

Most national morbidity and mortality surveys in the United States use ICD coding; however, even with these standards there are limitations. First, codes have been added or changed to account for new entities. Motor vehicles were rare when the first ICD was published, but the need for codes for motor vehicle accidents became quickly apparent. Tragically, these codes have been much used. The annual motor vehicle accident death rate rose steadily until the onset of World War II, when the supply of automotive fuel was restricted. Following a decline in the rate during that war, this type of homefront slaughter increased again to a peak in 1973, when the Arab Oil Embargo caused speed limits to be reduced (Wagstaff, 1986). Efforts are made to have continuity of codes over time, but this is not always possible (Harris and French, 1980; Klebba and Dolman, 1975).

Another limitation is the lack of sufficient detail in coding to suit all purposes. Poisonings caused by individual plant species are not coded separately. There is no code for tobacco in ICD-9, nor is there a listing for this plant even as a processed product in the index for ICD-9. But if there were a code for tobacco, it is doubtful that it would be used as much as it should. The Oregon Health Division has not been able to get physicians to indicate on death certificates when tobacco contributed to the cause of death (Oregon Health Division, 1987).

A further complication is that plant poisonings can be coded under many different codes in widely separated sections of ICD. Poisoning by fava bean might be coded as 282.2 together with other anemias resulting from disorders or glutathione metabolism. A poisoning by a berry might be coded under 988.2 as a noxious food, E965.2 as an external cause, E950.9 for suicide, or E980.9 for poisoning by liquid and solid substances not otherwise specified.

Even if all codes used for plant poisonings could be determined, the large number of other diseases also coded in this same set of codes would make it impossible to determine the exact number of plant poisonings. Therefore, the best we can do is to obtain estimates for particular subsets of plant poisonings. Even with these limitations, some patterns are remarkably plain. Annual death rates for hepatic cirrhosis are related to alcohol consumption. Cirrhosis death rates fell markedly after the passage of various laws to restrict alcohol availability in the period before and during World War I and ratification of the 18th constitutional amendment in 1919, which initiated national prohibition. After the repeal of the 18th amendment in 1933, rates gradually rose again as alcohol became more available (Wagstaff, 1986).

Interpreting coding in a one-way coding system presents another challenge. Of necessity, the codes are established from particular points of reference. A drug poisoning could not also be coded as a plant poisoning. However, efforts are under way to code multiple causes, which should alleviate this problem.

D. Determining the Subset of Diseases

Given all these challenges, one must define the subset of plant poisonings for which incidence is desired and which can reasonably be estimated. The classifications in ICD-9 for acute plant poisoning if the plant was eaten as food include 988.1 for mushrooms and 988.2 for berries and other plants. Cases are excluded if the plant was used as a drug, tonic, or herbal remedy. Other codes excluded are allergic reaction to food [e.g., gastritis (558) or rash (692.5, 693.1), bacterial food poisoning (005), and toxic effects of food contaminants such as aflatoxin and other mycotoxins (989.7) or mercury (985.0)]. In surveys, such as mortality, which use the codes for external causes, the included codes are E865.3 for berries and seeds, E865.4 for other plants, and E865.5 for mushrooms and other fungi. Those specific E codes include poisonous plants, berries, and mushrooms eaten as food, mistakenly eaten as food, or eaten by a child; they exclude bacterial food poisoning.

III. DATA SOURCES

A. Historical Sources

People have been poisoned by plants throughout human existence. In the Biblical account of the first humans, disease and death were first attributed to the eating of a fruit. Evidence of plant poisonings of the past is found in history, literature, and art. Some of the evidence is rather persuasive and some is circumstantial.

One of the more dramatic epidemics to ravage Europe during the Middle Ages was ergot poisoning. Its hideous effects were graphically portrayed in the Isenheim altarpiece in Colmar, France, by Mathias Grunewald in 1510 (Dotz, 1980). Available evidence indicates that Nancy Hanks Lincoln, the mother of Abraham Lincoln, was killed by milksickness resulting from drinking the milk of a cow that had eaten white snakerood (*Eupatorium rugosum*) (Jordan, 1944). The average human life span has been increasing for at least the past three centuries. The major factor was a decline in child mortality. In London in the seventeenth century, 60% of the children died before age 16; by the late eighteenth century the mortality of children by age 20 had decreased to 50% (Matossian, 1981). In 1865 in Massachusetts, mortality before age 20 was about 28% (U.S. Department of Commerce, Bureau of the Census, 1976). It has often been assumed that control of infectious diseases brought about this decrease in deaths of children, but Matossian (1981) is of the opinion that, at least in England and Western Europe, improvement of a food safety problem (i.e., awareness of mycotoxins such as ergot) may have significantly contributed to the decrease. The significance of ergot in the United States is suggested by a theory that ergotism was the cause of the unusual behavior in women of early Salem, Massachusetts, who were tried and sometimes burned at the stake as witches (Matossian, 1982). Lee (1981) theorized that the artist Van Gogh was given digitalis as a treatment for his mental problems and that the resulting visual images he experienced caused him to emphasize halos and the color yellow in his paintings during the latter part of his life. An even more speculative example is that of Khan (1984), who thinks that atropine may have been the means of revenge used by a cuckolded husband against the man who committed adultery with his wife in Nathaniel Hawthorne's novel *The Scarlet Letter*. But not all past misery is behind us: plant poisoning plagues like favism and lathyrism continue.

B. Mortality

Vital statistics (i.e., records of births and deaths) are generated by the states in the United States. In many other countries that role is performed by national governments, which took over the function from state churches. In the United States, no state church was ever formed and the federal government has never had authority over the recording of vital statistics. Soon after local and state governments were established they began to record vital statistics, and their programs gradually improved. The three major purposes for recording births and deaths are to obtain knowledge of the movement of the population, to protect the lives and health of people, and to protect the rights of individuals and of the community (e.g., inheritance, pension claims, and foul play) (U.S. Department of Commerce and Labor, Bureau of Census, 1908).

The key event in developing mortality data is the issuance and registration of a death certificate. The federal government receives mortality information from the states. Starting in 1880, local governments were gradually admitted to a national death-registration system operated by the Bureau of the Census. Annual national reports of mortality began in 1900; with the admission of Alaska into the death-registration area in 1960, the system was complete. Cause of death and other information about the decedent, including age, race, and sex, together with the place of death and the place of usual residence, are recorded on the death certificate. Later, the causes of death are classified and given numeric codes according to ICD rules (World Health Organization, 1977).

Mortality data have strengths and limitations. There is not always a one-to-one correspondence of codes from one revision of the ICD to the next. Time-trend analysis of death rates requires determination of equivalent ICD codes over different revisions. No complete set of equivalent codes covers all causes of death over all ICD revisions, but some subsets of equivalent codes have been created, principally by NCHS (Klebba and Dolman, 1975). The completeness of registration of deaths is not known. The standard for admission to the death-registration area was registration of 90% of the deaths that occurred. It is assumed that registration has approached 100% in recent years, but this has not been verified. The quality of mortality data depends on the care with which the cause of death and other information about the decedent were determined and recorded on the death certificate. Although quality control procedures in coding are followed and their effectiveness has been evaluated (Harris and French, 1980), some inaccuracies and improbable data still exist.

Poisoning from food was coded for 1779 deaths in the death-registration area in 1910, and deaths in this category decreased to 15 in 1978. However, it cannot be determined what portion of these deaths may have been due to microbial toxins rather than plants and other sources of toxic chemicals. Plant poisoning (ICD-9 codes E865.3-E865.4) has accounted for one to five deaths each year over the past few years. Deaths attributed to mushroom poisoning (ICD-9 code E865.5) have been in this same range. Deaths caused by chronic disease which may have been due to plants or plant products were probably far more numerous but are classified under various other ICD codes.

C. Morbidity

There are no total counts for cases of illness; therefore, morbidity rates must be estimated from samples and case series. A number of national surveys are concerned basically with morbidity, but some deaths are recorded in these surveys.

The National Health Interview Survey (NHIS) of NCHS is based on a sample of respondents from about 40,000 households per year, which include about 107,000 people from the civilian noninstitutionalized population. This survey has the advantage of covering all cases of illness regardless of severity and whether medical aid was sought; however, it is limited by the memory and understanding of the person who is interviewed and by the small number of cases of uncommon diseases. Estimates of injuries and impairments including toxic effects—nonmedical (ICD codes 980-989)—were made from NHIS of 1980 and 1981. Poisoning from all causes, including plants, was reported for 0.8% of the population, with a higher rate for persons under 17 years of age but nearly equal rates for both sexes (Collins, 1986a). Hay fever, which is often related to plant pollen, was the sixth leading chronic condition reported by 77.3 persons per 1000 population. Contact dermatitis, including reactions to plants such as poison ivy and other skin conditions, was tenth; it was reported by 36.9 persons per 1000 (Collins, 1986b). Of the people with hay fever about 7.3% sought medical attention.

The National Ambulatory Medical Care Survey (NAMCS) is a probability sample of visits by ambulatory patients to offices of nonfederally employed physicians in the coterminous states. These physicians are principally engaged in office-based patient care practice but not in the specialties of anesthesiology, pathology, or radiology. NAMCS is conducted periodically; the most recent survey for which data are published was conducted in 1985 by NCHS (Nelson and McLemore, 1988). The sample consisted of 2879 physicians, about 1% of office-based physicians. There were an estimated 636 million visits to physicians within the scope of the survey, an average rate of 2.7 visits per person in the population. However, not all segments of the population visited physicians with equal frequency. Those over 44 years of age visited more frequently than did younger people. Females had a higher rate than males and whites visited physicians oftener than did other races. In 1985 not a single case of poisoning by berries, seeds, mushrooms, or other plants (ICD-9 codes 988.2 and 988.3) was recorded in NAMCS. This does not mean that there were no plant-related illnesses in the population. In fact, allergic rhinitis, including hay fever, was diagnosed in 1.2% of the visits, and contact dermatitis including that due to plants such as poison ivy accounted for 0.9% of the diagnoses.

The National Hospital Discharge Survey (NHDS) is based on a sample of approximately 193,000 abstracts of medical records for patients discharged from 558 short-stay nonfederal hospitals in the United States (Graham, 1988). ICD 9-CM codes were used for up to seven diagnoses. From this sample it is estimated that there were 34,256,000 discharges in the scope population and 102,764,000 diagnoses. For ICD code 988, which includes poisoning from fish, shellfish, berries, mushrooms, other plants, and unspecified noxious substances eaten as food, there were an estimated 4000 diagnoses; however, a footnote to the published table warned that estimates of less than 5000 should not be used and those of less than 10,000 should be used with caution. Therefore, the number of hospitalizations in the scope population was probably less than 10,000, and some of these were due to animal poisonings. In the tables for 1987, ICD-9 code 988 was not even listed, indicating that perhaps the estimated number of discharges for plant poisonings may have been less than 4000.

Poison control centers report morbidity and mortality data through publication of case series and single cases of interest. The largest case series are published in annual reports of the American Association of Poison Control Centers (AAPCC) National Data Collection System. The system has grown from the first report in 1983 (Veltri and Litovitz, 1984) to 63 reporting centers in 1987, serving a total population of 137.5 million people in 35 states and the District of Columbia (Litovitz et al., 1988). Human exposure cases totaled 1,166,940 in 1987, or 8.5 reported exposures per 1000 population. One center had a reported exposure rate of 18.7 per 1000. Although these AAPCC case series are not probability samples, and the annual reports themselves contain cautions about extrapolating results to the entire population, it is of interest that the NHIS estimate was relatively close to that of AAPCC.

Poison exposures in the AAPCC system are not classified by ICD but rather by a classification unique to AAPCC. It is difficult, therefore, to compare statistics using the two different coding schemes. In fact, NCHS cautions that the various morbidity surveys cannot be compared among themselves because of differences in objectives and experimental designs. Poison ivy poisoning is classed among plant poisoning in poison control data, but with dermatitis in mortality and morbidity files that use ICD; and certainly not all poison ivy cases are reported to poison control centers. Thus care should be used in interpreting the data.

The 88,251 plant exposures in the AAPCC system in 1987 accounted for 7.2% of all poison exposures. Plant exposures were distributed differently from those of other exposure types. Plant exposures tended to occur at a younger age; 85% occurred in children of less than 6 years of age, compared to 62% for all poison exposures. This may be due to the popularity of houseplants. Not all species of plants involved were published in the report, but among exposures to the 10 most frequently recorded plants, 67% were houseplants. A lower proportion of the plant exposures required medical care. Only 6% of plant exposure cases were treated at a medical care facility, compared to 25% of all poison exposure types. In fact, a nontoxic plant was involved in over 25% of the plant exposures. Still there were 11,613 cases of overt intoxication plus one fatality due to *Cicuta* in a teenage boy. In addition to the plant exposures, there were 7023 mushroom exposures, of which 1045 had clinical illness.

In most poison exposures requiring medical aid, the subject was treated and released; only 17.7% were admitted for medical care. If this proportion holds for plant poisoning, about 937 patients could have been hospitalized for this cause. This estimate is somewhat in line with the low and statistically unreliable annual estimate of hospitalizations for plant poisoning by the NHDS. The proportion of deaths from annual plant exposures was 0.001%, which was much less than the 0.034% for all poison types combined. However, fatal plant intoxications tend to occur in young people and are almost always accidental compared to most fatal intoxications, which are suicides in older age groups. In addition to the exposures listed under plants or mushrooms, several other plant products were under various classifications. Some of these products were colchicine, ethanol, strychnine, caffeine, cocaine, and tobacco. The 20 most frequently recorded plants with common names and a statement of toxicity are listed in Table 1. Some of the 13 plants listed as being toxic have only moderate toxicity and then only under particular conditions.

None of the other government and private sources of national morbidity data seem to be designed to produce reliable data for low-incidence diseases such as plant poisoning. The Nutrition and Health Examination Survey (NHANES) conducted by NCHS, has the intriguing feature of determining detailed food intake information and health status in the same person; however, the survey is designed to address nutritional questions rather than those of food safety or clinical toxicology. Another problem is that for logistical reasons, season and geographic region are confounded. Sampling was done in the north in the summer and in the south in the winter.

IV. DISCUSSION

A. Broad Trends and Risk Factors

Plant exposures are the most diverse and troublesome class of poisons encountered by poison control centers, emergency rooms, and others dealing with clinical toxicology. Diagnostic difficulties, recording errors and ambiguities, and lack of detail and consistency in disease classification contribute to the low incidence of reported plant poisoning and the lack of published details, which preclude calculation of precise morbidity and mortality rates. Despite these limitations, general patterns in disease distribution can be discerned and tentative ideas of risk factors can be formed.

B. High-Risk Groups

An epidemiologic analysis of NHDS data for childhood poisonings caused by a wide variety of medicinal and nonmedicinal liquids and solids (Rodriguez and Sattin, 1987) indicate that some population groups are at higher risk than others for poisoning. Plant poisonings were not considered as a separate group and, indeed, risk factors are not the same for all groups of toxicants. However, the analysis illustrates that high-risk groups can be identified and intervention strategies can be applied to reduce the incidence of poisoning. The annual hospitalization rate for poisoning was 65.1 per 100,000 children

TABLE 1 Toxicities of Plants

Plant	Common name	Toxicity
1. *Dieffenbachia* spp	Dumbcane	Toxic
2. *Philodendron* spp.	Philodendron	Toxic
3. *Euphorbia pulcherrima*	Poinsettia	Toxic
4. *Crassula* spp.	Jade plant	Nontoxic
5. *Ilex* spp.	Holly	Toxic
6. *Schefflera* spp.	Schefflera	Nontoxic
7. *Phytolacca americana*	Pokewood	Toxic
8. *Capsicum annuum*	Chile pepper	Toxic
9. *Taxus* spp.	Yew	Toxic
10. *Rhus radicans*	Poison ivy	Toxic
11. *Saintpaulia* spp.	African violet	Nontoxic
12. *Epipremnum areum*	Pothos	Toxic
13. *Pyracantha* spp.	Firethorn	Nontoxic
14. *Solanum dulcamara*	Climbing nightshade	Toxic
15. *Rhododendron* spp.	Rhododendron, azalea	Toxic
16. *Sorbus* spp.	Mountain ash	Nontoxic
17. *Spathiphyllum* spp.	Peace lily	Toxic
18. *Chrysanthemum* spp.	Chrysanthemum	Toxic
19. *Begonia* spp.	Begonia	Nontoxic
20. *Chlorophytum* spp.	Spider plant	Nontoxic

Source: Lampe and McCann (1985).

0 to 9 years of age. The rate was higher in the northeast, mainly because of lead poisoning, and higher in the south than in the west. Nonwhite children had higher rates than whites, and rates for males were higher than for females. Hospitalization rates for poisoning were 17 times higher for those 1 to 2 years of age than for those 5 to 9 years of age, and 4 times higher than for those under 1 year of age and ages 3 to 4. The authors felt that intervention efforts should be directed at groups of highest risk and that past intervention efforts such as the Lead-Based Paint Poisoning Prevention Act and the Poison Prevention Packaging Act had contributed to the dramatic fall in childhood poisoning mortality rates from 1956 to 1978.

C. Problems of Low Numbers and Erratic Trends

Both the rate and type of plant poisonings vary with age, sex, and conditions. The environment of the newborn allows little opportunity for plant exposure.

As children grow older their environment expands, as does their desire to explore and to experience.

Infants eat almost anything; of concern with infants are leaves of house-plants, whereas children who can walk more often eat berries. Rauber (1975) published a smooth age distribution indicating that plant exposures start at about 5 months of age, peak at 7 and 8 months, and then taper off markedly to 1 year. This clustering may result because children in this age range are learning to pull themselves up and to crawl. New things to be tested become part of their environment. As children learn to walk, other things become available for exploration.

Young children explore their yards and nearby fields and woods. They also like to mimic and to play house, school, and doctor. The variety of plant exposures increases. Berries, seeds, and other plant parts are eaten. Un-usual or even unpleasant plants may be eaten as part of a game or an explora-tion (Hartman, 1976).

From their preteen years through young adulthood, young persons ex-plore areas far from home. Adventure and risk taking are appealing. Eating roots and using psychoactive plant products in various ways are sometimes part of the adventure. Intoxication from *Cicuta* roots has been reported a number of times (Landers et al., 1985; Litovitz et al., 1988). Companions are present in most cases, and the roots are eaten in the field rather than taken home to be shared with the family, as happens more often in mushroom-poisoning cases. Usually, only one or two of the group eat the roots, indica-ting a realization of some risk even if it is not well understood and appreciated.

In middle age the risk seems to shift somewhat to users of herbal products. Herbal teas and dietary supplements have become popular. It is not generally known that herbals and other products sold in so-called health food stores have not been tested for safety or efficacy. Some of these products are known to be toxic or carcinogenic. Such information may or may not appear on labels of the products. Canada is devoting considerable effort to developing lists of herbal products that should not be sold publicly (Health and Welfare Canada, 1986). The preliminary lists contain some products that are widely available in U.S. health food stores. Despite safety questions there are few data on plant poisonings from this source. But fatalities have followed the use of herbal products sold locally (Huxtable, 1980). A greater problem is misidenti-fication of medicinal plants grown or collected by people for their own use or for use by family members. Middle-aged women frequently are victims. In a number of cases their husbands misidentified plants which they gathered for herbal teas for their wives (Bain, 1985; Haynes et al., 1985).

Newcomers and others not acquainted with the plants of a region are an-other group at risk. The group includes military personnel and migrant work-ers (Wagstaff and Case, 1987). During the well-planned exploration of the Lewis and Clark company, the concern about poisonous plants was so great that even though the explorers were forced to eat native plants, mainly roots, for long periods of time, they invariably purchased these items from local Indians who regularly ate such foods. No member of the expedition, not even the Shoshone woman Sacajawea, was trusted to gather such plants (Lewis, 1814). Brigham Young spoke of plant poisoning among early Mormon pioneers of Utah (Roberts, 1958). Early settlers on the east coast also encountered poisonous plants; one of these incidents provided the common name of the

Jimson or Jamestown weed (Jennings, 1935). Sometimes answers to plant poisoning mysteries have been learned from longtime residents of a region. While searching for the cause of milksickness in the mid-1830s in southeastern Illinois, Anna Pierce Hobbs encountered an old Shawnee Indian medicine woman who pointed out white snakeroot as the cause of milksickness (Snively and Furbee, 1966). Hobbs confirmed this through animal feeding and controlled the outbreak in the local area by encouraging people to grub out the plant and to refrain from drinking milk during the growing season. Unfortunately, her information was not publicized or well received by the medical community and the disease continued to take its toll in various areas for several years.

Hunger forces humans and animals to eat disagreeable and dangerous foods; plant poisoning accompanies famines. An outbreak of gangrenous ergot poisoning in an isolated highland region of northern Ethiopia in the latter 1970s was associated with a number of factors, including war, drought, isolation, poverty, and starvation (Demeke et al., 1979). The prevalence was 2.2 cases per 1000 population and the death rate was 1.1 per 1000. Rates were more than twice as high for males, and 80% of the cases occurred in people 5 to 34 years of age. The immediate cause was ergot in wild oats which had infested local barley fields during drought. Early in the outbreak the local residents associated eating the poor-quality grain with the disease; however, those at the lower end of the socioeconomic scale had no choice but to eat contaminated grain.

In developed countries plants are seldom used for suicides, but in other areas they are commonly used. *Gloriosa superba* is used for suicide in Sri Lanka (Senanayake and Karalliedde, 1988). Another popular suicidal plant in that nation is the seed of *Thevetia peruviana* (Saravanapavananthan and Ganeshamoorthy, 1988). In a 3-year period following a newspaper story of the toxicity of the seeds, 170 cases were seen in just one hospital. About two-thirds of the cases were females and 65% of the cases were 16 to 25 years of age. There were seven fatalities.

D. Future Activities

If we can continue to avert war and famine in our nation and protect our young and newcomers, and if the call of the wild and the appeal of the natural can be kept within moderate bounds, we can expect the incidence of acute plant poisonings to remain low. But efforts should be made to better control a type of poisoning that causes concern, creates confusion, and endangers lives.

It may seem at times that the data on human plant poisonings are a confusing jumble. Small numbers make it difficult to discern patterns and associations, but morbidity and mortality trends tend to become fairly smooth as numbers get larger. There is every reason to believe that human plant poisonings also occur in definite patterns with fairly smooth distribution curves. Activities that are planned or are under way to improve epidemiologic data for plant poisoning include coding of multiple causes of death, the National Death Index to integrate death certificates with clinical and research records for a decedent, more detailed analysis of plant exposures, and comparison of poison control records with national mortality data.

REFERENCES

Ames, B. N. (1983). Dietary carcinogens and anticarcinogens: oxygen radicals and degenerative diseases. *Science 221*:1256-1264.

Amler, R. W., and Eddins, D. L. (1987). Cross-sectional analysis: precursors of premature death in the United States. In *Closing the Gap: The Burden of Unnecessary Illness*, R. W. Amler and H. B. Dull (Eds.). Oxford University Press, New York, pp. 181-187.

Bain, R. J. I. (1985). Accidental digitalis poisoning due to drinking herbal tea. *Br. Med. J. 290*:1624.

Collins, J. G. (1986a). *Types of injuries and impairments due to injuries: United States*. Vital and Health Statistics, Series 10, No. 159, DHHS Publ. No. (PHS) 87-1587. Public Health Service, U.S. Government Printing Office, Washington, D.C.

Collins, J. G. (1986b) *Prevalence of selected chronic conditions: United States, 1979-81*. Vital and Health Statistics, Series 10, No. 155, DHHS Publ. No. (PHS) 86-1583. Public Health Service, U.S. Government Printing Office, Washington, D.C.

Demeke, T., Kidane, Y., and Wuhib, E. (1979). Ergotism—a report on an epidemic, 1977-78. *Ethiop. Med. J. 17*:107-113.

Dotz, W. (1980). St. Anthony's fire. *Am. J. Dermatopathol. 2*:249-253.

Graham, D. (1988). *Detailed diagnoses and procedures for patients discharged from short-stay hospitals; United States, 1986*. Vital and Health Statistics, Series 13, No. 95, DHHS Publ. No. (PHS) 88-1756. Public Health Service, U.S. Government Printing Office, Washington, D.C.

Harchelroad, F., Scalise, J. A., Dean, B. S., and Krenzelok, E. P. (1988). Identification of common houseplants in the emergent care setting. *Vet. Hum. Toxicol. 30*:161-163.

Harris, K. W., and French, D. K. (1980). *A methodological study of quality control procedures for mortality medical coding*. Vital and Health Statistics, Series 2, No. 81, DHHS Publ. No. (PHS) 80-1355. Public Health Service, U.S. Government Printing Office, Washington, D.C.

Hartman, G. (1976). The deadly garden. *Time 107*(9):54-55.

Haynes, B. E., Bessen, H. A., and Wightman, W. D. (1985). Oleander tea: herbal draught of death. *Ann. Emerg. Med. 14*:350-353.

Health and Welfare Canada, Health Protection Branch. (1986). Report of the expert advisory committee on herbs and botanical preparations.

Hirono, I. (Ed.). (1987). *Naturally Occurring Carcinogens of Plant Origin: Toxicology, Pathology and Biochemistry*. Kodanshan, Tokyo and Elsevier, Amsterdam.

Huxtable, R. J. (1980). Herbal teas and toxins: novel aspects of pyrrolizidine poisoning in the United States. *Perspect. Biol. Med. 24*:1-14.

Jennings, R. E. (1935). Stramonium poisoning: a review of the literature and report of two cases. *J. Pediatr. 6*:657-664.

Jordan, P. D. (1944). Milksickness in the western country together with an account of the death of Lincoln's mother. *Ohio State Med. J. 40*:848-851.

Khan, J. A. (1984). Atropine poisoning in Hawthorne's *The Scarlet Letter*. *N. Engl. J. Med. 311*:414-416.

Klebba, A. J., and Dolman, A. B. (1975). *Comparability of mortality statis-*

tics for the seventh and eighth revisions of the International Classification of Diseases; United States. Vital and Health Statistics, Series 2, No. 66, DHEW Publ. No. (HRA) 76-1340. U.S. Government Printing Office, Washington, D.C.

Lampe, K. F., and McCann, M. A. (1985). *AMA Handbook of Poisonous and Injurious Plants*. Chicago Review Press, Chicago.

Landers, D., Seppi, K., and Blauer, W. (1985). Seizures and death on a white river float trip: report of water hemlock poisoning. *West. J. Med.* *142*:637-640.

Lee, T. C. (1981). Van Gogh's vision: digitalis intoxication? *J. Am. Med. Assoc.* *245*:727-729.

Lewis, M. (1814). *The Lewis and Clark Expedition*. J. B. Lippincott, Philadelphia.

Litovtiz, T. L., Schmitz, B., Matyunas, N., and Martin, T. G. (1988). 1987 annual report of the American Association of Poison Control Centers National Data Collection System. *Am. J. Emerg. Med.* *6*:479-515.

Matossian, M. K. (1981). Mold poisoning: an unrecognized English health problem, 1550-1800. *Med. Hist.* *25*:73-84.

Matossian, M. K. (1982). Ergot and the Salem witchcraft affair. *Am. Sci.* *70*:355-357.

Nelson, C., and McLemore, T. (1988). *The national ambulatory medical care survey: United States, 1975-81 and 1985 trends*. Vital and Health Statistics, Series 13, No. 93, DHHS Publ. No. (PHS) 88-1754. Public Health Service, U.S. Government Printing Office, Washington, D.C.

Nielsen, D. B. (1978). The economic impact of poisonous plants on the range livestock industry in the 17 western states. *J. Range Manage.* *31*:325-328.

Nielsen, D. B. (1988). Economic impact of poisonous plants on the rangeland livestock industry. *J. Anim. Sci.* *66*:2330-2333.

Oregon Health Division. (1987). Reporting tobacco use on death certificates. *Commun. Dis. Summ.* *36*(8):1-2.

Public Health Service and Health Care Financing Administration. (1980). *International Classification of Diseases*, 9th revision, *Clinical Modification*. DHHS Publ. No. (PHS) 80-1260. Public Health Service, U.S. Government Printing Office, Washington, D.C.

Rauber, A. (1975). Poisoning in children under 12 months of age. *Clin. Toxicol.* *8*:391-397.

Roberts, B. H. (1958). *Comprehensive History of the Church*, Vol. 3, Deseret News Press, Salt Lake City, Utah.

Rodriguez, J. G., and Sattin, R. W. (1987). Epidemiology of childhood poisonings leading to hospitalization in the United States, 1979-1983. *Am. J. Prev. Med.* *3*:164-170.

Saravanapavananthan, N., and Ganeshamoorthy, J. (1988). Yellow oleander poisoning—a study of 170 cases. *Forensic Sci. Int.* *36*:247-250.

Scalise, J. A., Harchelroad, F., Dean, B. S., and Krenzelok, E. P. (1988). Berry identification by emergency health care providers. *Vet. Hum. Toxicol.* *30*:426-428.

Senanayake, N., and Karalliedde, L. (1988). Patterns of acute poisoning in a medical unit in central Sri Lanka. *Forensic Sci. Int.* *36*:101-104.

Snively, W. D., Jr., and Furbee, L. (1966). Discoverer of the cause of milk sickness. *J. Am. Med. Assoc. 196*:1055-1060.

Snow, J. (1855). *Cholera.* Churchill, London.

U.S. Department of Commerce and Labor, Bureau of Census. (1908). *Mortality Statistics 1906.* U.S. Government Printing Office, Washington, D.C.

U.S. Department of Commerce and Labor, Bureau of Census. (1976). *Historical Statistics of the United States Colonial Times to 1970: Part I.* U.S. Government Printing Office, Washington, D.C.

U.S. Department of Health, Education, and Welfare, National Center for Health Statistics. (1979). *Vital statistics of the United States 1975*, Vol. II, *Mortality*, Part A. DHEW Publ. No. (PHS) 79-1114. U.S. Government Printing Office, Washington, D.C.

Veltri, J. C., and Litovitz, T. L. (1984). 1983 Annual report of the American Association of Poison Control Centers National Data Collection System. *Am. J. Emerg. Med. 2*:420-443.

Wagstaff, D. J. (1986). Public health and food safety: a historical association. *Public Health Rep. 101*:624-631.

Wagstaff, D. J., and Case, A. A. (1987). Human poisoning by *Zigadenus*. *Clin. Toxicol. 25*:361-367.

World Health Organization. (1977). *International Classification of Diseases.* WHO, Geneva.

26

Antineoplastic Potential and Other Possible Uses of Swainsonine and Related Compounds

Kenneth Olden

Howard University Cancer Center, Howard University Medical School, Washington, D.C. and National Cancer Institute, Bethesda, Maryland

Sandra L. White

Howard University Cancer Center and Department of Microbiology, Howard University Medical School, Washington, D.C.

Sheila A. Newton

Howard University Cancer Center, Howard University Medical School, Washington, D.C.

Russell J. Molyneux

Western Regional Research Center, Agricultural Research Center, USDA, Albany, California

Martin J. Humphries

Howard University Cancer Center, Howard University Medical School, Washington, D.C. and University of Manchester, Manchester, England

I. INTRODUCTION

Swainsonine and related compounds have been employed in biomedical research primarily as tools to study the role of the oligosaccharide moiety of glycoproteins in various biological systems (Gibson et al., 1980; Olden et al., 1982a,b; Schwarz and Datema, 1982,1984; Elbein, 1984,1987; Datema et al., 1987). Use in such studies is related to the ability of the drug to inhibit Golgi α-mannosidase II activity with the formation of hybrid oligosaccharides in lieu of oligosaccharides of complex structure (Tulsiani et al., 1982). In fact, swainsonine was the first compound shown to inhibit the processing of carbohydrate moieties of glycoproteins (Elbein et al., 1981).

To date, there are no reports that swainsonine-induced changes in the structure of oligosaccharides affect the function of a specific glycoprotein, which suggests that the formation of the hybrid oligosaccharides in lieu of the complex type is still sufficient for biological activity, and that protein conformation is not altered. For example, swainsonine did not influence the surface expression or function of the receptors for insulin (Duronio et al., 1986) or epidermal growth factor (Soderquist and Carpenter, 1984). However, we and others have shown that cell surface interactions involving carbohydrate mediation, such as recognition and adhesion, are influenced by swainsonine treatment (Bar-Shavit et al., 1984; Hino et al., 1985; Humphries et al., 1986a,b; Humphries and Olden, 1989). For example, the effect of glucocorticoids on bone cell attachment is blocked by the glycosylation inhibitor tunicamycin and the glycosylation modifier swainsonine. This review focuses on the potential use of swainsonine in the treatment of cancer and immunosuppressive disorders, diseases that may be influenced by this and related drugs.

II. INHIBITION OF METASTASIS

Hematogenous dissemination of malignant cells from the primary tumor to secondary sites represents the culmination of a complex series of events referred to as the metastatic cascade. The first phase of the metastatic cascade is that of detachment of malignant cells from the primary tumor mass and entry into the circulatory system, a process called invasion or intravasation; this is a multistep process involving many interactions between tumor cells and host. The second phase is that of transport in the blood vascular system. During this phase the vast majority of cells are destroyed by a combination of hemodynamic forces during passage of blood through narrow capillary beds (Fidler, 1970; Weiss et al., 1982; Weiss, 1986) and by host immune effector cells (Herberman, 1982). Survival in circulation is enhanced by the formation of homotypic or heterotypic aggregates. The final phase is that of colonization of the target organ; this is also a multistep process consisting of lodgement in capillary beds, by both specific and nonspecific mechanisms, where extravasation or invasion can occur.

The metastasis experiments described below were conducted using two animal model systems used previously for such studies (Fidler, 1978; Fidler et al., 1978). Initial studies were carried out using an experimental metastasis model system in which tumor cells were introduced into the circulatory system by intravenous injection. This model is adequate to examine the blood-vascular transport and colonization phases of the metastatic cascade, but obviously bypasses detachment or the intravasation phase of tumor dissemination. But our more recent studies were conducted using spontaneous metastasis models because of its relevance to metastasis in humans. Furthermore, the latter approach permitted us to examine the possible effect of swainsonine on all phases of the metastatic cascade.

Cell surface oligosaccharides play an important role in expression of the malignant behavior of tumor cells. The relationship between malignancy and structure of surface carbohydrates was suggested with the observation that oncogenic transformation led to an increase in the size and complexity of asparagine-linked oligosaccharides on cellular glycoproteins [reviewed by Warren et al. (1972, 1973, 1978), Van Beek et al. (1975), Warren and Buck (1980), Nicolson (1982), Yogeeswaran (1983), Raz and Lotan (1987), and Humphries and Olden (1989)]. This occurrence has been substantiated for cells from a variety of species, including humans, using various methods of transformation (Santer and Glick, 1979; Santer et al., 1984; Collard et al., 1985).

A. Modification of Surface Glycoproteins by In Vitro Treatment with Tunicamycin or Inhibitors of Oligosaccharide Processing

Asparagine-linked oligosaccharide synthesis occurs via a pathway involving dolichol phosphate-$Glc_3Man_9GlcNAc_2$ as a precursor. The sugar component of the precursor is transferred to the appropriate asparagine residue of the growing polypeptide on the rough endoplasmic reticulum; the transfer is catalyzed by glycosyl transferase that recognizes the asparagine in the tripeptide sequence Asn-X-Ser(Thr), where X can be any amino acid except proline. The glucosylated, high-mannose intermediate may give rise to either the "high-mannose," "hybrid," or "complex" structure characteristic of asparagine-linked oligosaccharides. This occurs by a series of trimming and elongation reactions that occur in the various compartments of the endoplasmic reticulum and Golgi apparatus. The glucose residues are removed by the sequential action of glucosidase I and II to give rise to the high-mannose oligosaccharide. The complex structure is formed by subsequent removal of six mannose residues by α-mannosidase I and II to give a trimannose core to which N-acetylglucosamine, galactose, and sialic acid are added sequentially. Branching is controlled by several specific branching enzymes that act at the level of the trimannose core. The removal of the three glucose residues and the first α-linked mannose occurs in the rough endoplasmic reticulum, whereas the remainder of the oligosaccharide processing reactions take place in the Golgi. These processing reactions are shown schematically in Fig. 1, and for a comprehensive review the reader is referred to the earlier publications of Hubbard and Ivatt (1981), Kornfeld and Kornfeld (1985), and Montreuil (1987). The structure of the oligosaccharide moiety of specific glycoproteins is relatively constant, even though considerable diversity exists in nature. The information encoded in the structure of the oligosaccharide chains is believed

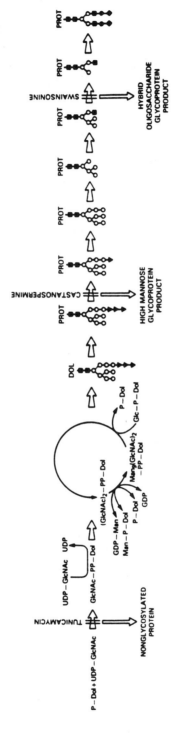

FIGURE 1 General pathway for glycoprotein processing. The high-mannose precursor molecule shown is synthesized on the lipid precursor dolichol and then transferred en bloc to the protein backbone. Subsequent processing steps are performed by specific glycosidases and glycosyl transferases located in the endoplasmic reticulum and Golgi apparatus. The reactions inhibited by tunicamycin, swainsonine, and castanospermine are shown. ○, mannose; ▼, glucose; ■, *N*-acetylglucosamine; ●, galactose; ◆, sialic acid.

to confer biological specificity which mediates cell surface functions such as cell-cell adhesion, recognition, and metastasis and invasion. By using processing inhibitors with specific sites of action, one can study the role of various oligosaccharides in the expression of the malignant phenotype. Presently, glycosylation inhibitors can be grouped into one of the following classes: (1) agents that prevent the transfer of the dolichol-linked oligosaccharide precursor to the protein backbone (e.g., tunicamycin); (2) agents that inhibit early events in the processing pathway and therefore generate glycoproteins with high-mannose oligosaccharide structures which would ordinarily possess complex structures (e.g., deoxynojirimycin, castanospermine, and deoxymannojirimycin), and (3) agents that act later in the processing pathway to generate glycoproteins with hybrid carbohydrate chains characteristic of both the high-mannose and complex structures (e.g., swainsonine).

Olden et al. (1979) reported that tunicamycin selectively killed transformed cells in culture and altered the morphology and adhesion of their normal counterparts. Based on these studies, Irimura et al. (1981) examined the effects of tunicamycin on the metastatic potential of B16 murine melanoma cells. Cells in culture were treated with tunicamycin, then viable cells were slowly injected into the lateral tail vein of syngeneic mice. Such treatment resulted in substantial inhibition of glycosylation and almost complete arrest in pulmonary colonization. This finding was later confirmed by Olden et al. (1985). Also, a slight therapeutic effect was obtained by the systemic administration of tunicamycin to tumor-bearing mice (Morin and Bernacki, 1983; Olden et al., 1985), but significant toxicity limits the use of this drug.

Since tunicamycin specifically inhibits the synthesis of the dolichol phosphate oligosaccharide intermediate (Tkacz and Lampen, 1975) (Fig. 1), its ability to decrease the metastatic potential of malignant cells suggests that asparagine-linked oligosaccharides play a crucial role in metastasis formation.

Subcutaneously injected tunicamycin-treated cells killed the recipient mice at a rate only slightly slower than did control cells, confirming that the effects of the drug are reversible (Humphries et al., 1986b). However, the retention of tunicamycin-treated cells in the lungs was only about half as efficient as that of untreated cells; that is, drug-treated cells, which initially lodged in the lungs, were lost at a reproducibly greater rate than were cells from control cultures. Such a finding suggests that the cell surface adhesive function is decreased in tunicamycin-treated cells. Consistent with this suggestion, the ability of tunicamycin-treated cells to attach to the adhesive macromolecules fibronectin and laminin was greatly diminished. The poorly adhesive cells exhibited rounding with abundant blebs and ruffles.

While similar results were obtained with murine sarcoma L-1 cells following in vitro treatment with tunicamycin (Pulverer et al., 1988), no specific effect on metastatic colonization of the lungs was observed following similar treatment of murine mammary tumor cells (Sargent et al., 1987). So although tunicamycin may inhibit the metastasis of diverse tumor types, the effect is apparently not universal.

It is possible that tumor cell surface oligosaccharides influence metastasis by facilitating interaction with extracellular matrix proteins. Such an involvement is supported by the following findings: (1) modification of cell surface carbohydrates with either glycosidases, lectins, or blood group antibodies disrupts adhesion (Grimstad et al., 1984); (2) purified glycopeptides exhibit specificity in inhibition of cell attachment to laminin or type IV collagen (Dennis et al., 1984); and (3) lectin-resistant mutants are poorly adhesive to fibronectin and collagens (Pena and Hughes, 1978; Dennis et al., 1982).

To date, four oligosaccharide-processing inhibitors have been tested for their effects on experimental metastasis: swainsonine, castanospermine, 1-deoxynojirimycin, and bromoconduritol. Swainsonine is a specific inhibitor of Golgi α-mannosidase II, the enzyme that catalyzes the removal of two mannose residues from the precursor $GlcNAcMan_5GlcNAc_2$ (Tulsiani et al., 1982). This step is required for the addition of N-acetylglucosamine, galactose, and sialic acid to the $\alpha1$-6 side of the mannose core. Since swainsonine does not prevent normal processing of the $\alpha1$-3 side of the mannose core, treatment with this drug results in formation of a biantennary structure composed of one high-mannose chain and one complex chain, the so-called "hybrid" structure (Tulsiani and Touster, 1983). Castanospermine inhibits endoplasmic reticulum glucosidase I (Saul et al., 1983); thus it prevents the trimming of the first two glucose residues from the precursor $Glc_3Man_9GlcNAc_2$. Therefore, the asparagine-linked oligosaccharides resulting from castanospermine treatment are predominantly of the unprocessed, high-mannose variety. 1-Deoxynojirimycin is an inhibitor of glucosidase I and II (Saunier et al., 1982), leading to the accumulation of unprocessed, high-mannose oligosaccharides. Finally, bromoconduritol is an inhibitor of glucosidase II and prevents trimming of the innermost glucose residue from the $Glc_3Man_9GlcNAc_2$ precursor (Schwarz and Datema, 1984).

Swainsonine treatment of either B16-F10 murine melanoma cells (Humphries et al., 1986a,b), MDAY-D2 murine lymphoreticular tumor cells (Dennis, 1986), or sarcoma L-1 tumor cells (Pulverer et al., 1988), but not naturally occurring murine mammary tumor lines (Sargent et al., 1987), resulted in substantial inhibition of metastasis, under conditions where hybrid oligosaccharides were formed. Similar results have been obtained with castanospermine with B16-F10 melanoma (Humphries et al., 1986b) and with bromoconduritol and 1-deoxynojirimycin using sarcoma L-1 tumor cells (Pulverer et al., 1988). Unlike tunicamycin, the antimetastatic activity of these inhibitors of oligosaccharide processing is optimal under conditions where toxicity is not evident.

The specific metastatic event impaired by carbohydrate alteration is still not clear. However, Schaaf-Lafontaine (1985) reported that blood-borne arrest of lymphoma cells in the spleen was sensitive to treatment with swainsonine, 1-deoxynojirimycin, or neuraminidase. Another possibility is that intravascular aggregation of tumor cells might be decreased by inhibiting normal oligosaccharide synthesis. But in contrast to tunicamycin, swainsonine- and castanospermine-treated cells were not less adhesive and their pulmonary retention was normal. Also, the carbohydrate-modified cells were not more susceptible to the tumoricidal activity of natural killer cells (Humphries et al., unpublished observation) or of macrophages (Mercurio, 1986).

B. Systemic Administration of Swainsonine and Castanospermine

In addition to inhibiting metastasis when incubated with cells in vitro, we and others have shown that swainsonine is also effective when administered systemically to mice in drinking water, or after intraperitoneal, subcutaneous, or intravenous injection (Dennis, 1986; Humphries et al., 1988; Newton et al., 1989; Humphries and Olden, 1989). For example, in our experiments the lung colonization potential of intravenously injected B16-F10 murine melanoma cells was inhibited by approximately 80% at 24, 48, and 72 h. Half-maximal inhibition of colonization was observed after only 6 h or drug administration. But to our surprise, the resistance of the animals to metastasis formation, once acquired, was sustained for up to 6 days following withdrawal of the drug from the drinking water (Olden et al., 1989). The latter two findings suggest that swainsonine initiates some sort of biological cascade that mediates antimetastatic activity.

In marked contrast to swainsonine, systemically administered castanospermine had only a slight effect (approximately 15% inhibition) on metastasis formation of B16-F10 melanoma cells. It is not presently understood why castanospermine is active in vitro but not when administered to animals. It is possible (1) that castanospermine is rapidly converted to an inactive metabolite; (2) that the in vivo mechanism of the antimetastatic activity of swainsonine is unrelated to inhibition of the formation of complex oligosacchardies, or (3) that there is strict specificity for the hybrid oligosaccharide structure.

While the foregoing studies using the intravenous injection of tumor cells are important in elucidating the biochemical basis of the colonization phase of metastasis, it is important to investigate the effect of swainsonine on authentic or spontaneous metastasis, as such results would be more relevant to the clinical experience. Additionally, by using a model in which metastatic cells in circulation are derived spontaneously from a primary tumor, one can evaluate the effect, if any, of swainsonine on the early events of the metastatic cascade.

The spontaneous metastasis assays were done in our laboratory using M5076 and B16-BL6 murine tumor cell lines (Newton et al., 1989). The former is a highly invasive reticulosarcoma that metastasizes to visceral organs, including liver and spleen, from dorsal scapular subcutaneous implants (Talmadge et al., 1982; Hart et al., 1981). The latter cell line is a melanoma that can spontaneously metastasize from a footpad injection to colonize the lungs (Hart, 1979; Poste et al., 1982; Stackpole et al., 1985). Our data indicated that swainsonine effectively inhibited the spontaneous metastasis of B16-BL6 melanoma (by 88%) and M5076 reticulum sarcoma (by 95%) murine tumor cells to the lung and liver, respectively. Additionally, we observed, for the first time, that swainsonine inhibited the growth of the B16-BL6 metastatic foci in the lungs. These findings indicate that the antimetastatic activity of swainsonine is not limited to artificial or experimentally induced metastasis or to a single tumor type or specific organ. Although these studies by no means document the principle that swainsonine is likely to be effective against all tumors, they do lend credence to this hypothesis.

III. INHIBITION OF TUMOR GROWTH AND PROLIFERATION

Authentic or spontaneous metastasis involves tumor growth and local invasion; therefore, an important question is whether swainsonine can influence the growth of the primary tumor. This question was first addressed by the experiments of Dennis (1986) in which he used swainsonine in combination with poly(I):poly(C), polyinosinic:polycytidylic acid (poly I:C) in tumor-bearing mice. The combination of the two drugs reduced the rate of growth of MDAY-D2 tumors by approximately 70% and prolonged the survival of mice with established metastases, whereas neither poly I:C nor swainsonine alone significantly inhibited tumor growth. Swainsonine also enhanced the antiproliferative effect of α/β interferon in vitro (Dennis, 1986). The fact that neither swainsonine nor poly I:C alone inhibited tumor growth indicates that the two agents act synergistically.

These findings were extended in our laboratory by determining (1) whether the reduction of metastasis described above translated into a prolongation of survival for the host, (2) whether swainsonine increases the survival of mice bearing subcutaneously implanted tumors, and (3) whether the response to swainsonine, if observed, can be potentiated by other known immunomodulators (Humphries et al., 1989). For these studies, the same treatment schedule, intravenous injection, and inoculum size (30,000 tumor cells) were used as for the colonization studies, but rather than killing the mice after 14 days, the animals were left indefinitely without further treatment and the times of their deaths noted. In such experiments, we observed that both swainsonine and poly I:C prolonged the survival of treated mice. However, when both agents were used in combination, the mean survival time was increased by 22% compared to 8% for poly I:C alone and 4% for swainsonine alone. Moreover, when the size of the tumor cell inoculum was reduced to 10,000, 88% of the mice receiving both agents were still alive after 100 days and were classified as long-term survivors, while untreated mice all died by 35 days postinjection. Similar results were obtained when swainsonine was used in combination with interleukin-2.

We observed that continuous administration of swainsonine was more effective in prolonging survival than a single dose, but interestingly, twice-weekly administration was significantly better than continuous exposure. For example, twice-weekly administration of swainsonine increased survival by 92% compared to 4% when administered continuously. Dennis and co-workers have shown that swainsonine has antiproliferative activity against human tumor cells (colon carcinoma, renal carcinoma, and melanoma) growing in tissue culture (Dennis et al., 1989). Swainsonine also inhibited the growth of colon carcinoma in athymic nude mice. These studies support earlier results with DNA transfected NIH-3T3 cells, which suggested that swainsonine has direct antitumor activity (DeSantis et al., 1987).

IV. MECHANISM OF SWAINSONINE INHIBITION OF TUMOR GROWTH AND METASTASIS

The view in our laboratory is that the antimetastatic effects of the various inhibitors of glycoprotein biosynthesis are due to at least two, and possibly three, independent mechanisms of action: alteration of surface oligosaccharides and enhancement of immune effector mechanisms. For example, in vitro treatment of cells with tunicamycin disrupts their adhesion and results in a more rounded morphology (Butlers et al., 1980; Irimura and Nicolson, 1981; Irimura et al., 1981). Consistent with this view, we found that the rate of loss of radiolabeled, tunicamycin-treated melanoma cells from the lungs of mice was significantly faster than that in untreated cells, suggesting a defect in retention (Humphries et al., 1986a). Also, treatment of lymphoma cells with deoxynojirimycin or swainsonine inhibited the blood-borne arrest of lymphoma cells in the spleen (Schaaf-Lafontaine, 1985).

The exact mechanism of inhibition of metastatic spread of malignant cells by in vitro treatment with inhibitors of glycosylation or oligosaccharide processing is not known. However, potential mechanisms of action, for which there is some evidence, include (1) alterations in adhesive/recognitional interactions between tumor cells and endothelial cell and/or basement membrane, or (2) disruption of heterotypic/homotypic aggregation of tumor cells and platelets.

In addition to exhibiting antimetastatic activity when incubated with cells in vitro, swainsonine was found to be active when administered systemically to mice in drinking water (Dennis, 1986; Humphries et al., 1988) or after intraperitoneal, subcutaneous, or intravenous injection (Humphries and Olden, 1989). Systemically administered swainsonine was reported to act additively with swainsonine treatment in vitro (Dennis, 1986). Kinetic studies of the administration of swainsonine revealed that its inclusion in drinking water was needed only for a very brief period (50% inhibition of metastasis in 6 h), and that administration of the drug as much as 1 week before tumor cells still elicited very significant inhibition (Humphries et al., 1988). These findings imply that swainsonine initiates some sort of biological cascade, and that it does not need to be present continually to exert its antimetastatic activity.

Subsequently, we discovered that swainsonine was completely inactive when administered to mice defective in natural killer cell function (Humphries et al., 1988). This finding suggests that swainsonine acts either directly or indirectly on natural killer cells to enhance their tumor-cell-killing capabilities. White et al. (1988) showed that swainsonine could enhance the proliferation of lymphocytes and the production of interleukin-2. Swainsonine has therefore been classified as a novel immunomodulator that promotes lymphoproliferation (Humphries et al., 1988; White et al., 1988).

Studies are currently under way to determine whether treatment of cells in vitro and systemic administration of swainsonine act by the same mechanism. Pharmacokinetic studies in our laboratory using radiolabeled swainsonine have suggested that it undergoes extremely rapid clearance from the circulation and never attains a concentration that would be required to alter oligosaccharide processing in situ.

V. CONCLUSIONS

The results presented here support four important conclusions with respect to swainsonine, potentially the most useful inhibitor of glycoprotein biosynthesis: first, that it is an effective inhibitor of tumor cell dissemination at a concentration that is unlikely to be toxic to the host; second, that swainsonine is a potent immunomodulator, promoting lymphoproliferation and interleukin-2 production; third, that the drug inhibits the proliferation of human tumors that are generally unresponsive to conventional chemotherapy; and finally, that swainsonine will continue to be useful as a chemical probe to investigate the function of N-linked complex-type oligosaccharides. Based on these findings, we predict that swainsonine will make its way into the clinic as a drug for the management of human malignancies and possibly for the treatment of immune deficiency disorders. Further development of this drug will require close collaboration between biologists and chemists and the testing of synthetic epimers and analogs of swainsonine against the multiple forms of human α-mannosidases.

ACKNOWLEDGMENTS

The authors wish to acknowledge the contribution of Ms. Kazue Matsumoto. The studies conducted in our laboratory were supported by grants from the National Cancer Institute (CA-14718 and CA-45290), the American Cancer Society (PDT-312A), and the Howard University Faculty Research Support Program. We thank Mrs. Joyce Dempsey for typing the manuscript.

REFERENCES

Bar-Shavit, Z., Kahn, A. J., Pegg, L. E., Stone, K. R., and Teitelbaum, S. L. (1984). Glucocorticoids modulate macrophage surface oligosaccharides and their bone binding activity. *J. Clin. Invest.* 73:1277-1282.

Butlers, T. D., DeValia, V., Aplin, J. A., and Hughes, R. C. (1980). Inhibition of fibronectin mediated adhesion of human fibroblasts to substratum: effects of tunicamycin and some cell surface modifying reagents. *J. Cell Sci.* 44:33-38.

Collard, J. G., Van Beek, W. P., Janssen, J. W. G., and Schijven, J. F. (1985). Transfection of human oncogenes: concomitant induction of tumorigenicity and tumor associated membrane alterations. *Int. J. Cancer* 35:207-214.

Datema, R., Olofsson, S., and Romero, P. A. (1987). Inhibitors of protein glycosylation and glycoprotein processing in viral systems. *Pharmacol. Ther.* 33:221-286.

Dennis, J. W. (1986). Effect of swainsonine and poylinosinic: polycytidylic acid on murine tumor cell growth and metastasis. *Cancer Res.* 46:5131-5136.

Dennis, J. W., Waller, C. A., Timpl, R., and Schirrmacher, V. (1982). Surface sialic acid residues attachment of metastatic cells to collagen type IV and fibronectin. *Nature* 300:274-276.

Dennis, J. W., Waller, C. A., and Schirrmacher, V. (1984). Identification of asparagine-linked oligosaccharides involved in tumor cell adhesion to laminin and type IV collagen. *J. Cell Biol.* 99:1034-1044.

Dennis, J. W., Koch, K., and Beckner, D. (1989). Inhibition of human HT 29 colon carcinoma growth in vitro and in vivo by swainsonine and human interferon-α2. *J. Natl. Cancer Inst.* 81:1028-1033.

DeSantis, R., Santer, U. N., and Glick, M. C. (1987). NIH 3T3 cells transfected with human tumor DNA lose the transformed phenotype when treated with swainsonine. *Biochem. Biophys. Res. Commun.* 142:348-353.

Duronio, V., Jacobs, S., and Cuatrecasas, P. (1986). Complete glycosylation of the insulin and insulin-like growth factor I receptors is not necessary for their biosynthesis and function. *J. Biol. Chem.* 261:970-975.

Elbein, A. D. (1984). Inhibitors of the biosynthesis and processing of N-linked oligosaccharides. *Crit. Rev. Biochem. 16*: 21-47.

Elbein, A. D. (1987). Inhibitors of the biosynthesis of N-linked oligosaccharide chains. *Annu. Rev. Biochem. 56*: 947-534.

Elbein, A. D., Solf, R., Dorling, P. R., and Vosbeck, K. (1981). Swainsonine: an an inhibitor of glycoprotein processing. *Proc. Natl. Acad. Sci. USA 78*: 7393-7397.

Fidler, I. J. (1970). Metastasis: quantitative analysis of distribution and fate of tumor emboli labeled with ^{125}I-iodo-2'deoxyuridine. *J. Natl. Cancer Inst. 45*: 773-779.

Fidler, I. J. (1978). General considerations for studies of experimental cancer metastasis. *Methods Cancer Res. 15*: 399-439.

Fidler, I. J., Gersten, D. M., and Hart, I. R. (1978). The biology of cancer invasion and metastasis. *Adv. Cancer Res. 28*: 149-250.

Gibson, R., Kornfeld, S., and Schlesinger, S. (1980). A role for oligosaccharides in glycoprotein biosynthesis. *Trends Biochem. Sci. 5*: 290-293.

Grimstad, I. A., Varani, J., and McCoy, J. P. (1984). Contribution of α-D-galactopyranosyl end groups to attachment of highly and low metastatic murine fibrosarcoma cells to various substrates. *Exp. Cell Res. 155*: 345-358.

Hart, I. R. (1979). The selection and characterization of an invasive variant of the B16 melanoma. *Am. J. Pathol. 97*: 587-600.

Hart, I. R., Talmadge, J. E., and Fidler, I. J. (1981). Metastatic behavior of a murine reticulum cell sarcoma exhibiting organ-specific growth. *Cancer Res. 41*: 1281-1287.

Herberman, R. B. (1982). Counterpoint: animal tumor models and relevance to human tumor immunology. *J. Biol. Response Modif. 2*: 39-46.

Hino, M., Nakayama, O., Tsurumi, Y., Adachi, K., Shibata, T., Terano, H., Kohsaka, M., Aoki, H., and Imanaka, H. (1985). Studies of an immunomodulator, swainsonine: I. Enhancement of immune response by swainsonine in vitro. *J. Antibiot. 38*: 926-935.

Hubbard, S. C., and Ivatt, R. (1981). Synthesis and processing of asparagine-linked oligosaccharides. *Annu. Rev. Biochem. 50*: 555-583.

Humphries, M. J., and Olden, K. (1989). Asparagine-linked oligosaccharides and tumor metastasis. *Pharmacol. Ther. 44*: 85-105.

Humphries, M. J., Matsumoto, K., White, S. L., and Olden, K. (1986a). Oligosaccharide modification by swainsonine treatment inhibits pulmonary colonization of B16-F10 murine melanoma cells. *Proc. Natl. Acad. Sci. USA 83*: 1752-1756.

Humphries, M. J., Matsumoto, K., White, S. L., and Olden, K. (1986b). Inhibition of experimental metastasis by castanospermine in mice: blockage of two distinct stages of tumor colonization by oligosaccharide processing inhibitors. *Cancer Res. 46*: 5215-5222.

Humphries, M. J., Matsumoto, K., White, S. L., Molyneux, R. J., and Olden, K. (1988). Augmentation of murine natural killer activity by swainsonine, a new antimetastatic immunomodulator. *Cancer Res. 48*: 1410-1415.

Humphries, M. J., Matsumoto, K., White, S. L., Molyneux, R. J., and Olden, K. (1990). An assessment of the effects of swainsonine on survival of mice injected with B16-F10 melanoma cells. *Clin. Exp. Metastasis 8*: 89-102.

Irimura, T., and Nicolson, G. L. (1981). The role of glycoconjugates in metastatic melanoma blood-borne arrest and cell surface properties. *J. Supramol. Struct. 17*: 325-336.

Irimura, T., Gonzalez, R., and Nicolson, G. L. (1981). Effects of TM on B13 metastatic melanoma cell surface glycoproteins and blood-borne arrest and survival properties. *Cancer Res. 41*: 3411-3418.

Kornfeld, R., and Kornfeld, S. (1985). Assembly of asparagine-linked oligosaccharides. *Annu. Rev. Biochem. 54*: 631-664.

Mercurio, A. M. (1986). Disruption of oligosaccharide processing in murine tumor cells inhibit their susceptibility to lysis by activated mouse macrophages. *Proc. Natl. Acad. Sci. USA 83*: 2609-2613.

Montreuil, J. (1987). Structure and conformation of glycoprotein glycans. In *Vertebrate Lectins*, K. Olden and J. B. Parent (Eds.). Van Nostrand Reinhold, New York, pp. 1-26.

Morin, M. J., and Bernacki, R. J. (1983). Biochemical effects and therapeutic potential of tunicamycin in murine L1210 leukemia. *Cancer Res. 43*: 1669-1674.

Newton, S. A., White, S. L., Humphries, M. J., and Olden, K. (1989). Swainsonine inhibition of spontaneous metastasis. *J. Natl. Cancer Inst. 81*: 1024-1028.

Nicolson, G. L. (1982). Cancer metastasis: organ colonization and the cell-surface properties of malignant cells. *Biochim. Biophys. Acta 695*: 113-176.

Olden, K., Pratt, R. M., and Yamada, K. M. (1979). Selective cytotoxicity of tunicamycin for transformed cells. *Int. J. Cancer 24*: 60-66.

Olden, K., Parent, J. B., and White, S. L. (1982a). Carbohydrate moieties of glycoproteins: a reevaluation of their function. *Biochim. Biophys. Acta 650*: 209-232.

Olden, K., Bernard, B. A., White, S. L., and Parent, J. B. (1982b). Function of the carbohydrate moieties of glycoproteins. *J. Cell. Biochem. 18*: 313-335.

Olden, K., Humphries, M. J., and White, S. L. (1985). Biochemical effects and cancer threapeutic potential of tunicamycin. In *Monoclonal Antibodies and Cancer Therapy*, R. Reisfeld and S. Sell (Eds.). Alan R. Liss, New York, pp. 443-472.

Olden, K., White, S. L., Mohla, S., Newton, S. A., Yasuda, Y., Bowen, D., and Humphries, M. J. (1989). Experimental approaches for prevention of hematogenous metastasis. *Oncology 3*: 83-91.

Pena, S. D. J., and Hughes, R. C. (1978). Fibronectin-plasma membrane interactions in the adhesion and spreading of hamster fibroblasts. *Nature 176*: 80-83.

Poste, G., Doll, J., Brown, A. E., Tzeng, J., and Zeidman, I. (1982). Comparison of the metastatic properties of B16 melanoma clones isolated from cultured cell lines, subcutaneous tumors, and individual lung metastases. *Cancer Res. 42*: 2770-2778.

Pulverer, G., Beuth, J., Ko, H. L., Yassin, A., Ohshima, Y., Roszkowski, K., and Uhlenbruck, G. (1988). Glycoprotein modifications of sarcoma L-1 tumor cells by tunicamycin, swainsonine, bromoconduritol or 1-desoxynojirimycin treatment inhibits their metastatic lung colonization in Balb/c-mice. *J. Cancer Res. Clin. Oncol. 114*: 217-220.

Raz, A., and Lotan, R. (1987). Endogenous galactoside-binding lectins: a new class of functional tumor cell surface molecules related to metastasis. *Cancer Metastasis Rev.* 6:433-452.

Santer, U. V., and Glick, M. C. (1979). Partial structure of a membrane glycoprotein from virus transformed hamster cells. *Biochemistry* 18:2533-2540.

Santer, U. V., Gilbert, F., and Glick, M. C. (1984). Change in glycosylation of membrane glycoproteins after transfection of NIH 3T3 cells with human tumor DNA. *Cancer Res.* 44:3730-3735.

Sargent, N. S. E., Price, J. E., Darling, D., Flynn, M. P., and Tarin, D. (1987). Effects of altering surface glycoprotein composition on metastatic colonization potential of murine mammary tumor cells. *Br. J. Cancer* 55:21-28.

Saul, R., Chambers, J. P., Molyneux, R. J., and Elbein, A. D. (1983). Castanospermine, a tetrahydroxylated alkaloid that inhibits β-glucosidase and β-glucocerebrosidase. *Arch. Biochem. Biophys.* 221:593-597.

Saunier, B., Kilker, R. D., Tkacz, J. S., Quaroni, A., and Herscovics, A. (1982). Inhibition of N-linked complex oligosaccharide formation by 1-deoxynorjirimycin, an inhibitor of processing glucosidases. *J. Biol. Chem.* 257:14155-14161.

Schaaf-Lafontaine, N. (1985). Modification of blood-borne arrest properties of lymphoma cells by inhibitors of protein glycosylation suggests the existence of endogenous lectins. *Carbohydr. Res.* 138:315-323.

Schwarz, R. T., and Datema, R. (1982). The lipid pathway of protein glycosylation and its inhibitors: the biological significance of protein-bound carbohydrates. *Adv. Carbohydr. Chem. Biochem.* 40:287-379.

Schwarz, R. T., and Datema, R. (1984). Inhibitors of trimming: new tools in glycoprotein research. *Trends Biochem. Sci.* 9:32-34.

Soderquist, A. M., and Carpenter, G. (1984). Glycosylation of the epidermal growth factor receptor in A-431 cells. *J. Biol. Chem.* 259:12586-12594.

Stackpole, C. W., Fornabaio, D. M., and Alterman, A. L. (1985). Phenotypic interconversion of B16 melanoma clonal cell populations: relationship between metastasis and tumor growth rate. *Int. J. Cancer* 35:667-674.

Talmadge, J. E., Wolman, S. R., and Fidler, I. J. (1982). Evidence for the clonal origin of spontaneous metastasis. *Science* 217:361-363.

Tkacz, J. S., and Lampen, J. O. (1975). Tunicamycin inhibition of polisoprenyl N-acetylglucosaminyl pyrophosphate formation of calf liver microsome. *Biochem. Biophys. Res. Commun.* 65:248-257.

Tulsiani, D. R. P., and Touster, O. (1983). Swainsonine causes the production of hybrid glycoproteins by human skin fibroblasts and rat liver Golgi preparations. *J. Biol. Chem.* 258:7578-7585.

Tulsiani, D. R. P., Harris, T. M., and Touster, O. (1982). Swainsonine inhibits the biosynthesis of complex glycoproteins by inhibition of Golgi mannosidase II. *J. Biol. Chem.* 257:7936-7939.

Van Beek, W. P., Smets, W. P., and Emmelot, P. (1975). Changes in surface glycoproteins as a marker of malignancy in human leukemic cells. *Nature* 253:457-460.

Warren, L., and Buck, C. A. (1980). The membrane glycoproteins of the malignant cell. *Clin. Biochem. 13*:191-197.

Warren, L., Fuhrer, J. P., and Buck, C. A. (1972). Surface glycoproteins of normal and transformed cells: a difference determined by sialic acid and a growth-dependent sialytransferase. *Proc. Natl. Acad. Sci. USA 69*:1838-1842.

Warren, L., Fuhrer, J. P., and Buck, C. A. (1973). Surface glycoproteins of cells before and after transformation by oncogenic viruses. *Fed. Proc. 32*:80-85.

Warren, L., Buck, C. A., and Tusgynski, G. P. (1978). Glycopeptide changes and malignant transformation a possible role for carbohydrates in malignant behavior. *Biochim. Biophys. Acta 516*:97-127.

Weiss, L. (1986). Metastatic inefficiency: causes and consequences. *Cancer Rev. 3*:1-24.

Weiss, L., Mayhew, E., Glaves-Rapp, D., and Holmes, J. C. (1982). Metastatic inefficiency in mice bearing B16 melanoma. *Br. J. Cancer 45*:44-53.

White, S. L., Schweitzer, K., Humphries, M. J., and Olden, K. (1988). Stimulation of DNA synthesis in murine lymphocytes by the drug swainsonine: immunodulatory properties. *Biochem. Biophys. Res. Commun. 150*:615-625.

Yogeeswaran, G. (1983). Cell surface glycolipids and glycoproteins in malignant transformation. *Adv. Cancer Res. 38*:289-350.

27

Ultrasonographic Studies on the Fetotoxic Effects of Poisonous Plants on Livestock

Kip E. Panter and Terrie L. Wierenga

Agricultural Research Service, Poisonous Plant Research Laboratory, USDA, Logan, Utah

Thomas D. Bunch

Utah State University, Logan, Utah

I. INTRODUCTION

Only recently has radio-ultrasound been used to study fetotoxicity and/or teratogenicity in poisonous plant-induced toxicoses in livestock (Panter et al., 1987, 1988a, 1990b). Numerous poisonous plants are known to cause abortion or fetal abnormalities in livestock. The mechanisms are not fully understood, and radio-ultrasound will facilitate their study.

   In 1983, Panter hypothesized that cleft palate and multiple congenital contractures (MCC) were induced when pregnant sows ingested poison-hemlock
(*Conium maculatum*) plant and seed, thus inhibiting fetal movement (Panter,
1983). The need to observe fetal movement inhibition in utero while under
the influence of poison-hemlock stimulated interest in radio-ultrasound techniques. We have used radio-ultrasound to observe the effects of *Conium*,
Nicotiana, and *Lupinus* (all known to induce cleft palate and MCC) on fetal
activity and physiology (Panter et al., 1990a,b). We also used radio-ultrasound to observe fetal cardiac function and placental aberrations in ewes fed
locoweed (Panter et al., 1987).
   Radio-ultrasound has provided new data and better understanding of the
mechanisms of toxicity and teratogenicity in livestock. It is a noninvasive,
humane technique of visualizing, measuring, and confirming the effects of
poisonous plants on the fetus.
   In this chapter we report on the theory and application of ultrasound
imaging, preliminary data on the normal growth and development of the sheep
and goat fetus as observed by ultrasound, the effects of locoweed on fetal
physiology, the effects of plants containing piperidine alkaloids on fetal movement and subsequent teratogenicity, mechanistic considerations related to
cleft palate and MCC, and the potential application of ultrasound imaging in
future research of poisonous plant toxicoses.

II. THEORY AND APPLICATION

Ultrasonography has been applied to animal studies since the mid-1960s when
Lindahl (1966) used ultrasound to diagnose pregnancy in sheep. However,
its use increased in domesticated animals following the development of real-
time or dynamic imaging scanners in the 1970s (Pierson et al., 1988), which
facilitated the study of anatomy in large (cattle and horses) and small (sheep,
goats and swine) domestic animals. Ultrasonography is widely used in research programs and has been integrated into human and veterinary diagnostics.
   The physics of ultrasound has been reviewed extensively (Carlsen, 1975;
Pierson et al., 1988). Ultrasound involves the generation of pulsed electrical
energy within a transducer to produce high-frequency sound waves. The
imaging system is based on the piezoelectric effect. The transducer contains
a piezoelectric crystal, which serves as a sending and receiving unit. The
crystal changes shape when exposed to an electrical potential. The resulting
compression and rarefaction creates a highly directed pulse of sound. The
pulse passes from the transducer through a coupling agent into the subject.
Returning echoes received by the transducer exert pressure on the piezoelectric crystal. An electrical impulse, generated as a radio-frequency signal,
is amplified and displayed as an image. Commonly used transducers in animal
research and diagnostics deliver sound frequencies of 3 to 7.5 MHz and consist of either a series of transducers arranged in linear order (linear array)
or one or more transducers that rotate or oscillate (sector scanner). The
electrical energy of the scanner is dispensed in microsecond impulses and
the focal point of the transducer is determined largely by the number of microsecond impulses generated. The lower the number of megahertz, the greater
the focal depth; the opposite effect occurs at the higher megahertz levels.

As the impulses pass through various tissues, some of the waves rebound or are reflected back from the tissue interfaces and are picked up by the transducer. The reflected echoes are displayed as a constellation of spots that form a gray scale image of 16 to 64 steps. Nonechogenic structures are black and represent fluid-filled cavities such as ovarian follicles or an embryo yolk sac. At the other end of the gray scale are the highly echogenic dense tissues such as bone, which are represented as white. Soft tissues such as the uterus and organs are intermediate shades. The resulting picture produced is animated and can be stored on magnetic tape by a video recorder (VHS or Beta) or viewed in freeze frame for critical analysis, measuring, and/or photography. The two-dimensional image on the monitor allows the ultrasonographer to visualize structures, a process similar to viewing a histologic specimen.

Diagnostic ultrasound has been used extensively in human and veterinary medicine. It has been used to study many organ systems, including (1) the reproductive system (pregnancy diagnosis, litter size, urogenital imaging, prostate disease, testicular torsion, detection of ovulation, follicular development, fetal growth, fetal movement, fetal abnormalities and disease, uterine contractions, uterine involution, etc.); (2) the abdomen (renal and hepatic disease; assessment of hepatic, splenic, and renal neoplasia; general interpretation of abdominal masses; comparative organ imaging; diagnosis of intra-abdominal abscesses; etc.); (3) echocardiography (features of pericardial effusion, congestive disease and acquired abnormalities, diagnosis of intra-cardiac fibrosarcoma, assessment of cardiac function, normal and paradoxical ventricular septal motion, volume determination, etc.); (4) the thorax (lung disorders, pleural effusion, pleuropneumonia, etc.); and (5) the eye (eye and orbit imaging, congenital microphthalmia, diagnosis of space-occupying ocular masses, etc.). An excellent bibliography covering the last 21 years of veterinary diagnostic ultrasound has been prepared by Christopher et al. (1988). Some recent articles not covered in the bibliography are Pierson and Ginther (1988) and Kastelic et al. (1988) for the cow; Pierson et al. (1988) and Squires et al. (1988) for the horse; Madec et al. (1988) for the pig; and Buckrell (1988) for sheep and goats.

Ultrasonography has also been used to measure body fat and estimate body condition in farm animals (Cassel et al., 1980; Kester, 1988; Westervelt et al., 1976), to measure muscle mechanics (Johnson et al., 1978), to determine teat milk flow (Delwiche et al., 1980), to identify obstructions in the bovine udder and teat (Cartee et al., 1986), to detect parasite cysts (Boyle, 1985), and to guide tissue biopsies (Hoope et al., 1986).

Ultrasonography has been most widely utilized in human obstetrics (Birnholz and Farrell, 1984). Hundreds of thousands of pregnant women each year receive ultrasound examinations to assess fetal movement and development. It is also used to image follicular development for human in vitro fertilization, embryo transfer, or gamete intrafallopian transfer (Edwards and Purdy, 1982; Wood and Trounson, 1984; Yee, 1988). Ultrasonography has also been used to predict ovulation to determine the optimal time for artificial insemination.

Recently, ultrasonography has been used to assess fetotoxic and teratogenic effects of poisonous plants in livestock and to determine normal fetal development and movement patterns in sheep and goats (Panter et al., 1988a, 1990b).

III. NORMAL FETAL GROWTH AND DEVELOPMENT
OF THE SHEEP AND GOAT

Patterns of normal fetal growth and development in sheep and goats by ultrasound are not well documented. Fetal growth in sheep has been studied in animals killed at various stages of gestation or recorded at birth (Wallace, 1948; Richardson et al., 1976). Surgical techniques have made possible continuous monitoring of the growth of individual fetuses (Mellor, 1983; Mellor and Murray, 1981, 1982a,b; Taylor et al., 1983). A nonsurgical approach using radio-ultrasound imaging has been used to study embryonic and fetal development in the cow (Pierson and Ginther, 1984) and sheep (Kleemann et al., 1987).

There is little information about the normal patterns of fetal activity, fetal cardiac function, and fetal physiology in the sheep and goat. Induction of certain types of malformations by toxicants appears to be related to specific periods when fetal movement is first observed and patterns of inhibited fetal activity.

Ultrasound data are extremely important in fetotoxicity and teratology studies in sheep and goats because they make it possible to compare fetal age to normal patterns of fetal movement and to relate that to certain types of malformations. For example, as discussed in Sections V and VI, there is a direct relationship between the initiation of mouth and tongue movement and palate closure and cleft palate anomalies induced by poisonous plants. Limb movement and body movement (strength and frequency) are related to the time during gestation when certain poisonous plants induce multiple congenital contractures. Fetal heart action, strength, and number of beats per minute have been related to fetal death, fluid accumulation, abnormal placental development, and subsequent abortion from locoweeds.

This section includes a review of the literature on the measurements of fetal size in relation to stage of gestation in the sheep and goat. Preliminary data, including growth curves, are presented and related to patterns of fetal movement and heart activity. These patterns of fetal growth and development with patterns of fetal movement are apparently important in predicting teratogenic effects of poisonous plants on livestock.

Data on fetal development in sheep are limited; even less information is available in the goat. We assume that fetal development in sheep and goats is very similar, but we recognize that there are inherent differences between the two species, even though the length of gestation is similar.

Different methods of measuring fetal size relative to gestational age have been reported (Thurley et al., 1973; Koong et al., 1975; Richardson et al., 1976; Mellor and Murray, 1981, 1982a,b; Wenham, 1981; Taylor et al., 1983). Many of these methods relate fetal growth patterns to nutritional status of the ewe. Richardson et al. (1976) used brain weight, long bone length, and appendicular ossification centers to estimate developmental age from 50 days' gestation until birth. Taylor et al. (1983) implanted ultrasound transducers subcutaneously on each side of the fetal skull in late pregnancy to measure growth of the fetal skull for 3 weeks. Fetal growth rate during the last 60 to 70 days of gestation was related to nutritional status as reflected in the measurement of fetal girth and crown rump length (Mellor and Murray, 1982a,b).

Techniques to measure fetal growth and development have been used late in gestation and usually describe the relationship between the fetus and nutritional status of the ewe. Radio-ultrasound has been used to predict fetal weight in sheep under field conditions (Kleemann et al., 1987). Ultrasound measurements were compared in fetuses obtained from slaughterhouses. The highest correlations between ultrasound and physical measurements were for thoracic depth ($r = 0.75$) followed by thoracic girth ($r = 0.63$), head width ($r = 0.39$), and thoracic width ($r = 0.17$). These measurements were taken between 83 and 125 days of gestation (Kleemann et al., 1987).

In teratology studies with sheep and goats, early ultrasound examination helps interpret fetal measurements and predict fetal age. It could also help understand normal fetal physiology and patterns of activity, factors that are particularly important during the time when lack of fetal movement appears to be related to the induction of cleft palate and MCC (Panter et al., 1989a,b).

Evans and Sack (1973) extensively reviewed the external characteristics of the sheep embryo and fetus by growth features and gestational age. Important points for this discussion include the appearance of the forelimb and hindlimb buds at 20 and 21 days' gestation, respectively. Subsequently, the hand and foot plates appear at 22 and 23 days' gestation. By 27 days' gestation, the third and fourth forelimb digits are prominent, and by day 29 grooves appear between the hindlimb digits. The facial clefts are closed and the tongue is visible by 30 days' gestation. By day 38 of gestation, the palate is fused.

The relationship between fetal growth and development and teratogenic effects reflects the fact that teratogenic activity is strongly dependent on exposure to an agent (in this case, poisonous plants or alkaloids therefrom) at a specific "sensitive" period in development (Shepard, 1976). Therefore, understanding teratogenesis of a particular agent or xenobiotic requires knowledge not only of the stage of development but also the patterns of movement, types of movement, heart action, and other parameters.

We speculate that the period of insult in the sheep and goat for cleft palate occurs soon after or at the time of initiation of fetal movement and between the time when the tongue is visible and the palate fuses (30 to 38 days' gestation). Similarly, during a later period (40 to 60 days) when fetal movement is at its peak and when apparently normal bone elongation, tendon, ligament, and muscle development is dependent on normal fetal movement, MCC malformations in sheep and goats may occur.

In a preliminary study (Panter and Bunch, 1989, unpublished data) we used ultrasound to monitor two pregnant ewes (western crossbred range ewes crossed with a Suffolk ram), both carrying twins, and two pregnant goats (Spanish type crossed with Angora bucks), also carrying twins. Each animal was monitored 3 weeks after mating and at weekly intervals to 110 days' gestation. In addition to measuring body size we recorded fetal movement (Fig. 1) and heart rate (Fig. 2). The number of fetal movements over a 5-min period and fetal heart rate over a 1-min period were recorded at weekly intervals. Early in gestation, fetal length was measured (Fig. 3). As the fetus grew, head length from the tip of the nose to the back of the head and head width at the widest region was measured.

Results of this preliminary study indicated that fetal movement was initiated near the time of palate closure (35 to 38 days). There was a bimodal pattern of fetal activity in sheep and goats (Fig. 1). It increased between

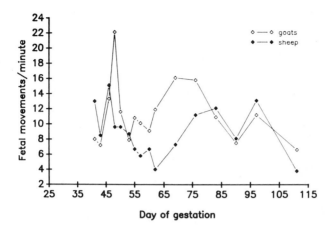

FIGURE 1 Mean number of fetal movements per minute measured in two pregnant sheep and two pregnant goats from 40 to 111 days' gestation.

38 and 50 days and again between 65 and 90 days. We hypothesize that the
early increase in activity is important in normal skeletal development, and
if inhibited for a sustained period, will result in MCC malformations. Data
shown in Sections V and VI and Fig. 4 support this hypothesis.

Fetal heart action begins early in gestation; the first heart beats were
observed by ultrasound near 35 days' gestation in both sheep and goats (Fig.
2). Early heart rate is high (near 200 beats per minute). As the stage of
gestation progresses, the fetal heart rate declines. Preliminary fetal measurements indicate that embryo length increases until about day 50 (crown rump
length measured by the internal calipers of the ultrasound equipment). From
45 to 100 days' gestation, fetal head width and length both increase in an
almost linear fashion (Fig. 3). These preliminary data must be confirmed.

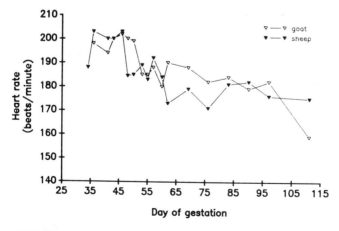

FIGURE 2 Mean fetal heart rate of two pregnant sheep and two pregnant goats
measured by radio-ultrasound from 35 to 111 days' gestation.

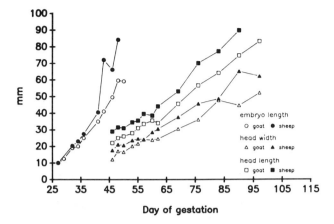

FIGURE 3 Mean embryo and fetal measurements from two pregnant sheep and two pregnant goats as observed by radio-ultrasound from 28 to 90 days' gestation.

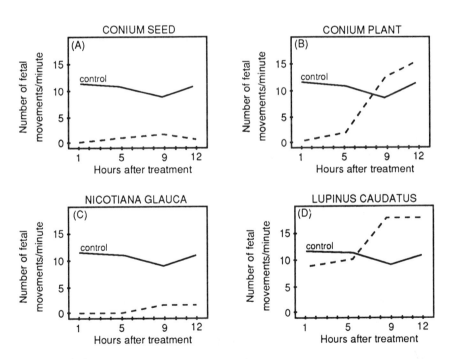

FIGURE 4 Comparision of fetal movement over a 12-h period at 45 days' gestation in pregnant goats gavaged water (control), *L. caudatus*, *N. glauca*, and *C. maculatum* fresh plant and seed). [Adapted from Panter et al. (1990b).]

However, early fetal measurements, fetal activity, and fetal heart action must be documented by ultrasound imaging in order to understand normal fetal growth and development and to clarify in teratology the relationship of animal studies to human studies. There is little of this type of information currently available for livestock species.

IV. EFFECTS OF LOCOWEED ON FETAL PHYSIOLOGY

Locoweed adversely affects reproduction in livestock. Necropsies show that locoweed causes fetal malformations, delayed placentation, reduced placental and uterine vascular development, hydrops amnii, abnormal cotyledonary development, interruption of fetal fluid balance, and abortion (Mathews, 1932; James et al., 1967, 1969, 1981; Van Kampen and James, 1971; James, 1972, 1976; McIlwraith and James, 1982). Locoweed poisoning occurs in all classes of grazing livestock, and multiple effects have been observed (James, 1974; James et al., 1981). Clinical symptoms of locoweed poisoning include aberrant behavior, ataxia, weakness, emaciation, rough hair coat, and death (James, et al., 1981). The severity of clinical symptoms varies with the length of time locoweed has been ingested.

A condition known as high mountain disease or congestive right-heart failure has been reported in cattle grazing locoweed at high elevations (James et al., 1983; Panter et al., 1988c). Based on gross observations and necropsies, the appearance of these animals was similar to that of fetuses from ewes that had ingested locoweed during pregnancy. There was severe edema along the underline, brisket, jaws, and in the thoracic and abdominal cavities. The hearts of calves grazing locoweed at high elevation and in fetal lambs from ewes fed locoweed had right-ventricular hypertrophy, dilatation, and rounding of the apex (Panter et al., 1987, 1988c). High mountain disease may result when the effects of locoweed exacerbate the hypoxia of high elevation, thus increasing the vascular resistance and/or vasoconstriction, causing the right ventricle to work excessively, thereby resulting in hypertrophy, cardiac insufficiency, edema, hydrothorax, and ascites.

The mammalian fetus is hypoxic and more hypertensive than the adult because the airways are filled with fluid (Brigham and Newman, 1979). Locoweed may cause a similar effect in the fetus as it does in cattle at high elevation (i.e., vasoconstriction or increased vascular resistance). The work load on the fetal heart may increase, causing hypertrophy, dilatation, cardiac insufficiency, fluid accumulation, fetal death, and abortion.

Panter et al. (1987) used radio-ultrasound to monitor the effects of locoweed on fetal and placental development in ewes. Their observations were similar to the results of others at necropsy (Van Kampen and James, 1971; James, 1972). Fluid accumulation in the placenta (hydrops allantois, hydrops amnii) altered cotyledonary development and fetal death followed by abortion were observed. The effects of locoweed on fetal heart rate, cardiac irregularity, and reduced strength of heart contractions were recorded. Fetal heart rate was reduced (Fig. 5), and fetal heart contractions were irregular and weak. Fetal cardiac insufficiency and right-heart failure, similar to that occurring in calves and cows that ingest locoweed at high elevation, may contribute to fluid accumulation in the fetus and placenta and thereby cause fetal death and abortion (Panter et al., 1987).

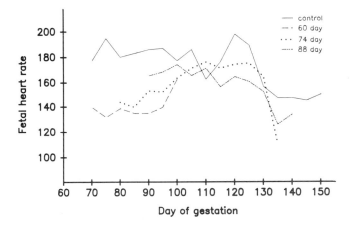

FIGURE 5 Reduction of fetal heart rate from pregnant ewes in which locoweed ingestion began at 60, 74, and 88 days' gestation.

Ellis et al. (1985) demonstrated that serum progesterone and cotyledonary prostaglandin levels were altered in pregnant ewes fed *Astragalus lentiginosus* (locoweed). Serum progesterone values were significantly reduced in a dose-dependent manner and cotyledonary prostaglandins (6-keto-PGF1α, PGF2α, and PGE2) were elevated. PGF1α and PGF2α were significantly higher than controls and PGE2 levels also tended to be higher. The results of ultrasound studies by Panter et al. (1987) suggested that at least one fetus in each ewe fed locoweed died 2 to 3 days before abortion occurred. Ellis et al. (1985) reported that myometrial concentrations of PGF1α, PGF2α, and PGE were significantly higher in ewes bearing dead fetuses than in those bearing live fetuses. Thus the ultrasound study by Panter et al. (1987) and the study reported by Ellis et al. (1985) are consistent with the hypothesis that fetal death or necrotic changes in the fetus induce the cotyledonary prostaglandin synthesis that results in abortion. In the case of locoweed-induced abortion, tissue necrosis after fetal death may stimulate prostaglandin production and subsequent abortion.

V. EFFECTS OF PIPERIDINE ALKALOID-CONTAINING PLANTS ON FETAL MOVEMENT AND SUBSEQUENT TERATOGENICITY

Conium maculatum (poison-hemlock) (Keeler, 1974; Keeler and Balls, 1978; Keeler et al., 1980; Panter, 1983; Panter et al., 1985a,b), *Nicotiana glauca* (tree tobacco) (Keeler, 1979; Keeler and Crowe, 1984, 1985; Keeler et al., 1984), *Nicotiana tabacum* (Burley tobacco) (Crowe, 1969; Menges et al., 1970; Crowe and Pike, 1973; Crowe and Swerczek, 1974), *Lupinus caudatus* (tail cup lupine) (Shupe et al., 1967; Keeler, 1973a,b, 1976), *Lupinus sericeus* (silky lupine) (Shupe et al., 1967; Keeler, 1973a,b, 1976), and *Lupinus formosus* (Lunara lupine) (Keeler and Panter, 1989) have been fed to livestock and have induced congenital birth defects. *Conium maculatum* (Panter et al., 1985a, 1990a) and *Nicotiana glauca* (Keeler et al., 1984; Panter et al., 1990a) induced cleft palate in pigs and goats and MCC (multiple congenital contractures) in pigs (Panter et al., 1985b, Keeler et al., 1984), goats (Panter et al., 1990a), sheep (Keeler et al., 1980; Keeler and Crowe, 1984; Panter et al., 1988b), and cattle (Keeler, 1974; Keeler and Balls, 1978; Keeler et al., 1980). *Nicotiana tabacum* induced MCC in pigs (Crowe, 1969; Menges et al., 1970; Crowe and Pike, 1973; Crowe and Swerczek, 1974). *Lupinus caudatus*, *L. sericeus*, and *L. formosus* induced cleft palate and MCC in cattle (Shupe et al., 1967, 1968; Keeler, 1976; Keeler and Panter, 1989). All of these plants contain teratogenic piperidine alkaloids except *L. caudatus* and *L. sericeus*, both of which contain a quinolizidine alkaloid anagyrine believed to be the teratogen (Keeler, 1976).

Keeler and Balls (1978) orally administered piperidine analogs of coniine to cattle. Keeler speculated that specific structures were necessary for these piperidine alkaloids to be teratogenic; for example, a teratogenic pipderidine alkaloid supposedly included a piperidine ring that was either saturated (as in coniine) or that contained a single double bond (as in γ-coniceine) and a side chain alpha to the nitrogen atom that contained at least three carbon atoms.

Many plant genera contain piperidine alkaloids that meet these requirements (Keeler and Crowe, 1985). Some of these include *Conium*, *Nicotiana*, *Lupinus*, *Lobelia*, *Pinus*, *Punica*, *Duboisia*, *Sedum*, *Withania*, *Carica*, *Hydrangea*, *Dichroa*, *Cassia*, *Prosopis*, *Genista*, *Ammondendron*, *Liparia*, *Collidium*, and others. Their structural similarity to known piperidine teratogens indicates that some of the piperidine alkaloids may be teratogenic (Keeler and Crowe, 1985).

Feeding trials using *Lupinus caudatus* and *L. sericeus* plants (sheep and goats) and anagyrine-rich extracts from these plants (sheep and hamsters) showed that these plants were not teratogenic in sheep (Keeler, 1984), goats (Panter et al., 1990a), and hamsters (Keeler, 1984); however, they were teratogenic in cattle (Shupe et al., 1967, 1968; Keeler, 1976). Anagyrine is a quinolizidine alkaloid whose structure is not closely related to that of the known teratogenic piperidines nor to that of the teratogenic piperidine analogs. Why would it induce clinical deformities in cattle identical to those induced by the piperidines, yet not do so in sheep, goats, and hamsters? Keeler and Panter (1989) hypothesized that cattle metabolize the anagyrine from lupine to a complex piperidine, thus meeting the structural requirements (Keeler and Balls, 1978) of teratogenic piperidines. This mechanism is consistent with the lack of teratogenicity of *L. caudatus* and *L. sericeus* in sheep and goats and of anagyrine-rich extracts therefrom in hamsters. In 1989, Keeler and Panter fed *Lupinus formosus* to pregnant cattle and induced cleft palate and MCC in their calves. *L. formosus* contains the piperidine alkaloid ammodendrine, which has the structure of teratogenic piperidine alkaloids proposed by Keeler and Balls (1978). Ammodendrine is believed to be the teratogen (Keeler and Panter, 1989). Thus the proximal teratogen causing cleft palate and MCC may actually be piperidines possessing the structures associated with teratogenicity. Anagyrine conversion has yet to be verified in cattle.

Panter (1983) hypothesized that the contracture-type birth defects and cleft palate induced in pigs from *Conium maculatum* were associated with the inhibition of fetal movement during critical stages of gestation. This was based on the clinical signs of toxicity (sedation and relaxation) in pregnant sows fed *Conium* and on the appearance of cleft palate and MCC in their offspring. Panter et al. (1985a) suggested that the alkaloids in *Conium* may cross the placental barrier to the fetus, thus reducing fetal movement due to a sedative or anesthetic effect, causing the tongue to lie immobile in the roof of the mouth and obstructing palate closure. Panter et al. (1988a) gavaged *C. maculatum* to pregnant ewes twice daily from gestation days 30 to 60. *Conium* causes MCC in cattle and cleft palate and MCC in pigs; however, results in sheep were not conclusive. Sheep were selected for ultrasound imaging because they were easy to handle even though they were somewhat resistant to the toxic and teratogenic effects of *Conium*. The pregnant ewes were monitored with ultrasound at 45, 54, and 60 days' gestation prior to gavage and 1 h after gavage. Fetal movement was significantly ($P < 0.01$) reduced in *Conium*-treated ewes (Table 1) for an undetermined duration; fetal movement was normal 12 to 18 h after treatment. Therefore, inhibition did not persist between doses. None of the lambs from treated ewes had a cleft palate, and the only skeletal malformations were modest-to-moderate carpal flexure of the front limbs, which were no longer apparent by 8 weeks' postpartum. Based on those findings, we hypothesized that the duration of reduced fetal movement must be a critical factor in permanent limb, spine, and neck deformities and perhaps in cleft palate induction. Perhaps sheep are more resistant to the toxic and teratogenic effects of *Conium* because reduced fetal movement may not persist as long as in other species.

We examined the relationship of reduced fetal movement and severity of induced terata in an experiment in goats (goats also being well suited for ultrasound). Twenty-four pregnant goats were divided into four groups, one of which was subdivided into two subgroups, each containing three pregnant goats. One subgroup was gavaged with fresh *Conium* as in the sheep experiment described above and the other subgroup was gavaged with *Conium* seed; one group was gavaged with *N. glauca*, one group was gavaged with *L. caudatus*, and one group consisted of water-gavaged controls. The *Conium* plant and seed were collected at a location where other collections had been teratogenic (Panter et al., 1985a,b, 1990a). Chemical analysis (Keeler, 1989, unpublished data) showed that the plant material contained teratogenic levels of coniine and γ-coniceine. The *N. glauca* was collected at a location where

TABLE 1 Reduced Fetal Movement in Response to Treatment with Poison Hemlock in Pregnant Sheep from 30-60 Days' Gestation

Days of gestation[a]	1 h Posttreatment[b]	12-16 h posttreatment	Control
45	0.44 ± 0.73	N/M[c]	4.79 ± 0.73
54	0.33 ± 0.52	5.83 ± 1.72	5.43 ± 4.36
60	0.33 ± 0.52	6.08 ± 1.80	7.92 ± 2.87

[a]Treatment period when monitored with ultrasound.
[b]Significantly reduced ($P \leqslant 0.01$) when compared to predosing and control values.
[c]Pretreatment fetal movements not measured at 45 days' gestation.

other collections had proven to be teratogenic in pigs (Keeler et al., 1984; Keeler and Crowe, 1985). The *L. caudatus* was a collection that had proven to be teratogenic in cattle and from an area where lupine was known to cause crooked calf disease (Shupe et al., 1967; Keeler, 1976). Chemical analysis confirmed teratogenic levels of anagyrine (Keeler, 1989, unpublished data). All pregnant goats were gavaged with a predetermined dose of plant material twice daily during gestation days 30 to 60. We fed *Conium* to see if results differed from the study involving sheep, *N. glauca* because it was known to cause cleft palate and MCC in sheep as well as cattle and pigs, and *L. caudatus* because it had been teratogenic in the cows (but not in sheep). Each dose was separated by 8 to 12 h.

The results suggested that the duration of reduced fetal movement was important in the induction of the described birth defects. All the pregnant goats were monitored with ultrasound 1, 5, 9, and 12 h after treatment at 45, 51, 55, and 60 days' gestation. The fetal movements in the four groups at 45 days' gestation over a 12-h period are compared in Fig. 4. The significant reduction in fetal movement in goats fed fresh *Conium* was similar to that which occurred in sheep; however, between 5 and 9 h after treatment, fetal movement increased and was almost normal by 12 h after treatment. The kids from these goats had no cleft palates and had modest-to-moderate carpal flexure, which was resolved spontaneously 8 to 10 weeks' postpartum, a pattern similar to that described by Panter et al. (1988a) in sheep. In goats fed *Conium* seed, the fetal movement was reduced over the entire monitoring period (12 h) at all four monitoring times (45, 51, 55, and 60 days' gestation). All kids had bilateral cleft palate and severe skeletal abnormalities (i.e., arthrogryposis, scoliosis, lordosis, torticollis, and rib cage anomalies) (Fig. 6 and 7). Fetal movement was also inhibited for 12 h between doses in the goats fed *N. glauca*. All kids from these goats had bilateral cleft palate and moderate to severe skeletal abnormalities as described for *Conium* seed. Fetal movement was not reduced and there were no malformations in the goats fed *L. caudatus*.

These results suggest that (1) the duration of reduced fetal movement was a factor in the induction of cleft palate and permanent limb, spine, and neck deformities; and (2) sheep and goats apparently do not metabolize anagyrine in *L. caudatus* to a teratogenic piperidine as suspected in cows.

In 1989, Keeler and Panter fed *L. formosus* to cows and induced limb and palate defects. The piperidine alkaloid ammodendrine, which meets the structural requirement proposed (Keeler and Balls, 1978) for teratogenic piperidines, was believed to be the teratogen (Keeler and Panter, 1989). If piperidine alkaloids must possess certain structural attributes for teratogenicity, *L. formosus* should be as teratogenic in the goat as *C. maculatum* and *N. glauca*. Goats will be administered *L. formosus* and fetal movement monitored and offspring examined for deformities to test this hypothesis.

VI. MECHANISM CONSIDERATIONS PERTAINING TO REDUCED FETAL MOVEMENT AND ITS RELATIONSHIP TO CLEFT PALATE AND MULTIPLE CONGENITAL CONTRACTURES

Only recently was it proposed that cleft palate and multiple congenital contractures (MCC) were induced by poisonous plants via the same mechanism

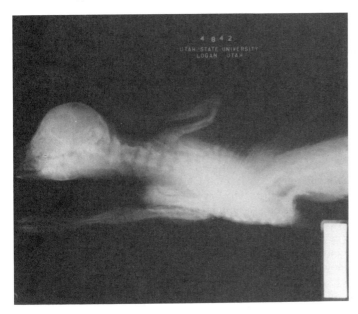

FIGURE 6 X-ray showing scoliosis and rib cage anomalies associated with ingestion of *C. maculatum* seed and *N. glauca*.

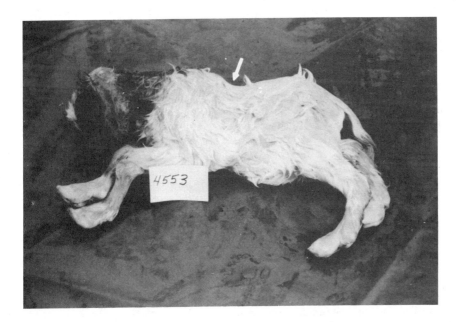

FIGURE 7 Arthrogryposis and lordosis associated with maternal ingestion of *C. maculatum* seed and *N. glauca*.

(Panter, 1983; Panter et al., 1985a,b, 1990b). Multiple congenital contractures and cleft palate of unknown etiology occur frequently in humans and livestock. Many causes have been proposed for these birth defects, including genetic errors, viruses, bacteria, mechanical restriction, chemical teratogens, and plant alkaloids (Keeler, 1980; Hall and Reed, 1982; Swinyard, 1982; Rousseaux and Ribble, 1988). Reduced fetal movement is the probable mechanism by which *Conium* (Panter, 1983; Panter et al., 1985a,b, 1990b), *Nicotiana* (Panter et al., 1990b), and *Lupinus* (Panter et al., 1990b) induce cleft palate and MCC. The incidence of MCC and cleft palate in goats (Panter et al., 1990b) (100% incidence in the kids with sustained inhibition of fetal movement over the dosage period) strongly suggests that similar mechanisms underlie the two types of malformations. A mechanical factor that changes fetal posture could also explain the association between cleft palate and MCC (Poswillo, 1966). The defect of the palate could be the result of tongue obstruction, and the limb defects could be produced by lack of fetal movement, resulting in postural intrauterine molding. Fetal positioning or fetal pressure from a sibling (in the case of multiple births) could result in some of the skeletal defects that we observed in goats (Panter et al., 1990b). Other reports support the relationship between sustained reduction of fetal movement and both of these malformations (cleft palate and MCC) (Poswillo, 1966; Panter et al., 1990b).

In humans, Pierre Robin syndrome is a birth defect in which cleft palate is associated with micrognathia and glossoptosis (Poswillo, 1966). Several workers have observed an association between the Pierre Robin syndrome cleft palate and MCC-type limb defects similar to those we have described. Smith and Stowe (1961) reviewed 35 cases of micrognathia associated with defects of the palate and reported that 8 had limb defects, including talipes, club feet, syndactyly, and missing carpal bones. Routledge (1960) reported 18 cases of the Pierre Robin syndrome cleft palate and found 5 cases with limb defects, including talipes, dislocation of the hips, congenital amputations, and multiple deformities of the lower limbs. Crabbe (1960) reviewed 232 cases of talipes and found this deformity to be associated with cleft palate.

Numerous mechanisms have been proposed for cleft palate in humans. One that fits our proposed hypothesis and is supported by many investigators is the mechanical obstruction hypothesis by the tongue at programmed palate closure time, first proposed by Poswillo (1966) and supported by Seegmiller and Fraser (1977), Panter (1983), Panter et al. (1985a), Clarke et al. (1988), and Panter et al. (1990a,b). Cleft palates have been induced in rats by amniotic sac puncture and subsequent removal of fluid from the amnion (Trasler et al., 1956; Walker, 1959). Fetal compression and mechanical obstruction were the probable causes of the cleft palate. Clarke et al. (1988) suggested that tongue obstruction during palatogenesis is responsible for cleft palate in chondrodystrophic mice, perhaps due to growth retardation of Meckel's cartilage, which in turn prevents the forward displacement of the tongue, leaving it positioned between the fetal palatal shelves and impairing normal shelf elevation and closure. This mandible-tongue-palate relationship is widely accepted as the pathogenetic mechanism underlying cleft palate associated with the Pierre Robin syndrome. Walker and Quarles (1976) observed that tongue removal allowed earlier palate closure in fetal mice, which is consistent with the tongue-palate obstruction hypothesis.

Recent observations by Panter and Bunch (1989, unpublished data) with ultrasound suggest that at 35 to 40 days the fetal head is tightly flexed such that the chin is tightly pressed against the sternum. If fetal movement is inhibited at this time, prevention of normal head and neck flexure and extension could induce cleft palate by the tongue through mechanical obstruction. Panter et al. (1985a) proposed that microsurgical removal of the tongue during palate closure would allow normal palate closure even under the influence of the cleft palate-inducing plant, *Conium maculatum* (they were not aware of the 1976 experiment of Walker and Quarles). This approach may still help elucidate the mechanism of cleft palate induciton by *Conium*.

Similarly, many causes of MCC in humans and animals have been proposed. Swinyard (1982) suggested that MCC in livestock is a very widespread problem that causes enormous financial losses and cited the ingestion of toxic alkaloids during foraging as the second most frequent cause (viral infections are the first). Many physiological or pathological factors may reduce fetal movement enough to be etiologically important: muscle aplasia or hypoplasia (Sheldon, 1932); myopathies (Banker et al., 1957), neuropathies (Price, 1933), connective tissue disturbances (Steindler, 1949), fetal compression (Smith, 1977; Graham et al., 1980), amniotic bands (Smith, 1977), and alkaloids from plants (Keeler, 1980). Several reports of MCC in plural births are believed to have resulted from intrauterine crowding, which may have restricted limb movement (Swinyard, 1982). Few specific etiologic agents have been recognized in humans. However, anything that decreases movement or mobility of limbs in a developing fetus may lead to contractures of the joints (Hall and Reed, 1982; Swinyard and Bleck, 1985; Hall, 1985; Banker, 1985; Hageman and Willemse, 1987; Panter et al., 1990b).

The first experimental model of xenobiotic-induced arthrogryposis involved the injection of *d*-tubocurarine into chicks, causing ankylosis of the joints, presumably from paralysis (Drachman and Coulombre, 1962). Similar experiments with rats had similar results (Moessinger, 1983). Amniocentesis-induced oligohydramnios in rats produced cleft palate and limb contractures (DeMeyer and Baird, 1969). Intra-abdominal pregnancies that resulted in arthrogryposis were the result of fetal compression (Margolis and Luginbeuhl, 1975; Guha-Ray and Hamblin, 1977). These studies, clinical findings in humans, and current research (Panter et al., 1990a,b) support the hypothesis that MCC is caused by loss of fetal movement. Furthermore, where disease conditions are associated with a loss of fetal movement, MCC occurs more frequently than in the general population (i.e., Potter's syndrome amyoplasia) (Swinyard and Bleck, 1985; Thompson and Bilenker, 1985; Banker, 1985; Hageman and Willemse, 1987; Thomas and Smith, 1974).

Joint twisting and rigidity has been attributed to a collagenous response around immobile joints (Swinyard, 1982). Clinical, anatomical, and biochemical evidence indicates that prenatal fixation of a given joint results from collagenous proliferation replacing atrophied muscle fibers with connective tissue and deposition of connective tissue around joint capsules. The joint capsule thickening results in loss of movement and rigidity of the joint (Swinyard, 1982).

We hypothesize that anything that may restrict fetal movement for a sustained period during critical stages of gestation may cause cleft palate, MCC, or both, depending on the stage of gestation in which inhibited fetal movement may occur. Further ultrasonographic measurements will allow us to test this hypothesis.

Although ultrasound imaging has been used in poisonous plant research only recently, it has found numerous applications in studies of the fetal physiology, growth, and development of livestock. Ultrasound imaging has increased our knowledge of these effects of poisonous plants on fetal physiology and the mechanism of subsequent malformations.

VII. CONCLUSION

Ultrasound imaging has provided new information about the fetotoxic effects of poisonous plants on livestock. We learned that the abortifacient action of locoweed probably involves fetal cardiac insufficiency. Reduced heart rate during early periods of gestation and reduced strength of contractions following ingestion of locoweed were first observed with ultrasound. These cardiac effects probably lead to fetal congestive right-heart failure, fetal death, and subsequent abortion. Locoweed-induced abortion is therefore secondary to fetal death. Ultrasound imaging clarified the critical role of fetal movement in normal growth and development (Panter et al., 1988a, 1990b). Inhibition of fetal movement by poisonous plants and their alkaloids may result in fetal malformations such as cleft palate and MCC (multiple congenital contractures). The poisonous plants *C. maculatum* (plant and seed) and *N. glauca* inhibit fetal movement in goats and cause several birth defects. The alkaloids believed responsible are coniine and γ-coniceine from *Conium* and anabasine from *N. glauca*, all simple piperidine alkaloids. *L. caudatus*, a plant containing the quinolizidine alkaloid anagyrine, did not inhibit fetal movement in goats (Panter et al., 1990b). It was teratogenic in cattle but not in goats, perhaps due to differences in the metabolic conversion of anagyrine by cattle and goats (Keeler and Panter, 1989). These findings resulted from the observation of fetal activity by ultrasound while their mothers were under the influence of poisonous plants.

Ultrasound imaging is a valuable diagnostic tool in human and veterinary medicine as described in this review and is also a valuable research tool. Radio-ultrasound is a noninvasive method of observing fetal activity, physiology, growth and development. Ultrasound may be used in conjunction with biopsy techniques to sample amniotic fluid, fetal blood or to introduce biological material directly to the fetus, thus bypassing the influence of the maternal metabolic or detoxification systems. Radio-ultrasound can be particularly valuable in studies of the effects of xenobiotics on the fetus.

REFERENCES

Banker, B. Q. (1985). Neuropathological aspects of arthrogryposis multiplex congenita. *Clin. Orthop. 194*: 30-43.

Banker, B. Q., Victor, M., and Adams, R. D. (1957). Arthrogryposis multiplex due to congenital muscular dystrophy. *Brain 80*: 319-334.

Birnholz, J. C., and Farrell, E. E. (1984). Ultrasound images of human fetal development. *Am. Sci. 72*: 608-613.

Boyle, N. P. (1985). Ultrasound imaging used to detect cysts of *Henneguya salminicola* (Protozoa: Myxozoa) in the flesh of whole Pacific salmon. *Can. J. Fish Aquat. Sci. 42*:1312-1314.

Brigham, K. L., and Newman, J. L. (1979). The pulmonary circulation. *Am . Thorac. Soc. News 8*:15.

Buckrell, B. C. (1988). Applications of ultrasonography in reproduction in sheep and goats. *Theriogenology 29*:71-84.

Carlsen, E. N. (1975). Ultrasound physics for the physician—a brief review. *J. Clin. Ultrasound 3*:69-75.

Cartee, R. E., Ibrahim, A. K., and McLeary, D. (1986). B-mode ultrasonography of the bovine udder and teat. *J. Am. Vet. Med. Assoc. 188*:1284-1287.

Cassel, E. K., Chase, L. E., Bui, T. V., and Hilderbrant, J. (1980). Quantitative measurement of body condition in dairy cattle using real time ADR ultrasound. *J. Dairy Sci. 63*(Suppl. 1):156-157 (abstract).

Christopher, R. L., Stowater, J. L., and Pipers, F. S. (1988). The first twenty-one years of veterinary diagnostic ultrasound. *Vet. Radiol. 29*: 37-45.

Clarke, L., Hepworth, W. B., Carey, J. C., and Seegmiller, R. E. (1988). Chondrodystrophic mice with coincidental agnathia: evidence for the tongue obstruction hypothesis in cleft palate. *Teratology 38*:565-570.

Crabbe, W. A. (1960). Aetiology of congenital talipes. *Br. Med. J. 2*:1060-1063.

Crowe, M. W. (1969). Skeletal anomalies in pigs associated with tobacco. *Mod. Vet. Pract. 50*:54-55.

Crowe, M. W., and Pike, H. T. (1973). Congenital arthrogryposis associated with ingestion of tobacco stalks by pregnant sows. *J. Am. Vet. Med. Assoc. 162*:453-455.

Crowe, M. W., and Swerczek, T. W. (1974). Congenital arthrogryposis in offspring of sows fed tobacco (*Nicotiana tabacum*). *Am. J. Vet. Res. 35*:1071-1073.

Delwiche, M. J., Scott, N. R., and Drost, C. J. (1980). Ultrasonic measurement of teat milk flow. *Agric. Eng. 6*:2660 (abstract).

DeMeyer, W, and Baird, I. (1969). Mortality and skeletal malformations from amniocentesis and oligohydramnios in rats: cleft palate, clubfoot, microstomia, and adactyly. *Teratology 2*:33-38.

Drachman, D. B., and Coulombre, A. J. (1962). Experimental clubfoot and arthrogryposis multiplex congenita. *Lancet 2*:523-526.

Edwards, R. G., and Purdy, J. M. (Eds.) (1982). *Human Conception In Vitro.* Academic Press, London.

Ellis, L. C., James, L. F., McMullen, R. W., and Panter, K. E. (1985). Reduced progesterone and altered cotyledonary prostaglandin levels induced by locoweed (*Astragalus lentiginosus*) in sheep. *Am. J. Vet. Res. 46*:1903-1907.

Evans, H. E., and Sack, W. O. (1973). Prenatal development of domestic and laboratory mammals: growth curves, external features and selected references. *Anat. Histol. Embryol. 2*:11-45.

Graham, J. M., Miller, M., Stephen, M. J., and Smith, D. W. (1980). Limb reduction anomalies and early in vitro limb compression. *J. Pediatr. 96*: 1052-1056.

Guha-Ray, D. K., and Hamblin, M. H. (1977). Arthrogryposis multiplex congenita in an abdominal pregnancy. *J. Reprod. Med. 18*:109-112.

Hageman, G., and Willemse, J. (1987). The pathogenesis of fetal hypokinesia: a neurological study of 75 cases of congenital contractures with emphasis on cerebral lesions. *Neuropediatrics 18*:22-23.

Hall, J. G. (1985). Genetic aspects of arthrogryposis. *Clin. Orthop. 194*: 44-53.

Hall, J. G., and Reed, S. D. (1982). Teratogens associated with congenital contractures in humans and in animals. *Teratology 25*:173-191.

Hoope, F. E., Hager, D. A., Poulos, P. W., Ekman, S., and Lindgren, P. G. (1986). A comparison of manual and automatic ultrasound-guided biopsy techniques. *Vet. Radiol. 27*:99-101.

James, L. F. (1972). Effects of locoweed on fetal development: preliminary study in sheep. *Am. J. Vet. Res. 33*:835-840.

James, L. F. (1974). Syndromes of locoweed poisoning in livestock. *Clin. Toxicol. 5*:567-573.

James, L. F. (1976). Effect of locoweed (*Astragalus lentiginosus*) feeding on fetal lamb development. *Can. J. Comp. Med. 40*:380-384.

James, L. F., Shupe, J. L., Binns, W., and Keeler, R. F. (1967). Abortive and teratogenic effects of locoweed on sheep and cattle. *Am. J. Vet. Res. 28*:1379-1388.

James, L. F., Keeler, R. F., and Binns, W. (1969). Sequence in the abortive and teratogenic effects of locoweed fed to sheep. *Am. J. Vet. Res. 181*:155-158.

James, L. F., Hartley, W. J., and Van Kampen, K. R. (1981). Syndromes of *Astragalus* poisoning in livestock. *J. Am. Vet. Med. Assoc. 178*:146-150.

James, L. F., Hartley, W. J., Van Kampen, K. R., and Nielsen, D. (1983). Relationship between ingestion of the locoweed *Oxytropis sericea* and congestive right-sided heart failure in cattle. *Am. J. Vet. Res. 44*:254-259.

Johnson, J. H., Amend, J. F., Ganer, H. E., and Franklin, D. L. (1978). Measurement of laryngeal muscle mechanics by ultrasound in the conscious horse. *Fed. Proc. 37*:215 (abstract).

Kastelic, J. P., Curran, S., Pierson, R. A., and Ginther, O. J. (1988). Ultrasonic evaluations of the bovine conceptus. *Theriogenology 29*:39-54.

Keeler, R. F. (1973a). Lupine alkaloids from teratogenic and nonteratogenic lupins: I. Correlation of crooked calf disease incidence with alkaloid distribution determined by gas chromatography. *Teratology 7*:23-30.

Keeler, R. F. (1973b). Lupine alkaloids from teratogenic and nonteratogenic lupins: II. Identification of the major alkaloids by tandem gas chromatography-mass spectrometry in plants producing crooked calf disease. *Teratology 7*:31-36.

Keeler, R. F. (1974). Coniine, a teratogenic principal from *Conium maculatum* producing congenital malformations in calves. *Clin. Toxicol. 7*:195-206.

Keeler, R. F. (1976). Lupine alkaloids from teratogenic and nonteratogenic lupins: III. Identification of anagyrine as the probable teratogen by feeding trials. *J. Toxicol. Environ. Health 1*:887-889.

Keeler, R. F. (1979). Congenital defects in calves from maternal ingestion of *Nicotiana glauca* of high anabasine content. *Clin. Toxicol. 15*:417-426.

Keeler, R. F. (1980). Plant toxins. In *Survey of Contemporary Toxicology*, Vol. I, A. T. Tu (Ed.). Wiley, New York, pp. 285-322.

Keeler, R. F. (1984). Teratogenicity studies on non-food lupins in livestock and laboratory animals. In *Proceedings of the Second International Lupine Conference*, L. L. Bellido (Ed.). Publicaciones Agrarias, Madrid, pp. 301-304.

Keeler, R. F., and Balls, L. D. (1978). Teratogenic effects in cattle of *Conium maculatum* and *Conium* alkaloids and analogs. *Clin. Toxicol. 12*: 49-64.

Keeler, R. F., and Crowe, M. W. (1984). Teratogenicity and toxicity of wild tree tobacco, *Nicotiana glauca* in sheep. *Cornell Vet. 74*:50-59.

Keeler, R. F., and Crowe, M. W. (1985). Anabasine, a teratogen from the *Nicotiana* genus. In *Plant Toxicology: Proceedings of the Australia-USA Poisonous Plants Symposium, Brisbane, Australia*, A. A. Seawright, M. P. Hegarty, L. F. James, and R. F. Keeler (Eds.). Queensland Poisonous Plants Committee, Yeerongpilly, Australia, pp. 324-333.

Keeler, R. F., and Panter, K. E. (1989). The piperidine alkaloid composition and relation to crooked calf disease-inducing potential of *Lupinus formosus*. *Teratology 40*:423-432.

Keeler, R. F., Balls, L. D., Shupe, J. L., and Crowe, M. W. (1980). Teratogenicity and toxicity of coniine in cows, ewes, and mares. *Cornell Vet. 70*:19-26.

Keeler, R. F., Crowe, M. W., and Lambert, E. A. (1984). Teratogenicity in swine of the tobacco alkaloid anabasine isolated from *Nicotiana glauca*. *Teratology 30*:61-69.

Kester, W. (1988). Ultrasound is here. *Beef* Oct:54-58.

Kleemann, D. O., Smith, D. H., Walker, S. K., and Seamark, R. F. (1987). A study of real-time ultrasonography for predicting ovine foetal growth under field conditions. *Aust. Vet. J. 64*:352-353.

Koong, L. J., Garrett, W. N., and Rattray, P. V. (1975). A description of the dynamics of fetal growth in sheep. *J. Anim. Sci. 41*:1065-1068.

Lindahl, I. L. (1966). Detection of pregnancy in sheep by means of ultrasound. *Nature 212*:642-643.

Madec, F., Marinat-Botte, F., Forgerit, Y., Le Denmat, M., and Vaudelet, J. C. (1988). Use of ultrasound echotomography in the sow: first trials attempting a codification of some lesions concerning the urogenital tract. *Rec. Med. Vet. 164*:127-133.

Margolis, S., and Luginbeuhl, B. (1975). Eye abnormalities associated with arthrogryposis multiplex congenita. *J. Pediatr. Ophthalmol. 12*:57-60.

Mathews, F. P. (1932). Locoism in domestic animals. *Tex. Agric. Exp. Stat. Bull. 456*:1-28.

McIlwraith, C. W., and James, L. F. (1982). Limb deformities in foals associated with ingestion of locoweed by mares. *J. Am. Vet. Med. Assoc. 181*:155-158.

Mellor, D. J. (1983). Nutritional and placental determinants of foetal growth rate in sheep and consequences for the newborn lamb. *Br. Vet. J. 139*: 307-324.

Mellor, D. J., and Murray, L. (1981). Effects of placental weight and maternal nutrition on the growth rates of individual fetuses in single and twin bearing ewes during late pregnancy. *Res. Vet. Sci. 30*:198-204.

Mellor, D. J., and Murray, L. (1982a). Effects of long term undernutrition of the ewe on the growth rates of individual fetuses during late pregnancy. *Res. Vet. Sci. 30:*177-180.

Mellor, D. J., and Murray, L. (1982b). Effects on the rate of increase in fetal girth of refeeding ewes after short period of severe undernutrition during late pregnancy. *Res. Vet. Sci. 32:*377-382.

Menges, R. W., Selby, L. A., Marienfeld, C. J., Ave, W. A., and Greer, D. L. (1970). A tobacco related epidemic of congenital limb deformities in swine. *Environ. Res. 3:*285-302.

Moessinger, A. C. (1983). Fetal akinesia deformation sequence: an animal model. *J. Pediatr. 72:*857-863.

Panter, K. E. (1983). Toxicity and teratogenicity of *Conium maculatum* in swine and hamsters. Ph.D. thesis, University of Illinois, Urbana.

Panter, K. E., Keeler, R. F., and Buck, W. B. (1985a). Induction of cleft palate in newborn pigs by maternal ingestion of poison hemlock (*Conium maculatum*). *Am. J. Vet. Res. 46:*1368-1371.

Panter, K. E., Keeler, R. F., and Buck, W. B. (1985b). Congenital skeletal malformations induced by maternal ingestion of *Conium maculatum* (poison-hemlock) in newborn pigs. *Am. J. Vet. Res. 46:*2064-2066.

Panter, K. E., Bunch, T. D., James, L. F., and Sisson, D. V. (1987). Ultrasonographic imaging to monitor fetal and placental developments in ewes fed locoweed (*Astragalus lentiginosus*). *Am. J. Vet. Res. 48:*686-690.

Panter, K. E., Bunch, T. D., Keeler, R. F., and Sisson, D. V. (1988a). Radio ultrasound observations of the fetotoxic effects in sheep from ingestion of *Conium maculatum* (poison-hemlock). *Clin. Toxicol. 26:*175-187.

Panter, K. E., Bunch, T. D., and Keeler, R. F. (1988b). Maternal and fetal toxicity of poison-hemlock (*Conium maculatum*) in sheep. *Am. J. Vet. Res. 49:*281-283.

Panter, K. E., James, L. F., Nielsen, D., Molyneux, R. J., Ralphs, M. H., and Olsen, J. D. (1988c). The relationship of *Oxytropis sericea* (green and dry) and *Astragalus lentiginosus* with high mountain disease in cattle. *Vet. Hum. Toxicol. 30:*318-323.

Panter, K. E., Keeler, R. F., Bunch, T. D., and Callan, R. J. (1990a). Congenital skeletal malformations and cleft palate induced in goats by infestation of *Lupinus, Conium* and *Nicotiana* species. *Toxicon 28:* (in press).

Panter, K. E., Bunch, T. D., Keeler, R. F., Sisson, D. V., and Callan, R. J. (1990b). Multiple congenital contractures (MCC) and cleft palate induced in goats by ingestion of piperidine alkaloid-containing poisonous plants: Reduction in fetal movement as the probable cause. *Clin. Toxicol. 28:*69-83.

Pierson, R. A., and Ginther, O. J. (1984). Ultrasonography for detection of pregnancy and study of embryonic development in heifers. *Theriogenology 22:*225-233.

Pierson, R. A., and Ginther, O. J. (1988). Ultrasonic imaging of the ovaries and uterus in cattle. *Theriogenology 29:*21-37.

Pierson, R. A., Kastelic, J. P., and Ginther, O. J. (1988). Basic principles and techniques for transrectal-ultrasonography in cattle and horses. *Theriogenology 29:*3-20.

Poswillo, D. (1966). Observations of fetal posture and causal mechanisms of congenital deformity of palate, mandible, and limbs. *J. Dent. Res.* 45:584-596.

Price, D. S. (1933). A case of amyoplasia congenita with pathological report. *Arch. Dis. Child.* 8:343-354.

Richardson, C., Hebert, C. N., and Terlecki, S. (1976). Estimation of the developmental age of the ovine fetus and lamb. *Vet. Rec.* 99:22-26.

Rousseaux, C. G., and Ribble, C. S. (1988). Developmental anomalies in farm animals: II. Defining etiology. *Can. Vet. J.* 29:30-40.

Routledge, R. T. (1960). The Pierre Robin Syndrome: a surgical emergency in the neo-natal period. *Br. J. Plast. Surg.* 13:204-218.

Seegmiller, R. E., and Fraser, F. C. (1977). Mandibular growth retardation as a cause of cleft palate in mice homozygous for the chondrodysplasia gene. *J. Embryol. Exp. Morphol.* 38:227-238.

Sheldon, W. (1932). Amyoplasia congenita. *Arch. Dis. Child.* 7:117-136.

Shepard, T. H. (1976). *Catalog of Teratogenic Agents*, 2nd ed. Johns Hopkins University Press, Baltimore, pp. XIII-XIX.

Shupe, J. L., Binns, W., James, L. F., and Keeler, R. F. (1967). Lupine, a cause of crooked calf disease. *J. Am. Vet. Med. Assoc.* 151:198-203.

Shupe, J. L., James, L. F., Binns, W., and Keeler, R. F. (1968). Cleft palate in cattle. *Cleft Palate J.* 1:346-354.

Smith, D. W. (1977). An approach to clinical dysmorphology. *J. Pediatr.* 91:690-692.

Smith, J. L., and Stowe, F. R. (1961). The Pierre Robin syndrome. *Pediatrics* 27:128-133.

Squires, E. L., McKinnon, A. O., and Shideler, R. K. (1988). Use of ultrasonography in reproductive management in mares. *Theriogenology* 29:55-70.

Steindler, A. (1949). Arthrogryposis. *J. Int. Coll. Surg.* 12:21-25.

Swinyard, C. A. (1982). Concepts of multiple congenital contractures (arthrogryposis) in man and animals. *Teratology* 25:247-258.

Swinyard, C. A., and Bleck, E. E. (1985). The etiology of arthrogryposis (multiple congenital contracture). *Clin. Orthop.* 194:15-29.

Taylor, M. J., Poore, E. R., Robinson, J. S., and Clewlow, F. (1983). Measurement of fetal growth in lambs by ultrasound. *Res. Vet. Sci.* 34:257-260.

Thomas, I. T. T., and Smith, D. W. (1974). Oligohydramnios, cause of the nonrenal features of Potter's syndrome including pulmonary hypoplasia. *J. Pediatr.* 84:811-814.

Thompson, G. H., and Bilenker, R. M. (1985). Comprehensive management of arthrogryposis multiplex congenita. *Clin. Orthop.* 194:6-14.

Thurley, D. C., Revfeim, K. J. A., and Wilson, D. A. (1973). Growth of the Romney sheep foetus. *N.Z. J. Agric. Res.* 16:111-114.

Trasler, D. G., Walker, B. E., and Fraser, F. C. (1956). Congenital malformations produced by amniotic sac puncture. *Science* 124:439.

Van Kampen, K. R., and James, L. F. (1971). Ovarian and placental lesions in sheep from ingesting locoweed *Astragalus lentiginosus*. *Vet. Pathol.* 8:193-199.

Wallace, L. R. (1948). The growth of lambs before and after birth in relation to the level of nutrition: II and III. *J. Agric. Sci.* 38:243-302.

Walker, B. E. (1959). Effects on palate development of mechanical interference with the foetal environment. *Science 130*: 981.

Walker, B. E., and Quarles, J. (1976). Palate development in mouse foetuses after tongue removal. *Arch. Oral Biol. 21*: 405-412.

Wenham, G. (1981). A radiographic study of the changes in skeletal growth and development of the foetus caused by poor nutrition in the pregnant ewe. *Br. Vet. J. 137*: 176-187.

Westervelt, R. G., Stouffer, J. R., Hintz, H. F., and Schrywer, H. R. (1976). Estimating fatness in horses and ponies. *J. Anim. Sci. 43*: 781-785.

Wood, C., and Trounson, A. (1984). *Clinical In Vitro Fertilization.* Springer-Verlag, Berlin.

Yee, B. (1988). Ultrasonography in human in vitro fertilization programs. *Theriogenology 29*: 85-94.

28

Cutaneous Responses to Plant Toxins

William L. Epstein

University of California, San Francisco, California

I. INTRODUCTION

Volume I, *Plant and Fungal Toxins*, contained a chapter, "Allergic Contact Dermatitis from Plants," which described one type of skin response to plant toxins (Baer, 1983). In this chapter the focus has been broadened to include all forms of skin reactions caused by exposure to plants. Space restriction and the breadth of the topic limit us to key references, recent relevant publications, and in-depth reviews where feasible. Nevertheless, the information presented should provide a perspective for understanding the range and degree of responses the human skin can give to externally contacted plant toxins.

Plant dermatitis is a common affliction of almost everybody who heeds the need to commune with nature and even for some who remain cloistered in their homes surrounded by beautiful house plants. All manner of plants, flowers, shrubs, and trees can wound the skin. Often, the injury is mild and simply annoying, or it can be severe and disabling. The main forms of dermatitis discussed in this chapter include (1) irritation, (2) allergy, (3) phytophoto-dermatitis, and (4) granulomas.

II. IRRITATION

By far the most common cause of skin rashes from plants is primary irritation. Mechanical injury from the spines and thorns of wild plants, shrubs, brambles, and briers cause superficial abrasions and linear tears which may become erythe-matous, bleed, and crust. Usually, these minor lesions heal uneventfully, but the danger is they may serve as a portal of entry into the body of serious infections (e.g., sporotrichosis) or may become secondarily infected with skin bacteria, so that these lesions should not be neglected. In addition to this obvious macrotrauma, a more refined form of microtrauma is produced by tiny, almost invisible hairs (called trichomes) or barbs (referred to as glochids) found along the outside of many weeds, fruits, and plants. Best known are the stinging hairs found on thistles. When the trichomes or glochids are stiff they tend to penetrate the skin, but when brittle or silicafied, the tips will break off by mere touching. In either case, chemicals within the hair cells are released or injected into or onto the skin. This results in a rapid, at times explosive, onset of swelling, urtication, redness, and itching or burning called nonimmunologic urticaria (see Epstein and Epstein, 1989). Sometimes blisters form and can be quite painful. Thus this type of irritation is a double-barreled attack by the plant, with a minor mechanical phase and an eruptive chemical assault. The irritant chemicals fall into several classes, including (1) low-molecular-weight acids, such as acetic, citric, formic, malic, and oxalic acid; (2) amines; (3) glycosides; (4) proteolytic enzymes [i.e., bromelin from pineapples, ficin from figs, mucain from cohage (itch powder), papain from papaya, and a trypsinlike protease from dieffenbachia]; and (5) crystals, notably calcium oxalate. Calcium oxalate is widely distributed in plants and appears to be important in plant cell metabolism (Franceschi and Horner, 1980). Crystals come in a variety of forms and are produced mainly in specialized cells called idioblasts, whose shape is thought to determine the nature of the crystals produced (Franceschi and Horner, 1980). Most of the irritant crys-tals form needle-shaped bundles called raphides. Although irritant plants are found almost universally throughout the plant kingdom, certain families have a particular propensity to produce primary contact irritation. In this context, three families are especially worrisome: Euphorbiaceae, Brassicaceae, and Ranunculaceae.

A. Plant Families

1. *Euphorbiaceae*

The spurge family (Euphorbiaceae) is a huge family of more than 7000 species, whose relatedness can be perceived only by expert botanists. Practically, there are five subfamilies and about 50 tribes (Webster, 1986). Fortunately, only three subfamilies (Acalyphoteae, Crotonoideae, and Euphorbioideae) account for the majority of primary irritation seen in humans. Table 1 lists some of the commonly recognized irritant plants in the spurge family, and as can be seen, the mechanism responsible for irritation is as variable as the family is large. The Euphorbioideae, or euphorbs, grow best in tropical and subtropical regions and appear as tall trees in rain forests or bushy shrubs in dry areas (Webster, 1986). In North America they are confined to southern Florida and the southwest. In Europe they are called wolfsmilk. The beach apple or manchineel tree (*Hippomane mancinella*) in Florida and the Caribbean is reputed to be among the most poisonous of these plants, but this may be a fiction of time, history, or mythology (Morton, 1982). Nevertheless, the milky latex that oozes out of any part of the injured tree or fruit is said to cause an immediate burning sensation with swelling and large blisters. In the eye it may produce blindness. While a number of irritating chemicals and biologically active amines have been extracted, the most recent studies fix blame on diterpene esters in the latex (Adolf and Hecker, 1984). These esters resemble the diterpenes in the irritant plants of the genus *Croton* found throughout the tropics. In the last century, oil from the seed of the croton plant (*Croton tiglium*) was imported into the United States for medicinal purposes as a rubefacient and cathartic. Contact with the oil produces a burning, erythematous blister or pustule in about 8 to 12 h. Croton oil contains several diterpenes composed of four isoprene units (C_5H_8) linked head to tail as the basic R unit, geranylgeraniol. These phorbol esters have been identified as the tumor-promoting cocarcinogens in croton oil (Boutwell, 1974). The literature attests to the widespread use of purified phorbol esters, such as 12-O-tetradecanoyl phorbol-13-acetate (TPA) in studies of cell proliferation and differentiation. Virtually all irritant plants of the genus *Croton* contain phorbol esters, while the latex from the majority of euphorbs is a mixture of polycyclic di- and triterpenes and other terpenoids, which can polymerize into rubber. In addition, these complex irritant terpenoids may be tumor promoters (Kinghorn, 1979).

Plants with stinging hairs as the cause of irritation also occur in the spurge family. The genus *Tragia* contains over 100 species and in the United States subsist in southern states. The stinging mechanism of these plants is unique and depends on peeling away of the idioblast cell wall to uncover a grooved, elongated calcium oxalate crystal which is inserted into the skin, allowing irritant chemicals to flow directly into the dermis (Thurston and Lersten, 1969; Franceschi and Horner, 1980). The toxic principles are not clearly known but may be amines, such as histamine (Thurston and Lersten, 1969). Other spurge family plants with stinging hairs belong to the genera *Cnidoscolus* and *Jatropha*. In the tropics stings from these plants can be very severe, with hemorrhagic blisters, skin necrosis, and possibly death. The stinging mechanism is different from *Tragia* but similar to stinging nettles (see below).

2. Brassicaceae

Sometimes called the mustard family, Brassicaceae contains 3200 species in more than 350 genera (Mitchell and Rook, 1979). Table 2 lists some of the well-known plants in this family which can be extremely irritating. The irri-

TABLE 1 Some Common Irritant Plants in the Spurge Family Euphorbiaceae

Subfamily	Tribe/genus	Common names	Mechanisms or irritant chemical
Crotonoideae	*Croton*	Croton bush	(Croton oil) phorbol esters
	Jatropha	Coral plant	(Mustard oil) thioglycoside
	Cnidoscolus	Spurge nettle Tread softly	Stinging hairs
Euphorbioideae	*Hippomane*	Manchineel Beach apple	Diterpenes and alkaloid
	Sapium	Aurou-wood	Terpenes
	Hura	Sandbox tree	Ricin-like tox-albumin and triterpenes
	Euphorbia	Beach spurge Red spurge Milkweed Wolf's milk Astham plant Candelabra cactus Caper spurge Snow-on-the-mountain Crown-of-thorns	Di- and triterpenes terpenoids
	Poinsettia	Poinsettia	Phorbol esters
	Pedilanthus	Slipper bush	Terpenes?
Acalyphoideae	*Tragia*	Nose-burn	Stinging hairs

Source: Reprinted from Epstein and Epstein (1989), with permission.

tant principle is found in the roots, seeds, and the leaves. Contact with the plant oil rapidly causes linear streaks of vesicles and later subepidermal blisters. The offending toxins are isothiocyanates, which in nature are complexed with glucose as inert thioglucosides. Upon injury the thioglucosides become substrates for a proteolytic enzyme, myrosinase, in the specialized idioblasts, and isothiocyanates in concentrations of greater than 0.1% are released into the environment (Kjaer 1966; Mitchell and Rook, 1979). Most plants contain mixtures of thioglucosides, so that allyl, benzyl, and/or phenyl isothiocyanates are usually produced (Mitchell and Rook, 1979). "Mustard oils" are not restricted to Brassicaceae but occur sporadically in many plant families. A few examples are papaya (*Carica papaya*), seeds of *Limnanthes douglasii* in the Pacific northwest, and Nasturtium, whose pickled seed is popular in Mexico and South America. It should also be noted that allergic sensitization to these plants may occur, but it is rare.

TABLE 2 Selected Irritant Plants in
the Brassicaceae Family (Cruciferae)

Genus/species	Common name
Armoracia	
A. *rusticana*	Horseradish
Brassica	
B. *campestris*	Turnip
B. *napus*	Rape
B. *nigra*	Mustard
B. *oleracea*	Cabbage
	Cauliflower
Eruca	
E. *sativa*	Rocket salad
Lepidium	
L. *campestre*	Pepperwort
L. *sativum*	Pepper grass
Raphanus	
R. *sativus*	Radish
Sinapis	
S. *albus*	White mustard

Source: Reprinted from Epstein (1990),
with permission.

3. *Ranunculaceae*

Buttercups personify this fairly large family of flowering weeds and cut
flowers. Not surprisingly, almost 400 species of buttercups exist in the genera
Ranunculus, and overall there are 1900 species of plants in 50 genera (Mitchell and Rook, 1979a). A sampling of the better-known irritant plants in
this family is presented in Table 3. The clinical appearance of irritation from
these plants ranges from mild to moderate erythema and itching to notable
edema, or eczema, and burning blisters with occasional ulcers. If chewed,
some plants elicit severe stomatitis, with swelling, burning, and small ulcers.
Chemical identification of the offending toxins remains unknown for many of
the irritating plants. The good news is that part of the puzzle has been solved
and seems related to chromosomal makeup. Plants in this family contain three
distinct types of chromosomes, C, R, and T, that have been useful in classification of the various genera (Ruijgrok, 1966). Plants with large, slender,
bent R chromosomes generally fall into four genera: *Ranunculus*, *Anemone*,
Clematis, and *Helleborus*. The chemical irritant in these beautiful wildflowers
turns out to be ranunculin, a glucoside (Ruijgrok, 1966). This substrate
is degraded by enzyme action to produce the active irritant protoanemonin,
an unsaturated lactone that with time dimerizes into inactive anemonin (Ruijgrok, 1966). Recent studies with high-performance liquid chromatography

TABLE 3 Selected Irritant Plants in the Family Ranunculaceae

Genus/species	Common name
Aconitum[a]	
A. lycoctonum	—
A. napellus	Wolfsbane
Actaea[a]	
A. rubra	Red baneberry
A. spicata	Baneberry
Anemone[b]	
A. hepatica	Liver leaf
A. nemorosa	Wind flower
A. patens	Wild crocus
Clematis[b]	
C. brachiata	—
C. grandiflora	—
C. virginiana	Virgin's bower
C. vitalba	Old man's beard
Delphinium[a]	Stave's acre
(250 spp.)	
Helleborus	
H. niger	Christmas rose
Nigella[a]	
N. sativa	Black cumin
Ranunculus[b]	Buttercup
(400 spp.)	
Thalictrum[a]	
T. foliolosum	Meadow rue
Trautvetteria	
T. caroliniensis	False bugbane

[a]Ranunculin not found (27).
[b]Ranunculin found (27).
Source: Reprinted from Epstein (1990), with permission.

(HPLC) analysis have detected trace amounts of protoanemonin in plants not containing R chromosomes (Bonora et al., 1987), but the genetic link seems amenable to investigation by modern biotechnology methods. Protoanemonin has powerful vesicant activity, on the order of cantharidin (Mitchell and Rook, 1979a), with a tense subepidermal blister appearing 12 to 24 h after contact. It is quite different from the blistering seen with isothiocyanates of the Brassicaceae.

4. Miscellaneous

It is presumptuous to conclude that all irritant plants reside in three families. Many other well-recognized species produce significant primary irritation, but they are widespread throughout the plant kingdom and no facile classification can bring them together. Without beleaguering the issue, a few seem worthy of consideration. The stinging nettles common to North America were alluded to previously. They belong to the family Urticaceae, which contains about 550 species (Mitchell and Rook, 1979b). Many, but not all, possess stinging hairs, such as the common thistle, *Urtica dioica*, which causes fierce urticaria, at times causes collapse, and can fell animals as large as a horse. Irritation occurs when the stiff hair is inserted into the skin, the tip breaks off, and a syringelike mechanism from the bulb cells forces toxins into the dermis (Thurston, 1974). The noxious chemicals are considered to be a mixture of histamine and similar amines (Thurston, 1974). The family Araceae also contains some common irritants. Perhaps best known is *Dieffenbachia*, whose species adorn homes and hotel lobbies by the millions and account for an inordinate amount of plant poisoning in the United States (Arditti and Rodriquez, 1982). When chewed, these plants cause marked tissue swelling and loss of voice for up to 2 weeks, supporting the common name "dumb cane" (Morton, 1982a). Skin contact gives a similar but not quite as dramatic response. The mechanism of irritation has generally been considered as being due to the oxalate crystals that abound in the plant. However, this seems inadquate, and a "dual-hit" hypothesis has been proposed: both calcium oxalate injury and proteolytic enzyme irritation (Arditti and Rodriguez, 1982). *Philodendron* is another well-known genus of this family of irritating plants. Thioglucosides in the caper bush (*Capparis spinosa*) and other species of the Capparidaceae family cause blistering upon contact.

An even bigger problem is distinguishing primary irritation from contact allergic sensitization. Even experts can be confused at times [see Benezra et al. (1985)]. Unfortunately, many plants contain both irritating and sensitizing chemicals. Table 4 lists some of these. Occasionally, but not invariably, the sensitizing chemical is also irritating. Separating allergy from irritancy presents a major challenge that should be dealt with only by experienced dermatologists.

B. Pathomechanisms

Despite its frequency, very little is known about the pathogenesis of skin irritation. Since the epidermis is most superficial and the first tissue to be injured by an irritant, it seems reasonable to assume that the epidermal cells should be first to respond with release of cytokines and other biologically active molecules and mediators of inflammation (Katz, 1985; Kupper, 1989; Stengl et al., 1989). It is also likely that the types, pattern, and sequence of mediator release will vary with different toxic attacks. Furthermore, the blistering responses, which tend to be subepidermal, may result from primary injury in the dermis, suggesting that the target may be the mast cell, which is capable of fast or slow release of mediators (see below). Irritant, nonimmunogenic urticaria is considered to be due to release of histamine from mast cells with dilation of small dermal blood vessels and leakage of plasma into the tissue. The molecular mechanism is thought to be similar to that for aller-

TABLE 4 Some Plants that Contain Sensitizers and/or Irritants

Family	Common name
Amaryllidaceae (1100 spp.)	Narcissus
Cannabaceae (3 spp.)	Hop
Commelinaceae (500 spp.)	Wandering jew
Compositae (13,000 spp.)[a]	Field camomile
Geraniaceae (750 spp.)	Geranium
Gesneriaceae (2000 spp.)	African violet, gloxinia, trumpet flower
Ginkgoaceae	Ginkgyo tree
Illiciaceae (42 spp.)	Star anise
Labiatae (3500 spp.)	Lavender, mint, sage, thyme, chives, leek, onion, colchicum, shallot, garlic, asparagus, tulip, squill, skunk cabbage
Orchidaceae (17,000 spp.)	
Pedaliaceae (50 spp.)	Sesame oil
Poaceae (10,000 spp.) (grass family)	Lemon grass Citronella
Solanaceae (2000 spp.)	Deadly nightshade Capsicum Thorn apple Tobacco
Zingiberaceae (700 spp.) (ginger family)	Ginger

[a]Mostly contact sensitizers.
Source: Reprinted from Epstein (1990) with permission.

gic urticaria, relying on opening of calcium channels and an inositol lipid second messenger-generated intracellular system to complete the cascade and degranulate mast cell products (see below). Certain differences exist. Specific IgE is not essential, but whether transmembrane signaling occurs through two bridged IgE receptors or elsewhere through membrane-attached G proteins remains uncertain. In addition, nonimmunogenic urticaria does not require that membrane phospholipids be methylated and signaling depends primarily on intracellular Ca^{2+} flux (Rosengard et al., 1986). Furthermore, the process is rapidly inactivated (Rosengard et al., 1986).

III. ALLERGY

In contrast to irritation, allergic reactions as a group tend to be more severe and often cause the victim to seek medical care. Practically speaking, these responses can be divided into immediate (serum mediated) and delayed (cell mediated, CMI), with some crossover in antibody-driven cellular cytotoxicity. Plant toxins are capable of producing many types of allergic reaction, either topically contacted or systemically administered.

A. Immediate Hypersensitivity

Allergists have long known that ingestion of certain foods, especially nuts, in sensitive persons can trigger bouts of urticaria, angioedema, and/or anaphylaxis (but that subject will not be discussed here). Hives or tissue edema after contact with plants, on the other hand, is quite common and is considered a major cause of immunogenic contact urticaria (Lahti, 1986). Table 5 is a partial list of the most common fruits, vegetables, spices, plants, and trees that can elicit contact urticaria. Patients usually become aware of itching or tingling 1 to 2 h after exposure, and over the next 6 to 24 h linear or grouped erythematous hives or solid tissue edema appear at the exposed site. Sometimes an entire limb can swell or the eruption can be subclinical with simply itching or tingling. This is a difficult occupational problem for food handlers, because repeated exposure can produce a more chronic, disabling, eczematous hand dermatitis (Hjorth and Roed-Patersen, 1976; Cronin, 1987).

The pathogenesis of immunogenic contact urticaria is established as an example of type I immediate hypersensitivity, in which specific IgE antibodies bound by their Fc portion to high-affinity receptors on mast cells behave like a blasting cap to explosively degranulate the mast cells when they attach to absorbed antigen by their exposed Fab fragments. The molecular mechanism of degranulation is beginning to be understood in some detail (Beaven and Cunha-Melo, 1988). First, the trigger is pulled when a divalent protein antigen appropriately bridges two specific IgE molecules to initiate a transmembrane signal through G proteins to activate an enzyme, phospholipase C, which in turn hydrolyzes a unique inositol lipid, phosphatidylinositol-4,5-bisphosphate (PIP_2) and gives two messengers, diacylglycerol (DG) and inositol triphosphate (IP_3), one result being release of free calcium ions (Ca^{2+}) from intracellular pools in endoplasmic reticulum (Beaven and Cunha-Melo, 1988; Berridge, 1988). In addition, another inositol lipid metabolite, IP_4, apparently influences intracellular calcium levels by regulating entry through the endoplasmic reticulum (Berridge, 1988). At the same time, calcium channels open in the plasma membrane and extracellular Ca^{2+} adds to the load of free cytoplasmic Ca^{2+}. Less is known about the external Ca^{2+} pathway. It may involve voltage-operated channels found mainly in excitable cells (least likely), receptor-operated stimulus-response coupling through G proteins, and/or second-messenger-operated channels (Berridge, 1988). In any event, the rise in intracellular Ca^{2+} allows DG to activate phosphokinase C (PKC), which phosphorylates a number of proteins and is required for stimulation of phospholipase A_2 and activation of a serine proteinase related to exocytosis of mast cell granules (Beaven and Cunha-Melo, 1988). A novel twist may provide more flexibility to the intracellular mechanisms for mast cell degranulation. Penner et al. (1988) have

TABLE 5 Some Plants and Plant Products
Causing Immunogenic Urticaria

Fruits	Spices
Apple	Cinnamon
Carrot	Garlic
Celery	Mustard
Parsley	Rapeseed
Parsnip	
Potato	Plants
Tomato	Tulips
Vegetables	Trees
Chives	Birch pollen
Grains	Teak
Lettuce	Western red cedar
Onion	Various nuts

Source: Reprinted from Epstein and
Epstein (1989), with permission.

described a Ca^{2+}-activated cAMP messenger system that may interact with,
and/or extend, inositol lipid-derived messengers in leading to mast cell degranulation.

Mast cell granules contain three types of products: (1) preformed and
rapidly released products (histamine, aryl sulfatase, chemotactic factors);
(2) preformed, slowly released products bound to heparin; and (3) newly
formed mediators. Histamine is probably the major mediator released in acute
urticaria, but when the lesions extend or persist after several hours, other
molecules, such as newly formed leukotrienes, heparin (or heparin fragments),
and proteases, may account for the persistent clinical picture.

Plant-induced immunogenic urticaria occurs most frequently, but not exclusively, in persons with an atopic background (Lahti, 1986; Cronin, 1987).
Since atopy with hay fever, asthma, and eczema occurs in about 10 to 20%
of the U.S. population, many people are at risk, given our propensity for
outdoor activities. As indicated in Table 5, the most likely offenders are fruits,
vegetables, and nuts, but spices are also offenders. Mustard or rapeseed,
which are commonly sold as vegetable oils and margarine, can induce contact
urticaria and even anaphylaxis (Meding, 1985).

Erythema multiforme (EM) is a generalized vasculitic skin eruption usually
caused by systemic drug drug allergy or associated with microbial skin infections, notably herpes simplex. Plants also have been reported to produce
erythema multiforme-like rashes from contact. Most celebrated is the EM-
like dermatitis observed after wearing necklaces and bracelets made of exotic
wood, such as *Dalbergia nigra* (Fisher, 1986). EM also has been seen after
contact with more common plants such as poison ivy and primula, and with
exposure to terpenes and even mugwort (Fisher, 1986). The pathogenesis
of EM is considered to be a vasculitis elicited by immune complexes in and
around superificial blood vessels, but no studies of plant-induced EM have
been published to determine the nature of the complexes.

B. Delayed Hypersensitivity

Type IV, contact-type delayed hypersensitivity reactions occur far more frequently than do type I contact urticaria. Poison ivy, poison oak, and poison sumac of the Anacardiaceae family are the most common offenders in the United States, and compositae are the leaders worldwide (Epstein and Epstein, 1989). The basic biology, botany, and chemistry of these has been described (Baer, 1983), so this section will simply be updated and expanded with perhaps greater emphasis on human biology. In addition to these common contact sensitizers, it has long been known that many natural plant toxins can induce allergic contact dermatitis. Historically, Bruno Bloch helped initiate the scientific investigation of contact and immediate plant allergens when he inadvertently became sensitized to the common European house plant *Primula obconica* (Bloch, 1929). One has only to peruse the literature of the toilet goods and fragrance industries to appreciate how many of the plant products used in these multibillion dollar industries have contact-sensitizing potential. Fortunately, these many different chemicals exist in very low concentrations in nature, and repeated exposure to concentrated preparations seems required for sensitization, so that problems surface primarily in an occupational setting or with exceptions, when indiscrete amounts of these chemicals are used in cosmetics.

1. Poison Ivy/Oak (Anacardiaceae)

The review by Baer (1983) requires only an update and a few additions.

Botany. Many laypersons are not clear as to where these weeds grow. Poison ivy flourishes east of the Rockies, while poison oak is found in the west. In Texas, where the mountains disappear, the species become mixed. As one travels north in Canada, poison oak, which is abundant in British Columbia, and the less populous eastern poison ivy tend to disappear. Neither plant grows in Alaska, in rain forests, or in Hawaii (Epstein, 1987). Their finicky growth requirements are further emphasized by their abhorrence of hot, dry deserts, so they are seldom seen in Mexico except in Baja California, where the moist temperate climate supports their subsistence. An important point for backpackers, hikers, and hunters is the failure of these weeds to grow above 4000 to 5000 ft elevation, so that Lake Tahoe, the Sierra Nevada and Rocky mountains, and much of the plateau in western Nevada and Idaho offer havens for poison oak-sensitive outdoorsmen. The United States is the prime spawning ground of these noxious plants, but over the years plants have been expatriated to Europe and escaped their confines, so that the weed is slowly taking hold, especially in the Netherlands, France, and Germany, and reports of its appearance are increasing in the foreign literature (Epstein and Epstein, 1989). This seems to be happening in Japan as well, so that cosmopolitan cases of urushi dermatitis are becoming more common (Epstein, 1987) and are not limited to workers in Japanese lacquer factories. In addition to the commonly recognized cross-reacting allergens (Baer, 1983), an ever-increasing number of plants that cause poison ivylike eruptions are being recognized worldwide, particularly in South America and Australia (Epstein and Epstein, 1989). The cross-reacting chemicals appear to be catechols, resorcinols, or salicylic acid with 13 to 17 carbon side chains at poisition 3 on the phenolic ring (Baer, 1983; Tomb et al., 1988; Epstein and Epstein,

1989). Floridonians should note that the commonplace Florida holly (also called
Brazilian pepper tree) can cause cross-reactions in some people (Morton, 1978).

Biology. In the United States about 50% of adults are sensitive to poison
oak/ivy and their first bout of dermatitis usually appears between the ages
of 8 and 16. They react to the leaf pressed on their skin, which is equivalent
to 2 to 2.5 µg purified urushiol (Epstein and Epstein, 1989). About 35% are
subclinically sensitive, which means that they never had the rash as a child,
will react only to higher concentrations (5 to 100 µg), and may become reactive as an adult after repeated exposures. The final 10 to 15% are biologically
tolerant, or nonreactive, even to amounts of urushiol as large as 1000 µg.
The mechanism of their tolerance is unknown but holds a key to biological
control of this unwanted human affliction (Epstein, 1987). From a medical
standpoint about 10 to 15% of patients are classified as exquisitely sensitive
and must have systemic corticosteroid therapy to control a bout of poison ivy
dermatitis. The activities of these 25 to 40 million individuals are severely
compromised by their sensitivity, which tends to be familial (Epstein, 1987).
Because so many people are sensitive, poison oak/ivy dermatitis is a major
cause of disability and time lost from work in outdoor industries, and much
effort has been expended toward preventative medicine (Epstein, 1989a), not
the least of which has been the development of topical barrier or binding preparations (Orchard et al., 1986; Epstein, 1989a).

Immunobiology. Hyposensitization by ingestion of active urushiol molecules has long been practiced, but the immunochemistry of urushiol predicted
that novel molecules could be synthesized, which would induce tolerance instead of contact sensitization (Baer, 1983; Epstein, 1987), and this has been
accomplished in animals (Dunn et al., 1986) (see below). Furthermore, it
was found that sensitization of animals with urushiol induced formation of anti-
receptor, anti-idiotypic antibodies which could be infused into naive recipients
and prevent subsequent experimental contact sensitization (Dunn et al., 1987).
And patients hyposensitized by oral ingestion of urushiol also may produce
these protective antibodies (Stamf et al., 1989). So the outlook for developing specific immunologic prevention seems a realistic possibility.

2. Compositae

The Compositae, an enormous family of 20,000 to 30,000 species in 1000
genera, is composed of many well-recognized plants, vegetables, wildflowers,
weeds, and industrially useful plants (Schmidt, 1986) (Table 6). As noted
previously (Baer, 1983; Epstein and Epstein, 1989), it is fortunate that casual
exposure, as with poison oak/ivy, does not induce compositae sensitivity or
the quality of outdoor life would be greatly compromised. Most reported cases
of "compositae dermatitis" occur in occupations intimately involved with the
plants. Exceptions are the epidemic of parthinin dermatitis observed in India
after inadvertent importation of the weed feverfew in shipments of grain from
the United States (Lonker et al., 1974), and the endemic airborne ragweed
dermatitis seen commonly in the U.S. midwest, which in recent years seems
due mostly to exposure to weeds such as dog fennel, cocklebur, and feverfew
(Menz and Winkelmann, 1987). As described previously (Baer, 1983), the
chemical toxins are sesquiterpene lactones, 15-carbon-ringed structures with
a complex organization and extensive ligand substitutions on six distinct skele-

TABLE 6 Some Compositae that Cause
Allergic Contact Dermatitis

Vegetables	Flowers
Artichoke	Black-eyed Susan
Chicory	Camomile
Endive	Cardoon
Lettuce	Chrysanthemum
Yarrow	Dahlia
	Daisy
Weeds	Dandelion
Burweed	Elecampane
Cocklebur	Gaillaridia
Dog fennel	Mountain tobacco
Goldenrod	Sunflower
Mugwort	Tansy
Stinking	
mayweed	Perfumery
Sneezeweed	Costus

Source: Reprinted from Epstein and
Epstein (1989), with permission.

tons (Epstein and Epstein, 1989). The sensitizing moiety appears to be an
α-methylene-γ-butyrolactone configuration which is available for nucleophilic
attack by amines (Baer, 1983; Epstein and Epstein, 1989). Unfortunately,
sesquiterpene lactones are not limited to the Compositae family; cross-reacting
chemicals have been found in plants of other families, including Magnoliaceae
and Lauraceae, as well as in liverworts of the genus *Frullania* (Mitchell et al.,
1970). A more recent molecular analysis of the patterns of cross-reactivity
of persons sensitized to costus indicated that chemicals with a lesser degree
of oxygenated substituents close to the α-methylene-γ-butyrolactone ring
produced the largest number of positive skin test reactions, and it seemed
that the six different skeletal classes acted as independent sensitizers (Benezra
and Epstein, 1986).

3. Toxic Woods

Contact dermatitis from trees and wood products is mainly an occupational
problem, but since the most potent sensitizers occur in beautiful tropical woods
of wide commercial use, the list of victims must be extended to boat lovers,
violinists, genteel hikers, art afficionados, and others (Hausen, 1986). Table
7 displays a few of the most common sensitizing trees. The chemistry of wood
sensitizers has been investigated in great detail (Hausen, 1981). Many of
these timbers contain complex quinones that can elicit cross-reactions in persons sensitized to the primin found in some primroses (*Primula obconica*)
(Benezra and Ducombs, 1987). Thus the sensitizing and cross-reacting chemical in Brazilian rosewood (*Dalbergia nigra*), R-4-methoxydalbergione, is,
immunologically speaking, structurally related to primin, 2-methoxy-6-pentyl-
benzoquinone. In recent years Brazilian rosewood has been replaced by a

TABLE 7 Some Trees that Cause Allergic Contact Dermatitis

Common name	Botanical name
African blackwood	*Dalbergia latifolia*
Australian blackwood	*Acacia melanoxylon*
California redwood	*Sequoia sempervirens*
Cocobolo	*Dalbergia retusa*
Mansonia	*Mansonia altissima*
Pao Ferro	*Machaerium scleroxylum*
Pine	*Pinus* (about 80 species in North America)
Rosewoods	*Dalbergia* species
Silky oak	*Grevillea robusta*
Spruce	*Picea* species
Teak	*Tectona grandis*
Western red cedar	*Thuja plica*

Source: Reprinted from Epstein and Epstein (1989), with permission.

similar South American timber, pao ferro (*Machaerium scleroxylon*), but unfortunately it also possesses a very potent sensitizer, R-3,4-dimethoxydalbergione, and may be the most hazardous timber in commercial use today (Hausen, 1986). Other examples include the Australian silky oak (*Grevillea robusta*), a shade tree in the United States and a source of plywood and furniture, which contains 5-n-tridecylresorcinol (grevillol) and may cross-react with urushiol (Baer, 1983). Pines yield terpenes that are purified into the potential sensitizers colophony (rosin) and turpentine. California redwoods (*Sequoia sempervirens*) can cause allergic alveolitis and/or contact dermatitis (Hausen, 1981, 1986). Western red cedar (*Thuja plicata*), a durable wood native to the western United States and Canada, is popular worldwide as building lumber. It contains at least two quinones and produces both immediate and delayed hypersensitivity reactions (Hausen, 1981, 1986).

4. Miscellaneous

Many other plants, shrubs, and trees cause clinical allergic contact dermatitis, but often the chemical responsible has not been identified. A list of known sensitizing chemicals in plants has been compiled (Benezra and Ducombs, 1987). Phytochemists throughout the world are slowly unraveling these knotty problems. For instance, the allergens in scorpion weed (*Phacelia crenulata*), which have been shown to be geranylhydroquinone (Reynolds et al., 1980) and related chemicals called phaceloids, are found in other members of this

genus (Benezra and Ducombs, 1987). The main contact sensitizer in English
and Algerian ivy (*Hedera helix* and *H. cannariensis*) has turned out to be
falcarinol (Hausen et al., 1987; Gafner et al., 1988).

5. Pathomechanisms

Although the immunologic nature of allergic contact dermatitis was discussed previously (Baer, 1983), it is worth briefly reviewing the various steps
since more is known now about the molecular events taking place at the T-
cell surface. As a prototype we will use poison oak/ivy urushiol because more
is known about its unique chemistry (Baer, 1983; Epstein, 1987). In the natural state urushiol is relatively unreactive; however, in the skin, in the presence of oxygen, with or without enzymic action, the hydroxyl groups at ring
positions 1 and 2 open up to produce a highly reactive *o*-quinone. During
the sensitization phase and in conjunction with class II HLA glycoproteins
on the surface of accessory cells (Langerhans cells in epidermis and/or macrophages in the dermis) (Epstein, 1987, 1990), the now complete antigen, which
depends on the hydrophobic carbon chain at ring site 3 for specificity (Baer,
1983; Epstein, 1987), is presented to T4 helper/inducer lymphocytes in the
dermis or more likely in regional lymph nodes. The antigen receptor complex
(TRC) consists of a disulfide-linked heterodimer (α/β) T_i molecule noncovalent-
ly bound to a set of invariant CD3 glycoproteins (Imboden and Weiss, 1988).
This receptor binding initiates a cascade involving rapid hydrolysis of inositol
lipids to second messengers and metabolites, a rise in intracellular Ca^{2+}, and
activation of PKC, all of which lead to a contingent series of about 70 gene
activations over a period of minutes to days (Crabtree, 1989) and a commit-
ment to T-lymphocyte activation, cell division, and clonal expansion of a population of urushiol-specific T4 cells (Horejsi and Bazil, 1988; Imboden and Weiss,
1988), resulting in a poison oak/ivy-sensitive individual. The next exposure
to these weeds will elicit allergic contact dermatitis. Presumably, the molecular process is the same, in that urushiol in the skin becomes an activated *o*-
quinone, a nucleophilic attack occurs, and the antigen is presented to T4
cells by the accessory cells. This time the T-cell response is specific and
the membrane changes are probably different (Imboden and Weiss, 1988).
Quite possibly the G proteins connected to the CD3/Ti complex are changed
so that the transduced signal now induces secretion of a variety of lymphokines which cause macrophage chemotaxis and additional cytokine secretion.
Epidermal cells are destroyed to give vesicles and blisters. Vasoactive peptides induce vasodilation, redness, and edema. Although urushiol is present
in skin for less than a day, it causes an inflammatory response that lasts 7
to 14 days before healing. Very little is known about modulation of allergic
contact dermatitis.

Other subsets of T cells are also induced by urushiol. Clinically, poison
oak/ivy sensitivity tends to persist throughout life, despite variations in the
level of sensitivity (Baer, 1983; Epstein, 1987; Epstein and Epstein, 1989).
This implies that specific T memory cells have been generated, presumably
T cells bearing Ta_1 and/or Tp 103 antigens (Horejsi and Bazil, 1988). Furthermore, the known regiospecificity of the nucleophilic attack on the *o*-qui-
none was taken advantage of by producing a urushiol molecule blocked at ring
position 5, which favored a sulfhydryl attack at position 6 and the induction
of T8 suppressor cells (Dunn et al., 1986). Blocking all available ring sites

(4, 5, and 6) also led to development of T8 suppressor cells (Dunn et al., 1986), so that the molecular mechanism for induction of tolerance remains unclear. It also seems that another mechanism of tolerance in animals and humans may rest on the induction of anti-T cell receptor antiidiotypic antibodies (Dunn et al., 1987; Stampf et al., 1989).

IV. PHYTOPHOTODERMATITIS

The basic biology and chemistry of photosensitization by plant toxins have been described (Johnson, 1983). This section is focused more on botanical and clinical issues in humans. Although photosensitizers can induce either a photoallergic or a phototoxic reaction, the response to natural plant toxins is almost invariably phototoxic (Epstein and Epstein, 1989).

The clinical presentation may simply be that of an excessive sunburn with bright erythema, but usually there is some swelling, or edema, and in severe cases tense bullae form. The eruption begins within hours of exposure, peaks in 12 to 36 h and persists for a week or so, healing with notable hyperpigmentation. The acute rash is limited to sun-exposed areas that were contacted by the plant toxin. This produces blotchy, linear, or confluent patterns of dermatitis.

The major phototoxic plant chemicals are furocoumarins (psoralens) (Johnson, 1983; Epstein and Epstein, 1989), and while reputed to be widely distributed throughout the plant kingdom (Pathak, 1986), are most commonly found in two distinct families: Rutaceae and Umbelliferae.

A. Psoralen-Containing Plant Families

1. Rutaceae

The Rutaceae, a family of 900 species, is famous for the photosensitizing citrus fruits, lemons, limes, and so on (Table 8). Oil of bergamot, extracted from bergamot oranges (*Citrus bergamia*) and used in cheap perfumes and colognes, has been responsible for some very unsightly, pigmented eruptions (Epstein and Epstein, 1989). Other unlikely members of this family include the gas plant (*Dictamnus albus*), the "burning bush" in the Bible; common rue (*Ruta graveolens*), a common yellow wild flower in temperate zones; and mokihana (*Pelea anisata*), whose anise-scented fruits are strung into traditional leis to greet visitors in Hawaii. It should be emphasized that this family of plants also contains irritating and sensitizing toxins, especially in the *Citrus* genus.

2. Umbelliferae

The Umbelliferae is by far the largest family with photosensitizing psoralen-containing plants, many of which are edible or ground into condiments (Table 9). *Ammi majus* was the original commercial source of psoralens used by Egyptian dermatologists to treat patients with vitiligo. However, it is likely that other genera, such as *Angelica*, used to make candied fruits and fine liqueurs, *Heracleum* (giant hogweed), *Ligusticum*, provider of potherbs, and *Peucedanum* (parsnip), cause much more of the phytophotodermatitis observed

TABLE 8 Some Common Photosensitizing Plants in the Family Rutaceae (900 Species)

Genus/species	Common name
Citrus	
C. *aurantifolia*	Lime
C. *aurantium*	Seville orange
C. *bergamia*	Bergamot
C. *bigaradia*	Pettigrain oil
C. *limon*	Lemon
Dictamnus	
D. *albus*	Gas plant
D. *dasycarpus*	—
Fagara	
F. *oilanthoides*	Artar prickly ash
Pelea	
P. *anisata*	Mokihana
Phebalium	
P. *anceps*	Blister bush
P. *argenteum*	Blister plant (Persian lime)
Ptelea	
P. *angustifolia*	Hop tree
P. *aptera*	—
P. *crenulata*	—
Ruta	
R. *graveolens*	Common rue
R. *montana*	—
Thamnosa	
T. *montana*	Turpentine broom

Source: Reprinted from Epstein (1990), with permission.

in nature, due to their wide distribution in temperate climes. Clinically, it should be noted that photodermatitis occurs only sporadically in the field and requires massive exposure to wet plants to deliver sufficient psoralen to the skin, followed by intense or prolonged sun exposure, because the eliciting wavelengths are in the ultraviolet, 320 and 400 nm.

An interesting case concerns celery (*Apium graveolens*). In the 1950s and early 1960s epidemics of photodermatitis in field workers were traced to pink rot (*Sclerotinia sclerotiorum*), which commonly infects celery. The problem was solved by breeding resistant celery. By the 1980s we were faced with mini-epidemics of photodermatitis in grocery store chains, because the new, improved celery now contained higher doses of psoralens; eruptions

TABLE 9 Some Common Photosensitizing Plants
in the Umbelliferae Family (2850 Species)

Genus/species	Common name
Ammi	
A. majus	Bishop's weed
A. visnaga	—
Anethum	
A. graveolens	Dill
Angelica (80 spp.)	
Anthriscus	
A. sylvestris	Wild chervil
Apium	
A. graveolens	Celery
Cuminum	
C. cyminum	Cumin
Daucus	
D. carota	Wild and cultivated carrot
Foeniculum	
F. vulgare	Fennel
Heracleum (70 spp.)	
H. dulce	Sweet cow parsnip
H. giganteum	Wild parsnip
H. lanatum	Cow-parsnip
H. mantegazzianum	Giant hogweed
H. sphondylium	Cow parsnip
Hippomarathrum	
H. capsicum	—
Ligusticum (60 spp.)	Pot herb
Peucedanum (120 spp.)	
P. galbanum	Blister bush
P. officinale	Sulfur root
P. sativum	Parsnip
Petroselinum	Parsley

Source: Reprinted from Epstein (1990), with
permission.

were triggered especially in grocery store employees who frequented suntan parlors [see Epstein and Epstein (1989) and Epstein (1990)].

Upon extraction, all of these phototoxic plants yield one or more linear tricyclic furocoumarin. The most common photosensitizers are 5- and 8-methoxypsoralens. Other families that harbor photosensitizing psoralens include Moraceae, which contains edible figs (*Ficus carica*), and Leguminosae, with the scurf pea (*Psoralea corylifolia*). But the suspected presence of linear psoralens in other potentially phototoxic plants (Pathak, 1986) remains to be demonstrated unambiguously. One possibility is the presence in certain plants of nonfurocoumarin photosensitizing toxins (see below). Another popular myth is that ingestion of plants containing psoralens can induce systemic photodermatitis. To be effective, huge amounts would have to be ingested (Pathak, 1986), and this could only happen to a determined food faddist.

B. Other Photosensitizers

One of the most difficult types of phytophotodermatitis presents the clinical picture of an airborne contact dermatitis, when in reality it is a phototoxic or photoallergic response (Pathak, 1986; Frain-Bell, 1986; Epstein and Epstein, 1989). The initial acute eruption quickly becomes chronic and tends to spread beyond the initial site of exposure to involve large areas of skin, sometimes as exfoliative dermatitis. These patients may eventuate as persistent light reactors (Frain-Bell, 1986; Epstein and Epstein, 1989). Psoralens rarely account for this pattern of response. The most likely culprits include the aromatic lichen compounds usnic acid and atranorin (Thune, 1987), compositae oleoresins, and other sesquiterpene lactones (Frain-Bell, 1986; Thune, 1987). The epidemic of airborne contact dermatitis from the importation of feverfew (*Parthenium hysterophorus*) into India also caused some cases of chronic phytophotodermatitis (Lonker et al., 1974).

C. Pathomechanisms

The photodynamic action of ultraviolet and psoralens has been described (Johnson, 1983), and its effect on skin, reviewed (Pathak, 1986; Epstein and Epstein, 1989). α-Terthienyl from marigolds (*Tagetes erecta*) apparently produces only a type I, nonphotodynamic phototoxic response (Towers et al., 1979). The mechanisms by which other plant toxins cause phytophotodermatitis remain to be deciphered (Thune, 1987). An intriguing but unsettled issue is the role of prior contact sensitization to Compositae in predisposing a person to develop photocontact dermatitis later (Pathak, 1986; Frain-Bell, 1986; Epstein and Epstein, 1989).

V. GRANULOMAS

Implantation into the skin of thorns, barbs, or spicules from plants can induce subacute, chronic, and/or granulomatous inflammation. Fortunately, this sort of response occurs uncommonly despite the frequency of these plant part injuries, probably because these painful thorns and slivers are manually removed or naturally extruded from the skin. The formation of skin granulomas from falling into cacti in the desert is well documented (Epstein and

Epstein, 1989). In recent years, however, a more subtle source of such injuries has moved closer to many of us as large collections of exotic cacti adorn parks, public places, and homes in metropolitan areas. The opportunity for accidental exposure to granulomagenic glochids has increased almost logarithmically.

The clinical lesions of cactus granuloma evolve slowly over a period of days to weeks and appear roughly to be the same age at time of presentation. Their emergence is not explosive. Nevertheless, one must consider various infections, so medical care should be sought. If the lesions remain firm and tumid to the touch, papular rather than pustular, a biopsy should be done, since the correct diagnosis then depends on interpretation by a trained pathologist.

True cacti belong to the family Cactaceae, which contains probably no more than 2000 species, but actual classification is confused by lack of agreement among experts (Mitchell and Rook, 1979c). Furthermore, plants in other families [e.g., the candelabra cactus (*Euphora lactea*) found in south Florida] are commonly called cacti. The cacti naturally inhabit hot, dry regions of tropical and subtropical America, but several centuries ago these attractive plants were domesticated and transplanted to the Mediterranean and other more temperate regions of the world as a cheap, easy-to-grow, nutritious plant and later for use as crude property boundaries and for protection. In the past century cacti have been adapted for purely ornamental purposes. Cacti tend to accumulate large amounts of calcium oxalate, up to 85% dry weight in some species (Franceschi and Horner, 1980). Handling of edible cacti such as prickly pears (*Opuntia* spp.) can induce an acute or subacute papulopustular eruption called "sabra dermatitis" (Shanon and Sagher, 1956). Sabra is a biblical term for aloe, but sometime during the sixteenth century the term was transferred to prickly pears, which by then had become indigenous to the Mediterranean (Shanon and Sagher, 1956). The eruption is caused by implantation of the readily detachable glochids from the skin of the fruit. Furthermore, the spines can be blown about in the wind, sticking to workers' clothing to give a more generalized rash. When floating spines land in the mucous membranes of the mouth and eyes, they can initiate a very inflammatory and disabling mucositis and keratoconjunctivitis (Epstein, 1990).

While cacti are most readily related to granuloma formation, many other plants with tough thorns, bristles, or splinters (e.g., roses, thistles, woods, and palm) can induce granuloma formation. In contrast to cactus granulomas, these are usually solitary and nearly always limited to an extremity (Epstein, 1989b). Plants with longer barbs may be responsible for deep tissue injury, and such thorn insertions have produced acute and chronic joint inflammation (Ormerod et al., 1984). This type of chronic wound is commonly caused by blackthorn (*Prunus spinosa*) in England and by palm trees (Palmae) in California (Epstein, 1990). When plant thorns lodge in or near bone, the ensuing inflammation can elicit osteolytic and/or osteoblastic responses that may mimic a bone tumor (Gerle, 1971).

Histologically, the response is a foreign body granuloma with periodic acid-Schiff-positive plant spicules often present in massive giant cells. The tissue response clearly is more inflammatory than seen in conventional foreign body granulomas. Despite much study, no additional toxins or antigens have been found in these lesions (Epstein, 1990). Perhaps it is best to consider these lesions exuberant, nonspecific, foreign body granulomas (Epstein, 1990). The predominant cells in such lesions are mixed-function macrophages with both secretory rough endoplasmic reticulum and dense lysosomal bodies in the cytoplasm (Epstein and Fukuyama, 1989). This anatomical observation supports the suggestion that an element of hypersensitivity exists, but the mere presence of T lymphocytes and dendritic mononuclear cells in an area of chemically induced hypersensitivity granulomas does not itself indicate the requirement for an intact cell-mediated immune system to initiate this type of granulomatous inflammation (Epstein, 1989b; Epstein and Fukuyama, 1989). Nevertheless, it is generally agreed that for organized granulomas to become amplified and fully formed depends on an activated cell-mediated immune system (Boros, 1981; Epstein, 1990; Epstein and Fukuyama, 1989; Williams and Jones Williams, 1983).

REFERENCES

Adolf, W., and Hecker, E. (1984). On the active principles of the spurge family: X skin irritants, cocarcinogens and cryptic cocarcinogens from the latex of the manchineel tree. *J. Nat. Prod. 47:* 482-496.

Arditti, J., and Rodriquez, E. (1982). Dieffenbachia: uses, abuses, and toxic constituents: a review. *J. Enthnopharmacol. 5:* 293-302.

Baer, H. (1983). Allergic contact dermatitis from plants. In *Handbook of Natural Toxins*, Vol. 1, R. F. Keeler and A. T. Tu (Eds.). Marcel Dekker, New York, pp. 421-442.

Beaven, M. A., and Cunha-Melo, J. R. (1988). Membrane phosphoinositide-activated signals in mast cells and basophils. In *Progress in Allergy: Membrane Activation in Immunologically Relevant Cells*, E. L. Becker (Ed.). S. Karger, Basel, pp. 123-184.

Benezra, C., and Ducombs, G. (1987). Molecular aspects of allergic contact dermatitis to plants. *Derm. Beruf. Umwelt 35:* 4-11.

Benezra, C., and Epstein, W. L. (1986). Molecular recognition patterns of sesquiterpene lactones in costus-sensitive patients. *Contact Dermatitis 15:* 223-230.

Benezra, C., Ducombs, G., and Sell, Y. (1985). *Plant Contact Dermatitis*, Marcel Dekker, New York.

Berridge, M. J. (1988). Inositol lipids and calcium signalling. *Proc. R. Soc. Lond. B234:* 359-378.

Bloch, B. (1929). The role of idiosyncracy and allergy in dermatology. *Arch. Dermatol. Syphilol. 19:* 175-197.

Bonora, A., Dall'Olio, G., and Donini, A. (1987). An HPLC screening of some Italian Ranunculaceae for the lactone protoanemonin. *Phytochemistry 26:* 2277-2279.

Boros, D. L. (1981). The role of lymphokines in granulomatous inflammations. *Lymphokines 3:* 257-281.

Boutwell, R. K. (1974). The function and mechanisms of promoters in carcinogenesis. *Crit. Rev. Toxicol. 2:* 419-443.

Crabtree, G. R. (1989). Contingent genetic regulatory events in T lymphocyte activation. *Science 243:* 355-361.

Cronin, E. (1987). Dermatitis of the hands in caterers. *Contact Dermatitis 17:* 265-269.

Dunn, I. S., Liberato, D. J., and Castagnoli, N. (1986). Influence of chemical reactivity of urushiol-type haptens on sensitization and induction of tolerance. *Cell. Immunol. 97*:189-196.

Dunn, I. S., Liberato, D. J., Stampf, J. L., et al. (1987). Regulation of murine contact sensitivity to urushiol components by serum factors. *J. Invest. Dermatol. 89*:296-298.

Epstein, W. L. (1987). The poison ivy picker of pennypack park: the continuing saga of poison ivy. *J. Invest. Dermatol. 88*:7s-11s.

Epstein, W. L. (1989a). Topical prevention of poison ivy/oak dermatitis. *Arch. Dermatol. 125*:499-501.

Epstein, W. L. (1990). Plants: house and garden. In *Irritant Contact Dermatitis*, E. M. Jackson and R. Goldner (Eds.). Marcel Dekker, New York, pp. 127-165.

Epstein, W. L., and Epstein, J. H. (1989). Emergency treatment of plant-induced dermatitis. In *Management of Wilderness and Environmental Emergencies*, 2nd ed., P. S. Auerbach and E. C. Geehr (Eds.). C. V. Mosby, St. Louis, Mo., Chap. 23, pp. 617-635.

Epstein, W. L., and Fukuyama, K. (1989). Mechanisms of granulomatous inflammation. In *Mechanisms in Cutaneous Disease*, D. A. Norris (Ed.). Marcel Dekker, New York, pp. 687-722.

Fisher, A. A. (1986). Erythema multiforme-like eruptions due to exotic woods and ordinary plants. *Cutis 37*:101-103, 1986.

Frain-Bell, W. (1986). Photosensitivity and compositae dermatitis. *Clin. Dermatol. 4*:122-126.

Franceschi, V. R., and Horner, H. T. (1980). Calcium oxalate crystals in plants. *Bot. Rev. 46*:361-426.

Gafner, F., Epstein, W., and Reynold, G. (1988). Human maximization test of falcarinol, the principal contact allergen of English ivy and Algerian ivy. *Contact Dermatitis 19*:125-128.

Gerle, R. D. (1971). Thorn-induced pseudo-tumours of bone. *Br. J. Radiol. 44*:642-645.

Hausen, B. M. (1981). *Woods Injurious to Human Health*. Walter de Gruyter, West Berlin.

Hausen, B. M. (1986). Contact allergy to woods. *Clin. Dermatol. 4*:65-76.

Hausen, B. M., Brohan, J., Konig, W. A., et al. (1987). Allergic and irritant contact dermatitis from falcarinol and didehydrofalcarinol in common ivy (*Hedera helix* L.). *Contact Dermatitis 17*:1-9.

Hjorth, N., and Roed-Petersen, J. (1976). Occupational protein contact dermatitis in food handlers. *Contact Dermatitis 2*:28-42.

Horejsi, V., and Bazil, V. (1988). Surface proteins and glycoproteins of human leukocytes. *Biochem. J. 253*:1-26.

Imboden, J. B., and Weiss, A. (1988). The initiation of human T lymphocyte activation. In *Progress in Allergy: Membrane Activation in Immunologically Relevant Cells*, E. L. Becker (Ed.). S. Karger, Basel, pp. 246-279.

Johnson, A. E. (1983). Photosensitizing toxins from plants and their biologic effects. In *Handbook of Natural Toxins*, Vol. 1, R. F. Keeler and A. T. Tu (Eds.). Marcel Dekker, New York, pp. 345-359.

Katz, S. I. (1985). The skin as an immunologic organ: a tribute to Marion B. Sulzberger. *J. Am. Acad. Dermatol. 13*:530-536.

Kinghorn, A. D. (1979). Cocarcinogenic irritant Euphorbiaceae in toxic plants. In *Toxic Plants*, A. D. Kinghorn (Ed.). Columbia University Press, New York, pp. 137-159.

Kjaer, A. (1966). The distribution of sulphur compounds. In *Comparative Phytochemistry*, T. Swain (Ed.). Academic Press, New York, pp. 187-194.

Kupper, T. S. (1989). Production of cytokines by epithelial tissues. *Am. J. Dermatopathol.* 11:69-73.

Lahti, A. (1986). Contact urticaria to plants. *Clin. Dermatol. 4*:127-136.

Lonker, A., Mitchell, J. C., and Calnan, C. D. (1974). Contact dermatitis from *Parthenium hysterophorus*. *Trans. St. John's Hosp. Dermatol. Soc. 60*:43-53.

Meding, B. (1985). Immediate hypersensitivity to mustard and rape. *Contact Dermatitis 13*:121-122.

Menz, J., and Winkelmann, R. K. (1987). Sensitivity to vegetation. *Contact Dermatitis 16*:169-173.

Mitchell, J. C., and Rook, A. (1979). *Botanical Dermatology*. Greengrass, pp. 227-236; (a) pp. 584-588; (b) pp. 70-113, (c) pp. 147-150.

Mitchell, J. C., Fritig, B., and Singh, B. (1970). Allergic contact dermatitis from *Frullania* and Compositae: the role of sesquiterpene lactones. *J. Invest. Dermatol. 54*:233-239.

Morton, J. F. (1978). Brazilian pepper—its impact on people, animals and the environment. *Econ. Bot. 32*:353-359.

Morton, J. F. (1982). *Plants Poisonous to People in Florida and Other Warm Areas*, 2nd ed. Published by the author, pp. 101-102; (a) pp. 85-86.

Orchard, S. M., Fellman, J. H., and Storrs, F. J. (1986). Poison ivy/oak dermatitis: use of polyamine salts of linoleic acid dimer for prophylaxis. *Arch. Dermatol. 122*:783-789.

Ormerod, A. D., White, M. I., and Eastmond, C. J. (1984). Plant-thorn synovitis occurring in a child with psoriatic arthritis. *Br. J. Rheumatol. 23*:296-297.

Pathak, M. A. (1986). Phytophotodermatitis. *Clin. Dermatol. 4*:102-121.

Penner, R., Mathews, G., and Neher, E. (1988). Regulation of calcium influx by second messengers in rat mast cells. *Nature 334*:499-504.

Reynolds, G. W., Epstein, W. L., and Rodriguez, E. (1980). Unusual contact allergens from plants in the family Hydrophyllaceae. *Contact Dermatol. 14*:39-44.

Rosengard, B. R., Mahalik, C., and Cochrane, D. E. (1986). Mast cell secretion: differences between immunologic and nonimmunologic stimulation. *Agents Actions 19*:133-140.

Ruijgrok, H. W. L. (1966). The distribution of ranunculin and cyanogenetic compounds in the Ranunculaceae. In *Comparative Phytochemistry*, T. Swain (ed.). Academic Press, New York, pp. 175-186.

Schmidt, R. J. (1986). Compositae. *Clin. Dermatol. 4*:46-61.

Shanon, J., and Sagher, F. (1956). Sabra dermatitis. *Arch. Dermatol. 74*:269-275.

Stampf, J. L., Castignoli, N., and Epstein, W. L., et al. (1990). Induction of immune tolerance to urushiol in mice with human IgG. *J. Invest. Dermatol. 95*: (in press, Sept.).

Stengl, G., Hauser, C., and Tschachler, E. (1989). Immune functions of epidermal cells. In *Mechanisms in Cutaneous Disease*, D. A. Norris (Ed.).

Marcel Dekker, New York, pp. 3-72.

Thune, P. (1987). Lichens, compositae and photosensitivity. *Photodermatol.*
4:1-4.

Thurston, E. L. (1974). Morphology, fine structure and ontogeny of the
stinging emergence of *Urtica dioica*. *Am. J. Bot.* 61:809-817.

Thurston, E. L., and Lersten, N. R. (1969). The morphology and toxicology
of plant stinging hairs. *Bot. Rev.* 35:393-412.

Tomb, R. R., Foussereau, J., and Sell, Y. (1988). Mini-epidemic of contact
dermatitis from ginkgo tree fruit. *Contact Dermatitis 19*:281-293.

Towers, G. N. H., Arneson, T., and Wat, C. K. (1979). Phototoxic polyacetylenes and their thiophene derivatives (effects on human skin). *Contact Dermatitis 5*:140-144.

Webster, G. L. (1986). Irritant plants in the Spurge family. *Clin. Dermatol.* 4:36-45.

Williams, G. T., and Jones Williams, W. (1983). Granulomatous inflammation.
J. Clin. Pathol. 36:723-733.

29

Congestive Right-Heart Failure in Cattle: High Mountain Disease and Factors Influencing Incidence

Lynn F. James

Poisonous Plant Research Laboratory, Agricultural Research Service, USDA, Logan, Utah

Russell J. Molyneux

Western Regional Research Center, Agricultural Research Service, USDA, Albany, California

A. F. Alexander

College of Veterinary Medicine, Colorado State University, Fort Collins, Colorado

I. CONGESTIVE RIGHT-HEART FAILURE

The heart is a biological pump that, via the blood, delivers to the body materials essential to sustain life and carries away wastes for disposal. Rather than being a specific disease, heart failure is a syndrome that results in the diminished capacity of the heart to circulate the blood.

Congestive heart failure in cattle can result from a number of causes. Among these are traumatic pericarditis and parasitism (Hull and Anderson, 1978; Hibbs et al., 1976); chronic anemia associated with diseases such as anaplasmosis (Jubb et al., 1985); valvular endocarditis (Alexander, 1978); congenital heart diseases which lead to a work overload on the heart (Alexander, 1978); diseases of the pulmonary system, such as pneumonia and emphysema, which could lead to an increased work load on the right ventricle of the heart; and toxic compounds in plants. Plants containing pyrrolizidine alkaloids [such as some *Senecio, Crotalaria*, and *Heliotropium* species (Alexander, 1978; Hibbs et al., 1976)] or other toxins that adversely affect various body systems could cause an increased work load on the heart or directly damage the myocardium proper. Locoweeds (certain species of *Astragalus* and *Oxytropis*) have been shown to enhance the incidence of right-heart failure in animals living at high altitude (James et al., 1983). Perhaps the most common and well-recognized cause of right-heart failure in cattle is residence at high elevations, as with cattle grazing the high mountain ranges of the western United States and certain other parts of the world (Alexander, 1978).

II. HIGH MOUNTAIN DISEASE

In cattle, congestive right-heart failure (CRHF) associated with residence at high elevations (above 7000 ft) is commonly referred to as high mountain disease (HMD). The basic cause of this condition is an hypoxic-induced pulmonary hypertension associated with the decreased oxygen tension found at high elevations (Alexander, 1978; Jensen et al., 1976).

Chronic hypoxia causes increased precapillary vascular resistance which results in pulmonary hypertension. The increased resistance causes an increased work load on the heart, resulting in hypertrophy or enlargement of the right ventricle (Blake, 1964). The structural changes that result are compensatory in nature; however, the compensatory action is often only temporarily effective as the enlargement of the heart introduces structural changes that cause the efficiency of the heart to decline (Jubb et al., 1985). As the heart enlarges, the strength of myocardial contraction decreases, right atrioventricular valve insufficiency develops, the effectiveness of the heart as a pump declines, and the outward signs of congestive right-heart failure may become apparent.

The clinical signs and lesions associated with HMD include right-ventricular hypertrophy and dilation, subcutaneous edema ascites, hydrothorax, profuse fluid diarrhea, chronic passive congestion of the liver, and hypervolemia with hemodilution. A jugular pulse is apparent. In advanced cases, death may follow slight exertion. Medial thickening with luminal restriction of the small pulmonary arteries and arterioles develops and becomes a prominent histological feature of the condition.

A genetic propensity to the disease exists in cattle (Will et al., 1975). Cattle native to high mountain areas, having been subject to a rigorous selection process imposed by humans and nature, have a lower incidence of the disease than do introduced cattle. The incidence of HMD is generally higher in cattle newly brought into a high-altitude-residence situation. The condition seems to be aggravated by cold temperatures (Will et al., 1978). Also at the elevations at which HMD occurs, marked changes in ambient temperatures occur, enhancing the possibility of pneumonia, which also predisposes an animal to heart failure (Will et al., 1978).

The incidence of high mountain disease in Wyoming and Colorado varies from 0.5 to 2% annually. Higher elevations cause an increase in incidence; lower elevations, a decrease. As elevation increases, the time required to develop pulmonary hypertension, and subsequently the time to produce heart failure and the signs of HMD, decreases. Cattle do not always develop HMD on ranges with elevations above 7000 ft (Blake, 1978). During residence on these ranges, cattle may have moved up and down the mountains (varying elevations) while grazing. The incidence of congestive heart failure HMD in cattle grazing high-altitude locoweed-infested range has been observed to approach a morbidity of 100% with a mortality of 10 to 15% (James et al., 1983). The mortality would be much higher if cattle showing signs of HMD were not removed to lower elevations.

III. LOCOWEED AND CONGESTIVE RIGHT-HEART FAILURE

Cattle, particularly calves, grazing on certain high-altitude ranges infested with the locoweed *Oxytropis sericea* have a much higher incidence of congestive right-heart failure than do those grazing ranges not infested with locoweed. Tissues from affected calves show histological lesions of both locoweed poisoning and congestive right-heart failure. The clinical signs, gross lesions, and microscopic lesions of congestive right-heart failure are similar to those of high mountain disease.

Poisoning results when cattle graze *O. sericea* over a period of several weeks. Clinical signs of locoweed poisoning include depression, rough dry hair coat, dull lusterless eyes, and excitement when placed under stress. No outstanding gross lesions are seen, but there are microscopic lesions of neurovisceral cytoplasmic vacuolation (James and Van Kampen, 1971). Emaciation, abortion, interference with other reproductive processes, and birth defects have also been associated with locoweed poisoning. No association of congestive heart failure with locoweed intoxication at lower elevations has been found (James et al., 1983).

Clinical signs in calves developing congestive right heart failure when grazing locoweed at high elevations are not typical of locoweed poisoning observed under usual field conditions at low altitude or as recorded in the literature (James et al., 1981, 1986; Panter et al., 1988). The signs of congestive right-heart failure enhanced by the grazing of locoweed are similar to those seen in the typical right-heart-failure condition. The clinical signs include dry nose; rough dry hair coat; depression; dark fluid diarrhea; edema under the jaw, brisket, and underline; labored respiration; visible jugular pulse; weakness; and death. However, some calves appear to dehydrate rather that become edematous, but on postmortem the gross lesions are the same. A few calves first develop the edema and then appear to become dehydrated. In some calves, the skin along the sides of the jaws becomes tight and the hair stands erect. These calves become quite ill and die in a short time. Gross and microscopic lesions are the same as those observed in calves showing the more typical signs.

At high elevations, pathologic changes of CRHF in calves fed locoweed are similar to those of nonlocoweed-fed calves in failure. The gross changes include right-ventricular dilation and hypertrophy, subcutaneous edema, ascites, hydrothorax, profuse fluid diarrhea, and chronic passive congestion of the liver. The heart has a rounded contour due to the dilation and hypertrophy. In advanced cases, the lungs have varying amounts of atelectasis or consolidation. Microscopic lesions reflect congestive heart failure and the neurovisceral cytoplasmic vacuolation characteristic of locoweed poisoning.

After only a few days of being fed locoweed at high elevations, calves become sensitive to exercise, showing weakness and a reluctance to walk. The outward signs of CRHF, such as edema, appear within 1 to 2 weeks (James et al., 1986). Uncomplicated HMD develops in about 6 months at 10,000 ft; at 12,500 ft, it requires only 9 weeks (Alexander and Will, 1980). Calves nursing cows grazing locoweed at high elevations seem prone to congestive heart failure (James et al., 1986). The locoweed toxin (swainsonine) is excreted in the milk (James and Hartley, 1977).

Cold and fluctuating temperatures seem to enhance the development of heart failure associated with cattle grazing on locoweed-infested ranges at high elevations, analogous to the situation with typical HMD. Some field cases on these ranges have shown pneumonia and signs and lesions of HMD with no lesions of locoweed poisoning. Like locoweed, pneumonia predisposes cattle to the development of congestive heart failure in very short periods of time (James et al., 1983, 1986).

White point locoweed (*O. sericea*) is the locoweed most often associated with the enhancement of HMD. Several *Astragalus* species are also classed as locoweeds. The *Astragalus* genera of plants can be divided into three general groups according to the toxin they contain: (1) locoweeds, which contain the indolizidine alkaloid swainsonine as the toxin; (2) nitro-containing *Astragalus*, the toxin being the glycoside of β-D-3-nitro-1-propanol or 3-nitro propionic acid; and (3) the selenium accumulators (James et al., 1981).

IV. SWAINSONINE: THE TOXIN IN LOCOWEED

The toxin responsible for the neurological defects produced by consumption of locoweeds by livestock is an indolizidine alkaloid, swainsonine (Molyneux and James, 1982) (see Chapter 10). Swainsonine is a specific inhibitor of the enzyme α-mannosidase. A deficiency of this enzyme is characteristic of the genetically induced lysosomal storage disease of Angus cattle, α-mannosidosis. Swainsonine completely inhibits acidic α-mannosidases isolated from a variety of mammalian tissues (Dorling et al., 1980) and is a potent inhibitor of Golgi mannosidase II but not of mannosidase IA and IB (Tulsiani et al., 1982). Inhibition of this enzyme results in incomplete processing of glycoproteins by the Golgi apparatus and the accumulation of lysosomal storage products, which eventually causes vacuolation in the cell.

The relationship of swainsonine to congestive right-heart failure produced at high altitudes is at present conjectural. Nevertheless, circumstantial evidence suggests a connection. Consumption of white point locoweed at high altitudes results in an increased incidence of HMD (James et al., 1983; Panter et al., 1988). Moreover, calves nursing cows consuming the plant exhibited the same symptoms, indicating that the causative agent is transferred in the milk. Swainsonine is present in white point locoweed, the highest levels occurring in the reproductive parts of the plant (see Chapter 10). Milk from cattle fed locoweed produces symptoms of locoism in calves, kittens, and lambs (James and Hartley, 1977). Calves fed pure swainsonine at high elevations develop CRHF similar to that produced by locoweed (L. F. James, K. E. Panter, H. Broquist, and W. J. Hartley, unpublished data, 1987). Since swainsonine is thought to be the only toxin in locoweed (Tulsiani et al., 1984), this is expected. The lesions observed in swainsonine poisoning are those of locoweed poisoning (Hartley et al., 1985).

The mechanism whereby swainsonine could enhance the development of CRHF is unknown. However, glycoprotein processing is such a fundamental process of cellular function that its disruption by swainsonine inhibition of the necessary enzymes could explain the syndrome. To produce the effects observed, it seems possible that the alkaloid could have an effect on lung tissue, which, in turn, would affect the circulatory function and ultimately the work load on the heart. Experiments designed to study the levels of α-mannosidase and the pathology of specific tissues could possibly resolve this question.

Nitro-containing *Astragalus* species grow on ranges from western Canada through the western United States and into northern Mexico. Examples include *A. emoryanus*, *A. tetrapterus*, *A. pterocarpus*, *A. miser* varieties *serotinus* and *oblongifolius*, and *A. hylophyllus*. Williams and Barneby (1977) have listed these plants in detail. The toxin is the β-D-glycoside of 3-nitro-1-propanol. Consumption of these plants can cause acute or chronic poisoning in cattle. The clinical signs of poisoning involve the respiratory tract and the central nervous system.

In acute poisoning, signs include general body weakness, knuckling at the fetlocks, incoordination (especially of the hind limbs), respiratory tract distress, cyanotic membranes, and sudden collapse of the animal. Sudden exertion may cause death. Gross lesions include pulmonary congestion, edema, petechial hemorrhage on the surface of the heart, and microhemorrhages in the central nervous system (James et al., 1980).

Grazing these plants at a much lower level than that consumed in acute cases over an extended period of time causes chronic poisoning. Signs include general depression, respiratory distress, cocked fetlocks, possible knuckling of the fetlocks, goose stepping, and incoordination. When walking, the animal's hindlimbs will knock against each other and interfere with movement. A roaring sound is made when the animal breathes. If the plant is ingested in sufficient amounts over time, pulmonary emphysema and often pneumonia may occur. The animal may become emaciated and die, and exertion may also cause death. Principal microscopic lesions are pulmonary alveolar emphysema, bronchiolar constriction, interlobular edema and fibrosis, Wallerian-type degeneration in the spinal cord and peripheral nerves, and focal hemorrhage in the brain (James et al., 1980). Since the lungs are one of the target organs of this toxin, one might postulate that consumption of this plant by cattle could contribute to an animal's responsiveness to high-altitude hypoxia and, subsequently, HMD. A mild intoxication would not necessarily be easily visible. Plants of this group grow on many of the mountain ranges of the western United States. Several species in this group also contain low levels of swainsonine.

Selenium, an element found in certain soils, may be taken up by some plants in sufficient quantities as to render them toxic (James and Shupe, 1984). About 25 species of *Astragalus* accumulate selenium at levels high enough to be toxic when consumed. One of the principal organs affected by selenium poisoning is the lung (James et al., 1982). It is questionable whether a relationship could exist between selenium poisoning and heart failure; however, it may be possible. Weakening of the heart muscle due to selenium toxicity could also possibly contribute to heart failure. White muscle disease in calves, a condition associated with selenium deficiency, can result in heart damage that could predispose these animals to such problems as HMD later in life. Other plants, such as those containing pyrrolizidine alkaloids (certain *Senecio* spp.), have been incriminated as a potential cause of congestive heart failure (Alexander, 1978).

V. FETAL IMPLICATIONS

Fetal lambs from ewes fed locoweed (*Astragalus lentiginosus*) during days 60 to 90 of gestation have enlarged right ventricles of the heart and edema about the neck area (James, 1972). Fetal lambs from ewes fed locoweed have lesions of locoweed poisoning (Hartley and James, 1975). The changes observed in these fetal lambs are reminiscent of HMD as it occurs in cattle. Panter et al. (1987), using ultrasonographic imaging techniques, observed right-ventricular dilation, rounded apex of the heart, and edema; they also observed a decrease in the strength of the heart contractions. These observations are very similar to those seen in calves fed locoweed at high elevations (James et al., 1986). The mammalian fetus is more hypoxic and more hypertensive than the adult because of the nature of the fetal circulation (Schimmel, 1981; Brigham and Newman, 1979). Thus pulmonary circulation from the fetus to the neonate changes from a high pressure-low flow system to a low pressure-high flow system (Reeves and Leather, 1964). These changes in pulmonary circulation are relevant to hypoxic reactivity later in life since generalized hypoxic vasoconstriction would never occur in extrauterine life if the lung were never hypoxic (Brigham and Newman, 1979). The normal changes that occur at birth include a rapid decrease in pulmonary artery pressure that takes place in two stages: (1) atrophy of smooth muscle in the pulmonary arteriole within the first weeks after birth, and (2) regression of the ratio of the right ventricle to total weight of the ventricles. There is a diametric decrease in pulmonary artery pressure in the first weeks postpartum to growth of lung parenchyma and increases in pulmonary and bronchial circulations (Reeves, 1973).

In their studies on the genetic resistance of calves to pulmonary hypertension, Will et al. (1975) found that resistant calves showed regression of fetal pulmonary arterial pressure as early as 10 days after birth, whereas calves susceptible to pulmonary hypertension showed a somewhat slower regression. The changes described suggest that hypoxia is a stimulus that affects pulmonary vascular resistance in utero. The persistence of pulmonary vasoconstriction into extrauterine life has been associated with the weak response of the adult to hypoxia (Reeves and Leather, 1967).

It is reasonable to speculate that the changes observed in the hearts of fetuses from ewes fed locoweed may be related to the congestive right-heart failure observed in calves fed locoweed at high elevations. Locoweed can also cause hydrops amnii (an accumulation of fluid in the placenta) in cattle grazing *A. wootonii*. Lesions of locoweed poisoning are also found in the calves of these cows (Charles Edwards, personal communication, 1980). These newborn calves have large fluid-filled abdominal cavities. This, too, could possibly be a result of a fetal heart defect or vascular defect related to the locoweed toxin.

VI. SUMMARY

According to Alexander (1978), "All work to date has supported the fact that chronic alveolar hypoxia and the resultant pulmonary hypertension remain the underlying mechanism in the pathogenesis of 'brisket disease' in cattle at high elevation." The more recent work on the look-alike locoweed-induced congestive right-heart failure at high elevations suggests that other factors may become involved which could markedly alter incidence, time lapse, severity, and possibly the elevation at which HMD can occur. This could also account for the differences in morbidity noted between years and locations.

REFERENCES

Alexander, A. F. (1978). The interaction of pathogenic mechanisms in bovine high mountain (brisket) disease. In *Effects of Poisonous Plants on Livestock*, R. F. Keeler, K. R. Van Kampen, and L. F. James (Eds.). Academic Press, New York, pp. 285-300.

Alexander, A. F., and Will, D. H. (1980). High mountain (brisket) disease. In *Bovine Medicine and Surgery*, 2nd ed., Vol. 2, A. E. Amstutz (Ed.). American Veterinary Publications, Santa Barbara, Calif., pp. 764-770.

Blake, J. T. (1964). Cardiac structural changes in cattle with brisket disease. *J. Am. Vet. Med. Assoc. 26*:76-82.

Blake, J. T. (1978). Occurrence and distribution of brisket disease in Utah. *Utah State Agric. Exp. Sta. Circ. 151.*

Brigham, K. L., and Newman, J. H. (1979). The pulmonary circulation. *Am. Thorac. Soc. News 8*:15

Dorling, P. R., Huxtable, C. R., and Colegate, S. M. (1980). Inhibition of lysosomal α-mannosidase by swainsonine, an indolizidine alkaloid isolated from *Swainsona canescens*. *Biochem. J. 191*:649-651.

Hartley, W. J., and James, L. F. (1975). Fetal and maternal lesions in pregnant ewes ingesting locoweed (*Astragalus lentiginosus*). *Am. J. Vet. Res. 36*:825-826.

Hartley, W. J., James, L. F., Broquist, H., and Panter, K. E. (1985). Pathology of experimental locoweed and selenium poisoning in pigs. In *Plant Toxicology*, A. A. Seawright, M. P. Hegarty, L. F. James, and R. F. Keeler (Eds.). Queensland Poisonous Plant Committee, Yeerongpilly, Australia, pp. 141-149.

Hibbs, C. M., White, R. G., and Nichols, J. T. (1976). Brisket edema—toxic weed can cause disease in cattle. *Farm Ranch Q.*, University of Nebraska, Spring.

Hull, M. W., and Anderson, C. K. (1978). Right ventricular heart failure of Montana cattle. *Cornell Vet.* 68:199.

James, L. F. (1972). Effects of locoweed on fetal development: preliminary study in sheep. *Am. J. Vet. Res.* 33:835-841.

James, L. F., and Hartley, W. J. (1977). Effects of milk from animals fed locoweed on kittens, calves, and lambs. *Am. J. Vet. Res.* 38:1263-1265.

James, L. F., and Shupe, J. L. (1984). Selenium poisoning in livestock. *Rangelands* 6:64-67.

James, L. F., and Van Kampen, K. R. (1971). Acute and residual lesions of locoweed poisoning in cattle and horses. *J. Am. Vet. Med. Assoc.* 158:614-618.

James, L. F., Hartley, W. J., Williams, M. C., and Van Kampen, K. R. (1980). Field and experimental studies in cattle and sheep poisoned by nitro-bearing *Astragalus* or their toxins. *Am. J. Vet. Res.* 41:377-382.

James, L. F., Hartley, W. J., and Van Kampen, K. R. (1981). Syndromes of *Astragalus* poisoning in livestock. *J. Am. Vet. Med. Assoc.* 178:146-150.

James, L. F., Smart, R. A., Shupe, J. L., Bowns, J., and Schoenfeld, J. (1982). Suspected phytotoxic selenium poisoning in sheep. *J. Am. Vet. Med. Assoc.* 180:1478-1481.

James, L. F., Hartley, W. J., Van Kampen, K. R., and Nielsen, D. (1983). Relationship between ingestion of the locoweed *Oxytropis sericea* and congestive right-sided heart failure in cattle. *Am. J. Vet. Res.* 44:254-259.

James, L. F., Hartley, W. J., Nielsen, D., Allen, S., and Panter, K. E. (1986). Locoweed (*Oxytropis sericea*) poisoning and congestive heart failure in cattle. *J. Am. Vet. Med. Assoc.* 189:1549-1556.

Jensen, R., Pierson, R. E., Braddy, P. M., Saari, D. A., Benitez, A., Horton, D. P., Lauerman, L. H., McChesney, A. E., Alexander, A. F., and Will, D. H. (1976). Brisket disease in yearling feedlot cattle. *J. Am. Vet. Med. Assoc.* 169:515-517.

Jubb, K. U. F., Kennedy, P. C., and Palmer, N. (1985). *Pathology of Domestic Animals*, 3rd ed. Academic Press, New York, pp. 3-12.

Molyneux, R. J., and James, L. F. (1982). Loco intoxication: indolizidine alkaloids of spotted locoweed (*Astragalus lentiginosus*). *Science* 216:190-191.

Panter, K. E., Bunch, T. D., James, L. F., and Sisson, D. V. (1987). Ultrasonographic imaging to monitor fetal and placental development in ewes fed locoweed (*Astragalus lentiginosus*). *Am. J. Vet. Res.* 48:686-690.

Panter, K. E., James, L. F., Nielsen, D., Molyneux, R. J., Ralphs, M. H., and Olsen, J. D. (1988). The relationship of *Oxytropis sericea* (green and dry) and *Astragalus lentiginosus* with high mountain disease in cattle. *Vet. Hum. Toxicol.* 30:318-323.

Reeves, J. T. (1973). Pulmonary vascular response to high altitude residences. *Cardiovasc. Clin.* 5:81.

Reeves, J. T., and Leather, J. E. (1964). Circulatory changes following birth of the calf and the effects of hypoxia. *Circ. Res.* 15:343.

Reeves, J. T., and Leather, J. E. (1967). Postnatal development of pulmonary and bronchial arterial circulation in the calf and the effect of chronic hypoxia. *Anat. Rec. 157*: 641.

Schimmel, J. C. (1981). Genetic aspects of high mountain disease in beef cattle. Ph.D. dissertation, Colorado State University, Fort Collins.

Tulsiani, D. R. P., Harris, T. M., and Touster, O. (1982). Swainsonine inhibits the biosynthesis of complex glycoproteins by inhibition of Golgi mannosidase II. *J. Biol. Chem. 257*: 7936-7939.

Tulsiani, D. R. P., Broquist, H. P., James, L. F., and Touster, O. (1984). The similar effects of swainsonine and locoweed on tissue glycosidases and oligosaccharides of the pig indicate that the alkaloid is the principal toxin responsible for the induction of locoism. *Arch. Biochem. Biophys. 232*: 76-85.

Will, D. H., Hicks, J. L., Card, C. S., and Alexander, A. F. (1975). Inherited susceptibility of cattle to high-altitude pulmonary hypertension. *J. Appl. Physiol. 38*: 491.

Will, D. H., McMurtry, I. F., Reeves, J. T., and Grover, R. F. (1978). Cold-induced hypertension in cattle. *J. Appl. Physiol. 45*: 469-473.

Williams, M. C., and Barneby, R. C. (1977). The occurrence of nitro-toxins in North American *Astragalus* (Fabaceae). *Brittonia 29*: 310-326.

Index